OIL AND GAS TERMS

WITHDRAWN
UTSA Libraries

Seventh Edition

Annotated Manual of
Legal
Engineering
Tax Words and Phrases

---

by

HOWARD R. WILLIAMS

Robert E. Paradise Professor of Natural Resources Law, Emeritus, Stanford University

Stella W. and Ira S. Lillick Professor of Law, Emeritus, Stanford University

and

CHARLES J. MEYERS

Gibson, Dunn & Crutcher, Denver, Colorado

Formerly Richard E. Lang Professor of Law and Dean, Stanford University

1987

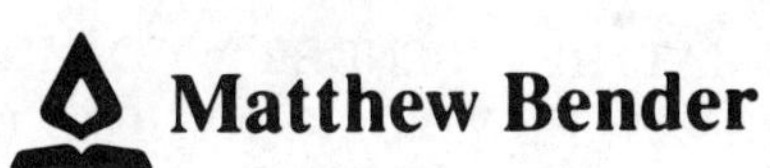

Times Mirror
Books

"This publication is designed to provide accurate and authoritative information in regard to the subject matter covered. It is sold with the understanding that the publisher is not engaged in rendering legal, accounting or other professional service. If legal or other expert assistance is required, the services of a competent professional person should be sought."

—From a Declaration of Principles jointly adopted by a Committee of the American Bar Association and a Committee of Publishers and Associations.

Copyright © 1964, 1971, 1976, 1981, 1984, 1987
By MATTHEW BENDER & COMPANY
INCORPORATED

All Rights Reserved
Printed in the United States of America

This material is also published in Volume 8 of
Williams and Meyers, *Oil and Gas Law.*

LIBRARY
The University of Texas
at San Antonio

MATTHEW BENDER & CO., INC.
11 PENN PLAZA, NEW YORK, NY 10001 (212) 967-7707
2101 WEBSTER STREET, OAKLAND, CA 94612 (415) 446-7100
1275 BROADWAY, ALBANY, NY 12201 (518) 462-3331

(Pub.821)

MATTHEW BENDER EDITORIAL STAFF

Fred D. Nation, Jr., J.D.
Editorial Director

Eben H. Carr, J.D.
Publication Manager

John Barker
Editorial Supervisor

Copy Editors:
Lucy Childs
Brett Threlkeld
Marj Young

FOREWORD

In making this manual of oil and gas terms, we had two purposes:

(1) To collect in one place the words and phrases that persons concerned with oil and gas matters are likely to encounter, and

(2) To define these with accuracy but with brevity and clarity.

We think the book will be useful to lawyers, landmen, accountants, investors in oil and gas properties, students, and others in the great variety of occupations in the industry. For example, the petroleum engineer may find the book helpful on the meaning of the Unless clause in an oil and gas lease; the landman may find help in explaining the purpose and meaning of various lease clauses; the lawyer, accountant, or investor may obtain a better understanding of terms descriptive of financing transactions and of their tax consequences.

Since many of the terms contained here are legal terms, we have seen the necessity of making these intelligible to laymen yet saying enough to be helpful to the lawyer. For the benefit of the former, we may have explained the obvious to the latter, but we have included for the lawyer references to statutes, cases, books, and law review articles we think are helpful.

In selecting terms, we have tried to include all those regularly used in the industry, emphasizing those concerned with exploration, development, production, and transportation of oil and gas. In defining terms, we have cross-checked a good many sources to promote accuracy. But a considerable number of oil and gas terms lack any standardized meaning: usage varies from place to place, or the same word conveys several meanings, not always consistent. Where we were aware of these ambiguities, we have noted them.

And lastly, about our errors, we adopt the statement of an earlier lexicographer, the forthright Dr. Samuel Johnson. Boswell relates the story that a lady once asked Johnson how he came to define "Pastern" as the *knee* of a horse. Instead of making an elaborate defense as she expected, he at once answered, "Ignorance, madam, pure ignorance."

OIL & GAS LAW
Table of Abbreviations
Law Reviews/Periodicals/Treatises

Ala. L. Rev.	Alabama Law Review
Alberta L. Rev.	Alberta Law Review
Alta. L. Rev.	Alberta Law Review
Am. L. of Prop.	American Law of Property
Am. Law Prop.	American Law of Property
Ariz. L. Rev.	Arizona Law Review
Ark. L. Rev.	Arkansas Law Review
Australian Mining & Petroleum L.J.	Australian Mining & Petroleum Law Journal
Baylor L. Rev.	Baylor Law Review
Brigham Young U. L. Rev.	Brigham Young University Law Review
Calif. L. Rev.	California Law Review
Cal. L. Rev.	California Law Review
Canadian-American L.J.	Canadian-American Law Journal
Can. Bar J.	Canadian Bar Journal
Can. Bar Rev.	Canadian Bar Review
Can. B.J.	Canadian Bar Journal
Can. B. Rev.	Canadian Bar Review
Colo. L. Rev.	Colorado Law Review
Columbia L. Rev.	Columbia Law Review
Colum. L. Rev.	Columbia Law Review
Cornell L.Q.	Cornell Law Quarterly
Corn. L.Q.	Cornell Law Quarterly
Creighton L. Rev.	Creighton Law Review
Cumberland-Samford L. Rev.	Cumberland-Samford Law Review
Denver L.J.	Denver Law Journal
Dick. L. Rev.	Dickinson Law Review
Duke L.J.	Duke Law Journal
Fla. St. U. L. Rev.	Florida State University Law Review
Geo. L.J.	Georgetown Law Journal

Geo. Wash. L. Rev.	George Washington Law Review
Gonzaga L. Rev.	Gonzaga Law Review
Gonz. L. Rev.	Gonzaga Law Review
Harv. L. Rev.	Harvard Law Review
Hous. L. Rev.	Houston Law Review
Houston L. Rev.	Houston Law Review
Idaho L. Rev.	Idaho Law Review
Ill. B.J.	Illinois Bar Journal
Ill. L. Rev.	Illinois Law Review
Interstate Oil Compact Comm'n Comm. Bull.	Interstate Oil Compact Commission Committee Bulletin
Interstate Oil Compact Q. Bull.	Interstate Oil Compact Quarterly Bulletin
J.B.A. Kan.	Kansas Bar Association Journal
J. Bar Assn. Kan.	Kansas Bar Association Journal
J. of Energy & Natural Resources Law	Journal of Energy and Natural Resources Law
J. of Law & Econ.	Journal of Law and Economics
J. of Mineral L. & Policy	Journal of Mineral Law & Policy
J. of Taxation	Journal of Taxation
John Marshall L.Q.	John Marshall Law Quarterly
J. Okla Bar Assn.	Oklahoma Bar Association Journal
J. Tax'n.	Journal of Taxation
Kan. B.A.J.	Kansas Bar Association Journal
Kan. L. Rev.	Kansas Law Review
Kansas L. Rev.	Kansas Law Review
Ky. L.J.	Kentucky Law Journal
La. B.J.	Louisiana Bar Journal
La. L. Rev.	Louisiana Law Review
Land & Water L. Rev.	Land and Water Law Review
Loyola L. Rev.	Loyola Law Review

L. Q. Rev.	Law Quarterly Review
Memphis St. U. L. Rev.	Memphis State University Law Review
Miami L. Rev.	Miami Law Review
Mich. L. Rev.	Michigan Law Review
Mich. S.B.J.	Michigan State Bar Journal
Minn. L. Rev.	Minnesota Law Review
Miss. L.J.	Mississippi Law Journal
Mo. L. Rev.	Missouri Law Review
Mont. L. Rev.	Montana Law Review
Nat. Res. & Envir.	Natural Resources & Environment
Nat. Res. J.	Natural Resources Journal
Nat. Res. Law.	Natural Resources Lawyer
Nat. Res. Lawyer	Natural Resources Lawyer
N.C.L. Rev.	North Carolina Law Review
N.D. Bar Briefs	North Dakota Bar Briefs
N.D. L. Rev.	North Dakota Law Review
Neb. L. Rev.	Nebraska Law Review
N. Mex. L. Rev.	New Mexico Law Review
No. Dak. L. Rev.	North Dakota Law Review
No. Ky. L. Rev.	North Kentucky Law Review
Northwestern L. Rev.	Northwestern Law Review
Notre Dame Law.	Notre Dame Lawyer
N.Y. State B.J.	New York State Bar Journal
N.Y.U. L. Rev.	New York University Law Review
Nw. L. Rev.	Northwestern Law Review
O.B.A.J.	Oklahoma Bar Association Journal
O.&G. Tax Q.	Oil & Gas Tax Quarterly
OGLTR	Oil and Gas Law and Taxation Review
Ohio St. L.J.	Ohio State Law Journal
Okla. B.A.J.	Oklahoma Bar Association Journal
Okla. B. Ass'n. J.	Oklahoma Bar Association Journal

Okla. B.J.	Oklahoma Bar Association Journal
Okla. L. Rev.	Oklahoma Law Review
Pacific L.J.	Pacific Law Journal
Pac. L.J.	Pacific Law Journal
Rocky Mt. L. Rev.	Rocky Mountain Law Review
Sask. B. Rev.	Saskatchewan Bar Review
Sask. L. Rev.	Saskatchewan Law Review
S.D.L. Rev.	South Dakota Law Review
So. Calif. L. Rev.	Southern California Law Review
So. Cal. L. Rev.	Southern California Law Review
So. Tex. L.J.	South Texas Law Journal
Southwestern L.J.	Southwestern Law Journal
Stanford L. Rev.	Stanford Law Review
Stan. L. Rev.	Stanford Law Review
St. Mary's L.J.	St. Mary's Law Journal
Sw. L.J.	Southwestern Law Journal
S.W.L.J.	Southwestern Law Journal
Texas Bar Ass'n Proceedings	Texas Bar Association Proceedings
Texas B.J.	Texas Bar Journal
Texas L. Rev.	Texas Law Review
Texas Tech L. Rev.	Texas Tech Law Review
Tex. L. Rev.	Texas Law Review
Trust Bull.	Trust Bulletin
Tulane L. Rev.	Tulane Law Review
Tul. L. Rev.	Tulane Law Review
Tulsa L.J.	Tulsa Law Journal
U.B.C. L. Rev.	University of British Columbia Law Review
U. British Columbia L. Rev.	University of British Columbia Law Review
UCLA-Alaska L. Rev.	UCLA-Alaska Law Review
U.C.L.A. L. Rev.	UCLA Law Review
U. Colo. L. Rev.	University of Colorado Law Review

U. Detroit J. Urban L.	University of Detroit Journal of Urban Law
U. Ill. L.F.	University of Illinois Law Forum
U. Kan L. Rev.	University of Kansas Law Review
U. of Kan. City L. Rev.	University of Kansas City Law Review
U. of Kan L. Rev.	University of Kansas Law Review
U. of Pa. L. Rev.	University of Pennsylvania Law Review
U. of Pitt. L. Rev.	University of Pittsburg Law Review
U. Pa. L. Rev.	University of Pennsylvania Law Review
Va. L. Rev.	Virginia Law Review
Valpariso L. Rev.	Valpariso Law Review
Vand. L. Rev.	Vanderbilt Law Review
Victoria U. of Wellington L. Rev.	Victoria University of Wellington Law Review
Washburn L.J.	Washburn Law Journal
Wash. & Lee L. Rev.	Washington and Lee Law Review
Wash. U.L.Q.	Washington University Law Quarterly
Wayne L. Rev.	Wayne Law Review
W. Va. L.Q.	West Virginia Law Quarterly
W. Va. L.Q.R.	West Virginia Law Quarterly Review
W. Va. L.Q. Rev.	West Virginia Law Quarterly Review
W. Va. L. Rev.	West Virginia Law Review
Wyo. L.J.	Wyoming Law Journal
Yale L.J.	Yale Law Journal

Reporter/Service Abbreviations

[Note that some of the case Reporters which follow have successive series—*e.g.,* D.L.R., D.L.R.(2d), D.L.R.(3d), D.L.R.(4th); Fed., F.2d; S.W., S.W.2d—and the numbering of the volumes begins anew with each new series.]

A.F.T.R.	American Federal Tax Reports
A.L.J.R.	Australian Law Journal Reports
All E.R.	All England Law Reports
A.L.R.	American Law Reports
Alta.	Alberta Law Reports
Am. Rep.	American Reports
At.	Atlantic Reporter
A.2d	Atlantic Reporter, Second Series
Blue Sky L. Rep. (CCH)	Blue Sky Law Reporter (CCH)
Cal. Rptr.	California Reporter
C.B.	U.S. Treasury Cumulative Bulletin
C.F.R.	Code of Federal Regulations
C.J.S.	Corpus Juris Secundum
Ct. Cl.	Court of Claims
Digest of Op. Att'y Gen.	Digest of Attorney General Opinions
D.L.R.	Dominion Law Reports
F.P.C.	Federal Power Commission Reports
FPS	Federal Power Service (Matthew Bender & Co.)
F. Supp.	Federal Supplement Reporter
GFS-BLM	Gower Federal Service—Bureau of Land Management
GFS OCS	Gower Federal Service—Outer Continental Shelf

GFS (O&G)	Gower Federal Service—Oil and Gas
IBLA	Interior Board of Land Appeals Decisions
I.D.	Decisions of the United States Department of the Interior
Interstate Oil Compact Q. Bull.	Interstate Oil Compact Quarterly Bulletin
IOCC Comm. Bull.	Interstate Oil Compact Commission Committee Bulletin
Misc.	Miscellaneous Reports
N.E.	Northeastern Reporter
NSWLR	New South Wales Law Reports
N.W.	Northwestern Reporter
N.Y.S.	New York Supplement Reporter
O.&G. Compact Bull.	Oil & Gas Compact Bulletin
O.&G.R.	Oil & Gas Reporter
Ont.Rep.2d	Ontario Reports, Second Series
O.W.N.	Ontario Weekly Notes
Pac.	Pacific Reporter
P.2d	Pacific Reporter Second Series
Pa. D.&C.	Pennsylvania District and County Reports
Qd.R.	Queensland Reports
Sask. L. Rep.	Saskatchewan Law Reports
S.C.R.	Canada Supreme Court Reports
S. Ct.	United States Supreme Court Reporter
S.E.	Southeastern Reporter
So.	Southern Reporter
S.W.	Southwestern Reporter
T.C.M.	Tax Court Memorandum Decisions

T.C. Memo	Tax Court Memorandum Decisions
T.D.	United States Treasury Decisions
Treas. Dec.	United States Treasury Decisions
U.S.	United States Reporter
U.S.L.W.	United States Law Week
U.S.T.C.	United States Tax Court Reports
V.R.	Victoria Reports
W.W.R.	Western Weekly Reports

Institute Abbreviations

Am. Bar Ass'n, Sect. of Mineral and Natural Resources Law, Proceedings	American Bar Association, Section of Mineral and Natural Resources Law, Proceedings
Eastern Min. L. Inst.	Eastern Mineral Law Institute
L.S.U. Annual Inst. on Mineral Law	Louisiana State University Annual Institute on Mineral Law
L.S.U. Min. L. Inst.	Louisiana State University Mineral Law Institute
Nat'l Inst. for Petroleum Landmen	National Institute for Petroleum Landmen
N.Y.U. Inst. on Federal Taxation	New York University Institute on Federal Taxation
N.Y.U. Inst. on Fed. Taxation	New York University Institute on Federal Taxation
Proc. Sec. of Mineral and Natural Resources Law (A.B.A.)	Proceedings Section of Mineral and Natural Resources Law (American Bar Association)
Proc. Sec. of Min. & Nat'l Res. L. (A.B.A.)	Proceeding Section of Mineral and Natural Resources Law (American Bar Association)
Rocky Mt. Min. L. Inst.	Rocky Mountain Mineral Law Institute
Sw. Legal Fdn. Nat'l. Inst. for Petroleum Landmen	National Institute for Petroleum Landmen
Sw. Legal Fdn. Oil & Gas Inst.	Institute on Oil and Gas Law and Taxation (The Southwestern Legal Foundation)
Tulane Tax Inst.	Tulane Taxation Institute
Tulane Tidelands Inst.	Tulane Tidelands Institute

Case/Writ History Abbreviations

aff'd	affirmed
aff'd as modified	affirmed as modified
aff'd in part	affirmed in part
aff'd on other grounds	affirmed on other grounds
aff'd per curiam	affirmed per curiam
aff'd sub nom.	affirmed sub nomine
app. dis.	appeal dismissed
app. dism'd	appeal dismissed
app. dis., sub nom.	appeal dismissed, sub nomine
app. for leave to appeal den.	application for leave to appeal denied
but cf.	but compare
cert. denied	certiorari denied
cert. denied, sub nom.	certiorari denied sub nomine
cert. dismissed	certiorari dismissed
cf.	compare
error dism'd	error dismissed
error dism'd j.c.	error dismissed, judgment correct
error dism'd w.o.j.	error dismissed for want of jurisdiction
error ref'd	error refused
error ref'd n.r.e.	error refused no reversible error
error ref'd n.r.e. sub nom.	error refused, no reversible error sub nomine
error ref'd w.o.j.	error refused for want of jurisdiction
error ref'd w.o.m.	error refused for want of merit
jurisdiction of dist. ct. aff'd	jurisdiction of district court affirmed
leave to app. ref'd	leave to appeal refused
on subsequent appeal sub nom.	on subsequent appeal sub nomine
q.v.	which see (This symbol indicates that the word is defined elsewhere in the

	manual and that the definition will aid the reader in understanding the subject.)
reh. denied	rehearing denied
rev'd	reversed
rev'd in part	reversed in part
rev'd sub nom.	reversed sub nomine
subsequent appeal dism'd	subsequent appeal dismissed
syn.	synonym
viz.	namely
writ denied	writ denied
writ ref'd	writ refused

Taxation Table Abbreviations

B.T.A.	Board of Tax Appeals Reports
C.B.	Cumulative Bulletin, Internal Revenue Service
D.T.C.	Dominion Tax Cases
G.C.M.	General Counsel's memorandum
I.R.B.	Internal Revenue Bulletin
I.T.	Income Tax Ruling
P-H Federal Taxes	(Prentice-Hall) Federal Taxes
P-H Oil and Gas Taxes	(Prentice-Hall) Oil and Gas Taxes
P-H Tax. Serv.	(Prentice-Hall) Taxation Service
P-H TC Memo Dec.	(Prentice-Hall) Tax Court Memorandum Decisions
Rev. Rul. (I.R.B.)	Revenue Rulings (Internal Revenue Bulletin)
Tax A.B.C.	Income Tax Appeal Board of Canada
T.C.	Tax Court of the United States Reports
T.C. Memo	Tax Court Memorandum Decisions
T.D.	Treasury Decision

. . A . .

AAODC

American Association of Oilwell Drilling Contractors.

AAPG

American Association of Petroleum Geologists. A professional organization of geologists primarily engaged in the oil industry.

AAPL

(1) The American Association of Petroleum Landmen.

(2) The Alberta Association of Petroleum Landmen. The successor to this organization is the CANADIAN ASSOCIATION OF PETROLEUM LANDMEN (CAPL) (*q.v.*).

AAPL Form 610-1977

A model form operating agreement. See Wigley, "AAPL Form 610–1977 Model Form Operating Agreement," 24 *Rocky Mt. Min. L. Inst.* 693 (1978).

For discussions of this and other operating agreement forms see the following:

Conine, "Rights and Liabilities of Carried Interest and Nonconsent Parties in Oil and Gas Operations," 37 *Sw. Legal Fdn. Oil & Gas Inst.* 3-1 (1986);

Wigley, "AAPL Form 610-1977 Model Form Operating Agreement," 24 *Rocky Mt. Min. L. Inst.* 693 (1978);

Rathert, "Use of the Model Form Operating Agreement for the Creation and Enforcement of a Security Interest," 62 *No. Dak. L. Rev.* 197 (1986);

Young, "Oil and Gas Operations: Who Does What, To Whom, For Whom And Who Pays, How, and When," 27 *Rocky Mt. Min. L. Inst.* 1651 (1982) (comparing the 1956 and the 1977 versions).

AAPL Form 610-1982

A modification of AAPL Form 610-1977. See Himebaugh, "An Overview of Oil and Gas Contracts in the Williston Basin," 59 *No. Dak. L. Rev.* 7 at 45 (1983);

Hardwick, "The 1982 Model Form Operating Agreement," *Rocky Mt. Min. L. Inst. on Oil and Gas Agreements* Paper 8 (1983);

Wood, "Oil and Gas: A.A.P.L. Form 610 Model Form Operating Agreement: Imposing Limitations on the Operator's Ability to Require Contribution from Nondefaulting Nonoperators," 36 *Okla. L. Rev.* 730 (1983);

Peters, "The Operating Agreement," in McKinney, *Oil and Gas Litigation* (Okla. Bar Ass'n, Dep't of Continuing Legal Education 1982).

Abandoned Oil

Waste oil permitted by an operator to escape from tanks or other storage facilities after production. If the operator makes no effort to recapture this escaping oil, it has been treated in some instances as abandoned, and hence a surface owner may recapture such oil in pits or other pick-up stations. See Humphreys Oil Co. v. Liles, 277 S.W. 100 (Tex. Com. App. 1925). Statutory or administrative regulation of wasteful practices now typically prevents an operator from wasting oil by permitting its escape over the surface.

Abandoned well

A well no longer in use, whether because it was drilled as a dry hole, or has ceased to produce or for some other reason cannot be operated. Statutes and regulations in many states require the plugging of abandoned wells to prevent the seepage of oil, gas or water from one stratum to another. See PLUGGING OF WELL.

See Douglass, "The Obligations of Lessees and Others to Plug and Abandon Oil and Gas Wells," 25 *Sw. Legal Fdn. Oil & Gas Inst.* 123 (1974).

Abandoning party

A term applied in a Rocky Mountain unit operating agreement to a person who consents to the proposed abandonment of a well by the unit operator and who is entitled under the terms of the agreement to receive from nonabandoning parties the salvage value of the well. See Rocky Mountain Unit Operating Agreement Form 1 (Undivided Interest) May, 1954, Section 25.2, TREATISE § 920.3.

Abandonment

(1) In law, one method of terminating an incorporeal interest in land. The requisites of abandonment are: (a) nonuser and (b) intent to relinquish the interest. In those states where an oil and gas lease creates an incorporeal interest in realty, the doctrine of abandonment

is applicable to such interests. Boatman v. Andre, 44 Wyo. 352, 12 P.2d 370 (1932); TREATISE § 210.1. In states where a lease creates a possessory interest, abandonment is not applicable in orthodox theory, but there are suggestions that it applies anyway. See Munsey v. Marnet Oil Co., 113 Tex. 212, 254 S.W. 311 (1923); King v. Hester, 200 F.2d 807, 2 *O.&G.R.* 285 (5th Cir. 1952).

(2) The Texas courts have spoken of another kind of abandonment, the abandonment of the lease purposes, which causes automatic termination of the lease under an implied special limitation. Texas Co. v. Davis, 113 Tex. 321, 254 S.W. 304, 255 S.W. 601 (1923); TREATISE § 210.1. See DEVOTIONAL LIMITATION DOCTRINE.

(3) Similarly, there has been confusion between cancellation of a lease for violation of implied drilling covenants and termination through abandonment. See, *e.g.*, Hodges v. Mud Branch Oil & Gas Co., 270 Ky. 206, 139 S.W.2d 576 (1937). In Doss Oil Royalty Co. v. Texas Co., 192 Okla. 359, 137 P.2d 934 (1943), the Oklahoma court repudiated abandonment as the grounds for relief for failure to explore. See TREATISE §§ 842–842.3. See also FURTHER EXPLORATION COVENANT.

(4) Plugging a well, removal of installation, and termination of operations for production from the well. For a discussion of temporary and permanent abandonment of offshore wells see Gates Rubber Co. & Subsidiaries v. Commissioner, 74 T.C. 1456, 67 *O.&G.R.* 647 (1980), *aff'd,* 694 F.2d 648 (10th Cir. 1982); Sun Oil Co. & Subsidiaries v. Commissioner, 74 T.C. 1481, 68 *O.&G.R.* 353 (1980), *aff'd,* 677 F.2d 294, 76 *O.&G.R.* 619 (3rd Cir. 1982), *acq.* I.R.B. 1983-26. See also White v. Conoco, Inc., 710 F.2d 1442, 77 *O.&G.R.* 559 (10th Cir. 1983), discussing requirements for finding "abandonment of well" and concluding that the requirements had not been met in the instant case.

See also TEMPORARY ABANDONMENT.

Abandonment costs

Costs incurred in abandonment, including the plugging of wells and the removal of installations. See Lochen, "Tax Treatment of Costs of Abandonment Work and Provisions for Such Costs," in International Bar Ass'n, *Proceedings of the Energy Law Seminar* (organized by the Committee on Energy and Natural Resources, Section on Business Law) Topic J, Paper 2 (1979).

Abandonment loss

A federal income tax term referring to the deduction allowed when the taxpayer relinquishes his interest in worthless property. See Internal Revenue Code (1954) § 165; Treas. Reg. § 1.165–1 (b) (1980). See also Harmon v. Commissioner, 1 T.C. 40 (1942); L. M. Fischer, 14 T.C. 792 (1950); Louisiana Land & Exp. Co. v. Commissioner, 161 F.2d 842 (5th Cir. 1947).

See also WORTHLESSNESS, LOSS FROM.

Abandonment of facilities or service

Under Section 7(b) of the Natural Gas Act, natural gas companies are prohibited from abandoning all or any part of its facilities subject to the jurisdiction of the FEDERAL POWER COMMISSION (*q.v.*) [or of its successor, the FEDERAL ENERGY REGULATORY COMMISSION (*q.v.*)], or any service rendered by means of such facilities, without the permission and approval of the Commission first had and obtained, after due hearing, and a finding by the Commission that the available supply of natural gas is depleted to the extent that the continuance of service is unwarranted, or that the present or future public convenience or necessity permit such abandonment. In Moss v. Federal Power Comm'n, 424 U.S. 494, 54 *O.&G.R.* 247 (1976), the court made it clear that the Commission had authority to issue a LIMITED TERM CERTIFICATE (*q.v.*) or a certificate authorizing abandonment at a future date certain (see PREGRANTED ABANDONMENT).

California v. Southland Royalty Co., 436 U.S. 519, 60 *O.&G.R.* 445 (1978), *reh. denied,* 439 U.S. 885 (1978), *on remand,* 578 F.2d 659 (5th Cir. 1978), held that termination of a lease at the expiration of its term did not cause the property to return to the lessor free of the burden of Federal Power Commission control arising from certification of the sale of the gas by the former lessee, and, therefore, Commission approval to abandonment of service was a prerequisite to removal of the gas from the regulated interstate to the unregulated intrastate market. In some situations this decision was overturned by § 2(18)(B)(iii) of the Natural Gas Policy Act of 1978, Pub. L. No. 95–621. See Columbia Gas Transmission Corp. v. Allied Chem. Corp., 470 F. Supp. 532 at 548 *et seq.*, 65 *O.&G.R.* 89 at 119 *et seq.* (E.D. La. 1979), *aff'd in part, rev'd in part and remanded,* 652 F.2d 503 73 *O.&G.R.* 147 (5th Cir. 1981), and Miles, "The Meaning of the *Southland* Exclusion—Complexity and Ambiguity in the Natural Gas Policy Act," 58 *Tex. L. Rev.* 435 (1980), for detailed exegeses of the statutory language and its legislative history.

Public Serv. Co. of N.C., Inc. v. Federal Energy Regulatory Comm'n, 587 F.2d 716, 64 *O.&G.R.* 83 (5th Cir. 1979), *cert. denied,* 444 U.S. 879 (1979), held that when royalty gas had been dedicated by the producer to interstate commerce, the election by the State of Texas to take royalty gas in kind did not remove the interstate dedication made by the producer without Commission abandonment authorization, following *Southland Royalty.*

In United Gas Pipe Line Co. v. McCombs, 442 U.S. 529, 63 *O.&G.R.* 401 (1979), *on remand sub nom.* McCombs v. Federal Energy Regulatory Comm'n, 705 F.2d 1177, 78 *O.&G.R.* 601 (10th Cir. 1980), *vacated and remanded on other grounds, appeal dism'd per stipulation,* 710 F.2d 611 (10th Cir. 1983), the court rejected the position taken by a divided court below that a 1953 producer's certificate had been abandoned on depletion of all known gas reserves even though no formal abandonment had been filed with the Federal Power Commission, holding that formal Commission action to effect abandonment is required by the plain language of the Natural Gas Act.

See also Phillips Petroleum Co. v. Federal Power Comm'n, 556 F.2d 466, 59 *O.&G.R.* 242 (10th Cir. 1977) (farmee reassigned interest in lease to farmor after sale of gas in interstate commerce; *held,* gas did not qualify as new gas within meaning of FPC Opinion No. 699–H).

See also LIMITED TERM ABANDONMENT.

Abandonment of lease

See ABANDONMENT.

Abbreviated abstract

Syn. for BOB-TAIL ABSTRACT (*q.v.*).

Abbreviated application

An application to the Federal Power Commission or to its successor, the Federal Energy Regulatory Commission, in an abbreviated form for a certificate of public convenience and necessity. 18 C.F.R. § 157.7 (1980).

A-B-C transaction

The name given to a certain form of transfer of producing oil and gas property. The form was dictated by tax advantages. For example, *A* and *B* agreed on the sale to *B* of producing property for

$1,000,000. *A* conveyed to *B* for $300,000 cash and reserved a $700,000 oil payment. *A* then sold the oil payment to *C*, a corporation created for this purpose. *C* pledged the oil payment to a bank to secure its note for $700,000, the proceeds of which were used to pay *A*. Thus *A* received cash, taxed at capital gain rates, and *B* paid part of the purchase price of the property with income from production, not taxable to him.

The tax advantages of the A-B-C transaction were eliminated by the Tax Reform Act of 1969. Under Internal Revenue Code § 636, the sale of a mineral interest subject to a reserved oil payment will be treated as a sale subject to a mortgage. The seller will treat the production payment as sales proceeds; the buyer will be taxed on production, subject to depletion.

See Hardwicke, "The Purchase of Producing Oil or Gas Properties by Use of a Production Payment," 33 *Tex. L. Rev.* 848 (1955); Wilkinson, "ABC—From A to Z," 38 *Tex. L. Rev.* 673 (1960); TREATISE § 423.11.

See also ADD-ONS; INCREMENT ACCRUAL; NASSAU PLAN; SQUEEZE; TAKE-OUT-LETTER; VARIABLE DEDICATION.

Abercrombie-type carried interest

A form of CARRIED INTEREST (*q.v.*), deriving its name from Commissioner v. J. S. Abercrombie, 162 F.2d 338 (5th Cir. 1947). In this type of carried interest, *A* assigned part of the working interest in a lease to *B* and mortgaged the retained interest to secure advances made by *B* to develop the property. The part of the proceeds from production attributable to *A*'s retained interest was taxable to him and not to *B*. While the case did not so hold, it was thought that *A* was entitled to the option to deduct intangible drilling costs as to his share of such costs.

Abercrombie was overruled in United States v. Cocke, 399 F.2d 433, 29 *O.&G.R.* 527 (5th Cir. 1968), *cert. denied,* 394 U.S. 922 (1969). Carried parties were held not to have an economic interest in the oil from which expenses were recouped by carrying parties and hence such oil was not a part of the gross income of the carried parties and such parties were not entitled to deductions for intangible drilling costs and other operating expenses and for depreciation.

See Burke and Bowhay, *Income Taxation of Natural Resources* ¶ 15.19 (1981); Fielder, "The Option to Deduct Intangible Drilling and Development Costs," 33 *Tex. L. Rev.* 825 at 840–841 (1955); Estate of Weinert v. Commissioner, 294 F.2d 750, 15 *O.&G.R.* 125 (5th Cir. 1961); TREATISE § 424.1.

ABG case

Aardolie Belangen Gemeenschap v. Esso Nederland BV and others (1977), 2 C.M.L.R. D1; BP v. E.C. Comm'n (1978), 3 C.M.L.R. 174, in which BP Holland defended an action brought by the European Commission for infringement of Article 86 of the Treaty of Rome. For a discussion of the case, see Walzer, "Rome Treaty: Case Study Under Article 86 (ABG)," in International Bar Ass'n, *Proceedings of the Energy Law Seminar* (organized by the Committee on Energy and Natural Resources, Section on Business Law) Topic K, Paper 1 (1979).

Abridged hearing procedure

A procedure employed by the Federal Power Commission and its successor, the Federal Energy Regulatory Commission, for the processing of certain noncontested applications. This procedure excuses the applicants from attendance at the hearings which are required by law to be held. See Federal Power Commission, *Thirty-Seventh Annual Report* 79 (1958); 18 C.F.R. § 1.32 (1980).

Absolute ownership theory

See OWNERSHIP IN PLACE THEORY.

Absolute pressure

See PSIG.

Absorber

A device containing an oil solution through which gas is flowed for the purpose of removing heavier hydrocarbons. See ABSORPTION PLANT.

Absorption

"The extraction of one or more fluids from an atmosphere or mixture of gases or liquids, by the substance of a sorbent material with which the atmosphere, gases or liquids come in contact. The assimilation or extraction process causes (or is accompanied by) a physical or chemical change, or both, in the sorbent material. Compare ADSORPTION." American Gas Association Bureau of Statistics, *Glossary for the Gas Industry* 1.

Absorption oil

Oil used in the removal of heavier hydrocarbons from natural gas in an absorption tower. The process is described in Hugoton Production Co. v. United States, 315 F.2d 868 at 882, 18 *O.&G.R.* 365 at 385 (Ct. Cl. 1963).

Absorption plant

A device that removes liquid hydrocarbons from natural gas, especially casinghead gas. The gas is run through oil of proper character, which absorbs the liquid constituents, which are then recovered by distillation.

See also COMBINATION PLANT; COMPRESSION PLANT; PROCESSING PLANT; SEPARATOR.

Abstract of title

A collection of all the recorded instruments affecting the title to a tract of land. Some abstracts contain full and complete copies of the instruments on record while others summarize their effect. In a number of states title examination is almost always done with the use of an abstract of title.

See Herd, "Title Opinions for Oil and Gas Purposes—Structure and Information Needed by a Client," 33 *Sw. Legal Fdn. Oil & Gas Inst.* 285 (1982).

See also BOB-TAIL ABSTRACT; CERTIFICATE OF TITLE; CERTIFICATION OF ABSTRACT; PENCIL ABSTRACT; TITLE OPINION; VERBATIM ABSTRACT.

Abu Dhabi National Oil Company (ADNOC)

For a study of the operation of this company see Suleiman, "The Abu Dhabi National Oil Company," International Bar Ass'n, *Energy Law 1981* at p. 103.

Abu Dhabi Petroleum Company (ADPC)

For a study of this company see Shwadran, *The Middle East, Oil and the Great Powers* 429 (3d Ed. revised and enlarged, 1973).

Accelerated Cost Recovery System (ACRS)

A depreciation system enacted as part of the ECONOMIC RECOVERY TAX ACT OF 1981 (*q.v.*) permitting all personal property to be placed in a three, five, or ten-year class for purposes of depreciation. Internal Revenue Code § 168(c)(2).

See Bandy, "ACRS Elections Can Minimize Taxes on Oil and Gas Income," 31 *Oil & Gas Tax Q.* 852 (1983).

See also DEPRECIATION.

Accelerator

A chemical additive that reduces the setting time of cement.

Accession system

The term applied to the system in the United States whereunder the landowner has certain ownership interests in minerals, as distinguished from the DOMANIAL LAW SYSTEM (*q.v.*), under which ownership of minerals is vested in the sovereign. Blinn, Duval, Le Leuch, and Pertuzio, *International Petroleum Exploration & Exploitation Agreements* 24 (1986).

Accommodation doctrine

A doctrine applicable to the relationship of the servient surface estate and the dominant mineral estate requiring that due regard to the rights of the surface owner be given in determining the mineral owner's rights to use the surface. See Hunt Oil Co. v. Kerbaugh, 283 N.W.2d 131, 65 *O.&G.R.* 202 (N.D. 1979). Under this doctrine, inconvenience to the surface owner is not the controlling element when no reasonable alternatives are available to the mineral owner or lessee. However, when there are other usual, customary, and reasonable methods practiced in the industry on similar lands put to similar uses which would not interfere with existing uses being made by the servient surface owner, it could be unreasonable for the lessee or mineral owner to employ an interfering method or manner of use. The burden of proof is on the surface owner to show that, under the circumstances, the use of the surface under attack is not reasonably necessary.

Norvell, "Developing Lands Characterized by Separate Ownership of Oil and Gas and Surface Coal and Uranium—The Other Side of *Acker v. Guinn* and Its Progeny," 33 *Sw. Legal Fdn. Oil & Gas Inst.* 183 at 217 (1982), discussed the "balancing of interests" required by this doctrine as follows:

> "To determine the nature of the accommodation required to equitably resolve the conflict, this test may weigh the harm, utility, priority by date of operations, times of severance, along with all other relevant factors including the public interest. Conceivably, the doctrine of accommodation, if necessary to protect the inter-

ests of the oil and gas lessee and the surface mining operator, could permit interference with the existing mining operation conditioned on payment of fair compensation to the injured party."

Accommodation sales

Purchases and sales of crude oil by a refiner supplied in part by its own production for the purpose of supplying its refineries with oil of the right type and at the right location. Basin, Inc. v. Mobil Oil Corp., 616 F.2d 1199 at 1201 (Temp. Emer. Ct. App. 1980).

Accounting agreement

See GAS ACCOUNTING AGREEMENT; PASO FORM; UNIT ACCOUNTING AGREEMENT.

Accounting methods

See ACCELERATED COST RECOVERY SYSTEM (ACRS); BALANCING; BASE PERIOD CONTROL LEVEL (BPCL); BTU METHOD; BY-PRODUCTS COST ACCOUNTING METHOD; COPAS ACCOUNTING PROCEDURE; COST OF PRODUCTION METHOD; DISCOUNTED CASH FLOW METHOD; FAIR FIELD PRICE METHOD; FULL COST ACCOUNTING; FUNCTIONAL COST BENEFIT METHOD; GAS ACCOUNTING AGREEMENT; INCH-MILE ALLOCATION METHOD; MARGINAL COST PRICING; MODIFIED BTU METHOD; MODIFIED SINGLE MARKETABLE PRODUCT METHOD; NET REALIZATION ACCOUNTING METHOD; RAR METHOD; RATE BASE APPROACH; REFUNDS INTEREST RATE (RIR) PROCEDURES; RELATIVE COST METHOD OF ALLOCATION; RELATIVE MARKET VALUE METHOD; RESERVES RECOGNITION ACCOUNTING; ROLLED-IN PRICE; SALES REALIZATION METHOD; SUCCESSFUL EFFORTS ACCOUNTING; TRACT ALLOCATION METHOD; VOLUMETRIC METHOD OF ALLOCATION; VOLUME VARIATION ADJUSTMENT CLAUSE; WEIGHTED AVERAGE METHOD.

Accredited investor

For purposes of REGULATION D (*q.v.*) of the Securities and Exchange Commission providing for a PRIVATE OFFERING EXEMPTION (*q.v.*) under the Federal Securities Act, an accredited investor (who need not be included in the 35 investors to whom a private offering may be made) is a person reasonably believed by the issuer not to fall within one of four categories specified by Rule 501, 17 C.F.R. § 230.501(a) (1982) (banks, insurance companies, investment companies, certain organizations with total assets in excess of $5,000,000, etc.). See TREATISE § 441.4.

Accrued royalty

Payments due the lessor or royalty owner for oil, gas or other minerals already produced by the lessee or operator. Whatever the local classification of a royalty as realty or as personalty, accrued royalty is treated as personalty. See United States v. Noble, 237 U.S. 74 at 80 (1915).

See also ROYALTY; UNACCRUED ROYALTY.

Achnacarry agreement

An agreement entered into in 1927 by Standard Oil Co. (New Jersey), Royal Dutch-Shell, and Anglo-Persian Oil Co., Ltd., said to involve a division of control over world oil consumption and prices. See U.S. Congress, Senate Committee on Interior and Insular Affairs, Trends in Oil and Gas Exploration, Hearings 1972, p. 1150; Danielsen, *The Evolution of OPEC* 120 (1982).

Acid bottle inclinometer

A device used in a deviational examination or survey of a well (as opposed to a directional survey). See Williams v. Continental Oil Co., 215 F.2d 4, 3 *O.&G.R.* 2080 (10th Cir. 1954), *cert. denied,* 348 U.S. 928 (1955).

See also DEVIATIONAL SURVEY.

Acid dip survey

A method of determining the inclination of a well bore by lowering a glass container of hydrofluoric acid into a borehole. In a brief period of time, the glass is etched by the acid, permitting the determination of the inclination of the borehole.

Acid fracturing

The process of opening cracks in hard carbonate productive formations by using a combination of oil and acid under high pressure.

See also FRACTURING.

Acid gas

Syn. for SOUR GAS (*q.v.*).

Acidizing of well

A technique for increasing the flow of oil from a well. Hydrochloric acid is introduced into the well to enlarge and reopen pores in oil-bearing limestone formations. An inhibited acid is used to prevent corrosion of the tubing. Pressure is applied to force the acid into the rock channels and pores, which causes their softer parts to become soluble. After a predetermined time, the acid is flowed or pumped out, leaving enlarged pores in the oil-bearing stratum. The acid attacks the limestone formation in all directions, and, amenable to the law of gravity, the downward pressure is greater than the lateral pressure, assuming equal density of strata. A blanket of calcium chloride or some other heavy inert liquid may be required at the bottom of the well to arrest the penetration of the acid downward to the salt water level. See Empire Oil & Refining Co. v. Hoyt, 112 F.2d 356 (6th Cir. 1940).

Acknowledgment

(1) In Louisiana, a method by which the PRESCRIPTION (*q.v.*) of a mineral servitude or a mineral royalty may be interrupted. See Articles 54–55, 93–96 of the Louisiana Mineral Code [(R.S. 31:54–55, 93–96 (1975)]; TREATISE § 216.3(c). See also PRESCRIPTION.

(2) A declaration or avowal of an act or a fact to give it legal effect.

ACMA

The ALASKA COASTAL MANAGEMENT ACT (*q.v.*).

Acoustical well logging

Determination of properties or dimensions of a borehole by acoustical means. See WELL LOG.

See also Hilchie, "Well Logging," in *Rocky Mt. Min. L. Fdn. Basic Oil and Gas Technology for Lawyers and Landmen* (1979).

Acquired federal lands

Those lands in federal ownership which have never been "public domain" and those lands in federal ownership which have once been public lands but have been disposed of as such and which the United States has subsequently reacquired by purchase, condemnation, or donation. Certain of the special problems of disposition of minerals in acquired lands are discussed in Fritz, "Mineral Problems Relating to Acquired Federal Lands," 3 *Rocky Mt. Min. L. Inst.* 379 (1957); *Rocky Mt. Min. L. Fdn. Law of Federal Oil and Gas Leases* Ch. 9–10 (1985).

The distinction between acquired lands and public domain lands is discussed in Bobby Lee Moore, A–30433 (Mimeo Dec., Dep't of the Interior, Nov. 1, 1965), holding that public land which has been patented and has passed into private ownership does not regain the status of public land upon being acquired subsequently by the United States through purchase or condemnation.

See also PUBLIC LANDS.

Acquired Lands Leasing Act of 1947

61 Stat. 913, 30 U.S.C. §§ 351–359.

Acquisition royalty trust

A ROYALTY TRUST (*q.v.*) created by a corporation in conjunction with an acquisition transaction.

Acquisitive prescription

Prescription *acquirendi causa.* The law of acquisitive prescription in Louisiana is codified in Articles 153–163 of the Louisiana Mineral Code [R.S. 31:153 to 31:163 (1975)]. See TREATISE § 224.6; Doyle, "Acquisitive Prescription in the Examination of Oil and Gas Titles," 8 *L.S.U. Min. L. Inst.* 88 (1961).

See also PRESCRIPTION.

Acre

43,560 square feet or 4840 square yards or 160 square rods.

See also MINERAL ACRE; ROYALTY ACRE.

Acreage attribution

For purposes of production allowables, the credit to a well of the acreage to be drained by the well in excess of the normal spacing unit drained thereby. Thus in Oklahoma where one well is to drain two 40-acre units, the ALLOWABLE (*q.v.*) is frequently fixed at between 125 per cent and 150 per cent of the regular 40-acre unit allowable, and where the well is to drain two 80-acre units, the allowable may be fixed at 180 per cent, as in Kingwood Oil Co. v. Corporation Commission, 396 P.2d 1008, 21 *O.&G.R.* 620 (Okla. 1964).

Acreage based royalty

A term occasionally used to describe a ROYALTY (*q.v.*) payable on a per acre basis, *e.g.*, a royalty expressed as a fixed sum per acre on a shut-in well or a royalty payable while drilling or other operations are excused during *force majeure.* See Greene v. Carter Oil Co., 152 So. 2d 611, 19 *O.&G.R.* 517 (La. App. 1963), *writ refused,* 244 La. 621, 153 So. 2d 414, 19 *O.&G.R.* 528 (1963).

Acreage basis

A basis for participation by parties within a unit area in production and expenses, *viz.*, participation in the proportion that the acreage of the party bears to the total acreage of all parties in the unit area. See Rocky Mountain Unit Operating Agreement Form 2 (Divided Interest) January 1955, Section 1.6, TREATISE § 920.4.

Acreage contribution agreement

See ACREAGE CONTRIBUTION LETTER.

Acreage contribution letter

A common form of agreement whereby *A* agrees to drill a test well in a certain location, making available to *B* all information from the well, in return for which *B* agrees to assign *A* certain leases held by *B* in the vicinity of the well. See TREATISE § 431. Such assignment is usually made upon completion of the test well. For a typical acreage contribution letter, see Williams, Maxwell, Meyers, and Williams, *Cases on Oil and Gas* 999 (5th ed. 1987).

For cases construing acreage contribution agreements see the following:

Superior Oil Co. v. Cox, 307 So.2d 350, 50 *O.&G.R.* 323 (La. 1975);

Harper Oil Co. v. Yates Petroleum Corp., 105 N.M. 430, 733 P.2d 1313, ____ *O.&G.R.* ____ (1987).

For other forms of letter agreements, see LETTER.

Acreage estimate provision

A lease clause providing that for designated purposes (*e.g.*, payment of bonus, rentals, shut-in royalties) the premises granted shall be treated as comprising a designated number of acres, whether there be more or less. See TREATISE § 665.6.

Syn.: "IN GROSS" PROVISION.

Acreage factor

The acreage allocated to a well for the purpose of determining allowable production. See Anderson-Prichard Oil Corp. v. Corporation Commission, 205 Okla. 672, 241 P.2d 363, 1 *O.&G.R.* 391 (1951), *appeal dism'd,* 342 U.S. 938 (1952). Thus the basic order considered in Stevens v. State Corporation Comm'n, 185 Kan. 190, 341 P.2d 1021, 11 *O.&G.R.* 804 (1959), provided that one well completed in a particular formation could adequately and sufficiently drain 640 acres without causing waste, and that the basic acreage unit to be used in the proration formula was 640 acres. The acreage factor of a well in this case equalled the number of acres held by production from said well divided by 640.

See also ALLOWABLE.

Acreage or cash contribution clause

See CONTRIBUTION CLAUSE.

Acreage retention clause

This term was used in Dawes v. Hale, 421 So. 2d 1208, 75 *O.&G.R.* 233 (La. App. 1982), as having the meaning of a RETAINED ACREAGE CLAUSE (*q.v.*).

Acreage selection clause

(1) A lease clause that permits the lessee to select certain acreage for drilling after conducting geophysical surveys. In the typical situation, the lessee takes a short term (60 or 90 days) oil and gas lease in sizeable acreage, for the purpose of making the geophysical survey. The clause permits the operator to extend the lease on the selected acreage when the survey has been completed, usually upon payment of a further sum. The same purpose can be served by making a contract for survey rights with an option to lease selected acreage. See Houston Farms Dev. Co. v. United States, 131 F.2d 577, 132 F.2d 861 (5th Cir. 1943); Bennett v. Scofield, 170 F.2d 887 (5th Cir. 1948); TREATISE §§ 696–696.1.

See also SHOOTING LEASE; SHOOTING OPTION; SHOOTING RIGHTS.

(2) A clause in a contract for the assignment of leases authorizing the purchaser to select the leases to be assigned. See Stekoll Petroleum Co. v. Hamilton, 152 Tex. 182, 255 S.W.2d 187, 2 *O.&G.R.* 102 (1953).

Acreage tolerance

The acreage (usually expressed by a percentage) by which a specified area may be exceeded for various purposes:

(1) in the formation of a unit of specified size under the provisions of a lease pooling clause [*viz.*, "Any unit formed by such pooling . . . shall not exceed 640 acres (plus a tolerance of 10%) for gas or gas condensate and shall not exceed 40 acres (plus a tolerance of 10%) for any other substance covered by this lease." See TREATISE § 669.10];

(2) the area for which a well will be viewed as adequate development [*viz.*, "in no event shall the lessee be required to drill more than one well per 640 acres plus an acreage tolerance of not more than 10% of 640 acres of the area retained hereunder and capable of producing gas in paying quantities."];

(3) the area for which an allowable based on acreage may be granted [*viz.*, "No gas proration unit shall contain more than three hundred twenty (320) acres except as hereinafter provided; . . . provided that tolerance acreage of ten (10) per cent shall be allowed for each unit so that an amount not to exceed a maximum of three hundred fifty two (352) acres may be assigned, and each unit containing less than three hundred twenty (320) acres shall be a fractional proration unit." Special Order Adopting Rules and Regulations for the Normanna Fields, Bee County, Texas, 14 *O.&G.R.* 885 at 887–888 (1961)].

Acre foot of sand

A unit of measurement applied to petroleum reservoirs. It is an acre of producing formation one foot thick. For purposes of fixing allowable or participation in a unit operations agreement, acre feet of sand under each tract provides an acceptable measure in most cases. See American Petroleum Institute, *Standards of Allocation of Oil Production* 55 (1942).

Acre yield

The average quantity of oil, gas or water produced from each acre of a reservoir.

Acromorph

A SALT DOME (*q.v.*).

ACRS depreciation

See ACCELERATED COST RECOVERY SYSTEM (ACRS).

ACT

The advance corporation tax required to be paid by a company resident in the United Kingdom when it pays a dividend. The Finance Act 1976, § 84. See Daintith and Willoughby, *A Manual of United Kingdom Oil and Gas Law* 93 (1977).

Act of God clause

See FORCE MAJEURE CLAUSE

Act of State doctrine

A doctrine formulated in Underhill v. Hernandez, 168 U.S. 250 (1897), under which the courts of the United States have refused to sit in judgment on the acts of the government of another country done within its own territory. Redress of grievances are to be obtained through the means open to be availed of by sovereign powers as between themselves. See Comment, "American Oil Investors' Access to Domestic Courts in Foreign Nationalization Disputes," 123 *U. Pa. L. Rev.* 610 at 617 (1975).

This doctrine was held to bar inquiry into the validity of Libya's nationalization of concession agreements. Hunt v. Mobil Oil Corp., 550 F.2d 68 (2d Cir. 1977), *cert. denied,* 434 U.S. 984 (1977); Hunt v. Coastal States Gas Producing Co., 583 S.W.2d 322 (Tex. 1979), *cert. denied,* 444 U.S. 992 (1979), *reh. denied,* 444 U.S. 1103 (1980).

The applicability of the Act of State doctrine to conduct of the OPEC cartel is discussed in Joelson and Griffin, "The Legal Status of Nation-State Cartels Under United States Antitrust and Public International Law," 9 *International Lawyer* 617 (1975).

See also BERNSTEIN LETTER.

ACT system (ACTS)

See AUTOMATIC CUSTODY TRANSFER SYSTEM.

Actual calendar day allowable

The ALLOWABLE (*q.v.*) on a per day basis. It is calculated as follows: (1) the NONPRORATABLE ALLOWABLE (*q.v.*) is deducted from the total SCHEDULE ALLOWABLE (*q.v.*); (2) the remainder is multiplied by the number of producing days in the month; (3) the product is added to the allowable of the marginal and exempt fields to arrive at the actual calendar day allowable for the month. See Zimmermann, *Conservation in the Production of Petroleum* 219 (1957).

Also the allowable for a well or leasehold on a per day basis.

Actual drilling operations

This term has been construed by an Interior Department decision as requiring the actual penetration of the ground by the drill bit. Preliminary work as grading roads and well sites and moving equipment onto the leased land were viewed as insufficient. Estelle Wolf, IBLA 77–145, GFS(O&G) 1978–157. Distinguished were such terms as "drilling operations," "commencement of drilling operations," "commencement of a well," and the like. See also Classic Mining Corp., IBLA 78–183, GFS(O&G) 1978–166; Webb Resources, Inc., IBLA 78–499, GFS(O&G) 1979–8; Phoenix Resources Co., IBLA 78–343, GFS(O&G) 1979–21.

See also DRILLING OPERATIONS.

Ada mud

A conditioning material which may be added to drilling mud in order to obtain satisfactory cores and samples of formations. See MUD.

Adaptation Clause

A clause in an oil or gas supply agreement designed to permit adaptation of price provisions of the agreement in the event of substantial economic change. See Daniel, "Adaptation Clauses in North Sea Oil Supply Agreements," 1 *J. of Energy & Natural Resources Law* 100 (1983):

"There now exist three main types of adaptation clauses:

(i) the clause providing for a review of the price within a period of three months ('a quarter');

(ii) the 'hardship' or 'change of circumstances' clauses;

(iii) the *force majeure* clause.

"Each of these clauses is drafted to cover events which were unforeseen at the time the contract was made, and each of these clauses, it is suggested, *ought* to concern itself with a change which *materially* affects the agreement.

". . .

". . . Also encountered in North Sea supply agreements are what are commonly known as hardship clauses. The circumstances which give rise to the hardship must of course be beyond the control of both parties and should, on any view, be uncontemplated and unforeseeable.

"Although these clauses are referred to as 'hardship' clauses and at first sight afford protection to both parties to the oil supply agreement, the economic necessity of obtaining a continued access to North Sea oil has resulted in the development of what is termed a 'Change in Seller's Circumstances' clause. By the use of the 'Change in Seller's Circumstances' clause, parties to North Sea oil supply agreements have gone one stage further than the normal view of hardship clauses. Whereas the original concept of the hardship clause was to cover substantial hardship, so that the change of circumstances results in consequences and effects fundamentally different from that which was contemplated by the parties at the time of entering into the agreement, the 'Change in Seller's Circumstances' clauses in North Sea supply agreements do not rely for their effect on there having been a substantial alteration in the terms of the contract. Some clauses are sufficiently widely drafted to allow their use in every possible circumstance. Thus a typical 'Change in Seller's Circumstances' clause would provide that if at any time in the life of the agreement there is a change 'of any kind' in the circumstances in which a seller carries on his business as a crude oil seller, then the seller may be entitled to invoke the clause and request a meeting with the buyer. Some clauses do not even provide that the change of circumstances need have had a significant or material effect on the way in which the seller carries on his duties under the agreement."

See also the following:

Biller, "Special Features of Norwegian North Sea Gas Contracts," International Bar Ass'n Section on Energy and Natural Resources, *International Energy Law* (1984) (Topic 5);

Kemp, "Applying the Hardship Clause," 1 *J. of Energy & Natural Resources Law* 119 (1983) (discussing Superior Overseas Development Corp v. British Gas Corp., [1982] 1 Lloyd's Rep. 262).

Ad coelum doctrine

The doctrine that ownership of land extends from the heavens to the core of the earth: *cujus est solum, ejus est usque ad coelum et ad inferos* .

Additional Profits Tax

An additional tax provided for by some agreements between host governments and foreign oil companies chargeable whenever profits net of company income tax exceed a specified rate of return on capital employed. See Hossain, *Law and Policy in Petroleum Development* 198, 225, 230 (1979).

See also CONCESSION.

Additional royalty

The Outer Continental Shelf Lands Act of 1953, 43 U.S.C. § 1331 *et seq.*, provided a procedure under which prior state leases, the status of which were rendered uncertain by Supreme Court decisions, would be validated by the federal government, subject to certain conditions. One such condition was that the lessee agree to pay a royalty of not less than 12 1/2 per centum and as "additional royalty" on the production from the lease, less the United States' royalty interest in such production, a sum of money equal to the amount of the severance, gross production, or occupation taxes which would have been payable on such production to the state issuing the lease under its laws as they existed on August 7, 1953. 43 U.S.C. § 1335(a)(9). In Ocean Drilling & Exploration Co. v. United States, 600 F.2d 1343, 63 *O.&G.R.* 417 (Ct. Cl. 1979), the court concluded that the "additional royalty" was in fact "royalty," which was excludible from taxpayer's gross income, rather than a continuation of the former severance tax, and therefore deductible as such.

See also ROYALTY.

Additive

Chemical added to oil or other products to enhance certain characteristics of the product. See Asiatic Petroleum Corp. v. United States, 183 F. Supp. 275, 12 *O.&G.R.* 841 (Customs Court 1959).

Add-ons

(1) Additional sums added on to the amount of an oil payment in an A-B-C TRANSACTION (*q.v.*), representing certain taxes and expenses of the owner of the production payment. See Sack, "ABC's of the ABC Oil Transaction," 59 *Northwestern L. Rev.* 591 (1964).

(2) This term is also applied to clauses of gas purchase and sale contracts providing for increases in prices, *e.g.*, in the amount of new severance taxes or in the amount of increased compression, gathering, or treatment costs. See Watson, "The Natural Gas Policy Act of

1978 and Gas Purchase Contracts," 27 *Rocky Mt. Min. L. Inst.* 1407 at 1429 (1982).

Adjoining

Meeting or touching at some point. See, *e.g.*, Acree v. Shell Oil Co., 548 F. Supp. 1150, 75 *O.&G.R.* 5 (M.D. La. 1982), *aff'd,* 721 F.2d 524 (5th Cir. 1983), holding that properties that touch at a corner are "adjoining."

Adjusted allowable

The allowable production a well or proration unit receives after all adjustments are made. New Mexico Oil Conservation Comm'n, Rules and Regulations 1 (1958).

See also ALLOWABLE.

Adjusted base price

For purposes of the CRUDE OIL WINDFALL PROFIT TAX OF 1980 (*q.v.*), this term means the base price for the barrel of crude oil being sold plus an amount equal to—

(1) such base price multiplied by

(2) the inflation adjustment for the calendar quarter in which the crude oil is removed from the premises. Internal Revenue Code § 4989.

Adjusted deliverability formula

A proration formula for natural gas based on a well's ability to produce into a pipeline against a specific back pressure, adjusted for the well's attributed acreage, each well being allocated an allowable in proportion to the total field allowables as its adjusted deliverability bears to the total adjusted deliverability of all wells. Cities Service Oil Co. v. State Corporation Comm'n, 205 Kan. 655 at 660, 472 P.2d 257 at 261, 38 *O.&G.R.* 379 at 385 (1970); 207 Kan. 43, 483 P.2d 1123, 38 *O.&G.R.* 402 (1971).

See also ALLOWABLE.

Adjusted posted price

POSTED PRICE (*q.v.*) adjusted for quality and gravity of the crude oil and a fixed selling charge in lieu of charging any selling or other marketing expense in the cost of operation. See the Oil Concession Agreement between Kuwait, the Kuwait National Petroleum Co.

and Hispanica de Petroles [OPEC, *Selected Documents of the International Petroleum Industry* 1968 at p. 156].

See also CONCESSION.

Adjustment of unit interests

A reallocation of interests in a unit agreement after the formation of the unit on the basis of facts known at the time of the reallocation or adjustment. If a unit agreement is entered into before the property is fully developed, it is impossible to estimate accurately the reserves beneath the various unitized properties. Under these circumstances, the agreement may provide that for a period of time the participants reserve the right to redetermine the interests accruing to each participant in the agreement. The reallocation of interests may be prospective in character or may be both prospective and retroactive. For the tax consequences of an adjustment of unit interests, see Burke and Bowhay, *Income Taxation of Natural Resources* ¶¶ 17.12–17.14 (1980).

ADMA

The Abu Dhabi Marine Areas, Ltd. See Shwadran, *The Middle East, Oil and the Great Powers* 439 (3d ed. revised and enlarged, 1973).

Administrative overhead

A term employed loosely in the oil and gas industry to describe a variety of expenses. Thus, in Mason v. Ladd Petroleum Corp., 630 P.2d 1283, 70 *O.&G.R.* 586 (Okla. 1981), the court quoted different definitions given the term by witnesses and by the trial court, concluding that expenses so described should not be considered in determining whether production was in paying quantities.

Ladd Petroleum Corp. v. Eagle Oil & Gas Co., 695 S.W.2d 99, 87 *O.&G.R.* 116 (Tex. App. Fort Worth 1985, error ref'd n.r.e.), concluded that district expense and administrative overhead which would continue in effect even if the operation of a well were to cease should not be included as overhead in determining whether a well was producing in paying quantities.

See also DISTRICT EXPENSES.

ADNOC

The Abu Dhabi National Oil Company (ADNOC) (*q.v.*).

Adoption

In Louisiana, a method whereby a mineral servitude owner may cause operations or production by some other person to be treated as his own. See Articles 44–53 of the Louisiana Mineral Code [R.S. 31:44–53 (1975)]; TREATISE § 216.3(b).

ADPC

The Abu Dhabi Petroleum Company. See Shwadran, *The Middle East, Oil and the Great Powers* 439 (3d ed. revised and enlarged, 1973).

Adsorption

The attraction exerted by the surface of solid matter for a liquid or gas with which there is contact.

"The extraction from an atmosphere or mixture of gases or liquids of one or more fluids, by surface adhesion to that material with which the atmosphere, gases or liquids come in contact. The adsorption or extraction process does not cause and is not accompanied by either a physical or chemical change in the sorbent material. Compare ABSORPTION." American Gas Association Bureau of Statistics, *Glossary for the Gas Industry* 1.

Adsorption process

A process for the extraction of various products from gas involving the circulation of gas through beds of charcoal followed by separation of the products adhering to the charcoal through vaporization by the application of heat.

Ad valorem charge

A form of lease rental based upon the appraised value of the unproduced mineral in the ground. As new information is obtained by discovery and proving of reserves, the appraisal of the unproduced mineral in the ground will change and with it the amount of the rental. See Gaffney, *Oil and Gas Leasing Policy: Alternatives for Alaska in 1977* (1977).

See also LEASE BIDDING SYSTEMS.

Ad valorem tax

A local property tax based on the assessed value of the property taxed.

Lynch v. State Board of Equalization, 164 Cal.App.3d 94, 210 Cal.Rptr. 335 (1985), sustained the validity of the State Board of Equalization's Rule 468 establishing valuation principles for taxation of oil and gas reserves. For purposes of ad valorem taxation under the acquisition system adopted by the voters in 1978 by Proposition 13, value of an oil and gas property is based on proven reserves. Additions to proven reserves in the course of a year may be assessed on the basis of value at the time of recognition, but existing proven reserves are not subject to reassessment on the basis of increase in value due to inflation.

See also FLUSH PRODUCTION

Advance payment

Money paid to gas suppliers for exploration, development, or production of natural gas, which amount is to be repaid in cash, by delivery of gas or recovered in cost of service. American Gas Ass'n, *Glossary for the Gas Industry* (3d ed. 1981).

Advance payment agreement

An agreement to make an advance payment to a producer for gas to be delivered at a future date. See ADVANCE PAYMENT ORDER.

In Tennessee Gas Pipeline Co., 56 F.P.C. 120, 10 FPS 5–240.1 (Opinion No. 769, July 9, 1976), the Federal Power Commission declared that front-end advance payments are presumptively extravagant and affirmed the exclusion of a pipeline's Canadian advance payments from its rate base.

Advance payment financing

A method of financing oil and gas development whereunder a sum of money is advanced for development of a property in exchange for the right to receive a portion of the oil and gas produced and saved. Thus, for each advance of $1 the party making the advance might become entitled to receive a portion of the oil or gas produced until such time as the cumulative value of the oil or gas received equals $1.50. In this respect, advance payment financing is akin to a PRODUCTION PAYMENT (*q.v.*). The advancing party may also acquire a preferential right to purchase the remaining oil and gas produced. See Ladbury, "Recent Trends in Limited Recourse Financing with Particular Reference to Limited Recourse Loans, Production Payments and Forward Sale and Purchase Agreements," 2 *Austl. Mining & Petroleum L.J.* 68 at 74 (1979).

See also PROJECT FINANCING.

Advance payment order

An order of the Federal Power Commission authorizing natural gas pipelines to include in their rate bases certain advance payments made to producers for gas to be delivered at a future date. A challenge to such orders was remanded to the Commission for further consideration to permit the Commission to engage in a meaningful review, analysis and evaluation of the experience under the program. Public Service Comm'n v. Federal Power Comm'n, 511 F.2d 338, 50 *O.&G.R.* 231 (D.C. Cir. 1975). See also Michigan Wisconsin Pipe Line Co. v. Federal Power Comm'n, 520 F.2d 84 (D.C. Cir. 1975). On remand, the Commission terminated the program with conditions. Docket Nos. R–411 and RM74–4 (Dec. 31, 1975), 8 FPS 5–158.1, *clarified and amended on rehearing,* Feb. 27, 1976, 8 FPS 5–527.

For reviews of the history of the advance payment order, see the following:

United Gas Pipe Line Co. v. Federal Energy Regulatory Comm'n, 597 F.2d 581 (5th Cir. 1979), *cert. denied,* 445 U.S. 916 (1980);

Tennessee Gas Pipeline Co. v. Federal Energy Regulatory Comm'n, 606 F.2d 1094 (D.C. Cir. 1979), *cert. denied,* 447 U.S. 922 (1980);

Natural Gas Pipeline Co. of America v. Federal Energy Regulatory Comm'n, 590 F.2d 664 (7th Cir. 1979).

See also PRICE CONTROL OF OIL, GAS OR PETROLEUM PRODUCTS.

Advance Petroleum Revenue Tax (APRT) System

A part of the system established by the Finance Act 1981 for the collection of the PETROLEUM REVENUE TAX (PRT) (*q.v.*). See North, "The New Advance Petroleum Revenue Tax (APRT) System," [1982] 3 *OGLTR* 73.

Advance royalty

(1) At one time for Federal income taxation purposes lease bonus was referred to and treated as advance royalty, and thus was subject to the depletion allowance but was not subject to capital gains treatment. Herring v. Commissioner, 293 U.S. 322 (1934). Where bonus was received, a well drilled and abandoned as a dry hole and the lease released, all in the same year, no depletion was allowed. Camp-

bell v. Commissioner, 41 T.C. 91 (1963). See also Treas. Reg. § 1.612–3(b) (1980).

(2) In certain lease forms (particularly in California) the term is used to describe a SHUT-IN ROYALTY (*q.v.*) payment for gas wells paid during the period the gas well is shut-in for want of a market. The lessee may be authorized by the lease to deduct any such payments made out of some fraction, *e.g.*, ½, of the royalties on production thereafter payable.

(3) Minimum royalty is also referred to as advance royalty, for the lessee is obligated to pay certain sums in advance, subject to his right to recoup from royalty oil. See McFaddin, 2 T.C. 395 (1943); Alice G. K. Kleberg, 43 B.T.A. 277 (1941).

Pittsburgh National Bank v. Allison Engineering Co., 279 Pa. Super. 442, 421 A.2d 281 (1980), concluded that it was so well-established as to be a rule of law that a minimum royalty provided for by a coal lease was not an advance royalty, to be recouped against later tonnage royalties, but was a liquidated rental for property whether or not the coal is mined, and the minimum royalty may not be applied to payment for the coal remaining in place unless expressly so provided.

Engle v. Comm'r of Internal Revenue, 677 F.2d 594, 74 *O.&G.R.* 617 (7th Cir. 1982), reversing a Tax Court decision, held that percentage depletion could be claimed on advance royalty although there was no physical extraction of minerals in the taxable year. Farmar v. United States, 689 F.2d 1017 (Ct. Cl. 1982), held that percentage depletion could not be claimed on lease bonus granted in both cases, 103 S. Ct. 722 (1983). *Engle* was affirmed and *Farmar* was reversed in Comm'r v. Engle, 464 U.S. 206, 104 S. Ct. 597, 79 *O.&G.R.* 391 (1984). The Tax Reform Act of 1986 overruled the Supreme Court holding in *Engle.* Independent producers and royalty owners can no longer claim percentage depletion for lease bonuses, advance royalties or other amounts payable without regard to production from the property received or accrued after August 16, 1986.

See also DEPLETION PERCENTAGE; ROYALTY.

AEOT

AVERAGE EVALUATION OF TRACT (*q.v.*).

AFE

(1) Authority for Expenditure or Authorization for Expenditure. See Buttes Gas & Oil Co. v. Willard Pease Drilling Co., 467 F.2d 281, 43 *O.&G.R.* 481 (10th Cir. 1972); Lammerts v. Humble Oil &

Refining Co., 489 P.2d 485, 40 *O.&G.R.* 238 (Okla. 1970); Haas v. Gulf Coast Natural Gas Co., 484 S.W.2d 127, 43 *O.&G.R.* 381 (Tex. Civ. App. 1972). For a discussion of problems arising from the provisions of an operating agreement relating to the AFE see Heaney, "The Joint Operating Agreement, the AFE and COPAS—What They Fail to Provide," 29 *Rocky Mt. Min. L. Inst.* 743 (1983), and Young, "Oil and Gas Operating Agreements," 20 *Rocky Mt. Min. L. Inst.* 197 at 203 (1975).

M & T, Inc. v. Fuel Resources Development Co., 518 F. Supp. 285, 70 *O.&G.R.* 232 (D. Colo. 1981), commented as follows concerning an AFE:

> "An AFE is a form which is widely used in the oil and gas industry when wells are drilled by multiple parties. The AFE sets forth the location of the well, its objective geological formation, an estimated depth at which that formation will be encountered, the estimated costs of drilling and completion, and miscellaneous other information. It is prepared by the 'operator' of the well, and execution of the AFE by the nonoperating owners of working interests in the underlying leaseholds is a written manifestation of their consent to participate in the well. It is axiomatic that drilling costs cannot be estimated with certainty and that an AFE is at best a good-faith estimate. AFE's are usually exceeded, often by very substantial amounts. . . .
>
> "In the oil and gas industry, it is understood and accepted that when one signs an AFE, he is committed to his proportionate share of the necessary costs in drilling to the objective specified in the AFE, unless the parties mutually agree to terminate drilling earlier or to attempt a completion at a shallower formation."

The court rejected as "novel and somewhat imaginative, but nevertheless meritless" the contention that the AFE set a ceiling upon expenditures to which consent was given by a party and further rejected as "meritless" the contention that a party had the right to go nonconsent at the time the AFE estimate was surpassed.

> "In sum, I hold that the AFE was only an estimate; that approval of an AFE is a commitment to pay one's proportionate share of all reasonable and necessary costs incurred until the objective formation or casing point is reached or until the parties mutually agree to terminate. Further I hold that an AFE gives no right to go nonconsent and that the point at which a party can go nonconsent, in the absence of express written agreement, is determined by industry custom and practice."

Renaissance Resources Ltd. v. Metalore Resources Ltd., [1984] 4 W.W.R. 430 (Alta. Q.B. 1984), *app. and cross-app. dism'd,* [1985] 4

W.W.R. 633 (Alta. Ct. App. 1985), concluded that once a participant in a drilling project approved an AFE, the party became liable for its share of the total costs of the undertaking, including both the drilling and the abandonment of the well.

Grynberg v. Roberts, 102 N.M. 560, 698 P.2d 430, 85 *O.&G.R.* 582 (1985), held that parties to an AFE who failed to make timely payment of money due were liable for prejudgment interest.

Sonat Exploration Co. v. Mann, 785 F.2d 1232, 89 *O.&G.R.* 498 (5th Cir. 1986), concluded that execution of an AFE by the owner of a working interest who had not signed or ratified the pertinent operating agreement did not obligate the signer to pay drilling costs demanded by the operator, the AFE utilized by the parties not containing language which could be taken as a promise to pay a part of the reflected costs.

(2) This acronym is also used for Authorized Field Expenditure, "a detailed explanation of costs to be incurred, which is supplemented as costs change; its purpose is to provide full, fair, and complete cost estimates, and it is a practice in the petroleum industry for consultants who are hired to serve clients without expertise or knowledge of the industry to prepare AFEs for their clients." Sedco International, S.A. v. Cory, 522 F. Supp. 254 at 291 (S.D. Iowa 1981) (declaring that managers of a joint venture violated professional standards by providing no AFEs for an investor), *aff'd,* 683 F.2d 1201 (8th Cir. 1982), *cert. denied,* 459 U.S. 1017, 103 S. Ct. 379 (1982).

Affidavit of noncompliance

An affidavit filed by the owner of land when a lease shall become forfeited by failure of the lessee to comply with its provisions and the lessee has failed to execute and record a release of record. Iowa Code Ann., § 84.22 (1980 Supp.)

Affidavit of nondevelopment

An affidavit which may be required by a title examiner for oil properties when there is of record an unreleased lease on the premises which is believed to have terminated by reason of nondevelopment. If the primary term of the lease has not expired, the affidavit will cover both nondevelopment and nonpayment of rentals. See *Rocky Mt. Min. L. Fdn., Landman's Legal Handbook* 141 (3d ed. 1977).

Affidavit of production

An affidavit setting forth the description of a lease, that the affiant is the owner thereof, and the facts showing that the required contingency for extending the lease into the secondary term has occurred. See *e.g.*, Kan. Stat. Ann. § 55–205 (1976). Where required, such affidavit should be filed by each partial assignee of a lease and each owner of a lease included in a joint operating, pooling or unit agreement where the lease is extended by production or other operations. See Cities Service Oil Co. v. Adair, 273 F.2d 673, 12 *O.&G.R.* 660 (10th Cir. 1959).

In Superior Oil Co. v. Devon Corp., 458 F. Supp. 1063, 61 *O.&G.R.* 61 (D. Neb. 1978), the court ruled that, under Nebraska law, there was no absolute duty to file an affidavit of production and that failure of the lessee to file the affidavit did not alter the contractual relationship between the parties to a lease. The lease was preserved into the secondary term as to all of the leased premises by production under the lease despite failure to file the affidavit. On other grounds, however, the lease was held to have been terminated in part by reason of breach of the covenant of further development. On appeal, the judgment was reversed and remanded with directions. 604 F.2d 1063, 65 *O.&G.R.* 368 (8th Cir. 1979). The appellate court agreed that failure to file the affidavit of production did not affect the contractual relationship between the lessor and the lessee. However, it concluded that, after the expiration of the primary term of the lease, the lease "did not provide notice to subsequent purchasers of its existence." Hence, a purchaser of a new lease from the lessor upon undeveloped acreage included in the earlier lease "who relied upon the public records and who did not otherwise have actual or constructive notice of the [earlier] lease would therefore be a subsequent good faith purchaser for value, and his leasehold interest would be prior to that of the lessees under the [earlier] lease." 604 F.2d at 1072, 65 *O.&G.R.* at 382.

Affreightment

See CONTRACT OF AFFREIGHTMENT.

AFRA

Average Freight Rate Assessments, published by the London Tanker Brokers Panel.

See also WORLDSCALE.

AFRA LR I

Freight valuation calculated for Long Range I oil tankers (45,000–79,999 DWT), expressed in terms of percent of WORLDSCALE (*q.v.*).

AFRA LR II

Freight valuation calculated for Long Range II oil tankers (80,000–159,999 DWT), expressed in terms of percent of WORLDSCALE (*q.v.*).

African Petroleum Producers' Association (APPA)

An organization comprised of four OPEC members (Algeria, Gabon, Libya, and Nigeria) and five non-OPEC states (Angola, Benin, Cameroon, the Congo, and Egypt). CCH, *Energy Management* (Issue No. 739, March 17, 1987); [1986/87] 9 *OGLTR* D-99.

After acquired rights clause

A clause in a lease, joint venture, farmout, or other agreement designed to afford parties to the agreement the right to share in specified future acquisitions of interests by another party to said agreement. See TREATISE § 428.4.

After-acquired title doctrine

The doctrine (also called ESTOPPEL BY DEED) barring one who has conveyed an interest in land from asserting an after-acquired title inconsistent with the effectiveness of the instrument conveying an interest in land. See TREATISE § 311.

AGA

The American Gas Association, a trade association of companies that provides natural gas distribution and transmission service to consumers in all 50 states.

AGD

The Associated Gas Distributors.

Agency contract

The term applied to the type of agreement which has increasingly replaced the concession as the dominant form of petroleum development agreement in the Middle East. Under the agency contract, title to local installations and oil produced is vested in the national partner but the host state does not bear the cost and risk of initial exploration. The foreign company does not have a long-term exclusive right to exploit oil, as under the concession. See Best, "Middle East Oil and the U.S. Energy Crisis: Prospect for New Ventures in a Changed Market," 5 *Law & Policy in International Business* 215 at 233 (1973).

For specific aspects or provisions of agreements of this kind see the entries under CONCESSION.

Aggregate programmed quantity system

See APQ SYSTEM.

Aggregation of properties

A Federal income tax term referring to the combination of different properties to form a single property unit for tax purposes. Statutory authority for aggregation of properties was added to the Internal Revenue Code in 1954, § 614(b) and (c). See also Treas. Reg. §§ 1.614–2 through 1.614–6 (1980).

See also DEPLETION, PERCENTAGE; IVY OPTION; NONOPERATING MINERAL INTEREST, FOR TAX PURPOSES; OPERATING MINERAL INTEREST, FOR TAX PURPOSES; OPERATING UNIT, FOR TAX PURPOSES; PROPERTY UNIT, FOR TAX PURPOSES.

AGIP

Azienda Generale Italiana Petroli, established in Italy in 1926 to carry out exploration ventures as well as operating in the petroleum marketing and processing field. See Mughraby, *Permanent Sovereignty Over Oil Resources* 63 (1966).

Agreement on Principles

The Agreement Between the United States of America and Canada on Principles Applicable to a Northern Natural Gas Pipeline. The Agreement was signed by representatives of the two governments on September 20, 1977. Final Rule, Recovery of Alaska Natural Gas Transportation System Charges, 18 C.F.R. Part 154, 24 FPS 5-600 at 5-604.

AIMME

American Institute of Mining and Metallurgical Engineers.

AIOC

The Anglo-Iranian Oil Company. For a discussion of the history of this company, see Shwadran, *The Middle East, Oil and the Great Powers* 127 *et seq.* (3d ed. revised and enlarged, 1973).

Air drilling

Drilling using compressed air (or natural gas) as the circulation medium (rather than water or drilling mud) to remove cuttings. In some instances this method is more efficient for the purpose, and the rate of penetration is increased. There are problems arising from the penetration of formations containing water.

Air injection

A SECONDARY RECOVERY (*q.v.*) method to increase production by mechanically forcing the oil from the reservoir rock into well bores. The disadvantages of air as compared to gas make this method rare, save for those areas where a gas supply is lacking.

See also GAS INJECTION.

Air injection well

An air input well in repressuring by AIR INJECTION (*q.v.*).

Air lift

See GAS LIFT.

AL

APPRAISAL LICENSE (AL) (*q.v.*).

Alaska Coastal Management Act (ACMA)

AS 46.40.010.210, providing for the establishment of an Alaska Coastal Management Program (ACMP) which is partly designed to ensure that the development of industrial and commercial enterprises is consistent with the environmental and cultural interests of the state. See Hammond v. North Slope Borough, 645 P.2d 750 (Alaska 1982).

Alaska National Interest Lands Conservation Act (ANILCA)

Public Law 96-487, 94 Stat. 2374 *et seq.*, 16 U.S.C. § 3101 *et seq.* (1980), governing the use and development of federal lands in Alaska. Among other things, the Act directs the Secretary of the Interior to establish an oil and gas leasing program on federal lands in Alaska, including the identification of areas favorable for the discovery of oil and gas. Such an area is known as a FAVORABLE PETROLEUM GEOLOGICAL PROVINCE (FPGP). Land in such a province may be leased only by competitive bidding.

See also Linxwiler, "Federal Oil and Gas Leasing in Alaska," *Rocky Mt. Min. L. Fdn. Law of Federal Oil and Gas Leases* ch. 27 (1984).

Alaska Native Claims Settlement Act of December 18, 1971 (ANCSA)

An Act, 85 Stat. 688, as amended, 43 U.S.C. §§ 1601–1628, pertaining to the selection of lands and interests in land in satisfaction of the land selections conferred by the act upon Alaska Natives and Alaska Native Corporations. Procedures are provided by the regulations in 43 C.F.R. § 2650 *et seq* (1978).

See also the following:

Linxwiler, "Federal Oil and Gas Leasing in Alaska," *Rocky Mt. Min. L. Fdn. Law of Federal Oil and Gas Leases* ch. 27 (1984);

Walsh, "Settling the Alaska Native Claims Settlement Act," 38 *Stan. L. Rev.* 227 (1985);

Shively, "Alaska Native Corporations and Native Lands," *Rocky Mt. Min. L. Fdn. Alaska Mineral Development Inst.* Paper 4 (1978).

See also ALASKA'S (d)(2) LANDS.

Alaska Natural Gas Pipeline Financing Act

Public Law 97-93 (1981), waiving restrictions contained in the ALASKA NATURAL GAS TRANSPORTATION ACT OF 1976 (*q.v.*) and permitting builders of the pipeline to recoup some of their investment before completion of the whole system and allowing Alaskan gas producers to hold interests in the pipeline. The validity of the Act was sustained in Metzenbaum v. Federal Energy Regulatory Comm'n, 675 F.2d 1282 (D.C. Cir. 1982). For a criticism of the Act, see Tannenbaum, "Waivers of the Alaska Natural Gas Transportation Act," 14 *Toledo L. Rev.* 39 (1982).

See also PIPELINE.

Alaska Natural Gas Transportation Act of 1976 (ANGTA)

Public Law 94-586, 90 Stat. 2912 (1976), 15 U.S.C. §§ 719–719o. This Act established a procedural framework to expedite a final decision on an Alaskan natural gas transportation system. See Midwestern Gas Transmission Co. v. Federal Energy Regulatory Comm'n, 589 F.2d 603 (D.C. Cir. 1978). Certain provisions of this Act were waived by Public Law 97-93, 95 Stat. 1204 (1981). The validity of the latter act was sustained in Metzenbaum v. Federal Energy Regulatory Comm'n, 675 F.2d 1282 (D.C. Cir. 1982). In particular, this Act permitted builders of the pipeline to begin recouping their investment through higher gas rates prior to the time when the system was completed, and it allowed both debt and equity participation in the pipeline by Alaskan gas producers, so that they could own an aggregate of up to 30% of the system.

For a case sustaining the determination of the rate base for a leg of ANGTS (*q.v.*) see Iowa State Commerce Comm'n v. Office of Federal Inspector, 730 F.2d 1566 (D.C. Cir. 1984).

Alaska's (d)(2) lands

The term applied to lands withdrawn by the Secretary of the Interior as authorized by Section 17(d)(2) of the ALASKA NATIVE CLAIMS SETTLEMENT ACT (*q.v.*) for inclusion as units of the National Park, Wildlife Refuge, Forest and Wild and Scenic Rivers Systems. See Stenmark, "An Introduction to Alaska," *Rocky Mt. Min. L. Fdn. Alaska Mineral Development Inst.* 2–13 (1978), Norman and Silver, "Alaska's D–2 Lands," *id.*, Paper 5.

Alberta border price

See IMPUTED ALBERTA BORDER PRICE.

Alberta Petroleum Marketing Commission (APMC)

The agent of the Crown to market petroleum produced under Alberta Crown leases. See Hollingsworth and Snider, "Some Aspects of 1985 Deregulation of Petroleum," 25 *Alta. L. Rev.* 36 at 40 (1986).

Alberta Royalty Tax Credit

A credit, popularly known as the small explorer's credit, allowed certain taxpayers for royalties paid to the province of Alberta. See Bell, "Petroleum Taxation in Canada," [1982] 3 *OGLTR* 82 at 89.

Alberta Surface Rights Act

An Act substantially increasing the rights of a surface owner to compensation for use of the surface for the development of minerals by a mineral owner. See TREATISE § 218 at note 8.

See also FOUR HEADS APPROACH; GLOBAL APPROACH.

Albino oil

Syn. for GAS CONDENSATE (*q.v.*) or WHITE OIL (*q.v.*). See "Big, Small Energy Firms Fight Over Texas Gas," *The Wall Street Journal,* Sept. 21, 1984, p. 33; "Angry Texas Town Faces End of Joyride Fueled by 'White Oil,' " *The Wall Street Journal,* July 18, 1985, p. 1, col. 4.

See also LOW TEMPERATURE EXTRACTION (LTX); NATURAL GASOLINE; WATER-WHITE OIL.

Alcohol slug injection

See ALCOHOL SLUG PROCESS; AMPHIPATHIC SLUG INJECTION.

Alcohol slug process

A miscible flood process involving the introduction into the reservoir of a small amount of an organic solvent such as isopropyl alcohol. See Slobod, "Research on Methods for Improving Oil Recovery from Pennsylvania Oil Fields," *The Interstate Oil Compact Commission Committee Bulletin* 11 (vol. 1, No. 2, Dec. 1959); Smith, "The Engineering Aspects of Pressure Maintenance and Secondary Recovery Operations," 6 *Rocky Mt. Min. L. Inst.* 211 at 230 (1961).

See also SECONDARY RECOVERY.

Alien land or mineral ownership restrictions

Statutes and regulations governing the ownership by aliens of interests in land or minerals. For discussions of the matter see the following:

Horigan, "Foreign Participation in Domestic Oil and Gas Ventures," 28 *Rocky Mt. Min. L. Inst.* 969 (1982);

Fiske and Meagher, "Alien Ownership of Mineral Interests," 24 *Rocky Mt. Min. L. Inst.* 47 (1978).

See also Santa Fe International Corp. v. Watt, 591 F.Supp. 929, 84 *O.&G.R.* 221 (D. Dela. 1984) (invalidating a decision of the Secretary of the Interior barring Kuwaiti citizens and corporations from acquiring interests in oil and gas leases on public lands under the Mineral Lands Leasing Act of 1920).

ALJ

Administrative Law Judge.

Alkylation

A process of combining light hydrocarbon molecules to form high octane gasoline.

All-inclusive clause

See COVER-ALL CLAUSE.

Allocated pool

A pool in which the total oil or natural gas production is restricted and allocated to various wells therein in accordance with proration schedules. New Mexico Oil Conservation Comm'n, *Rules and Regulations* 1 (1958).

Allocation formula

The formula employed in fixing the ALLOWABLE (*q.v.*) for a well, pool or field. See Zimmermann, *Conservation in the Production of Petroleum* 331–336 (1957).

Allocation of oil and gas

See APQ SYSTEM; BUY-SELL LIST; BUY/SELL OIL; CHANDELEUR INCENTIVE DOCTRINE; CURTAILMENT PLAN; ECONOMIC REGULATORY AGENCY; ENTITLEMENT PROGRAM; 533 PROGRAM; HIGH PRIORITY USERS; NATIONAL ENERGY CONSERVATION POLICY ACT OF 1978; POWERPLANT AND INDUSTRIAL FUEL USE ACT OF 1978; SMALL REFINER BIAS.

All or nothing clause

A Pooling clause (*q.v.*) providing that if any part of the leased acreage is to be pooled, all must be pooled. Scott, "Unusual Provisions in Oil and Gas Leases," 33 *Sw. Legal Fdn. Oil & Gas Inst.* 139 at 151 (1982).

See also Pugh clause.

Allotment

"[A]n allocation to a Native of land of which he has made substantially continuous use and occupancy for a period of five years and which shall be deemed the 'homestead' of the allottee and his heirs in perpetuity, and shall be inalienable and nontaxable except as otherwise provided by the Congress." 43 C.F.R. § 2561.0–5 (b) (1978).

See also Indian allotment; Indian lands; Public lands.

Allotted lands

See Indian lands.

Allowable

The amount of oil (or gas) which a well, leasehold, field, or state is permitted to produce under proration orders of a state regulatory commission. The allowable may be stated in terms of number of barrels per day for a stated number of days per month, *e.g.*, 120 barrels per day for 20 days per calendar month. In such instances, operators may produce daily during the entire calendar month but must limit gross monthly production to the amount allowed by the regulatory commission, determined by multiplying the daily allowance by the number of producing days allowed per month. See Kingwood Oil Co. v. Loehr, 200 F.2d 551, 2 *O.&G.R.* 296 (5th Cir. 1952). Alternatively, the allowable may be stated in terms of a percentage of the Maximum efficient rate (*q.v.*). Actual production does not necessarily equal the allowable.

For a detailed discussion of the fixing of allowables in the United States, see S. L. McDonald, *Petroleum Conservation in the United States: An Economic Analysis* (1971).

Methods employed in the several states to fix allowables are described in Interstate Oil Compact Commission, *A Study of Conservation of Oil and Gas* 63 *et seq.* (1964), and in Lovejoy and Homan, *Economic Aspects of Oil Conservation Regulation* (1967). For discussions of procedures in particular states and provinces see the following:

Vavra, "An Appraisal of Alberta's New Prorationing Scheme," 7 *Alberta L. Rev.* 379 (1969);

Schell, "The Impact of Oil and Gas Conservation Orders Upon Implied Covenants in Oil and Gas Leases," 34 *J.B.A. Kan.* 181 (1965) (discussing the procedure in Kansas);

Porter, "Oil and Gas Conservation in New Mexico," 22 *Oil and Gas Compact Bull.* 15 (Dec. 1963);

Blazier, "The Lease Allowable System: New Method in Regulating Oil Production in Texas," 47 *Texas L. Rev.* 658 (1969).

A study of allowables in Texas up to 1948 revealed that 17% of the reporting fields were prorated on a per well basis only, 35% were prorated on a 50–50 acreage-per well basis, 26% were prorated on a 75–25 acreage-per well basis, and less than 7% were prorated on an acreage basis alone. See Dutton, "Proration in Texas: Conservation or Confiscation?", 11 *Sw. L.J.* 186 at 195:n22 (1957).

For a chart showing schedule allowable, actual calendar day allowable, and actual production in Texas, 1945–55, see Zimmermann, *Conservation in the Production of Petroleum* 222–223 (1957).

It has been held in Texas that the Railroad Commission may not, for the purpose of protecting correlative rights, establish a ceiling on the monthly allowable of gas to be produced from a reservoir. Railroad Comm'n v. Woods Exploration & Producing Co., 405 S.W.2d 313, 24 *O.&G.R.* 831 (Tex. 1966), *cert. denied sub nom.* Aluminum Co. of America v. Woods Exploration & Producing Co., 385 U.S. 991 (1966). Future allowables may be reduced to make up earlier overproduction. Railroad Comm'n v. Sample, 405 S.W.2d 338, 25 *O.&G.R.* 85 (Tex. 1966).

In Chevron Oil Co. v. Oil and Gas Conservation Comm'n, 150 Mont. 351, 435 P.2d 781, 27 *O.&G.R.* 635 (1967), it was held that the State Oil and Gas Commission had authority to limit the production rate or otherwise control the quantity of oil and gas produced from a well drilled under an exception to field spacing rules in order to protect the correlative rights of owners of interests in production from adjoining land.

Osborn v. Texas Oil & Gas Corp., 661 P.2d 71, 76 *O.&G.R.* 101 (Okla. App. 1982), held:

> "the corporation commission—once it found that a gas well offsetting a water driven secondary recovery unit maintained by gas pressure was 'causing waste and [would] continue to . . . so long as it is produced'—had authority to either shut the well in or permanently limit its production to a nonwasteful level."

Robert-Gay Energy Enterprises, Inc. v. State Corporation Comm'n, 235 Kan. 951, 685 P.2d 299, 82 *O.&G.R.* 272 (1984), sustained the power of the regulatory commission to punish a violation of commission orders or rules by restricting the allowable for the violator's well.

See also ACREAGE ATTRIBUTION; ACREAGE FACTOR; ACRE FOOT OF SAND; ACTUAL CALENDAR DAY ALLOWABLE; ADJUSTED ALLOWABLE; ADJUSTED DELIVERABILITY FORMULA; ALLOCATION FORMULA; ALLOWABLE FORMULA; ALLOWABLE PENALTY; ALLOWABLE PERIOD; ASSOCIATED GAS PRORATION; ASSOCIATED RESERVOIR ALLOWABLE; ATTRIBUTABLE ACREAGE; BACK ALLOWABLE; BALANCING PERIOD; BASE ALLOWABLE; BONUS ALLOWABLE; CANCELLED UNDERAGE; CAPACITY ALLOWABLE; COUNTY REGULAR FIELDS; DA; DEFICIENT WELL; DEPTH BRACKET ALLOWABLE; DEPTH BRACKET METHOD OF PRORATION; DISCOVERY WELL ALLOWABLE; ECONOMIC ALLOWANCE; EXCESS OIL; EXEMPT ALLOWABLES; 50–50 ALLOWABLE FORMULA; GAS CAP ALLOWABLE; GAS-OIL RATIO ADJUSTMENT; GAS-OIL RATIO PENALTY FACTOR; GAS PRORATION UNIT; GENERAL SHUT-DOWN ORDER; HENZE TYPE PRORATION ORDER; HOT OIL; INCENTIVE ALLOWABLE; LEASE ALLOWABLE SYSTEM; LIMITED CAPACITY WELL; MARGINAL UNIT; MARGINAL WELL ALLOWABLE; MER ALLOWABLE; MINIMUM ALLOWABLE; NET PAY PRORATION FORMULA; NOMINATIONS BY PURCHASERS; NONMARGINAL UNIT; NONPRORATABLE ALLOWABLE; 1/3–2/3 ALLOWABLE FORMULA; OVERAGE; OVER-PRODUCTION; PERMITTED PRODUCTION; PRORATABLE ALLOWABLES; PRORATIONING; PRORATION FORMULA; PRORATION UNIT; PURCHASER PRORATIONING; RATABLE TAKING; REASONABLE MARKET DEMAND; RESERVE INDEX FORMULA; RETROACTIVE ADJUSTING ALLOWABLE; SALT WATER SHUT-IN ALLOWABLE; SCHEDULE ALLOWABLE; SCHEDULED ALLOWABLE DAYS; SHAPE OF TRACT BASIS; SHORTAGE; SHUT-DOWN DAYS; SISTRUNK FORMULA; STRUCTURAL ADVANTAGE; TEMPORARY ALLOWABLE; TOKEN ALLOWABLE; TOP WELL ALLOWABLE; TRANSFERRED ALLOWABLE; UNDERAGE; UNDERPRODUCTION; VOLUMETRIC DISPLACEMENT RULE FOR GAS WELLS; WATERFLOOD ALLOWABLE; WATER-OIL RATIO PENALTY FACTOR; YARDSTICK ALLOWABLE.

Allowable days

See SCHEDULED ALLOWABLE DAYS.

Allowable formula

A formula for the allocation of a field ALLOWABLE (*q.v.*) among the wells in a field.

Allowable penalty

A reduction in the normal allowable for a well as a penalty for a location exception. See Halpin v. Corporation Comm'n, 575 P.2d 109, 59 *O.&G.R.* 314 (Okla. 1977) (sustaining a 30 percent allowable penalty), and GMC Oil & Gas Corp. v. Texas Oil & Gas Corp., 586 P.2d 731, 62 *O.&G.R.* 187 (Okla. 1978) (sustaining a 25 percent allowable penalty).

Allowable period

The time within which an ALLOWABLE (*q.v.*) of oil or gas may be produced. Interstate Oil Compact Commission, *A Suggested Form of General Rules and Regulations for the Conservation of Oil and Gas* (1960) Rule III.

Allowable production

See ALLOWABLE.

Allowable work expenditure

Under certain Canadian permits for oil and gas exploration, deposits are required which are refundable as an expenditure, known as an allowable work expenditure, is incurred in performing exploratory work. A permit holder may also satisfy the work expenditure requirement by acquiring allowable work expenditures from other permit holders. See Wright v. Commissioner, T.C. Memo 1980–279, 67 *O.&G.R.* 494 (1980).

Alsands project

A project to manufacture synthetic crude oil from the bitumen deposits in the tar sands located in northeastern Alberta. See Re Athabasca Tribal Council and Amoco Canada Petroleum Co. Ltd., [1981] 1 S.C.R. 699, 124 D.L.R.3d 1 (Sup. Ct. of Canada 1981); Pettigrew, "New Frontiers in Resource Technology—A Legal Overview," 19 *Alberta L. Rev.* 1 at 5 (1980); Holland, "The Syncrude and Alsands Oil Shale and Oil Sands Projects," International Bar Ass'n, *Energy Law 1981* at p. 445.

See also PETROLEUM TAR SANDS.

Alternate fuel cap

See CONTRACTUAL CAP.

Alternate fuel capability

A situation where an alternate fuel (other than natural gas) could have been utilized whether or not the facilities for such use have actually been installed. State of Louisiana v. Federal Power Comm'n, 503 F.2d 844 at 859 (5th Cir. 1974).

Alternative decree

The court decree in an implied covenant case that orders cancellation of the lease for breach of covenant if, after a stated period of time (usually not more than 6 months and often 30 or 60 days), the obligations imposed by the covenant have not been met. Also called a CONDITIONAL DECREE OF CANCELLATION (*q.v.*). The alternative decree differs from an absolute decree of cancellation in that the latter allows no time for the performance of the covenant. For examples of an alternative decree, see Sauder v. Mid-Continent Petroleum Corp., 292 U.S. 272 (1934); Sinclair Oil & Gas Co. v. Masterson, 271 F.2d 310, 11 *O.&G.R.* 632 (5th Cir. 1959), *cert. denied,* 362 U.S. 952 (1960); Humble Oil and Refining Co. v. Romero, 194 F.2d 383, 1 *O.&G.R.* 358 (5th Cir. 1952); Gregg v. Harper-Turner Oil Co., 199 F.2d 1, 1 *O.&G.R.* 1685 (10th Cir. 1952); Doss Oil Royalty Co. v. Texas Co., 192 Okla. 359, 137 P.2d 934 (1943).

See TREATISE §§ 834, 844.1.

See also CANCELLATION DECREE; CONDITIONAL DECREE OF CANCELLATION; PARTIAL CANCELLATION.

Alternative fuel clause

A lease clause permitting the lessee to utilize in its lease operations fuel brought onto the leasehold in lieu of oil and gas produced from the leasehold and providing for a credit to the lessee for the cost of the alternate fuel against the value or proceeds of the oil and gas produced from the leasehold. Thus, during periods of price controls, the oil or gas produced from the leasehold might have a higher value than alternative fuel available on the market for lease operations, *e.g.,* for generation of steam employed in secondary recovery operations of heavy crude oil. Under such circumstances, it may be to the mutual interest of lessor and lessee for the lessee to purchase cheaper alternate fuel rather than to employ the higher priced crude oil produced from the leasehold. The alternative fuel provision causes the lessor to share in the cost of the fuel employed just as the lessor would have shared in the cost had oil and gas produced from the leasehold been employed by the lessee in its operations under a lease provision permitting royalty-free use of lease products in connection with lease operations. See TREATISE § 644.5.

See also SUBSTITUTE FUEL CLAUSE.

Alternative fuel cost

For purposes of INCREMENTAL PRICING (*q.v.*) under the Natural Gas Policy Act of 1978, each nonexempt industrial gas user was subject to incremental pricing until its cost for gas reached its alternative fuel cost. The alternative fuel cost was the price per million Btu paid for No. 2 fuel oil by industrial users of such fuel in a designated region. See Cormie, "Incremental Pricing Under the Natural Gas Policy Act of 1978," 57 *Denver L.J.* 1 at 13 (1979).

See also PRICE CONTROL OF OIL, GAS AND PETROLEUM PRODUCTS.

American ton

See TON.

AMI

An AREA OF MUTUAL INTEREST AGREEMENT (*q.v.*).

Amphipathic slug injection

A secondary recovery method involving the injection of a slug of alcohol or other fluid miscible with both water and oil into injection wells followed by water injection. See Smith, "The Engineering Aspects of Pressure Maintenance and Secondary Recovery Operations," 6 *Rocky Mt. Min. L. Inst.* 211 at 230 (1961).

See also ALCOHOL SLUG PROCESS; SECONDARY RECOVERY.

Analysis

See CORE ANALYSIS; MUD ANALYSIS.

ANCAP

The Administracion Nacional de Combustiles Alcohol Y Portland of Uruguay.

Anchor string

Syn. for OUTER CONDUCTER (*q.v.*).

ANCSA

The ALASKA NATIVE CLAIMS SETTLEMENT ACT OF DECEMBER 18, 1971 (*q.v.*).

Anderson v. Helvering assignment

A term occasionally used to describe a transaction involving the assignment of a working interest for cash in which assignment it is also provided that an additional payment shall be made by the assignee out of oil, if produced, but payable in any event whether or not there is production. See Appleman, "Sales and Assignments of Leases and Other Interests in Oil and Gas," 1 *Sw. Legal Fdn. Oil & Gas Inst.* 427 at 446 (1949).

See also ASSIGNMENT.

Aneth letter

The name given a form employed by the Federal Power Commission since 1958 requesting evidence of prices paid by pipe lines, contract terms, favored nations clauses, and cost information. See Johnson, "Producer Rate Regulation in Natural Gas Certification Proceedings: CATCO in Context," 62 *Colum. L. Rev.* 773 at 805 (1962).

Angle of deflection

The angle, expressed in degrees, at which a DIRECTIONAL WELL (*q.v.*) is deflected from the vertical by means of a WHIPSTOCK (*q.v.*) or other deflecting tool.

ANGTA

The ALASKA NATURAL GAS TRANSPORTATION ACT OF 1976 (*q.v.*).

ANGTS

The Alaska natural gas transportation system. See ANGTA.

Angularity test

Syn. for SLOPE TEST (*q.v.*).

Angular unconformity

See DISCONFORMITY; UNCONFORMITY.

ANILCA

The ALASKA NATIONAL INTEREST LANDS CONSERVATION ACT (ANILCA) (*q.v.*).

Anniversary date

The date on which payment of delay rental or shut-in gas well royalty must be made in order to keep a lease effective under the DELAY RENTAL CLAUSE (*q.v.*). or SHUT-IN GAS WELL CLAUSE (*q.v.*).

Annual acreage rental

Syn. for DELAY RENTAL (*q.v.*).

Annual inflation adjustment factor

A factor specified by Section 101 of the Natural Gas Policy Act of 1978 (Pub. L. No. 95–621) to be applied in adjusting price ceilings for regulated natural gas.

See also PRICE CONTROL OF OIL, GAS OR PETROLEUM PRODUCTS.

Annual quantity entitlement (AQE)

The basis on which delivery volumes of gas are calculated in time of curtailment. See, *e.g.,* Texas Eastern Transmission Corp., 4 FPS 5–190 (Feb. 12, 1975).

See also CURTAILMENT PLAN.

Annular blow-out preventer

A wellhead device that will seal around any object in the well bore as well as seal off an open well bore. An annular preventer fills the annular space by hydraulically extruding a resilient packing element inward from the housing of the preventer.

See also BLOW-OUT PREVENTER.

Annular space

The space between the outer wall of pipe suspended in a well bore and the side of the open hole or the inner side of a larger pipe.

Annulus of well

The space between the surface casing and the producing casing. Cummings & McIntyre v. Corporation Comm'n, 319 P.2d 602, 8 *O.&G.R.* 604 (Okla. 1957).

Anticipation of income

A federal income tax term meaning that a transfer purporting to shift the incidence of the income tax to another person fails in its purpose, leaving the income taxable to the transferor. At one time the assignment of an oil payment could be treated as anticipation of income with the assignor liable for the tax as on ordinary income. See Commissioner v. P.G. Lake, Inc., 356 U.S. 260, 8 *O.&G.R.* 1153 (1958). Since December 30, 1969, a carved-out production payment has been treated as if it were a mortgage loan on the property, and a production payment retained on the sale of a mineral property has been treated as if it were a purchase money mortgage loan, neither qualifying as an economic interest in the mineral property. I.R.C. § 636.

Anticline

A subsurface, geological structure in the form of a sine curve; that is, the formation rises to a rounded peak. Anticlinal structures in sedimentary rocks are good prospects for drilling, since any oil in the deposit will normally rise to the highest point in the structure. Such reservoirs are called anticlinal traps.

See also GEOLOGICAL STRUCTURE; STRUCTURAL TRAP.

Anticlinical trap

See ANTICLINE

Anti-passthrough provision

The term applied to a provision in a tax law designed to prevent the taxpayer from passing the burden of the tax through to consumers by adding to the price of products sold. Such provisions in a New York "gross receipts" tax levied on oil companies and in a Connecticut "gross earnings" tax levied on integrated petroleum companies have been invalidated. See Mobil Oil Corp. v. Tully, 653 F.2d 497(Temp. Emer. Ct. of App. 1981), *vacated and remanded for reconsideration in light of expiration of federal price control authority,* 455 U.S. 245 (1982), *remanded to Distsrict Court,* 689 F.2d 186 (Temp. Emer. Ct. App. 1982); Mobil Oil Corp. v. Dubno, 639 F.2d 919 (2d Cir. 1981), *cert. denied,* 452 U.S. 967 (1981).

For a detailed discussion of New York's attempt to prevent major oil companies from passing through their tax liabilities to New York consumers in the prices of petroleum products, see Brown, "New

York State Oil Company Gross Receipts Taxation," 32 *O.&G. Tax Q.* 271 (1983).

See also PASS-THROUGH PROHIBITION; PASS-THROUGH PROVISION.

Anti-washout provision

The name sometimes given an EXTENSION AND RENEWAL CLAUSE (*q.v.*) of a lease assignment. See Robinson v. North American Royalties, Inc., 463 So.2d 1384, 84 *O.&G.R.* 281 (La. App. 1985), *modified,* 470 S.2d 112 (La. 1985).

AOPL

The Association of Oil Pipe Lines.

APB

The Accounting Principles Board of the American Institute of Certified Public Accountants. From time to time the Board issues opinions dealing with accounting practices and tax consequences.

APD

Application for Permit to Drill in Wilderness Study Area. See Rocky Mountain Oil and Gas Ass'n v. Watt, 696 F.2d 734 at 741, 78 *O.&G.R.* 152 at 161 (10th Cir. 1982).

APGA

The American Public Gas Association.

API

The American Petroleum Institute, a trade organization.

See also EVERYTHING IS A.P.I.

API gravity

SPECIFIC GRAVITY (*q.v.*) measured in degrees on the American Petroleum Institute scale. The specific gravity of oil is normally specified not as a fraction in relation to water taken at the figure "1" but in terms of API degrees. On the API scale, oil with the least specific gravity has the highest API gravity. Other things being equal, the higher the API gravity, the greater the value of the oil. Most crude oils range from 27 degrees to 35 degrees API gravity.

See also DENSITY OF PETROLEUM.

API neutron unit

A unit devised by the American Petroleum Institute for the calibration of the scales of neutron logs.

APMC

The ALBERTA PETROLEUM MARKETING COMMISSION (APMC) (*q.v.*).

APOC

The Anglo-Persian Oil Company, the predecessor of AIOC (the Anglo-Iranian Oil Company). See Shwadran, *The Middle East, Oil and the Great Powers* 13 *et seq.* (3d ed. revised and enlarged, 1973).

APPA

(1) The American Public Power Association.

(2) The AFRICAN PETROLEUM PRODUCERS' ASSOCIATION (APPA) (*q.v.*).

Appalachian basin

"[A] sedimentary dispositional BASIN (*q.v.*) with thick sediments in the interior and thinner sediments at the edges extending from New York to Alabama. Topographically it forms the Appalachian Mountains and to the west the Allegheny Plateau." Snyder and Christian, "Oil and Gas Operations Through Coal Seams in West Virginia," 1 *Eastern Min. L. Inst.* 5–110 (1980).

Applicant

Under the vacancy laws of Texas, any person, other than a good faith claimant, who discovers and files application to purchase or lease a VACANCY (*q.v.*). Tex. Nat. Res. Code § 51.172 (1978).

See also QUALIFIED APPLICANT.

Apportionment

Division of royalties (and sometimes of other lease proceeds) among the owners of interests in the land subject to the lease.

Apportionment problems arise whenever there is production by a lessee under a lease which covers and includes segregated parcels in which separate mineral or royalty interests exist (*e.g.*, the lease covers and includes Blackacre, which is owned by *A*, and Whiteacre, which is owned by *B*). Under the apportionment theory, each of the owners of mineral or royalty interests in the several parcels subject to the lease is entitled to a share of the royalty paid upon the production from the well. Under the nonapportionment theory, which is accepted in most of the states, the royalty is payable only to the owners of interests in the particular parcel upon which the producing well is located.

In the states adopting the latter theory, apportionment may nevertheless result from (1) a pooling or unitization agreement, (2) a community lease, (3) an entirety clause in the lease, (4) a "subject-to" clause in a mineral or royalty deed, (5) a proportionate reduction clause in the lease, (6) spacing and drilling regulations, (7) the duty of fair dealing owed by a person with exclusive leasing power to the owner of a nonparticipating mineral or royalty interest, or (8) implication of intent arising from the duration of a mineral or royalty grant. See TREATISE §§ 520–521.8.

Appraisal license (AL)

Under the December 1984, United Kingdom regulations [The Petroleum (Production) (Landward Areas) Regulations (1984)], an Appraisal license (AL) may issue for a five-year term (extendable at the Secretary of State's discretion) following a discovery on an Exploration license (EXL). The AL will enable the licensee to appraise the field, prepare a suitable development program, and obtain long-term planning permission for its development. The Secretary of State has discretion to extend the term of the AL to provide, if necessary, further time to complete these processes. Case Digest and National News [1984/85] 12 *OGLTR* D-130; J. Salter, *U.K. Onshore Oil and Gas Law* 1-320 (1986).

See also DEVELOPMENT LICENSE (DL); EXPLORATION LICENSE (EXL).

Appraisal well

A well, *e.g.*, a STEP-OUT WELL (*q.v.*), drilled into a formation shown to be potentially productive of oil or gas by an earlier well for the purpose of obtaining more information about the reservoir.

Appropriated public lands

"Original public domain lands which are covered by an entry, patent, certification, or other evidence of land disposal; for certain purposes, public lands which are within a reservation, which contain improvements constructed with the aid of Federal funds, or which are covered by certain classes of leases are also considered appropriated." United States Department of the Interior Bureau of Land Management, *Glossary of Public-Land Terms* 3 (1949).

See also PUBLIC LANDS.

Approximation, rule of

See RULE OF APPROXIMATION

APQ system

The Aggregate Programmed Quantity system employed to set production levels and to allocate supply among members of the so-called Iranian consortium of oil producers. See "Multinational Oil Corporations and U.S. Foreign Policy," Report to the Committee on Foreign Relations, United States Senate by the Subcommittee on Multinational Corporations, 93d Cong., 2d Sess. (Jan. 2, 1975) at p. 110.

See also CONCESSION.

APRT

The ADVANCE PETROLEUM REVENUE TAX (APRT) SYSTEM (*q.v.*).

APT

ADDITIONAL PROFITS TAX (*q.v.*).

AQE

ANNUAL QUANTITY ENTITLEMENT (*q.v.*).

Aquagel

A specially prepared bentonite clay widely used as a conditioning material in the preparation of drilling MUD (*q.v.*).

Aquifer

Water-bearing rock strata; in a WATER-DRIVE FIELD (*q.v.*) the water zone of the reservoir. Since water is only slightly compressible, there must be a large aquifer in order to recover completely the oil in the reservoir by water encroachment. See Buckley (ed.), *Petroleum Conservation* 204–206 (1951).

Aquifer storage

See GAS STORAGE, UNDERGROUND.

Arabian light oil

A term used to describe Saudi Arabian light oil, also known as BENCHMARK CRUDE (*q.v.*). *The Wall Street Journal,* Jan. 27, 1983, p. 16 col. 2.

See also BONNY LIGHT OIL.

Arab Petroleum Service Company

A joint venture established by OAPEC in 1977 to engage in drilling activities in member countries. Al-Chalabi, *OPEC and the International Oil Industry: A Changing Situation* 143 (1980).

ARAMCO

The Arabian American Oil Company. See Shwadran, *The Middle East, Oil and the Great Powers* 349 *et seq.* (3d ed. revised and enlarged, 1973).

For another discussion of the history of ARAMCO's dealings with Saudi Arabia and the United States government, see "Multinational Oil Corporations and U.S. Foreign Policy," Report to the Committee on Foreign Relations, United States Senate, by the Subcommittee on Multinational Corporations, 93d Cong., 2d Sess. (Jan. 2, 1975).

For a discussion of Saudi Arabia's influence in the world energy market, see Quandt, *Saudi Arabia's Oil Policy* (Brookings Institution 1982).

Area fee

An annual fee paid in advance for use of the area covered by a Norwegian PRODUCTION LICENSE (*q.v.*). Should the area fee for the period in question exceed the calculated royalty, no royalty has to be paid. See Krohn, Kaasen, *et al., Norwegian Petroleum Law* 2–24, 2–32 (1978).

Area of interest

(1) A federal income tax term used in allocating GEOPHYSICAL AND GEOLOGICAL COSTS (*q.v.*) to certain properties. A large-scale geophysical survey may indicate several areas of interest. The cost of the survey must be allocated to each area of interest, and when leases are

obtained therein, the geophysical costs become part of the basis of the property. See I.T. 4006, 1950–1 C. B. 48.

(2) This phrase is sometimes used in partnership, joint adventure, or similar agreements to refer to an area affected by the agreement. Palmer v. Fuqua, 641 F.2d 1146, 69 *O.&G.R.* 119 (5th Cir., Unit A, 1981), held that the phrase was not limited to property already owned by a partnership but that, at the very least, it included properties contiguous to lands owned by the partnership. The court further indicated that the phrase sufficiently described the property affected for purposes of the Statute of Frauds and the Statute of Conveyances; in any event, there was a fiduciary relationship in the instant case and a constructive trust could be imposed irrespective of a failure to meet the requirements of the Statute of Frauds.

See also Blackmore v. Davis Oil Co., 671 P.2d 334, 80 *O.&G.R.* 431 (Wyo. 1983), denying specific performance of the area of interest provision of a letter agreement absent proof that defendant used information received from plaintiff in making its drilling decisions.

For discussion of area of interest provisions of operating and other agreements, see the following:

Pennebaker, "Recent Developments in Oil and Gas Law With Drafting Suggestions," 34 *Sw. Legal Fdn. Oil & Gas Inst.* 353 at 357 (1983);

Himebaugh, "An Overview of Oil and Gas Contracts in the Williston Basin," 59 *No. Dak. L. Rev.* 7 at 32 (1983);

Zarlengo, "Area of Mutual Interest Clauses Regarding Oil and Gas Properties: Analysis, Drafting, and Procedure," 28 *Rocky Mt. Min. L. Inst.* 837 (1982);

Harrell, "Recent Developments in the Nonregulatory Law of Oil and Gas," 33 *Sw. Legal Fdn. Oil & Gas Inst.* 17 at 55 (1982).

See also AREA OF MUTUAL INTEREST AGREEMENT.

Area of mutual interest agreement

An agreement between or among parties to a FARM-OUT AGREEMENT (*q.v.*) or other agreement by which the parties attempt to describe a geographical area within which they agree to share certain additional leases acquired by any of them in the future. See Westland Oil Development Corp. v. Gulf Oil Corp., 637 S.W.2d 903, 73 *O.&G.R.* 359 (Tex. 1982), noted, 35 *Baylor L. Rev.* 629 (1983) (holding that the covenant relating to this matter ran with the land at law).

First Nat. Bank & Trust Co. v. Sidwall Corp., 234 Kan. 867, 678 P.2d 118, 80 *O.&G.R.* 263 (1984), concluded that the Rule against

Perpetuities did not apply to an area of mutual interest agreement "because the transaction was purely contractual, creating no rights in any real property."

Grimes v. Walsh & Watts, Inc., 649 S.W.2d 724, 77 *O.&G.R.* 590 (Tex. App., El Paso, 1983, error ref'd n.r.e.), held that for want of privity of estate, an area of mutual interest agreement contained in a farm-out letter agreement did not run with the land.

Molero v. Bass, 478 So.2d 929, 89 *O.&G.R.* 258 (La. App. 1985), was concerned with the construction of an agreement requiring one party to pay an overriding royalty to the other on any leases acquired in a described area. The trial court construed the agreement as being applicable only to leases acquired from landowners; the court of appeal construed the agreement as being applicable also to leasehold interests acquired from lessees by assignment or a FARM-OUT AGREEMENT (*q.v.*). On subsequent hearing by a five judge panel, the court held (two judges dissenting) the trial court correctly determined that the agreement was applicable only to leases acquired from landowners. Molero v. Bass, 486 So.2d 780, 89 *O.&G.R.* 273 (La. App. 1986), *writs denied,* 488 So.2d 1020 (La. 1986).

See also the following:

Vander Ploeg, "Particular Problems in the Structuring of Broad Area Exploration Contracts," 5 *Eastern Min. L. Inst.* 14-1 (1984);

O'Byrne, "Canadian Commentary on Farmouts," 32 *Rocky Mt. Min. L. Inst.* 18-1 at 18-46 (1986);

Himebaugh, "An Overview of Oil and Gas Contracts in the Williston Basin," 59 *No. Dak. L. Rev.* 7 at 32 (1983).

See also AREA OF INTEREST; CONTRACT AREA.

Area price

See AREA PRICING POLICY.

Area pricing policy

A policy of the Federal Power Commission and of its successor, the Federal Energy Regulatory Commission, whereby approval was given to proposed rates on the basis of prices determined for various producing areas. Seven areas were utilized in the area pricing policy: Permian Basin (West Texas and New Mexico), Texas Gulf Coast, Southern Louisiana, Rocky Mountain, Hugoton-Anadarko (Kansas and the Texas and Oklahoma panhandles), Appalachian-Illinois, and Other Southwest (miscellaneous fields in East Texas, Oklahoma, Arkansas and throughout the Southeast). See 18 C.F.R. § 2.56, 154.015–154.109b (1980).

The first area pricing policy decision was the Permian Basin Area Rate Proceeding, 34 F.P.C. 159, 23 *O.&G.R.* 103 (Opinion No. 468, Aug. 5, 1965), *remanded,* Skelly Oil Co. v. Federal Power Comm'n, 375 F.2d 6, 26 *O.&G.R.* 237 (10th Cir. 1967), *aff'd in part and rev'd in part sub nom. In re* Permian Basin Area Rate Cases, 390 U.S. 747, 28 *O.&G.R.* 689 (1968). For a detailed analysis of the cost studies in this proceeding see Hawkins, *The Field Price Regulation of Natural Gas* (1969). See also Meeks and Landeck, "Area Rate Regulation of the Natural Gas Industry," 1970 *Duke L. J.* 653.

The second opinion of the Supreme Court sustaining the area pricing policy was Mobil Oil Corp. v. Federal Power Comm'n, 417 U.S. 283, 49 *O.&G.R.* 543 (1974).

See also PRICE CONTROL OF OIL, GAS AND PETROLEUM PRODUCTS.

Area rate ceiling

See AREA PRICING POLICY.

Area rate clause

A price ESCALATOR CLAUSE (*q.v.*) in a GAS PURCHASE CONTRACT (*q.v.*) permitting the increase of the price of gas in the event of an increase in area rates established by order of the Federal Power Commission or by order of its successor, the Federal Energy Regulatory Commission. This escalator clause was not permitted in contracts certificated under the optional procedure [18 C.F.R. § 2.75 (1980)] authorized by FPC Order No. 455, 48 F.P.C. 218 (Aug. 3, 1972).

Freeport Oil Co. v. Federal Energy Regulatory Comm'n, 638 F.2d 702 (5th Cir. 1980), held that a producer certified for a limited term under 18 C.F.R. § 2.70 was not precluded from obtaining a rate increase under the provisions of an area rate clause in its contract for the sale of gas. The rationale applicable to a certificate issued under § 2.75 was held inapplicable to a certificate issued under § 2.70.

Independent Oil and Gas Association of West Virginia, 20 FPS 5–177 (FERC Opinion No. 77, March 4, 1980), *petition for review dism'd without prejudice,* Pennzoil v. Federal Energy Regulatory Comm'n, 645 F.2d 394, 71 *O.&G.R.* 137 (5th Cir., Unit A, 1981), *cert. denied,* 454 U.S. 1142 (1982), deals at length with the procedures and standards to be applied in determining whether particular area rate clauses confer contractual authority to charge and collect the rates prescribed by the Natural Gas Policy Act of 1978. The opinion is discussed in Veis, "The Effect of the Natural Gas Policy Act of 1978 on Administrative Interpretation of Natural Gas Sales

Contracts," 69 *Georgetown L.J.* 133 (1980). See also Pennzoil Co. v. Federal Energy Regulatory Comm'n, 645 F.2d 360, 22 FPS 6–23 (5th Cir., Unit A, 1981), affirming in part, setting aside and modifying in part, commission orders dealing with area rate clauses in natural gas purchase contracts.

See also PRICE CONTROL OF OIL, GAS AND PETROLEUM PRODUCTS.

Argon

A colorless, odorless, inert gaseous element.

For many years the Ontario Natural Gas Conservation Act provided that when helium, argon, or any other rare gas was found or was capable of production in commercial quantities, an order might issue compelling the closing in of gas wells until steps had been taken for the extraction and conservation of any such rare gas. Rev. Stat. Ont. 1937, c. 49, § 5; Rev. Stat. Ont. 1950, c. 251, § 5. The Ontario Fuel Board Act of 1954, Stat. Ont. 1954, c. 63, § 27, provided that when the Board was "of the opinion that a well may produce helium, argon or any other of the rare gases in commercial quantities, the Board may order the well to be closed until such steps have been taken as the Board directs for the conservation of the helium, argon or other of the rare gases." This Act was repealed by the Ontario Energy Board Act, which makes no specific reference to argon. Stat. Ont. 1960, c. 75.

ARPEL

ASISTENCIA RECIPROCA PETROLERA ESTATAL LATINOAMERICANA (*q.v.*).

Artificial gas

See MANUFACTURED GAS; NATURAL GAS.

Artificial lift

Pumping of a well to bring oil to the surface when natural pressure is insufficient to lift the petroleum. See 16 Tex. Admin. Code § 3.22

Artificial processes

Methods used to stimulate the flow or production of oil or gas in excess of the flow or production resulting from natural reservoir pressures and conditions, *e.g.*, by use of a pump, or by SHOOTING A

WELL (*q.v.*) or by SECONDARY RECOVERY (*q.v.*) or REPRESSURING OPERATION (*q.v.*).

ASCOPE

An acronym for the ASEAN COUNCIL ON PETROLEUM (*q.v.*).

ASEAN

The Association of Southeast Asian Nations, a regional association of five nations formed in Bangkok in 1967. See Chandler, "Current Developments in Oil and Gas Law: The ASEAN Countries," International Bar Ass'n, 1 *Energy Law 1981* at p. 217.

ASEAN Council on Petroleum (ASCOPE)

A council formed on October 15, 1975, in Jakarta when the national oil companies of ASEAN met to coordinate efforts in dealing with petroleum needs of member nations of ASEAN. See Tan Boon Teik, "ASCOPE," *International Business Lawyer* 10(vi) (June 1982).

As-Is agreement

Syn.: ACHNACARRY AGREEMENT (*q.v.*).

Asistencia Reciproca Petrolera Estatal Latinoamericana (ARPEL)

The Association for Reciprocal Assistance by the State-owned petroleum companies of Latin America. See Hossain, *Law and Policy in Petroleum Development* 74 (1979); Mikdashi, *The Community of Oil Exporting Countries* 93-94 (1972).

ASME

American Society of Mechanical Engineers.

Asphalt

A solid hydrocarbon which may be deposited within the reservoir rock, in well equipment, or in surface lines and tanks. Asphalt is sometimes found as a natural deposit, and if mixed with mineral grains it can be used as road-surface material with little or no special treatment.

Crude oils of high asphaltic content may be subjected to distilling operations wherein lighter fractions, such as naphtha and kerosene are removed, leaving as a residue asphalt, which at normal temperatures is a solid.

See also CUTBACK ASPHALT.

Asphalt base (or napthene base) oil

Crude oil containing an appreciable amount of napthenes or similar hydrocarbons. Oils produced in the Gulf Coast area of southern Texas and Louisiana are predominately napthenic, as is some of the oil produced from Rocky Mountain fields and much of the oil produced in California. Asphalt base oils are superior sources of motor fuels.

See also MIXED BASE OIL; PARAFFIN BASE OIL.

Asphaltum

A solid hydrocarbon with the general appearance of coal from which by a treatment and manufacturing process gasoline, fuel oil and coke may be obtained. See also GILSONITE.

ASSE

American Society of Safety Engineers.

Assessment work

Work required by law to keep certain leases or claims on government land in effect.

The assessment work requirement is discussed in Tosco Corp. v. Hodel, 611 F.Supp. 1130 at 1179 *et seq.* (D. Colo. 1985). This case was settled by an Aug. 4, 1986 agreement. See 2 *Nat. Res. & Environment* 74 (Fall 1986), 804 F.2d 590 (10th Cir. 1986).

Assignee

In law generally, a transferee; a recipient of an interest in property or a contract. In oil and gas law, the term commonly means, but is not limited to, the transferee of an oil and gas lease.

Assignment

In law generally, a transfer. In oil and gas law, usually a transfer of a property interest or of a contract. The most common usage refers to the assignment of an oil and gas lease. See TREATISE §§ 402–414.

See also ANDERSON V. HELVERING ASSIGNMENT; CROSS-ASSIGNMENT; CROSS-TRANSFER OF ROYALTIES; FLEMING ASSIGNMENT; GAS LEASE-SALES AGREEMENT (GLA); HORIZONTAL ASSIGNMENT; LOOK-SEE ASSIGNMENT; PALMER V. BENDER ASSIGNMENT; PARTIAL ASSIGNMENT; PRODUCTION ASSIGNMENT; SUBLEASE.

Assignment clause

A standard clause in the oil and gas lease, allowing free transfer of lessor's or lessee's interest, in whole or in part, in such manner as the following:

> "The rights of either party hereunder may be assigned, in whole or in part, . . . No change in the ownership of the land, or any interest therein, shall be binding on Lessee until Lessee shall be furnished with a certified copy of all recorded instruments, all court proceedings and all other necessary evidence of any transfer, inheritance, or sale of said right."

In drafting an assignment clause, careful attention should be given to the language employed with reference to: (a) requirement of notice to the lessee in appropriate form of an assignment by the lessor before the lessee shall be required to give effect to such assignment as concerns payment of rentals, royalties or other sums; (b) the effect of partial assignments by the lessee as concerns the future payment of delay rentals or royalty as to a subdivided portion of the leased premises; and (c) the effect of the assignment by the lessee upon his continued contractual liability under the lease. See TREATISE §§ 677–677.4.

Assignment of reserves

A transfer of oil or gas produced from described premises for a specified period of time.

See also BANKING OF GAS; BROKERAGE OF GAS.

Associated companies

As used in the Uniform System of Accounts Prescribed for Natural Gas Companies Subject to the Provisions of the Natural Gas Act, the term means "companies or persons that directly, or indirectly through one or more intermediaries, control, or are controlled by, or under common control with the accounting company." 18 C.F.R. Part 201, Definitions 5A (1980).

Associated gas

Gas occurring in the form of a gas cap associated with an oil zone. See Dutton, "Proration in Texas: Conservation or Confiscation?" 11 *Sw. L.J.* 186 at 191 (1957); GAS.

Martin v. Kostner, 231 Kan. 315, 644 P.2d 430, 73 *O.&G.R.* 279 (1982), found that gas produced with oil from a well was associated gas rather than casinghead gas and hence, under the pooling clause of the lease in question, the gas rights could be pooled although the pooling clause excluded casinghead gas from the provision authorizing pooling of gas rights.

Associated gas proration

Proration of ASSOCIATED GAS (*q.v.*). In Texas this is governed by State-wide Rule 6(b). See Dutton, "Proration in Texas: Conservation or Confiscation?," 11 *Sw. L.J.* 186 at 191, 198 (1957), in which it is asserted that the operation of this rule is confiscatory in character.

See also ALLOWABLE; PRORATION.

Associated reservoir allowable

A special reduced gas ALLOWABLE (*q.v.*) for an associated gas well which is based on the equivalent volumetric withdrawals of an oil well in the same reservoir. See Blazier, "The Lease Allowable System: New Method of Regulating Oil Production in Texas," 47 *Texas L. Rev.* 658 (1969).

Association for tax purposes

Under Internal Revenue Code § 7701(a) (3), certain associations of persons engaged in a common effort but not in a corporate form may so resemble a corporation as to be taxable as such. In oil and gas operations, this danger is presented by unit operations. Avoidance of the association classification may be achieved by following the provisions of I.T. 3930 and I.T. 3948. See Treas. Reg. 301.7701–1 (1980); Sneed, "More about Associations in the Oil and Gas Industry," 33 *Texas L. Rev.* 168 (1954); Hill, "Tax Problems Arising out of Unitization Agreements," 3 *Sw. Legal Fdn. Oil & Gas Inst.* 427 (1953); Burke and Meyer, "Federal Income Tax Classification of Natural Resource Ventures: Co-Ownership, Partnership, or Association?," 37 *Sw. L.J.* 859 (1984).

ASTM

American Society for Testing Materials.

Atlantic Accord

An agreement entered into in February 1985 by the Canadian federal and the Newfoundland government dealing with mineral exploration and development in the continental shelf offshore Newfoundland. Clause 3 of the Accord establishes the Canada-Newfoundland Offshore Petroleum Board to make decisions relating to exploration, production and management of the offshore. See Edmond, "A Critical Evaluation of the Atlantic Accord," 12 *Resources* (The Newsletter of the Canadian Institute of Resources Law, Aug. 1985); Penney, "The Atlantic Accord: A Model of Cooperative Federalism: A Response to D. Paul Edmond," 14 *Resources* (Feb. 1986); MacDonald and Thompson, "The Atlantic Accord: The Politics of Compromise," 24 *Alberta L. Rev.* 61 (1985).

Atlantic Seaboard classification method

A method of classifying costs as demand or commodity costs, laid down by the Federal Power Commission in Matter of Atlantic Seaboard Corp., 11 F.P.C. 43 (Opinion No. 225, April 25, 1952) and in Matter of Northern Natural Gas Co., 11 F.P.C. 123 (Opinion No. 228, June 11, 1952). The method is discussed in Matters of Southern Natural Gas Co., 29 F.P.C. 323 at 341, 18 *O.&G.R.* 144 at 166 (Opinion No. 379, Feb. 18, 1963). See also Consolidated Gas Supply Corp. v. Federal Power Comm'n, 520 F.2d 1176 (D.C. Cir. 1975); Cheatham, "Regulation in the Post-World War II Period," American Gas Ass'n, *Regulation of the Gas Industry* 4-1 at 4-54 (1981).

ATP

Authority to prospect (*q.v.*).

"At risk" rule

The rule established by the Tax Reform Act of 1976 under which deductions which may be taken (other than by corporations) in the "activity of . . . exploring for, or exploiting, oil and gas resources" are limited to the amount the taxpayer has "at risk." Internal Revenue Code § 465.

At the well

See SOLD AT THE WELL.

Attributable acreage

Acreage which may be attributed to a well for the purpose of determining ALLOWABLE (*q.v.*) where there is an acreage factor in the allowable formula. See Stevens v. State Corporation Comm'n, 185 Kan. 190, 341 P.2d 1021, 11 *O.&G.R.* 804 (1959).

Auction

The term applied to various competitive bidding systems, *e.g.*, BONUS BIDDING; NET PROFITS BIDDING; PERFORMANCE-TYPE LEASING; ROYALTY BIDDING; WORK COMMITMENT BIDDING (*q.v.*). See K.W. Dam, *Oil Resources* (1976).

See also LEASE BIDDING SYSTEMS; ROYALTY OIL AUCTION.

Auger hole

A "hole drilled with power driven augers." Report of the Committee on Regulatory Practices for Stratigraphic Test Holes, 17 *Interstate Oil Compact Bull.* 43 (Dec. 1958).

Austin Chalk

A formation in east Texas from which there has been substantial production since about 1973. Robert L. Lyon, IBLA 82-566, GFS (O&G) 1982-205 (Aug. 10, 1982), sustained a determination of the U.S. Geological Survey that land within this formation was within a KNOWN GEOLOGICAL STRUCTURE (*q.v.*).

Authority for expenditure

See AFE.

Authority to prospect (ATP)

In Australia the conferring of the right to prospect for petroleum setting forth the areas affected and the terms or conditions imposed on the holder of the Authority. Australian Energy Ltd. v. Lennard Oil N/L [1986] Qd. R. ____ (Sup.Ct. of Queensland, 14 March 1986).

Authorization for expenditure

See AFE.

Authorized field expenditure

See AFE.

Automatic contraction clause

Syn. for AUTOMATIC ELIMINATION CLAUSE (*q.v.*).

Automatic Custody Transfer System (ACTS)

An automatic system for receiving and measuring oil. See *API Bulletin* 2502, "Recommended Practice for Lease Automatic Custody Transfer," and Nutter, "The Application of Engineering Principles to the Conservation Rules of New Mexico," 5 *IOCC Committee Bull.* 3 (Dec. 1963), (discussing the rules and forms adopted by the New Mexico Oil Conservation Commission on the matter).

Automatic elimination clause

A provision in unit agreements providing for automatic elimination of certain lands in the unit area upon a certain date if prescribed development operations are not then being carried forward. Ryan, "Current Problems in Federal Unitization," 2 *Rocky Mt. Min. L. Inst.* 157 at 160 (1956).

Syn.: AUTOMATIC CONTRACTION CLAUSE.

Automatic fuel adjustment clause

Syn. for PURCHASED GAS ADJUSTMENT CLAUSE (*q.v.*).

Automatic gauge

A method of determining automatically the quantity of oil in a tank. See Irving and Draper, *Accounting Practices in the Petroleum Industry* 59 (1958).

See also INNAGE GAUGE; OUTAGE GAUGE.

Automatic termination of lease

Ending of a lessee's interest by operation of law by virtue of a general or special limitation in the lease.

Thus, at the expiration of the primary term of a lease if there is then no production (or, in some cases, if drilling or reworking operations are not then being pursued) the lessee's interest automatically terminates by operation of the clause of general limitation in the habendum clause. Baldwin v. Blue Stem Oil Co., 106 Kan. 848, 189 P. 920 (1920). See TREATISE § 604. Similarly, if during the primary term of an UNLESS LEASE (*q.v.*), delay rentals are not tendered on or before the anniversary date (and the lease is not being kept alive in accordance with its terms by production or drilling operations), the lessee's interest automatically terminates by operation of the clause of special limitation in the delay rental clause. Phillips Petroleum Co. v. Curtis, 182 F.2d 122 (10th Cir. 1950). See TREATISE § 606. When the shut-in gas well clause of a lease governs by reason of the shutting in of a gas well capable of production in paying quantities, in most states failure to make timely payment of the shut-in gas well royalty occasions the automatic termination of the lease. Freeman v. Magnolia Petroleum Co., 141 Tex. 274, 171 S.W.2d 339 (1943); Gulf Oil Corp. v. Reid, 161 Tex. 51, 337 S.W.2d 267, 12 *O.&G.R.* 1159 (1960). See TREATISE § 633.3.

The definition in this MANUAL was quoted in Canadian Superior Oil Ltd. v. Murdoch, 65 W.W.R. 473 at 479 (Alberta Sup. Ct. 1968), *appeal dism'd,* 68 W.W.R. 390, 4 D.L.R.3d 629 (Alberta Sup. Ct. App. Div. 1969), *appeal dism'd,* [1969] S.C.R. vi, 6 D.L.R.3d 464, 70 W.W.R. 768 (1969).

See also DEVOTIONAL LIMITATION DOCTRINE; LIMITATION CLAUSE; TERMINATION OF LEASE.

Available alternative means

See ACCOMMODATION DOCTRINE.

Average evaluation of tract (AEOT)

A factor employed by the Secretary of the Interior in evaluating competitive lease bids on submerged lands of the Outer Continental Shelf. This factor is the average of all bids submitted on a tract plus the MEAN OF THE RANGE OF VALUES (MROV) (*q.v.*).

> "Thus if four bids were submitted, the AEOT would be calculated by adding the four bids and the MROV and dividing by five. High bids above the MROV, the DMROV [DISCOUNTED MROV (DMROV) (*q.v.*)] and the AEOT are generally accepted while high bids which fall below all three values are generally rejected."

Greater difficulty is presented by high bids exceeding fewer than all of these factors. See Kerr-McGee Corp. v. Watt, 517 F. Supp. 1209 at 1210, 71 *O.&G.R.* 494 at 496 (D.D.C. 1981).

A bid which falls below the MEAN OF THE RANGE OF VALUE (MROV) (*q.v.*) and the DISCOUNTED MROV (DMROV) (*q.v.*) but which equals or exceeds the AEOT is described as a PROBLEM BID (*q.v.*). See Superior Oil Co. v. Watt, 548 F. Supp. 70, 74 *O.&G.R.* 423 (D. Del. 1982).

California Energy Co. (On Reconsideration), 85 IBLA 254, 92 I.D. 125 (March 6, 1985), deals with the authority of the Secretary of the Interior to reject a bid for a lease in a KNOWN GEOTHERMAL RESOURCES AREA (KGRA) (*q.v.*). The government's reliance on oil and gas drilling data to calculate geothermal resource exploration costs was found to be in error.

See also ONE-EIGHTH RULE.

Aviation fuels

Petroleum-based fuels designed for use in aircraft internal combustion engines and refined petroleum fuel designed to operate aircraft turbine engines. Regulations concerning the allocation of these fuels are contained in 10 C.F.R. § 211.141 *et seq.* (1980).

See also ECONOMIC REGULATORY ADMINISTRATION (ERA).

. . B . .

Back allowable

The authorization for production of any shortage or underproduction resulting from pipeline prorationing. New Mexico Oil Conservation Comm'n, Rules and Regulations 1 (1958).

See also ALLOWABLE; PURCHASER PRORATIONING.

Back-haul arrangement

An arrangement between two pipeline gas carriers under which pipeline carrier *A* agrees to deliver gas to an off-system purchaser of pipeline carrier *B*, and in exchange *B* agrees to collect an equivalent amount of gas from *A's* producers and deliver it by back-haul to *B*. Tennessee Gas Pipeline Co. v. Federal Energy Regulatory Comm'n, 809 F.2d 1138 (5th Cir. 1987).

Back-in farm-out

A FARM-OUT AGREEMENT (*q.v.*) in which it is agreed that a retained nonoperating interest of the grantor may be converted at a later date into a specified undivided working interest. See Bowden, "Federal Income Tax Consequences Under Typical Farm-Out Agreements," 3 *Nat. Res. J.* 470 at 483 (1964).

See also CONVERTIBLE INTEREST.

Back-in interest

Syn. for BACK-IN RIGHT (*q.v.*). Occasionally a pooling order will provide for such interest as one of the options given the owner of an operating interest affected by the order. See Nesbitt, "A Primer on Forced Pooling of Oil and Gas," 50 *Okla. B.A.J.* 648 at 651 (1979).

Back-in option

The term used to describe the right given Petro-Canada by the Canada Oil and Gas Land Regulations by which Petro-Canada is given the right to acquire an interest in subsisting permits. S.0.R./61–253, § 120 *et seq.* See Harrison, "State Involvement in the Canadian Petroleum Industry: The Petro-Canada Experience," in International Bar Ass'n, *Proceedings of the Energy Law Seminar* (organized by the Committee on Natural Resources, Section on Business Law) Topic R, Paper 4 (1979).

"Back-in" provision

A term used to describe a provision in a FARM-OUT AGREEMENT (*q.v.*) whereby the farmor retains an option to exchange a retained override for a share of the working interest. See Lamb, "Farmout Agreements—Problems of Negotiation and Drafting," 8 *Rocky Mt. Min. L. Inst.* 139 at 146 (1963).

See also CONVERTIBLE INTEREST.

Back-in right

(1) The privilege created by certain joint venture agreements whereunder participants in the agreement will be entitled to participate in a leasehold acquired by another participant as a result of a competitive bid made by the latter which is higher than the bid made by the joint venture. See Energy Data Requirements of the Federal Government (Part III—Federal Offshore Oil and Gas Leasing Policies), Hearings before the Subcommittee on Activities of Regulatory Agencies of the Permanent Select Committee on Small Business, House of Representatives, 93rd Cong., 2d Sess. (1974) at p. 412, 457; Smith, "Participation Agreements in Offshore Operations," *Rocky Mt. Min. L. Fdn. Offshore Exploration, Drilling and Development Institute* 2–26 (1975).

(2) The reversionary interest of a FARMOR (*q.v.*) or of an assignor of a lease whereunder the farmor or assignor is to become entitled to a specified share of the working interest when the assignee has recovered specified costs from production. See Mengden v. Peninsula Prod. Co., 544 S.W.2d 643, 55 *O.&G.R.* 477 (Tex. 1976).

See also CONVERTIBLE INTEREST; PAY OUT; SALE FOR CASH WITH RETAINED BACK-IN.

(3) A provision in the Canada Oil and Gas Act requiring a free 25% government share in all exploration rights on the four million square miles of federally controlled land and offshore prospects. *Wall Street Journal,* Dec. 8, 1981, p. 30, col. 2; 1 *Resources* (Newsletter of the Canadian Institute of Resources Law, May 1982) (discussing the right of compensation under international law in the event of the exercise of the back-in right).

For an argument that the back-in provision of the Crown under the Canada Oil and Gas Act constitutes an expropriation under international law and is therefore subject to the principle of customary international law requiring prompt, adequate and effective compensation, see Olmstead, Krauland and Orentlicher, "Expropriation in the Energy Industry: Canada's Crown Share Provision as a Violation of International Law," 29 *McGill L.J.* 439 (1984).

Back-off wheel

See STRIPPER WHEEL.

Back pressure

The pressure within a well against the exposed face of the reservoir rock. The pressure may be imposed at the wellhead by control valves, chokes or surface conditions, and may be influenced by tubing design. Maintenance of back pressure reduces the pressure differential between the formation and the well bore so that oil is moved into the well from the reservoir rock with a smaller pressure loss. The rate of flow is somewhat reduced below what it would be under open-flow conditions, but there will be an expenditure of a smaller volume of gas, the gas-oil ratio will be reduced, and ultimate recovery will be increased.

"Pressure against which a fluid is flowing; may be composed of friction in lines, restrictions in pipes, valves, pressure in vessel to which fluid is flowing, hydrostatic head, or other resistance to fluid flow." American Gas Association Bureau of Statistics, *Glossary for the Gas Industry* 4.

See also MULTIPOINT BACK PRESSURE TEST; PRESSURE.

Back pressure method

A method to determine the productive capacity or potential of gas wells. The wellhead pressures and quantities of gas produced are measured at various rates of flow. From a plot of these data the amount of gas the well would be able to deliver may be computed. This method makes it possible to determine the capacity of a gas well without waste of gas and it eliminates the hazards of damage to the formation and well equipment. See Interstate Oil Compact Commission, *Oil and Gas Production* 110 (1951).

Back-up crude

The term applied in the LIBYAN PRODUCERS AGREEMENT (*q.v.*) to refer to Middle East crude to be supplied by participants in the agreement to replace Libyan crude of which they were deprived by action of the Libyan government. See Hunt v. Mobil Oil Corp., 465

F. Supp. 195 at 202 (S.D. 1978), *aff'd without opinion,* 610 F.2d 806 (2d Cir. 1979).

BACT

BEST AVAILABLE CONTROL TECHNOLOGY (BACT) (*q.v.*).

Bad faith trespasser

An operator who enters upon land of another without authority and in bad faith. If such a person drills and secures production, he is liable to the true owner for the value at the surface of the oil and gas produced, that is, without a credit for drilling and operating expenses.

The determination of the good or bad faith of a trespasser may be left to the jury or may be decided as a matter of law. Several factors affect the determination: (1) the subjective state of mind of the trespasser; (2) the reasonableness of the trespasser's claim of title; (3) the presence or absence of drainage under the land; (4) entry upon advice of reputable counsel.

It has been held, however, that despite a jury finding of good faith, a trespasser is in bad faith as a matter of law if he enters and drills after written notice of an adverse claim (that proves to be good) and after filing of a title suit. Houston Prod. Co. v. Mecom Oil Co., 62 S.W.2d 75 (Tex. Com. App. 1933). See TREATISE §§ 226–226.3.

See also GOOD FAITH TRESPASSER; SUBSURFACE TRESPASS.

Bailer

A piece of equipment in a cable rig. It is a bucket-like device which is lowered in the hole periodically to remove the cuttings. One advantage of cable tool drilling is that the cuttings can be removed from the hole and examined at will.

Bailing

A term used in cable tool drilling. It refers to the act of lowering a bailer in the hole to remove the cuttings therefrom.

Balancing

The process by which persons having an interest in production from a well, unit or reservoir adjust their take therefrom to insure that each such person receives his proportionate part of production. Basic methods of balancing include:

(1) balancing in kind, *viz.*, the underproduced party takes a certain percentage of the overproduced's party's oil or gas until the "imbalance" has been "made up;"

(2) periodic cash balancing, *viz.*, the underproduced party receives cash and the production is immediately brought into balance; and

(3) cash balancing upon depletion, *viz.*, the overproduced party accounts to the underproduced party in cash upon depletion.

52 Okla. Stat. §§ 541–547 (enacted in 1983) permits all owners of an interest in a gas well to share ratably in revenues from the sale of the well's production, regardless of who may be producing it. Seal v. Corporation Comm'n, 725 P.2d 278, 90 *O.&G.R.* 500 (Okla. 1986), *appeal dism' for want of a properly presented federal question sub nom.* Amerada Hess Corp. v. Corporation Comm'n, ___ U.S. ___, 107 S.Ct. 1265 (1987), sustained the constitutionality of this legislation while invalidating certain of the Rules promulgated by the Corporation Commission to administer the provision of the Act.

See also La. Act 345 of 1984 amending 30 La. R.S. § 10 (unleased interest included in a compulsory unit is entitled to pro rata share of proceeds of sale of production).

Northern Michigan Exploration Co. v. Public Service Comm'n, 153 Mich. App. 635, 396 N.W.2d 487 at 493, ___ *O.&G.R.* ___ (1986), sustained the authority of a regulatory commission to adopt a NET PAY PRORATION FORMULA (*q.v.*) based upon the commission's authority to require cumulative balancing, to control production retroactively and to transfer underproduction. "These are common devices in the industry to assure that each interest owner obtains a fair and equitable share of production. See 8 Williams & Meyers, [Oil and Gas Law] *supra,* 'Balancing,' pp. 62–63; 'Retroactive Adjusting Allowable,' p. 756; 'Transferred Allowable,' p. 919; 'Underproduction,' p. 933 and 'Overproduction,' p. 606."

Chevron U.S.A., Inc. v. Belco Petroleum Corp., 755 F.2d 1151, 84 *O.&G.R.* 471 (5th Cir. 1985), *reh. denied,* 761 F.2d 695 (5th Cir. 1985), *cert. denied,* ___ U.S. ___, 106 S.Ct. 140 (1985), construed a gas balancing agreement entered into by a farmor and farmee to provide only for a balancing "in kind" rather than in cash. The court concluded that the farmor who underdrew his share of the gas prior to the failure of production bore the risk of lost production.

In the United States, problems of balancing have arisen primarily in connection with the production of gas; in a number of major oil producing countries problems of balancing of oil production have arisen by reason of shipping or marketing problems of a party with an interest in production under a CONCESSION (*q.v.*) or similar agreement. Major variants in balancing agreements include the following:

(a) LIFTING TOLERANCE (*q.v.*),

(b) the applicable period employed in determining underlift/overlift status of a party,

(c) the method of balancing to be employed,

(d) the effect of termination of production while an imbalance exists,

(e) the permissible period during which an underlift may be accumulated, and

(f) circumstances, if any, under which an underlift may be forfeited.

The difficulty experienced in negotiating balancing agreements is evidenced by the fact that many oil balancing agreements provide that the parties "agree to agree" on a balancing agreement for gas if and when commercial production of gas is obtained, thus postponing to a later day the complex negotiating process.

For other discussions of balancing problems see the following:

Symposium: Workshop on Natural Gas Prorationing and Ratable Take Regulation, 57 *U. Colo. L. Rev.* 149–393 (1986);

Kutzschbach, "Operating Agreement Considerations in Acquisitions of Producing Properties," 36 *Sw. Legal Fdn. Oil & Gas Inst.* 7-1 at 7-33 (1985);

McNamara, "Unitized Production—Rights of Operators and Non-Operators," 31 *L.S.U. Min. L. Inst.* 194 (1984) (discussing orders of the Louisiana Commissioner of Conservation designed to resolve disputes among coowners of unit production);

Heisler, "Ownership, Disposition and Control of Production From Unitized or Jointly Owned Wells," 30 *L.S.U. Min. L. Inst.* 1 (1984).

Taylor, "The Excess Gas Market—Recent Legal Problems Precipitated by Excess Gas Deliverability, and Applicable Regulatory Provisions," 35 *Sw. Legal Fdn. Oil & Gas Inst.* 87 (1984);

Park, "Developments in Natural Gas Purchase Contracts," 22 *Alta. L. Rev.* 43 (1984);

Campbell, "Gas Balancing Agreements," *Rocky Mt. Min. L. Fdn. Inst. on Oil and Gas Agreements* Paper 9 (1983);

Fell, "Marketing of Production From Properties Subject to Operating Agreements," 33 *Sw. Legal Fdn. Oil & Gas Inst.* 115 (1982);

Upchurch, "Split Stream Gas Sales and the Gas Storage and Balancing Agreement," 24 *Rocky Mt. Min. L. Inst.* 665 (1978);

Niebrugge, "Oil and Gas: Production Imbalance in Split Stream Gas Wells—Getting Your Fair Share," 30 *Okla L. Rev.* 955 (1977);

Ellis, "The Production of Gas from Joint Interest Properties, 21 *Sw. Legal Fdn. Oil & Gas Inst.* 47 (1970);

Hillyer, "Problems in Producing and Selling by Split or Single Stream, Gas Allocable to Diverse Working Interest Ownerships," 16 *Sw. Legal Fd. Oil & Gas Inst.* 243 (1965);

United Petroleum Exploration, Inc. v. Premier Resources, Ltd., 511 F. Supp. 127, 70 *O.&G.R.* 53 (W.D. Okla. 1980) (adopting the cash balancing method, calculated on the basis of the actual price received for the gas sold);

Beren v. Harper Oil Co., 546 P.2d 1356, 53 *O.&G.R.*, 531 (Okla. App. 1975, *as corrected on limited grant of certiorari*);

HBOP, Ltd. v. Delhi Pipeline Corp., 645 P.2d 1042, 73 *O.&G.R.* 47 (Okla. App. 1982; *cert. denied*).

See also TREATISE § 951.

See also CANCELLED UNDERAGE; DEEMED PURCHASE FORMULA; DEFERRED PRODUCTION AGREEMENT; GAS BANK AGREEMENT; GAS STORAGE AND BALANCING AGREEMENT; LIFTING; LIFTING TOLERANCE; "OUT OF BALANCE" PRODUCTION PLAN; OVERLIFT; SPLIT CONNECTION; TAKE-OR-LOSE PROVISION; UNDERAGE; UNDERLIFT; UNDERLIFT/OVERLIFT PROVISION.

Balancing dates

The beginning and end of a BALANCING PERIOD (*q.v.*). See In re Conservation and Prevention of Waste of Crude Petroleum and Natural Gas in the Alco-Mag Fields, Harris County, Texas, 5 *O.&G.R.* 423 (Railroad Comm'n of Texas, Dec. 12, 1955); 16 Tex. Admin. Code § 3.31.

Balancing period

A period of time during which OVERPRODUCTION (*q.v.*) and U NDERPRODUCTION (*q.v.*) may be made up by the operator of a gas well which has overproduced or underproduced. See Administrative Ruling, Railroad Commission of Texas, 5 *O.&G.R.* 1100 at 1104 (1956); 16 Tex. Admin. Code § 3.31.

For a discussion of the allowable adjustments on the balancing dates, see Weymouth v. Colorado Interstate Gas Co., 367 F.2d 84 at 98, 25 *O.&G.R.* 371 at 389 (5th Cir. 1966).

See also IOCC, *General Rules and Regulations for the Conservation of Oil and Gas* 26–27 (1969); ALLOWABLE.

Balancing rule

The name sometimes given to the Texas Railroad Commission rule for the balancing of periods of overproduction and periods of underproduction of gas wells. See Stayton, "Proration of Gas," 14 *Sw. Legal Fdn. Oil & Gas Inst.* 1 at 29 (1963); 16 Tex. Admin. Code § 3.31.

Bank

See BANKING OF GAS; COST BANK; DEPOSITORY BANK; GAS BANK AGREEMENT; QUALITY BANK.

Banking of cost

See COST BANK.

Banking of gas

The term applied to an arrangement for the delivery of gas at a designated price coupled with the obligation upon request to redeliver equivalent amounts of gas at roughly the same price. See Railroad Comm'n v. City of Austin, 524 S.W.2d 262 at 277, 51 *O.&G.R.* 231 at 252 (Tex. 1975).

See also GAS BANK AGREEMENT; "OUT-OF-BALANCE" PRODUCTION PLAN.

Bankruptcy

The effect of bankruptcy of a lessor upon unexpired oil and gas leases is discussed in Jones, "Rejection of Unexpired Oil and Gas Leases in Bankruptcy Proceedings," 19 *Tulsa L.J.* 68 (1983).

See also Practicing Law Institute, *The Oil and Gas Industry and the Bankruptcy Laws* (Alan Gover, Chairman, 1985).

BAPCO

The Bahrain Petroleum Company. See Shwadran, *The Middle East, Oil and the Great Powers* 390 *et seq.* (3d ed. revised and enlarged 1973).

Barefoot

A well completed without casing or screen at the bottom.

Barite

A mineral employed as a weighting material in drilling MUD (*q.v.*).

American Petroleum Institute v. Environmental Protection Agency, 787 F.2d 965, 89 *O.&G.R.* 8 (5th Cir. 1986), sustained the validity of limitations imposed on the mercury-cadmium content of barite used in offshore Alaskan operations.

Baroid

A specially processed barite (barium sulphate) to which Aquagel has been added, used as a conditioning material in drilling MUD (*q.v.*) in order to obtain satisfactory cores and samples of formation.

Barrel mile

For purposes of the Michigan Business Receipts Tax, this term was defined as the transportation of the equivalent of a barrel of oil a distance of one mile for a consideration. Act No. 17 of the Public Acts of 1954, State of Michigan, Mich. Stat. Ann. § 7.557 (1)(q), 4 *O.&G.R.* 491 (1955) (subsequently repealed in 1967).

Barrel of oil

"Fifteen [states] describe a barrel [of crude oil] as being 42 U.S. gallons measured at 60 degrees F., three as 42 U.S. gallons (no temperature prescribed), two as 42 U.S. gallons of 231 cubic inches each, and eleven do not define a barrel of oil." 26 *Oil & Gas Compact Bull.* 55 (June 1967).

A 42 gallon barrel of crude oil weighs about 306 pounds. One barrel equals 5.6 cubic feet or O.159 cubic meters. For crude oil 1 bbl is about O.136 metric tons, O.134 long tons, and O.150 short tons. See CONVERSION FACTORS.

One U.S. gallon is equal to O.832672 Canadian gallon and hence one U.S. barrel (42 gallon) is equal to 34.9722 Canadian (Imperial) gallons. For many purposes this is rounded off and a barrel is viewed as containing 35 Imperial gallons. See Canada Oil and Gas Drilling and Production Regulations (SOR/61–253) § 2.

For an interesting account of the history and legends of this unit of measurement, see Hardwicke, *The Oilman's Barrel* (1958). As explained in this work at page 97, a specified number of barrels of crude oil in the original underground reservoir measures more than that number in the stock tank shortly after production because the change from reservoir pressure to the lower atmospheric pressure results in considerable shrinkage, in part by escape from the liquid of gas and some of the lighter fractions. For this reason, contracts for purchase of a specified number of barrels of crude oil in the reservoir should state clearly whether the unit is a barrel as measured in the reservoir or in the stock tanks, with all the applicable corrections, as for gravity, temperature, and BS AND W (*q.v.*).

See also PAPER BARREL; VIDEO BARREL.

Barrel payment

Syn. for OIL PAYMENT (*q.v.*).

Base allowable

"[T]he amount of production which according to a [Oil and Gas Conservation] Board order could be taken if no penalty factor, whether its purpose be for proration, for avoidance of waste or for protection of the rights of others, were to be applied." The Alberta Oil and Gas Conservation Act, R.S.A. 1970, c. 267, § 2(1) (2). When a well is completed outside its primary and secondary TARGET AREA (*q.v.*), its base allowable is reduced. See Province of Alberta Energy Resources Conservation Board Order No. SU 1088 (Aug. 10, 1981).

See also ALLOWABLE.

Base gas

Syn. for CUSHION GAS (*q.v.*).

Base line

"A line which runs in an east-west direction from an initial point and from which are initiated other lines for the cadastral survey of the public lands within the area governed by the principal meridian that runs through the same initial point. Three base lines (in Ohio) are irregular owing to the fact that they follow river courses." United States Department of the Interior Bureau of Land Management, *Glossary of Public-Land Terms* 4 (1949).

See GENERAL LAND OFFICE SURVEY.

Basement rock

Either igneous or metamorphic rock. It does not contain petroleum. Ordinarily, it lies below sedimentary rock, and when it is encountered in drilling, the well is abandoned.

Base period control level (BPCL)

An adjusted approximation by the Department of Energy based on the natural rate of decline of production from an old well indicating the amount of oil the well should be capable of producing in a given period. Production from the well in excess of this level is considered new, or upper tier, oil for pricing purposes. The procedure is designed to give the producer an incentive to keep production above the BPCL. Congressional Budget Office, *The Decontrol of Domestic Oil Prices: An Overview* 6 (1979).

See Department of Energy Regulations for Control of Petroleum Prices, 10 C.F.R. § 212.72 (1980).

See also PRODUCED AND SOLD.

Base-point pricing

A pricing system under which one geographical location (SINGLE BASE-POINT SYSTEM (*q.v.*)) or multiple geographical locations (MULTIPLE BASE-POINT SYSTEM (*q.v.*)) are accepted by buyers and sellers of oil as the assumed shipping point of the oil for purposes of the posted price and shipping costs. See Danielsen, *The Evolution of OPEC* 59, 139 (1982).

See also BASING POINT; EQUALIZATION POINT; GULF-PLUS PRICING STRUCTURE; PERSIAN GULF PRICING SYSTEM; PHANTOM FREIGHT.

Base pressure

"A standard to which measurements of a volume of gas are referred." American Gas Association Bureau of Statistics, *Glossary for the Gas Industry* 4.

Base royalty

The ROYALTY (*q.v.*) reserved by the landowner on the making of an oil and gas lease or the granting of an interest in oil and gas.

Base survey

A tract described in an original sale from the state. Discussion Notes, 3 *O.&G.R.* 1950 at 1952 (1954).

Basic sediment

Impurities contained in the fluid as produced from an oil well. Purchasing companies will ordinarily not accept oil having more than 1% of water and other foreign matter. If the fluid as produced contains more than this proportion of foreign matter, some of the impurities may be removed by settling in the bottom of tanks into which the fluid is run on the lease. The impurities gradually settle and thicken in the bottom of the tank as an emulsion which is called basic sediment or B.S. The emulsion is scraped out of the tank periodically and disposed of as waste matter or treated for recovery of additional hydrocarbons. Alternatively, the fluid as produced may be processed in a treating and steaming plant on the lease to separate the basic sediment and water from the oil.

Director of Taxation v. Kansas Krude Oil Reclaiming Co., 236 Kan. 450, 691 P.2d 1303, 83 *O.&G.R.* 252 (1984), held that the Board of Tax Appeals improperly exempted from the Mineral Severance Tax oil which was recovered from basic sediment and water.

See also DEHYDRATION PLANT; HEATER-TREATER; TREATING PLANT.

Basin

A synclinal structure in the subsurface, formerly the bed of an ancient sea. Because basins are composed of sedimentary rock, and are thought to have contained the source material for petroleum, and because basin contours provide traps for petroleum, basins are regarded as good prospects for petroleum exploration. The Tyler Basin in East Texas and the Williston Basin in North Dakota are examples of major oil producing basins.

Basing point

A location employed for the purpose of determining the transportation charge ingredient in the price of oil. For some years the GULF-PLUS PRICING STRUCTURE (*q.v.*), under which crude oil was priced at the U.S. price plus tanker rates from the United States Gulf to the point of delivery, was employed. In other words, there was a phantom transportation charge for Middle East oil delivered to Eastern Hemisphere purchasers. During the Second World War a Double basing point structure was established, *viz.*, the Arabian Gulf as well as the Gulf of Mexico came to be used as a basing point. Al-Chalabi, *OPEC and the International Oil Industry: A Changing Structure* 62 (1980).

See also BASE-POINT PRICING; EQUALIZATION POINT; GULF-PLUS PRICING STRUCTURE; MULTIPLE BASE-POINT SYSTEM; PERSIAN GULF PRICING SYSTEM; PHANTOM FREIGHT; SINGLE BASE-POINT SYSTEM.

BAST regulations

Regulations relating to the use of the "best available and safest technologies" determined to be feasible which the Secretary of the Interior is obliged by 43 U.S.C. § 1347(b) to require on all new drilling and production operations wherever failure of equipment would have a significant effect on safety, health, or the environment, except where he determines that the incremental benefits are clearly insufficient to justify the incremental costs of utilizing such technologies. See Conservation Law Foundation of New England, Etc. v. Andrus, 623 F.2d 712 at 719 (1st Cir. 1979).

Battery

See TANK BATTERY.

Battery site

That portion of the surface of land, other than a well site or roadway, required for access to and to accommodate separators, treaters, dehydrators, storage tanks, surface reservoirs, pumps and other equipment, including above ground pressure maintenance facilities, that are necessary to measure, separate or store prior to shipping to market or disposal, or necessary to produce, the fluids, minerals and water, or any of them, from wells. Saskatchewan Surface Rights Acquisition and Compensation Act, 1968 (Sask. Stat. 1968, c. 73) § 2 (a).

See also TANK BATTERY.

Baumé system

A system of determining the density of oil. See DENSITY OF PETROLEUM.

bbl

Abbreviation for barrel. See BARREL OF OIL.

bcf

Billion cubic feet.

Bé

Abbreviation for Baum é.

Bean

See CHOKE.

Behind the meter storage

See OFF-SYSTEM STORAGE.

Behind the pipe

See GAS BEHIND THE PIPE.

Behind the pipe exclusion

The provision of the NATURAL GAS POLICY ACT OF 1978 (NGPA) (*q.v.*) providing that production is not NEW NATURAL GAS (*q.v.*) for pricing purposes if the reservoir was penetrated before April 20, 1977, by an old well from which natural gas or oil was produced in commercial quantities (whether or not such production was from such reservoir); and natural gas could have been produced in commercial quantities from such reservoir through such old well before April 20, 1977. 15 U.S.C. § 3312(c)(1)(C)(ii). See True Oil Co. v. Federal Energy Regulatory Commission, 663 F.2d 75 (10th Cir. 1981).

Benchmark crude

Saudi Arabian (gravity API 34 degrees) light crude oil employed as the standard on which OPEC price changes have been based.

Syn.: Arabian light oil.

See also BONNY LIGHT OIL.

Beneficial interest

(1) As defined in a Rocky Mountain unit operating agreement, the proportion (expressed as a percentage) that the net acreage of a party's Committed Working Interest or Interests bears to the total net acreage of all the Committed Working Interests of the parties. See Rocky Mountain Unit Operating Agreement Form 1 (Undivided Interest) May, 1954, Section 1.7, TREATISE § 920.3.

(2) A term used to describe the fraction or percentage of production allocated under a unit operating agreement to a particular party in interest.

Benton plan

The name applied to a plan under which changes may be made from time to time in the allocation of unitized substances on the basis of newly acquired information. Kirk, "Content of Royalty Owners, and Operator's Unitization Agreements," 3 *Sw. Legal Fdn. Oil & Gas Inst.* 19 at 53-58 (1952). See TREATISE § 980.2.

Bentonite

A material used in the preparation of drilling MUD (*q.v.*).

United States v. Kaycee Bentonite Corp., 89 I.D. 262, 64 IBLA 183 (1982), held that bentonite was a locatable mineral under the federal mining laws. The case includes a detailed discussion of the characteristics and use of this mineral.

Benzine

A volatile inflammable liquid derived from petroleum and used in cleaning, dyeing and painting.

Bernstein letter

A letter from the State Department informing a court that the foreign policy needs of the United States do not necessitate application of the ACT OF STATE DOCTRINE (*q.v.*). See Comment, "American Oil Investors' Access to Domestic Courts in Foreign Nationalization Disputes," 123 *U.Pa. L.Rev.* 610 at 635 (1975). In First National City Bank v. Banco Nacional de Cuba, 406 U.S. 759 (1972), six members of the Court disapproved the so-called *Bernstein* exception to the Act of State doctrine. See also Alfred Dunhill of London, Inc. v. Republic of Cuba, 425 U.S. 682 (1976).

Best available control technology (BACT)

A concept taken from the Clean Air Act designed to preserve air quality from degradation by requiring that emissions from new facilities, temporary facilities, and even existing facilities in some instances be controlled to the extent possible. What is determined to be BACT is based on cost, available technology, and other factors. See 30 C.F.R. §§ 250.2(ww) (definitions), 250.57-1(g) (1981); Kirwan, "Offshore Oil and Gas Development—1980 Environmental Update," 32 *Sw. Legal Fdn. Oil & Gas Inst.* 1 at 14 (1981).

Better market clause

See ESCALATOR CLAUSE.

BGC

The British Gas Corporation, which enjoys monopoly buying power over United Kingdom offshore natural gas.

Bid-away problem

The term applied to the possibility of potential deliverability shortages faced by intrastate gas pipelines and their customers arising from a disparity between gas acquisition costs of interstate and of intrastate natural gas pipelines which enable interstate pipelines to bid away a disproportionate share of new gas supplies from intrastate pipelines. See Allison, "Natural Gas Pricing: The Eternal Debate," 37 *Baylor L. Rev.* 1 at 44 *et seq.* (1985).

Bid files

Collections of documents developed for and used in nominating and bidding for the right to lease tracts in the federal domain for oil and gas exploration. Federal Trade Comm'n v. Texaco, Inc., 555 F.2d 862 at 876 (D.C. Cir. 1977), *cert. denied,* 431 U.S. 974, *reh. denied,* 434 U.S. 883 (1977).

Big frac

This term is defined by Stoltz, Wagner & Brown v. Cimarron Exploration Co., 564 F. Supp. 840 at n. 3, 77 *O.&G.R.* 529 at n. 3 (W.D. Okla. 1981), as follows:

> "A 'big frac' is a method of completion of a gas well which consists of perforating the prospectively productive interval in the formation with approximately one perforation per foot and injecting into the well bore some 100,000 gallons of gel water and 100,000 pounds of river salt at a rate of 100 to 150 barrels per minute."

See also FRACTURING; LITTLE FRAC.

Big inch pipeline

A 24-inch pipeline from Longview in east Texas to Norris City, Illinois, built during World War II to meet the problem caused by tanker losses at sea as a result of submarine warfare. Oil was moved through the pipeline to Illinois whence it moved by rail tank cars to New York and Philadelphia. Later during the war the pipeline was extended to Pennsylvania. Following the war the pipeline was sold to Texas Eastern Transmission Corp. and converted to a gas pipeline. See Johnson, *Petroleum Pipelines and Public Policy, 1906–1959,* 322–326, 341–348 (1967).

Billing notice

See COURTESY BILLING NOTICE.

Bio gas

Methane produced by decomposition or processing of organic matter.

Bit

A drilling tool that cuts the hole. Bits are designed on two basic and different principles: the cable tool bit, which moves up and down to pulverize; and the rotary bit which revolves, to grind.

Bit, Cable tool

A metal bar, rounded on two sides and flat on the other two. The flat sides are grooved. The bottom is wedge-shaped. A cable tool bit operates on a percussion principle; it pulverizes the rock by its weight as it is dropped and raised continuously in the hole. Added to this force is that of suction, created by the rising movement of the bit in a hole full of mud.

Bit, Core

A special bit for removing a sample of the formation from the bottom of the hole. The essential elements of design are a sharp cutting surface, which will carve out a cylinder of rock, and a hollow center which holds the core as it is being cut.

See also CORING; DIAMOND DRILL CORE BIT.

Bit, Drag

A bit sometimes used to drill the hole in soft formations. Drilling may be faster with the use of a drag bit rather than a rock bit through certain formations. See McGhee, "Did We Bury the Drag Bit Too Soon?" 55 *Oil and Gas Journal* 125 (Dec. 16, 1957).

Bit, Dressing of

The repair and sharpening of a bit that has been worn down from use.

Bit, Drilling

The bit used to drill the hole after the well is spudded in. Two types of drilling rigs are in common use in the United States: rotary and cable tool. The bits for each type of rig differ in construction and operation. For a description see the entry for each.

Bit, Fishtail

A type of rotary bit used primarily in soft formations. There are a variety of designs for fishtail bits, but their distinguishing characteristic is one or more blades which do the cutting. While these bits revolve as do other rotary bits, they do not use the revolving cone with teeth.

Bit, Rock

The drilling tool used to cut the hole once the well is spudded in and the top soil penetrated. On a rotary rig, a common type rock bit has three conical cutters mounted on ball and roller bearings. This tool is lowered to the bottom of the hole, where it is rotated to cut away the rock.

Bit, Roller

The cutting tool used in rotary drilling. It consists of a cluster of conical cutters, with teeth, that rotate on ball and roller bearings.

Bit, Rotary

There are several types. One of the most common is a cluster of revolving cones serrated with wedge-shaped teeth. The bit rests on the bottom of the hole and grinds up the rock as it revolves. Mud is run through the drill pipe, into the hole, to lubricate the bit, and to remove the cuttings.

Bit, Spudding

The bit used to start the hole. When the hole is deep enough, regular drilling tools are substituted.

Bitumen

A name for various solid and semisolid hydrocarbons.

See also CRUDE BITUMEN; HEAVY OIL.

Black Oil

An asphalt-base oil as distinguished from a paraffin-base oil, known as green oil. See Ball, Ball, and Turner, *This Fascinating Oil Business* 210 (2d ed. 1965).

Blackstock formula

A formula employed to determine the value of land taken for a well site. See Canadian Reserve Oil & Gas Ltd. v. Lamb, 49 D.L.R.3d 759 at 765, [1975] 1 W.W.R. 414 at 421 (Saskatchewan Ct. of Appeal 1974); *appeal allowed,* [1977] 1 S.C.R. 517, 70 D.L.R.3d 201, [1976] 4 W.W.R. 79 (Sup. Ct. of Canada 1976); Re Cochin Pipe Lines Ltd. and Rattray, 117 D.L.R.3d 442 (Alta. Ct. of App. 1980).

Blanchard case

A term used to describe Shell Oil Co. v. Corporation Commission, 389 P.2d 951, 20 *O.&G.R.* 841 (Okla. 1963).

For discussion of the Blanchard case and the WEIGHTED AVERAGE METHOD (*q.v.*) of allocating unit production to royalty owners adopted therein, see the following:

Upchurch, "Split Stream Gas Sales and the Gas Storage and Balancing Agreement," 24 *Rocky Mt. Min. L. Inst.* 665 (1978);

Mosburg, "Practical Effects of the 'Blanchard' Case," 35 *Okla. B.A.J.* 2331 (1964);

TREATISE § 951.

See also BALANCING.

Blasting

Use of explosives, *e.g.,* for purposes of a seismologic survey.

Bleeder pipe

An open pipe sometimes placed through the center of a plug in an abandoned well, extending to the surface to permit the free passage of gas. Code of Virginia, 1950 § 45.1–129(b).

"Bleeding" a well

See PERIODIC FLOWING.

Bleedline

A line which may be opened to relieve excess gas pressure and prevent a blow-out. See Anderson-Prichard Oil Corp. v. Parker, 245 F.2d 831, 7 *O.&G.R.* 1419 (10th Cir. 1957).

Blending stock

Any of the stocks used to make commercial gasoline. These include: natural gasoline, straight-run gasoline, cracked gasoline, polymer gasoline, alkylate, and aromatics.

Blind pool drilling fund

See DRILLING FUND; PUBLIC DRILLING FUND.

BLM

THE BUREAU OF LAND MANAGEMENT (*q.v.*).

Block

(1) Several leases within an immediate vicinity. Skeeters v. Granger, 314 S.W.2d 364, 9 *O.&G.R.* 771 (Tex. Civ. App. 1958, error ref'd n.r.e.).

(2) An area, composed of separate contiguous leaseholds, appropriate in size for the drilling of an exploratory well. Before drilling an exploratory well, particularly when it is proposed to drill to a considerable depth at great expense, the operator will normally seek to acquire a sizable block of leases surrounding the site of the proposed exploratory well. See DRILLING BLOCK.

(3) For purposes of the Alberta Oil and Gas Conservation Act, the term Block is defined as an area or part of a pool consisting of production spacing units grouped for the purpose of obtaining a common, aggregate production allowable. R.S.A. 1970, c. 267, § 2 (1)(4).

(4) For purposes of administration of the United Kingdom Continental Shelf Act of 1964, the territorial seabed of Great Britain and the continental shelf have been divided into rectangular blocks (measuring 12 degrees of longitude by 10 degrees of latitude) each of approximately 250 square kilometers (100 square miles). Production licenses may be issued in respect of one or more blocks. See

Crommelin, "Offshore Oil and Gas Rights: A Comparative Study," 14 *Nat. Res. J.* 457 at 466 (1974).

(5) In Australia for purposes of administration of submerged lands the adjacent lands are divided into blocks measuring five minutes of latitude by five minutes of longitude (the area varying from 23 square miles in the south to 30 square miles in the north). *Id.* at 479. See Lang and Crommelin, *Australian Mining and Petroleum Law* 233 (1979).

(6) For purposes of Norwegian production licenses, a block is approximately 500 square kilometers, but certain blocks can be considerably smaller, *i.e.*, those which are bounded by a base line or by the median line. See Krohn, Kaasen, *et al.*, *Norwegian Petroleum Law* 3–1 (1978).

Block lease

A lease executed by the owners of separate tracts (or separate leases executed by the owners of the individual tracts) which provides that drilling of one or more test wells within the combined area or block will satisfy the delay rental and habendum clause of the lease or leases as to each of the separate tracts included in the combined area or block. Such leases are fairly common in unexplored territory where land is owned in comparatively small tracts and when a single tract is not extensive enough to warrant the capital investment required for exploration and development. Wilson v. Mitchell, 245 Ky. 55, 53 S.W.2d 175 (1932).

Blowing

Dissipation of casinghead gas into the atmosphere.

Blowing a well

Periodic flowing of a well to remove accumulation of dirt, liquids, shale, rocks, water and, in the case of a gas well, oil which settle around the well and reduce the flow. The object of blowing the well is to remove this accumulation, to blow it out of the well. The general practice is to open the top of the pipe and "let her blow." More pressure and velocity are thereby obtained and more rubbish blown out of the well. The most efficient way to clean gas wells is to open them directly to the atmosphere. When the gas well contains salt water, oil, or perhaps some other objectionable or poisonous substance, a less efficient method of blowing into a catcher, separator or sump is followed; this technique causes a loss of pressure differential and hence a less efficient cleaning operation. See Wohlford v. American Gas Production Co., 218 F.2d 213, 4 *O.&G.R.* 448 (5th Cir. 1955).

See also PERIODIC FLOWING.

Blowing off

The release of gas into the atmosphere for a brief period of time. When gas is withdrawn from underground gas storage it is sometimes necessary to release some of the gas into the atmosphere for a minute or two. This is done to clear the well bore of hydrates and water which have collected and which cause a decrease in the flow of gas from the well. See Pitsenbarger v. Northern Natural Gas Co., 198 F. Supp. 665 at 674, 16 *O.&G.R.* 267 at 278 (S.D. Iowa, 1961).

Blow out

A sudden, violent expulsion of oil, gas and MUD (*q.v.*) (and sometimes water) from a drilling well, followed by an uncontrolled flow from the well. It occurs when high pressure gas is encountered in the hole and sufficient precautions, such as increasing the weight of the mud, have not been taken.

For discussions of the meaning of the term "blow out" see Creole Explorations, Inc. v. Underwriters at Lloyd's London, 151 So. 2d 382, 18 *O.&G.R.* 293 (La. App. 1963), *rev'd,* 245 La. 927, 161 So. 2d 768, 20 *O.&G.R.* 320 (1964); Equity Oil Co. v. National Fire Insurance Co., 247 F.2d 393, 8 *O.&G.R.* 85 (10th Cir. 1957); Fidelity-Phenix Fire Insurance Co. v. Dyer, 220 F.2d 697, 4 *O.&G.R.* 973 (5th Cir. 1955); Feeney and Meyers v. Empire State Insurance Co., 228 F.2d 770, 5 *O.&G.R.* 728 (10th Cir. 1955).

See also Phillip Rosamond Drilling Co. v. St. Paul Fire & Marine Insurance Co., 305 So. 2d 630, 51 *O.&G.R.* 36 (La. App. 1974) (finding that there had been a "blow out" of a well within the meaning of that term in an insurance contract and rejecting the contention that there must be an expulsion of drilling fluid from the surface opening on the drilling hole in an upward direction to constitute a blow out).

For various definitions of the term "blow out," see Sutton Drilling Co. v. Universal Insurance Co., 335 F.2d 820, 21 *O.&G.R.* 363 (5th Cir. 1964).

See also KICK; GELATION.

Blow-out preventer

A casinghead control designed to prevent the uncontrolled flow of fluids from the well bore by closing around the drill pipe or completely sealing the hole in the absence of drill pipe. See California Division of Oil and Gas, *Oil and Gas Well Blowout Prevention in California* (Manual No. M07, 1977).

A heavy casinghead control filled with special gates or rams which can be closed around the drill pipe, or which completely close the top of the casing. Interstate Oil Compact Commission, *A Suggested Form of General Rules and Regulations for the Conservation of Oil and Gas* (1960) Rule III.

For a discussion of the nature and operation of this device, see Sutton Drilling Co. v. Universal Insurance Co., 335 F.2d 820, 21 *O.&G.R.* 363 (5th Cir. 1964).

See also ANNULAR BLOW-OUT PREVENTER; RAM BLOW-OUT PREVENTER.

Blue Sky law

A statute which regulates the issuance and sale of securities. The term is usually restricted to state statutes; the corresponding federal statute and regulations are the Federal Securities Act and the regulations of the Securities and Exchange Commission (SEC). The various states differ about subjecting the sale of property interests in oil and gas to Blue Sky regulation. See TREATISE §§ 441–441.5.

See also SECURITIES REGULATION; LIMITED OFFER EXEMPTION; PRIVATE OFFERING EXEMPTION; UNIFORM LIMITED OFFERING EXEMPTION.

BNOC

The BRITISH NATIONAL OIL COMPANY (BNOC) (*q.v.*).

See also BRITOIL, LTD.

Board of Land Appeals

The agency of the Department of the Interior which decides finally for the department appeals to the head of the department from decisions rendered by departmental officials relating to the use and disposition of public lands and their resources, and the use and disposition of mineral resources in certain acquired lands of the United States and in the submerged lands of the Outer Continental Shelf. 43 C.F.R. § 4.1 (1981).

Bob-tail abstract

An ABSTRACT OF TITLE (*q.v.*) containing a brief summary of instruments of record in the chain of title rather than copies of the instruments themselves.

Syn.: Briefed abstract.

Boiler

A vessel in which steam is generated.

Boil-off

Natural gas that is spontaneously converted from a liquid (LNG) to a gaseous state as a result of normal heat leaks in the piping. Southern Natural Gas Co. v. Federal Energy Regulatory Comm'n, 780 F.2d 1552 (1986).

Boll weevil

An inexperienced rig or oil field worker.

Bona fide offer provision

A provision in a gas purchase contract providing that the contracting purchaser will meet any bona fide offer made to the contracting seller at an increased price for the gas being sold under the contract. Matters of Union Oil Co. of California, 16 F.P.C. 100, 6 *O.&G.R.* 1108 at 1114 (1956). See TREATISE § 726.

See also ESCALATOR CLAUSE; GAS PURCHASE CONTRACT.

Bona fide purchaser

A person who buys property in good faith for valuable consideration and without knowledge (actual or imputed) of outstanding claims in a third party. A bona fide purchaser will prevail over the holder of a prior equitable title. See NRG Exploration, Inc. v. Rauch, 671 S.W.2d 649, 81 *O.&G.R.* 400 (Tex. App., Austin, 1984, *error ref'd n.r.e.*).

Bonny light oil

A name applied to high-quality Nigerian crude oil which by reason of its quality and proximity to the principal world markets commanded a premium over so-called BENCHMARK CRUDE (*q.v.*). *Wall Street Journal,* Jan. 27, 1983, p. 16, col. 2.

Bonus

Usually, the cash consideration paid by the lessee for the execution of an oil and gas lease by a landowner. Carroll v. Bowen, 180

Okla. 215 at 217, 68 P.2d 773 at 775 (1937). Bonus is usually figured on a per acre basis.

Bonus is defined by Article 213 of the Louisiana Mineral Code [R.S. 31:213 (1975)] as "money or other property given for the execution of a mineral lease, except interests in production from or attributable to property on which the lease is given." As a result of the complementary definitions of bonus and of royalty by the Code, where a lease provides for a production payment or an overriding royalty in addition to payments described as royalty, such additional payments will be payable to the person or persons entitled to royalty where the payments are to be made out of production from the property being leased; if such payments are to be made out of production from other property, such payments will be viewed as bonus. "Coupled with the provisions concerning executive rights, this means that one holding an executive interest cannot, by the device of calling an interest in production an overriding royalty rather than a lessor's royalty, deprive the holder of a mineral royalty or other nonexecutive interest of the right to share in production." Comment to Article 213. See TREATISE § 339.4

Bonus for the execution of a lease may take other forms than cash. One form is called oil bonus or royalty bonus. Sheppard v. Stanolind Oil and Gas Co., 125 S.W.2d 643 at 647–648 (Tex. Civ. App. 1939). This bonus may be in the form of an overriding royalty reserved to the landowner in addition to the usual landowner's royalty of one-eighth. Wright v. Brush, 115 F.2d 265 (10th Cir. 1940). Or it may be in the form of an oil payment. State National Bank v. Morgan, 135 Tex. 509, 143 S.W.2d 757 (1940). See TREATISE § 301.

Where the ownership of bonus and royalty has been separated, the classification of overriding royalty and oil payments reserved by the lessor has presented difficulty. See State National Bank v. Morgan, *supra;* Morriss v. First National Bank, 249 S.W.2d 269, 1 *O.&G.R.* 1371 (Tex. Civ. App. 1952, error ref'd n.r.e.); Giffith v. Taylor, 156 Tex. 1, 291 S.W.2d 673, 5 *O.&G.R.* 1371 (1956).

For another discussion of the meaning of bonus, see Kelley v. Zamarello, 486 P.2d 906, 40 *O.&G.R.* 1 (Alaska 1971).

Bonus is distinguished from "royalties" and "rent" as those terms are used in the Small Business Corporation Act in Swank & Son, Inc. v. United States, 362 F. Supp. 897, 46 *O.&G.R.* 291 (D. Mont. 1973).

For federal income tax purposes, prior to the Tax Reduction Act of 1975, cash bonus was treated as advance royalty which could be depleted. Burnet v. Harmel, 287 U.S. 103 (1932); Campbell v. Commissioner, 41 T.C. 91 (1963). The availability of percentage depletion on a lease bonus since The Tax Reduction Act of 1975 is discussed in "Continued Availability of Percentage Depletion," 24 *O.&G. Tax Q.* 209 (1975); Administrative Ruling, 1976–12 I.R.B. 28, 52 *O.&G.R.* 467 (March 22, 1976). Bonus was held not to be entitled to percentage depletion in Engle v. Commissioner, 76 T.C. 915, 69 *O.&G.R.* 375 (1981); *reversed,* 677 F.2d 594, 74 *O.&G.R.* 617 (7th Cir. 1982), insofar as it denied percentage depletion [See DEPLETION, PERCENTAGE] on advance royalties in a year in which there was no production. Farmar v. United States, 689 F.2d 1017 (Ct. Cl. 1982), held that percentage depletion could not be claimed on lease bonus. *Engle* was affirmed and *Farmar* was reversed in Comm'r v. Engle, 464 U.S. 206, 104 S. Ct. 597, 79 *O.&G.R.* 391 (1984). The Tax Reform Act of 1986 overruled the Supreme Court holding in *Engle.* Independent producers and royalty owners can no longer claim percentage depletion for lease bonuses, advance royalties or other amounts payable without regard to production from the property received or accrued after August 16, 1986.

The definition in this MANUAL was cited in Whitehall Oil Co. v. Eckart, 197 So. 2d 664, 26 *O.&G.R.* 778 (La. App. 1966), *rev'd sub nom.* Gardner v. Boagni, 252 La. 30, 209 So. 2d 11, 29 *O.&G.R.* 229 (1968).

See also COMMERCIAL DISCOVERY BONUS; DEFERRED BONUS; EXPLORATORY WORK BONUS; LEASE ACQUISITION COSTS; NET PROFITS ROYALTY; OIL BONUS; PRODUCTION BONUS; RISK BONUS; ROYALTY BONUS; SELECTION BONUS; SIGNATURE BONUS.

Bonus allowable

An extra well ALLOWABLE (*q.v.*) granted to operators for returning salt water produced with oil to the reservoir. It may be transferred to other leases in the field. See "Transferred Allowables and Substitute Royalties," 5 *O.&G. Tax Q.* 59 (1956).

A Commission order allowing a bonus allowable for water injection was sustained in Texaco, Inc. v. Railroad Comm'n, 583 S.W.2d 307, 63 *O.&G.R.* 346 (Tex. 1979), over an objection that it was resulting in net uncompensated drainage. The court reasoned that the injection program would allow ultimate recovery of an additional 800,000 barrels, one-half of which would be lost unless oil was produced at the bonus allowable rate before wells were destroyed by encroaching water. Under such circumstances, the "elementary rule of property that a landowner is entitled to an opportunity to produce his fair share of oil from a common reservoir" was qualified by both the rule of capture and the Commission's authority to prevent waste. "Between protecting correlative rights and protecting the public interest of preserving our state's natural resources, the prevention of waste has been held to be the dominant purpose."

See also TRANSFERRED ALLOWABLE.

Bonus bidding

Competitive bidding for leases in which the lease providing for a fixed royalty (*e.g.*, 1/8 or 1/6) is offered to the person offering to pay the largest bonus to the lessor.

On the authority of the Secretary of the Interior to reject bonus bids as inadequate, see Kerr-McGee Corp. v. Morton, 527 F.2d 838 (D.C. Cir. 1975); Arkla Exploration Co., IBLA 76–394, GFS (O&G) 1976–65.

See also LEASE BIDDING SYSTEMS.

Bonus penalty

A term used in Holmes v. Corporation Commission, 466 P.2d 630, 36 *O.&G.R.* 635 (Okla. 1970), to describe a NONCONSENT PENALTY (*q.v.*).

Bonus royalty

See ROYALTY BONUS.

Bonus title opinion

See TITLE OPINION.

Boomer

(1) A transient oil field worker who often moves from one center of activity to another.

(2) A slang term for a device to tighten chains on a load of pipe or other equipment on a truck to make it secure.

Booster

A compressor used to raise pressure in a gas or oil pipeline.

Booster station

Pipe line station with equipment to increase the rate of flow through the pipeline. See PUMPING STATION.

Boot

An additional consideration paid by one party to the other in an exchange of properties. For federal income tax purposes, the exchange of like kinds of properties may be nontaxable except to the extent of any boot received by one party.

BOP

A Blow-out preventer (*q.v.*).

Bore hole

The hole made by drilling or boring a well.

See also Pooling by the borehole; Preplatform well.

Borrowed gas

Gas obtained from another operator in the event of mishap which interrupts deliveries by an operator. The agreement may provide for the return of the gas in kind at a later date or for payment at an agreed price if not returned. See Fiske, *Federal Taxation of Oil and Gas Transactions* § 8.10 (1983 Revision), *Miller's Oil and Gas Federal Income Taxation* § 9–9 (1980 edition).

See also Gas.

Bottle well

A well used for gas storage purposes by connecting the casing to a high pressure gas line so that the gas will flow in and out of the shaft of the well as the pressure varies on the gas lift system. Gas from an extraneous source is allowed in and out without the production of oil from the well, *viz.*, the well is used merely as oil field equipment and not as a producing well. Kleas v. Mayfield, 404 So. 2d 500, 71 *O.&G.R.* 503 (La. App. 1981).

Bottled gas

See Liquefied petroleum gas.

Bottom hole abandonment pressure

"The lowest pressure at which a well will produce in commercial quantities. Calculation of this pressure is necessary to determine the amount of commercially recoverable minerals (recoverable reserves) within a particular field." Mississippi River Transmission Corp. v.

Tabor, 757 F.2d 662 at note 17, 85 *O.&G.R.* 542 at note 17 (5th Cir. 1985).

Bottom hole agreement

See BOTTOM HOLE LETTER.

Bottom hole choke

A choke placed at the bottom of the tubing to regulate the gas-oil ratio and the flow. See FLOWING WELL.

Bottom hole contribution

The payment made or the land transferred pursuant to a BOTTOM HOLE LETTER (*q.v.*). See TREATISE § 431.2.

Rev. Rul. 80–153, 1980–24 I.R.B. 8, 65 *O.&G.R.* 165 (June 6, 1980), concluded: (1) the recipient of a bottom hole contribution on a nonproducing well is not permitted to use the contribution to reduce or offset the cost of drilling the well but must include the contribution in income, and (2) the payor may not expense but must capitalize the contribution.

Bottom hole contribution agreement

See BOTTOM HOLE LETTER.

Bottom hole donation letter

The same form of agreement as a BOTTOM HOLE LETTER (*q.v.*), except no transfer of an interest in property takes place. The inducement for such an agreement by the payor is often his ownership of adjacent land or leases; the drilling by the payee will provide data valuable in determining whether (or where) to drill.

Bottom hole heater

Equipment employed to increase temperature at the bottom of a hole and thereby increase recovery of low gravity oil. See Nelson and McNiel, "Oil Recovery by Thermal Methods," 17 *Interstate Oil Compact Bull.* 56 at 57 (Dec. 1958).

See also SECONDARY RECOVERY; TERTIARY RECOVERY.

Bottom hole letter

An agreement by which an operator contemplating the drilling of a well on his own land secures the promise of another to contribute to the cost of the well, usually in return for an assignment of part of the payee's lease to the payor upon completion of the well. In contrast to the dry hole letter, the bottom hole letter requires payment upon completion of the well to a specified depth, whether the well produces or not. See Louisiana Progress Oil Co. v. McDaniel, 154 S.W.2d 985 (Tex. Civ. App. 1941); Anderson v. Bell, 70 Wyo. 471, 251 P.2d 572, 2 *O.&G.R.* 111 (1952); Brown, "Assignment of Interests in Leases," 5 *Sw. Legal Fdn. Oil & Gas Inst.* 25 at 81 (1954); 54 *Oil & Gas J.* 170 (Sept. 26, 1955); TREATISE § 431.

For a typical form of Bottom hole letter, see Williams, Maxwell, Meyers, and Williams, *Cases on Oil and Gas* 992 (5th ed. 1987).

Bottom hole letters are often used by the payee as security for financing costs of drilling the well. See First National Bank v. Republic Supply Co., 166 S.W.2d 373 (Tex. Civ. App. 1942).

Syn.. Bottom hole purchase letter.

For other forms of letter agreements, see LETTER.

Bottom hole pressure

The reservoir or rock pressure at the bottom of the hole, whether measured under flowing conditions or not. If measured under flowing conditions, pressure readings are usually taken at different rates of flow in order to compute a theoretical value for maximum productivity. Decline in pressure furnishes a guide, in some reservoirs, to the amount of depletion from the reservoir.

Prindle, *Petroleum Politics and the Texas Railroad Commission* 29 (1981), reports on the role measurement of bottom hole pressure had in the development of conservation in Texas:

> "By December of 1932, the Commission was able to shut down the [East Texas] field while its engineers, using pressure gauges borrowed from the major oil companies, recorded bottom-hole pressure in twenty-eight wells, running from east to west. In the initial tests, pressure varied from fourteen hundred pounds per square inch on the west side to seven hundred on the east. Seventy-two hours later, when the same wells were retested, pressure on the west side was unchanged, but on the east is had almost doubled.
>
> "This finding was significant because, in an ordinary gas-drive reservoir, pressure does not rise again once it had decreased. The only way to explain the rise in pressure on the east side of the field

was by admitting that a water drive existed. The acceptance of a water drive implied that production would have to be regulated to protect the field. This scientific understanding of East Texas was thus the first great victory for conservationists in the proration war."

See also RESERVOIR PRESSURE.

Bottom hole well

A term without a precise meaning; usually a well which has been drilled to a practically impenetrable substance. See Anderson v. Bell, 70 Wyo. 471, 251 P.2d 572, 2 *O.&G.R.* 111 (1952).

Bottom lease

(1) The existing lease covering a mineral interest upon which a second lease or TOP LEASE (*q.v.*) has been granted. Ernest, "Top Leasing—Legality v. Morality," 26 *Rocky Mt. Min. L. Inst.* 957 (1980).

(2) This term has also been applied to a lease covering deep horizons when more shallow horizons or formations are held under another lease. Thus when a lease held by production in a shallow horizon is terminated as to deeper unexplored horizons under the "DEEP HORIZONS" LEGISLATION (*q.v.*) in Kansas, a new lease covering the deeper horizons has been described as a bottom lease.

Bottom water

Free water in a permeable reservoir rock just below the space in the reservoir trap which is filled with oil and gas. Whether reservoir water is bottom water or edge water depends, not on its quality but on its location. If the entire reservoir is underlain with a zone of water bearing rock, so that a well almost anywhere in the field will strike water if drilled through the oil zone, then the reservoir water is bottom water. If the water is on the sides of the reservoir (as viewed in cross-section), it is EDGE WATER (*q.v.*).

See also CONNATE WATER.

Boyle's law

A law of physics stating that when gas is subject to compression and kept at a constant temperature, the product of the pressure and volume is a constant quantity, *i.e.,* the volume is inversely proportional to the pressure. *Webster's New International Dictionary.*

BPCL

BASE PERIOD CONTROL LEVEL (*q.v.*).

Bpd

Abbreviation for barrels per day.

BPH

Barrels per hour.

Bradenhead

A head, screwed into the top of the casing, used to confine gas in the well until released through an outlet to be piped away. See 16 Tex. Admin. Code § 3.17.

Bradenhead gas

Gas enclosed or confined in a well by a bradenhead until released through an outlet to be piped away.

See also CASINGHEAD GAS.

Bradenhead gas well

Any well producing gas through wellhead connections from a gas reservoir which has been successfully cased off from an underlying oil or gas reservoir. New Mexico Oil Conservation Comm'n, *Rules and Regulations* 1 (1958).

Branded independent marketer

A person who is engaged in the marketing or distributing of refined petroleum products under an agreement or contract authorizing the use of a trademark, trade name, service mark or other identifying symbol or name owned by the refiner (or a person who controls, is controlled by, or is under common control with such refiner) or under an agreement or contract granting authority to occupy premises owned, leased, or in any way controlled by a refiner (or such other person), but who is not affiliated with, controlled by, or under common control with any refiner (other than by means of such supply contract or agreement), and who does not control such refiner. 38 F.R. 34,419 (Dec. 13, 1973).

Brent blend

A sweet high-quality North Sea oil that, beginning in November, 1983, has been traded on the INTERNATIONAL PETROLEUM EXCHANGE (*q.v.*), London's oil-futures market, in contracts of 1,000 U.S. barrels. Previously the International Petroleum Exchange traded only heating-oil contracts. *The Wall Street J.*, Aug. 8, 1983, p. 25.

Bridge

An obstruction placed in a well at any specified depth. Pa. Stat. Ann. § 52–2102(14) (1966).

Any solid material inserted into a well bore or a casing string to provide a support for cement and to protect it from ascending waters until it can attain its initial set. Uren, *Petroleum Production Engineering* 367 (2d ed. 1934).

Bridge over

Collapse of well bore around the drill stem.

Bridge plug

A down-hole tool designed to isolate a lower zone while testing an upper section.

Bridging crude

The share of PARTICIPATION CRUDE (*q.v.*) which an operating oil company is guaranteed the right to "buy back" from the host nation in order to meet established long term commitments. See "The Economics of Energy and Natural Resource Pricing," Committee Print, A Compilation of Reports and Hearings of the Ad Hoc Committee on the Domestic and International Monetary Effect of Energy and Other Natural Resource Pricing, House Committee on Banking, Currency and Housing, 94th Cong. 1st Sess., (March 1975) at p. 100.

See also BUYBACK OIL; CONCESSION; PHASE-IN CRUDE.

Bridging of hole

Caving of walls and accumulation of material in some interval of the hole that prevents access to the bottom of the well.

Briefed abstract

Syn.: Bob-tail abstract (*q.v.*).

Brine

Water impregnated with salt frequently produced with oil. The disposal of this salt water by the operator is sometimes quite difficult. In many areas, a Salt Water Disposal District (*q.v.*) has been established for the purpose of disposing of salt water. The problem of disposal of oil field brines is discussed in "Production and Disposal of Oilfield Brines in the United States and Canada," a study conducted by the Research Committee, Interstate Oil Compact Commission (1960).

Brine disposal well

A well utilized for reinjection of oilfield brine into an underground structure.

Brine storage pit

A surface pit utilized for the disposal of oilfield brine by evaporation or seepage.

Bringing in a well

Completing a producing well and beginning production.

British National Oil Company (BNOC)

A company established by the Petroleum and Submarine Pipe-Lines Act 1975, Stat. 1975, c. 74.

For discussions of this company see the following:

Cameron, *Property Rights and Sovereign Rights: The Case of North Sea Oil* (1983);

Forster and Zillman, "The British National Oil Corporation: The State Enterprise as Instrument of Energy Policy," 3 *J. of Energy L. & Policy* 57 (1982);

Daintith and Willoughby, *A Manual of United Kingdom Oil and Gas Law* 15–19 (1977);

Woodliffe, "State Participation in the Development of United Kingdom Offshore Petroleum Resources," [1977] *Public Law* 249.

Exploration and production interests formerly owned by BNOC were transferred to Britoil, Ltd. (*q.v.*), a state-owned company organized in 1981.

See also INTERLOCKERS.

British thermal unit (Btu)

The amount of heat needed to raise the temperature of one pound of water one degree Fahrenheit.

For the energy values of various petroleum products, see CONVERSION FACTORS.

Britoil, Ltd.

The state-owned company organized in August 1981, to which was transferred the exploration and production interests formerly owned by the state-owned BRITISH NATIONAL OIL COMPANY (BNOC) (*q.v.*). The British Conservative Party in October 1982 proposed to sell 51 percent of Britoil to private investors. *The Wall Street Journal,* Oct. 7, 1982, p. 32, col. 2; [1982] 3 *OGLTR* 96.

Broad form deed

A loosely-defined term applied to a deed severing the mineral estate from the surface estate. The history of the form and a discussion of the constitutionality of legislation designed to restrict the rights of the grantee under such a deed are discussed in Pfeiffer, "Kentucky's New Broad Form Deed Law—Is It Constitutional?" 1 *J. of Min. Law & Policy* 57 (1985), and in Greenwell, "On the Constitutionality of Kentucky's Mineral Deed Act," 13 *No. Ky. L. Rev.* 219 (1986).

Broker

See LEASE BROKER.

Brokerage of gas

The term applied to the activities and compensation in arranging for the sale of gas between producers and buyers. See Railroad Comm'n v. City of Austin, 524 S.W.2d 262 at 278, 51 *O.&G.R.* 231 at 253 (Tex. 1975).

Brown Book

In the United Kingdom this term is applied to an annual report and account to Parliament by the Board of Trade, "Development of the Oil and Gas Resources of the United Kingdom," charting the development of the U.K.'s oil and gas resources during the year in question, and describing exploration, development and production aspects as well as the economic, industrial and environmental impact on the U.K. of oil and gas production. The report has been known as the Brown Book since it acquired a brown colored cover in or before 1974. J. Salter, *U.K. Onshore Oil and Gas Law* 1-121, 1-515, 5-025 *et seq.* (1986).

Brownsville Loop

The name given an arrangement made to qualify Mexican crude oil for the overland exemption to the system of import quotas for oil. Inasmuch as no pipeline linked Mexican producing areas and U.S. consuming areas, the only economically feasible means of transportation for Mexican crude oil was by tanker from Mexico to East Coast refineries. Such imports would not qualify for the overland exemption. To qualify, oil was shipped by ocean tanker to Brownsville, Texas (where it was treated as being landed in bond), loaded on a truck, hauled across the border into Mexico and immediately brought over the border into the United States, reloaded on tankers and shipped to the East Coast. The second entry qualified for the overland exemption, whereas the first entry, being under bond, was not counted under the Mandatory Program. In 1971 the Brownsville Loop was converted into what amounted to a country-of-origin quota for Mexico. See Dam, "Implementation of Import Quotas: The Case of Oil," 14 *J. of Law and Economics* 1 at 35–36 (1971); Chester, *United States Oil Policy and Diplomacy 138 (1983).*

Syn.: BROWNSVILLE U-TURN; EL LOOPHOLE.

See also OIL IMPORT QUOTA.

BRPM

Bureau de Recherches et de Participations Minieres of Morocco.

BS and W

Basic sediment and water. See BASIC SEDIMENT.

Btu

British thermal unit. The amount of heat needed to raise the temperature of one pound of water one degree Fahrenheit.

For the energy values of various petroleum products, see CONVERSION FACTORS.

See also MEASUREMENT UNITS.

Btu adjustment clause

An ESCALATOR CLAUSE (*q.v.*) in a GAS CONTRACT PURCHASE (*q.v.*) based on variation of gas from a specified standard, *e.g.*, a provision for a price increase of 1/100 of 1 cent for each Btu in excess of 1000 Btu content per cubic foot. See Holloway, "Some FPC Problems Encountered in General Oil and Gas Practice," 12 *Sw. Legal Fdn. Oil & Gas Inst.* 59 at 74 (1961); J. M. Huber Corp. v. Federal Power Comm'n, 294 F.2d 568, 15 *O.&G.R.* 189 (3d Cir. 1961); Pure Oil Co. v. Federal Power Comm'n, 292 F.2d 350, 15 *O.&G.R.* 196 (7th Cir. 1961); Northern Natural Gas Co. v. Grounds, 292 F. Supp. 619 at 671, 33 *O.&G.R.* 505 at 598 (D. Kan. 1968), *aff'd in part and remanded with directions,* 441 F.2d 704, 39 *O.&G.R.* 574 (10th Cir. 1971), *cert. denied,* 404 U.S. 951 (1971); TREATISE § 726.

Btu method

A method of allocating costs between different operations or between different products. Thus joint exploration and production costs may be allocated between gas and liquids in proportion to the amount of gas and the amount of liquids produced, using Btu's as the common denominator. See Joseph, "Background and Analysis of Trial Examiner's Decision in Phillips Case," 11 *Sw. Legal Fdn. Oil & Gas Inst.* 1 at 24 (1960). Expenses may be allocated by this method between transportation and processing operations.

For a discussion of this method see In re Other Southwest Area Rate Case, 484 F.2d 469 at 481 (5th Cir. 1973), *cert. denied,* 417 U.S. 973 (1974).

For other methods of allocating costs, see ACCOUNTING METHODS.

Btu rejection clause

A provision of a GAS PURCHASE CONTRACT (*q.v.*) permitting the refusal of gas which yields less than a specified number of Btu's per cubic foot of gas. Northern Natural Gas Co. v. Grounds, 292 F. Supp. 619 at 671, 33 *O.&G.R.* 505 at 598 (D. Kan. 1968), *aff'd in part and remanded with directions,* 441 F.2d 704, 39 *O.&G.R.* 574 (10th Cir. 1971), *cert. denied,* 404 U.S. 951 (1971).

Bubble

See GAS BUBBLE; ILLINOIS OIL BUBBLE.

Bubble point of oil

The pressure at which the oil begins to release gas from solution.

Lowe and McKeown, "Mineral Law Section Annual Survey of Significant Developments," 57 *Okla. B.J.* 735 at 738 (1986), discuss efforts in Oklahoma to maintain pressure above the bubble point:

> "Reservoir maintenance remains a major concern of the [Oklahoma Corporation] Commission. The issue of when an oil reservoir reaches its critical 'bubble point' was closely scrutinized during the past year. The 'bubble point' is the industry term to describe the phenomenon which occurs when reservoir pressure necessary to allow an effective rate of recovery is endangered by rapid depletion of such pressure through imprudent rates of production. If the 'bubble point' is passed (as determined by a laboratory examination of pressure, volume and temperature tests of reservoir fluids) loss of oil recovery will result. The immediate implementation of a planned pressure maintenance program is necessary to prevent this potential loss of oil recovery. In one case, the Commission ordered a reduction in allowables on several wells and scheduled testing to ensure that a volatile reservoir would not go below its 'bubble point.' Extensive monitoring of the wells and reservoir and further conferences continue among the Commission's technical and legal staffs and many other interested parties."

Bubble-point pump

A pump with an extension between the bottom of the barrel and the standing valve. It is very sensitive to free gas, and will gas-lock when the pressure drops below the saturation or bubble-point pressure permitting gas to break out of solution. This action tends to maintain a back pressure on the formation in excess of the bubble-point pressure, and with the casinghead closed, bubble-point pumps have served to maintain oil production at a rate that will not be damaging to ultimate recovery.

Buddy swap

"An arrangement whereby, during a period of severe curtailment, one industrial or commercial customer, that can use an alternate fuel, agrees to do so temporarily, and transfers that part of his gas allocation to another customer that cannot use an alternate fuel." American Gas Ass'n, *Glossary for the Gas Industry* (3d ed. 1981).

Budget-type certificate application

A form of certificate application covering in general outline along the lines of a budget estimate proposed routine construction intended to be undertaken during the current or ensuing fiscal year. F.P.C. Order No. 185, 15 F.P.C. 793 (Feb. 7, 1956). See Tennessee Gas Transmission Co. v. Federal Power Comm'n, 340 F.2d 100, 22 *O.&G.R.* 93 (10th Cir. 1964), *cert. denied,* 381 U.S. 950 (1965); 18 C.F.R. §§ 2.58, 157.7 (1980).

Bullet perforator

A tool that fires bullets through the casing in order to provide holes through which the well fluids may enter.

See also PERFORATION.

Bunker "C" Fuel Oil

A heavy residual fuel oil used by ships, industry, and for large-scale heating installations. It is often referred to as No. 6 fuel.

Bureau of Land Management

A bureau of the United States Department of Interior which administers the statute and regulations applicable to the leasing of land owned by the federal government for oil and gas purposes.

See also BOARD OF LAND APPEALS; CHERRYSTEMMING PRACTICE; COURTESY BILLING NOTICE; FEDERAL LAND POLICY AND MANAGEMENT ACT OF 1976 (FLPMA); FEDERAL LEASE; LAND STATUS BOOK; LEASE CASE FILE; NOTATION RULE; NON-CONVENTIONAL OIL RECOVERY STIPULATION; OFFICE OF APPEALS AND HEARINGS; OFFICE OF HEARINGS AND APPEALS; ONE-EIGHTH RULE; OVER-THE-COUNTER LEASE; OVER-THE-COUNTER LEASE OFFER; POST SALE ANALYSIS CHART; SERIAL REGISTER; SURFACE MANAGEMENT REGULATIONS; SUSPENSION OF OPERATIONS AND PRODUCTION.

Buried pipe covenant

A typical oil and gas lease provision for the benefit of the lessor requiring, upon request, the lessee to bury pipe lines on the leasehold below plow depth. The clause usually limits the obligation to cultivated land. See TREATISE § 673.4.

Burning

Disposal of casinghead gas by fire. In many states statutes prohibit wasteful burning of gas. *Syn.:* Flaring.

Burn out pit

A salt water pit or oil field refuse pit used for the evaporation of salt water or brine or the burning of oil field waste or refuse.

Burn pit

An unlined pit built to contain flares and minimize the dangers of overpressure conditions that may result from a flowing gas well. Amoco Production Co. v. Carter Farms., 103 N.M. 117, 703 P.2d 894, 86 *O.&G.R.* 84 (1985).

See also RESERVE PIT; SPILLOVER PIT.

Business trust

See MASSACHUSETTS TRUST.

Butane

A hydrocarbon associated with petroleum. It is gaseous at ordinary atmospheric conditions. It is readily converted to the liquid state. See Interstate Oil Compact Commission, *Oil and Gas Production* 26 (1951); LIQUEFIED PETROLEUM GAS.

Buy-back agreement

An agreement by a company performing services for clients, in connection with the Bureau of Land Management's Simultaneous Oil and Gas Lease Filing System, by which the company promises to purchase from the client at a specified price any lease won by the client in the lottery. In Securities & Exch. Comm'n v. Energy Group of America, Inc., 459 F. Supp. 1234, 62 *O.&G.R.* 372 (S.D. N.Y. 1978), it was held that this transaction did not involve the sale of an unregistered security in violation of the Securities Act of 1933 and the Securities Act of 1934.

See COMPETITIVE LEASE; NONCOMPETITIVE LEASE; SIMULTANEOUS FILINGS.

Buyback oil

Under participation agreements between host countries and producing oil companies some portion of the oil produced accrues to the government and then is sold back to the producing oil company. The price paid by the oil company for the buyback oil is usually some percentage (*e.g.*, 93%) of the posted price. Equity oil, on the other hand, is that produced by the company for its own account. The cost of oil to the producing company is the weighted average of the tax-paid cost of equity oil (taxes and royalties paid the government plus production expense) and the buyback price for government oil. Thus the cost of crude oil to the producing company is affected by any government action changing the posted price, percentage of participation, royalty, tax, or buyback price. See *The Wall Street Journal,* Oct. 1, 1974, p. 3, col. 1.

See also BRIDGING CRUDE; CONCESSION; PARTICIPATION CRUDE; PHASE-IN CRUDE.

Buyer protection clause

A provision in a GAS PURCHASE CONTRACT (*q.v.*) permitting the buyer, under specified circumstances, to reduce the price below the amount redetermined under an ESCALATOR CLAUSE (*q.v.*).

> "One of the most common provisions allows the pipeline to request a redetermination if the price paid by the pipeline is disallowed by the Commission in ratemaking decisions. Normally, the price will then fall to a price the pipeline is allowed to recover. Other escape clauses, called 'market-out,' deal with the marketability of the gas or the economic conditions regarding sale of gas in certain locations." Energy Information Administration Office of Oil and Gas, U.S. Department of Energy, *The Natural Gas Market Through 1990* 82 (1983).

Buy-in option

A provision of certain agreements between a host government and a foreign oil company under which the government has the option to "buy-in" to a project upon assuming a proportionate share of exploration and development costs. See Hossain, *Law and Policy in Petroleum Development* 214 (1979).

See also CONCESSION.

Buy-out

The term applied in proposed regulations of the Department of Energy for certain payments made by pipelines to extinguish future minimum payment or purchase obligations [TAKE-OR-PAY CLAUSE (*q.v.*)] in gas purchase contracts. 50 *Fed. Reg.* 24130 (June 7, 1985).

Buy-sell list

A list published by the Federal Energy Administration each quarter designed to control transfers by larger integrated oil companies which were required to sell specified amounts of price controlled crude oil to smaller refiners. See Cockrell, "Exceptions to Federal Regulations for Management of the Energy Crisis: The Emerging Agency Case Law," 28 *Okla. L. Rev.* 530 at 531 (1975).

Buy/Sell oil

Crude oil that smaller refiners may demand from major companies under the crude oil allocation program of the Department of Energy to insure that they have sufficient raw materials to keep their facilities in operation.

The Buy/Sell program previously administered by the Federal Energy Administration is discussed in Task Force on Reform of Federal Energy Administration, *Federal Energy Administration Regulation* 10 *et seq.* (MacAvoy ed. 1977).

By-passing

A reservoir condition in a water drive field, whereby less permeable portions of the stratum are by-passed by the encroaching water table, leaving unrecovered oil in place in the formation. Interstate Oil Compact Commission, *Oil and Gas Production* 46 (1951). This condition sometimes occurs in a water flood project when the injected water channels through the looser connected sections of a sand, leaving the tighter sections by-passed and unexploited. Brown and Meyers, "Some Legal Aspects of Water Flooding," 24 *Tex. L. Rev.* 456 at 466 (1946).

See also CHANNELING; FINGERING.

By-products cost accounting method

A method of allocating costs between dry gas and liquid hydrocarbons, helium, or other products extracted from gas as produced from the ground. See Ashland Oil, Inc. v. Phillips Petroleum Co., 463 F. Supp. 619 at 634 (N.D. Okla. 1978).

See also ACCOUNTING METHODS.

. . C . .

Cable tool bit

See BIT, CABLE TOOL.

Cable tool drilling

One of the two primary methods of drilling oil wells. Cable tool drilling operates on a combination hammer-suction principle. A heavy, sharp-pointed bit is raised and dropped continuously in the hole, so that it chips and breaks the rock away. The bottom of the hole is kept full of MUD (*q.v.*) and water, and the motion of the bit is so regulated that the moment it hits bottom it starts up again, adding the effect of suction to the pounding. Cable tool drilling has been substantially replaced by rotary drilling, but occasional instances of its use are still found.

See also CANADIAN POLE SYSTEM; CHURN DRILLING; DRILLING RIG; ROTARY DRILLING; TURBODRILLING.

Cadastral survey

"The establishment of land boundaries and their identification on the ground by monuments or marks and their identification in the records by field notes and plats." United States Department of the Interior Bureau of Land Management, *Glossary of Public-Land Terms* 5 (1949).

See SURVEY.

Calendar day allowable

See ACTUAL CALENDAR DAY ALLOWABLE.

California method

A method of depreciating leasehold costs which involves estimates of future capital investments and of undeveloped reserves as well as past capital expenditures. See Irving and Draper, *Accounting Practices in the Petroleum Industry* 18 (1958).

Caliper log

A log of the diameter of the well bore or the internal diameter of tubular goods. The log will indicate undue enlargement of the well bore due to caving, wash-out, or other causes, and will reveal internal corrosion, scaling, or pitting of tubular goods.

See also WELL LOG.

Call

An option retained by the farmor in a FARM-OUT AGREEMENT (*q.v.*) to purchase the production from the test well to be drilled or a right to process gas. Schaefer, "The Ins and Outs of Farmouts: A Practical Guide for the Landman and the Lawyer," 32 *Rocky Mt. Min. L. Inst.* 18-1 at 18-27 (1986).

Callery case

United Gas Improvement Co. v. Callery Properties, 382 U.S. 223, 23 *O.&G.R.* 832 (1965), *reh. denied,* 382 U.S. 1001 (1966).

Call on oil

An option to buy oil for an extended period of time.

Calvo clause

The name given an agreement by an alien, as a condition of engaging in economic activity in the territory of a state, that he is to be treated as if he were a national in respect of such activity, and that his only remedy for injury in this respect is that available under the law of the state. The clause is named for Carlos Calvo, Argentine diplomat and publicist, who propounded in 1868 the propositions which came to be known as the Calvo doctrine. See American Law Institute, Restatement of the Law Second, *Foreign Relations Law of the United States* § 202 (1965).

The use of the Calvo clause in agreements with foreign oil companies is discussed in Lucas, "Doing Petroleum Business Abroad; General Legal Considerations," 24 *Sw. Legal Fdn. Oil & Gas Inst.* 295 at 347 (1973).

CAMPSA

Compania Arrendataria Del Monopolio de Petroleos SA of Spain.

Canada-Newfoundland Offshore Petroleum Board

See ATLANTIC ACCORD.

Canada Oil and Gas Land Administration (COGLA)

An administrative body established by the Canada Oil and Gas Act, R.S.C. 1980-81, c. 81, to administer the new system created by the act. See Gault, *Petroleum Operations on the Canadian Continental Margin* 94 (1983); Lucas, "The Canadian National Energy Program Legislation," 1 *J. of Energy & Natural Resources Law* 104 at 109 (1983).

Canada Petroleum Resources Act (CPRA)

An Act which received first reading on December 20, 1985, designed to repeal the existing Canada Oil and Gas Act (COGA) and to be a comprehensive code governing the acquisition, exploration for and production of oil and gas on federal frontier lands. See Evans, "Bill C-92: The Canada Petroleum Resources Act," 25 *Alta. L. Rev.* 59 (1986).

Canadian Association of Petroleum Landmen (CAPL)

The successor to the Alberta Association of Petroleum Landmen (AAPL). This association has developed standard forms, one of which is discussed in Boyer, "The 1981 CAPL Operating Procedure," 21 *Alberta L. Rev.* 82 (1983).

Canadian crude oil allocation program (CAP)

See MANDATORY CANADIAN CRUDE OIL ALLOCATION REGULATIONS; NATIONAL ENERGY PROGRAM (NEP).

Canadian pole system

A system similar to the CABLE TOOL DRILLING (*q.v.*) system except that wooden rods screwed together are used instead of a rope.

Cancellation decree

An equitable decree of a court nullifying a lease. While a cancellation decree may be entered against a lease that was void or voidable in its inception, or to remove from the record a lease that has terminated by its own terms, such decrees are also used to nullify a lease, the obligations of which have been violated by the lessee. Thus the equitable remedy of cancellation is used to terminate a lease that otherwise is valid and in force. The grounds for a cancellation decree of the first sort include fraud, incapacity, illegality, insufficient writing to satisfy the statute of frauds, failure to pay delay rentals under an unless lease and expiration of the primary term without production. The most usual ground for cancelling a lease good at its inception and in force under its express terms is breach of an implied covenant. A decree of cancellation may be absolute or it may be conditional, in that the lessee is given a stated period of time to perform his obligations. Failure to comply results in cancellation when the time limit set by the decree expires. See TREATISE §§ 825.1, 834, 844.1.

See also ALTERNATIVE DECREE; CONDITIONAL DECREE OF CANCELLATION; PARTIAL CANCELLATION.

Cancellation of lease

The nullifying of a lease by court order. See CANCELLATION DECREE.

Cancelled underage

UNDERAGE (*q.v.*) of allowable production which, after having been permitted by the Regulatory Commission to accumulate to a specified level, is then cancelled. See Northwest Central Pipeline Corp. v. State Corporation Comm'n, 237 Kan. 248, 699 P.2d 1002, 86 *O.&G.R.* 276 (1985) (sustaining a Commission order providing, under specified circumstances, for permanent cancellation of certain accumulated underages), *vacated and remanded,* ___ U.S. ___, 89 L.Ed.2d 289, 106 S.Ct. 1169 (1986), for further consideration in light of Transcontinental Gas Pipe Line Corp. v. State Oil & Gas Board of Mississippi, 474 U.S. ___, 106 S.Ct. 709 (1986), *on remand,* 240 Kan. 638, 732 P.2d 775, ___ *O.&G.R.* ___ (1987).

See also BALANCING; DEEMED PURCHASE FORMULA; DEFERRED PRODUCTION AGREEMENT; GAS BANK AGREEMENT; LIFTING; LIFTING TOLERANCE; "OUT OF BALANCE" PRODUCTION PLAN; OVERLIFT; SPLIT CONNECTION; UNDERAGE; UNDERLIFT; UNDERLIFT/OVERLIFT PROVISION.

CAP

CANADIAN CRUDE OIL ALLOCATION PROGRAM (*q.v.*).

Cap

See CONTRACTUAL CAP.

Capable well

A well capable of producing oil or gas in paying quantities. Sheffield v. Exxon Corp., 424 So. 2d 1297, 76 *O.&G.R.* 419 (Ala. 1983).

Capacity allowable

A special ALLOWABLE (*q.v.*) available when a secondary recovery project is initiated in a reservoir that is so depleted of natural reservoir energy that the injection of fluid is necessary to push the oil toward the well bore. See Blazier, "The Lease Allowable System: New Method of Regulating Oil Production in Texas," 47 *Tex. L. Rev.* 658 (1969).

Capillarity

The attraction of the surface of a liquid to the surface of a solid at the point of contact. Capillarity adversely affects recovery of oil from a reservoir, since it tends to hold the oil in the rock. An increase in the gas in solution decreases the capillary attraction of the oil and the rock.

Capital allowances

The British term for depreciation. See Wheeler, "The UK Corporation Tax," [1982] 1 *OGLTR* 4 at 5.

Capital assets

An asset acquired for investment and not for sale and requiring no personal services or management duties. In federal income tax law, oil and gas leases are ordinarily property used in the taxpayer's trade or business (Section 1231 assets), and not capital assets. On the other hand, if held for investment, royalty is usually a capital asset.

Capital cost

A cost incurred in acquiring leases, geological and geophysical exploration, and in the drilling and completion of wells which is capitalized rather than expensed as INTANGIBLE DRILLING AND DEVELOPMENT COSTS (IDC) (*q.v.*).

Capital cost allowance

In Canada, a tax allowance for depreciation. See Katchen and Bowhay, *Federal Oil and Gas Taxation* 59 (3d ed. 1979).

Capital expenditure

In federal income tax law, a nondeductible expenditure which must be recovered through depletion or depreciation. In the oil industry, the following items are illustrative of expenditures which must be capitalized: geophysical and geological costs, oil well equipment costs, lease bonus paid by the lessee.

Capital gain (or loss)

The profit or loss resulting from the sale or exchange of a capital asset. For federal income tax purposes, this value is determined by the difference between the sale price and the basis of the property. The capital gains provisions of the Internal Revenue Code are also applicable, under certain circumstances, to gain from the sale of an asset used in the trade or business (Section 1231 asset).

Capital recovery factor

A factor in a VARIABLE NET PROFIT SHARE BIDDING SYSTEM (*q.v.*) setting forth the capital costs recoverable and the allowable rate of return on such costs. See 46 Fed. Reg. 15,484 at 15,486 (March 5, 1981), 46 F.R. 29,680 at 29,686 (June 2, 1981). Under proposed regulations (10 C.F.R. § 376.110), the lessee is entitled to recoup all recoverable costs plus an additional percentage of costs incurred during the capital recovery period through application of the capital recovery factor before any net profit-share payments are owed. Under these regulations, the capital recovery factor would in general tend to be set at lower levels for higher net profit-share rate bids.

CAPL

CANADIAN ASSOCIATION OF PETROLEUM LANDMEN (*q.v.*).

CAPL Operating Procedure

A form developed by the CANADIAN ASSOCIATION OF PETROLEUM LANDMEN (CAPL) (*q.v.*). See Boyer, "The 1981 CAPL Operating Procedure," 21 *Alberta L. Rev.* 82 (1983).

Capped-in royalty

Syn. for SHUT-IN ROYALTY (*q.v.*).

Capital string

The casing set in a producing horizon.

Syn.: FLOW STRING; OIL STRING; PAY STRING; PRODUCTION STRING.

Capping

Closing in well to prevent escape of gas.

Caprock

"The impervious geological stratum that overlays the reservoir rock and retains gas or oil in a reservoir." American Gas Ass'n, *Glossary for the Gas Industry* (3d ed. 1981).

Captive mine

Syn. for COST COMPANY (*q.v.*).

Capture, Rule of

See RULE OF CAPTURE.

Carbon black

A carbon substance of considerable commercial importance, particularly in the rubber industry, which uses some 95% of the carbon black produced. Carbon black may be produced by the incomplete combustion of oil and gas. It may also be manufactured from other products in more abundant supply, and hence the use of oil or gas for this purpose is generally the subject of state law or regulations. Typical legislation or regulation prohibits the use of sweet gas for the manufacture of carbon black where sour gas (gas containing hydrogen sulphide) is available, or prohibits certain manufacturing processes which are less efficient in total recovery of carbon black or in the utilization of the energy generated in the process. The authority of the state in this area has regularly been sustained. See Moses, "Statutory Regulations in the Carbon Black Industry," 20 *Tulane L. Rev.* 83 (1945).

See also CHANNEL TYPE CARBON BLACK PLANT.

Carried interest

A fractional interest in oil and gas property, usually a lease, the holder of which has no personal obligation for operating costs, which are to be paid by the owner or owners of the remaining fraction, who reimburse themselves therefor out of production, if any. The person advancing the costs is the carrying party and the other is the carried party. Three general types of carried interest are recognized: the ABERCROMBIE-TYPE CARRIED INTEREST, the HERNDON-TYPE CARRIED INTEREST, and the MANAHAN-TYPE CARRIED INTEREST (*q.v.*).

The details of a carrying agreement vary considerably, *e.g.*, whether the operator (the party who is putting up the cost of development) has control of the oil and the right to sell it or the carried party can sell his part of the oil; whether the carried interest is to be carried for the initial development period only of the operation or for the life of the lease; whether interest is to be charged and, if so, the rate; who would own the equipment, such as pipe, motors and pumps, if and when production ceased; *etc.* See Ashland Oil & Refining Co. v. Beal, 224 F.2d 731, 5 *O.&G.R.* 387 (5th Cir. 1955), *cert. denied,* 350 U.S. 967, 6 *O.&G.R.* 456 (1956). As observed by Professor Masterson, Discussion Notes, 5 *O.&G.R.* 396 (1956):

> "The numerous different forms these interests are given from time to time make it apparent that the terms 'carried interest' and 'net profits interest' do not define any specific form of agreement but rather serve merely as a guide in preparing and interpreting instruments."

Professor Masterson further noted the close kinship between carried interests and net profits interest. Either type may be employed where one coowner is to advance the entire costs of drilling. The major difference between the two interests is that it is customary for a carried interest relationship to cease when all costs as to the carried interest are paid; thereafter the carried and carrying parties jointly own the working interest and share in costs and receipts. A net profits interest, on the other hand, usually continues for the duration of the leasehold, one party continuing to bear costs and the other receiving a share of proceeds after payment of such costs. See Estate of Weinert v. Commissioner, 294 F.2d 750, 15 *O.&G.R.* 125 (5th Cir. 1961); TREATISE §§ 424–424.4.

See also Byrd v. Smyth, 590 S.W.2d 772 at 775, 64 *O.&G.R.* 530 at 535 (Tex. Civ. App. 1979):

> "As used in the oil industry, the holder of a carried interest of a working interest has no personal obligation for operating costs while the coowners who advance such costs are entitled to reimburse themselves first from future production. . . . [Citing this Manual]. As the term was used here, it meant that the coowners who advanced expenses were entitled to reimburse themselves first from the profits of the venture before equal distribution to all shareholders was made."

Del-Ray Oil & Gas, Inc. v. Henderson, 797 F.2d 1313, ____ *O.&G.R.* ____ (5th Cir. 1986), declared that a reserved interest described by the transfer agreement as a "Carried Working Interest" amounted to an overriding royalty for purposes of the Louisiana rule under which reservation of an overriding royalty causes a transfer to be classified as a sublease rather than an assignment.

See also Conine, "Rights and Liabilities of Carried Interest and Nonconsent Parties in Oil and Gas Development," 37 *Sw. Legal Fdn. Oil & Gas Inst.* 3-1 (1986), discussing at length Railroad Commission v. Olin Corp., 690 S.W.2d 628, 88 *O.&G.R.* 579 (Tex. App., Austin, 1985) (holding nonconsent parties under a widely used form of operating agreement liable under Texas statutes for the cost of plugging a well in which they had declined to participate), error ref'd n.r.e., 701 S.W.2d 641, 88 *O.&G.R.* 586 (Tex. 1985) (approving only the result reached by the court of appeals requiring the nonconsent parties to pay for the plugging of the well).

The duration of a carry may be the subject of litigation. See, *e.g.*, Berryhill v. Marshall Exploration, Inc., 420 F. Supp. 198, 57 *O.&G.R.* 25 (W.D. La. 1976) (reporting a conflict in the evidence as to the existence or nature of a local custom on the matter).

For discussions of the employment of the carried interest device in the licensing of oil exploration, see the following:

Krohn, Kaasen, *et al.*, *Norwegian Petroleum Law* (1978);

K.W. Dam, *Oil Resources* (1976);

K.W. Dam, "The Evolution of North Sea Licensing Policy in Britain and Norway," 17 *J. Law & Econ.* 213 (1974).

See also NON-CONSENT INTEREST: OVERRIDING ROYALTY: FLIP; LIMITED CARRIED INTEREST; NET PROFITS INTEREST; PAY-UP PRIVILEGE; PERMANENT CARRIED INTEREST; SHARING ARRANGEMENT.

Carried interest arrangement

An agreement creating a CARRIED INTEREST (*q.v.*).

Carried party

The coowner for whom costs are advanced under a CARRIED INTEREST ARRANGEMENT (*q.v.*). If one concurrent owner develops a tract and obtains production without the joinder of another or others, the latter may be entitled to recover a share of the production less a share of the costs. See TREATISE §§ 504–504.3. The tax consequences may be the same in this instance as in the case of a MANAHAN-TYPE CARRIED INTEREST (*q.v.*). Burke and Bowhay, *Income Taxation of Natural Resources* ¶ 15.17 (1981).

See also PAY-UP PRIVILEGE.

Carrier

(1) A company engaged in the business of transporting oil or gas; (2) *Syn.* for CARRYING PARTY (*q.v.*).

Carry forward provision

A provision of a PETROLEUM INTERNATIONAL AGREEMENT (PIA) (*q.v.*) or CONCESSION (*q.v.*) permitting the levelling of the crests and valleys of expenditures by adding under-expenditures or subtracting excess-expenditures in one year to (or from) the expenditures required in the succeeding year. See Blinn, Duval, Le Leuch, and Pertuzio, *International Petroleum Exploration & Exploitation Agreements* 127 (1986).

Carrying party

(1) The coowner who advances the costs for the carried party under a CARRIED INTEREST ARRANGEMENT (*q.v.*).

(2) This term is also used in pooling and unitization agreements to describe a party who assumes responsibility for that share of the costs of drilling which another party has elected not to assume. See Rocky Mountain Unit Operating Agreement Form 2 (Divided Interest) January, 1955, Exhibit 4 (Flexible Drilling Block Partial Non-Consent).

Carrying rental

A term occasionally employed as a synonym for a DELAY RENTAL (*q.v.*). See Davis v. Hardman, 148 W. Va. 82, 133 S.E. 2d 77, 19 *O.&G.R.* 713 (1963).

Carryover

A feature in a CURTAILMENT PLAN (*q.v.*) allowing volumes not used in one period to be used in the following period. American Gas Ass'n, *Glossary for the Gas Industry.*

Carved-out drill site arrangement

See DRILL SITE ARRANGEMENT.

Carved out interest

An interest, *e.g.*, an oil payment or overriding royalty, conveyed by the owner of a greater interest. Several examples are: the grant of an overriding royalty out of a working interest; the grant of an oil payment out of perpetual, nonparticipating royalty.

See also CARVED OUT OIL PAYMENT; RETAINED INTEREST.

Carved out oil payment

A form of OIL PAYMENT (*q.v.*) so classified because the owner of an interest in oil and gas assigns a production payment out of an interest previously owned. The reverse transaction occurs when the owner of an oil and gas interest assigns such interest reserving an oil payment. The distinction between retained and carved out oil payments lies primarily in the federal income tax field.

Under Commissioner v. P. G. Lake, 356 U.S. 260 (1958), a carved out oil payment was an assignment of income and the proceeds therefrom were taxable to the assignor as ordinary income.

The Tax Reform Act of 1969 adopted new rules for oil payments, causing them to be treated as loans. In the case of carved-out oil payments, the money received by the seller will not be income, but the seller will be taxed on production, subject to depletion. I.R.C. § 636.

See also WRAP-AROUND CARVED-OUT PRODUCTION PAYMENT.

Carved-out property

A terminating interest sold in a CARVE-OUT TRANSACTION (*q.v.*).

Carve-out transaction

In Canada this term has been applied to a sale of a terminating interest in an oil and gas property from a taxpayer likely to have taxable income in the current period or in the near future to a purchaser who had accumulated loss carryforwards, resource pools or other "shelter" or who was himself exempt from tax. See Emes, "Recent Developments in Federal Taxation Treatment of Canada's Petroleum Industry—Part II," [1986/87] 6 *OGLTR* 144.

Case file

A file containing the original instruments which have been filed relating to any particular offer for oil and gas lease or other application that may have been made, which is maintained in a District

Land Office of the Bureau of Land Management. See *Rocky Mt. Min. L. Fdn., Landman's Legal Handbook* 115 (3d ed. 1977).

Case oil

The term applied in the nineteenth century to kerosine packed in ten-gallon tins, two tins to the case, shipped from the United States and from Russia to the European market. Danielsen, *The Evolution of OPEC* 98 (1982).

Cash bonus

See BONUS.

Cash bonus bidding

See BONUS BIDDING.

Cash consideration

In oil and gas transactions, the cash money paid in return for a promise or an act of another. For example, in the execution of an oil and gas lease, it is customary for the lessee to pay a cash consideration to the lessor. This is also called BONUS (*q.v.*).

Cash contribution clause

See CONTRIBUTION CLAUSE.

Cash substitute royalty

A payment which, under the terms of an applicable lease, is a substitute for production by the lessee. A typical cash substitute royalty is that paid under a SHUT-IN GAS WELL CLAUSE (*q.v.*). An occasional lease provides for the payment of a substitute royalty in lieu of the drilling of offset or protection wells or of development wells under certain circumstances. See Robinson v. Milam, 125 W.Va. 218, 24 S.E.2d 236 (1942).

Syn.: COMPENSATORY ROYALTY (*q.v.*).

See also OFFSET ROYALTY; SUBSTITUTE ROYALTY.

Cash surrender value provision

A provision in a DRILLING FUND (*q.v.*) program under which the program manager may buy a certain number or percentage of the program interests each year for a cash surrender value. The program manager determines both the number or percentage (which is frequently quite small) of interests which it will buy as well as the amount it will pay for such interests.

Casing

Heavy steel pipe used to seal off fluids from the hole or to keep the hole from caving in. There may be several strings of casing, one inside the other, in a single well.

Most oil wells are completed with two strings of cemented casing, the surface pipe and the production string. The surface pipe serves as conductor of the drilling fluid through loose, near-surface formations during deeper drilling, protects potable water supplies, anchors blowout preventers for deeper drilling, and supports at the surface deeper casing strings when hung. The production string serves as a conduit to the surface for produced fluids and confines each fluid-bearing zone to its native place. In many cases a third casing, called the intermediate or protective string is also cemented in place. This string sometimes accomplishes some of the purposes of surface strings but generally it is set for the purpose of protecting sections of formations which would prove troublesome if exposed during deeper drilling. See Bugbee, "An Introduction to Oil Well Cement Technology," 16 *Oil and Gas Compact Bull.* 26 (June 1957).

"Production casing is the series of steel pipe lengths, screwed or welded together and called the 'string,' through which the oil flows to the surface. Surface-casing is not the same as the production string. It usually is an outer casing or jacket of the string. One purpose of surface-casing is to prevent contamination of fresh water strata which have been penetrated and to seal off fluids from the hole. Another purpose is to prevent caving at the surface. Surface-casing is a tubular product lighter than the string. Sometimes, however, the production string itself serves as the surface-casing. Surface-casing may go down a thousand feet or more." Harper Oil Co. v. United States, 425 F.2d 1335 at 1336, 36 *O.&G.R.* 190 at 192 (10th Cir. 1970).

See also OUTER CONDUCTOR.

Casinghead

The head or top of the casing set in a well.

See also CHRISTMAS TREE.

Casinghead gas

Gas produced with oil in oil wells, the gas being taken from the well through the casinghead at the top of the well, as distinguished from gas produced from a gas well. Casinghead gas contains liquid hydrocarbons in solution which may be separated in part by a reduction in pressure at the well head and which may be separated more completely in a separator, absorption plant or by other manufacturing process.

The term "casinghead gas" is sometimes defined in particular contracts in such a way as to include gas from gas wells. See *e.g.*, Saulsbury Oil Co. v. Phillips Petroleum Co., 142 F.2d 27 (10th Cir. 1944), *cert. denied,* 323 U.S. 727 (1944).

For a collection of definitions of casinghead gas and a discussion of its characteristics see the appendix to Reynolds v. McMan Oil & Gas Co., 11 S.W.2d 778 at 787–790 (Tex. Com. App. 1928). See also Magnolia Petroleum Co. v. Connellee, 11 S.W.2d 158 (Tex. Com. App. 1928); Mussellem v. Magnolia Petroleum Co., 107 Okla. 183, 231 Pac. 526 (1924).

An Attorney General's opinion in Louisiana suggests that there are two types of casinghead gas, true casinghead gas and secondary casinghead gas. True casinghead gas is described as that gas which is taken from the ANNULAR SPACE (*q.v.*) of an oil well and run through some type of simple separator. Secondary casinghead gas is described as gas released from oil run through a modern separator. *Report and Opinions of the Attorney General of the State of Louisiana* March 15, 1960 to March 1, 1962 at page 193 (March 28, 1960).

See also BRADENHEAD GAS; CASINGHEAD PETROLEUM SPIRIT; CASINGHEAD VAPOR.

Casinghead gas clause

The lease clause providing for a royalty on casinghead gas produced and saved. Originally gas royalty clauses typically provided for the annual payment of a relatively small sum of money, $50 or $100 per year. Later it became customary to provide that gas royalty should be paid on 1/8 or some other fraction or percentage of the value of the gas produced. Most modern leases now contain express provision concerning casinghead gas or other gaseous substances sold or used for the extraction of gasoline or other product therefrom. See Hardwicke, "Evolution of Casinghead Gas Law," 8 *Tex. L. Rev.* 1 (1929); Moses, "Casing-Head Gas Law in Louisiana," 15 *Tulane L. Rev.* 262 (1941); TREATISE § 643.3.

Casinghead gas contract

A contract for the purchase and sale of casinghead gas. A form of casinghead gas contract is reproduced in TREATISE § 741.2. See Howell, "Gas Purchase Contracts," 4 *Sw. Legal Fdn. Oil & Gas Inst.* 151 (1953); Siefkin, "Rights of Lessor and Lessee With Respect to Sale of Gas and as to Gas Royalty Provisions," *Id.* at 181.

Casinghead gasoline

Liquid hydrocarbons separated from casinghead gas by reduction of pressure at the well head or by a separator, absorption plant, or a manufacturing process. A highly volatile, water white liquid.

Syn.: NATURAL GASOLINE (*q.v.*).

See also CASINGHEAD PETROLEUM SPIRIT; NATURAL GASOLINE.

Casinghead gasoline plant

A plant or device by the use of which gasoline or natural gasoline or casinghead gasoline, or any of them, is extracted by any process or method from natural gas or casinghead gas, or from any gas liberated from petroleum in the process of refining. 30 C.F.R. § 222.2(1)(1980).

Casinghead gas royalty

The royalty payable on casinghead gas produced and saved from an oil well.

The casinghead gas royalty clause has undergone a number of changes as the economic importance of gas increased and as the science of removing liquid hydrocarbons from casinghead and wet gas developed. Originally gas royalty clauses typically provided for the annual payment of a relatively small sum of money, $50 or $100 per year. Considerable litigation resulted from the efforts of lessors to recover a share of the liquid hydrocarbons (or of the economic value thereof) when the royalty clause was of this type. See Lone Star Gas Co. v. Harris, 45 S.W.2d 664 and 998 (Tex. Civ. App. 1931, error ref'd); Reynolds v. McMan Oil & Gas Co., 11 S.W.2d 778 (Tex. Com. App. 1929); Wemple v. Producers Oil CO., 145 La. 1031, 83 So. 232 (1919); Gilbreath v. States Oil Corp., 4 F.2d 232 (5th Cir. 1925), *cert. denied,* 268 U.S. 705 (1925).

Later it became customary to provide that gas royalty should be paid on 1/8 or some other fraction or percentage of the value of the gas produced. This clause also gave rise to controversy. Most modern leases now contain express provisions concerning casinghead gas or other gaseous substances sold or used for the extraction of gasoline or other product therefrom. See Hardwicke, "Evolution of Casinghead Gas Law," 8 *Tex. L. Rev.* 1 (1929); Moses, "Casing-Head Gas Law in Louisiana," 15 *Tulane L. Rev.* 262 (1941); TREATISE § 643.3.

See also ROYALTY.

Casinghead petroleum spirit

A term used in the United Kingdom and Australia to refer to liquid hydrocarbons recovered from natural gas or casinghead gas. See Institute of Petroleum in London, *A Glossary of Petroleum Terms* 30; South Australian Mining (Petroleum) Act 1940 § 35; Queensland Petroleum Acts Amendment Act of 1958 § 40A.

See also CASINGHEAD GASOLINE; NATURAL GASOLINE.

Casinghead pressure

See SHUT-IN PRESSURE.

Casinghead vapor

A term occasionally used to describe the liquid hydrocarbons in solution in oil produced from an oil well. See L. Boone, *The Petroleum Dictionary* 83 (1952) (under definition of Casinghead gas).

The term may be used to describe CASINGHEAD GAS (*q.v.*) or to describe WET GAS (*q.v.*) from a gas well.

Casing point

A term used in a joint operating agreement to refer to the time when a well has been drilled to the objective depth stated in the initial notice, appropriate tests have been made, and operator notifies drilling parties of his recommendation with respect to the running and setting of a production string of casing and completing the well. Rocky Mountain Joint Operating Agreement Form 3, November 1959, Section 9.4, TREATISE § 920.5.

Casing pressure

The pressure built up between the casing and tubing when the casing and tubing are packed off at the top of the well. Interstate Oil Compact Commission, *A Suggested Form of General Rules and Regulations for the Conservation of Oil and Gas* (1960), Rule III.

Casing, pull

Removal of casing. Most oil and gas lease forms give the lessee the right at any time to remove casing from wells. See TREATISE §§ 674–674.6.

Casing, set

See SET CASING.

Casual condition

See POTESTATIVE CONDITION.

Catalytic cracking

A refining process for breaking down large, complex hydrocarbon molecules into smaller, more useful ones. A catalyst is used to accelerate the chemical reactions in the cracking process. This method is an improvement upon THERMAL CRACKING (*q.v.*) since it produces a larger quantity of gasoline base stock of a substantially higher octane than is produced by thermal cracking.

See also CRACKING; HYDROCRACKING; REFINER; TOPPING PROCESS.

Catch all clause

Syn. for COVER-ALL CLAUSE (*q.v.*). See Thomas v. Standard Development Co., 70 Mont. 156, 224 Pac. 870 (1924).

CATCO case

A term used to describe In the Matters of Continental Oil Co., 17 F.P.C. 732, 7 *O.&G.R.* 515 (May 20, 1957), *on rehearing.* 17 F.P.C. 880, 7 *O.&G.R.* 925 (June 24, 1957), *rev'd sub nom.* Public Service Comm'n v. Federal Power Comm'n, 257 F.2d 717, 9 *O.&G.R.* 141 (3d Cir. 1958), *aff'd sub nom.* Atlantic Refining Co. v. Public Service Comm'n, 360 U.S. 378, 10 *O.&G.R.* 1021 (1959).

CATCO is an acronym formed from the initial letters of the applicants for a CERTIFICATE OF PUBLIC CONVENIENCE AND NECESSITY (*q.v.*)—Cities Service Production Co., Atlantic Refining Co., Tidewater Oil Co., and Continental Oil Co.

See also CERTIFICATE CONDITION; IN LINE PRICE; RAYNE FIELD CASE.

Caveat

A notice of a claim which may or may not be a valid one, filed in accordance with the provisions of a title registry act to warn the registered owner and all persons who might deal on the faith of a certificate of title that the caveator claims an interest which is not disclosed on the certificate of title. See Canadian Pacific Railway Co. v. District Registrar of Dauphin Land Titles Office, 18 W.W.R. 241, 5 *O.&G.R.* 1279 (Manitoba Queen's Bench 1956).

CDE

Canadian development expense. See 66.3 COMPANY.

CEDOT

The Committee for Equitable Development of Texas Oil and Gas Resources, an organization of independent oil producers.

CEE

Canadian exploration expense. See 66.3 COMPANY.

Ceiling price

"The maximum lawful price which may be charged." American Gas Ass'n, *Glossary for the Gas Industry* (3d ed. 1981).

Cement, oil well

The substance used to fix the casing in the hole. Cement is pumped into the hole, between the walls of the hole and the outside of the casing. Upon hardening, it keeps the pipe in the hole stationary and prevents leakage from or to other strata that have been drilled through. See Bugbee, "An Introduction to Oil Well Cement Technology," 16 *Oil and Gas Compact Bull.* 26 (June 1957).

Cement squeeze

A method whereby perforations and fissures in well walls may be sealed off. The process is discussed in Birch v. Virden Drilling Company Ltd., 23 W.W.R. 673 (Manitoba Queen's Bench 1957).

See also SQUEEZE A WELL; SQUEEZE CEMENTING; SQUEEZE JOB.

Cemotron log

A gamma ray-gamma ray log used to locate the top of cement in a well.

See also GAMMA RAY-GAMMA RAY LOGGING; WELL LOG.

Centipoise

A unit of measurement of viscosity.

Century case, Rule of

The principle announced in Railroad Comm'n v. Magnolia Petroleum Co., 130 Tex. 484, 109 S.W.2d 967 (1937). Where a tract of land has been voluntarily subdivided contrary to RULE 37 (*q.v.*), the Texas state-wide oil-well spacing rule, so that no subdivision is entitled to a drilling permit as of right, the Century Rule permits the subdivided tract to be reconstructed and granted a drilling permit as an exception to prevent confiscation. A recurring difficulty with the Century Rule is, which subdivision gets the permit? See Ryan Consol. Petroleum Corp. v. Pickens, 285 S.W.2d 201, 5 *O.&G.R.* 99 (Tex. 1955), *cert. denied,* 351 U.S. 933 (1956); Railroad Comm'n v. Miller, 165 S.W.2d 504 (Tex. Civ. App. 1942); Magnolia Petroleum Co. v. Railroad Com'n, 127 S.W.2d 230 (Tex. Civ. App. 1939).

See also VOLUNTARY SUBDIVISION.

CEPE

Cautivo Empresa Petrolera of Ecuador.

CEQ

The Council on Environmental Quality created by 83 Stat. 854, 42 U.S.C. § 4342, and charged with the performance of a number of duties and functions, including (1) assisting and advising the President in the preparation of the Environmental Quality Report required by 42 U.S.C. § 4341, (2) gathering information concerning the conditions and trends in the quality of the environment, (3) reviewing and appraising programs and activities of the Federal Government for the purpose of determining the extent to which they contribute to the achievement of the policy set forth in the Act, and (4) developing and recommending to the President national policies to foster and promote the improvement of environmental quality.

CEQA

The California Environmental Quality Act of 1970, Cal. Pub. Resources Code § 21050 *et seq.* (1975). The application of this Act to the drilling of oil wells is considered in No Oil Inc. v. City of Los Angeles, 13 Cal.3d 68, 118 Cal.Rptr. 34, 529 P.2d 66, 50 *O.&G.R.* 293 (1974).

CERDS

The CHARTER OF ECONOMIC RIGHTS AND DUTIES OF STATES (*q.v.*), Article 2(2)(c) of United Nations Resolution 3281 (XXIX), of December 12, 1974.

CERT

The COUNCIL OF ENERGY RESOURCE TRIBES (*q.v.*).

Certificate condition

A condition imposed by the Federal Power Commission or its successor, the Federal Energy Regulatory Commission, to the granting of a CERTIFICATE OF PUBLIC CONVENIENCE AND NECESSITY (*q.v.*). In Atlantic Refining Co. v. Public Service Comm'n, 360 U.S. 378, 10 *O.&G.R.* 1021 (1959), the court concluded that the Commission was authorized to exercise its power to condition certificates in such manner as the public convenience and necessity may require. Certificate conditions have related to such matters as postponement of the effectiveness of a new rate schedule, modification of take-or-pay provisions of contracts, omission of escalator clauses, and related matters. See Williams, Maxwell and Meyers, *Cases on Oil and Gas* 49 (4th Ed. 1979).

In Algonquin Gas Transmission Co. v. Federal Power Comm'n, 534 F.2d 952 (D.C. Cir. 1976), the court declared that the Commission should not be able to defeat substantial rights of regulated companies indefinitely by engrafting permanent rate conditions to a § 7 certificate.

For a case imposing limitations on the power of the Commission to impose certificate conditions, see Panhandle E. Pipe Line Co. v. Federal Energy Regulatory Comm'n, 613 F.2d 1120 (D.C. Cir. 1979), *cert. denied,* 449 U.S. 889 (1980).

Certificated capacity

The amount of natural gas which a pipe line is legally allowed to transmit under orders of the Federal Power Commission. See Gulf Oil Corp. v. American Louisiana Pipe Line Co., 282 F.2d 401 (6th Cir. 1960).

Certificate of beneficial interest

A certificate issued to the beneficiary when an enterprise is operated in the form of a Massachusetts or business trust. See Helvering v. Combs, 296 U.S. 365 (1935), holding that such an enterprise created for the purpose of operating an oil and gas lease is taxable as an association. See TREATISE § 907.1

Certificate of clearance

A permit for the transportation or the delivery of oil, gas or products, approved and issued or registered under the authority of a regulatory commission or board.

Certificate of compliance

A certificate issued by a regulatory commission or board showing compliance with the conservation laws of the state, and conservation rules, regulations and orders of the commission or board, prior to connection with a pipe line. With limited exceptions, pipe line connection with a well is prohibited in some states until a certificate of compliance has issued. See, *e.g.*, Miss. Code 1942, § 6132–31.

Certificate of compliance and authorization to transport oil or gas from lease

A form, prescribed by a regulatory commission, which, when executed by an operator, certifies that the operation of the wells described and the production of oil or gas therefrom has been done in compliance with the orders, rules, and regulations of the commission. This certificate also authorizes a purchaser of oil or gas to transport the same from the lease. Thereby, the commission is informed of the purchaser, and the purchaser is informed that the oil or gas purchased has been produced legally. Interstate Oil Compact Commission, *A Suggested Form of General Rules and Regulations for the Conservation of Oil and Gas* (1960), Rule III.

Certificate of conformance

A certification that a well has been plugged and abandoned in accordance with the provisions of law and valid rules and regulations. Burns' Ind. Stat. Ann. § 13–4–7–23 (Code ed. 1973).

Certificate of public convenience and necessity

A certificate issued by the Federal Power Commission or its successor, the Federal Energy Regulatory Commission, under section 7 of the Natural Gas Act. See 18 C.F.R. § 157.5 *et seq.* (1980).

See also CERTIFICATE CONDITION; GRANDFATHER CERTIFICATE; GRANDFATHER CLAUSE; OPTIONAL CERTIFICATING PROCEDURE.

Certificate of title (or Report of title or Memorandum of title)

An abbreviated type of ABSTRACT OF TITLE (*q.v.*) wherein the abstracter reports his opinion as to the present owner of lands, prior unreleased oil and gas leases, conveyances of minerals and outstanding encumbrances and liens of record. See Rocky Mt. Min. Law Fdn., *Landman's Legal Handbook* 123 (3d ed. 1977).

Certification of abstract

A certification by the abstracter that the abstract contains a full and complete abstract of all the instruments affecting title to the described lands as shown by the records to the date of certification. See ABSTRACT OF TITLE.

Cessation clause

Syn. for CESSATION OF PRODUCTION CLAUSE (*q.v.*). D. Pierce, *Kansas Oil and Gas Handbook* § 11.16 (1986).

Cessation of production

The termination of production of oil and gas from a well. Such stoppage may be due to mechanical breakdowns, clogging of the hole, reworking operations, governmental orders or exhaustion of the deposit. For legal purposes, cessation of production is either temporary or permanent. Permanent cessation of production terminates the ordinary oil and gas lease and defeasible term interest. Temporary cessation of production does not have this effect. See Gillespie v. Wagoner, 28 Ill.2d 217, 190 N.E.2d 765, 18 *O.&G.R.* 863 (1963) (oil and gas lease); Midwest Oil Corp. v. Winsauer, 159 Tex. 560,

323 S.W.2d 944, 10 *O.&G.R.* 1123 (1959) (term royalty); TREATISE § 604.4.

See also PERMANENT CESSATION OF PRODUCTION; TEMPORARY CESSATION OF PRODUCTION.

Cessation of production clause

A lease clause providing that under certain circumstances a lease may be preserved despite cessation of production in the primary or secondary term. Usually the lessee must resume the payment of rentals (if within the primary term) or commence reworking, redrilling or new drilling operations upon the premises within a designated period of time after the cessation of production in order to keep the lease alive. See TREATISE §§ 615–616.4.

See also THIRTY DAY-SIXTY DAY CLAUSE.

CFP

Compagnie Francaise des Petroles. See Krueger, *The United States and International Oil* § A.15 (1975).

CGA

The Canadian Gas Association.

Champerty

A bargain, made by one with no legitimate concern in a suit, to aid in the suit or carry on its prosecution or defense, in consideration of receipt of a share of the matter in suit in the event of success. The doctrine of champerty is of decreasing significance in the United States. Mitchell v. Amerada Hess Corp., 638 P.2d 441, 72 *O.&G.R.* 104 (Okla. 1981), concluded that it was not champertous to obtain a contract for a TOP LEASE (*q.v.*), conditioned upon successful prosecution by the top lessee of a suit to be brought seeking cancellation of a BOTTOM LEASE (*q.v.*).

Chandeleur incentive doctrine

The doctrine providing that producers may reserve gas from the offshore federal domain for their own use in order to provide them with an incentive for exploration and development. The doctrine was first promulgated by the Federal Power Commission in a proceeding involving the use of natural gas in a producer's refinery and involved a reservation of 100 percent of the gas. Chandeleur Pipeline Co., 40

F.P.C. 20 (Opinion No. 560), *remanded,* 436 F.2d 904 (D.C. Cir. 1970), 44 F.P.C. 1747 (Opinion No. 560–A), *aff'd sub nom.* Public Serv. Comm'n v. Federal Power Comm'n, 453 F.2d 24 (D.C. Cir. 1972). In Public Serv. Comm'n of the State of N.Y. v. Federal Energy Regulatory Comm'n [Chandeleur remand], 575 F.2d 892 (D.C. Cir. 1978), the court remanded orders to the Commission for further consideration in the light of the existing status of the doctrine.

The program of providing incentive by use of this doctrine was abandoned in FERC Opinion No. 10, 14 FPS 5–390 (March 20, 1978). In FERC Opinion No. 10–A, issued June 21, 1978, rehearing was denied. Issuance of the latter opinion, which made the matter ripe for judicial review, was followed by a frenzied race to the Courts of Appeals for the District of Columbia and for the Fifth Circuit, in both of which appeals were docketed. Details of the race are reported in Tenneco Oil Co., 17 FPS 5–390 (March 28, 1979), in response to an order issued by the Fifth Circuit referring the matter to the Commission for findings of fact on the question of which petition for review was filed first. Tenneco, which filed in the Fifth Circuit, had a five-person human chain extending from the Commission's office to a public telephone where an open line had been established to a Tenneco representative at the Fifth Circuit Clerk's office. The Associated Gas Distributors and the Public Service Commission of the State of New York had a similar chain and telephone connection with the District of Columbia Circuit Clerk's office. The petition was stamped as filed in the Fifth Circuit at 3:02 PM EDT and was stamped as filed in the District of Columbia Circuit at 3:02:10 PM EDT.

Air Products & Chemicals, Inc. v. Federal Energy Regulatory Comm'n, 650 F.2d 687 (5th Cir. 1981), reviewed the action of the Commission, sustaining it in large part, and remanded the case for consideration of a payback demand made by consumer petitioners. *On remand,* Tenneco Oil Co., 23 FPS 5-938 (FERC Opinion No. 10-8, Dec. 23, 1982), the payback demand was denied.

See also PRODUCER RESERVATION GAS.

Change in seller's circumstances clause

See ADAPTATION CLAUSE.

Change of ownership clause

A lease clause providing for the effect upon the relationship of lessor and lessee of a change in the ownership of the landowner or working interest. The typical lease will provide that the rights of either party may be assigned, in whole or in part. To protect the lessee, the lease may further provide that

> "No change in the ownership of the land, or any interest therein, shall be binding on Lessee until Lessee shall be furnished with a certified copy of all recorded instruments, all court proceedings and all other necessary evidence of any transfer, inheritance, or sale of said rights."

Typically the lease will also provide that the assignee of the lease as to a specific part of the leased premises may keep the lease alive as to his assigned interest by paying his proportionate part of the delay rentals during the primary term:

> "It is hereby agreed in the event this lease shall be assigned as to a part or parts of the above described lands and the assignee or assignees of such part or parts shall fail or make default in the payment of the proportionate part of the rents due from him or them, such default shall not operate to defeat or affect this lease insofar as it covers a part or parts of said lands as to which the said lessee or any assignee thereof shall make due payment of said rental."

Brubaker v. Branine, 237 Kan. 488, 701 P.2d 929, 86 *O.&G.R.* 35 (1985), ruled that, by reason of failure to notify the lessee of a change of ownership of leased premises, the lessee was under no contractual duty to pay royalties to the transferee. However the assignee of the lease was held entitled to an accounting from the assignor for the assignee's share of royalties paid by the lessee to the assignor.

See Gulf Refining Co. v. Shatford, 159 F.2d 231 (5th Cir. 1947); Atlantic Refining Co. v. Shell Oil Co., 217 La. 576, 46 So. 2d 907 (1950); Pearce v. Southern Natural Gas Co., 220 La. 1094, 58 So. 2d 396, 1 *O.&G.R.* 690 (1952); TREATISE § 677.4.

Channeling

The by-passing of oil in a water drive field due to erratic, uncontrolled water encroachment. There are two types of channeling: (1) coning off, in which the oil rides on top of water encroaching into the well bore; and (2) by-passing, in which water encroaches into the well bore through the more permeable streaks in the formation, leaving oil trapped in the less permeable streaks. The natural tendency toward channeling is aggravated by production at excessive rates, which encourages premature water encroachment.

See also BY-PASSING; FINGERING.

Channel type carbon black plant

A plant which manufactures CARBON BLACK (*q.v.*) by burning natural gas in an atmosphere with insufficient oxygen and collecting the soot so formed.

Charcoal test

A test to determine the gasoline content of casinghead or wet gas. Bosworth v. Eason Oil Co., 202 Okla. 359, 213 P.2d 548 (1949). This test is said generally to indicate a higher content of gasoline than does the FIELD COMPRESSION TEST (*q.v.*). *Ibid.*

Charge

A tax, lien or other assessment upon an interest in land or minerals.

Chargeability

A phrase used in connection with leases of federal lands to indicate that an operator is charged with a particular leasehold for purposes of the federal rule limiting an operator to 46,080 acres of direct leaseholdings and 200,000 acres of lease option holdings, in any one state except Alaska, where an operator may have 100,000 acres of direct leaseholdings. See Nelson, "Factors to be Considered in the Formation of Units on Public Lands," *1959 Sw. Legal Fdn. National Institute for Petroleum Landmen* 31 at 36 (1960).

See also FEDERAL LEASE.

Charitable interest

See QUALIFIED CHARITABLE INTEREST.

Charter

See OIL CHARTER.

Charter of Economic Rights and Duties of States (CERDS)

Article 2(2)(c) of United Nations Resolution 3281 (XXIX), of December 12, 1974.

See also the following:

El Sheikh, *The Legal Regime of Foreign Private Investment in the Sudan and Saudi Arabia* 127 *et seq.* (1984);

Hossain and Chowdhury, *Permanent Sovereignty Over Natural Resources in International Law* (1984).

Chattel real

A personal property interest in land; a nonfreehold interest in land.

Checkerboard farm-out

A FARM-OUT AGREEMENT (*q.v.*) in which it is agreed to transfer a full interest in one or more of the offsetting or cornering checkerboard tracts (drill sites), or perhaps a checkerboard throughout the entire lease if an obligation well is drilled. See Bowden, "Federal Income Tax Consequences Under Typical Farm-Out Agreement," 3 *Nat. Res. J.* 470 at 478 (1964).

Checkerboarding

The acquisition of mineral rights upon a checkerboard pattern. For example, a company may be forced to lease land in a large area before it has made adequate geological studies; leases may be taken on one quarter section in each section in such case. In cases of partition in kind between cotenants of minerals, it has been suggested that division on a checkerboard pattern is appropriate. See Henderson v. Chesley, 116 Tex. 355, 292 S.W. 156 (1927); Williams, "The Effect of Concurrent Interests on Oil and Gas Transactions," 34 *Tex. L. Rev.* 519 at 539 (1956); TREATISE § 506.3.

Checkerboard leasing

A system of leasing in which the lessor retains unleased acreage in the immediate vicinity of leased acreage, the consequence being a relationship between leased and unleased acreage resembling spaces in a checkerboard. The Alberta Checkerboard leasing system is described by Professor A.R. Thompson, University of Alaska Institute of Social, Economic and Government Research *Review of Business and Economic Conditions* (Vol. 7, No. 3, July 1970, p. 6) as follows:

> "For the payment of an annual fee which starts at 20 cents an acre and escalates over the years to $1 per acre, oil companies are allowed to acquire exploration rights on a first-come, first-served basis over just about any part of the public domain. Such permits may include up to 99,840 acres and run from five to seven years. At any time during that period the permit holder may lease, at $1 per acre, up to one-half of the land in each township (36 sections)

within any particular permit. The land so selected, however, may not be in one continguous block but must be made up of separate lease parcels, none of which may be larger than a square three miles on a side, or a rectangle two miles wide and four miles long. Each such parcel must be separated from any adjacent section by at least one mile.

"Thus, it is the oil company that within the statutory time limits must decide when and what to lease, and which parcels to return to the government. As lease selection proceeds, the 50 per cent which is not selected reverts to the government as reserves, and, when the permit lapses, all unselected lands become reserves as well. These reserves are, by law, subject only to competitive bidding. If, at the time the reserves are established, oil company interest is very high, as indicated by requests to offer the reserves for sale, the government will ordinarily auction them immediately. In other cases, it may await the results of drilling which the original permit holder may be expected to undertake in the near future.

"Offering large parcels without bids, at low rentals, provides substantial incentive for exploration, yet the corridor requirement assures that parts of the acreage which are proven or semi-proven by the exploratory work will revert to the state for competitive leasing. The system provides a mechanism which leaves judgment and initiative with the individual oil operator and calls mainly for automatic responses from state administrators."

See also CORRIDOR ACREAGE.

Checkerboard relinquishment

A system of relinquishment of lands held under lease or under an agreement between a host government and a foreign oil company requiring the company, after discovery of oil or gas in commercial quantities, to yield certain acreage to the lessor or government, which would then be free to sell the relinquished area to the highest bidder. See Hossain, *Law and Policy in Petroleum Development* 217 (1979).

See also CONCESSION; RELINQUISHMENT CLAUSE.

Chemical treatment of well

See ACIDIZING OF WELL.

Cherrystemming practice

A practice of the BUREAU OF LAND MANAGEMENT (*q.v.*) of designating certain lands occupied by roads or other intrusions as "nonwilderness corridors" in establishing wilderness study areas under the FEDERAL LAND POLICY AND MANAGEMENT ACT OF 1976 (FLPMA) (*q.v.*).

"These lands are occupied by roads or other intrusions which would seemingly disqualify a parcel from wilderness consideration. This practice is commonly employed when a road enters, but does not bisect an area otherwise possessing wilderness characteristics. In such a case, the area occupied by the road is designated a nonwilderness corridor. Such corridors frequently appear on inventory maps in the shape of a cherrystem. The boundaries of an inventory unit 'containing' a cherrystem are drawn around the intrusion so as to exclude it from the area being considered for wilderness values." National Outdoor Coalition, IBLA 80-274, GFS (MIN) 1982-6 (Oct. 30, 1981).

Chilling the bid

A term applied to an alleged practice of participants in a proposed joint venture of reducing a proposed bonus bid for Outer Continental Shelf Lands. See Energy Data Requirements of the Federal Government (Part III—Federal Offshore Oil and Gas Leasing Policies), Hearings before the Subcommittee on Activities of Regulatory Agencies of the Permanent Select Committee on Small Business, House of Representatives, 93d Cong., 2d Sess. (1974) at pp. 319, 339, 364, 395, 401, 418, 450, 470, 475, 484, 496.

See also LEASE BIDDING SYSTEMS.

China National Oil and Gas Exploration and Development Corporation (CNOGC)

An offshoot of the PETROLEUM CORPORATION OF THE PEOPLE'S REPUBLIC OF CHINA (PCRC) (*q.v.*). This company bears responsibility for the discovery and extractive aspects of the China petroleum industry, and it has been the principal Chinese participant in geophysical activities with Western oil companies. See the following:

Bevan, "Exploration in China: What Next?," International Bar Association, 1 *Energy Law 1981* at p. 193;

Lubman and Gniffke, "The Emerging Legal Environment of Foreign Economic Activity in China," *Id.* at 201;

Hoyt, "Current Developments in Petroleum Exploration Offshore China," *Proceedings of the Energy Law Seminar of the International Bar Ass'n Committee on Energy and Natural Resources, Section on Business Law* Topic I, Paper 3 (1979).

See also CHINA PETROLEUM CORPORATION (CPC).

China Petroleum Corporation (CPC)

The corporation which supervises the CHINA NATIONAL OIL AND GAS EXPLORATION AND DEVELOPMENT CORPORATION (CNOGC) (*q.v.*), and, in turn, reports to the Ministry of Petroleum. See Hoyt, "Current Developments in Petroleum Exploration Offshore China," *Proceedings of the Energy Law Seminar of the International Bar Ass'n Committee on Energy and Natural Resources, Section on Business Law* Topic I, Paper 3 (1979).

Chinese National Offshore Oil Corporation (CNOOC)

The corporation charged with exploiting offshore petroleum resources in the People's Republic of China. See "The Offshore Petroleum Regulations of China," [1982] 2 *OGLTR* 60; McAfee, "The Utilization of Foreign Capital and Technology in the Development of China's Oil and Gas Resources," [1982] 3 *OGLTR* 77.

CHLA

The COMBINED HYDROCARBON LEASING ACT OF 1981 (*q.v.*), P.L. 97-98, 95 Stat. 1070, which amended several provisions of the Mineral Leasing Act of 1920.

Chlorinilog

A log run to determine the relative presence of chlorine. See Well Surveys, Inc. v. McCullough Tool Co., 199 F. Supp. 374 (N.D. Okla. 1961).

Choice of forum clause

See FORUM SELECTION CLAUSE.

Choice of law clause

A clause in a multi-jurisdictional contract providing that the law of a specified jurisdiction shall be applicable to the resolution of disputes between or among the parties. See Wertz and Eisen, "Forum

Selection and Governing Law Provisions in Multi-Jurisdictional Agreements—Preparation and Implementation," 32 *Rocky Mt. Min. L. Inst.* 4-1 (1986).

Choke

Heavy steel nipples inserted into the production string of pipe, closing off the flow except through an orifice in the nipple. These orifices are of various sizes. It is customary to speak of the production of a well as so many barrels on a *(e.g.)* one-inch choke.

Syn.: Bean; flow plug; flow nipple.

See also DOWN-HOLE STORM CHOKE.

Christmas tree

The assembly of valves, pipes and fittings used to control the flow of oil and gas from the casinghead.

See also DRY TREE; WET TREE.

Churn drilling

Drilling by cable tool or related methods, as opposed to rotary drilling.

See also CABLE TOOL DRILLING; CANADIAN POLE SYSTEM; DRILLING RIG; ROTARY DRILLING; TURBODRILLING.

CIF pricing

The pricing provision of an oil purchase and sale contract which locates the burden of shipping costs by specifying that the oil will be delivered at the destination at a price including "cost, insurance and freight" (CIF). See Danielsen, *The Evolution of OPEC* 56 (1982); Daniel, "Carriage of Oil by Sea Crude Oil Sale Agreements," [1982] 5 *OGLTR* 163.

See also FAS PRICING; FOB PRICING.

Circle flood

A modification of the dump flood method of secondary recovery in which additional wells are drilled around the area of advancing water where the old wells are spaced too far apart for efficient flooding. See Lytle, "History, Present Status, and Future Possibilities of Secondary Recovery Operations in Pennsylvania," 1 *IOCC Committee Bulletin* 29 at 33 (Dec. 1959).

See also SECONDARY RECOVERY; WATER FLOODING.

Circulation

The movement of drilling fluids through the drill pipe to the bottom of a well and back to the surface to remove drill cuttings.

See also LOST CIRCULATION.

Circulation of mud

The return to the surface of a portion of the drilling MUD (*q.v.*) used in the drilling of a well. Unless some portion of the mud is returned to the surface, it becomes evident that the mud is going into some porous formation and is not sealing the hole. Sealing the hole by drilling mud helps to prevent cave-ins. See Vickers v. Peaker, 227 Ark. 587, 300 S.W.2d 29, 7 *O.&G.R.* 1177 (1957).

See also LOST CIRCULATION.

City gate

The point or measuring station at which a distributing gas utility receives gas from a natural gas pipe line company. Leeston, Crichton and Jacobs, *The Dynamic Natural Gas Industry* 173 (1963).

See also GATE STATION.

City gate rate

The rate charged for natural gas by a pipeline to a distribution company in a particular city or area.

Class A (or B, or C or D) Natural Gas Companies

A classification of Natural Gas Companies made by 18 C.F.R. Part 201 (1980), for purpose of applying the Uniform System of Accounts for Natural Gas Companies. The several classifications are based on operating revenues. Depending on the classification, different accounts are prescribed.

Classification and Multiple Use Act of Sept. 19, 1964

An Act (78 Stat. 986, 43 U.S.C. 1411–18) providing for the classification of public lands and the multiple use thereof.

Class of service

A classification based on the type of ultimate consumer of gas. The common classes are residential service, commercial service and industrial service. American Gas Ass'n, *Glossary for the Gas Industry* (3d ed. 1981).

Claus recovery process

A process employed to oxidize hydrogen sulphide recovered from sour gas into sulphur. See Piney Woods Country Life School v. Shell Oil Co., 539 F. Supp. 957, 74 *O.&G.R.* 485 (S.D. Miss. 1982), *aff'd in part, rev'd in part and remanded,* 726 F.2d 225, 79 *O.&G.R.* 244 (5th Cir. 1984), *reh. denied,* 750 F.2d 69 (5th Cir. 1984), *cert. denied,* 471 U.S. 1005, 105 S. Ct. 1868 (1985).

CLC

COST OF LIVING COUNCIL (*q.v.*).

Clean Air Act

84 Stat. 1676, 42 U.S.C. § 1857 *et seq.*

See also BEST AVAILABLE CONTROL TECHNOLOGY (BACT).

Cleaning a well

The process of removing drilling mud, silt, debris, water, brine, oil scum, paraffin, or other material from the bore of a completed well.

Many wells, especially gas wells, require periodic cleaning. See Welport Oil Co. v. Fairchild, 51 Cal.App.2d 533, 125 P.2d 97 (1942). The flow of reservoir fluids into the well bore carries with it some or all of the substances listed above, which settle around the bottom of the hole and materially reduce production. In addition the hole may mud up or sand up due to cavings in the hole. Cleaning may be done by SWABBING (*q.v.*) or PERIODIC FLOWING (*q.v.*). See Rogers v. Osborn, 152 Tex. 540, 261 S.W.2d 311, 2 *O.&G.R.* 304, 1439 (1953). More often, however, it requires moving a string of tools to the well. The tools remove part of the accumulation from the sand face by mechanical means. The cleaning may be carried further by washing with proper solvents, shooting with nitroglycerine, or acidizing with hydrochloric acid if the productive formation is limestone. Paraffin deposits may be removed by mechanical methods such as cable tools and paraffin knives; by solvents like natural gasoline and other light petroleum fractions; by exothermic chemical reactions; and by steam and application of heat by electrical or combustion methods.

Cleaning is one type of REWORKING OPERATIONS (*q.v.*). See also REDRILLING; WORK-OVERS.

Clean oil

(1) Under a contract for the carriage of oil by sea this term covers motor spirit, aviation spirit, benzene, white spirit, aviation turbine fuel, kerosene, and sometimes gas oil or high-speed diesel. See "The Tonnage Contract," [1982] 1 *OGLTR* 32.

(2) *Syn.* for DRY OIL (*q.v.*).

Clearance, certificate of

See CERTIFICATE OF CLEARANCE.

Closed-in pressure

See SHUT-IN PRESSURE.

Closed pressure

Pressure on a well that has been closed or shut-in long enough to attain a maximum.

Closure

The vertical distance between the top of an anticline or dome and the point of closure, on a contour map. The point of closure is the lowest point on the lowest closing contour. Closure is important as it indicates the maximum amount of producing formation that can be expected to be encountered.

CNOGC

The CHINA NATIONAL OIL AND GAS EXPLORATION AND DEVELOPMENT CORPORATION (*q.v.*).

CNOOC

The CHINESE NATIONAL OFFSHORE OIL CORPORATION (*q.v.*).

Coalbed gas

A term loosely used to describe gas contained in and emitted from coal deposits.

See the following:

Regelin, "Coalbed Gas Ownership in Pennsylvania—A Tenuous First Step with *U.S. Steel v. Hoge,*" 23 *Duquesne L. Rev.* 735;

Cohen, "Leasing of Coalbed Methane Gas Rights—Are Oil and Gas Lease Clauses Analogous?" 15 *Cumberland L. Rev.* 703 (1985);

Dunn, "Methane from Coal Seams via Vertical Wells: A Commercial Success," 26 *IOCC Comm. Bull.* 1 (June 1984);

Dunn, Gremillion and Pearson, "The Technological, Economic, and Legal Aspects of Methane Production from Coal Seams," International Bar Ass'n Section on Energy and Natural Resources, *International Energy Law* (1984) (Topic 9);

Ownership of and Right to Extract Coalbed Gas in Federal Coal Deposits, 88 I.D. 538 (1981);

Bowles, "Coalbed Gas: Present Status of Ownership Issue and Other Legal Considerations," 1 *Eastern Min. L. Inst.* 7–1 (1980);

McGinley, "Legal Problems Relating to Ownership of Gas Found in Coal Deposits," 80 *W. Va. L. Rev.* 369 (1978);

Craig and Myers, "Ownership of Methane Gas in Coalbeds," 24 *Rocky Mt. Min. L. Inst.* 767 (1978);

Olson, "Coalbed Methane: Legal Consideration Affecting Its Development As an Energy Resource," 13 *Tulsa L.J.* 377 (1978).

United States Steel Corp. v. Hoge, 503 Pa. 140, 468 A.2d 1380, 79 *O.&G.R.* 96 (1983), reversing the judgments of the Superior Court and the Court of Common Pleas, held that gas present in coal seams, as long as it remains withn the coal, belongs to the owner of the coal rather than to the owner of "the right to drill and operate through said coal for oil and gas."

See also METHANE; METHANE DRAINAGE LICENSE.

Coal gas

An artificial gaseous fuel produced by pyrolysis of coal. The energy content of this fuel, also known as town gas, is about 450 Btu per standard cubic foot. Use of coal gas in the United States stopped when inexpensive natural gas became widely available. See Hammond, Metz, and Maugh, *Energy and the Future* 158 (1973).

See also POWER GAS.

Coal liquefication

The conversion of coal into liquid hydrocarbons and related compounds by hydrogenation.

Coal oil

(1) An oil produced by the destructive distillation of bituminous coal. New York State Natural Gas Corp. v. Swan-Finch Gas Development Corp., 173 F. Supp. 184 at 187, 11 *O.&G.R.* 54 at 58 (W.D. Pa. 1959), *aff'd,* 278 F.2d 577, 12 *O.&G.R.* 918 (3d Cir. 1960).

(2) An archaic term for kerosine made from petroleum.

COAS

CRUDE OIL ALLOCATION SCHEME (*q.v.*).

Coastal Zone Management Act of 1972

An Act [16 U.S.C. §§ 1451–1464] creating a procedure for the development and administration of a management program for the land and water resources of the coastal zone of a state. Once a state's coastal zone management plan (CZMP) has been approved by the United States Secretary of Commerce, federal agencies are required to conduct activities affecting the coastal zone of a state in a manner which is, to the maximum extent practicable, consistent with approved state management programs.

For discussions of the impact of this Act on the development of mineral resources, see the following:

Breeden, "Federalism and the Development of Outer Continental Shelf Mineral Resources," 28 *Stanford L. Rev.* 1107 (1976);

Rubin, "The Role of the Coastal Zone Management Act of 1972 in the Development of Oil and Gas from the Outer Continental Shelf," 8 *Nat. Res. Law.* 399 (1975).

For a case dealing with the application of this Act to a lease sale, see State of California *et al.* v. Watt et al. 520 F. Supp. 1359, 70 *O.&G.R.* 455 (C.D. Cal. 1981), *aff'd in part, rev'd in part, vacated in part and stayed in part,* 683 F.2d 1253, 73 *O.&G.R.* 447 (9th Cir. 1982), *rev'd sub nom.* Secretary of the Interior v. California, 464 U.S. 312, 104 S.Ct. 656, 79 *O.&G.R.* 448 (1984).

COE

CRUDE OIL EQUIVALENT (*q.v.*).

Cogeneration

"(1) Any of several processes which either use waste heat from generation of electricity to satisfy thermal needs or process waste heat in the steam generation of electricity or production of mechanical energy.

"(2) The use of a single prime fuel source in a reciprocating engine or gas turbine to generate electricity and thermal energy in order to optimize the efficiency of the fuel used. The dominant demand for energy may be either electrical or thermal." American Gas Ass'n, *Glossary for the Gas Industry* (3d ed. 1981).

COGLA

The CANADA OIL AND GAS LAND ADMINISTRATION (COGLA) (*q.v.*)

Colessor's ratification agreement

An agreement by a concurrent owner ratifying and confirming a lease excecuted by another concurrent owner.

Syn.: Colessor's agreement.

Collateral estoppel

A bar to relitigating an issue which has already been tried between the same parties or their privies. On the question whether the collateral estoppel doctrine applies to a judicial proceeding after an earlier administrative proceeding see Richardson v. Phillips Petroleum Co., 791 F.2d 641, 89 *O.&G.R.* 44, *rehearing en banc denied with opinion,* 799 F.2d 426 (8th Cir. 1986), *cert. denied,* 107 S.Ct. 929 (1987).

See also EQUITABLE ESTOPPEL; ESTOPPEL BY DEED; ESTOPPEL IN PAIS.

Collecting system

The system of pipe lines, pumps, tanks, valves, and other incidental equipment by means of which oil is transported and the flow contolled from the wells to a main storage or shipping point.

Syn.: GATHERING SYSTEM.

See also DISTRIBUTION SYSTEM.

Combination drive

The energy used in the production of oil derived from a combination of two or more of the energy sources available for primary production.

See also RESERVOIR ENERGY.

Combination gas

A term which has been applied to WET GAS (*q.v.*) from a gas well or to CASINGHEAD GAS (*q.v.*) from an oil well. L. Boone, *The Petroleum Dictionary* 94 (1952).

Combination lease

(1) A term used to classify leases producing, or capable of producing, from both oil and gas reservoirs. See Permian Basin Area Rate

Proceeding, 34 F.P.C. 159 at 295, 23 *O.&G.R.* 103 at 274 (Opinion No. 468, Aug. 5, 1965), *remanded,* Skelly Oil Co. v. Federal Power Comm'n, 375 F.2d 6, 26 *O.&G.R.* 237 (10th Cir. 1967), *aff'd in part and rev'd in part sub nom. In re* Permian Basin Area Rate Cases, 390 U.S. 747, 28 *O.&G.R.* 689 (1968).

(2) A term applied to a lease which provides for exploration, production, and storage. Emanuel, "Tribulations and Trials of the Lessor (Land Owner)," 3 *Eastern Min. L. Inst.* 17–1 at 17–20 (1982).

Combination plant

A device which removes liquid hydrocarbons from natural gas, especially casinghead gas. It uses both compression and absorption to recover the liquid.

See also ABSORPTION PLANT; COMPRESSION PLANT; PROCESSING PLANT; SEPARATOR.

Combination trap

An underground formation that contains the characteristics of both a STRUCTURAL TRAP and a STRATIGRAPHIC TRAP (*q.v.*). For example, a monocline that loses porosity and permeability up dip is a combination trap. The monocline gives it the structural characteristic; the change in the character of the reservoir rock gives it the stratigraphic characteristic. The East Texas oil field, in which the sandstone reservoir rock pinches out between two planes of impervious rock, is regarded by some geologists as a combination trap. See TREATISE § 102.

See also TRAP.

Combination well

The term applied by Martin v. Kostner, 231 Kan. 315, 644 P.2d 430, 73 *O.&G.R.* 279 (1982), to a well producing significant quantities of both gas and oil. The court concluded that, for purposes of a pooling clause of the lease, the gas was not "casinghead gas produced from oil wells" as it was apparently produced from a gas cap rather than from the oil zone, but the gas was "[a]ssociated gas or gas from a gas cap [which] constitutes a gas right under the oil and gas lease permitting unitization or pooling of such right."

Combine

A term sometimes used for a JOINT ADVENTURE (*q.v.*). Gates Rubber Co. & Subsidiaries v. Commissioner, 74 T.C. 1456, 67 *O.&G.R.*

647 (1980), *aff'd,* 694 F.2d 648 (10th Cir. 1982); Sun Oil Co. & Subsidiaries v. Commissioner, 74 T.C. 1481, 68 *O.&G.R.* 353 (1980), *aff'd,* 677 F.2d 294, 76 *O.&G.R.* 619 (3rd Cir. 1982), *acq.* I.R.B. 1983-26.

Combined hydrocarbon lease

A lease issued in a special tar sand area pursuant to Section 17 of the Combined Hydrocarbon Leasing Act of 1981, P. L. 97–98, 95 Stat. 1070.

Combined Hydrocarbon Leasing Act of 1981 (CHLA)

Public Law 97–98, 95 Stat. 1070, amending several provisions of the Mineral Leasing Act of 1920. The Act established a combined hydrocarbon lease and eliminated the distinction between oil and tar sands. Regulations implementing the Act are contained in 43 C.F.R. Parts 3140 and 3150.

Comeback

A term sometimes used to describe a reversionary interest. See Hamilton and Maxwell, "The Sale of Oil and Gas in Place—Redetermination and Reversionary Interests," *P-H Oil and Gas Taxes* ¶ 1017 at ¶ 1017.4 (1977).

COMECON

The Council for Mutual Economic Assistance (*q.v.*).

Comfort letter

A letter from the parent company of a borrowing subsidiary to a potential lender reciting, in substance, that it is the parent company's policy to ensure that its subsidiaries meet their obligations or, alternatively, that the parent company would be displeased if its subsidiary did not meet its obligations. The letter is not usually intended to create any legal obligation (although legal liability may arise in some circumstances by reason of fraud or negligence) but is designed to set out certain facts or attitudes or expressions which lenders are, or may be, influenced by. See "Discussion of Financing Mineral Project," 1 *Austl. Mining & Petroleum L.J.* 175 (1977).

See also Project financing.

Commence drilling clause

A term sometimes applied to the delay rental, the drilling operations, or the continuous drilling operations clause of a lease. See *e.g.*, Gulf Oil Corp. v. Reid, 161 Tex 51, 337 S.W.2d 267 at 280, 12 *O.&G.R.* 1159 at 1178 (1960), in which this term was used to describe a continuous drilling operations clause.

"Commence" lease

A lease under the terms of which the commencement of a well during the primary term will suffice to keep such lease alive into the secondary term while such drilling operations are prosecuted with reasonable diligence. State ex rel Comm'rs of Land Office v. Carter Oil Co., 336 P.2d 1086, 10 *O.&G.R.* 790 (Okla. 1958); Moncrief v. Pasotex Petroleum Co., 280 F.2d 235, 12 *O.&G.R.* 1087 (10th Cir. 1960), *cert. denied*, 364 U.S. 912, 13 *O.&G.R.* 622 (1960).

See also "COMPLETION" LEASE.

Commencement clause

The name sometimes applied to a DRILLING OPERATIONS CLAUSE (*q.v.*) or to a CONTINUOUS DRILLING OPERATIONS CLAUSE (*q.v.*). See D. Pierce, *Kansas Oil and Gas Handbook* § 11.14 (1986).

Commencement lease

Syn. for "COMMENCE" LEASE (*q.v.*).

Commencement of drilling

The first operations on the land preliminary to the drilling of a well. Generally speaking, the courts have been ready to find commencement of operations for drilling on the land where only the most modest preparations for drilling have been made. In Guleke v. Humble Oil & Refining Co., 126 S.W.2d 38 (Tex. Civ. App. 1939), for example, commencement of drilling operations was found when on the last day of the year the lessee erected a part of the steel derrick, and was working on the water well to be used to supply water for drilling the oil well.

It is clear that such operations, once commenced, must be pursued with reasonable diligence if termination of the lessee's interest is to be avoided. Flanigan v. Stern, 204 Ky. 814, 265 S.W. 324 (1924). In Goble v. Goff, 327 Mich. 549, 42 N.W. 845 (1950), the lessee moved an oil rig on the lease, dug a slush pit and started the drilling of a well before the anniversary date of a lease, but by reason of his failure to secure a permit to drill from the regulatory agency, it was held that a well had not been commenced.

For other cases dealing with the problem of construing the phrase "commence drilling operations," see Muth v. Aetna Oil Co., 188 F.2d 844 (7th Cir. 1951); Haddock v. McClendon, 223 Ark. 396, 266 S.W.2d 74, 3 *O.&G.R.* 1219 (1954); Hughes v. Ford, 406 Ill. 171, 92 N.E.2d 747 (1950). See TREATISE § 606.1.

In Stoltz, Wagner & Brown v. Duncan, 417 F. Supp. 552, 55 *O.&G.R.* 315 (W.D. Okla. 1976), the court concluded that there had been commencement of drilling during the primary term of a COMMENCE LEASE (*q.v.*) even though the drilling bit did not pierce the earth before the end of the primary term. Dirt work had been commenced on the well location during the primary term but a drilling rig was not moved to the location until more than three weeks had elapsed after the expiration of the primary term.

Olinkraft, Inc. v. Gerard, 364 So. 2d 639, 63 *O.&G.R.* 165 (La. App. 1978), held that a "commencement of drilling" requirement had not been satisfied by an 18-inch diameter 22-foot hole drilled by a water drilling rig and insertion of a conductor pipe. A deep well drilling rig was brought to the site three weeks later. The activity with the water drilling rig was not a good-faith attempt to drill the well.

See also A & M Oil, Inc. v. Miller, 11 Kan. App. 2d 152, 715 P.2d 1295, 88 *O.&G.R.* 453 (1986) (commencement of slant well on adjacent premises before expiration of primary term of lease was commencement of well on lease even though the property line of the lease had not been penetrated during the primary term).

The term "commence to drill a well," is defined by Burns' Ind. Stat. Ann., § 14–4–3–1(1)(1973) as follows:

> "The institution of work in good faith with drilling equipment adequate for the drilling of a well to a depth that will reasonably test the oil and gas productiveness of the public lands where such well is commenced."

Ferrell Construction Co. v. Russell Creek Coal Co., 645 P.2d 1005 (Okla. 1982), found that preliminary activities constituted "commencement" of strip mining, declaring that:

> "We see no distinction in law or logic between the mining of hard minerals and the mining of an oil or gas deposit which would vary the meaning of 'commencement' under the law pertaining to minerals."

For purposes of liberative prescription of a mineral servitude in Louisiana, commencement of drilling operations requires the "spudding-in" of a well. See Article 30 of the Louisiana Mineral Code [R.S. 31:30(1975)]; TREATISE § 216.3(a).

See also ACTUAL DRILLING OPERATIONS; DRILLING; DRILLING OPERATIONS.

The definition in this MANUAL was cited by the court in Hilliard v. Franzheim, 180 So. 2d 746 at 747 (La. App. 1965).

Commencement provision

Syn. for DRILLING OPERATIONS CLAUSE (*q.v.*). See Nickel v. Jackson, 380 F. Supp. 1389 at 1392, 49 *O.&G.R.* 246 at 250 (W.D. Okla. 1974).

Commercial deposit

A deposit of oil, gas or other minerals in sufficient quantity for PRODUCTION IN PAYING QUANTITIES (*q.v.*). As generally used in the industry, it is sufficient oil or gas to repay the cost of drilling, equipping, completing and operating as well plus some profit. But in some instances, it is merely sufficient oil or gas to repay the expenses of operation but not the expenses of drilling. See COMMERCIAL QUANTITY.

Commercial discovery bonus

A bonus payable under the provisions of some agreements between a host government and a foreign oil company when the latter makes a commercial discovery. See Hossain, *Law and Policy in Petroleum Development* 216 (1979).

See also CONCESSION.

Commercial oil pool

A pool which appears to contain sufficient quantities of recoverable oil to justify the economical development thereof. Ark. Stat. 1947, § 53–131(J) (1971 Repl.).

Commercial quantity

A quantity of oil, gas or other minerals sufficient for PRODUCTION IN PAYING QUANTITIES (*q.v.*).

This definition was accepted in Texaco, Inc. v. Fox. 228 Kan. 589 at 592, 618 P.2d 844 at 847, 67 *O.&G.R.* 360 at 365 (1980), in which the court held that the term "commercial quantity" was synonymous with the term "paying quantity."

This term is defined by the Saskatchewan Petroleum and Natural Gas Regulations, 1969, § 3(d), O.C. 8/69, as:

"the production from a well of such quantity of oil or gas as would, in the opinion of the minister [of Natural Resources], economically warrant the drilling of a like well in the vicinity thereof for the taking of such production, consideration having been given to the cost of drilling and production operations, available market and the value, nature and quality of oil or gas."

This term, like the term "paying production," may be defined as meaning production exceeding in value current operating costs (as in the habendum clause) or as meaning production which will produce a profit after satisfying cost of drilling and current operating costs (as in the case of implied covenants). See TREATISE § 604.6(a). Thus in General American Oil Co. of Texas v. Superior Oil Co., 416 So. 2d 251, 80 *O.&G.R.* 75 (La. App. 1982), *writ of ref'd,* 421 So. 2d 908 (La. 1982), in construing a contract for the sharing of costs of drilling, this term was given its habendum clause meaning rather than the meaning ascribed to it for purposes of implied covenants.

Commercial quantity of gas was distinguished from paying quantity of gas in Pan American Petroleum Corp. v. Shell Oil Co., 455 P.2d 12, 33 *O.&G.R.* 477 (Alaska 1969), and in State v. Wallace, 52 Ohio App.2d 264, 6 Ohio Op.3d 262, 369 N.E.2d 781, 58 *O.&G.R.* 549 (1976).

See also the following:

Schnell v. Hudson, 141 Ill. App. 3d 617, 96 Ill. D. 16, 490 N.E.2d 1052 (1986) (citing this MANUAL);

Solicitor's Opinion, "Section 2(a)(2)(A) of the Mineral Leasing Act of 1920," 92 I.D. 537 (Feb. 12, 1985);

Garner, "Mineral Leasing: Toward a Workable Definition of 'Commercial Quantities,'" 47 *U. Colo. Rev.* 707 (1976).

Syn.: COMMERCIAL DEPOSIT (*q.v.*).

Commercial well

(1) A well capable of PRODUCTION IN PAYING QUANTITIES (*q.v.*), which in this sense usually means a well that will make a profit over the costs of drilling, equipping, completing and operating it.

(2) In some instances, the term means merely a well with sufficient production to cover current operating expenses, without regard to original drilling costs.

For a discussion of certain of the considerations going into the determination of whether a particular well is a commercial well and of various meanings of such terms in different contexts see Discussion Notes, 12 *O.&G.R.* 695 (1960).

Yates Petroleum Corp., 89 I.D. 480 at 482, 67 IBLA 246 (Sept. 24, 1982), commented as follows:

> "The term 'commercial well,' just like the term 'paying quantities,' is amenable to differing interpretations dependent upon the context of its usage. Thus the term 'commercial well' has been defined as 'a well capable of production in paying quantities, which in this sense usually means a well that will make a profit over the costs of drilling, equipping, completing and operating it.' [Citing this MANUAL OF TERMS]. But, when terms such as 'commercial quantity' appear in the habendum clause of an oil and gas lease, they are normally defined as including costs of marketing but excluding recapture of the costs of drilling. . . . In this regard, therefore, the term 'commercial well' is synonymous with 'a well capable of producing in paying quantities,' since it has long been recognized that where that latter phrase is found in the habendum clause, it, too, encompasses recovery only of the costs of production and marketing and excludes drilling costs."

Commingled well

A well producing crude oil from two or more oil-bearing formations through a common well casing and a single tubing string. The crude oil from each producing formation is mixed with the crude oil from all other oil producing formations which have been tapped through the common well casing. This type of well is distinguished from a MULTIPLE COMPLETION WELL (*q.v.*), which produces from two or more formations through separate tubing strings to each formation, and from a RECOMPLETED WELL (*q.v.*), which produces from only one formation. See Energy Consumers & Producers Ass'n, Inc. v. Department of Energy, 632 F.2d 129 (Temp. Emer. Ct. of App. 1980), *cert. denied,* 449 U.S. 832 (1980) (sustaining the validity of a ruling that in calculating "average daily production" for purposes of the exemption from price controls of STRIPPER WELL OIL (*q.v.*), a multiple completion well was considered as two (or more) wells but a commingled well was considered as a single well).

For a detailed discussion of the history and enforcement of Texas Railroad Commission Rule 10 relating to commingling, see Douglass & Whitworth, "Practice Before the Oil and Gas Division of the Railroad Commission of Texas," 13 *St. Mary's L.J.* 719 at 733 *et seq.* (1982).

Tex. Nat. Res. Code §§ 85.053, 85.055, and 86.081(b), enacted in 1981, deal with the fixing of allowables for commingled production.

See also RULE 10.

Commingling agreement

See TANK BATTERY COMMINGLING AGREEMENT.

Commingling theory

Syn. for MOLECULAR THEORY (*q.v.*).

Commissioner's unit

In Louisiana, a single-well unit created by the Commissioner of Conservation of the State of Louisiana. *Syn.:* Compulsory unit. See La. R.S. 30:5, 9–10; 31:213 (1975).

See also UNIT.

Committed working interest

As defined in a Rocky Mountain unit operating agreement, a working interest which is owned by a party to the agreement and which is committed thereto. See Rocky Mountain Unit Operating Agreement Form 1 (Undivided Interest) May, 1954, Section 1.5, TREATISE § 920.3.

Commodity charge

A charge for gas based on the gas actually taken by the gas purchaser, as distinguished from a demand charge which is based on the maximum volume a buyer has the right to take, though no gas is taken. The commodity charge is substantially smaller than the demand charge, and hence the larger the volume of gas taken, the lower the unit cost. See Lynchburg Gas Co. v. Federal Power Comm'n, 336 F.2d 942 (D.C. Cir. 1964); Atlantic Seaboard Corp. v. Federal Power Comm'n, 404 F.2d 1268 (D.C. Cir. 1968).

See also DEMAND CHARGE; DEMAND RATE; MINIMUM COMMODITY BILL; RATE TILTING; SEABOARD METHOD; UNITED METHOD.

Commodity charge theory

A theory of the Federal Power Commission for approving pipe line company costs which was adopted in the Matter of Panhandle Eastern Pipe Line Co., 13 F.P.C. 53 (Op. No. 269, April 15, 1954). This theory accepted as a rate component of the total cost-of-service charge to consumers, the fair price of gas in the field. Glassberg v. Boyd, 35 Del.Ch. 293, 116 A.2d 711, 4 *O.&G.R.* 2038 (1955).

Commodity rate

A charge or rate for gas delivered beyond the quantity to meet the needs of firm and space heating customers. A higher rate or charge is made for the demand quantity than is made for this excess gas made available on an interruptible basis.

Commodity value of natural gas

A value for natural gas determined on the basis of the cost of competing sources of energy. See *e.g.*, the definition proposed by Holland, "Thoughts on the Arbitration of Price Redetermination under Gas Purchase Contracts in Alberta," 12 *Alberta L. Rev.* 26 at 31 (1974):

"'Commodity value of natural gas' means the overall or weighted average market value of competitive alternative energy sources in the regional market areas in which the natural gas is being or is to be consumed, as obtained by weighting the volumes and prices of the said alternative energy sources in each of the said market areas having regard to the mix of end uses and the volume of natural gas consumed or to be consumed by end use in each of the said market areas, plus any value that may be attributable to natural gas as a premium form of energy as a result of consumer preference for or the necessity to use natural gas as compared to alternative energy sources."

The Alberta Arbitration Act, R.S.A. 1970, C. 21, § 16.1 defines "commodity value of gas" as the aggregate of

(i) the thermal value of gas determined by reference to the volume-weighted average prices of substitutable energy sources competing with gas for the various end uses of gas in the consuming markets served, directly or through exchange, by the buyer of gas under a gas purchase contract, and

(ii) the premium value of gas determined by reference to its inherent special qualities when compared with competing energy sources.

See Re Canadian Western Natural Gas Co., Ltd. and Shell Canada Resources, Ltd., 108 D.L.R.3d 431 (Alta. Q.B. 1979), *appeal allowed,* 118 D.L.R.3d 607 (Alta. Ct. of App. 1980).

For a study of the commodity value of natural gas in U.S. Markets, see Foster Associates, Inc., *An Analysis of the Regulatory Aspects of Natural Gas Supply* (Environmental Protection Agency Publication No. APTD–1459) at p. VI–4 (1973).

In Shell Oil Co. v. Federal Power Comm'n, 520 F.2d 1061 (5th Cir. 1975), *rehearing denied,* 525 F.2d 1261 (5th Cir. 1976), *cert. denied,* 426 U.S. 941 (1976), the court rejected the contention that the Federal Power Commission should fix rates for jurisdictional sales of natural gas on the basis of the commodity value of the natural gas.

The Federal Energy Regulatory Commission has proposed to limit the maximum lawful price of HIGH COST NATURAL GAS (*q.v.*) to ensure that the ceiling prices do not go above the commodity value of the natural gas. FERC Dkt. No. RM82-32-000, 18 C.F.R. Part 271, 24 FPS 3-1113 (Feb. 10, 1983).

See also FIELD VALUE OF GAS; OIL EQUIVALENCY CLAUSE.

Common carrier

A person engaged in the transportation of petroleum as a public utility and common carrier for hire.

For a discussion of the problems of obtaining carriage for DIRECT SALE GAS (*q.v.*), see Airey and Teater, "Transportation of Direct Sale Natural Gas," 5 *Eastern Min. L. Inst.* 17-1 (1984).

For a brief discussion of certain of the difficulties that might arise from common carrier status of gas pipelines, see Anonymous, "Natural Gas Regulation and Market Disorder," 18 *Tulsa L.J.* 619 at 645 (1983).

Common carrier law

A law declaring certain corporations, individuals or associations of individuals engaged, directly or indirectly, in the transportation of crude oil or petroleum or the products thereof, for hire or otherwise, to be common carriers and public utilities, and subjecting them to regulation.

For discussions of proposed legislation and regulations to impose common carrier status on gas pipelines see the following:

Allison, "Natural Gas Pricing: The Eternal Debate," 37 *Baylor L. Rev.* 1 at 74 (1985);

Means and Cohn, "Common Carriage of Natural Gas," 59 *Tulane L. Rev.* 529 (1985).

Syn.: MANDATORY CONTRACT CARRIAGE.

Common deposit clause

A clause in an international agreement providing for compulsory cooperation in case of the discovery of a mineral deposit extending across the boundary line between the nations. Blinn, Duval, Le

Leuch, and Pertuzio, *International Petroleum Exploration & Exploitation Agreements* 218 (1986).

Common pool

An accumulation of oil and/or gas underlying an area.

Common pool problem

"[T]he tendency toward present overproduction that arises when competitors seek to exploit an exhaustible resource in which no one has adequately defined and protectable rights. It is basically a problem of externality, a divergence between the private and social cost of exploitation." Friedman, "The Economics of the Common Pool: Property Rights in Exhaustible Resources," 18 *U.C.L.A. L. Rev.* 855 (1971).

For a study of firm bargaining to mitigate rent dissipation from competitive production on five common oil pools where contracting success varied sharply, see Libecap and Wiggins, "Contractual Responses to the Common Pool: Prorationing of Crude Oil Production," 74 *American Economic Review* 87 (1984).

Common purchaser

See COMMON PURCHASER ACT.

Common purchaser act

A statute which requires the ratable taking of oil or gas by a purchaser, usually a pipe line, without discrimination between producers or sources of supply. Such statutes have been upheld as constitutional. Republic Nat. Gas Co. v. State, 198 Okla. 350, 180 P.2d 1009 (1947); Oklahoma Nat. Gas Corp. v. State, 161 Okla. 104, 17 P.2d 488 (1932); and see opinion of Rutledge, J., Republic Nat. Gas Co. v. State, 334 U.S. 62 (1948). Although the Texas statute was held unconstitutional in Texoma Nat. Gas Co. v. Railroad Comm'n, 59 F.2d 750 (W.D. Tex. 1932), the Texas Supreme Court has since assumed the validity of the statute. Col-Tex Ref. Co. v. Railroad Comm'n, 150 Tex. 340, 240 S.W.2d 747 (1951). See Stayton, "Proration of Gas," 14 *Sw. Legal Fdn. Oil & Gas Inst.* 1 (1963).

The application of common purchaser acts to purchasers of gas moving in interstate commerce has been held to infringe upon the exclusive jurisdiction of the Federal Power Commission. Under the doctrine of preemption, such application is void. Northern Natural Gas Co. v. State Corp. Comm'n, 372 U.S. 84 (1963). For the possible import of this case on state conservation regulations see Meyers, "Federal Preemption and State Conservation in Northern Natural Gas," 77 *Harv. L. Rev.* 689 (1964). See also Note, "Conservation of Natural Gas and the Federal-State Conflict," 64 *Colum. L. Rev.* 888 (1964).

It was held by Foree v. Crown Central Petroleum Corp., 431 S.W.2d 312, 30 *O.&G.R.* 374 (Tex. 1968) (one justice dissenting), that a determination by the Railroad Commission of discrimination was not a prerequisite to bringing suit under the Common Purchaser Act for damages.

For a discussion of Common purchaser acts see Symposium: Workshop on Natural Gas Prorationing and Ratable Take Regulation, 57 *U. of Colo. L. Rev.* 149–393 (1986).

See also RATABLE TAKING.

Common reservoir

"[A]ll or part of any oil or gas field or oil and gas field that comprises and includes any area that is underlaid or that, from geological or other scientific data or experiments or from drilling operations or other evidence, appears to be underlaid by a common pool or accumulation of oil or gas or oil and gas." Texas Natural Res. Code § 86.002(4) (1978).

In Railroad Comm'n v. Graford Oil Corp., 557 S.W.2d 946, 59 *O.&G.R.* 338 (Tex. 1977), the court concluded that under the statutory definition of common reservoir in Tex. Rev. Civ. Stat. Art. 6008, Section 2, the word "common" modifies both "pool" and "accumulation," *viz.*, to be a common reservoir it must appear that the area is underlain by a "common pool" or a "common accumulation" of oil and/or gas. Hence, separate and distinct pools of oil or gas, which are not connected and which do not communicate with one another, do not constitute a "common reservoir."

> "Each separate pool or accumulation is, under the statute, a separate reservoir, even though several different reservoirs may underlie a single gas-producing area and an entire gas-producing area may often be loosely referred to as a 'field.' " 557 S.W.2d at 950, 59 *O.&G.R.* at 342.

In Gage v. Railroad Comm'n, 582 S.W.2d 410, 63 *O.&G.R.* 218 (Tex. 1979), the court concluded: (1) the Commission was without authority to consolidate separate reservoirs for proration purposes; and (2) communication among vertically separated producing zones obtained by well completions in two or more zones was not sufficient to constitute a common reservoir. Subsequent to this decision, §

85.046 and § 86.012 of the Texas Natural Resources Code were amended, apparently to overturn *Gage* and related cases, to give the Railroad Commission authority to permit commingled production.

Railroad Commission v. Mote Resources, 645 S.W.2d 639, 76 *O.&G.R.* 113 (Tex. App., Austin, 1983), reaffirmed the holdings in *Graford Oil Corp.* and in *Gage* which denied to the Commission authority to combine a number of separate accumulations of oil or gas and prorate them together as a single field.

See also RESERVOIR.

Common source of supply

An underground reservoir containing a common accumulation of oil or gas, or both. Each zone of a general structure, which zone is completely separated from any other zone in the structure, is covered by the word "pool" or "common source of supply." Colo. Rev. Stat. 1973 § 34–60–103.

An underground reservoir, all parts of which are permeably connected so as to permit the migration of oil or gas or both from one portion thereof to another wherever and whenever pressure differentials are created as a result of the production of oil or gas from said producing formation. Palmer Oil Corp. v. Phillips Petroleum Co., 204 Okla. 543, 231 P.2d 997 (1951), *appeal dism'd,* 343 U.S. 390 (1952).

This term is defined in Transcontinental Gas Pipeline Corp. v. State Oil & Gas Board of Mississippi, 457 So.2d 1298 at 1324, 83 *O.&G.R.* 295 at 337 (Miss. 1984), as "that geological configuration or area within which a significant drainage problem would result if there be unratable taking from one well to another. It is synonymous with 'pool'." The judgment in this case sustaining a state ratable take order was reversed, 470 U.S. 1083, 106 S.Ct. 709, 87 *O.&G.R.* 550, *reh. denied,* ____ U.S. ____, 106 S.Ct. 1485 (1986), the court holding, by five to four, that a state ratable take order continued subject to federal preemption.

Syn.: POOL (*q.v.*).

Common variety minerals

Mineral materials including, but not limited to, sand, stone, gravel, pumice, pumicite and cinders. Common varieties are defined by Federal Regulations to mean deposits having no distinct or special economic or commercial value. See Pruitt, "Mineral Terms—Some Problems in Their Use and Definition," 11 *Rocky Mt. Min. L. Inst.* 1 at 30 (1966); Holme, " 'Common Varieties' and the 'Distinct and Special Value' Exception in the Mining Act of 1955," 38 *U. Colo. L. Rev.* 220 (1966).

Communitization

Syn. for POOLING (*q.v.*).

Community knowledge test

A term which has been applied to a test utilized in some states in ascertaining the substances included in a grant or reservation of minerals, *viz.*, ascertaining the custom or usage of the community in the use of the term "minerals" at the time of the mineral severance. D. Pierce, *Kansas Oil and Gas Handbook* § 6.04 (1986). See TREATISE § 219.3.

Community lease

A single lease covering two or more separately owned tracts of land. A community lease may arise from the execution of a single lease by the several owners of separate tracts or by the execution of separate but identical leases by the owners of separate tracts individually when each lease purports to cover the entire consolidated acreage. The usual result of the execution of a community lease is to cause the apportionment of royalties in proportion to the interests owned in the entire leased premises as a consequence of the judicially ascertained intent of the parties. See Hoffman, *Voluntary Pooling and Unitization* 9–86 (1954); Hardwicke and Hardwicke, "Apportionment of Royalty to Separate Tracts: The Entirety Clause and the Community Lease," 32 *Tex. L. Rev.* 660 (1954); TREATISE § 521.2.

Syn.: JOINT LEASE.

See also MULTIPLE COMMUNITY LEASE.

Community property

A form of marital property that exists in eight states which adopted the community property system of marital rights from the civil law, especially the law of France and Spain. The states are: Arizona, California, Idaho, Louisiana, Nevada, New Mexico, Texas and Washington. Three of these states are principal producing states and others have an active oil and gas industry. Since the community property system governs all property of married persons in these states, it has an important effect on titles, and hence on leasing of land for exploration and development purposes. Leading secondary authorities on the law of community property include, Armstrong,

California Family Law (1953); De Funiak, *Principles of Community Property* (2d ed. 1971); McKay, *The Law of Community Property* (1925); Reppy and De Funiak, *Community Property in the United States* (1975).

Comparable sales

The term applied to sales of gas to which may be compared the sale under analysis in a particular case for the purpose of the determination of market value of gas under the provisions of a MARKET VALUE LEASE (*q.v.*). For a detailed discussion of the factors of time, quality, and availability to market employed in determining comparable sales, see Piney Woods Country Life School v. Shell Oil Co., 539 F. Supp. 957 at 982, 74 *O.&G.R.* 485 at 530 (S.D. Miss. 1982), *aff'd in part, rev'd in part and remanded,* 726 F.2d 225, 79 *O.&G.R.* 244 (5th Cir. 1984), *reh. denied,* 750 F.2d 69 (5th Cir. 1984), *cert. denied,* 471 U.S. 1005, 105 S. Ct. 1868 (1985).

See also TREATISE § 650.4.

Compensation for risk

Syn. for NONCONSENT PENALTY (*q.v.*). See *in re* Application of Kohlman (Kohlman v. Depco, Inc.), 263 N.W.2d 674, 60 *O.&G.R.* 402 (S.D. 1978).

Compensation interests

Certificates of participation in the net proceeds of oil properties. New v. New, 148 Cal.App.2d 372, 306 P.2d 987, 7 *O.&G.R.* 213 (1957).

Compensation payment

The term applied to a payment proposed to be required of higher priority customers for natural gas to compensate lower priority customers for the greater costs of alternative fuels they were forced to use as a consequence of curtailment. In Mississippi Public Service Comm'n, v. Federal Power Comm'n, 522 F.2d 1345 (5th Cir. 1975), *rehearing denied,* 526 F.2d 816 (1976), *cert. denied,* 429 U.S. 870 (1976), the court concluded that the imposition of compensation payments as a condition for the receipt of higher priority gas was within the statutory power of the Federal Power Commission over the movement of such gas in interstate commerce.

Compensatory drainage

A term used to describe drainage onto particular premises which may be viewed as compensating the owner for minerals drained from the premises. See Hughes, "Legal Problems of Water Flooding, Recycling and Other Secondary Operations," 9 *Sw. Legal Fdn. Oil & Gas Inst.* 105 at 110 (1958).

See also DRAINAGE.

Compensatory royalty

A royalty paid in lieu of drilling a well which would otherwise be required under the covenants of a lease, express or implied. When a lessee has leases covering two or more contiguous tracts, *e.g.*, Tracts *A* and *B*, if he drills a well on Tract *A*, he will normally be obligated under the offset well covenant to drill a well on Tract *B*. If existing development of the two tracts is adequate to recover the oil or gas in place, he may elect to pay the royalty owners of Tract *B* a compensatory royalty in lieu of drilling the offset well, if the lease of Tract *B* contains a COMPENSATORY ROYALTY CLAUSE (*q.v.*). See TREATISE § 644.4.

Syn.: CASH SUBSTITUTE ROYALTY (*q.v.*).

See also OFFSET ROYALTY; ROYALTY; SUBSTITUTE ROYALTY.

Compensatory royalty clause

A clause providing for the payment of a royalty on oil produced from other premises in lieu of drilling an obligatory well, usually an offset well. This type of clause is of particular value to a lessee who owns leases on adjoining tracts and who has developed the consolidated tracts in an efficient manner. Without this clause, he must drill wells on each leasehold to protect it from drainage from other leaseholds in the consolidated tract. This type of clause may enable him to pay relatively nominal compensatory royalties and thereby escape the necessity of drilling additional offset wells which are not needed for the efficient drainage of the consolidated tracts. See TREATISE § 644.4.

Competitive lease

An oil and gas lease on federal owned land over a known geologic structure in a producing oil or gas field. These leases cannot cover more than 640 acres and are awarded to the highest bonus bidder after notice. See Hoffman, *Oil and Gas Leasing on Federal Lands*

(1957); *Rocky Mt. Min. L. Fdn. Law of Federal Oil and Gas Leases* ch. 7 (1985).

The Secretary of the Interior has the authority to reject a high bid in a competitive oil and gas lease sale where the record discloses a rational basis for the conclusion that the amount of the bid was inadequate. See, *e.g.*, Vierson & Cochran, IBLA 82-616, GFS(O&G) 1982-226 (Sept. 1, 1982) (remanding case to the Bureau of Land Management for reconsideration of rejection of bid when bidder raised considerable doubt whether the bid was, in fact, inadequate); L. B. Blake, IBLA 82-778, GFS(O&G) 1982-236 (Sept. 15, 1982) (finding that the grounds for rejection of a bid by the Minerals Management Service were rational).

See also AVERAGE EVALUATION OF TRACT (AEOT); BACK-IN RIGHT; CHILLING THE BID; FEDERAL LEASE; MONEY LEFT ON THE TABLE; NON-COMPETITIVE LEASE.

Completed well

A dry hole; or a well capable of producing oil or gas; or a well drilled to such depth that oil or gas is not likely to be encountered at greater depths; or a well drilled to that reasonable depth at which the existence of oil or gas is usually proved or disproved in the locality. Smith v. Hayward, 193 F.2d 198, 200 (C.C.P.A. 1951).

In Michigan, Howard v. Hughes, 293 N.W. 740, 294 Mich. 533 (1940), approved the following definition:

> "(1) An oil well is completed when it has been drilled to the oil formation prevailing in that district and (2) such means have been employed to produce oil as are known to the industry in that community and (3) to the extent that a reasonably experienced driller would use and employ same in good faith effort to make a well an oil producer of a nonproducer (a dry hole)."

For purposes of cancellation of a bond required of drillers, Cal. Pub. Res. Code § 3208 (1972) (1980 Supp.) defines a properly completed well as one which "has been shown to the satisfaction of the supervisor that the manner of producing oil or gas therefrom is satisfactory and that the well has maintained production of oil or gas from a continuous six-month period."

For purposes of required filing of a log, core record, and history with the supervisor, Cal. Pub. Res. Code § 3217 (1972) declares that a well is completed "thirty days after it has commenced to produce oil, water or gas, unless drilling operations are resumed before the end of the thirty-day period."

For purposes of construing a lease provision requiring the commencement of operations on a second well within 3 months of the completion of the first well, the court in Siemon v. Lyon, 51 Cal. App.2d 350, 124 P.2d 893 (1942), quoted the latter definition in concluding that a well had been completed within the meaning of this lease provision, declaring that "there is nothing in the lease itself, or in the law, which requires that for a well to be a completed well, it must be a well that produces in paying quantities."

In Niles v. Luttrell, 61 F. Supp. 778 (W.D. Ky. 1945), drilling of a well ceased on May 25. On June 4 the well was shot with nitroglycerin but without satisfactory results. In August or September the well was acidized. It still did not produce oil in paying quantities. The court concluded that the well was "completed" after it had been acidized without results.

For purposes of a shut-in royalty clause, there may be dispute as to the time of completion of a well. Thus in Bennett v. Sinclair Oil & Gas Co., 275 F. Supp. 886, 27 *O.&G.R.* 716 (W.D. La. 1967), *aff'd,* 405 F.2d 1005, 33 *O.&G.R.* 256 (5th Cir. 1968), one ground for the lessor's refusal of a tender of shut-in royalty payment was that the payment was premature in that it was designated for a period beginning May 29, 1965, when in fact the well was not completed until June 13, 1965. The argument was rejected by the court which observed:

> "Viewing the evidence as a whole and in a light most favorable to plaintiffs, we find the dispute over the completion date of the well involved a mere technicality based on whether the well should have been deemed 'completed' when the 'Christmas tree' was installed or when the liner was perforated. We fail to see the significance this distinction has in this case. In no event have petitioners been prejudiced by the payment with respect to Lease # 1 and they certainly have not been injured by a payment which represents more than they were due." 275 F. Supp. at 892, 27 *O.&G.R.* at 723.

In Seale v. Major Oil Co., 428 S.W.2d 867 at 869, 29 *O.&G.R.* 292 at 295 (Tex. Civ. App. 1968), the court concluded that a contract reference to the completion of a well "does not as contended by appellant mean the completion of such well as an oil or gas producer but has a broader meaning and refers to completion of the required work on the well whether it became a producer or not."

Barrett v. Ferrell, 550 S.W.2d 138 at 142, 57 *O.&G.R.* 590 at 597 (Tex. Civ. App. 1977, error ref'd n.r.e.), declared that "the term 'completing' a well as used in the oil and gas industry does not mean that the operator is required to install completion equipment on a dry hole."

See also Lerblance v. Continental Oil Co., 437 F. Supp. 223 at 229, 59 *O.&G.R.* 50 at 61 (E.D. Okla. 1976).

The definition in this MANUAL was cited in Canadian Superior Oil Ltd. v. Paddon-Hughes Development Co., 65 W.W.R. 461 at 470 (Alberta Sup. Ct. 1968), *appeal dismissed,* 67 W.W.R. 525, 3 D.L.R.3d 10 (Alberta Sup. Ct. App. Div. 1969), *appeal dismissed,* [1970] S.C.R. 932, 12 D.L.R.3d 247, 74 W.W.R. 356 (1970).

Complete pay-out period

A term employed in the 1956 proposed Treas. Reg. § 1.612–4(a)(2), defined as the period of time it takes for the operating net income from a well, after payment of all costs of operations, to equal all expenditures for drilling and development, both tangible and intangible, less all such expenditures which are recoverable out of production payments, royalties and net profits interests. See Stroud, "Major Points of Impact of New Natural Resources Regulations on Oil and Gas," 8 *Sw. Legal Fdn. Oil & Gas Inst.* 393 at 404 (1957).

Completion clause

The name applied by D. Pierce, *Kansas Oil and Gas Handbook* § 11.15 (1986), to a DRILLING OPERATIONS CLAUSE (*q.v.*) or to a CONTINUOUS DRILLING OPERATIONS CLAUSE (*q.v.*).

Completion contract

A form of DRILLING CONTRACT (*q.v.*) between an operator and an independent drilling contractor. The contractor may be paid on a footage or day work basis but the operator's obligation to pay is postponed until the well is completed. See Bankoff v. Wycoff, 233 F.2d 476, 6 *O.&G.R.* 417 (10th Cir. 1956).

Completion funding

See COMPLETION PARTNERSHIP.

"Completion" lease

A lease under the terms of which a well must be completed, as opposed to commenced, during the primary term in order to keep the lease alive into the secondary term. State ex rel Comm'rs of Land

Office v. Carter Oil Co., 336 P.2d 1086, 10 *O.&G.R.* 790 (Okla. 1958); Moncrief v. Pasotex Petroleum Co., 280 F.2d 235, 12 *O.&G.R.* 1087 (10th Cir. 1960), *cert. denied,* 364 U.S. 912 (1960).

See also Steinkuehler v. Hawkins Oil & Gas Inc., 728 P.2d 520, ____ *O.&G.R.* ____ (Okla. App. 1986) (finding that lease construed was a "commencement lease" rather than a "completion lease").

See also "COMMENCE" LEASE.

Completion location

This term is defined by Section 402 of the Natural Gas Policy Act of 1978 (Pub. L. No. 95–621), as the subsurface location from which crude oil or natural gas is or has been produced from a reservoir.

Completion of a well

An indefinite term, meaning something more than mere completion of drilling. At the least it means the cleaning out of the well after reaching a specified depth, or the shooting of the well if there is doubt as to whether it is a producer or nonproducer. Totah Drilling Co. v. Abraham, 64 N.M. 380, 328 P.2d 1083, 9 *O.&G.R.* 682 (1958). Completion of a well involves those processes necessary before production occurs and after drillers have hit the pay sand, *viz.,* perforating the casing and washing out the drilling mud. In Edwards v. Hardwick, 350 P.2d 495, 12 *O.&G.R.* 684 (Okla. 1960), the court emphasized that the term "completed well" has different meanings in various contexts, *e.g.,* when used in drilling contracts or drilling clauses or when used to determine the commencement of a period of time in which an act is to be performed or a right is to be exercised.

This term was said in Modern Exploration, Inc. v. Maddison, 708 S.W.2d 872, ____ *O.&G.R.* ____ (Tex. App., Corpus Christi, 1986), to mean the time production from a well actually began.

Completion of drilling

A term often used interchangeably with the term COMPLETION OF A WELL (*q.v.*). Modern Exploration, Inc. v. Maddison, 708 S.W.2d 872, ____ *O.&G.R.* ____ (Tex. App., Corpus Christi, 1986), construed the term "completion of drilling" as meaning "the time when no further drilling is needed, when oil or gas has been reached and the well is capable of producing—in short, when the well's total depth is reached, not when the operator chooses to perforate the cement plug that he chose to insert into the well." This court viewed the term "completion of a well" as meaning the time production actually began.

Completion operations

This term is defined by Ariz. R.S. § 27–551 as "work performed in an oil or gas well after the well has been drilled to the point where the production string of casing is to be set, including setting the casing, perforating, artificial stimulation, production testing and equipping the well for production, all prior to the commencement of the actual production of oil or gas in paying quantities, or in the case of an injection or service well, prior to when the well is ready for use, or in the case of a dry hole, prior to when the well is plugged and abandoned."

Completion partnership

A partnership organized to obtain financing of the obligation of a general partner in a drilling program to contribute completion and other capital costs. See Mann, "Financing Oil and Gas Operations—Recent Developments," 33 *Sw. Legal Fdn. Oil & Gas Inst.* 407 at 421 (1982):

> "If conventional financing from banks or other financial institutions is unavailable or considered too expensive or restrictive, additional funding from a 'completion partner' may be sought. The function of the completion partner is to provide funds for completion and other capital costs of successful wells. Because the well is known to be successful, the risk may be low to the completion partner."

See also DRILLING FUND.

Completion program

A program to provide funds for the acquisition of leases and prospects and/or to pay all capital costs incurred in completing wells. Baggett, Dole, and Short, *Coopers & Lybrand Anatomy of a Drilling Fund* 7 (1980).

See also DRILLING FUND.

Completion report

A report required by the conservation regulations of many states to be filed with the conservation commission after the completion of a well. Such reports are to contain some or all of the following information: name and/or number of the well; location; lease name; date of completion; date of first production, if any; name and depth of reservoir being produced from; initial production test data; casing and cementing records; perforation data; shooting or chemical treatment record; the well log. Some states also require filing of copies of the electrical well logs.

Compliance, certificate of

See CERTIFICATE OF COMPLIANCE.

Compliance with laws clause

A clause in the Alberta Crown Petroleum and Natural Gas pro forma lease obligating the lessee to comply with all provincial statutes and regulations in force from time to time.

See also REFERENTIAL INCORPORATION.

Composite price ceiling

Under the provisions of the Emergency Petroleum Allocation Act of 1973 (EPAA), as amended by the Energy Policy and Conservation Act of 1975 (EPCA) and the Energy Conservation and Production Act of 1976 (ECPA), price ceilings for oil produced in the United States were established. Under EPAA a two-tier price system was established, with a ceiling imposed on the price of OLD OIL (*q.v.*) and an exemption from price control given NEW OIL, RELEASED OIL and STRIPPER WELL OIL (*q.v.*). Following enactment of EPCA in December of 1975, ceilings were imposed on new oil, released oil, and stripper well oil, which came to be known as upper tier or second tier oil to distinguish it from old oil, which came to be described as lower tier or first tier oil. The EPCA also imposed a composite price ceiling, *viz.* an average price ceiling, on all domestic crude oil, of $7.66 a barrel for February 1976, with provision for escalation of the composite or average price ceiling at annual rate not exceeding 10 percent. Under EPCA, effective September 1, 1976, stripper production was exempted from controls and there emerged a three tier price system consisting of lower tier, upper tier, and exempt crude oil. Thereafter for purposes of determining compliance with the Composite price ceiling, there was attributed to stripper well production an IMPUTED STRIPPER WELL OIL PRICE (*q.v.*) of $11.63 per barrel (subject to an escalator provision).

See also PRICE CONTROL OF OIL, GAS AND PETROLEUM PRODUCTS.

Compression plant

A device which removes liquid hydrocarbons in natural gas, especially casinghead gas. The plant compresses and cools the gas, which causes the liquid constituents to condense out.

See also ABSORPTION PLANT; COMBINATION PLANT; PROCESSING PLANT; SEPARATOR.

Compression test car method

A method of testing the gasoline content of gas which involves the use of compression and refrigeration equipment mounted on a truck by means of which the gas is compressed and then cooled, resulting in the gasoline condensing out of the gas. See Gregg, "Negotiating and Drafting Gas Purchase Contracts on Behalf of the Seller," 13 *Sw. Legal Fdn. Oil & Gas Inst.* 87 at 96 (1962).

Compressor plant

A pipe line installation to pump natural gas through the pipe line. See Gault v. Transcontinental Gas Pipe Line Corp., 102 F. Supp. 187, 1 *O.&G.R.* 362 (D. Md. 1952), *aff'd,* 198 F.2d 196, 1 *O.&G.R.* 1213 (4th Cir. 1952).

Syn.: BOOSTER STATION.

Compressor station

An installation in which the pressure of gas is raised for transmission through pipe lines while the gas is cooled, scrubbed and dehydrated. See Calvert v. Panhandle Eastern Pipe Line Co., 255 S.W.2d 535, 2 *O.&G.R.* 843 (Tex. Civ. App. 1953), *rev'd,* 347 U.S. 157, 3 *O.&G.R.* 354 (1954), for a schematic diagram of the operations of such a station.

Compulsory pooling

The bringing together, as required by law or a valid order or regulation, of separately owned (or separate interests in) small tracts sufficient for the granting of a well permit under applicable spacing rules. Compulsory process for pooling is now available in nearly all producing states. See TREATISE § 905.1. Pooling is important in preventing the drilling of unnecessary and uneconomic wells, which will result in physical and economic waste.

Anderson, "Compulsory Pooling in North Dakota: Should Production Income and Expenses Be Divided from Date of Pooling,

Spacing, or 'First Runs'?" 58 *No. Dak. L. Rev.* 537 at 573 (1982), argues that "a well spacing order should be retroactive to the date of first production and a compulsory pooling order should be retroactive to the effective date of spacing."

For a case giving retroactive operation to a compulsory pooling order, see Murphy v. Amoco Production Co., 590 F.Supp. 455, 83 *O.&G.R.* 108 (D. N.D. 1984), discussed in TREATISE § 953 note 1.

See also COMPULSORY UNITIZATION; ELECTION TO PARTICIPATE; MUSCLE-IN CLAUSE; POOLING; WELL SPACING.

Compulsory unit

A UNIT (*q.v.*) formed by order of a governmental agency.

Compulsory unitization

The bringing together, as required by law or a valid order or regulation, of separately owned tracts (or separate interests therein) into a unit constituting all or some portion of a producing reservoir and the joint operation of such unit. Unitization is important where there is separate ownership of portions of the rights in a common producing pool in order that it may be made economically feasible to engage in cycling, secondary recovery operations, pressure maintenance, reinjection, or explorations in depth.

Compulsory unitization of rather comprehensive scope is now available in many states. See TREATISE § 912. In general, under these statutes, a state regulatory agency is given authority to impose unitization on a pool or part thereof as against the objection of a small minority interest if a proposed plan has been approved by a requisite majority (*e.g.*, 75 percent) of the owners of operating interests and certain nonoperating interests. In some states compulsory process is available to accomplish unitization for purposes of cycling operations, but not for other purposes. In Washington, unitization may be ordered by the regulatory commission when in its judgment production in any pool or field shall have declined to a point where secondary recovery operations are necessary.

To achieve the maximum objectives of a unitization program it is necessary that all persons having an interest in the program area become subject to the agreement. Without statutory compulsion, however, unanimity is frequently impossible to obtain. The principal obstacle to full, voluntary agreement is the problem of dividing the proceeds of production. Even under a compulsory unitization statute, the problem of dividing the proceeds of production creates considerable difficulty inasmuch as most compulsory unitization statutes require prior agreement of a substantial majority of the persons interested in the area to be unitized to a unitization plan, and agreement must be reached by such persons on such matters as division of the proceeds of development before the regulatory commission may act upon the plan.

For a detailed study of the extent to which Texas has achieved voluntary unitization without the impetus of a compulsory unitization statute, see Weaver, *Unitization of Oil and Gas in Texas* (1986).

See also COMPULSORY POOLING; ELECTION TO PARTICIPATE; UNITIZATION.

Concession

An agreement (usually from a host government) permitting a foreign petroleum company to prospect for and produce oil in the area subject to the agreement. The terms ordinarily include a time limitation and a provision for royalty to be paid to the government.

For discussion of legislation and contractual provisions relating to mineral production by foreign producers, see the following:

Blinn, Duval, Le Leuch, and Pertuzio, *International Petroleum Exploration & Exploitation Agreements* (1986);

Mikesell, *Petroleum Company Operations & Agreements in the Developing Countries* (1984);

Cameron, *Petroleum Licensing: A Comparative Study* (1984);

Gray and Walter, "Investment-related Trade Distortions in Petrochemicals," 17 *J. World Trade Law* 283 (1983).

Cameron, *Property Rights and Sovereign Rights: The Case of North Sea Oil* (1983);

Hossain and Chowdhury, *Permanent Sovereignty Over Natural Resources in International Law* (1984);

Barrows, *Worldwide Concession Contracts and Petroleum Legislation* (1983) (a collection and brief analysis of oil laws and contracts around the world);

Chester, *United States Oil Policy and Diplomacy* (1983);

Fisher, "Law and Policy for Accelerating Petroleum Exploration and Development in New Zealand," 16 *Victoria U. of Wellington L. Rev.* 11 (1986);

Kuehne, "Oil and Gas Licensing: Some Comparative United Kingdom-German Aspects," 4 *J. of Energy & Natural Resources Law* 150 (1986);

Vock, "Bilingual Agreements in the Petroleum Industry," 4 *J. of Energy & Natural Resources Law* 188 (1986);

Black, "Comparative Licensing Aspects of Canadian and United Kingdom Petroleum Law," 21 *Tex. Int. L. J.* 471 (1986);

Fitzpatrick, "Interesting Legal Aspects of the Netherlands' Petroleum Regime," [1985/86] 12 *OGLTR* 312;

McPherson, "Recent Developments in Petroleum Laws and Contracts," International Bar Association Section on Energy and Natural Resources, *International Energy Law* (1984) (Topic 1);

Murphy, "State Entities and Private Oil Companies: The Contest for Leadership in the Development of Latin American Oil and Gas," International Bar Association Section on Energy and Natural Resources, *International Energy Law* (1984) (Topic 2);

"Developments in Concessions and Licenses," International Bar Ass'n Section on Energy and Natural Resources, *International Energy Law* (1984) (Topic 7);

Meijer, "The Dutch Offshore Licensing Regime," [1983/84] *OGLTR* 227 (1984);

Blackshaw, "Legal and Fiscal Aspects of Foreign Investments in the Hydrocarbons Sector in Spain," [1983] 9 *OGLTR* 198;

Davies, "Recent Concession Agreements in the Arab Republic of Egypt," [1983] 4 *OGLTR* 61;

"Developments in Concessions and Licenses," International Bar Ass'n Section on Energy and Natural Resources, *International Energy Law* (1984) (Topic 7);

Shwadran, *The Middle East, Oil and the Great Powers* (3d Ed. revised and enlarged, 1973):

Kirchner, Schanze, *et al., Mining Ventures in Developing Countries* (1977);

Ascante, "Restructuring Transnational Mineral Agreements," 73 *Am. J. Int. Law* 335 (1979);

Tavern, "Concessions and New Types of Exploration/Production Contracts," in International Bar Ass'n, *Proceedings of the Energy Law Seminar* (organized by the Committee on Energy and Natural Resources, Section on Business Law) Topic H, Paper 1 (1979);

Adebe, "A Profile of Trends in the State Contracts for Natural Resources Development Between African Countries and Foreign Companies," 12 *N.Y.U. J. Int'l Law & Politics* 479 (1979);

Roberts, "Government Participation in the Minerals Industry," 1 *Australian Mining and Petroleum L.J.* 271 (1978);

Taverne, "Methods of Participation of Host Countries in Crude Oil Exploration and Production Ventures in the Middle East and Northern Africa," in International Bar Ass'n, *World Energy Laws* (proceedings of the IBA Seminar on World Energy Law held in Stavanger, Norway) 133 (1975);

Multinational Oil Corporations and U.S. Foreign Policy, Report to the Committee on Foreign Relations, United States Senate, by the Subcommittee on Multinational Corporations, 93d Cong., 2d Sess. (Jan. 2, 1975);

Moran, "The Evolution of Concession Agreements in Underdeveloped Countries and the United States National Interest," 7 *Vanderbilt J. of Transnational Law* 315 (1974);

Note, "From Concession to Participation: Restructuring the Middle East Oil Industry," 48 *N.Y.U. L. Rev.* 774 (1973);

Olisa, "Comparison of Legislation Affecting Foreign Exploitation of Oil and Gas Resources in Oil Producing Countries," 10 *Alberta L. Rev.* 478 (1972);

Barraz, "The Legal Status of Oil Concessions," 5 *J. of World Trade Law* 609 (1971);

Mughraby, *Permanent Sovereignty Over Oil Resources* (1966).

See also AGENCY CONTRACT; CONTRACT OF WORK; CONTRACTOR AGREEMENT; EQUITY JOINT VENTURE; LICENSE; PARTICIPATION; PETROLEUM INTERNATIONAL AGREEMENT (PIA); PRODUCTION LICENSE; PRODUCTION SHARING CONTRACT; PURE SERVICE AGREEMENT; RISK SERVICE CONTRACT; SERVICE AGREEMENT; SERVICE CONTRACT; WORK CONTRACT.

For specific aspects or provisions of concessions and similar agreements, see the following: ANCHANARRY AGREEMENT; ACT OF STATE DOCTRINE; ADDITIONAL PROFITS TAX; ADJUSTED POSTED PRICE; APQ SYSTEM; AREA FEE; BACK-IN OPTION; BALANCING; BENCHMARK CRUDE; BRIDGING CRUDE; BUY-IN OPTION; BUYBACK OIL; CALVO CLAUSE; CARRY FORWARD PROVISION; CHECKERBOARD RELINQUISHMENT; COMMERCIAL DISCOVERY BONUS; COMMON DEPOSIT CLAUSE; CONSORTIUM ACCORD; COST OIL; COST RECOVERY CLAUSE; COST RECOVERY OIL (OR GAS); CREDITED ROYALTY SYSTEM; D'ARCY CONCESSION; DEAD RENT; DEEMED INTEREST; DEEMED PURCHASE FORMULA; DESTINATION AND RESALE RESTRICTIONS; DISREPUTE CLAUSE; DIVESTMENT; DOMANIAL LAW SYSTEM; ECONOMIC DEVELOPMENT AGREEMENT (EDA); ECONOMIC INTEGRATION CLAUSE; EQUITY OIL; EXPECTED THIRD PARTY PRICE; EXPENSED ROYALTY SYSTEM; EXPLORATION LICENSE; EXPLORATION RETENTION LEASE; EXPLORATORY STAGE; EXPLORATORY TITLE; EXPROPRIATION; FADE-OUT POLICY; FIRST TIER OIL; FLAT SALE OF CRUDE OIL; FORCE MAJEURE CLAUSE; FOREIGN INVESTMENT REVIEW ACT; FOREIGN TAKEOVERS ACT; FOREIGN TAX CREDIT; FORUM SELECTION CLAUSE; GHOST TRAINING; GOVERNMENT TAKE; GUARANTEED SALES PRICE; HARDSHIP PROVISION; INCENTIVE OIL; INTERNATIONAL MARKET PRICE; INVESTMENT GUARANTEE; INVITED APPLICATION; IRANIAN CONSORTIUM; LAW STABILIZING CLAUSE; LIBYAN PREMIUM; LIBYAN PRODUCERS

AGREEMENT; LIFTING; LIFTING TOLERANCE; MAKE-UP PAYMENT; MANDATORY WORK PROGRAM; MOST FAVORED NATION CLAUSE; NATIONAL ENERGY PROGRAM (NEP); NATIONALIZATION; NOMINATIONS (IN CONCESSIONS AND PARTICIPATIONS); NONINVITED APPLICATION; NONRECURRENT FEE; OFFTAKE; OFFTAKE PRICE; OIL SERVICE COMPANY OF IRAN; OPEC; OSCO; "OUT OF BALANCE" PRODUCTION PLAN; OVERLIFT; PARTICIPATING INTEREST; PARTICIPATION CRUDE; PERFORMANCE GUARANTEE; PETRODOLLARS; PETROLEUM LICENSE; PHASE-IN CRUDE; POSTED PRICE; PRODUCTION BONUS; PROFIT OIL; REALIZED PRICE; REDLINE AGREEMENT; REFERENCE CRUDE; REFERENCE PRICE; REFERENTIAL INCORPORATION; RELINQUISHMENT CLAUSE; RENEGOTIATION CLAUSE; RETENTION LEASE; ROYALTY EXPENSING; SABBATINO AMENDMENT; SAFETY NET; SHARING AGREEMENT; SIGNATURE BONUS; SOLE RISK CLAUSE; TAX-PAID COST (TPC); TAX REFERENCE PRICE; TEHERAN AGREEMENT OF FEBRUARY 14, 1971; UNDERLIFT; UNDERLIFT/OVERLIFT PROVISION; WORK-BACK VALUATION METHOD.

Concurrent ownership

A form of divided ownership where two or more persons own fractional, undivided interests in the whole. The typical forms of concurrent ownership are tenancy in common, joint tenancy, and tenancy by the entirety. See TREATISE §§ 502–510.

See also INDUSTRY DEAL.

Concursus proceeding

A proceeding in Louisiana "in which two or more persons having competing or conflicting claims to money, property, or mortgages or privileges on property are impleaded and required to assert their respective claims contradictorily against all other parties to the proceeding." La. Code of Civil Procedure Art. 4651 (1961).

Condensate

(1) Liquid hydrocarbons recovered by conventional surface SEPARATORS (*q.v.*) from gas produced from a CONDENSATE GAS RESERVOIR (*q.v.*). Typical condensates grade from colorless liquids of high API gravity to light-colored liquids of red, green or blue cast with gravities as low as 40–45 degrees API Some condensates are indistinguishable from nonasphaltic, light crude oil, except that in the reservoir they are associated with sufficient methane at such pressure as to be found in the gas phase, until pressure is reduced.

"Condensate, as generally generally defined by fifteen states, is the liquid hydrocarbons recovered at the surface that result from condensation due to reduced pressure or temperature of petroleum hydrocarbons existing initially in a gaseous phase in the reservoir. Eleven refer to and, for the most part, adequately define condensate in the definition of crude oil, and five states do not define the term at all." 26 *Oil & Gas Compact Bull.* 55 (June 1967).

The term is defined by the Alberta Oil and Gas Conservation Act as a mixture mainly of pentanes and heavier hydrocarbons that may be contaminated with sulphur compounds, that is recovered or is recoverable at a well from an underground reservoir and that may be gaseous in its virgin reservoir state but is liquid at the conditions under which its volume is measured or estimated. R.S.A. 1970, c. 267, § 2(1)(8).

(2) The term is also used to refer to any liquid hydrocarbon recovered by surface separators from natural gas.

(3) The term is defined in § 1.16 of the Model Form for an Oil and Gas Conservation Statute (1959), approved by the Legal Committee and the Interstate Oil Compact Commission, as follows: " 'Condensate' means liquid hydrocarbons that were originally in the gaseous phase in the reservoir."

The exemption from price controls of STRIPPER WELL OIL (*q.v.*) was held not to be applicable to gas well condensate in Southern Union Production Co. v. Federal Energy Administration, 569 F.2d 1147 (Temp. Emer. Ct. of App. 1978).

The importance of distinguishing condensate from NATURAL GAS LIQUIDS (NGL) (*q.v.*) is emphasized in Seddelmeyer, "Royalties on Processed Gas," 36 *Sw. Legal Fdn. Oil & Gas Inst.* 5-1 (1985).

Syn.: NATURAL GASOLINE; DISTILLATE (older usage).

See also RETROGRADE CONDENSATION.

Condensate gas reservoir

A reservoir in which the fluids under initial reservoir pressure and temperature conditions exist in a single phase (all gas). For that reason, engineers frequently call them single phase reservoirs. The dense gas that occurs there originally has liquid in varying amounts dissolved in it, depending upon the geologic conditions of deposition and upon pressure and temperature conditions in the reservoir. It generally is believed that the fluids exist initially at or near their dew point in the reservoir and that components in certain proportions begin to condense to liquid in the reservoir when reservoir pressure declines. The formation of liquid from mixtures when pressure decreases at constant temperature is called retrograde condensation.

As both pressures and temperatures change during the producing processes, liquids may be separated from gas through retrograde and normal condensation under a wide variety of conditions. As hydrocarbon substances are taken from a natural gas-condensate reservoir (without putting gas back into the formation through a cycling process), the pressure is reduced, the temperature may be reduced slightly by expansion of the fluids, and the average composition of the material may be changed somewhat by a condensation of liquid in the reservoir and the resultant production of a gaseous fluid that is lighter than the original reservoir fluid. When liquid condenses in the reservoir, it "wets" the formation and may not come out with the gas that is produced. It follows, therefore, that if conditions of pressure, temperature, and composition can be maintained in a natural gas-condensate reservoir so that all the liquid fractions remain in solution in the gas until the gas reaches the surface, substantially all of them can be removed. If, however, conditions are induced in the natural reservoir that permit liquids to condense in the sand or porous limestone and "wet" the formation, a large proportion of the liquids will not be extracted by any ordinary means.

This type of reservoir is most commonly encountered below 5,000 feet and will typically have a pressure above 2,000 feet per sq. inch. The frequency of discovery of condensate reservoirs has increased in recent years with deeper drilling.

See also CYCLING; GAS CAP FIELD; RECYCLING; RESERVOIR; RETROGRADE CONDENSATION.

Condensate well

A well producing oil with a high gas-oil ratio.

Condensing gas drive

Syn. for ENRICHED GAS INJECTION (*q.v.*).

Conditional decree of cancellation

The form of decree granted under the equitable powers of a court which conditions nullification of the lease on the nonperformance by the lessee of designated obligations within a specified period of time. It can be contrasted with an absolute or outright cancellation decree, in that the latter allows no time for performance after entry of the decree and before cancellation. The conditional decree is not appropriate where cancellation is sought as the remedy for an invalid or terminated lease. It is often used where the lessee has breached an express or implied covenant in the lease. Examples of such a decree may be found in Sinclair Oil & Gas Co. v. Masterson, 271 F.2d 310, 11 *O.&G.R.* 632 (5th Cir. 1959), *cert. denied,* 362 U.S. 952 (1960); Sauder v. Mid-Continent Petroleum Corp., 292 U.S. 272 (1934); Gregg v. Harper-Turner Oil Co., 199 F.2d 1, 1 *O.&G.R.* 1685 (10th Cir. 1952); Humble Oil & Ref. Co. v. Romero, 194 F.2d 383, 1 *O.&G.R.* 358 (5th Cir. 1952). See TREATISE §§ 825.1, 834, 844.1.

See also ALTERNATIVE DECREE; CANCELLATION DECREE; PARTIAL CANCELLATION.

Conditional landowner

In Louisiana, a landowner whose title terminates at a particular time or upon the occurrence of a certain condition. See Louisiana Mineral Code Article 25 [R.S. 31:25 (1975)].

Conditional lease

In Alaska, a lease issued by the State on lands that have been selected by the State under laws of the United States granting lands to Alaska but on which no patent to Alaska has become effective. See the Alaska Mineral Leasing Regulations, 11 AAC 83.165.

Condition subsequent

See POWER OF TERMINATION.

Conductor pipe

See CASING.

Confidential pool

A DESIGNATED POOL (*q.v.*) other than a NONCONFIDENTIAL POOL (*q.v.*).

Confidential well

In Alberta, a well for which data has not been made available to the public concerning such matters as the well's location, elevation, current depth, status, casing, *etc.,* Alberta Oil and Gas Conservation Regulations (Alta. Reg. 151/71) § 12–150 (1)(2).

A Wisconsin statute providing for disclosure to the public of confidential mining exploration data and core samples amounted to an unconstitutional taking of private property without just compensation. Noranda Exploration, Inc. v. Ostrom, 113 Wis. 2d 612, 335 N.W.2d 596, 77 *O.&G.R.* 380 (1983).

Roberts v. Gulf Oil Corp., 147 Cal. App. 3d 770, 195 Cal. Rptr. 393 (1983), liberally construed the authority of a County assessor to obtain "raw data" and "interpretative data" relating to the oil company's properties located in the county.

Confinement of gas

Preventing the escape of gas by properly equipping a well, or in the case of an abandoned well, by plugging the well.

Confirmation well

A well drilled to prove the formation or producing zone encountered by an exploratory well.

Confiscation

This is not a word of art with a general definition which can be applied in all instances. In its most common usage the term appears to refer to depriving an owner or lessee of a fair chance to recover the oil and gas in or under this land; in this sense the term refers principally to drainage. This is the meaning of the term as used in RULE 37 (*q.v.*) of the Texas Railroad Commission as one ground for granting an exception for the drilling of a well on an undersized tract under the Texas spacing rule. Gulf Land Co. v. Atlantic Refining Co., 134 Tex. 59, 131 S. W. 2d 73 (1939).

See also EXPROPRIATION; NATIONALIZATION.

Conformance, certificate of

See CERTIFICATE OF CONFORMANCE.

Conglomerates

A type of sedimentary rock composed of pebbles of various sizes held together by cementing material. The cementing material in conglomerates is the same as that in sandstone; the only difference between the two types of rocks is the nature of the grains cemented together. Congomerates are a common form of reservoir rock.

Coning, water

See CHANNELING.

Connally Act

49 Stat. 33; 15 U.S.C.A. §§ 715 to 715L, enacted in 1935. An act regulating the interstate transportation of petroleum and petroleum products produced in violation of conservation laws. See Humble Oil & Refining Co. v. United States, 198 F.2d 753, 1 *O.&G.R.* 1677 (10th Cir. 1952); HOT OIL.

Connate water

The water present in a petroleum reservoir in the same zone occupied by oil or natural gas. This water is to be contrasted with edge water and bottom water. Connate water is a film of water around each grain of sand in granular reservoir rock and is held in place by capillary attraction. The finer the pore channels between the mineral grains of the rock, the greater the percentage of connate water in the oil and gas zones of the reservoir. Very little connate water is produced in oil or gas wells.

See also BOTTOM WATER; EDGE WATER.

Connected person

A term used with reference to United Kingdom corporation taxes as meaning a company controlled by another company or companies under common control. See Daintith and Willoughby, *A Manual of United Kingdom Oil and Gas Law* 113 (1977).

Connected well

A gas well connected to a pipeline or an oil well connected to the refinery through an unbroken series of trunk and gathering pipelines.

See UNCONNECTED WELL.

Connection order

An order of the Texas Railroad Commission requiring common carrier lines on application of the producer to connect lease batteries to the carrier (a) within a field when any common carrier is the only pipeline serving this field or common reservoir, and (b) within the general area served by a common carrier which is an affiliate or subsidiary of a common purchaser. See Street, "The New Texas Well Connection Order and Its Implications," 17 *Oil and Gas Compact Bull.* 12 (Dec. 1958).

Conselho Nacional de Petróleo

The National Petrolcum Council of Brazil. See Chester, *United States Oil Policy and Diplomacy* 196 (1983).

Consent clause

A clause in a financing agreement stipulating that certain things cannot be done without the consent of the lender. See Krohn, Kaasen, *et al.*, Norwegian Petroleum Law 4–11 (1978).

See also PROJECT FINANCING.

Consent decree (or order)

A decree or order entered by consent of both parties to settle pending litigation or dispute. Thus, consent decrees or consent orders have been extensively employed as a procedure to settle compliance proceedings throughout the period of petroleum price controls. See Bachman, "Developments and Trends in DOE Enforcement," 31 *Sw. Legal Fdn. Oil & Gas Inst.* 61 (1980); 10 C.F.R. § 205.199J (1980).

See also PIPELINE CONSENT DECREE OF 1941.

Consent party

A party to a joint venture, a joint operating agreement, or a pooling or unitization agreement, who consents in advance to participate in drilling, reworking, deepening, or plugging back of a well. See NON-CONSENT PARTY.

Conservation

The prevention of the loss of natural resources without economic or beneficial use; the prevention of waste.

Conservation is, of course, a relative matter. One method of conserving a natural resource is by complete or partial prohibition of production or consumption. The policy of setting aside petroleum reserves for the Navy was based on this theory. In a less restrictive manner, conservation of oil and gas is accomplished by prohibition of their use for particular purposes, *e.g.*, for industrial or domestic heating or as energy sources where coal, in much more abundant supply, may be utilized for the same purpose, or by prohibition of their employment in nonefficient processes or for inferior uses. In a still less restrictive sense, conservation means the attaining of maximum production from known fields by more efficient utilization of reservoir energy and by early institution of secondary recovery operations; requiring maximum possible recovery of liquid hydrocarbons from natural gas and casinghead gas and from condensate fields, with reinjection or sale of the dry gas; and limiting certain inefficient and inferior uses of natural gas or oil.

The term is defined by Zimmermann, *Conservation in the Production of Petroleum* 7 (1957) as "(1) the prevention of physical waste and (2) a sparing use of [minerals] in order to delay inevitable exhaustion."

Conservation (of oil) is defined by S. L. McDonald, "Unit Operation of Oil Reservoirs as an Instrument of Conservation," 49 *Notre Dame Law.* 305 at 309 (1973), as follows:

> "[I]t is that method of recovery and distribution of use over time which maximizes the present value of oil resources to society, expected future net proceeds from them being discounted at the prevailing rate of interest. Implied in this definition are at least three propositions: (1) oil and gas physically recoverable will be recovered for current or future use when the discounted value of them exceeds the cost of their recovery; (2) in discovered and developed reservoirs production will be postponed when the discounted value of future net proceeds thereby made possible exceeds the value of current net proceeds sacrificed; (3) exploration for new reserves will be expanded when the discounted values of expected discoveries, these to be operated in accordance with propositions (1) and (2), exceeds the necessary investment outlays. All of these propositions imply continuous cost-benefit comparisons and action to maximize net benefit to society."

See Hartman v. State Corporation Comm'n, 215 Kan. 758, 529 P.2d 134 (1974), sustaining the validity of regulations requiring the delivery to a regulatory commission of formation samples, well logs and other such information. The challenge was based on the alleged lack of authority of the commission to require such information and on the taking of property inasmuch as there was a substantial risk of loss of confidentiality of valuable information required to be supplied to the commission.

For a detailed study of conservation regulation in the petroleum industry of the United States, see S.L. McDonald, *Petroleum Conservation in the United States: An Economic Analysis* (1971).

See also W.T. Doherty, Jr., *Conservation in the United States: Minerals* (1971) (collecting many of the source documents relating to the history of conservation of oil, gas and other minerals).

See also WASTE.

Conservation Committee of California Oil Producers

A private organization which, in the absence of effective state conservation and prorationing laws and regulations, has exercised by voluntary agreement certain conservation and prorationing functions. See Comment, "Conservation and Price Fixing in the California Petroleum Industry," 29 *So. Cal. L. Rev.* 470 (1956). By an act adopted in 1955, it was declared that recommendations of the committee with respect to MER (*q.v.*) and for the intrapool distribution of such MER's are in the interest of the conservation of the oil and gas resources of the State and are lawful. Calif. Pub. Resources Code § 3450.

For a detailed study of this Committee, see Langum, "Private Limitations of Petroleum Production—California's Approach to Conservation," 17 *Stanford L. Rev.* 942 (1965).

Consideration

See SERIOUS CONSIDERATION.

Consortium

(1) As used in United Kingdom tax legislation, the term is defined in the Income and Corporation Taxes Act 1970, § 258(8), as meaning a company all of whose share capital is owned by five or fewer companies, all resident in the United Kingdom.

(2) This term is occasionally used to describe a JOINT ADVENTURE (*q.v.*). See Ryan, "Joint Adventure Agreements," 4 *Australian Mining & Petroleum L.J.* 101 at 119 (1982).

Consortium accord

The 1954 agreement between the Iranian government and a consortium of western oil companies settling the dispute arising from nationalization of oil properties in Iran and providing for exploration, development and marketing of Iranian oil. See Shwadran, *The Middle East, Oil and the Great Powers* (3d ed. revised and enlarged, 1973).

Construction contract

This term, as used in Tex. Prop. Code Ann. § 162.001(a)(1984), was held not to include a contract for drilling an oil and gas well.

Holley v. NL Industries/NL Acme Tool Co., 718 S.W.2d 813 (Tex. App., Austin, 1986, error ref'd n.r.e.).

See also DRILLING CONTRACT.

Constructive production

By virtue of express lease clauses, in some instances a lessee may pay COMPENSATORY ROYALTY (*q.v.*) or SHUT-IN ROYALTY (*q.v.*) under specified circumstances, and so long as there is timely payment of such royalty there is constructive production from the lease for habendum clause purposes.

See also West Bay Exploration Co. v. Amoco Production Co., 148 Mich. App. 197, 384 N.W.2d 407, ____ *O.&G.R.* ____ (1986) (holding that non-timely payment of shut-in royalty did not constitute constructive production, citing this MANUAL), *vacated and remanded,* 425 Mich. 878, 389 N.W.2d 865 (1986), *on remand,* 155 Mich. App. 429, 399 N.W.2d 549 (1986) (adhering to court's prior decision).

Constructive production, doctrine of

The doctrine applicable to unitized leases for purposes of extension by production under which the extension of any unitized lease by production under the unit agreement will extend all other leases committed to the same unit. Burton/Hawks Inc. v. United States, 553 F. Supp. 86 at 90 note 7, 75 *O.&G.R.* 618 at 625 note 7 (D. Utah C.D. 1982).

Consumer gas

Gas sold by an interstate gas pipeline company to a utility for resale to consumers. In the Matters of Transcontinental Gas Pipe Line Corp., 21 F.P.C. 138, 9 *O.&G.R.* 1199 (Jan. 30, 1959).

The term is employed to distinguish gas sold for resale from so-called TRANSPORTATION GAS (*q.v.*), which is gas purchased by a buyer from a producer rather than from a pipe line company and is transported by the pipeline company for a fee. Also distinguished thereby is so-called DISPLACED GAS (*q.v.*), which is transportation gas, the delivery of which has been delayed by the prior carriage of consumer gas which preempted the capacity of the pipeline. The displaced gas is carried later when capacity is available.

Contact line

See GAS-OIL CONTACT LINE; OIL-WATER CONTACT LINE.

Contemporaneous construction

An aid sometimes employed by a court in the construction of an ambiguous instrument. The construction given the instrument by the parties contemporaneously with the execution thereof is viewed as highly persuasive as to its construction at a later time in a dispute between successors to the original contracting parties. See, *e.g.*, Souders v. Montana Power Co., 203 Mont. 483, 662 P.2d 289, 79 *O.&G.R.* 278 (1983); Superior Oil Co. v. Stanolind Oil & Gas Co., 150 Tex. 317, 240 S.W.2d 281 (1951); Sunburst Exploration, Inc. v. Jensen, 635 P.2d 822, 72 *O.&G.R.* 363 (Wyo. 1981). See also Fedman, "Looking Behind the Record—An Analysis of Contemporaneous Construction Discovery," 17 *Tulsa L.J.* 448 (1982).

Lowman v. Chevron U.S.A., Inc., 748 F.2d 320, 83 *O.&G.R.* 55 (5th Cir. 1984), rejected a contemporaneous construction argument as applied to an instrument which was unambiguous.

Contiguous

For purposes of construction of this word as used in oil and gas leases and other instruments affecting interests in oil and gas, several courts have concluded that tracts of land which touch at corners are contiguous. See Elf Acquitaine, Inc. v. Amoco Production Co., 485 So.2d 1023, 89 *O.&G.R.* 491 (Miss. 1986), and cases cited therein.

Continental margin

The submerged prolongation of adjacent land extending to an average water depth of 200 meters (approximately 660 feet). Kash, *et al., Energy Under the Oceans* 365 (1973).

For a discussion of joint venture agreements for development of offshore leases, see Gremillion, "Offshore Leases in the Gulf of Mexico—Joint Venture Agreements and Related Matters," 25 *Sw. Legal Fdn. Oil & Gas Inst.* 205 (1974).

See also "Outer Continental Shelf Oil and Gas Development," Hearings before the Subcommittee on Minerals, Materials and Fuels of the Senate Committee on Interior and Insular Affairs, 93rd Cong., 2d Sess. (1974).

Continental Offshore Stratigraphic Test (COST)

A drilling project to obtain information about soil conditions before an offshore lease transaction is entered into. The drilling is done to obtain core samples of the subsoil and not to develop or remove oil or gas. See Rev. Rul. 80–64, 1980–10 I.R.B. 9, 64 *O.&G.R.* (1980); Rev. Rul. 80-342, 1980-50 I.R.B. 9, 67 *O.&G.R.* 342 (1980).

For a discussion of the late penalty imposed upon a party who wishes to participate despite failure of timely assent to participation in the project, see Shell Oil Co., 66 IBLA 397, 89 I.D. 430 (Aug. 31, 1982).

Sohio Alaska Petroleum Co., IBLA 82-619, GFS(OCS) 1983-96 (Nov. 16, 1982), sustained a decision of the Director of the Geological Survey denying an applicant the right to participate in certain COST wells without penalty as an original participant, rejecting the contention that applicant had been denied the opportunity to participate.

For a discussion of drilling of COST wells in the Georges Bank area see MacLeish, *The Struggle for Georges Bank* 101 (1985).

Continental shelf

The extension of the continental land mass into the oceans, under relatively shallow seas, as opposed to the deeper basins.

The continental shelf is defined in Article 1 of THE CONVENTION ON THE CONTINENTAL SHELF (1958) (*q.v.*) "as referring (a) to the sea-bed and the subsoil of the submarine areas adjacent to the coast but outside the area of the territorial sea, to a depth of 200 metres or, beyond that limit, to where the depth of the superjacent waters admits of the exploitation of the natural resources of the said areas; (b) to the sea-bed and subsoil of similar submarine areas adjacent to the costs of islands."

Continental Shelf Act, 1964

Statutes of England, 1964, c.29, regulating the exploration and exploitation of the continental shelf of the United Kingdom.

Continuing part

See PRODUCTION LICENSE.

Continuous drilling clause

A term occasionally employed to describe the lease provision which is referred to herein as a DRILLING OPERATIONS CLAUSE (*q.v.*). See *e.g.*, Sword v. Rains, 575 F.2d 810 61 *O.&G.R.* 339 (10th Cir. 1978); 2 Kuntz, *Oil & Gas* § 26.14 (1964).

Continuous drilling operations clause

A lease clause providing that a lease may be kept alive after the expiration of the primary term and without production by drilling operations of the type specified in the clause continuously pursued. A typical clause of this type provides:

"It is agreed that this lease shall remain in force for a term of ten years from date and as long thereafter as oil, or gas, of whatsoever nature or kind, or either of them is produced from said land or drilling operations are continued as hereinafter provided. If, at the expiration of the primary term of this lease, oil or gas is not being produced on or from said land, but lessee is then engaged in drilling or reworking operations thereon, then this lease shall continue in force so long thereafter as drilling or reworking operations are being continuously prosecuted on said land or on a drilling or development or operating unit which includes all or a part of said land; and drilling or reworking operations shall be considered to be continuously prosecuted if not more than sixty days shall elapse between the completion or abandonment of one well and the beginning of operations for the drilling or reworking of another well. If oil or gas shall be discovered and/or produced from any such well or wells drilled, being drilled or reworked at or after the expiration of the primary term of this lease, this lease shall continue in force so long thereafter as oil or gas is produced from the leased premises or from any such unit which includes all or a part of said lands."

For a discussion of the difference between the effect of this type of clause and the somewhat simpler DRILLING OPERATIONS CLAUSE, see that title.

See also St. Louis Royalty Co. v. Continental Oil Co., 193 F.2d 778, 1 *O.&G.R.* 538 (5th Cir. 1952); TREATISE §§ 617–618.9; THIRTY DAY-SIXTY DAY CLAUSE.

Continuous flow

Flow of oil from a well without interruption, the energy source being natural reservoir energy. When reservoir pressure is greater than that necessary to support a column of the well fluid extending from the reservoir rock to the surface, the flow from the well is continuous.

Continuous operations clause

A term occasionally employed to describe the lease provision which is referred to herein as a DRILLING OPERATIONS CLAUSE (*q.v.*) [See *e.g.*, Sword v. Rains, 575 F.2d 810, 61 *O.&G.R.* 339 (10th Cir. 1978)] and also occasionally employed to describe the lease provision which is referred to herein as a CONTINUOUS DRILLING OPERATIONS CLAUSE (*q.v.*) [see *e.g.*, 2 Kuntz, *Oil & Gas* § 26.12 (1964)].

Contour map

See CONTOURS.

Contours

A line on which every point is at the same elevation above or below sea level. Structure contour maps are used extensively by geologists and geophysicists to depict subsurface conditions.

Contraband oil

"[P]etroleum which, or any constituent part of which, was produced, transported, or withdrawn from storage in excess of the amounts permitted to be produced, transported, or withdrawn from storage under the laws of a State or under any regulation or order prescribed thereunder by any board, commission, officer, or other duly constituted agency of such State, or any of the products of such petroleum." 15 U.S.C.A. § 715a.

Contract area

The area affected by an AREA OF MUTUAL INTEREST AGREEMENT (*q.v.*), a JOINT OPERATING AGREEMENT (*q.v.*), or other agreement relating to the acquisition, exploration or development of minerals.

Contract carriage arrangement

See PURCHASE-CONTRACT CARRIAGE ARRANGEMENT.

Contract carriage obligation

See COMMON CARRIER.

Contract date vintaging

A system for determining the permissible price to be charged for natural gas subject to price control regulations under which price was based on VINTAGE (*q.v.*) of gas [*viz.*, as NEW GAS (*q.v.*) or OLD GAS (*q.v.*)] and the determination whether the gas was new or old was based on the date of sale of the gas in question. City of Farmington v. Amoco Gas Co., 568 F. Supp. 1265, 78 *O.&G.R.* 504 (D. N.M. 1983), *aff'd*, 777 F.2d 554 (10th Cir. 1985).

See also WELL COMMENCEMENT DATE VINTAGING.

Contract for extension of lease

An agreement extending the primary term of a previously executed lease.

Contract landman

A person employed to obtain oil and gas leases. A contract landman has been declared to be an employee for purposes of federal employment taxes. Rev. Rul. 65–277, I.R.B. 1965–47, 54 (Nov. 22, 1965).

See also LANDMAN.

Contract leaseman

"A person who engages in the acquisition of oil and gas leases for the account or accounts of various independent producers and, in addition thereto, also negotiates and acquires oil and gas leases for his own account which he then sells to a producing oil and gas company at a profit." Aladdin Oil Corp. v. Perluss, 230 Cal. App.2d 603, 41 Cal. Rptr. 239 at 241 (1964).

See also LANDMAN.

Contract of affreightment

The term customarily applied to a contract for the carriage of oil by sea. See "The Tonnage Contract," [1982] 1 *OGLTR* 32.

See also OIL CHARTER; SHORT DELIVERY (0.5% ALLOWANCE) ISSUE.

Contract of work

The term applied to certain agreements between a host government and a foreign oil company having certain of the characteristics of a CONCESSION (*q.v.*). See Hossain, *Law and Policy in Petroleum Development* 159 (1979).

The contract of work has been employed in Indonesia since 1967 to authorize a mining company to conduct operations on behalf of the Government or the state enterprise. "The mining company has full responsibility for its operations and assumes all related risk. Unlike the situation with production sharing agreements . . ., the mining company has full control and management of its operations." See Herron, "Foreign Participation in Mineral Development and Operations in Indonesia," *Rocky Mt. Min. L. Fdn. International Minerals and Operations Inst.* 17–5 (1974) (discussing certain details of the contract of work and problems of negotiation).

Contracted reserves

Natural gas reserves dedicated to the fulfillment of gas purchase contracts. American Gas Institute Bureau of Statistics, *Glossary for the Gas Industry* 13.

Contractor agreement

An agreement between a host country and an oil company under which the oil company engages in exploration and development under a contract for an agreed fee rather than as a principal under a concession. These agreements "vary considerably from nation to nation and even within a nation. In some instances the contractor assumes little risk; he simply performs a specific task for a prescribed fee. In other instances, the contractor is paid in a share of the oil he finds, if any, thus sharing part of the risk. In still other instances, he must sell all the oil he produces to the government. But, in some cases, he has almost all the prerogatives of a concession owner except the name, being free to sell any oil he produces to any customer he desires at any price he can obtain, paying the government a specified percentage of profits." Jacoby, *Multinational Oil* 118 (1974).

For specific aspects or provisions of agreements of this kind see the entries under CONCESSION.

Contract price

For purposes of section 105(c) of the NATURAL GAS POLICY ACT OF 1978 (*q.v.*) this term is said to mean the total amount of proceeds paid by the purchaser to obtain the subject gas, and, therefore, the term includes all proceeds paid or payable by the seller even if specifically earmarked as reimbursement for state severance taxes or production-related costs. Final Regulations Under Section 105 and 105(b) of the Natural Gas Policy Act of 1978, FERC Order No. 68 (Jan. 18, 1980), 20 F.P.S. 5–12.

Contract pricing area

The area in which a MOST FAVORED NATION CLAUSE (*q.v.*) is operative. Matters of Sun Oil Co., 17 F.P.C. 174 at 178, 6 *O.&G.R.* 1422 at 1428 (Sept. 11, 1956).

Contract system

A system developed in Russia along the western coast of the Caspian Sea near Baku for the development of oil.

> "Ownership of land and mineral rights resided in the hands of the czar. Under the contract system the government granted a monopoly for exploitation of a specific plot for a period of four years. The contract could be revoked without notice by the czarist administration and there were no options for renewal. Under these circumstances, those working the oil pits were primarily interested in maximizing current production."

Thus the contract system was similar in its effect to the RULE OF CAPTURE (*q.v.*) in the United States. Danielsen, *The Evolution of OPEC* 99 (1982).

Contract theory of pooling

A theory concerning the nature of interests arising from a pooling or unitization agreement. Under this theory the relationship of the parties is treated as one arising from a contract without a transfer of interests in land. The matter is discussed in Myers, *The Law of Pooling and Unitization* § 13.02 (2d Ed. 1967). See TREATISE §§ 929–930.10.

See also CROSS-ASSIGNMENT; POOLING.

Contractual cap

A provision of a GAS PURCHASE CONTRACT (*q.v.*) imposing a limit on the increase in price during the term of the contract, *e.g.*, (1) a regulatory-pass through cap, stating that the pipeline will not be required to pay a price higher than that which the pipeline is allowed by its regulatory agency to pass through to its customers; (2) an alternate fuel cap, protecting the purchaser from paying more than the MMBtu equivalent of some alternate fuel, usually No. 2 Fuel Oil or No. 6 Fuel Oil; or (3) a market cap, based on some analysis of the pipeline's market for resale of the gas being purchased. See Watson, "The Natural Gas Policy Act of 1978 and Gas Purchase Contracts," 27 *Rocky Mt. Min. L. Inst.* 1407 at 1426 (1982).

Contractual unit

In Louisiana, a unit specifically created by joint agreement of the mineral lessee and the owners of all the other mineral or royalty interests in the land in question, as distinguished from a DECLARED UNIT (*q.v.*), *viz.*, one formed by the lessee acting under the provisions of a lease pooling clause. See Humble Oil & Refining Co. v. Jones, 157 So. 2d 110, 19 *O.&G.R.* 545 (La. App. 1963), *writ refused,* 245 La. 568, 159 So. 2d 284, 19 *O.&G.R.* 559 (1964).

See also CONVENTIONAL UNIT.

Contribution agreement

An agreement to contribute to the cost of drilling a well. The agreement, usually in the form of a letter signed by the contributor and the party planning to drill the well may be in the form of a D ONATION LETTER (*q.v.*) or of a PURCHASE LETTER (*q.v.*).

See also TEST WELL CONTRIBUTION AGREEMENT.

Contribution clause

A clause in a JOINT OPERATING AGREEMENT (*q.v.*) providing in substance as follows:

> "If any party receives, while this agreement is in effect, a contribution of cash toward the drilling of a well or any other operation on the subject leases such contribution shall be paid to the party or parties who conducted the drilling or other operation and same shall be applied against the cost of drilling or other operation. If the contribution be in form of acreage, the party to whom the contribution is made shall promptly execute an assignment of the acreage, without warranty of title, to the other parties who participated in such operation for which the acreage contribution was made to support in the proportion of their interest therein. Each party shall promptly notify the other parties of all acreage and money contributions it may obtain in support of any well or other operation on the Joint Area."

See Superior Oil Co. v. Cox, 307 So. 2d 350, 50 *O.&G.R.* 323 (La. 1975) (holding that clause was inapplicable under facts of instant case to a contribution made after the drilling of a well rather than as an incentive or compensation for drilling a well); Hazlett, "Drafting of Joint Operation Agreements," 3 *Rocky Mt. Min. L. Inst.* 277 at 299 (1957).

Contributor

The person who contributes money toward drilling costs or who agrees to make a contribution toward drilling costs in a PURCHASE LETTER (*q.v.*) or DONATION LETTER (*q.v.*).

Control well

A well capable of producing which is within a block or project and which is completed nearer than the least side dimension of its drilling spacing unit to a portion of the boundary or project which is also a boundary of a drilling spacing unit containing a producing well outside the block or project. Alberta Oil and Gas Conservation Regulations (Alta. Reg. 151/71) § 1–020 (2) (5).

Controlled crude oil

Crude oil subject to a first sale ceiling price under section 4(a) of the EMERGENCY PETROLEUM ACT OF 1973 (*q.v.*)

Controlled gravity drainage

A method of recovering additional oil from fields which are no longer producible by conventional drilling techniques. The method, said to have been successfully employed in Europe and the Soviet Union, requires sinking a shaft to a level slightly below the reservoir, then tunneling beneath the field. Collecting pipes are inserted in the bottom of the reservoir, and the oil is pumped to the surface. CCH, *Energy Management* p. 4 (March 6, 1984).

Conventionalization of lease-sale

The process by which a lease-sale transaction which did not survive the test of public convenience and necessity for certification by the Federal Power Commission was modified so as to more nearly conform to a normal gas-sale contract. See Public Service Comm'n of the State of N.Y. v. Federal Power Comm'n, 543 F.2d 757 at 779–787 (D.C. Cir. 1974).

Conventional life estate

A life estate created by a volitional act, as distinguished from a LEGAL LIFE ESTATE which arises by operation of law, *e.g.*, under local law creating a dower, curtesy or homestead interest.

Conventional gamma ray-gamma ray log

See GAMMA RAY-GAMMA RAY LOGGING.

Conventional license

The term used by K.W. Dam, *Oil Resources* 14 (1976), to describe the conventional CONCESSION (*q.v.*) agreement between a host nation and a foreign oil company.

Conventional sales contract

A contract for the sale of gas wherein the producer promises to sell all the gas produced from either specific wells or specific fields. Under a so-called WARRANTY CONTRACT (*q.v.*), on the other hand, the producer agrees to sell a specific amount of gas and the gas delivered in satisfaction of this obligation may come from fields or sources outside of the designated fields. Shell Oil Co. v. Federal Power Comm'n, 531 F.2d 1324 at note 6, *petition for rehearing denied,* 535 F.2d 957 (5th Cir. 1976).

See also GAS PURCHASE CONTRACT.

Conventional unit

In Louisiana, a unit established by contract as distinguished from a compulsory unit.

See also CONTRACTUAL UNIT; DECLARED UNIT.

Conventional usufruct

A USUFRUCT (*q.v.*) created by a volitional act, as by a donation *inter vivos* or *mortis causa.*

Convention of the Continental Shelf (1958)

An international agreement emerging from the First United Nations Conference on the Law of the Sea held at Geneva in 1958 which came into force on June 10, 1964. About fifty States are parties to the Convention but a sizable number of States, including some European States, have not become parties and some signatory States have entered reservations in respect to particular articles of the Convention. The Convention (1) declares that the coastal State exercises exclusive rights over the continental shelf for the purpose of exploring it and exploiting its natural resources, (2) provides for certain restrictions of the exercise of such rights (*e.g.,* impeding the laying or maintenance of submarine cables or pipelines on the continental shelf, unjustifiable interference with navigation, fishing, or the conservation of the living resources of the sea), and (3) establishes a scheme for determining the boundary of the continental shelf appertaining to two or more States whose coasts are opposite each other.

Conversion clause

A clause in an assignment or other instrument providing for the conversion, either automatically or at the option of one of the parties, of one interest granted or reserved into another interest (*e.g.*, conversion of an overriding royalty or net profits interest into a share of the working interest).

See also CONVERTIBLE INTEREST; DRILL SITE ARRANGEMENT.

Conversion factors

Energy equivalents for various fuels commonly used.

Coal:

Anthracite—25.4 million Btu/ton

Bituminous—26.2 million Btu/ton

Sub-bituminous—19.0 million Btu/ton

Lignite—13.4 million Btu/ton

Petroleum:

Crude petroleum—5.60 million Btu/bbl (42 gal)

Residual fuel oil—6.29 million Btu/bbl

Distillate fuel oil—5.83 million Btu/bbl

Gasoline (including aviation)—5.25 million Btu/bbl

Jet fuel (kerosene type)—5.67 million Btu/bbl

Jet fuel (naphtha type)—5.36 million Btu/bbl

Asphalt and Road oil—6.64 million Btu/bbl

Natural gas:

Dry—1031 Btu/cu. ft. at STP

Wet—1103 Btu/cu. ft. at STP

Liquids (avg)—4.1 million Btu/bbl.

The energy content of most fuels can vary depending on their source and composition.

APPROXIMATE CONVERSION FACTORS FOR CRUDE OIL

	Into—				
	Metric tons	Long tons	Short tons	Barrels	Kiloliters (cubic meters)
From—	Multiply by—				
Metric tons	1	0.984	1.102	7.33	1.16
Long tons	1.016	1	1.120	7.45	1.18
Short tons	.907	.893	1	6.65	1.00
Barrels	.136	.134	.150	1	.159
Kiloliters (cubic meters)	.863	.849	.951	6.29	1

Source: Energy Facts, Committee Print prepared for the Subcommittee on Energy of the House Committee on Science and Astronautics, 93rd Cong., 1st Sess. (Nov. 1973).

To convert metric tons per year into a rough estimate of barrels per day, divide the tons-per-year figure by 50.

See also BTU; MEASUREMENT UNITS.

Convertible interest

A varicty of (usually nonoperating) interests in oil and gas or other minerals which, at the option of its owner or upon the happening of a specified event, may be changed into another (usually operating) interest. Thus, by the terms of an instrument creating an overriding royalty, it may be provided that at the owner's option, after the completion of a well, the override may be converted into another interest, *e.g.*, a specified undivided share of the working interest. A FARM-OUT AGREEMENT (*q.v.*) may provide for payment of an overriding royalty to the FARMOR (*q.v.*) until the FARMEE (*q.v.*) has recovered costs after which the overriding royalty is convertible automatically, or at the option of the farmor, to a share of the working interest. See, *e.g.*, the following:

Aminoil USA, Inc. v. OKC Corp., 629 F.Supp. 647, 90 *O.&G.R.* 234, (E.D. La. 1986) (letter agreement provided for conversion of an overriding royalty to a net profits interest when the farmed-out interest reached a "net profits status"; the court concluded that the farmee was not entitled to charge interest, actual or imputed, or its legal expenses incurred in an action between the farmor and farmee against the net profits account), *aff'd sub nom.* Phillips Oil Co. v. OKC Corp., 812 F.2d 265, ____ *O.&G.R.* ____ (5th Cir. 1987);

Groebl v. Walker, 567 S.W.2d 622, 61 *O.&G.R.* 408 (Tex. Civ. App. 1978, error ref'd n.r.e.) (override of 1/8 of 7/8 convertible into a 1/2 working interest when operator recovered costs; the court concluded that the operator was not entitled to interest on the sums advanced as a recoverable expense);

Inexco Oil Co. v. Crutcher-Tufts Corp., 389 F. Supp. 1032, 51 *O.&G.R.* 321 (W.D. La. 1975) (upon recovery of costs by farmee, farmor's reserved 5% overriding royalty at option of the farmor would terminate and 35% of the leasehold interests previously assigned would revert to the farmor, free and clear of costs);

Vreeland v. Federal Power Comm'n, 528 F.2d 1343, 54 *O.&G.R.* 397 (5th Cir. 1976) (farmor's 1/8 overriding royalty could be converted to a 1/4 operating interest).

See also the following:

Act Oils Ltd. v. Pacific Petroleums Ltd., 27 D.L.R.3d 444, [1972] 4 W.W.R. 23 (Alberta Sup. Ct. 1972), *appeal dism'd,* 60 D.L.R.3d 658 (Alberta Sup. Ct., App. Div. 1975), *application for leave to appeal denied,* 61 D.L.R.3d 316, [1976] 1 W.W.R. 369 (Alberta Sup. Ct., App. Div. 1975), *leave to appeal refused,* [1975] 2 S.C.R. vii (Supreme Court of Canada 1975) (convertible carried interest);

Sinclair Canada Oil Co. v. Pacific Petroleums Ltd., 61 D.L.R.2d 437 (Alberta Sup. Ct. 1967), *appeal dismissed,* 67 D.L.R.2d 519 (Alberta Sup. Ct., App. Div. 1968), *appeal dismissed,* [1969] S.C.R. 394, 2 D.L.R.3d 338 (Supreme Court of Canada 1969).

Care is required in the drafting of instruments creating convertible interests to avoid the possibility of future dispute as to the precise event or events triggering the convertible right. See, *e.g.*, Energy Oils, Inc. v. Montana Power Co., 626 F.2d 731, 68 *O.&G.R.* 255 (9th Cir. 1980).

Conversion of an overriding royalty into a share of the working interest did not effect a withdrawal of natural gas from the regulated interstate market without the approval of the Federal Power Commission or its successor, the Federal Energy Regulatory Commission, nor did it entitle the owner of the interest to claim a NEW GAS (*q.v.*) classification. See Atlantic Richfield Co. v. Federal Power Comm'n, 585 F.2d 943 (9th Cir. 1978); Phillips Petroleum Co. v. Federal Power Comm'n, 556 F.2d 466, 59 *O.&G.R.* 242 (10th Cir. 1977).

For discussions of convertible interests, see the following:

Westin, "Relationship Between the Rule Against Perpetuities and the Convertible Override," 35 *O.&G. Tax Q.* 238 (1986);

Schenkkan, "Convertible Oil and Gas Interests After Southland Royalty and Phillips," 24 *Rocky Mt. Min. L. Inst.* 547 (1978);

Cook, "The Disposition of Oil and Gas Interests," a paper delivered before the A.B.A. Section of Real Property, Probate and Trust Law, July 12, 1957;

Appleman, "Use of the Partnership as an Instrumentality in Oil Operations," 14 *N.Y.U. Inst. on Fed. Tax.* 519 at 526, 528 (1956);

TREATISE § 426.

For a discussion of certain convertible interest provisions in Australian joint venture agreements, see Nicholls, "Some Practical Problems of Joint Venture Agreements," 3 *Australian Mining and Petroleum L.J.* 41 (1981).

See also BACK-IN FARM-OUT; BACK-IN PROVISION; BACK-IN RIGHT; DRILL SITE ARRANGEMENT; EQUITY KICKER; OPTION TO EXCHANGE.

Convertible override farm-out

A transaction which "is essentially the same arrangement as the deferred working interest type of farmout, except, in lieu of a deferred working interest, the farmor retains an overriding royalty which may be, at the option of the farmor, converted into a share of the working interest on the farmee's payout. Therefore, this type of farmout is also a subleasing transaction.

"As in the deferred working interest type farmout, the farmee should be entitled to deduct all IDCs which he pays, including that portion attributable to the fraction of the working interest which the farmor may acquire by conversion of his overriding royalty. The conversion of the farmor's retained overriding royalty into a portion of the working interest is generally viewed as a like-kind exchange which results in no recognition of income to either party under Section 1031 of the Code. However, if exchange treatment is followed to its logical conclusion, potential Section 1245 recapture attributable to the interest in the equipment received by the farmor would be triggered in an amount up to the fair market value of the non-Section 1245 property (the overriding royalty) received by the farmee in the exchange transaction." Crichton, "Recapture of Intangibles Under Section 1254," 30 *Sw. Legal Fdn. Oil & Gas Inst.* 509 at 539 (1979).

See also BACK-IN FARM-OUT; FARM-OUT AGREEMENT.

Cooperative agreement

An agreement or plan of development and operation for the recovery of oil and gas made subject thereto in which separate ownership units are independently operated without allocation of production. 30 C.F.R. § 226.2(b) (1978).

Cooperative development

Independent operation of separate ownership units without allocation of production under an agreement or plan of development and operation for the recovery of oil or gas entered into by the owners of working interests (and sometimes by owners of royalty interests) in separate tracts.

Cooperative plan of development

A plan or agreement for cooperative development of separately owned tracts or units.

Coowners' group

A term used colloquially to describe a variety of groups formed for the financing of the acquisition, exploration and development of oil and gas properties. See TREATISE § 503.3.

See also DRILLING FUND.

COPAS accounting procedure

An accounting procedure prepared by Council of Petroleum Accountants Societies of North America (COPAS).

For discussions of this accounting procedure, see the following:

Heaney, "The Joint Operating Agreement, the AFE and COPAS—What They Fail to Provide," 29 *Rocky Mt. Min. L. Inst.* 743 (1983);

Dutton, "Accounting Procedures: Contracts or Controversies," 19 *Rocky Mt. Min. L. Inst.* 117 (1974);

Cook, "The Accounting Procedure of Joint Operating Agreements," 12 *Sw. Legal Fdn. Nat'l Inst. for Petroleum Landmen* 193 (1971);

Kennedy, "Joint Venture Accounting, A La COPAS—1962," 6 *Sw. Legal Fdn. Nat'l Inst. for Petroleum Landmen* 157 (1965).

See also ACCOUNTING METHODS.

COPE

The Compagnie Orientale des Petroles d'Egypte. See Shwadram, *The Middle East, Oil and Great Powers* 484 (3d Ed. revised and enlarged, 1973).

Core

A solid column of rock, usually from two to four inches in diameter, taken as a sample of an underground formation. It is common practice to take cores from wells in the process of being drilled. Cores may also be taken independent of drilling wells, as an incident of a geological study of an area to determine its oil and gas prospects.

Core is also used as a verb, meaning to take a core. See CORING.

Core analysis

Laboratory examination of geological samples taken from the well bore to determine the capacity of the formation to contain oil and gas, the possibility of oil and gas passing through the formation, the degree of saturation of the formation with oil, gas, and water, and for other purposes.

Core bit

See BIT, CORE.

Core drilling

See CORING.

Core hole

A "hole drilled with slim hole rig. Core is not necessarily taken today, as common practice is to use a rock bit and run an electric log." Report of the Committee on Regulatory Practices for Stratigraphic Test Holes, 17 *Interstate Oil Compact Bull.* 43 (Dec. 1958).

Core record

A record which shows the depth, character, and fluid content of cores obtained, so far as determined. Cal. Pub. Res. Code § 3212 (1972).

Core test

One of the methods of subsurface geology. Core samples are taken just below the top soil to determine the nature of the formations and, so far as possible, their structure. This type of coring differs from ordinary oil well coring in that it is not incident to the drilling of a well and the cores are taken at shallow depths.

Coring

The act of taking a core. A core bit is attached to the end of the drill pipe; this tool then cuts a column of rock from the formation being penetrated; the core is then removed and tested for evidences of oil or gas, and its characteristics (porosity, permeability, *etc.*) are determined. Coring tools permit the taking of full-hole cores (*i.e.*, a large diameter core), small-diameter cores, and side-wall cores. Many wells are now cored all the way through potentially productive formations.

Corner target area

A TARGET AREA (*q.v.*) for a new oil and gas well located in the corner (rather than in the center) of a DRILLING SPACING UNIT (*q.v.*) under the provisions of Alberta Energy Resources Conservation Board Order No. SU 800, effective June 1, 1974, so as to minimize interference between petroleum and agricultural operations in irrigated areas.

Corporación Venezolana del Petróleo (CVP)

A Venezuelan oil corporation established in 1960. See Chester, *United States Oil Policy and Diplomacy* 154 (1983).

Corporate rollup

The transfer by some part of the public to a new corporation of limited or general partnership interests and fractional operating or nonoperating interests. See Mann, "Financing Oil and Gas Operations—Recent Developments," 33 *Sw. Legal Fdn. Oil & Gas Inst.* 407 at 427 (1982):

> "The purpose of the rollup primarily is to permit the corporation to obtain control immediately over a group of diverse assets valuable and sizable enough to support financing on more favorable terms than were available to the properties separately."

See also ROLL-UP PROVISION.

Corporeal estate

A possessory interest in land. In some states (*e.g.*, Texas), minerals are capable of corporeal ownership separate from the ownership of the surface. In other states (*e.g.*, Oklahoma) a severed interest in minerals is an incorporeal or nonpossessory interest in land. The difference in the classification of the severed interest as corporeal or incorporeal may have important legal consequences with regard to the following: (1) ABANDONMENT (*q.v.*); (2) remedies, such as ejectment and partition; (3) state taxation; (4) procedure, such as jurisdiction and venue; and (5) adverse possession. See TREATISE §§ 210–211. For many important purposes, *e.g.*, the construction of a lease or deed, or the application of the Rule of Capture, this classification is without significance.

See also INCORPOREAL INTEREST.

Correction lease

A lease executed to correct a mistaken provision, *e.g.*, description, in a previously executed lease. Care must be taken when a correction lease has been executed in making timely payment of delay rentals. In Humble Oil & Refining Co. v. Mullican, 144 Tex. 609, 192 S.W.2d 770 (1946), a correction lease was executed to rectify a mistake in the original lease. The court held that the first and not the correction lease determined the anniversary date for delay rental payments.

Correlative rights

This terms is defined by Nev. Rev. Stat. § 522.020(1) as follows:

> "[T]he opportunity afforded, so far as it is practicable to do so, to the owner of each property in a pool to produce without waste his just and equitable share of the oil or gas, or both, in the pool; being an amount, so far as can be practically determined, and so far as can practicably be obtained without waste, substantially in the proportion that the quantity of recoverable oil or gas, or both, under such property bears to the total recoverable oil or gas, or both, in the pool, and for such purposes to use his just and equitable share of the reservoir energy."

There appear to be two aspects of the doctrine of correlative rights: (1) as a corollary of the rule of capture, each person has a right to produce oil from his land and capture such oil or gas as may be produced from his well, and (2) a right of the land owner to be protected against damage to a common source of supply and a right to a fair and equitable share of the source of supply.

When a legislature or administrative body regulates production practices to protect against waste, it may also regulate to insure an equitable distribution of the source of supply. There is some dispute over the power of the state to regulate production practices to insure an equitable distribution of the source of supply, apart from waste. See TREATISE § 204.6.

In Texaco Inc. v. Railroad Comm'n, 583 S.W.2d 307, 63 *O.&G.R.* 346 (Tex. 1979), the court concluded that the correlative right of a property owner to the opportunity to produce his fair share of oil from a common reservoir was qualified by both the Rule of Capture and the Commission's authority to prevent waste. In the instant case the court sustained the validity of a bonus allowable for water injection under a program which would increase the ultimate recovery of oil from a reservoir while causing net uncompensated drainage from some tracts.

Big Piney Oil & Gas Co. v. Wyoming Oil and Gas Conservation Comm'n, 715 P.2d 557, ____ *O.&G.R.* ____ (Wyo. 1986), concluded that the power of the Commission to protect correlative rights justified issuance of an order restricting gas cap production from a lease when such production caused migration of oil from adjoining premises, which oil became nonrecoverable after migration, and when the gas cap producer had produced more gas from the common pool than was estimated to have been under its lease originally.

Seal v. Corporation Comm'n, 725 P.2d 278, 90 *O.&G.R.* 500 (Okla. 1986), *app. dism'd for want of a properly presented federal question sub nom.* Amerada Hess Corp. v. Comm'n, ____ U.S. ____, 107 S.Ct. 1265 (1987), concluded (one judge dissenting) that the doctrine of correlative rights was not limited to mutual duties and obligations of owners of a common source of supply, but it extended to regulation of the allocation of benefit derived from production from a single well. The court sustained the validity of 1983 legislation permitting all owners of an interest in a gas well to share ratable in revenues from the sale of the well's production, regardless of who may be producing it.

This definition was quoted in Amoco Production Co. v. North Dakota Industrial Comm'n, 307 N.W.2d 839 at 842, n.4, 70 *O.&G.R.* 283 at 289, n.4 (N.D. 1981). See also Hystad v. Industrial Comm'n, 389 N.W.2d 590, 90 *O.&G.R.* 260 (N.D. 1986).

For a discussion of the correlative rights doctrine in Oklahoma see Haymaker v. Oklahoma Corporation Comm'n, 731 P.2d 1008, ____ *O.&.G.R.* ____ (Okla. App. 1986) (holding that Commission order denying application for additional well in 80-acre spacing unit was not supported by substantial evidence).

For a collection of definitions of this term, see Gilmore v. Oil and Gas Conservation Comm'n, 642 P.2d 773, 75 *O.&G.R.* 172 (Wyo. 1982).

See also ACCOMMODATION DOCTRINE; FAIR SHARE OF OIL OR GAS IN PLACE; RULE OF CAPTURE.

Correlative rights theory

The theory adopted by the courts in a number of states that all land owners whose tracts overlay a producing formation have correlative rights in the formation. This theory is frequently termed the "qualified ownership" theory. See TREATISE § 203.2. The principal states adopting this theory in general are California, Indiana, Louisiana and Oklahoma. The interest created in a mineral grantee in a state following this theory is a *profit à prendre.*

See also NON-OWNERSHIP THEORY; OWNERSHIP IN PLACE THEORY; OWNERSHIP OF STRATA THEORY; QUALIFIED OWNERSHIP THEORY.

Corridor acreage

The acreage included within a corridor of land surrounding the boundaries of a lease required to be transferred back to the Crown as Crown reserves when an operator has selected a lease out of his permit area. The corridor acreage no longer forms part of the permit area under the control of the operator and ownership of the permit holder but it is available for subsequent sale at public auction to bidders who might include the operator. Pine Pass Oil & Gas Ltd. v. Pacific Petroleum Ltd., 70 D.L.R.2d 196 at 199–200 (British Columbia Supreme Court 1968).

For a description of the leasing system resulting in Corridor acreage, see CHECKERBOARD LEASING.

COST

CONTINENTAL OFFSHORE STRATIGRAPHIC TEST (*q.v.*).

Cost allocation methods

See ACCOUNTING METHODS.

Cost bank

Under the price control system applicable to petroleum products, refiners and dealers were entitled to a dollar-for-dollar pass through of product and nonproduct costs. Because of seasonal or other marketing factors, they were sometimes unable to recoup costs that they would otherwise be permitted to pass on to their customers. Under such circumstances, sellers could "bank" such costs to be passed on when market conditions permitted. See 10 C.F.R. § 212.83(e) and (f) (1980). The operation of the cost bank is discussed in Task Force on

Reform of Federal Energy Administration, *Federal Energy Administration Regulation* 20 *et seq.* (MacAvoy ed. 1977).

In settling compliance proceedings during the period of price control, the Department of Energy relied to a considerable extent on consent orders. Some of these orders called for reductions in the refiner's bank of unrecovered increased costs. "On a dollar-for-dollar basis, a bank reduction is more favorable to the firms than a refund obligation, since market conditions and subsequent decontrol may prevent the firms from ever exhausting their banks. For this reason, however, DOE is likely to require a relatively greater bank reduction in exchange for a reduced refund obligation during consent order negotiations." Bachman, "Developments and Trends in DOE Enforcement," 31 *Sw. Legal Fdn. Oil & Gas Inst.* 61 at 71, n. 41 (1980).

See also PRICE CONTROL OF OIL, GAS AND PETROLEUM PRODUCTS.

Cost bearing interest

Syn. for EXPENSE BEARING INTEREST (*q.v.*).

Cost company

"[A] corporation with nominal capital which holds title to a mineral interest and related production and processing facilities; the shareholders agree to take the product of the corporation pro rata in accordance with their shares. The stockholders are deemed for federal income tax purposes to have the economic interest in the minerals and the 'equitable ownership interest' in the nonmineral assets of the cost company. The cost company files a return showing no income or deductions, and its shareholders report their pro rata shares of all items of income, deduction, loss, and credit of the cost company." Hunt and Camp, "Project Financing—Oil and Gas Venture," 27 *Sw. Legal Fdn. Oil & Gas Inst.* 215 at 239 (1976).

Rev. Rul 77–1, 1977–1 C.B. 161, held that a cost company should be treated as a separate taxpayer; since that ruling, cost companies have not generally been utilized. See Maxfield and Houghton, *Taxation of Mining Operations* §§ 2.01[1][b], 10.01 (1981); Bruen and Taylor, *Federal Income Taxation of Oil and Gas Investments* ¶ 1.02[3] (1980).

Cost depletion

See DEPLETION, COST

Cost equalization plan

A pricing system formulated by the Federal Energy Administration commonly known as the ENTITLEMENT PROGRAM (*q.v.*).

Cost of exploration and development

An element in the determination of whether rates of a natural gas producer are just and reasonable. In Forest Oil Corp. v. Federal Power Comm'n, 263 F.2d 622, 10 *O.&G.R.* 242 (5th Cir. 1959), the court concluded that "this item represents the cost of finding potential fields as well as the drilling of the dry wells that seems to be a necessary part of any continuing oil or gas business."

Cost of Living Council (CLC)

The agency that administered the wage and price controls issued under the ECONOMIC STABILIZATION ACT OF 1970 (ESA) (*q.v.*). See Aman, "Institutionalizing the Energy Crisis: Some Structural and Procedural Lessons," 65 *Cornell L. Rev.* 491 (1980).

Cost of production method

A method of determining the value of company produced gas for rate purposes. Under this method the natural gas in place and the properties and equipment used in producing it are included in the rate base along with the Company's other utility properties at the original cost of the properties less the accrued depreciation and depletion reserves. In addition to a return on such production properties, there are included in the costs of service, all operating expenses chargeable to production. All expenses associated with the production of liquid hydrocarbons, such as natural gasoline, are included in expenses and corresponding credits are made to expenses for the sale of the products extracted. Such income taxes as are actually paid by the Company are included in allowable expenses. Savings in Federal and State income taxes arising from the statutory allowance of percentage depletion and intangible well drilling costs are distributed to functions, thus reducing the allowable expense of each function. See Matter of Arkansas Louisiana Gas Co., 5 *O.&G.R.* 127 at 136 (Ark. Public Serv. Comm'n 1955), *rev'd sub nom.* Acme Brick Co. v. Arkansas Public Service Comm'n, 227 Ark. 436, 299 S.W.2d 208, 6 *O.&G.R.* 1395 (1957).

See also ACCOUNTING METHODS; FAIR FIELD PRICE METHOD; RATE BASE APPROACH.

Cost oil

That share of oil produced which is applied to the recovery of costs under a PRODUCTION SHARING CONTRACT (*q.v.*).

See also PROFIT OIL.

Cost recovery clause

The clause in certain CONCESSION (*q.v.*) and similar contracts allowing the foreign petroleum company to deduct all or some specified share of development costs from the oil produced before the host country receives its share of the petroleum products produced. *The Wall Street Journal,* March 5, 1982, p. 7, col. 3.

Cost recovery oil (or gas)

That share of oil or gas produced which is applied to the recovery of actual operating costs under a SERVICE CONTRACT (*q.v.*) or other contract between a host government and a foreign petroleum company to prospect and produce oil and gas in the area subject to the agreement. In addition, the petroleum company may be entitled to a share of the production to be applied to the recovery of exploration costs (INVESTMENT RECOVERY OIL) and to a share of the annual gross production after payment of tax and royalty and payment of COST RECOVERY OIL and INVESTMENT RECOVERY OIL (REMAINDER OIL).

COST well

See CONTINENTAL OFFSHORE STRATIGRAPHIC TEST (COST).

Council for Mutual Economic Assistance (COMECON)

A council composed of the Soviet Union, Poland, Romania, Hungary, the German Democratic Republic, Czechoslovakia, and Bulgaria. For a study of production and reserves in these countries, see Park, *Oil and Gas in Comecon Countries* (1979).

Council of Energy Resource Tribes

An organization, established in 1975, of twenty-five American Indian tribes having lands rich in energy resources, established to facilitate collective action of the tribes in the development of energy resources. See Ruffing, "Fighting the Substandard Lease," 6 *Am. Indian J.* 6:2 (1980).

Counter letter

(1) An agreement to reconvey where property has been passed by absolute deed with the intention that it shall serve as security only. Karcher v. Karcher, 138 La. 288, 70 So. 228 at 229 (1915).

(2) An unrecorded letter indicating the real party in interest in a purchase transaction. In Republic Petroleum Corp. v. United States, 397 F. Supp. 900 at 923 (E.D. La. 1975), the court observed:

> "Louisiana courts have, on many occasions, enforced counter letters or similar agreements, such as the one here at issue, in which the purchaser of real property discloses that he purchases not for himself but on behalf of the true owner. So long as uninfluenced by fraud or duress or the product of error, the principal is well established that such secret, unrecorded agreements are binding and enforceable upon the parties to them."

In the instant case the counter letter indicated that the real purchaser of Square 187 was Republic, who agreed to pay the entire purchase price including interest on the mortgage.

> "Under Louisiana law, then, Republic, though not the title owner of record, may nonetheless be regarded as the equitable owner of Square 187 by virtue of the counter letter, and as such, indirectly obligated to make the payments in dispute."

For other forms of letter agreements, see LETTER.

Counterpart leases

Separate leases executed by owners of separate tracts each of which describes the leased acreage as including the separate tracts. The result of the execution of such leases is to give rise to a presumption that the lessors have pooled their royalty interests, and will participate pro rate in production from a well drilled on any tract in the proportion of their respective surface acreage contributions. Eberhardt, "Effect of Conservation Laws, Rules and Regulations on Rights of Lessors, Lessees and Owners of Unleased Mineral Interests," 5 *Sw. Legal Fdn. Oil & Gas Inst.* 125 at 188 (1954).

Country Regular Fields

Small, relatively shallow fields in Railroad Commission Districts 7B and 9 (North Central Texas) which "often produce at rates high enough to disqualify them from the marginal well category but at rates substantially below the 'yardstick' allowable usually applied to nonexempt wells. These fields are considered to be in the stripper category and thus exempt from production restrictions." Lovejoy,

"Oil Conservation in a New Setting." 4 *Nat. Res. J.* 332 at 339 (1964).

See also ALLOWABLE.

Courtesy billing notice

A notice sent by the appropriate state office of the Bureau of Land Management of the due date of rental payment on oil and gas leases. This billing notice is sent as a courtesy. Reliance on the receipt of a courtesy billing notice is not a justifiable excuse for failure to timely pay rental. Richard C. Corbyn, IBLA 77-321, GFS (O&G) 1977-145 (Sept. 28, 1977).

Covenant

Formerly a written promise under seal, for the breach of which a special form of action lay. Now, any promise, express or implied.

In the law of oil and gas, any instrument may contain one or more covenants. The typical oil and gas lease contains a number, some of which do not appear on the face of the instrument, *viz.*, IMPLIED COVENANTS (*q.v.*).

See also DIVISIBLE COVENANTS; EXPRESS COVENANT.

Cover-all clause

A clause commonly included in contemporary leases to meet the problem of adequately describing strips of land owned by a lessor contiguous to the land specifically described by the lease and intended to be covered by the lease. A typical clause will follow the specific description of the land leased and will provide:

> "It being intended to include herein all lands and interests therein contiguous to or appurtenant to said described lands owned or claimed by lessor."

There are innumerable variations in the language of such clauses. See McRae, "Granting Clauses in Oil and Gas Leases: Including Mother Hubbard Clauses," 2 *Sw. Legal Fdn. Oil & Gas Inst.* 43 (1951); TREATISE §§ 221–221.8.

Syn.: MOTHER HUBBARD CLAUSE; ALL-INCLUSIVE CLAUSE.

Cover lease

A second lease obtained to "cover" a possible defect in a prior lease. Johnson v. Brewer, 427 So. 2d 118, 77 *O.&G.R.* 302 (Miss. 1983).

See also PROTECTION LEASE; TOP LEASE.

CPA

Canadian Petroleum Association.

CPC

The CHINA PETROLEUM CORPORATION (*q.v.*).

CPRA

The CANADA PETROLEUM RESOURCES ACT (CPRA) (*q.v.*).

Cracked gasoline

See THERMAL CRACKING; GASOLINE.

Cracking

The process of breaking down the larger, heavier and more complex hydrocarbon molecules into simpler and lighter molecules, thus increasing the gasoline yield from crude oil. Cracking is done by application of heat and pressure, and in modern time the use of a catalytic agent.

See also CATALYTIC CRACKING; HYDROCRACKING; REFINER; THERMAL CRACKING; TOPPING PROCESS.

Crater

A bowl shaped depression around a blow out well caused by the caving in and collapse of the earth's structure. See Midwestern Insurance Co. v. Rapp, 296 P.2d 770, 5 *O.&G.R.* 757 (Okla. 1956).

Credited royalty system

A term applied to the system of international petroleum exploration and exploitation agreements under which royalties are directly credited to the income tax to be paid the host country by the international oil company. Blinn, Duval, Le Leuch and Pertuzio, *International Petroleum Exploration & Exploitation Agreements* 231 (Barrows 1986).

See also CONCESSION; EXPENSED ROYALTY SYSTEM.

Creekology theory

An ancient theory, not now supported by geologists, that a substructure could be defined by a river bank. See Creslenn Oil Co. v.

Corporation Comm'n, 206 Okla. 428, 244 P.2d 314, 1 *O.&G.R.* 813 at 820 (1952).

CRISTAL

The Contract Regarding an Interim Supplement to Tanker Liability for Oil Pollution which establishes a fund from contributions of participating oil companies to supplement the monies available under TOVALOP (*q.v.*) or under the proposed IMCO CONVENTIONS (*q.v.*). CRISTAL will reimburse the owner of a tanker which has spilled oil for cleanup costs which exceed $125 per gross ton or $10 million, whichever is less, up to $30 million. See Wood, "Requiring Polluters to Pay for Aquatic Natural Resources Destroyed by Oil Pollution," 8 *Nat. Res. Lawyer* 545 at 559 (1976).

See also PLATO.

Crooked well

A well which deviates from the vertical. See DIRECTIONAL WELL; WHIPSTOCKING.

Syn.: DOG'S LEG; ELBOW; SLANT WELL.

Cross-assignment

A multiple assignment of property interests, whereby an assignor also receives an assignment from his assignee.

The term has special reference to the execution of pooling and unitization agreements, which some courts have treated as cross-assignments of property interests. For example, where *A* and *B* are lessors of adjoining 40-acre tracts, and they join in a pooling agreement based on surface acreage, it is conceived that *A* assigns *B* a one-half interest in the royalty in his tract and *B* assigns *A* a one-half interest in the royalty in his tract. Opinions seeming to adopt this theory include: Brown v. Smith, 141 Tex. 425, 174 S.W.2d 43 (1943); Veal v. Thomason, 138 Tex. 341, 159 S.W.2d 472 (1942); *contra,* Phillips Petroleum Co. v. Peterson, 218 F.2d 926, 4 *O.&G.R.* 746 (10th Cir. 1954), *cert. denied,* 349 U.S. 947, 4 *O.&G.R.* 1178 (1955). See Hoffman, *Voluntary Pooling and Unitization* (1954); TREATISE §§ 929–930.10.

See also ASSIGNMENT.

Cross-charge

The term applied to a security agreement in an Australian joint venture by each party in favor of the others covering the party's interest in the joint venture assets, its interest in the joint venture agreement, and its share of the production. See Ryan, "Joint Adventure Agreements," 4 *Australian Mining & Petroleum L.J.* 101 at 127 (1982):

"Thus if a party defaults in its contributions to the manager/operator for joint venture costs, the other parties can pay these moneys on its behalf, in the knowledge that they will be able to obtain reimbursement from the sale of production belonging to the defaulting party, or from the sale of the defaulting party's interest in the joint venture. The cross charges will usually rank ahead of the security given by a party to a third party financier."

Cross-default clause

A provision of a bond issue or other financing agreement the effect of which is to give the lender the right to accelerate repayment if there should be a default in any financing entered into by the borrower. For a discussion of the problems created by such a provision upon a subsequent PROJECT FINANCING (*q.v.*) agreement of the borrower see McCormick, "Legal Issues in Project Finance," 1 *J.E.R.L.* 21 at 28 (1983).

Cross-flow

A phenomenon which may occur when a well is completed in separate strata without the use of separate tubing to avoid commingling. In this situation the gas from the zone with the higher pressure may move through the wellbore and enter the zone with the lower pressure. See Douglass & Whitworth, "Practice Before the Oil and Gas Division of the Railroad Commission of Texas," 13 *St. Mary's L.J.* 719 at 734 (1982).

Cross-transfer of royalties

The same concept as CROSS-ASSIGNMENT (*q.v.*) as applied to royalty interests. For example, if *A* and *B* each own in severalty an eighth royalty under the terms of a lease on adjoining 40-acre tracts of land, and they agree to pool the two tracts on a surface acreage basis, the pooling agreement would result in a cross-transfer of royalties, by which *A* received a 1/16 royalty in *B*'s tract and *B* received a 1/16 royalty in *A*'s tract.

See also ASSIGNMENT.

Crown block

Part of the equipment of a drilling rig, either rotary or cable tool. It is housed at the top of the derrick and consists of a stationary pulley system used for raising and lowering drilling tools.

Crown reserve

In Canada Crown reserves are of two kinds: (1) lands which were set aside as Provincial Reserves and on which no applications or leases have been accepted, and (2) lands set up as Crown Reserves at the time leases are selected from reservations. The latter reserves are created when leases are granted to the holder of a reservation of Provincial petroleum and natural gas rights. Where the holder of a reservation discovers minerals in commercial quantities, he may lease one-half of the reservation. An equal amount of the reservation is set up as Crown Reserves to be disposed of on a competitive basis as and when and on whatever terms the Lieutenant Governor in Council may decide. See Tanner, "The Oil and Gas Law of the Province of Alberta, Canada," 1 *Sw. Legal Fdn. Oil & Gas Inst.* 313 at 329 (1949); Lewis and Thompson, *Canadian Oil and Gas* § 78 (1955).

Crown reserve drilling reservation

A reservation of petroleum and natural gas rights granted pursuant to provincial regulations. See, *e.g.*, 3 *O.&G.R.* 1189 (1954), 4 *O.&G.R.* 1474 (1955). The holder of a reservation, under certain prescribed conditions, has the exclusive right before the expiration or termination of the reservation to apply for a lease or leases of the petroleum and natural gas rights described in the reservation. The holder of a reservation must perform certain mandatory drilling operations.

See also CHECKERBOARD LEASING; CORRIDOR ACREAGE; DRILLING RESERVATION.

Crude bitumen

A naturally occurring viscous mixture, mainly of hydrocarbons heavier than pentane, that may contain sulphur compounds and that in its naturally occurring viscous state is not recoverable at a commercial rate through a well. The Alberta Oil Sands Technology and Research Authority Act (S.A. 1974, c.49) § 1(b).

Crude oil

Liquid petroleum as it comes out of the ground, as distinguished from refined oils manufactured out of it. Also called, simply, "crude." Crude oil varies radically in its properties, *viz.*, specific gravity and viscosity. Depending on the chemical nature of its chief constituents, crude oil is classified as ASPHALT BASE OIL, PARAFFIN BASE OIL, or MIXED BASE OIL (*q.v.*).

"Crude oil is defined generally by twenty states as crude petroleum oil and all other hydrocarbons, regardless of gravity, produced at the well in liquid form by ordinary production methods and which are *not* the result of condensation of gas. Some seven states include liquids which *are* the result of condensation and four do not define crude oil." 26 *Oil & Gas Compact Bull.* 55 (June 1967).

See also OIL; PETROLEUM; REFERENCE CRUDE.

Crude Oil Allocation Scheme (COAS)

In Australia, a mechanism for the allocation of indigenous crude oil to refiners (and marketers) on the basis of their market shares of sales of certain petroleum products. The mechanism is designed to facilitate an equitable distribution of indigenous crude oil priced at import parity. See Eves, "The Indigenous Crude Oil Allocation Scheme and Its Relationship With Indigenous Crude Oil Pricing Policies," 4 *Australian Mining & Petroleum L.J.* 159 (1982).

Crude oil equalization tax

The tax imposed by Section 2031 of the National Energy Act (H.R. 8444), as passed by the House of Representatives on August 5, 1977, on the first purchase of LOWER TIER CRUDE OIL (*q.v.*) during 1978 or 1979 and of CONTROLLED CRUDE OIL (*q.v.*) after 1979 and on or before the termination date of controlled crude oil. This provision died in the Senate and was not included in The Energy Tax Act of 1978 (Pub. L. No. 95–618).

Crude oil equivalent

The energy equivalent, expressed in terms of barrels of crude oil, of specified quantities of natural gas.

Crude oil self sufficiency

The extent to which an integrated oil company has sufficient production of crude oil to satisfy its requirements for refining and marketing.

"The degree of crude oil self sufficiency, in combination with vertical integration and the tax advantages resulting from percentage depletion allowance, has special importance in terms of crude oil price policies. Depletion allowance creates an incentive for resources to flow into crude oil production and, initially, tends to lower crude oil and product prices. The integrated firm is generally both a buyer and seller of crude oil; in the former role it has an incentive for lower crude prices but in the latter role an incentive exists for higher prices. The net balance of these opposing interests depends on the degree of crude oil sufficiency and the extent to which higher crude prices are passed on to refined products. De Chazeau and Kahn report that a company with a crude oil self sufficiency in excess of 77 percent stands to gain from higher crude oil prices if none of the increase were passed on to product prices." [Other estimates indicate that about 93 percent self sufficiency would be required.] Duchesneau, *Competition in the U.S. Energy Industry* 132–134 (1975).

Crude Oil Windfall Profit Tax Act of 1980

Pub. L. No. 96–223 (I.R.C. § 4986 *et seq.*), imposing an excise tax on the windfall profit (as defined) from taxable crude oil removed from the premises after February 29, 1980.

This Act was held to be unconstitutional in Ptasynski v. United States, 550 F. Supp. 549, 75 *O.&G.R.* 215 (D. Wyo. 1982), by reason of its lack of uniformity in that one state, Alaska, was not subject to the tax. This judgment was reversed and the constitutionality of the Act sustained by the United States Supreme Court on June 6, 1983, 462 U.S. 74, 103 S. Ct. 2239, 77 O.&G.R. 195 (1983).

Amerada Hess Corp. v. Director, Division of Taxation, 208 N.J. Super. 201, 505 A.2d 186, 88 *O.&G.R.* 214 (1986), petition for certification granted, concluded that for purposes of a New Jersey Corporate Business Tax the federal Windfall Profits Tax is an excise tax, deductible as a business expense, and not a tax on or measured by profits or income.

Some oil and gas leases and other instruments contain provision placing the burden of taxation on one party. The applicability of such provisions to the Crude Oil Windfall Profit Tax Act has been the subject of dispute. See *e.g.*, the following:

Tenneco West, Inc. v. Marathon Oil Co., 564 F. Supp. 381, 77 *O.&G.R.* 421 (C.D. Cal. 1983) (holding that tax burden was shifted to lessee by some but not by all leases in controversy), *rev'd,* 756 F.2d 769, 84 *O.&G.R.* 609 (9th Cir. 1985), *cert. denied,* ____ U.S. ____, 106 S.Ct. 134 (1985) (holding that tax shifting clause in lease requiring lessee to pay any and all taxes referrable to operations or acts of the lessee did not shift from the lessor to lessee incidence of the windfall profits tax upon royalty oil);

Exxon Corp. v. City of Long Beach, 812 F.2d 1256, ____ *O.&G.R.* ____ (9th Cir. 1987) (crude oil windfall profits tax was not an excise tax chargeable to a net profits interest);

Crocker National Bank v. McFarland Energy, Inc., 140 Cal. App. 3d 6, 189 Cal. Rptr. 302, 75 *O.&G.R.* 414 (1983) (tax burden not shifted by clause construed).

For discussions of the Act and its operation see the following:

Crumbley and Reese, *Readings in the Crude Oil Windfall Profit Tax* (1982);

Attermeier and Reveley, "Characterizing the Windfall Profit Tax for State Income Tax Purposes," 32 *O.&G. Tax Q.* 465 (1984).

See also ADJUSTED BASE PRICE; DISQUALIFIED TRANSFEROR; ECONOMIC INTEREST; ECONOMIC RECOVERY TAX ACT OF 1981; EXEMPT ALASKAN OIL; EXEMPT FRONT-END OIL; EXEMPT INDIAN OIL; EXEMPT ROYALTY OIL; EXEMPT STRIPPER WELL OIL; FRONT-END TERTIARY OIL; FRONT-END TERTIARY PROVISIONS; HEAVY OIL; INCREMENTAL TERTIARY OIL; INDEPENDENT PRODUCER OIL; NEWLY DISCOVERED CRUDE OIL; PAYOUT; PROPERTY; PROVEN OIL OR GAS PROPERTY TRANSFER; QUALIFIED CHARITABLE INTEREST; QUALIFIED GOVERNMENTAL INTEREST; QUALIFIED OVERRIDING ROYALTY INTEREST; QUALIFIED PRODUCTION; QUALIFIED ROYALTY PRODUCTION; QUALIFIED TERTIARY INJECTANT EXPENSES; QUALIFIED TERTIARY RECOVERY PROJECT; RELATED GROUP; REMOVAL PRICE; RESIDENTIAL CHILD CARE AGENCY EXEMPTION; SADLEROCHIT OIL; SEVERANCE TAX; SUBSTITUTE FUEL CLAUSE; TAX SHIFTING CLAUSE; TIER 1 OIL; TIER 2 OIL; TIER 3 OIL; WINDFALL PROFIT.

Cryogenics

The study and production of very low temperatures and their associated phenomena.

Cryogenic techniques

Techniques involving extremely low temperatures used to keep certain fuels in liquid form, *i.e.,* liquefied hydrogen, methane, propane, etc.

Cubic foot of gas

See STANDARD CUBIC FOOT.

Current Btu related price

This term is defined by Section 402 of the National Energy Act (H.R. 8444), as passed by the House of Representatives on August 5, 1977, as the most recently published Btu related price calculated pursuant to section 403, *viz.*, by dividing per barrel domestic refiner cost of acquiring domestic crude oil during the preceding 3 calendar months by a Btu conversion factor of 5.8 million Btu's per barrel.

Curtailment plan

A plan for the curtailment of certain natural gas service to designated consumers when there is insufficient gas available to satisfy the requirements of all potential consumers. See Consolidated Edison Co. of N.Y., Inc. v. Federal Power Comm'n, 511 F.2d 372 (D.C. Cir. 1974), *petition for clarification granted and rehearing denied,* 512 F.2d 1332, 518 F.2d 448 (D.C. Cir. 1975); Louisiana Power & Light Co. v. Federal Power Comm'n, 526 F.2d 898 (5th Cir. 1976); Houston Lighting & Power Co. v. Railroad Comm'n, 529 S.W.2d 763, 52 *O.&G.R.* 427 (Tex. 1975).

Process Gas Consumers Group v. U.S. Department of Agriculture, 661 F.2d 1322 (D.C. Cir. 1981), sustained in part rules governing natural gas curtailment plans of interstate pipelines and remanded in part for revision of certain of the rules.

Consolidated Edison Co. of New York v. Federal Energy Regulatory Comm'n, 676 F.2d 763 (D.C. Cir. 1982), held that the Commission's curtailment was not arbitrary and capricious, by reason of failure to provide compensation to low-priority users for converting to alternate fuels, as compensation schemes are not a required part of a curtailment plan.

For a discussion of the operation of the curtailment plan under the NATURAL GAS POLICY ACT OF 1978 (NGPA) (*q.v.*), see Process Gas Consumers Group v. United States Dept. of Agriculture, 694 F.2d 728 (D.C. Cir. 1981), *modified on rehearing en banc,* 694 F.2d 778 (D.C. Cir. 1982), *cert. denied,* 461 U.S. 905, 103 S. Ct. 1874 (1983).

For a detailed discussion of curtailment plans, see Merriman and Bowman, "The 1970's—A Period of Momentous Change," American Gas Ass'n, *Regulation of the Gas Industry* ch. 5 (1981).

See also AQE; CARRYOVER; END USE CONTROL; END USE PLAN; 467 PLAN; OVERRUN PENALTY; PAYBACK OF GAS; PRO RATA PLAN; RESTITUTION GAS; SELF-HELP ARRANGEMENT; STORAGE SPRINKLING.

Cushion gas

The gas required in a reservoir used for storage of natural gas so that reservoir pressure is such that the storage gas may be recovered. Mississippi River Transmission Corp. v. Simonton, 442 So. 2d 764 (La. App. 1983), *writ denied,* 444 So.2d 1240 (La. 1984), *cert. denied,* ____ U.S. ____, 105 S. Ct. 58 (1984); State *ex rel.* Hughes v. State Board of Land Comm'rs, 137 Mont. 510, 353 P.2d 331, 13 *O.&G.R.* 20 at 29 (1960). See also Leeston, Crichton and Jacobs, *The Dynamic Natural Gas Industry* 245 (1963).

Arkla, Inc. v. United States, 765 F.2d 487, 85 *O.&G.R.* 431, *reh. denied,* 772 F.2d 904 (5th Cir. 1985), *cert. denied,* 106 S.Ct. 1374 (1986), held that recoverable cushion gas was not subject to depreciation and the taxpayer was not entitled to the investment tax credit for cost of the gas.

See also GAS STORAGE, SUBSURFACE; NATIVE GAS; NATIVE GAS ENTITLEMENT; WORKING GAS.

Cut and cap operation

An operation upon a well abandoned as a non-producer involving the digging of a trench around the well pipe, severing the inner and outer casing about three feet below ground by a cutting torch, welding a cap over the top of the pipe, and covering the hole with dirt. Gutierrez v. Exxon Corp., 764 F.2d 399, 85 *O.&G.R.* 341 (5th Cir. 1985).

Cutback asphalt

Asphalt to which is added a solvent to make the asphalt transportable or to permit its use for various purposes, *e.g.*, as a binder of an aggregate of stones and gravel in road building. As the solvent evaporates, the asphalt hardens into a solid again. The controlled or "curing" rate of hardening is determined by the type and amount of solvent that is mixed with the solid asphalt at the time the cut-back asphalt is prepared. See American Bitumuls & Asphalt Co. v. United States, 185 F. Supp. 955 (Ct. of Customs, 1960) (dealing with question of duty applicable to this product).

Cut of oil

Percentage of impurities in oil.

Cut-off point

A term applied for purposes of PERCENTAGE DEPLETION (*q.v.*) to the point at which the value attributable to post-production processes is not included in "gross income from the property." See Nix and Snyder, "Percentage Depletion: A Review and Update," 2 *Eastern Min. L. Inst.* 3–20 (1981).

Cut oil

An emulsified mixture of oil and water. Brown & Myers, "Some Legal Aspects of Water Flooding," 24 *Tex. L. Rev.* 456 at 457 (1946).

Cuttings

Bits and pieces of rock cut out of a formation by the bit. See WELL CUTTINGS.

CVP

Corporación Venezolana del Petroleo of Venezuela.

Cycling

A primary recovery method by which condensate is recovered from gas produced from a CONDENSATE GAS RESERVOIR (*q.v.*) and the residue gas is compressed and returned to the reservoir from which it was originally produced. The return of the residue gas tends to maintain the pressure and thereby prevent RETROGRADE CONDENSATION (*q.v.*) and resultant waste of hydrocarbon liquids in the reservoir.

Among some engineers, cycling is distinguished from RECYCLING (*q.v.*) as follows: in cycling the gas condensate moves as a unit across the reservoir to the output wells, the front between the wet gas and the reinjected dry gas remaining relatively stable. Thus the operation is a one-cycle process, and when all the wet gas has been removed, the process is finished. In recycling, the wet gas and the reinjected dry gas intermix, so that over the period of the operation, progressively less liquid is recovered from the gas produced.

See also FISKE FORMULA.

Cycling plant

A plant for the processing of wet gas produced from wells and after the processing thereof the injection of the residue dry gas into the reservoir through other wells for purpose of pressure maintenance.

CZMA

The COASTAL ZONE MANAGEMENT ACT OF 1972 (*q.v.*).

..D..

DA

The daily ALLOWABLE (*q.v.*) established for a gas well. See Provisions Governing the Limitation and Allocation of Production of Gas, Saskatchewan MRO 119/68 A 63, 5 Lewis and Thompson, *Canadian Oil and Gas* Div. D, Part X [5A] (1971).

DAC

The DEVELOPMENT ASSISTANCE COMMITTEE (*q.v.*).

Daily contract quantity (DCQ)

The daily quantity of gas to be delivered or taken under a gas purchase contract.

In Gulf Oil Corp. v. Federal Power Comm'n, 563 F.2d 588, 59 *O.&G.R.* 191 (3d Cir. 1977), *cert. denied,* 434 U.S. 1062 (1978), *reh. denied,* 435 U.S. 981 (1978), *cert. dism'd under Rule* 60, 435 U.S. 911 (1978), the court was called upon to construe a contract requiring the buyer to "purchase or pay for" a quantity of gas equal to 80 percent of the Daily Contract Quantity multiplied by the number of days in the year and entitling the buyer to purchase greater quantities of gas providing that the seller was not obligated to deliver in any day a quantity in excess of 125 percent of the Daily Contract Quantity. The court concluded that the contract entitled the buyer to demand and required the seller to deliver 125 percent of the Daily Contract Quantity "every day" until the buyer demands less. For a subsequent appeal of this case, see Gulf Oil Corp. v. Federal Energy Regulatory Comm'n, 706 F.2d 444 (3d Cir. 1983), *cert. denied,* 464 U.S. 1038, 104 S. Ct. 698 (1984).

See also Superior Oil Co., F.P.C. Opinion No. 766 (June 10, 1976), 10 FPS 5–93 at 5–98.

Daily take

The amount of gas required to be delivered and taken each day under the provisions of a GAS PURCHASE CONTRACT (*q.v.*).

Daisy Chain

A string of buyers and sellers of a single cargo of oil constructed as the cargo changes hands, sometimes several times a day and sometimes passing by the same company or buyer a number of times. These chains offer participants advantages of speculating and hedging. *The Wall Street Journal,* March 6, 1986, p. 6.

Dansk Olie og Naturgas A/S (DONG A/S)

The state oil company of Denmark. See Engel, "State-to-State Deals in the Crude Oil Trace—The Danish Experience," International Bar Ass'n, *Energy Law 1981* 17; Dragsted, "Recent Developments in Denmark," International Bar Ass'n Section on Energy and Natural Resources, *International Energy Law* (1984) (Topic 7); Ronne and Budtz, "The Legal Framework for Exploration for and Production of Oil and Natural Gas in Denmark," 3 *J. of Energy & Nat. Res. L.* 153 (1985).

Dansk Undergrunds Consortium (DUC)

A group composed of several oil companies that is the sole concessionaire of the Danish sector of the North Sea.

Darcy

The unit of permeability; the rate of flow in milliliters per second of a fluid having a viscosity of one centipoise, through a cross section of one sq. cm. of the rock, under a pressure gradient of one atmosphere (760 mm. Hg) per centimeter, and conditions of viscous flow. A millidarcy is one one-thousandth (.001) darcy.

See also PERMEABILITY OF ROCK.

D'Arcy Concession

A 1901 concession for mineral development in Persia. See Shwadran, *The Middle East, Oil and the Great Powers* 14 (3d ed. revised and enlarged, 1973).

Darcy's law

A statement of flow conditions. See Nelson and McNeil, "Oil Recovery by Thermal Methods," 17 *Interstate Oil Compact Bull.* 56 at 57 (Dec. 1958).

Dawson Acts

The Act of April 22, 1954 (68 Stat. 57) and the Act of July 11, 1956 (70 Stat. 529), providing for the transfer of certain mineral school lands to the states.

Day rate contract

A contract for the drilling of an oil and gas well under which "the drilling contractor furnished the drilling crew and drilling equipment; he is paid an agreed sum of money for each day spent in drilling regardless of the number of days involved; all materials, services and supplies that are not agreed to be furnished by the contractor are furnished by the well owner." Haas v. Gulf Coast Natural Gas Co., 484 S.W.2d 127 at 131, 43 *O.&G.R.* 381 at 389 (Tex. Civ. App. 1972).

For a discussion of the circumstances under which a day rate rather than a footage rate is charged, see Startex Drilling Co. v. Sohio Petroleum Co., 680 F.2d 412, 74 *O.&G.R.* 384 (5th Cir. 1982).

See also DRILLING CONTRACT; GULF COAST CLAUSE; TERM DAY-WORK CONTRACT.

Syn.: Day-work contract.

Day work

In a DRILLING CONTRACT (*q.v.*), one basis for determining the compensation of the independent drilling contractor. For example, a contract may provide a footage rate (see FOOTAGE CONTRACT) except when the well is coring and for SHUT DOWN TIME (*q.v.*) when operations have ceased at the operator's request. The day rate protects the drilling contractor against loss under the footage rate, when the well is not drilling at a normal rate because of special work requested by the operator.

Day-work contract

Syn. for DAY RATE CONTRACT (*q.v.*).

DCC

DESIGNATED CROWN CORPORATION (*q.v.*).

DCQ

DAILY CONTRACT QUANTITY (*q.v.*) of gas to be delivered or taken under a GAS PURCHASE CONTRACT (*q.v.*).

DD&A

Depletion, depreciation and amortization.

Dead oil

Oil containing no dissolved gas.

Dead rent

A term used in certain CONCESSION (*q.v.*) agreements for a payment agreed to be made annually to the host country until the date of commencement of regular exports of the substances covered by the agreement. See *e.g.*, Article 10 of the Convention of 29 July 1938 between the Basrah Petroleum Company and the Government of Iraq [*Petroleum Legislation, Middle East: Basic Oil and Laws and Concession Contracts* (Vol. II, 1959)].

Dead well

A well from which oil will not flow without a pump.

Dealer day in court statute

The term applied to franchising statutes enacted in a number of states affecting gasoline dealers. Such statutes require written disclosure to a dealer of the material terms of the franchise agreement and prohibit termination of or failure to renew the agreement unless justified by good cause. See Meriwether and Smith, "Gasoline Marketing Divestiture Statutes: A Preliminary Constitutional and Economic Assessment," 28 *Vanderbilt L. Rev.* 1277 at 1279 (1975); Cal. Corp. Code §§ 31,005, 31,101 (1980 Supp.); Mass. Ann. Laws ch. 93E, §§ 1–8 (1975).

For a discussion of the Petroleum Marketing Practices Act of 1978 (establishing federal standards for termination and nonrenewal of franchise relationships in gasoline marketing), see Boyce, "State Gasoline Divorcement Statutes: Legal and Economic Implications," 28 *Cath. U.L. Rev.* 511 at 551 (1979).

DEC

A DRAWING ENTRY CARD (*q.v.*) submitted in a simultaneous oil and gas lease filing for a noncompetitive lease on federal land.

Decatherm

A unit of heat in the metric system employed to measure the heating value of gas. This unit is equal to ten therms. See THERM.

Deceptive Trade Practices-Consumer Protection Act (DTPA)

A Texas statute, Tex. Bus. & Com. Code Ann. §§ 17.41–17.63, providing consumer remedies for unconscionable conduct and for breaches of express or implied warranties. See Dwyre, "Practical Applications and a Survey of Cases: The DTPA and Oil and Gas," 18 *Texas Tech L. Rev.* 145 (1987).

Declared unit

A unit formed by the lessee acting under the provisions of a lease pooling clause. In Louisiana the legal consequences of forming such a unit may be different from those following the formation of a VOLUNTARY UNIT (*q.v.*) or CONTRACTUAL UNIT (*q.v.*), *viz.,* one specifically created by joint agreement of the mineral lessee and the owners of all the other mineral or royalty interests affecting the land in question. See Humble Oil & Refining Co. v. Jones, 157 So. 2d 110, 19 *O.&G.R.* 545 (La. App. 1963), *writ refused,* 245 La. 568, 159 So. 2d 284, 19 *O.&G.R.* 559 (1964).

See also UNIT AGREEMENT.

Decline analysis

A method of estimating petroleum reserves by determining the natural production decline and extrapolating to predict future production. See Graham, "Fair Share or Fair Game?," 8 *Nat. Res. Law.* 61 at 64 (1975).

Declining balance method

See DEPRECIATION.

Dedicated reserve contract

A term employed in the Texas Dedicated Reserve Tax Act for "any written contract for a designated term specified therein which confers upon a dedicated reserve producer the right to take title to gas from particular lands, leases and reservoirs in this State, and imposes upon a severance producer the duty to supply all or a designated quantity or portion of gas produced by that severance producer (or by that severance producer in conjunction with others) to the dedicated reserve producer at a fixed or determinable price." The Act was held to be unconstitutional in Calvert v. Panhandle Eastern Pipe Line Co., 371 S.W.2d 601, 19 *O.&G.R.* 742 (Tex. Civ. App. 1963, error ref'd n.r.e.).

Dedicated reserve producer

A term employed in the Texas Dedicated Reserve Tax Act for "any person holding a written contract for a designated term specified therein which confers upon such person the right to take title to gas from particular lands, leases and reservoirs in this State and imposes upon a severance producer the duty to supply all or a designated quantity or portion of gas produced by that severance producer (or by that severance producer in conjunction with other severance producers) to the dedicated reserve producer at a fixed or determinable price." The Act was held to be unconstitutional in Calvert v. Panhandle E. Pipe Line Co., 371 S.W.2d 601, 19 *O.&G.R.* 742 (Tex. Civ. App. 1963, error ref'd n.r.e.).

Dedication contract

A gas purchase and sale contract under which the producer contracts to furnish the purchaser all the gas produced from specified reserves, thus "dedicating" those reserves to the customer. In Louisiana Land & Exploration Co. v. Texaco, Inc., 478 So.2d 926, 89 *O.&G.R.* 472 (La. App. 1985), a dedication contract was distinguished from a WARRANTY CONTRACT (*q.v.*), under which the producer is obligated to deliver to the purchaser certain quantities of gas, but the source of the gas is unspecified and the producer may fulfill his obligation from any source he chooses. The judgment in this case was reversed and remanded on other grounds, 491 So.2d 363, 89 *O.&G.R.* 479 (La. 1986).

Dedication of reserves

The assurance of an adequate supply of natural gas to a pipeline company, usually accomplished by a GAS PURCHASE CONTRACT (*q.v.*) between a natural gas producer and the pipe line company. A typical contract will provide that "seller hereby dedicates to the performance of this contract all gas located in, under, or hereafter produced from the units, leases, and lands described in Exhibit 'A' (hereafter referred to as dedicated reserves)." Such contracts normally run for a period of at least twenty years. Dedication of reserves is required by the Federal Power Commission and its successor, the Federal Energy Regulatory Commission, acting under the Natural Gas Act, 52 Stat. 821, 15 U. S. C. § 717 *et seq.*, which requires the issuance of a certificate of public convenience and necessity by the Commission as the prerequisite of constructing or operating an interstate gas pipe line. Issuance of the certificate depends upon a showing, *inter alia,* of an ability to provide adequate, continuous and reasonable service, which obviously includes an adequate gas supply. See Linz, "Federal Power Commission—It's Always in the Middle," 52 *Oil and Gas J.* 84 (1953); Wheat, "Administration of the Certificate Provisions of the Natural Gas Act," 14 *Geo. Wash. L. Rev.* 194 (1945); Comment, 28 *Ind. L.J.* 587 (1953); TREATISE § 724.6.

The definition in this MANUAL was quoted in Nordan-Lawton Oil & Gas Corp. of Texas v. Miller, 272 F. Supp. 125 at 129, note 12 and 136, 27 *O.&G.R.* 593 at 596, note 12 and 606 (W.D. La. 1967), *aff'd,* 403 F.2d 946, 31 *O.&G.R.* 526 (5th Cir. 1968) (citing this MANUAL).

Deed

See BROAD FORM DEED; MINERAL DEED; QUITCLAIM; ROYALTY DEED.

Deemed interest

An agreed rate of interest applicable to development costs incurred under a SERVICE CONTRACT (*q.v.*) which the contractor is entitled to recover out of actual production, if any.

Deemed purchase formula

A formula, sometimes utilized when one party to an operating agreement is unable to market its share of available or optimum production but the other or others can, under which the overlifter purchases the share of production not taken by the underlifter at a discount price. H.P. Williams, "Matters to be Taken Into Consideration in the Negotiation of Farmouts and Operating Agreements," 1 *Austl. Mining & Petroleum L.J.* 509 at 520 (1978).

See also BALANCING; CANCELLED UNDERAGE; DEFERRED PRODUCTION AGREEMENT; GAS BANK AGREEMENT; JOINT OPERATING AGREEMENT; LIFTING; LIFTING TOLERANCE; "OUT OF BALANCE" PRODUCTION PLAN; OVERLIFT; SPLIT CONNECTION; UNDERAGE; UNDERLIFT; UNDERLIFT/OVERLIFT PROVISION.

Deeper drilling exception

An exception to the "vintaging" rules of the Federal Power Commission and its successor, the Federal Energy Regulatory Commission, providing that production from reservoirs penetrated for the first time through deeper drilling in an existing well was eligible for the same price rate as if the deeper drilling constituted the commencement of such well. See Falcon Petroleum v. Federal Energy Regulatory Comm'n, 642 F.2d 780, 69 *O.&G.R.* 205 (5th Cir., Unit A, 1981).

See also PRICE CONTROL OF OIL, GAS AND PETROLEUM PRODUCTS.

Deep gas

"Gas found at depths greater than the average for a particular area; for FERC purposes it is gas found at depths of more than 15,000 feet." American Gas Ass'n, *Glossary for the Gas Industry* (3d ed. 1981).

"Deep Horizons" legislation

The colloquial name given House Bill No. 2208, Kans. Stat. Ann. §§ 55-223 to 55-229 (1983), which recognized the implied covenant of further exploration and shifted the burden of proof in implied covenant cases to the lessee in specified circumstances. See Lungren, "Deep Horizons—Legislative Shifting of the Burden of Proof in Implied Covenant Cases," 24 *Washburn L.J.* 30 (1984).

Deep Rights Act

Kan. Stat. Ann. §§ 55-223 to 55-229 (1983), which recognized the implied FURTHER EXPLORATION COVENANT (*q.v.*) and shifted the burden of proof in implied covenant cases to the lessee in specified circumstances.

Syn.: "DEEP HORIZONS" LEGISLATION. (*q.v.*)

Deep Seabed Mineral Resources Act

Pub. L. 96–283 (1980). The Act:

1. Disclaims extraterritorial sovereignty by the U.S. over deep seabeds. (Title I)

2. Requires licensing, in accordance with this Act, for exploration of or commercial recovery from deep seabeds. (Title II)

3. Directs the Secretary of the Interior to administer the Act and to enforce civil and criminal penalties which the Act establishes. (Title II)

4. Determines the effects of subsequent international agreements upon the licenses granted under the Act. (Title III)

5. Imposes a tax on hard mineral resources removed from the deep seabed. (Title IV)

6. Establishes a Deep Seabed Fund in the U.S. Treasury. (Title V)

See also OUTER CONTINENTAL SHELF (OCS).

Deep well

This term is defined by W. Va. Code §§ 22–4–1 and 22–4B–2 (Cum. Supp. 1980) as "any well drilled and completed in a formation at or below the top of the uppermost member of the 'Onondaga Group' or at a depth of or greater than six thousand feet, whichever is shallower."

See also SHALLOW WELL; WELL.

Default clause

A clause found in some leases providing that in the event the lessee violates any of the terms or conditions of the lease and fails to remedy the violation within a stipulated number of days after written notice from the lessor, the lessor, at his option, may terminate the lease.

See also GOOD FAITH CLAUSE; JUDICIAL ASCERTAINMENT CLAUSE; NOTICE AND DEMAND CLAUSE.

Defeasible term interest

A mineral, royalty or nonexecutive mineral interest for a fixed term of years and for an indefinite period of time thereafter, usually so long as oil or gas is produced. See TREATISE § 331 at n 2, §§ 333–336.

See also TERM MINERAL OR ROYALTY INTEREST; MASTERSON CLAUSE.

Defensive clause

The term utilized by Lowe, *Oil and Gas Law in a Nutshell* 209 (1983), to describe a variety of clauses (*e.g.*, dry hole clause, drilling operations clause, shut-in royalty clause, force majeure clause) sought by a lessee to protect his lease from termination as a result of strict construction policies applied by the courts to the oil and gas lease.

Deferred bonus

Landowner's BONUS (*q.v.*) paid in installments spread over a number of years, as distinguished from the usual mode of payment, which is in a lump sum on execution and delivery of the lease.

The tax treatment of deferred bonus prior to the Tax Reduction Act of 1975 is discussed in Burke and Bowhay, *Income Taxation of Natural Resources* ¶ 4.09 (1981), and *Miller's Oil and Gas Federal Income Taxation* § 18–12 (1980 edition).

Deferred bonus bidding

A system of bidding for leases under which the operator pays the bonus in installments and retains the option to surrender the rights and discontinue the payments at any time.

"Advocates of this system claim that it encourages participation by smaller companies and reduces the necessity of discounting bids to take account of uncertainty. There is also a substantial incentive for rapid exploration, should this be a government objective. Nevertheless, there would appear to be formidible problems in the administration of such a system as it encourages overbidding and frequent surrender of rights without detailed evaluation of oil and gas reserves." Crommelin, "Offshore Oil and Gas Rights: A Comparative Study," 14 *Nat. Res. J.* 457 at 494 (1974). See also LEASE BIDDING SYSTEMS.

Deferred minimum annual royalty

A MINIMUM ROYALTY (*q.v.*), the liability for which is incurred each year, but payment is deferred until production is obtained or a date certain, whichever occurs earlier. As a condition to permitting the deferral of payment, the lessor usually obtains security, guarantees, assumptions of liability, or other assurances beyond the existence of the mineral that the deferred royalty will be paid. From an economic standpoint, this royalty is a hybrid of a production payment and a lease bonus.

"To a lessor, it has the advantage of guaranteeing a minimum return without regard to production. It should also encourage prompt development of a lease since a lessee will desire to avoid incurring subsequent minimum annual royalties on unproductive acreage. To an accrual basis lessee, it has greater tax advantages than a lease bonus because it is deductible in the year paid or incurred. Although it exposes the lessee to more economic risk, this risk can be reduced through proper planning." Martin, "Tax Advantages of a Deferred Annual Royalty Provision in Oil and Gas Leases," 30 *O.&G. Tax Q.* 241 at 261 (1981).

Deferred net royalty

A "deferred right of participation, limited to the terms of an existing lease, in the net proceeds from the sale of oil and/or gas produced from a specified tract of land or well after payment of a certain fixed preferred amount in dollars as set out in a 'Trust Agreement'; but such right of participation is subject to prior payment of (a) 'Landowner's Royalty' and 'Overriding Royalty' and (b) production equipment, acidization, operating cost, taxes, assessment and any other deductions authorized by the 'Trust Agreement' under which the right of such participation is created. After payment of said fixed preferred amount Deferred Net Royalties shall rank pari passu with 'Preferred Net Royalties' and 'Net Royalties' in the net proceeds from the sale of oil and/or gas." Saskatchewan Amended Regulations, Securities Act, O.C. 1704/52, July 14, 1952; 1 *O.&G.R.* 1541 at 1549.

See also NET ROYALTY; PREFERRED NET ROYALTY, ROYALTY.

Deferred oil payment

See DEFERRED PRODUCTION PAYMENT.

Deferred-payment open-end sale

A sale of operating properties in which the grantor reserves a production payment which terminates when the production by the grantee equals a specified amount or when the reserves equal another specified amount, whichever occurs first. Under this plan, if the reserves are accurately estimated, the sellers will continue to receive proceeds from the production payment until the buyer takes all the gas which was anticipated, but if the reserves prove smaller, the production payment will end. See Jewell, "Deferred-Payment Open-End Sales of Oil and Gas Interests to Obtain Capital Gains," 11 *Tulane Tax Inst.* 260 at 280–81 (1962).

See also OIL PAYMENT.

Deferred production agreement

An agreement entered into by owners entitled to take gas in kind whereby one such owner is permitted to take gas as produced and the other owner postpones his right to take such gas. Such agreement may be entered into where one owner has accepted a temporary certificate and another has elected to await the issuance of a permanent certificate from the Federal Power Commission or its successor, the Federal Energy Regulatory Commission. See Park, "Developments in Natural Gas Purchase Contracts," 22 Alta. L. Rev. 43 (1984); Richardson, "Producer Contracts for Sale of Natural Gas in Interstate Commerce," 11 *Sw. Legal Fdn. Oil & Gas Inst.* 201 at 214 (1960); Interstate Oil Compact Commission, General Counsel Report No. 39, May 8, 1961; Jameson, "Significant Problems in the Production of Natural Gas," 4 *Sw. Legal Fdn. National Inst. for Petroleum Landmen* 201 at 206 (1963).

Syn: Gas balancing agreement.

See also BALANCING; CANCELLED UNDERAGE; DEEMED PURCHASE FORMULA; GAS BANK AGREEMENT; LIFTING; LIFTING TOLERANCE; "OUT OF BALANCE" PRODUCTION PLAN; OVERLIFT; SPLIT CONNECTION; UNDERAGE; UNDERLIFT; UNDERLIFT/OVERLIFT PROVISION.

Deferred production payment

A production payment which does not commence until after the operator has realized a specific sum from production from the lease or after a primary production payment. See Bergen, "Oil Payments and the Investor," 4 *Rocky Mt. Min. L. Inst.* 87 at 97 (1958) (observing that the Bureau of Internal Revenue took the position that to the extent payment was received for deferral, such payment was taxable as ordinary income subject to depletion). See TREATISE § 422.1.

Syn.: Secondary production payment.

See also OIL PAYMENT.

Deferred working interest farm-out

A form of transaction in which "the farmee agrees to pay a share (usually 100 percent) of the cost of a well or wells on the property which is disproportionately greater than the permanent share of the working interest he acquires in the transaction; however, the farmee is given the additional right to hold a similarly disproportionate share (usually 100 percent) of the operating rights in the well or wells (and to receive the production income therefrom) until payout—defined as the time the farmee has recouped his costs. The farmor retains a deferred working interest which does not participate in production revenue until the farmee achieves payout, at which time the working interest share of the farmee automatically drops to his permanent interest. The farmee is entitled to deduct all IDC's which he pays, including that portion attributable to the farmor's deferred working interest. Upon reversion of the farmor's share of the working interest, the farmee must reclassify the portion of his undepreciated basis in tangible equipment attributable to the farmor's working interest as depletable leasehold cost. It does not appear that potential Section 1245 recapture attributable to the interest in the lease and well equipment, which reverts to the farmor, is triggered on the basis that either no disposition has occurred, or no realized gain has resulted from the transaction." Crichton, "Recapture of Intangibles Under Section 1254," 30 *Sw. Legal Fdn. Oil & Gas Inst.* 509 at 538 (1979).

See also FARM-OUT AGREEMENT.

Deficiency agreement

See THROUGHPUT AND DEFICIENCY AGREEMENT.

Deficient well

A well incapable of producing its allowable. See Minor v. Pan American Petroleum Corp., 216 F. Supp. 86 at 88 (W.D. La. 1962).

Definite escalation clause

Any provision in an independent producer's contract for the sale of natural gas in interstate commerce for resale or the transportation of natural gas in interstate commerce which sets forth the price to be paid for natural gas delivered thereunder in terms of a specific price per unit, including, in addition to the initial price, any increases therein by specific amounts at definite future dates, or any provision which changes the specific price in order to reimburse the seller for all or any part of the changes in production, severance, or gathering taxes levied upon the seller. See TREATISE § 726.

See also ESCALATOR CLAUSE; INDEFINITE ESCALATION CLAUSE.

Degree day

A measure of the coldness of the weather based on the extent to which the daily mean temperature falls below a reference temperature, usually 65°F.

Dehydration

Removal of water from fluid produced from oil wells.

Dehydration plant

A plant designed to remove basic sediment and water from the fluid produced from oil wells. Efficiency of such plants varies materially. In the more elaborate type of plant designed to serve a number of wells, the fluids produced from the wells are collected through the pipe lines from the various wells and run into large receiving tanks and there commingled. From these tanks it passes through entirely closed, large pipes, which are heated with steam, and then into entirely closed reservoirs, where it is further treated with chemicals. This treatment removes practically all water and other impurities, and the oil in good marketable condition is delivered into stock tanks or run into pipelines for further shipment. In this treatment substantially all gasoline vapor is saved as well as substantially all the oil in the B. S. (amounting to about 30%). See Hamilton v. Empire Gas and Fuel Co., 117 Kan. 25, 230 Pac. 91 (1924).

See also BASIC SEDIMENT; GLYCOL DEHYDRATOR; HEATER-TREATER; TREATING PLANT.

Dekatherm

A thermal unit of energy equal to 1,000,000 British thermal units (Btu's), that is, the equivalent of 1,000 cubic feet of gas having a heating content of 1,000 Btu's per cubic foot.

Delay rental

A sum of money payable to the lessor by the lessee for the privilege of deferring the commencement of drilling operations or the commencement of production during the primary term of the lease.

Under the UNLESS LEASE (*q.v.*), nonpayment of delay rental on or before the due date (anniversary date) occasions automatic termination of the lease unless the lease is being held by production, by drilling operations, or by virtue of some special clause of the lease, *e.g.*, the shut-in gas well clause. Under the OR LEASE (*q.v.*), nonpayment of delay rental on the due date does not cause termination of the lease automatically, but the lessor may elect to sue to recover the delay rental or to have the lease forfeited.

The lessee under an Unless lease has made no promise to pay the rental, whereas the lessee under an Or lease has promised to pay the rental or to do something else, *e.g.*, pay rental or drill a well, pay rental or forfeit the lease. Under neither type of lease will payment of rental serve to keep the lease alive after the expiration of the primary term of the lease.

The term is defined in Treasury regulations § 1.612–3(c)(1) (1980) as follows:

> "A delay rental is an amount paid for the privilege of deferring development of the property and which could have been avoided by abandonment of the lease, or by commencement of development operations, or by obtaining production."

Subsection (2) further provides that:

> "Since a delay rental is in the nature of rent it is ordinary income to the payee and not subject to depletion. The payor may at his election deduct such amount as an expense, or under section 266 and the regulations thereunder, charge it to depletable capital account."

The term "rental" is defined by Article 213 of the Louisiana Mineral Code [R.S. 31:213 (1975)] as meaning "money or other property given to maintain a mineral lease in the absence of drilling or mining operations or production of minerals. 'Rental' does not include payments classified by a lease as constructive production." As the Comment to this article indicates, this definition includes "so-called 'shut-in rentals' commonly found in many oil and gas lease forms as a means of maintaining leases when a well producing gas or gaseous substances in paying quantities is shut in. Payments of this type are to be distinguished from other payments deemed to be constructive production under certain lease forms. For example another common type of lease form provides for the making of shut-in payments in the royalty clause of the lease and states that when such payments are made, it shall be considered that there is production under the habendum clause of the lease. Compensatory royalty payments may also be classified as constructive production for purposes of maintaining a lease."

The definition in this MANUAL was cited in the following cases:

Beverly Hills Oil Co. v. Beverly Hills Unified School District, 264 Cal. App. 2d 603 at 608, 70 Cal. Rptr. 640 at 643, 31 *O.&G.R.* 14 at 19 (1968);

Whitehall Oil Co. v. Eckhart, 197 So. 2d 664 at 667, 26 *O.&G.R.* 778 at 783 (La. App. 1966), *rev'd sub nom.* Gardner v. Boagni, 252 La. 30, 209 So. 2d 11, 29 *O.&G.R.* 229 (1968).

See also DELAY RENTAL CLAUSE.

Delay rental clause

The lease clause providing for the payment of delay rentals to keep a lease alive during the primary term despite failure to obtain production or to commence drilling operations. In an UNLESS LEASE (*q.v.*) a typical delay rental clause provides as follows:

"If no well be commenced on said land on or before one year from the date hereof, this lease shall terminate as to both parties, unless the lessee on or before that date shall pay or tender to the lessor or to the lessor's credit in the . . . . Bank at . . . ., or its successors, which shall continue as the depository for rental regardless of changes in the ownership of said land, the sum of . . . . Dollars, ($. . . . .) which shall operate as a rental and cover the privilege of deferring the commencement of a well for twelve months from said date. In like manner and upon like payments or tenders the commencement of a well may be further deferred for like periods of the same number of months successively."

In an OR LEASE (*q.v.*) a typical delay rental clause provides as follows:

"Commencing with . . . ., if the Lessee has not theretofore commenced drilling operations on said land or terminated this lease as herein provided, the Lessee shall pay or tender to Lessor . . . . in advance, as rental, the sum of . . . . Dollars per acre per . . . . for so much of said land as may then still be held under this lease, until drilling operations are commenced or this lease terminated as herein provided."

On the delay rental clause see TREATISE §§ 605–607.8.

Delay rental division order

A document addressed to the owner of a lease giving instructions concerning the payment of delay rentals to persons having interests therein. See TREATISE § 702.

See also DIVISION ORDER.

Delay rental title opinion

A statement of opinion by an attorney as to the persons entitled to receive payment of delay rentals on leased land. See Atlantic Refining Co. v. Shell Oil Co., 217 La. 576, 46 So. 2d 907 (1950).

See also TITLE OPINION.

Deliverability standard pressure

The standard used in calculating deliverability of gas wells. See "Annual Review of Significant Legislative, Judicial and Administrative Activities during 1976," 10 *Nat. Res. Law.* 3 at 151 (1977).

Delivery in kind

Delivery to the owner of an interest in production of the hydrocarbons which have been produced rather than accounting to such person for the value or price thereof. See ROYALTY IN KIND.

Delivery pressure

The agreed pressure at which delivery of gas is to be made under a GAS PURCHASE CONTRACT (*q.v.*).

Delivery ticket

Any expense bill or written document covering oil or products delivered. Tex. Rev. Civ. Stat. Ann. Art. 6066a § 1(j) (1962).

Demand billing

The demand upon which billing to a customer is based, as specified in a rate schedule or contract. It may be based on the contract year, a contract minimum, or a previous minimum and, therefore, does not necessarily coincide with the actual measured demand of the billing period. American Gas Association Bureau of Statistics, *Glossary for the Gas Industry* 16.

Demand charge

That portion of a rate for gas service which is based on the actual or estimated peak daily (monthly or hourly) usage of the customer. Compare COMMODITY CHARGE. American Gas Association Bureau of Statistics, *Glossary for the Gas Industry* 16.

See also RATE TILTING; SEABOARD METHOD; UNITED METHOD.

Demand clause

See ECONOMY ENERGY TRANSACTION; NOTICE AND DEMAND CLAUSE

Demand rate

The charge for gas which a distributor may demand under a gas sales contract to meet the requirements of the distributor's firm and space heating customers.

See also COMMODITY CHARGE; RATE TILTING.

Demonstrated reserves or resources

A collective term for the sum of MEASURED and INDICATED RESERVES OR RESOURCES. 2 *OCS Oil and Gas—An Environmental Assessment,* A Report to the President by the Council on Environmental Quality (April 1974) at p. 11.

See also INDICATED RESERVES OR RESOURCES; MEASURED RESERVES OR RESOURCES; RESERVES.

Density logging

See GAMMA RAY-GAMMA RAY LOGGING.

Density of petroleum

The specific gravity or weight of petroleum. Density or specific gravity is ordinarily expressed as the ratio between equal volumes of water and another substance, measured at a standard temperature and pressure. The weight of the water is assigned a value of 1. Sincc most petroleum has a lesser density than water, the specific gravity of petroleum is a fraction. For example, the specific gravity of octane is .7064. In the oil industry, however, the density of crude oil is normally expressed in API degrees. On this scale, the ratio is inverted, so that the greater the density of the petroleum, the lower the degree of API gravity. Most crude oil ranges in density between 27 degree to 35 degree API.

See also API GRAVITY; BAUME SYSTEM.

Density order

An order by a regulatory commission regulating well locations. See Railroad Comm'n v. DeBardeleben, 297 S.W.2d 203, 7 *O.&G.R.* 360 (Tex. Civ. App. 1956), *aff'd,* 157 Tex. 518, 305 S.W.2d 141, 8 *O.&G.R.* 466 (1957).

Departmental lease

A NON-COMPETITIVE LEASE (*q.v.*) on federally-owned land. For federal income tax purposes, first-year rentals paid under such leases are deductible. United States v. Dougan, 214 F.2d 511, 3 *O.&G.R.* 1597 (10th Cir. 1954); Commissioner v. Miller, 227 F.2d 326, 5 *O.&G.R.* 173 (9th Cir. 1955); Featherstone v. Commissioner, 22 T.C. 765, 3 *O.&G.R.* 1587 (1954), *acq.* 1956 I.R.B. 23, 6, 6 *O.&G.R.* 271 (1956), *withdrawing former non-acq.*

Department of Energy

The Department established by Pub. L. No. 95–91 (Aug. 4, 1977), 42 U.S.C. § 7101 *et seq.*, as a consolidation of a number of Commissions and energy-related activities of the federal government.

See also ECONOMIC REGULATORY AADMINISTRATION (ERA); FEDERAL ENERGY REGULATORY COMMISSION (FERC).

Depleted formation

A petroleum reservoir from which all the recoverable oil and gas has been removed. It has become common practice in recent years for natural gas pipe line companies to store gas near the consumer market in depleted formations.

See also GAS STORAGE, SUBSURFACE.

Depletion

Several usages of the word should be distinguished:

(1) *Physical depletion* is the exhaustion of a mine or a petroleum reservoir by extracting the minerals.

(2) *Economic depletion* is the reduction in the value of a wasting asset by removing the minerals.

(3) *Depletion for tax purposes* is the removal *and sale* of minerals from a mineral deposit. The tax concept of depletion differs from the physical and economic concept in that the former depends on sale and the latter only on removal.

The Internal Revenue Code (1954), §§ 611–613A, authorizes a deduction from income for depletion in the case of oil and gas wells. The taxpayer is entitled to cost depletion or percentage depletion, whichever is higher. The availability of percentage depletion was greatly limited by the Tax Reduction Act of 1975. See DEPLETION, PERCENTAGE.

The right to a depletion allowance for tax purposes depends on ownership of an economic interest in minerals in place. For many years ownership of the following interests entitled the taxpayer to a depletion allowance: mineral interest, working interest in a lease, royalty, overriding royalty, production payment, lease bonus (considered advance royalty), and net profits interest. See Anderson v. Helvering, 310 U. S. 404 (1940), and the many cases cited therein. A Supreme Court decision held that the owner of beach land, who agreed to the use of his land as the site for a directional well bottomed under the sea on land owned by another, was entitled to a depletion allowance on the interest acquired in the production from the well. Commissioner v. Southwest Exploration Co., 350 U.S. 308, 5 *O.&G.R.* 839 (1956).

See also DEPLETION, COST; EARNED DEPLETION; FIRST MARKETABLE PRODUCT; FRONTIER EXPLORATION ALLOWANCE; PROPORTIONATE PROFITS METHOD; SUCCESSOR EARNED DEPLETION; SUPPLEMENTARY DEPLETION ALLOWANCES.

Depletion, cost

In federal income taxation, the method of figuring the depletion allowance in relation to the taxpayer's investment. U.S. Treas. Reg. § 1.611–2(a) (1980) provides a formula for the calculation, which may be expressed as follows:

$$B \left(\frac{s}{u+s}\right)$$, where

B = the adjusted basis of the property;

u = units of oil or gas remaining at the end of the tax year;

s = units of oil or gas sold in the tax year.

Depletion drive

A drive mechanism for the production of oil which depends upon solution gas or dissolved gas.

See also RESERVOIR ENERGY.

Depletion, economic

The reduction in the value of a mineral deposit as the minerals are produced.

Depletion, percentage

In federal income taxation, the method of figuring the depletion allowance on the basis of an arbitrary percentage of gross income from production. For many years the Internal Revenue Code, for oil and gas wells, allowed a deduction of 27 1/2% of gross income from production, excluding royalty payments, such figure not to exceed 50% of the taxable (net) income from the property, as computed without allowance for depletion. The Tax Reform Act of 1969 reduced the rate of percentage depletion for oil and gas wells from 27 1/2% to 22%. The Tax Reduction Act of 1975 further limited the availability of percentage depletion. Internal Revenue Code § 613A. See Burke and Russell, "The New Percentage Depletion Rules," 25 *O.&G. Tax Q.* 13 (1975).

See also ADVANCE ROYALTY; AGGREGATION OF PROPERTIES; BONUS; CUT-OFF POINT; DEPLETION, RESTORATION OF; ECONOMIC INTEREST FOR TAX PURPOSES; IPRO EXEMPTION; NET INCOME FOR DEPLETION ALLOWANCE: NON-OPERATING MINERAL INTEREST, FOR TAX PURPOSES; OPERATING MINERAL INTEREST, FOR TAX PURPOSES; OPERATING UNIT, FOR TAX PURPOSES; PROPERTY UNIT, FOR TAX PURPOSES; TRANSFER RULE.

Depletion, physical

The exhaustion of supply of a wasting asset.

Depletion, restoration of

In federal income taxation, the adding back to income of depletion allowance taken on minerals not produced. Where a lessee had paid a bonus or had made advance royalty payments not derived from production, and the lessor had taken depletion on such income in the year received, then upon abandonment or termination of the lease without production, the lessor was required to restore to income the deductions for depletion in the prior years and make such restoration in the year the lease terminated. U. S. Treas. Reg. § 1.612–3 (b)(2) (1980), Douglas v. Commissioner, 322 U.S. 275 (1944); Campbell v. Commissioner, 41 T.C. 91, 19 *O.&G.R.* 467 (1963).

Restoration was not required if there had been production or if the lessee retained part of the lease. See Crabb v. Comm'r, 119 F.2d 772 (5th Cir. 1941); Houston Farms Dev. Co. v. Comm'r, 147 F.2d 493 (5th Cir. 1945).

See also DEPLETION, PERCENTAGE.

Depletion type reservoir

The term employed in Sinclair Oil & Gas Co. v. Bishop, 441 P.2d 436, 30 *O.&G.R.* 614 (Okla. 1967), to describe a RESERVOIR (*q.v.*) in which the necessary energy to produce oil from the reservoir is supplied by the gas pressure in a gas cap. Unless gas pressure is maintained in such a reservoir by repressuring or other operations, much of the oil in the reservoir will become nonrecoverable by reason of reduction of pressure incident to production, particularly where wells are permitted to produce with a high gas-oil ratio.

Depletory covenant

A term employed by one writer to describe the asserted obligation of a lessee to refrain from, or to account for, drainage from beneath the lessor's land through wells drilled and operated by the lessee himself upon adjoining lands, either owned by the lessee, or leased by him from other landowners. The covenant is said to include protection against FRAUDULENT DRAINAGE (*q.v.*) and other depletory acts, *e.g.*, destroying a producing well either by pulling the casing or by plugging it, or driving oil from beneath lessor's land by converting an offset well into a repressuring well. Seed, "The Implied Covenant in Oil and Gas Leases to Refrain from Depletory Acts," 3 *U.C.L.A. L. Rev.* 508 (1956); TREATISE §§ 824–824.3.

See also DRAINAGE.

Deposit

An accumulation of oil, gas or other minerals capable of production.

Depository bank

The bank to which payment of DELAY RENTAL (*q.v.*) may be made to the credit of the lessor or his successors in interest in accordance with the provisions of the DELAY RENTAL CLAUSE (*q.v.*) of the lease. When timely payment is made to the depository bank in accordance with the terms of this clause, the payment has the same effect as if made directly to the lessor or his successors in interest. See TREATISE §§ 605.5, 606.5.

Depreciation

A charge reflecting the loss in useful value of physical equipment by reason of wear and tear.

For a discussion of the various methods of depreciation of oil and gas equipment and leasehold costs, see Fiske, *Federal Taxation of Oil and Gas Transactions,* ch. 5–6 (1983 Revision); Irving and Draper, *Accounting Practices in the Petroleum Industry* (1958).

For a discussion of methods of depreciation employed in calculating cost of service for rate purposes see In the Matter of Olin Gas Transmission Corp., 17 F.P.C. 685 at 695, 7 *O.&G.R.* 936 (1957).

See also ACCELERATED COST RECOVERY SYSTEM (ACRS); CAPITAL ALLOWANCES; CAPITAL COST ALLOWANCE.

Depropanizer

A portion of a processing plant wherein the separation of propane from natural gas is accomplished.

Depth bracket allowable

In Louisiana, an ALLOWABLE (*q.v.*) based entirely on depth of a well. Since 1960 an acreage factor has also been utilized in the allocation formula for new pools. See McKie and McDonald, "Petroleum Conservation in Theory and Practice," 64 *Q. J. Econ.* 98 at 117 (1964); Smith, "Depth Bracket Allowable Determination and Proration of Oil Production in Louisiana," 24 *La. L. Rev.* 638 (1964).

Depth-bracket method of proration

A proration method whereunder all wells of a particular depth are permitted an established production. See Daggett, *Mineral Rights in Louisiana* 491 (rev. ed. 1949); Dutton, "Proration in Texas: Conservation or Confiscation?" 11 *Sw. L.J.* 186 (1957).

Syn.: DEPTH BRACKET ALLOWABLE; YARDSTICK ALLOWABLE.

See also ALLOWABLE.

Derrick

A tapering tower, usually of open steel framework although formerly of wood, used in the drilling of oil and gas wells as support for the equipment lowered into the well. Both methods of drilling—cable tool and rotary—use derricks, but the latter are larger. Derricks may be as high as a twenty-story building.

See also DRILLING RIG.

Description

That part of a lease or other conveyance describing, tracing and delineating the specific tract of land in which the specific interest conveyed, leased, excepted or reserved exists.

Desertion of well

"The removal of production equipment or the failure to produce oil or gas (other than a gas well shut in for lack of a market) for a period of one year is prima facie evidence of desertion of a well. Such well shall be plugged in accordance with the rules and regulations of the commission and the site restored." North Dakota Administrative Code 43-02-03-55. See Amerada Hess Corp. v. Furlong Oil and Minerals Co., 348 N.W.2d 913, 81 *O.&G.R.* 545 (N.D. 1984).

See also ABANDONED WELL.

Designated area

In the United Kingdom this is a National Park, Area of Outstanding Natural Beauty, Site of Special Scientific Interest, National Nature Reserve, Conservation Area, or other area (presumably of similar kind) given protection for environmental reasons from mineral development. J. Salter, *U.K. Onshore Oil and Gas Law* 1-508 (1986).

Designated Crown Corporation (DCC)

A corporation (such as Petro-Canada) to which the 25% Crown share out of all federal oil and gas lands may be disposed under the provisions of the 1978 amendments to the Canada Oil & Gas Act and the 1980 NATIONAL ENERGY PROGRAM (NEP) (*q.v.*), providing for the Canadianization of petroleum exploration and production on federal lands. See Hunt, "Private Sector Legal Problems Arising from Canadianization of Petroleum Activities," in *Resources, The Newsletter of the Canadian Institute of Resources Law* (No. 5, June 1983) at page 2.

Designated pool

In Alberta, a pool described in an order of the Energy Resources Conservation Board by surface area vertically above the pool and named by geological formation, member or zone in which the pool occurs or by such other method of identification as the Board considers suitable. Alberta Oil and Gas Conservation Act, R.S.A. 1970, c. 267, § 33.

See also POOL.

Desk and Derrick Club

An organization of women employed in the oil industry.

For a number of years the Association of Desk and Derrick Clubs has followed a policy of providing educational programs, study courses and field trips for its membership. A Program Committee, operating at national level, reviews and grades each program to insure compliance with the regulation that each club must maintain 80 percent educational programs.

De-spacing

Syn. for DOWN-SPACING (*q.v.*).

Destination and resale restrictions

Provisions in an international exploration and development contract providing restrictions on the buyer. See, *e.g.*, the following portion of the Saudi Arabian-Aramco contract:

"Article 8: Buyer/user requirement and destination

"8.1 It is expressly understood that BUYER will process Crude Oil sold under this Contract in its own processing facilities or under processing arrangements with other refineries for BUYER's own account. BUYER undertakes that under no circumstances shall BUYER resell the said Crude Oil in its original form or blend it with any other crude oil or crude oil deliveries for purposes of resale. . . . The following exceptions to the foregoing principles will be permitted:

"(1) BUYER may transfer Crude Oil sold under this Contract to Buyer Affiliates at cost;

"(2) Buyer may exchange Crude Oil sold under this Contract with Buyer Affiliates; and

"(3) provided Seller's written consent is first obtained (which consent will not unreasonably be withheld) BUYER may make Crude Oil exchanges with companies other than Buyer Affiliates. . . . ([However,] if SELLER requests, BUYER shall provide documentation with regard to the terms of such exchanges.)

"8.2 BUYER shall comply with the Laws of Saudi Arabia concerning the country of destination of Crude Oil sold under the terms of this Contract.

"8.3 In the event of any breach by BUYER of paragraphs 1 and 2 of this Article, SELLER shall have the right to terminate this Contract at its sole discretion without any notice or responsibility for compensation or payment and/or any claim from Buyer." Danielsen, *The Evolution of OPEC* 260 (1982).

See also CONCESSION.

Det norske stats oljeselskap a.s. (STATOIL)

The Norwegian state oil company. See STATOIL.

Develop

Gorenflo v. Texaco, Inc., 566 F. Supp. 722 at 727, (M.D. La. 1983), *aff'd*, 735 F.2d 835, 81 *O.&G.R.* 284 (5th Cir. 1984), declared that "the word 'develop' as used in the oil and gas industry contemplates any step taken in the search for, capture, production and marketing of hydrocarbons. Thus, the word 'develop' as used in the industry clearly contemplates and includes exploration."

See also Adolph v. Stearns, 235 Kan. 622, 684 P.2d 372, 82 *O.&G.R.* 64 (1984), construing the term "developed or operated" as employed in the habendum clause of a lease, citing this MANUAL.

Developed area or developed unit

"[A] drainage unit having a well completed thereon capable of producing oil or gas in paying quantities." Ariz. Rev. Stat. § 27–501 (5)(1976)(1979 Supp.).

See also DRAINAGE UNIT.

Development

The drilling and bringing into production of wells in addition to the exploratory or discovery well on a lease. The drilling of development wells may be required by the express or implied covenants of a lease.

See also REASONABLE DEVELOPMENT COVENANT.

Developmental program well

This term, as employed in a prospectus for a limited partnership drilling program, is defined as:

> "A well to be drilled (or a pre-existing well to be completed or recompleted or reworked) whose primary objective is a defined geological feature in a confined geographic area where prior drilling has established hydrocarbon production and where productive geologic reservoirs have been identified. A Developmental Program Well differs from and presents higher risks than a Development well because, among other reasons, it may be drilled more than one location away from a well producing from the same reservoir or it may be drilled to a reservoir from which there has been no production."

See also DRILLING FUND.

Developmental unit

A term employed by one writer to describe a unit "formed for the purpose of permitting rapid and systematic development of a field as an integral step leading to a program of conservation of unitized substances by means of regulation of production and injection of fluids into the producing reservoir." Roark, "Matters of Mutual Concern to the Lawyer and Engineer in the Unitization Agreement," 7 *Sw. Legal Fdn. Oil & Gas Inst.* 275 at 276 (1956).

See also UNIT.

Development Assistance Committee (DAC)

A committee of 17 nations established by the ORGANIZATION FOR ECONOMIC COOPERATION AND DEVELOPMENT (OECD) (*q.v.*) "to secure an expansion of the aggregate volume of resources made available to less-developed countries and to improve their effectiveness." See "The Economics of Energy and Natural Resource Pricing," A Compilation of Reports and Hearings of the Ad Hoc Committee on the Domestic and International Monetary Effect of Energy and Other Natural Resource Pricing, House Committee on Banking, Currency and Housing, 94th Cong., 1st Sess. (March 1975) at p. 463.

Development clause

(1) The drilling and delay rental clause of a lease. (See DELAY RENTAL CLAUSE.)

(2) An express clause specifying the number of development wells to be drilled. See TREATISE § 671.4.

Development contract

A federal contract designed to promote timely and full operations in areas where special development incentive and acreage-relief treatment is required if reserves are to be developed. The contract frees the holder from application of the acreage limitation restrictions for a specified period of time, conditioned on meeting certain requirements as to minimum expenditures on geological or geophysical activities and test well drilling. See Abbott, "Federal Oil and Gas Leasing Laws: Full Symphony or Overture?" *1959 Sw. Legal Fdn. Nat'l Inst. for Petroleum Landmen* 81 at 105 (1960).

Development covenant

See REASONABLE DEVELOPMENT COVENANT

Development license (DL)

Under the December, 1984, United Kingdom regulations [The Petroleum (Production) (Landward Areas) Regulations (1984)], a Development license (DL) may be issued for a 20-year term (extendable at the Secretary of State's discretion) after a suitable development program has been submitted and long-term planning permission has been obtained. The Secretary of State has discretion to extend the DL if there is still production from the licensed area. See Case Digest and National News, [1984/85] 12 *OGLTR* D-130; J. Salter, *U.K. Onshore Oil and Gas Law* 1-132 (1986).

See also APPRAISAL LICENSE (AL); EXPLORATION LICENSE (EXL).

Development well

A well drilled to a known producing formation in a previously discovered field as distinguished from a wildcat, or exploratory, well and from an offset well. The legal duty to drill development wells sometimes is expressly set out in the lease, but more often depends on the implied covenant of reasonable development. Even development wells can be dry holes, where, for example, the exact boundaries of a field have not been determined and the well penetrates below the oil-water contract line.

Sun Exploration & Production Co. v. Jackson, 715 S.W.2d 199, ____ *O.&G.R.* ____ (Tex. App., Houston, 1986), distinguished exploratory development wells from exploratory wildcat wells and sustained in part a trial court decree unconditionally canceling a lease as to a portion of the leased acreage and conditionally canceling other portions of the lease for prolonged failure of the lessee to drill exploratory development wells.

See also EXPLORATORY WELL; FIELD DEVELOPMENT WELL; FURTHER EXPLORATION COVENANT.

Deviation

A divergence or deflection from the vertical in the drilling of a well. The deviation may be intentional, as the result of WHIPSTOCKING (*q.v.*), or may be accidental as the result of the drilling bit coming in contact with a slanting, hard or tough stratum of rock which causes a deviation in the direction of the downward slope of the stratum.

See also DIRECTIONAL DEVIATION; RANDOM DEVIATION; RULE 54; TOTCO TEST.

Deviational survey

A survey of a well to determine whether a well bore deviates from the vertical and the extent of such deviation, if any. On the power of a court to order a deviational or directional survey, see L & G Oil Co. v. Railroad Comm'n, 368 S.W.2d 187, 18 *O.&G.R.* 664 (Tex. 1963); Williams v. Continental Oil Co., 215 F.2d 4, 3 *O.&G.R.* 2080 (10th Cir. 1954); Hastings Oil Co. v. Texas Co., 149 Tex. 416, 234 S.W.2d 389 (1950).

See also ACID BOTTLE INCLINOMETER; ACID DIP SURVEY; DIRECTIONAL SURVEY; RULE 54.

Devonian shale

Gas-bearing black or brown shale of the Devonian geologic age underlying large portions of the Appalachian Basin. It has been estimated that the reserves of gas in Devonian shales is about equal in size to the proved reserves of conventional natural gas. Landsberg, Chairman, *Energy: The Next Twenty Years* 241 (Report of a Study Group Sponsored by the Ford Foundation, 1979).

Devotional limitation doctrine

The term occasionally applied to the rule laid down in Texas Co. v. Davis, 113 Tex. 321, 254 S.W. 304 (1923), to the effect that there is an implied special limitation in certain leases that the premises will be devoted to exploration, development and production. Upon failure so to devote the premises, the leasehold terminates by operation of this implied special limitation. Clearly the presence of a delay rental clause in the lease negates the existence of this implied special limitation while the rental clause is operative. However, the doctrine may have application when it is not. See TREATISE §§ 604.3, 955.5.

See also LIMITATION CLAUSE.

Diagonal offsetting

See OFFSET WELL

Diamond drill core bit

A cylindrical shaped drilling tool, rounded at the bottom and having a hole in the center, used in CORING (*q.v.*). The rounded bottom has industrial diamond chips set in place to aid cutting out of the core. It is used for extremely hard formations or in a program of continuous coring.

Diesel oil

A petroleum fraction composed primarily of aliphatic (linear or unbranched) hydrocarbons. Diesel oil is slightly heavier than kerosine and distills in the range 250 to 400 degrees C. It is used as a fuel in internal combustion engines in which ignition results from high temperatures produced by compression of air, and as a light fuel oil (No. 2 fuel oil). Hammond, Metz, and Maugh, *Energy and the Future* 159 (1973).

Differential

A premium added to the price of oil by reason of certain advantages, *e.g.*, a low sulfur content.

See also GRAVITY DIFFERENTIAL; MARKER PRICE; OIL PURCHASE AND SALE CONTRACT; SULFUR DIFFERENTIAL; TRANSPORT COST DIFFERENTIAL.

Differential pressure

The difference between the hydrostatic pressure in a bore hole and that of the surrounding formation. See J. C. Trahan Drilling Contractor, Inc. v. Cockrell, 255 So. 2d 599, 34 *O.&G.R.* 384 (La. App. 1969), *writ refused,* 254 La. 922, 228 So. 2d 482 (1969). Normally the hydrostatic head rises as depth increases and differential pressure is kept slightly positive which tends to cause some fluid to be lost into the formation. If fluids are entering the formation, a negative differential (kick) is created which must be controlled.

Differential pressure flow meter

Woods Petroleum Corp. v. Delhi Gas Pipeline Corp., 54 *Okla. B.J.* 1075 at 1076 (Okla. App. 1983), *opinion vacated only with regard to attorney fee,* 56 *Okla. B.J.* 48 (Okla. 1984), described this as a metering device which:

> "works by placing a restriction of a certain known size, known as an orifice plate, in a line of a certain known size, known as the meter run, and measuring the difference in pressure on either side of the orifice plate. Due to the physical fact that for a certain volume of gas to move through such a restriction a certain percentage of the pressure of the gas is translated into velocity, it becomes possible to determine precisely the volume of gas moving through the meter by measuring this pressure drop across the orifice plate. The critical factors in determining the flow are the size of the

opening in the orifice plate, the pressure on the system and the temperature of the gas."

See also METER; PRESSURE.

Diluent

A fluid (*e.g.*, diesel oil) added to heavy oil to improve the transmissibility of the oil through a gathering or other pipeline. Many leases provide for the cost of the diluent, if any, to be shared proportionately by owners of operating and nonoperating interests in production.

Diluent clause

A lease clause authorizing the lessee to deduct from royalty a reasonable charge for the cost of any diluent used in connection with production.

Dip

The incline or slope of a geological formation. Usually, sedimentary formations are not level; the rock plane slopes in some direction, as, for example south and southeast along the Gulf Coast of Texas. In any reservoir trap, petroleum is more likely to occur up dip than down dip, because petroleum rises.

Direct customer

A term used to describe a purchaser of gas directly from a gas pipeline company. State of Louisiana v. Federal Power Comm'n, 503 F.2d 844 at 869 (5th Cir. 1974).

Directional deviation

The intentional DEVIATION (*q.v.*) of a well from vertical in a predetermined compass direction. Texas Railroad Commission, Special Order No. 54, 17 *O.&G.R.* 109 at 111 (1963); 16 Tex. Admin. Code § 3.11.

See also RANDOM DEVIATION.

Directional drilling

(1) The drilling of a well that departs materially from the vertical. In the 1920's most directional drilling resulted from accident. At present, however, such drilling is usually done on purpose. Examples of such are: the drilling of a directional well to shut off a blowout;

the drilling of a number of directional wells from one drilling platform erected on water; the drilling of a directional well to land, the surface of which cannot be used for a well location, as a railroad right of way. A common device employed in directional well drilling is a WHIPSTOCK (*q.v.*), a joint that translates motion into a different direction.

Texas Railroad Commission Rule 11 (16 Tex. Admin. Code § 3.11) requires that wells be drilled as nearly vertical as possible by normal, prudent, practical drilling operations. If the necessity for directionally deviating a well arises unexpectedly, after drilling has begun, the operator may continue drilling after notice to the Commission: "The operator proceeds with the drilling of a deviated well under such circumstances at his own risk, and should he fail to show good and sufficient cause for such deviation, no permit will be granted for the production of the well." See Superior Oil Co. v. Railroad Comm'n, 546 S.W.2d 121, 56 *O.&G.R.* 617 (Tex. Civ. App. 1977, error ref'd n.r.e.) (sustaining the validity of a Commission order approving the bottom hole location of a deviated well and assigning a permanent allowable to the well).

For a discussion of the abuses of directional drilling, particularly in the East Texas field, see Prindle, *Petroleum Politics and the Texas Railroad Commission* 81 *et seq.* (1981).

(2) This term has also been used by the Federal Power Commission to describe the ability of producers to direct their drilling activities toward either oil or gas. See Permian Basin Area Rate Proceeding, 34 F.P.C. 159 at 184, 23 *O.&G.R.* 103 at 122 (Opinion No. 468, Aug. 5, 1965), *remanded,* Skelly Oil Co. v. Federal Power Comm'n, 375 F.2d 6, 26 *O.&G.R.* 237 (10th Cir. 1967), *aff'd in part and rev'd in part sub nom. In re* Permian Basin Area Rate Cases, 390 U.S. 747, 28 *O.&G.R.* 689 (1968).

Directional drilling clause

A lease clause providing that actual drilling from a surface location off the leasehold of a well to be completed or bottomed on the leased premises shall be considered as actual drilling under the lease terms. See *e.g.,* State of Alaska Department of Natural Resources Lease Form No. DL–1 (revised Sept. 1974), ¶ 40; Alaska Mineral Leasing Regulations, 11 AAC 83.145.

Directional survey

A well survey that measures the degree of departure of a hole from the vertical and the direction of departure. Thus, it may be determined whether a well trespasses on the land of another, for the bottom may be accurately determined. In several cases a plaintiff has secured a court order requiring the owner of a well to permit a directional survey to be made to determine if the well trespasses on the plaintiff's land. Williams v. Continental Oil Co., 215 F.2d 4, 3 *O.&G.R.* 2080 (10th Cir. 1954); Hastings Oil Co. v. Texas Co., 149 Tex. 416, 234 S.W.2d 389 (1950).

See Special Rule 54 of the Texas Railroad Commission, 17 *O.&G.R.* 109 (1963), for regulations concerning the taking of directional surveys in Texas. 16 Tex. Admin. Code § 3.11.

See also DEVIATIONAL SURVEY; RULE 54.

Directional well

A well that departs from the vertical. See DIRECTIONAL DRILLING.

Direct offsetting

See OFFSET WELL

Direct producer sale

A sale of natural gas by a producer to an end-user or distributor. See Means and Angyal, "The Regulation and Future Role of Direct Producer Sales," 5 *Energy L.J.* 1 (1984).

See also DIRECT SALE GAS.

Direct sale customer

A gas customer who purchases gas primarily for his own needs as distinguished from a RESALE CUSTOMER (*q.v.*) who does not use gas for its own purposes but resells it. Fort Pierce Utility Authority v. Federal Power Comm'n, 526 F.2d 993 at 995 (5th Cir. 1976).

See also GAS PURCHASE CONTRACT.

Direct sale gas

Gas purchased by natural gas end users and local distribution companies at the wellhead. These purchases were "set up to avoid the end users' and local distribution companies' total dependency on traditional interstate pipeline suppliers whom they had historically relied on for their natural gas needs." Airey and Teater, "Transportation of Direct Sale Natural Gas," 5 *Eastern Min. L. Inst.* 17-1 at 17-2 (1984) (discussion of state and federal regulation of direct sale gas and the problems of obtaining carriage for such gas).

Dirt work

A term sometimes applied to preliminary operations at a drill site, usually limited to road construction and site preparation and not including drilling operations. William Perlman, 93 I.D. 159 (April 2, 1986).

Dirty oil

Under a contract for the carriage of oil by sea this term is used for crude oil, diesel oil, fuel, and furnace oils and also for gas oil. See "The Tonnage Contract," [1982] 1 *OGLTR* 32.

Disclaimer by tenant (or surface owner)

A statement by the person in possession or the owner of the surface to the effect that such person claims no interest in the minerals underlying the land. See *Rocky Mt. Min. Law Fdn. Landman's Legal Handbook* 142–143, 303–304 (3d ed. 1977).

Disconformity

A type of UNCONFORMITY (*q.v.*) A disconformity occurs when an older sedimentary deposit has been folded, then eroded, and then a younger sediment laid down on top. The two sediments will then dip at different angles, hence the name disconformity or angular unconformity.

Discounted cash flow method

A method of estimating unit cost for gas. See McLean, "How to Evaluate New Capital Investments," 36 *Harv. Bus. Rev.* 59 (Nov.–Dec. 1958).

For discussions of the employment of this method by the Federal Power Commission, see the following:

The Second National Natural Gas Rate Cases (American Public Gas Ass'n v. Federal Power Comm'n), 567 F.2d 1016, 59 *O.&G.R.* 351 (D.C. Cir. 1977), *cert. denied,* 435 U.S. 907 (1978);

Shell Oil Co. v. Federal Power Comm'n, 520 F.2d 1061 at 1079 (5th Cir. 1975), *reh. denied,* 525 F.2d 1261 (5th Cir. 1976), *cert. denied,* 426 U.S. 941 (1976).

See also ACCOUNTING METHODS.

Discounted MROV (DMROV)

A calculation made by the Geological Survey in evaluating competitive lease bids on submerged lands of the Outer Continental Shelf designed to estimate the effect on the value of the tract to the government if the high bid was rejected and the tract was held to be reoffered at a future lease sale. Normally, the DRMOV will be less than the MEAN OF THE RANGE OF VALUES (MROV) (*q.v.*), since any delay in reoffering results in a loss of the use of receipts. However, in certain cases, the DMROV will exceed the MROV because of rising energy prices. "The DMROV is not considered in evaluating the high bid in these circumstances. . . . However, a high bid above DMROV is almost always accepted." Kerr-McGee Corp. v. Watt, 517 F. Supp. 1209 at 1210, 71 *O.&G.R.* 494 at 496 (D.D.C. 1981).

Discoveries

"[P]roved reserves credited to new fields and new pools in old fields as the result of successful exploratory drilling and associated development drilling during the current year." American Petroleum Institute Division of Statistics, *Organization and Definitions for the Estimation of Reserves and Productive Capacity of Crude Oil* 15 (Technical Report No. 2, June 1970).

See also RESERVES.

Discovery

Drilling of a well to a formation capable of production of oil and/or gas.

Some cases have held that discovery alone is sufficient to keep a lease alive beyond the primary term, but the majority rule is that production is required for this purpose, absent some savings clause in the lease such as a SHUT-IN GAS WELL CLAUSE, DRILLING OPERATIONS CLAUSE, or CONTINUOUS DRILLING OPERATIONS CLAUSE (*q.v.*). See Cantwell, "Term Royalty," 6 *Sw. Legal Fdn. Oil & Gas Inst.* 339 at 351 *et seq.* (1956); TREATISE § 604.1.

For purposes of extension of certain federal leases, "discovery" does not require the completion of a well capable of producing oil and gas in paying quantities. Joseph I. O'Neill, Jr., 77 I.D. 181, IBLA 70–39, GFS-BLA-CON-1970–12 (Oct. 9, 1970).

Discovery is distinguished from "a well capable of producing oil or gas in paying quantities" by Arlyne Lansdale, 16 IBLA 42, GFS(O&G) 1974–47 (June 20, 1974). It was held in this case that although a well had been drilled into a formation capable of producing gas, the casing set and cemented, since the casing had not been perforated the well was not in a physical condition to produce and hence it was not a well capable of producing oil or gas in paying quantities within the meaning of that term in 30 U.S.C. § 226(f).

In Gladys City Co. v. Amoco Production Co., 528 F. Supp. 624 at 626, 73 *O.&G.R.* 88 at 90 (E.D. Tex. 1981), the parties were in agreement that "discovery" of a "valuable mineral" as used in the instrument construed "means that a mineral covered by the grant in the lease is found in sufficient quantity, with a sufficient market, that it can be produced at a profit."

The discovery requirement under early mining laws and the Mineral Leasing Act of 1920 is discussed in Tosco Corp. v. Hodel, 611 F.Supp. 1130 at 1170 *et seq.* (D. Colo. 1985). This case was settled by an Aug. 4, 1986 agreement. See 2 *Nat. Res. & Environment* 74 (Fall 1986), 804 F.2d 590 (10th Cir. 1986).

Discovery lease selection

The selection for lease which a permittee who has made a commercial discovery of oil or gas may make from the lands subject to a permit to explore. See *e.g.*, Saskatchewan Petroleum and Natural Gas Regulations, 1969 (O.C. 8/69) § 22.

Discovery royalty

A special lower royalty of five percent (rather than the usual 12½%) payable under certain leases of the State of Alaska by the leaseholder who drilled and made the first discovery of oil and gas in commercial quantities in a geologic structure. AS 38.05.180(a). By legislative amendments in 1967 and 1969 the discovery royalty system was curtained and finally abolished. See Union Oil Co. of California v. State of Alaska, Department of Natural Resources, 526 P.2d 1357 (Alaska 1974), *on second appeal,* 574 P.2d 1266 (Alaska 1978).

Discovery well

An exploratory well that encounters a new and previously untapped mineral deposit. A discovery well may open up a new field, or it may locate a new and previously unknown producing horizon in an old field.

Discovery well allowable

An additional ALLOWABLE (*q.v.*) granted to a discovery well. In Mississippi, for example, the owners and producers of a discovery well may certify to the oil and gas board an itemized list of the expenses incurred in the actual drilling of such well. Upon certification by the Oil and Gas Board of the amount of such costs, the discovery well is not subject to restrictions on production until the cost of drilling such well shall have been recovered in oil or gas from such discovery well. Miss. Code 1972, § 53–1–17(12) (1979 Supp.).

This allowable normally exceeds the average per well allowable for older reservoirs. It is not subject to shutdown days. See Dutton, "Proration in Texas: Conservation or Confiscation?," 11 *Sw. L.J.* 186 at 189 (1957); 16 Tex. Admin. Code § 3.42.

See also Zimmermann, *Conservation in the Production of Petroleum* 218 (1957).

Displaced gas

TRANSPORTATION GAS (*q.v.*) which has been displaced by the carrier in order to deliver CONSUMER GAS (*q.v.*) and which is delivered at a later time when capacity becomes available.

Displacement

See TRANSPORTATION BY DISPLACEMENT.

Disposal well

A well employed for the reinjection of salt water produced with oil into an underground formation. See 16 Tex. Admin. Code § 3.9.

Disqualified transferor

For purposes of the CRUDE OIL WINDFALL PROFIT TAX ACT OF 1980 (*q.v.*), this term means, with respect to any quarter, any person who: (1) had qualified production for such quarter which exceeded such person's independent producer amount for such quarter, or (2) was not an independent producer for such quarter. Internal Revenue Code § 4992.

Disrepute clause

A clause said to be included in all Petromin contracts with foreign government oil purchasers which enables the Saudi government entity to terminate the contract if the Saudis conclude that the other government acts in a manner which brings discredit to the Saudi government. Conant, "Government-to-Government Agreements," *Energy Law 1981,* Seminar of the International Bar Association Committee on Energy and Natural Resources at p. 8 (1981).

See also CONCESSION.

Dissolved gas drive

The energy, derived from expansion of solution gas, used in the production of oil. *Syn.:* Solution-gas expansion. Gas escapes from solution within the oil upon reduction of pressure and drives the oil from the reservoir into the well. This form of drive is characterized by rapidly declining pressure and an increasing amount of gas necessary to produce a barrel of oil, with rapidly increasing gas-oil ratios.

See also RESERVOIR ENERGY.

Distillate

Liquid hydrocarbons, usually colorless and of high API gravity (above 60 degrees), recovered from wet gas by a separator that condenses the liquid out of the gas. This is the older name for the substance; generally at present the term NATURAL GASOLINE (*q.v.*) or CONDENSATE (*q.v.*) is used.

Any product separated, or purified, or identified by distillation. See Asiatic Petroleum Corp. v. United States, 183 F. Supp. 275, 12 *O.&G.R.* 841 (Customs Court 1959).

Distillate fuel oil

A term subject to a variety of definitions. Sometimes the definition is based on the method of production (distillation), but other definitions are based on boiling range, viscosity, or use. See RESIDUAL FUEL OIL. Most commonly the term is used in connection with diesel oil and the light fuel oils used for residential heating. See Hammond, Metz, and Maugh, *Energy and the Future* 159 (1973). Distillates are classified in grades, called Number 1, 2, 3, 4, 5, and 6 fuels. The specific gravity of fuel oils range from O.92 to O.99.

As distinguished from residual fuel oils which are leftovers of refining processes, distillate fuel oils are products of distillation and are lighter. They are used for a variety of purposes, including diesel fuel and for space heating. Residual fuel oils are used under boilers in ships and in power plants. See Zimmermann, *Conservation in the Production of Petroleum* 85 (1957).

Distribution line

A pipeline other than a GATHERING LINE (*q.v.*) or TRANSMISSION LINE (*q.v.*). 49 C.F.R. § 192.3 (1982). See Hamman v. Southwestern Gas Pipeline, Inc., 721 F.2d 140, 78 *O.&G.R.* 552 (5th Cir. 1983) (concerned with classification of pipeline in order to determine whether it was subject to regulation under the NATURAL GAS PIPELINE SAFETY ACT (NGPSA) (*q.v.*).

Distribution system

". . . [T]he mains which are provided primarily for distributing gas within a distribution area, together with land, structures, valves, regulators, services and measuring devices, including the mains for transportation of gas from production plants or points of receipt located within such distribution area to other points therein. The distribution system owned by companies having no transmission facilities connected to such distribution system begins at the inlet side of the distribution system equipment which meters or regulates the entry of gas into the distribution system and ends with and includes property on the customer's premises. For companies which own both transmission and distribution facilities on a continuous line, the distribution system begins at the outlet side of the equipment which meters or regulates the entry of gas into the distribution system and ends with and includes property on the customer's premises. The distribution system does not include storage land, structures, or equipment." 18 C.F.R. Part 201, Definitions 26(c) (1980).

See also COLLECTING SYSTEM; GATHERING SYSTEM.

District expenses

When a particular leasehold is included by the operator within a district in which many other wells are being operated, a proportionate part of the expenses of the district may be allocated to the particular leasehold, *e.g.*, on the basis of the relation of the number of wells on the particular leasehold to the number of wells in the district. See Luling Oil & Gas Co. v. Humble Oil & Refining Co., 144 Tex. 475, 191 S.W.2d 716 (1946).

In Mason v. Ladd Petroleum Corp., 630 P.2d 1283, 70 *O.&G.R.* 586 (Okla. 1981), after describing the work of a district office and the nature of district expenses, the court concluded that district expenses should not be considered in determining whether production was in paying quantities:

"The district office is the first level in defendant's chain of command. But while a district office may be convenient and even necessary as a pragmatic approach to making a corporate giant functional in the corporate administration of its lease operations, we deem the expense of such an office to be too indirectly and too remotely related to defendant's lifting or producing operations in connection with the Sherman No. 1 well to be included in determining whether the well operates at a profit." 630 P.2d at 1285, 70 *O.&G.R.* at 589.

Ladd Petroleum Corp. v. Eagle Oil & Gas Co., 695 S.W.2d 99, 87 *O.&G.R.* 116 (Tex. App., Fort Worth, 1985, error ref'd n.r.e.), concluded that district expenses and administrative overhead which would continue in effect even if the operation of a well were to cease should not be included as overhead in determining whether well was producing in paying quantities.

See also ADMINISTRATIVE OVERHEAD.

Divestment

In the petroleum and mining industries this term is applied to the process by which concessionaires relinquish their properties to host governments gradually over a period of years or at the end of the lease period. See Mikdashi, "Policy Issues in Primary Industries," 7 *Vanderbilt J. Transnational Law* 281 at 305 (1974).

See also CONCESSION; EXPROPRIATION; NATIONALIZATION.

Divided type of unit operating agreement

A unit operating agreement whereunder the sharing of costs and benefits is dependent upon participating areas which may be established from time to time. The undivided type of unit operating agreement, on the other hand, provides for the sharing of costs and benefits in accordance with a formula agreed upon at the time the unit is formed, without regard to the location and size of any participating areas which may be established from time to time. See *Rocky Mt. Min. Law Fdn. Landman's Legal Handbook* 155 (3d ed. 1977).

See also UNIT AGREEMENT.

Divisibility of covenants

The doctrine which concerns the effect on covenants of an assignment, by lessor or lessee, of part of the tract subject to the lease. As regards partial assignments by the lessor, the question is whether one assignee can proceed to enforce the lease covenants without joinder of other owners of lessor interests. As regards partial assignments by the lessee, the question is whether the covenants relate to each subdivision of the leasehold in severalty or apply to the entire leasehold without regard to the partial assignment. See DIVISIBLE COVENANTS.

Divisibility of lease

See PUGH CLAUSE; RULE OF INDIVISIBILITY.

Divisible covenants

Those duties imposed by an oil and gas lease that are apportioned to each individual subdivision of the leasehold after an assignment by the lessor or the lessee.

The typical oil and gas lease expressly makes the royalty clause divisible. As to the implied covenants relating to drilling, the cases are divided. Holding that these covenants are divisible upon partial assignment by the lessee are: Cosden Oil Co. v. Scarborough, 55 F.2d 634 (5th Cir. 1932); Standard Oil Co. v. Geller, 183 Ark. 776, 38 S.W.2d 76 (1931). Holding that the implied drilling covenants are indivisible are: Da Camera v. Binney, 146 S.W.2d 440 (Tex. Civ. App. 1941); see Amerada Petroleum Co. v. Sledge, 151 Okla. 160, 3 P.2d 167 (1931). See the argument for non-divisibility of these covenants in Brown, "Assignments of Interests in Oil and Gas Leases," 5 *Sw. Legal Fdn. Oil & Gas Inst.* 25 at 43 (1954). See also Walker, "Nature of Property Interests Created by an Oil & Gas Lease in Texas," 11 *Texas L. Rev.* 399 at 452 (1933); TREATISE §§ 409–409.4.

A different aspect of the subject is presented when the lessor assigns a portion of the leasehold, and thereafter some but not all owners of the lessor's interest bring suit for breach of covenant. The cases once again divide on the divisibility of the covenants. Holding that the covenants are divisible and hence the joinder of all owners in the action is unnecessary are: Theissen v. Weber, 128 Kan. 556, 278 Pac. 770 (1929); Toklan Royalty Corp. v. Panhandle Eastern Pipe Line Co., 172 Kan. 305, 239 P.2d 927 1 *O.&G.R.* 56 (1952); Compton v. Ficher-McCall, 298 Mich. 648, 299 N.W. 750 (1941). *Contra:* Callahan v. Martin, 3 Cal. 2d 110, 43 P.2d 788, 101 A.L.R. 871 (1935); Sun Oil Co. v. Oswell, 258 Ala. 326, 62 So. 2d 783, 2 *O.&G.R.* 145 (1953). It is not suggested that the joinder of parties question is always decided by reference to the divisibility, *vel non,* of the implied covenant in issue. See Hunt v. McWilliams, 218 Ark. 922, 240 S.W.2d 865 (1950).

A somewhat related subject is the divisibility of lease clauses other than express or implied covenants. The typical lease expressly makes the rental clause divisible, upon assignment by either lessor or lessee. On the other hand, the habendum clause is usually treated as indivisible. After subdivision, production anywhere on the tract keeps the lease alive after the primary term as to assignees of both lessor and lessee. Berry v. Tidewater Associated Oil Co., 188 F.2d 820 (5th Cir. 1951); Cosden Oil Co. v. Scarborough, 55 F.2d 634 (5th Cir. 1932); Gypsy Oil Co. v. Cover, 78 Okla. 158, 189 Pac. 540 (1920). *Contra,* Roberson v. Pioneer Gas Co., 173 La. 313, 137 So. 46, 82 A.L.R. 1264 (1931); Noel Estate v. Murray, 223 La. 387, 65 So. 2d 886, 2 *O.&G.R.* 951 (1953).

For a good general discussion, see Merrill, "The Partial Assignee—Done in Oil," 20 *Texas L. Rev.* 298 (1942).

Divisible lease covenants

See DIVISIBLE COVENANTS.

Divisible sharing arrangement

A SHARING ARRANGEMENT (*q.v.*) in which some consideration in addition to the development contribution [EXCESS CASH (*q.v.*)] passes between the grantor and grantee. The name derives from the fact that the arrangement is not a simple sharing arrangement but is a mixed sharing arrangement, "divisible" in the sense that for tax purposes, part of the transaction may be treated as a simple sharing arrangement (with no realization of income) and part treated otherwise, depending upon its nature. See Burke and Bowhay, *Income Taxation of Natural Resources* ¶¶ 7.06, 7.14 (1980).

Division order

A contract of sale to the purchaser of oil or gas. The order directs the purchaser to make payment for the value of the products taken in the proportions set out in the division order.

Even though the lessee by the terms of the lease has authority to dispose of any products produced, the purchaser usually requests the operator to furnish complete abstracts of title which the purchaser causes to be examined, after which a division order is prepared by the purchaser on the basis of the ownership shown in the title opinion prepared after examination of the abstracts. The purchaser usually requires that the division order be executed by the operator, the royalty owners and other persons having an interest in the production. When the division order is executed and returned to the purchaser, payment is commenced for the products removed. The division order is typically terminable at the will of either party.

As to the effect of a division order as a conveyance of interests in the producing property, see Snider v. Snider, 208 Okla. 231, 255 P.2d 273, 2 *O.&G.R.* 711 (1953). Execution of a division order permits payment to be made by a purchaser in accordance with the terms thereof even though in conflict with the actual ownership of interests in production. Chicago Corp. v. Wall, 293 S.W.2d 844, 6 *O.&G.R.* 703 (Tex. 1956). The execution of a division order by a nonleasing concurrent owner may operate as a ratification of a lease [Texas & Pacific Coal & Oil Co. v. Kirtley, 288 S.W. 619 (Tex. Civ. App. 1926, error ref'd)], or alter the terms of a lease [Simpson v. United Gas Pipe Line Co., 196 Miss. 356, 17 So. 2d 200 (1944)].

See also the following:

Hollimon, "Division Orders—A Primer," 34 *Sw. Legal Fdn. Oil & Gas Inst.* 313 (1983);

Knowlton and Morrow, "Division Orders," *Rocky Mt. Min. L. Fdn. Inst. on Oil and Gas Agreements* Paper 12 (1983);

Jacobson, "Division Orders are Unilaterally Revocable Agreements that Bind the Parties Until Properly Revoked: Exxon Corp. v. Middleton," 13 *Texas Tech L. Rev.* 142 (1982);

Edwards, "A Suggested Analysis for Gas Division Orders," 17 *Tulsa L.J.* 534 (1982);

Bounds, "Division Orders," 5 *Sw. Legal Fdn. Oil & Gas Inst.* 91 (1954);

Ethridge, "Oil and Gas Division Orders," 19 *Miss. L.J.* 127 (1948);

TREATISE §§ 701–715.

See also DELAY RENTAL DIVISION ORDER; ONE HUNDRED PERCENT OIL DIVISION ORDER.

The definition of division order in this MANUAL was cited by Kaufman v. Arnaudville Co., 186 So. 2d 337 at 342, 25 *O.&G.R.* 290 at 297 (La.App. 1966), *writ ref'd,* 249 La. 575, 187 So. 2d 739, 25 *O.&G.R.* 299 (1966).

Division order title opinion

See TITLE OPINION.

DL

DEVELOPMENT LICENSE (DL) (*q.v.*).

DLR

Abbreviation of *Dominion Law Reports,* a set of reports containing decisions of various Canadian courts.

DMROV

DISCOUNTED MROV (*q.v.*).

Doctrine of accommodation

See ACCOMMODATION DOCTRINE.

Doctrine of due regard

See ACCOMMODATION DOCTRINE.

Doctrine of obstruction

See OBSTRUCTION, DOCTRINE OF.

Doctrine of repudiation

See REPUDIATION, DOCTRINE OF.

DOE

The Department of Energy, established by Pub. L. No. 95–91 (Aug. 4, 1977), 42 U.S.C. § 7101 *et seq.*

DOE Act

The Department of Energy Organization Act, Pub. L. No. 95–91, 91 Stat. 565 (Aug. 4, 1977).

Doghouse

The small shed near the derrick where the driller and tool dressers keep their clothes. *API Quarterly* 3 (Spring 1957).

See Champlin Petroleum Co. v. Heinz, 665 S.W.2d 544 (Tex. App., Corpus Christi, 1983, error ref'd n.r.e.) (holding that maintenance of a doghouse on a leasehold was not a sufficient basis for establishing venue under a statute referring to "a fixed and established place of business").

This term is also used in offshore drilling operations for a part of the deck which serves as an office and base of operations for the driller and for a compression or decompression chamber in a diving installation.

Dog's leg

See CROOKED WELL.

Domanial law system

A term applied to the system under which ownership of mineral substances is vested in the sovereign, as distinguished from the so-called ACCESSION SYSTEM (*q.v.*) in the United States under which the landowner has certain ownership interests in minerals. Blinn, Duval, Le Leuch, and Pertuzio, *International Petroleum Exploration & Exploitation Agreements* 24 (1986).

For a brief discussion of ownership of minerals under Islamic law and of United Nations Resolutions on the ownership concepts applicable to natural resources, see *Id.* at 27-32.

Dome

See SALT DOME.

Dominant estate

The term applied to the estate to which a servitude or easement is due, or for the benefit of which it exists, or to the parcel of land benefitted by an easement or a servient estate. Oil and gas leases and mineral deeds generally contain express or implied rights of surface user; the lessee or mineral owner is viewed as owning the dominant estate and the lessor or surface owner is viewed as owning the SERVIENT ESTATE (*q.v.*). See TREATISE §§ 218–218.14.

See also ACCOMMODATION DOCTRINE.

Donation letter

An agreement by which one person agrees to contribute money toward the drilling of a well by another. Such payment is usually conditioned on completion of the well by the latter party as a dry hole [a DRY HOLE DONATION LETTER (*q.v.*)] or to a specified depth [a BOTTOM HOLE DONATION LETTER (*q.v.*)]. The inducement for such contribution is often the desire of the payor to have a test well drilled in the vicinity of his leaseholds. The absence of an assignment of a property interest in a donation letter distinguishes it from a PURCHASE LETTER (*q.v.*). See TREATISE §§ 431–431.2.

For other forms of letter agreements, see LETTER.

DONG A/S

DANSK OLIE OG NATURGAS A/S (DONG A/S) (*q.v.*), the state oil company of Denmark.

Donkey head

The term used to describe 15 to 20 foot head of a beam pump at the wellhead of a pumping well.

Syn.: GRASSHOPPER; NODDING DONKEY.

Doodle bug

A device alleged to be of value in the location of a site for an oil and gas well or a water well. The simplest form of doodle bug is a twig which, when held in the hands of an "expert" DOWSER (*q.v.*) walking over the premises, is said to react in a certain way, *e.g.*, by bending downwards, when the "expert" comes to a favorable portion of the land for the drilling of a well. There are instances in which production has been obtained by drilling a well at the site indicated by the doodle bug but contemporary informed opinion attributes this to chance and places no value in doodle bugs, whether a simple twig or a more complex device. See Frank v. United States, 220 F.2d 559, 4 *O.&G.R.* 1116 (10th Cir. 1955).

Rhabdomancy, the science of divination by rods or wands, has long had a substantial following and substantial success in discovering underground streams of water has been claimed by practitioners. It has been suggested that the history of success is based on discoveries in such areas as New England, where it is hard not to find water. Early in 1962 a design patent was granted for a divining rod to be employed as a prospecting tool for oil and gas to an inventor who claimed to have had success (not yet verified by drilling) in discovering petroleum deposits. See *The New York Times*, January 13, 1962.

This term is also employed in connection with seismograph operations.

Door mats

Small tracts—*e.g.*, 1/20 of an acre—just large enough to accommodate a derrick. At the time of the Spindletop development in 1901, many such small tracts were conveyed. See Norvell, "The Railroad Commission of Texas: Its Origin and History," 68 *Southwestern Historical Q.* 464 at 475 (1965).

Dormant minerals act

The term sometimes applied to a statute designed to extinguish mineral and royalty interests when there has been no exporation, development, or operations for a substantial number of years. See Mask v. Shell Oil Co., 77 Mich. App. 25, 257 N.W.2d 256, 58 *O.&G.R.* 535 (1977); TREATISE § 216.7.

The constitutionality of the Indiana act was sustained in Texaco, Inc. v. Short, 454 U.S. 516, 72 *O.&G.R.* 217 (1982).

See also REPOSE, RULE OF.

Double basing point structure

See BASING POINT.

Double suspension plug

An oil tool used in the wellhead of an oil well to suspend the tubing. It consists of a doughnut shaped outer plug tapered on the outside to fit in the tubing head, and on the inside to seat the inner plug. The latter is a smaller tapered plug which is screwed to the top of the tubing and actually suspends the tubing in the well. Basin Oil Co. v. Baash-Ross Tool Co., 125 Cal. App. 2d 578, 271 P.2d 122, 3 *O.&G.R.* 971 (1954).

Down-dip lease

A lease on the lower part of a formation. Amoco Production Co. v. Alexander, 622 S.W.2d 563 at 566, 72 *O.&G.R.* 125 at 127, 18 A.L.R.4th 1 (Tex. 1981).

See also UP-DIP LEASE.

Down-dip well

A well located low on the structure where the oil is furtherest from the surface of the field. Hunter v. Hussey, 90 So. 2d 429, 6 *O.&G.R.* 1172 (La. App. 1956).

Down-hole steam generation

A process of generation of steam for use in a heavy oil reservoir to reduce viscosity and increase recovery of the oil. Steam generation at the surface for this purpose has environmental problems and is effective only in relatively shallow horizons by reason of the decline in the temperature of the steam as it moves from the surface to the formation. Downhole steam generation may solve certain of the environmental problems and enable use of the technique in deeper horizons. See Department of Energy, *Energy Insider* (Vol. 4, No. 8, Apr. 14, 1980, p. 4).

See also THERMAL METHOD OF OIL RECOVERY.

Down-hole storm choke

A safety valve inside the tubing of flowing wells in the ocean which automatically shuts off production whenever there is an abnormal flow through the tubing. Thus if an accident were to open the production assembly by severing the wellhead connection, the storm choke automatically stops the flow of oil or gas within the system. See CHOKE.

Down-spacing

A regulatory commission order providing for denser spacing by infill drilling. Anderson, "New Directions in Oil and Gas Conservation Law," *Institute on Oil and Gas Conservation Law and Practice* 14-1 at 14-14 (Rocky Mt. Min. L. Fdn. 1985).

Syn.: De-spacing.

Downstream

This term is used in describing operations performed after those at a point of reference. Thus marketing may be described as a downstream operation and production as an upstream operation when the refinery is used as a point of reference. On a gas pipeline, downstream denotes a location further removed from the source of supply.

See also UPSTREAM.

Down-structure

Below the high point of a STRUCTURE (*q.v.*); down-dip. Since oil and gas rise in any structural formation, the most favorable place for discovering them is on the high point of the formation. As movement is always from this high point, the chances of successful production diminish.

Down the hole

Industry slang for the costs of drilling, testing, completing, and equipping a well for production or plugging and abandonment. Himebaugh, "An Overview of Oil and Gas Contracts in the Williston Basin," 59 *No. Dak. L. Rev.* 7 at 24 (1983).

Downtime

The period of time a well is shut down for workover, maintenance or for other reasons. By reason of price control regulations authorizing a higher price for old oil produced from a stripper well (one averaging 10 barrels a day or less) than for other "old oil", the question whether downtime could be used in calculating a well's production average became of substantial importance inasmuch as exclusion of downtime could cause some wells to lose their status as stripper wells. See Interstate Oil Compact Commission, *Compact Comments* 5 (Sept. 1975).

Dowser

The term applied to one who utilizes a DOODLE BUG (*q.v.*) to locate a site for an oil and gas well or a water well.

See also RHABDOMANCY.

DPC

The Dubai Petroleum Company. See Shwadran, *The Middle East, Oil and the Great Powers* 442 (3d ed. revised and enlarged, 1973).

Drag bit

See BIT, DRAG.

Drainage

Migration of oil or gas in a reservoir due to a pressure reduction caused by production from wells bottomed in the reservoir. Local drainage is the movement of oil and gas toward the well bore of a producing well. FIELD DRAINAGE (*q.v.*) is a reservoir-wide migration. Under the RULE OF CAPTURE (*q.v.*) there is no liability for producing oil or gas drained from beneath the land of another, absent negligent waste and destruction of the product drained. Elliff v. Texon Drilling Co., 146 Tex. 575, 210 S.W.2d 558, 4 A.L.R.2d 191 (1948).

Under the OFFSET WELL COVENANT (*q.v.*), a lessee may be liable for local drainage away from the leasehold or for FIELD DRAINAGE (*q.v.*) if he fails to drill offset wells to prevent the drainage.

See also COMPENSATORY DRAINAGE; CONTROLLED GRAVITY DRAINAGE; DEPLETORY COVENANT; FRAUDULENT DRAINAGE; NET DRAINAGE; PERMITTED DRAINAGE; RADIAL DRAINAGE; UNCOMPENSATED DRAINAGE.

Drainage method of evaluation

See PROVEN OR SEMI-PROVEN ACREAGE ("DRAINAGE") METHOD OF EVALUATION.

Drainage sale

A term used to describe the leasing of land in danger of being drained by production on adjacent lands. See Crommelin, "Off-shore Oil and Gas Rights: A Comparative Study," 14 *Nat. Res. J.* 457 at 460 (1974).

Drainage unit

"[T]he maximum area in a pool which may be drained efficiently by one well so as to produce the reasonable maximum amount of recoverable oil or gas in the area." Ariz.Rev.Stat. § 27–501(6) (1976) (1979 Supp.).

This term is defined by Saskatchewan Petroleum and Natural Gas Regulations, 1969, O/C 8/69, § 3(h) as "the area allocated to a well for the purpose of drilling for and producing oil or gas and includes subsurface areas bounded by the vertical planes in which surface boundaries lie."

Drawing entry card (DEC)

A card filed for the drawing conducted of simultaneously filed oil and gas lease offers. See W. C. Yahmel, IBLA 78–203, GFS(O&G) 1978–68.

See also FEDERAL LEASE; LEASING SERVICE COMPANY; MULTIPLE FILING; NON-COMPETITIVE LEASE; PUT OPTION; SIMULTANEOUS FILINGS.

Drawdown plan

See STRATEGIC PETROLEUM RESERVE.

Draw works

The collective name for the hoisting drum, shaft, clutches, and other operating machinery used in the drilling of a well. Draw works are situated at one side of the derrick floor, connected with a source of power, and embody a housing drum and powerful brakes to control the rotation of the drum under load. Draw works serve as a power-control center for the hoisting gear and usually for the rotary elements of the drill column.

See also DRILLING RIG.

Dressing of bit

See BIT, DRESSING OF.

Drill and earn agreement

A term which has been applied to a FARM-OUT AGREEMENT (*q.v.*) under which a farmee receives a working interest only in the drill site when he completes a well; he is, however, then entitled to earn an interest in additional sites as he drills on them, usually within specified time intervals. Kuntz, Lowe, Anderson and Smith, *Cases on Oil and Gas* 641 (1986); Scott, "How to Prepare an Oil and Gas Farm-out Agreement," 33 *Baylor L. Rev.* 63 (1981).

See also EARNED INTEREST.

Drill collar

A part of the hollow drill stem used to drill a well, located immediately above the bit. It is the means of attaching the drilling bit to the drill column.

Drill column

The assemblage of cylindrical steel tubes connected, end to end, by collars or tool joints, which connect the rotary table at the top and the bit at the bottom of a well being drilled.

Driller

The chief of the crew that drills an oil or gas well. Wells are usually drilled continuously on the three 8-hour shifts called tours (see TOUR), and a driller is in charge of each crew and is responsible for carrying out the orders of the geologist, tool pusher or other person supervising the well.

Driller's log

A record, kept by the driller, that is supposed to show the following: when the well was spudded in, the size of the hole, the drilling tools used, when and at what depth the different drilling tools were hooked on, the number of feet drilled each day, the point at which each string of casing is landed, and in the case of cable tool drilling, the character, color, and description of each rock stratum penetrated. In addition, any unusual event should be noted, such as twisting off in the hole, *etc.* In modern practice, data in the driller's log is supplemented by ELECTRICAL WELL LOGS (*q.v.*).

Drilling

Act of boring a hole through which oil and/or gas may be produced if encountered in commercial quantities. CABLE TOOL DRILLING (*q.v.*) and ROTARY DRILLING (*q.v.*) are the common methods. The former operates on a percussion or pounding principle, and the formations in the bottom of the hole are pulverized. Rotary drilling, which is the common method today, involves the rotation of a bit in the hole, thereby cutting or boring through the various strata.

See also ACTUAL DRILLING OPERATIONS; AIR DRILLING; COMMENCEMENT OF DRILLING; DRILLING OPERATIONS; HORIZONTAL DRILLING; TURBODRILLING.

Drilling and operating restrictions

Governmental regulations or lease provisions which restrain or limit drilling and operating activities of a lessee. Depending on the situation at the time of the leasing transaction as to the existence of improvements on the leased premises or as to the utilization of the surface for agricultural or grazing purposes, a variety of restrictions on the lessee's activities may be imposed by a lease. The following are typical:

"When requested by lessor, lessee shall bury lessee's pipe lines below plow depth."

"No well shall be drilled nearer than 200 feet to the house or barn now on said premises without written consent of lessor."

"Lessee shall pay for damages caused by lessee's operations to growing drops on said land."

The lease may contain detailed provisions relating to such matters as maintenance of fences by the lessee or the restoration of the premises by the lessee upon the termination of the lease to the conditions prevailing before the commencement of operations.

Typical governmental regulations restrict the right to drill in urban areas.

See TREATISE §§ 673–673.6.

Drilling and rental clause

The delay rental clause of an oil and gas lease.

See also DELAY RENTAL CLAUSE; OR CLAUSE; UNLESS CLAUSE.

Drilling bit

See BIT, DRILLING

Drilling block

An area upon which an exploratory well is proposed to be drilled. See Rocky Mountain Unit Operating Agreement Form 2 (Divided Interest), January 1955, Exhibit 4, TREATISE § 920.4.

This term was defined by an early Oklahoma City zoning ordinance, allowing the drilling of only one well to a drilling block, as follows:

> "[A] tract of land which has for its exterior boundary lines public streets, United States government lot lines, the channels of streams, the corporate limits of the city of Oklahoma City, Railway rights-of-ways or unplotted tracts of land, provided that in unplotted tracts the term 'block' shall mean one contiguous tract of not less than five (5) acres." Phillips Petroleum Co. v. Davis, 194 Okla. 84 at 95, 147 P.2d 135 at 145 (1942).

The history of the Oklahoma Corporation Commission's regulation of drilling and spacing units is discussed in Dancy and Dancy, "Regulation of the Oil and Gas Industry by the Oklahoma Corporation Commission," 21 *Tulsa L.J.* 613 (1986).

See also BLOCK.

Drilling bond

An indemnity bond for each well drilled, redrilled, or deepened, required to be filed in some states at the time of the filing of a notice of intention to drill, redrill or deepen. See Calif. Pub. Res. Code § 3204 (1972) (1980 Supp.).

Drilling, cable tool

See CABLE TOOL DRILLING.

Drilling clause

A term sometimes applied to the DELAY RENTAL CLAUSE (*q.v.*) or to the DRILLING OPERATIONS CLAUSE (*q.v.*) of a lease. See *e.g.*, Gulf Oil Corp. v. Reid, 161 Tex. 51, 337 S.W.2d 267 at 276, 12 *O.&G.R.* 1159 at 1172 (1960), in which this term was used to describe a drilling operations clause. See also D. Pierce, *Kansas Oil and Gas Handbook* § 11.14 (1986).

Drilling contract

An agreement to drill and complete a well, setting forth the obligations of each party, compensation, indemnification, method of drilling, depth to be drilled, etc.

A contract between a lessee (sometimes called "operator") and a drilling contractor for the drilling of a well. Generally the contract will take one of four forms: (1) a footage contract "whereby the contractor is paid on a footage basis as work progresses, the price per foot sometimes changing as drilling progresses, with special provisions covering day work; (2) a turnkey contract, which is one whereby the contractor agrees to drill to a designated depth or formation for a fixed price; (3) a completion contract based on a footage and day work basis but postponing operator's liability until well completion; (4) a contract whereby in consideration for drilling, contractor is granted an interest in operator's leasehold estate." Discussion Notes, 6 *O.&G.R.* 422 (1956). See Masterson, "The Legal Position of the Drilling Contractor," 1 *Sw. Legal Fdn. Oil & Gas Inst.* 183 (1949).

Calvert Western Exploration Co. v. Diamond Shamrock, 234 Kan. 699, 675 P.2d 871, 79 *O.&G.R.* 522 (1984), concluded, for purposes of application of the mechanics' lien law, that the agreement construed was a drilling contract rather than a lease of personal property (the drilling rig) by reason of the variety of personnel, equipment, and services required to be provided with the rig.

For a discussion of the application of the third party beneficiary doctrine to provisions of a drilling contract, see Cornwell v. Jespersen, 238 Kan. 110, 708 P.2d 515, 87 *O.&G.R.* 40 (1985).

Dews v. Halliburton Industries, Inc., 288 Ark. 532, 708 S.W.2d 67, 89 *O.&G.R.* 455 (1986), sustained the recovery under a quasi-contract theory for services and materials contributed to the drilling of a well.

For a discussion of typical provisions of drilling contracts and problems in negotiation and construction, see the following:

Calkins, "The Oil Well Drilling Contract: Its Significant Provisions and Problems," *Rocky Mt. Min. L. Inst. on Oil and Gas Agreements* Paper 3 (1983);

Calkins, "The Drilling Contract—Legal and Practical Considerations," 21 *Rocky Mt. Min. L. Inst.* 285 (1976);

Shelton, "The Drilling Contract," in Slovenko (ed.) *Oil and Gas Operations: Legal Considerations in the Tidelands and on Land* 113 (1963).

See also COMPLETION CONTRACT; CONSTRUCTION CONTRACT; DAY RATE CONTRACT; DAY WORK; DUE DILIGENCE CLAUSE; EVERGREEN CLAUSE; EXCULPATORY CLAUSE; FOOTAGE CONTRACT; GULF COAST CLAUSE; IADC FORM; INDEPENDENT DRILLING CONTRACTOR; KNOCK-FOR-KNOCK INDEMNITY CLAUSE; SHUT-DOWN TIME; SOLE RISK CLAUSE; SPECIALTY CONTRACT; STAND-BY RIG TIME; TAKE-OVER PROVISION; TURNKEY CONTRACT.

Drilling fluids

Special chemical fluids, usually called MUD (*q.v.*), introduced into the hole to lubricate the action of a rotary bit, to remove the cuttings and to prevent blow-outs. Drilling fluid circulates continuously down the drillpipe, into the hole and upwards between the drill pipe and the walls of the hole to a surface pit, where it is purified and begins the cycle again.

Drilling fund

The generic term employed to describe a variety of organizations established to attract venture capital to oil and gas exploration and development. Typically the fund is established as a joint venture or limited partnership with minimum investments of $5,000 or $10,000. The fund is designed to give a high-bracket taxpayer investor the benefit of expensing intangibles and percentage depletion. See TREATISE §§ 503.3, 530.

For discussions of the organization and regulation of drilling funds and their tax consequences, see the following:

Wright, *Oil & Gas Drilling Programs: Preparing the Documentation* (1985);

Baggett, Dole and Short, *Coopers & Lybrand Anatomy of a Drilling Fund* (1980);

Practicing Law Institute, *Oil and Gas Financings: Current Practice and Anticipated Developments* (1983);

"Petroleum Law Supplement: Drilling Funds and Other Oil and Gas Industry Matters," 16 *Alberta L. Rev.* 127 (1978);

Close, "Drilling Funds: The 1977 Perspective," 28 *Sw. Legal Fdn. Oil & Gas Inst.* 421 (1977);

Welter, "Tax Structuring the Drilling Deal," 19 *Rocky Mt. Min. L. Inst.* 81 (1974);

Record, "Recent Developments in Exploration Financing," 24 *Sw. Legal Fdn. Oil & Gas Inst.* 111 (1973);

Cossey, "Financing Oil and Gas Exploration—Past, Present, and Future," *Id.* at 135;

Mosburg, "Regulation of Tax Shelter Investments," 25 *Okla. L. Rev.* 207 (1972);

Rathwell, "Problems Related to the Registration in Western Canada of Foreign Limited Partnerships and the Ownership by Such Partnerships of Interests in Oil and Gas Leases," 10 *Alberta L. Rev.* 477 (1972).

For a detailed discussion of several varieties of drilling funds, see Brountas v. Commissioner, 73 T.C. 491 (1979), 74 T.C. 1062, 67 *O.&G.R.* 477 (1980), *vacated and remanded,* 692 F.2d 152, 75 *O.&G.R.* 193 (1st Cir. 1982), *cert. denied,* 462 U.S. 1106 103 S. Ct. 2453 (1983).

For a description of a number of the features of a program to raise capital for a secondary recovery operation, see Moore v. Tristar Oil and Gas Corp., 528 F. Supp. 296 (S.D.N.Y. 1981). As indicated in the opinion, 528 F. Supp. at 305, there appear to be no standard fees for services provided by underwriters and other parties to transactions of this kind.

For discussion of a drilling fund program designed to enable an investor to deduct twice the amount invested from his federal income tax return in the first year of investment, thus recovering his investment in the first year by tax savings if he is in a 50 percent or higher tax bracket, see Sharp v. Coopers & Lybrand, 649 F.2d 175, 71 *O.&G.R.* 555 (3d Cir. 1981, *reh. denied*), *cert. denied,* 455 U.S. 938 (1982).

Molchan v. Omega Oil & Gas Ltd., 7 D.L.R.4th 216, [1984] 3 W.W.R. 246 (Alta. Q.B. 1984), was concerned with a conveyance by the general partner and 59 of 60 limited partners in an exploration fund of lands held by the partnership. The court held the transfer of the land made it impossible for the partnership to carry on its ordinary business, and was, therefore in breach of the Partnership Act. Consequently the purchaser held the land in trust for the limited partnership, and the non-consenting limited partner was entitled to an accounting. Appeal was allowed in this case, 21 D.L.R.4th 253, [1986] 1 W.W.R. 398 (Alta. Ct. App. 1985), the court concluding that the possibility of conflicts of interest was known and understood from the beginning, and the general partner was not liable to the plaintiff in the absence of proof of bad faith.

See also CASH SURRENDER VALUE PROVISION; COMPLETION PARTNERSHIP; COMPLETION PROGRAM; DEVELOPMENTAL PROGRAM WELL; END-USER PROGRAM; EQUITY KICKER; EXPLORATORY DRILLING PROGRAM; FLIP-FLOP PROVISION; FUNCTIONAL ALLOCATION SHARING ARRANGEMENT; INCOME PROGRAM; LEASE ACQUISITION FUND; LEVERAGED DRILLING FUND; LIMITED PARTNERSHIP; LISTED DEPOSITORY RECEIPT;

MONEY MANAGEMENT FUND; PAY-AS-YOU-GO BASIS; PER WELL CHARGE; PLATO; POGO PLAN; POOL OF CAPITAL DOCTRINE; PREPAID IDC; PRIVATE PLACEMENT DRILLING FUND; PRODUCTION FUND; PROGRAM MANAGEMENT FEE; PUBLIC DRILLING FUND; ROLL-UP PROVISION; 66.3 COMPANY; THIRD FOR A QUARTER DEAL.

Drilling log

See DRILLER'S LOG.

Drilling mud

See MUD.

Drilling operations

Any work or actual operations undertaken or commenced in good faith for the purpose of carrying out any of the rights, privileges or duties of the lessee under a lease, followed diligently and in due course by the construction of a derrick and other necessary structures for the drilling of an oil or gas well, and by the actual operation of drilling in the ground. Under various lease clauses (*e.g.*, the delay rental, the drilling operations clause), the question may arise whether drilling operations have commenced or whether such operations have been prosecuted with reasonable diligence, or whether such operations have ceased for a given period of time. See Ariz. R.S. § 27–551; Rogers v. Osborn, 152 Tex. 540, 261 S.W.2d 311, 2 *O.&G.R.* 304, 1439 (1953). See also ACTUAL DRILLING OEPRATIONS; COMMENCEMENT OF DRILLING; DRILLING.

In Reid v. Gulf Oil Corp., 323 S.W.2d 107, 10 *O.&G.R.* 830 (Tex. Civ. App. 1959), *aff'd,* Gulf Oil Corp. v. Reid, 161 Tex. 51, 337 S.W.2d 267, 12 *O.&G.R.* 1159 (1960), the court discussed the meaning of the term "drilling operations" as used in a lease clause:

> "It may be—though there is no affirmative evidence to that effect—that drilling operations are not normally thought of, either inside or outside the oil and gas industry, as embracing the installation of marketing facilities, but we are nonetheless of the opinion that, as used in the lease, the term 'drilling operations' was intended to embrace all of the physical and mechanical aspects of bringing about the production of oil or gas in paying quantities. A pipe line was as essential to production in the circumstances as was the casing that was placed in the well itself. . . . We are therefore impelled to the conclusion that the term 'drilling operations' was intended to have the broad meaning we have indicated, be-

cause the parties are presumed to have known, and to have executed the lease knowing that the reasonable-time doctrine would not be available to bridge a gap between the capping stage and the production stage in a well's program. . . . It would be idle to argue that the term was intended to embrace nothing more than the mere cutting of hole; and once past that point, there would seem to be no justification for excluding from its meaning any intervening step necessary to ultimate production." 10 *O.&G.R.* at 838–839.

Sheffield v. Exxon Corp., 424 So. 2d 1297, 76 *O.&G.R.* 419 (Ala. 1983), in analyzing the meaning of this term, declared:

"The key element is whether the operation is associated or connected with the *physical* site of the well or unit. . . . Mere negotiations for purchases or subcontracts do not contribute to the *physical* efforts necessary to make a well capable of production."

For a liberal construction of the term "drilling operations" see 21st Century Investment Co. v. Pine, 724 P.2d 834, ____ *O.&G.R.* ____ (Okla. App. 1986, *cert. denied*).

See also REWORKING OPERATIONS.

Drilling operations clause

A savings clause which operates to keep the lease alive after the expiration of the primary term despite the failure to obtain production by that time if drilling operations are then being pursued. There is limited authority that without such a clause, a lease may be kept alive by drilling operations begun before the expiration of the primary term and pursued with reasonable diligence thereafter until production is obtained [Simons v. McDaniel, 154 Okla. 168, 7 P.2d 419 (1932)], but by the weight of authority, if there is no production at the expiration of the primary term the lease then terminates even though drilling operations then being pursued result in production shortly after the expiration of the primary term.

A common drilling operations clause provides:

"It is expressly agreed that if lessee shall commence drilling operations at any time, while this lease is in force, this lease shall remain in force and its terms shall continue so long as such operations are prosecuted."

In Tate v. Stanolind Oil & Gas Co., 172 Kan. 351, 240 P.2d 465, 1 *O.&G.R.* 341 (1952), the drilling operations clause provided:

"If the lessee shall commence to drill a well within the term of this lease or any extension thereof, the lessee shall have the right to drill such well to completion with reasonable diligence and dis-patch, and if oil or gas, or either of them, be found in paying quantities, this lease shall continue and be in force with the like effect as if well had been completed within the term of years herein first mentioned."

Steinkuehler v. Hawkins Oil & Gas, Inc., 728 P.2d 520, ____ *O.&G.R.* ____ (Okla. App. 1986), held that there was a continuous drilling operation of a single well when, after the initial bore hole had been damaged beyond reclamation, the rig was skidded followed by a second penetration of the surface and drilling the well to completion.

In some instances a drilling operations clause has been denominated a CONTINUOUS DRILLING OPERATIONS CLAUSE (*q.v.*). See, *e.g.*, Sword v. Rains, 575 F.2d 810, 61 *O.&G.R.* 339 (10th Cir. 1978). This regrettable practice fails to recognize two important distinctions:

(1) When a lease includes a drilling operations clause and a well being drilled at the expiration of the primary term fails to attain commercial production, the lease terminates upon the completion of said well, even though another well, commenced after the expiration of the primary term but before the completion of the well being drilled at the expiration of the primary term, does attain commercial production. Skelly Oil Co. v. Wickham, 202 F.2d 442, 2 *O.&G.R.* 559 (10th Cir. 1953); Stanolind Oil & Gas Co. v. Newman Bros. Drilling Co., 157 Tex. 489, 305 S.W.2d 169, 7 *O.&G.R.* 1496 (1957).

(2) When a lease includes a continuous drilling operations clause, even though the well being drilled at the expiration of the primary term fails to gain paying production, a well commenced subsequent to the expiration of the primary term and completed as a paying well will suffice to preserve the lease into the secondary term so long as there has not been a cessation of drilling operations for a period longer than that specified by the clause. See TREATISE §§ 617–617.9.

See also THIRTY DAY-SIXTY DAY CLAUSE.

Drilling party

(1) As defined in a Rocky Mountain unit operating agreement, a party obligated to contribute to the costs incurred in drilling, deepening or plugging back a well in accordance with the agreement, See Rocky Mountain Unit Operating Agreement Form 1 (Undivided Interest) May, 1954, Section 1.10, TREATISE § 920.3.

(2) The party to a unit agreement who conducts or is responsible for drilling operations. See Upchurch, "Formation of the Explora-

tion and Development Unit," *1959 Sw. Legal Fdn. Nat'l Inst. for Petroleum Landmen* 1 at 21 (1960).

See also UNIT AGREEMENT.

Drilling permit

In those states that regulate WELL SPACING (*q.v.*), the authorization from the regulatory agency to drill a well.

Litigation over the issuance of drilling permits has been especially profuse in Texas. See the following:

Murphy (ed.), *Conservation of Oil and Gas—A Legal History, 1948* (1949);

Hardwicke, "Oil Well Spacing Regulations and Protection of Property Rights in Texas," 31 *Texas L. Rev.* 99 (1952);

Hyder, "Some Difficulties in the Application of Exceptions to the Spacing Rule in Texas," 27 *Texas L. Rev.* 481 (1949);

Walker, "The Problem of the Small Tract under Spacing Regulations," *Texas L. Rev.* 157 (Bar Ass'n No., Oct. 1938);

Meyers, "'Common Ownership and Control' in Spacing Cases," 31 *Texas L. Rev.* 19 (1952).

See also TARGET FORMATION; WELL PERMIT.

Drilling program

Syn. for DRILLING FUND (*q.v.*).

Drilling reservation

"[T]he right, license, privilege and authority to explore the lands therein described for oil and gas, but not to remove, produce or recover such oil and gas, except such production as is necessary to establish that the well is or is not a producer in commercial quantities, until a lease pursuant to these regulations has been applied for and approved." Saskatchewan Petroleum and Natural Gas Regulations, 1969, O.C. 8/69, § 30.

See also CHECKERBOARD LEASING; CORRIDOR ACREAGE; CROWN RESERVE; CROWN RESERVE DRILLING RESERVATION.

Drilling rig

The structures and equipment used in drilling an oil or gas well. This includes the derrick, the engine, the engine house, plus other equipment, the nature of which depends upon whether the rig is cable tool or rotary.

Principal additional items in a cable tool drilling rig are: bull wheel, walking beam, temper screw, drilling tine, calf wheel, casing line, band wheel, bailing line, headache post, and lazy bench.

Principal additional items in a rotary rig are: traveling block, hook and swivel, mud hose, kelly, rotary table, pipe rack, pumps, and hoisting works.

See also CABLE TOOL DRILLING; DRAW WORKS; JACK-UP RIG; MOBILE RIG; ROTARY DRILLING; TURBODRILLING.

Drilling, rotary

See ROTARY DRILLING

Drilling spacing unit

The area specified by applicable regulations or orders for the drilling of a well.

In Alberta the normal drilling spacing unit for an oil well is one quarter section with a target area within the quarter section and having sides 660 feet from the sides of the drilling spacing unit and parallel to them; where the drilling spacing unit for an oil well is one legal subdivision (1/16 of a section), it shall have a target area within the legal subdivision and having sides 330 feet from the sides of the drilling spacing unit and parallel to them; the normal drilling spacing unit for a gas well is one section with a target area within the section and having sides 1320 feet from the sides of the drilling spacing unit and parallel to them. Alberta Oil and Gas Conservation Regulations (Alta. Reg. 151/71) § 4–020. After notice and public hearing the Energy Resources Conservation Board may prescribe special drilling spacing units which may differ from normal drilling spacing units in size, shape or target area. *Id.*, § 4–030.

See also DRILLING UNIT; SPACING UNIT; STANDUP DRILLING UNIT (STANDUP SPACING); TARGET AREA; WELL SPACING.

Drilling title opinion

See TITLE OPINION.

Drilling tools

The equipment used in the boring of the hole, in drilling a well. See BIT; BAILER; DRILL STEM; FISHING TOOLS.

Drilling to the sale

Under certain circumstances the driller of a well in Saskatchewan is required by regulations to file with the Department of Mineral Resources all pertinent information obtained from the well and within 30 days of "rig release" all information about the well is available to the general public. "[I]f a land owner or lessee wishes to acquire land near to his present holding and wishes to assess that other parcel which is going to come on to the market on a certain day, he would locate his evaluation well as close as possible to that parcel and drill as close to the sale as possible, so that probably a few hours before the sale time he would have the best information available to use in determining his bid for the parcel being sold. This 'drilling to the sale' is a practice followed because the security screen about a well can be broken in a short space of time." Guyer Oil Company, Ltd. v. Fulton and Gladstone Petroleum Ltd., [1973] 1 W.W.R. 97 at 100 (Saskatchewan Q.B. 1972), *appeal dism'd,* [1976] 5 W.W.R. 356 (Saskatchewan Ct. of App. 1976), *appeal dism'd,* [1977] 2 S.C.R. 791, [1977] 4 W.W.R. 112 (Sup. Ct. of Canada 1977).

Drilling unit

The area prescribed by applicable well spacing regulations for the granting of a permit by the regulatory agency for the drilling of a well; the area assigned in the granting of a well permit.

The customary method of regulating drilling is to establish the area which one well can efficiently drain and to prohibit drilling on small tracts. The size of the prescribed drilling unit may vary from 10 acres in oil fields to 640 acres in gas fields. However, twenty- to forty-acre spacing is typical in oil fields. (Another way of stating a spacing formula is by distances to property lines and to other wells. For example, RULE 37 (*q.v.*)—the statewide spacing rule in Texas—for many years provided that no well should be drilled closer than 933 feet to another well in the same producing horizon nor closer than 330 feet to a property line. This resulted in 20-acre spacing.) For a discussion of the operation of Rule 37 in Texas, see Meyers, " 'Common Ownership and Control' in Spacing Cases," 31 *Tex. L. Rev.* 19 (1952).

In arriving at the proper size of drilling units, of first importance, of course, should be reservoir conditions. The permeability of the reservoir rock and the viscosity of the oil will have an important bearing on how large an area one well will drain. But considerations beyond the purely technical are influential and sometimes decisive of the spacing pattern. Operators usually favor wide spacing in order to minimize development costs. Landowners can be counted on to seek close spacing for a quick return. Since regulation is ordinarily entrusted to elected officials, the spacing order that emerges is a compromise between the two groups. The spacing pattern may not be uniform all over a state but may vary in the several fields on the basis of the time of application of the rule to the field, local geological conditions and other factors.

The history of the Oklahoma Corporation Commission's regulation of drilling and spacing units is discussed in Dancy and Dancy, "Regulation of the Oil and Gas Industry by the Oklahoma Corporation Commission," 21 *Tulsa L.J.* 613 (1986).

Manufacturers National Bank of Detroit v. Director of the Department of Natural Resources, 420 Mich. 128, 362 N.W.2d 572, 84 *O.&G.R.* 103 (1984), held that the creation of a drilling unit by the Director of the Department of Natural Resources in his capacity of Supervisor of Wells did not amount to the pooling of the legal interests of those whose lands were within the unit.

The distinction to be drawn between a drilling or spacing unit and a proration unit is noted in Rutter & Wilbanks Corp. v. Oil Conservation Comm'n, 87 N.M. 286, 532 P.2d 582, 50 *O.&G.R.* 488 (1975).

See also DRILLING SPACING UNIT; POOLING BY A DRILLING AND SPACING UNIT; SPACING UNIT; STANDUP DRILLING UNIT (STANDUP SPACING); TARGET AREA; WELL SPACING.

Drill or drop provision

A provision of a partnership agreement that upon discovery of oil or gas in commercial quantities, partners may choose to invest additional cash in the ratio of their partnership interests for completion and production. Any partner choosing not to contribute capital for such additional costs would drop its interest in income from the particular well and would not share in revenue from that well or the "block" surrounding the well site. Allison v. United States, 701 F.2d 933, 76 *O.&G.R.* 379 (Fed. Cir. 1983).

See also PROJECT FINANCING.

Drill or forfeit lease

A type of OR LEASE (*q.v.*). The lease contains the usual primary term and thereafter clauses but provides that the lessee covenants to drill a well within a stated term or forfeit the lease. See TREATISE § 605.1.

Drill or pay lease

A type of Or lease (*q.v.*). The lease contains the usual primary term and thereafter clauses but provides that the lessee covenants to drill a well within a stated term or pay delay rentals. Although drilling or paying rentals may occasionally be the only alternatives available to the lessee, usually the lease gives him a third alternative of surrendering the lease, *e.g.*:

> "Lessee agrees to commence operations on said premises on or before . . . ., or thereafter pay to Lessor . . . . dollars per acre per . . . . until a well is drilled, or the property hereby granted is conveyed to the first party."

Upon failure of the lessee to commence drilling a well or surrender, the lessor has a cause of action to recover rentals. Cohn v. Clark, 48 Okla. 500, 150 Pac. 467 (1915). In some early cases it was contended that the presence of the surrender alternative rendered the obligations of the lessee illusory and therefore there was a failure of consideration for the grant by the lessor. Inasmuch as the typical leases required the execution of the surrender in a specified manner and required the payment of $1 to the lessor, the courts concluded that the obligations of the lessee were not illusory and that there was no failure of consideration. See Treatise § 605.1.

Drill pipe

In rotary drilling, the heavy seamless tubing used to rotate the bit and circulate the drilling mud. Individual pipe lengths are normally 30 feet and are coupled together with tool joints.

Drill ship

A self-propelled vessel used for drilling offshore wells. See Kash, *et al., Energy Under the Oceans* 37 (1973).

See also Mobile rig.

Drill site arrangement

An arrangement wherein a lessee assigns his entire interest in a drill site, reserving an overriding royalty or net profits interest in the drill site, and also assigns a fractional interest in the balance of the lease. The overriding royalty or net profits interest reserved by the assignor may or may not contain a Conversion clause (*q.v.*). See Appleman, "Use of the Partnership as an Instrumentality in Oil Operations," 14 *N.Y.U. Inst. on Federal Taxation* 519 at 528 (1956).

For discussions of the tax consequences of a drill site arrangement and the effect of Revenue Ruling 77–176, see the following:

Chapoton, "Income Tax on Transactions Commonly Handled by Natural Resource Practitioners," 27 *O.&G. Tax Q.* 209 at 223 (1978);

Gregg, "Oil and Gas Farmouts—Implications of Revenue Ruling 77–176," 29 *Sw. Legal Fdn. Oil & Gas Inst.* 601 (1978).

See also FARM-OUT AGREEMENT.

Drill site royalty

A ROYALTY (*q.v.*) paid for the privilege of locating a well on one tract of land and using it to produce oil from another tract. See Stucky, "Current Developments and Views Concerning Rights and Status of Landowner-Lessors," 21 *Sw. Legal Fdn. Oil & Gas Inst.* 83 at 88 (1970).

Drill site title opinion

A TITLE OPINION (*q.v.*) relating to the site of a proposed well drilled on a unit embracing two or more separate tracts of land. See Canik v. Texas International Petroleum Corp., 308 So. 2d 543, 52 *O.&G.R.* 363 (La. App. 1975), *writ denied,* 310 So. 2d 850 (La. 1975).

Drill stem

The assembly of kelly, drill pipe, tools, collars and drilling bit which is suspended from a swivel in the derrick and rotated by the rotary table in ROTARY DRILLING (*q.v.*).

Drill stem test

A method of determining the presence of oil or gas in a formation. When the depth to be tested has been reached in a well being drilled, a special tool is lowered into the hole and placed next to the wall. The drilling mud is removed from this vicinity and the contents of the formation allowed to flow into the tool, while an instrument measures the pressure. The tool is then removed from the hole and the contents examined.

Drill string

A "string" or column of drill pipe.

In some instances the entire assembly consisting of kelly, drill pipe, tools, collars and drilling bit which is suspended from a swivel in the derrick, and rotated by the rotary table is described as a drill string, but more properly that assembly is described as a drill stem.

"Drill to earn" farm-out

A FARM-OUT AGREEMENT (*q.v.*) under which the rights of the farmee are earned regardless of whether the test well is a producer or dry hole. See Schaefer, "The Ins and Outs of Farmouts: A Practical Guide for the Landman and the Lawyer," 32 *Rocky Mt. Min. L. Inst.* 18-1 at 18-21 (1986).

See also "PRODUCE TO EARN" FARM-OUT.

Drip gasoline

NATURAL GASOLINE (*q.v.*) recovered at the surface as the result of the separation (or dripping out) of certain of the liquid hydrocarbons which were dissolved in gas in the formation under high pressure but which come out of solution on the reduction of pressure at the surface.

Drip pot

An installation between the wellhead of a well and the gas meter designed to collect small amounts of water and substances referred to as drips, condensate or natural gas liquids which are components of the produced natural gas stream but which, because of their molecular structure, tend to separate from the stream as liquids. The drips consist of heavier hydrocarbon molecules which take a liquid form when subject to a mechanical separation process or to reduction in temperature or pressure. Sowell v. Natural Gas Pipeline Co. of America, 604 F.Supp. 371 at 373, 84 *O.&G.R.* 407 at 409 (N.D. Tex. 1985), *aff'd,* 789 F.2d 1151, ____ *O.&G.R.* ____, *rehearing denied,* 793 F.2d 1287 (5th Cir. 1986).

Drips

See GAS CONDENSATE.

Drive

See COMBINATION DRIVE; DEPLETION DRIVE; DISSOLVED GAS DRIVE; GAS CAP DRIVE; GAS EXPANSION RESERVOIR; GRAVITATIONAL FORCE; RESERVOIR ENERGY; SOLUTION GAS FIELD; WATER DRIVE.

Drowning

Infiltration of water at the well bore into a formation formerly productive of oil so that the well produces only water.

Dry gas

Natural gas which does not contain dissolved liquid hydrocarbons.

Minor variations in statutory and case definitions of the term may be found. See Huie, Walker & Woodward, *Cases and Materials on Oil and Gas* 621 n. 30 (1960). The authors point out that under a statutory definition of dry gas as "any natural gas produced from a stratum that does not produce crude oil," the antithetical term, WET GAS (*q.v.*), would be synonymous with casinghead gas. They observe further:

> "A similar but not always identical meaning is ascribed when 'dry gas' is defined as gas from a gas well, while 'wet gas' is gas produced from an oil well. [Citations omitted.] The term 'dry gas' is also frequently employed to mean a gas which contains no appreciable quantities of dissolved liquid hydrocarbons while 'wet gas' does contain such liquids in solution in quantities of commercial importance. [Citations omitted.] There is a similar although again not an identical use of the term 'dry gas' to mean gas from which liquid hydrocarbons have been removed by processing."

Dry gas well

A well producing gas only and no oil. Lynch v. State Board of Equalization, 164 Cal. App.3d 94, 210 Cal. Rptr. 335 (1985).

Dry hole

A completed well which is not productive of oil and/or gas (or which is not productive of oil and/or gas in paying quantities).

To qualify as a dry hole, a well must have been completed [see COMPLETED WELL]; there is some controversy over the question of whether a well which produces a limited amount of oil or gas but not in paying quantities is a dry hole. In Murphy v. Garfield Oil Co., 98 Okla. 273, 225 P. 676 (1924), it is suggested that a well producing oil or gas, although not in paying quantities, cannot be regarded as a dry hole. In Cox v. Miller, 184 S.W.2d 323 (Tex. Civ. App. 1944, error ref'd), the court declared that "The terms 'dry hole' and a well 'producing gas in paying quantities' are not necessarily the converse of the other."

Whether or not a well is a dry hole is important in a number of contexts including (1) construction and application of a DRY HOLE CLAUSE (*q.v.*), and (2) determining liability under a DRY HOLE AGREEMENT (*q.v.*). See Berryman v. Sinclair Prairie Oil Co., 164 F.2d 734 (10th Cir. 1947); Rogers v. Osborn, 152 Tex. 540, 261 S.W.2d 311, 2 *O.&G.R.* 304, 1439 (1953); Superior Oil Co. v. Stanolind Oil & Gas Co., 150 Tex. 317, 240 S.W. 281 (1951); TREATISE § 614.1.

A dry hole is generally not viewed as a "gas well" or as an "oil well" as those terms are customarily used in contracts unless required by express wording of the contract or necessary implication. See Nafco Oil & Gas, Inc. v. Tartan Resources Corp., 522 S.W.2d 703, 52 *O.&G.R.* 273 (Tex. Civ. App. 1975, error ref'd n.r.e.).

In Sunac Petroleum Corp. v. Parkes, 416 S.W.2d 798, 26 *O.&G.R.* 689 (Tex. 1967), the court concluded that a well drilled on a unit pooled for gas and completed as an oil well was *not* to be viewed as a "dry hole" for purposes of a dry hole clause of a lease of land included in the gas unit. The case is discussed in the TREATISE § 614.1. note 5.

L & B Oil Co. v. Federal Energy Regulatory Commission, 665 F.2d 758, 73 *O.&G.R.* 399 (5th Cir., Unit A, 1982), cited this TREATISE in holding that under the facts of the instant case, a dry hole was not a well.

See also Lerblance v. Continental Oil Co., 437 F. Supp. 223 at 229, 59 *O.&G.R.* 50 at 61 (E.D. Okla. 1976), emphasizing that to qualify as a dry hole, a well must have been *completed.*

Dry hole agreement

An agreement similar to a BOTTOM HOLE LETTER (*q.v.*) except that it creates an obligation to be performed upon the drilling of a dry hole whereas the latter creates an obligation to be performed upon the drilling of a well to a specified depth, whether or not the well is dry. The agreement, usually evidenced by a letter signed by both parties thereto, is in one of two forms:

(1) Dry Hole Donation Letter, in which a person owning land or leases in the vicinity agrees to pay the driller an agreed sum of money if the driller will complete a well to a designated depth and if the well so drilled is a dry hole; usually the obligor will be entitled to receive certain information concerning the well drilled (*e.g.*, the well log and electrical log);

(2) Dry Hole Purchase Letter, in which the driller agrees to sell and transfer designated leases or portions thereof, the other party agreeing to make a stipulated payment upon the completion of a well

by the first party as a dry hole. See Brown, "Assignments of Interests in Oil and Gas Leases," 5 *Sw. Legal Fdn. Oil & Gas Inst.* 25 at 81 (1954).

Dry hole agreements are utilized to finance the drilling of a well in unproven territory. An operator may use such agreements as collateral in borrowing money for drilling expenses. If the well is completed as a producer, no obligation to pay arises under the agreements, but the loan to the driller will be repaid from the proceeds of production. The signatories of the agreement in the form of a Dry Hole Donation Letter obtain for their contingent liability the drilling of a well in the community which may serve to prove their land. They may also be entitled to copies of the well log and electrical log which may provide geological information valuable to them in the determination of whether (or where) to drill on their own land. Signatories of the agreement in the form of a Dry Hole Purchase Letter are entitled to a conveyance of an interest in the leases owned by the driller in exchange for their contingent liability in the event the well drilled is a dry hole.

For a typical form of dry hole agreement, see Williams, Maxwell, Meyers, and Williams, *Cases on Oil and Gas* 991 (5th ed. 1987).

For a case involving use of such agreements in financing drilling, see First National Bank of Post v. Republic Supply Co., 166 S.W.2d 373 (Tex. Civ. App. 1942, error ref'd w.o.m.). See TREATISE §§ 431–431.2.

For other forms of letter agreements, see LETTER.

Dry hole clause

A lease clause specifying the means by which a lessee may keep a lease alive after the drilling of a dry hole. A typical clause provides:

> "Should the first well drilled on the above described land be a dry hole, then, and in that event, if a second well is not commenced on said land within twelve months from the expiration of the last rental period for which rental has been paid, this lease shall terminate as to both parties, unless the lessee on or before the expiration of said twelve months shall resume the payment of rentals in the same amount and in the same manner as hereinbefore provided." Superior Oil Co. v. Stanolind Oil & Gas Co., 150 Tex. 317, 240 S.W.2d 281 (1951).

A clause in this form will not suffice to keep a lease alive after the expiration of the primary term; for this purpose a CONTINUOUS DRILLING OPERATIONS CLAUSE (*q.v.*) is requisite.

Another form of the dry hole clause combines the dry hole feature with a provision concerning cessation of production as follows:

"If prior to discovery of oil or gas on said land Lessee should drill a dry hole or holes thereon, or if after discovery of oil or gas the production thereof should cease from any cause, this lease shall not terminate if lessee commences additional drilling or reworking operations within sixty (60) days thereafter or (if it be within the primary term) commences or resumes the payment or tender of rentals on or before the rental paying date next ensuing after the expiration of three months from date of completion of dry hole, or cessation of production. If at the expiration of the primary term oil, gas or other mineral is not being produced on said land but lessee is then engaged in drilling or reworking operations thereon, this lease shall remain in force so long as operations are prosecuted with no cessation of more than thirty (30) consecutive days, and if they result in production of oil, gas or other mineral so long thereafter as oil, gas or other mineral is produced from said land." Rogers v. Osborn, 152 Tex. 540, 261 S.W.2d 311, 2 *O.&G.R.* 304, 1439 (1953); Stanolind Oil & Gas Co. v. Newman Bros. Drilling Co., 157 Tex. 489, 305 S.W.2d 169, 7 *O.&G.R.* 1496 (1957).

For the protection of the lessee, a properly drafted dry hole clause will be sufficiently explicit to prevent a construction which might cause a change in the anniversary date of rental payments and to insure that the lessee will have ample time after the completion of a dry hole to resume payment of rentals. See Walker, "Defects and Ambiguities in Oil and Gas Leases," 28 *Tex. L. Rev.* 895 at 903 (1950); TREATISE §§ 612–614.5.

See also THIRTY DAY-SIXTY DAY CLAUSE.

Dry hole contribution

Money or property given to an oil operator in accordance with the terms of a DRY HOLE AGREEMENT (*q.v.*) in payment for drilling of a well on property in which the contributor has no direct interest, but payable only in the event that the well is a dry hole. The contribution is made only where the well is drilled to a specified depth and is a dry hole.

Dry hole contribution agreement

See DRY HOLE AGREEMENT.

Dry hole donation letter

See DRY HOLE AGREEMENT.

Dry hole letter

See DRY HOLE AGREEMENT.

Dry hole money

Sum to be paid in accordance with the terms of a DRY HOLE AGREEMENT (*q.v.*) in the event a well to be drilled is a dry hole. See Kaye v. Smitherman, 225 F.2d 583, 5 *O.&G.R.* 691 (10th Cir. 1955).

Dry hole plug

A plug inserted in a well completed as a dry hole to close off formations penetrated by the well.

Dry hole purchase letter

See DRY HOLE AGREEMENT.

Dry oil

As distinguished from wet oil, dry oil is oil containing less than a stated amount (*e.g.*, 3%) of BASIC SEDIMENT (*q.v.*) and water. See Alamitos Land Co. v. Shell Oil Co., 3 Cal. 2d 396, 44 P.2d 573 (1935).

Dry rule

A rule of the Federal Energy Regulatory Commission requiring that the Btu content of a gas stream be determined for purposes of wellhead pricing under the Natural Gas Policy Act (NGPA). This rule, in contrast to the WET RULE (*q.v.*), measured the Btu content of gas at the conditions under which natural gas was actually delivered for first sales and thus, in most cases, indicated a lower water vapor content than was assumed under the wet rule. See Interstate Natural Gas Ass'n of America v. Federal Energy Regulatory Comm'n, 716 F.2d 1 at 4, 81 *O.&G.R.* 631 at 634 (D.C. Cir. 1983), *cert. denied,* 465 U.S. 1108, 104 S. Ct. 1615, 1616 (1984).

Dry tree

A CHRISTMAS TREE (*q.v.*) installed above water as distinguished from a WET TREE which is one installed on a wellhead at the seabed and exposed to the water.

Dry well

A well completed as a dry hole; a well not capable of production in commercial quantities.

DSP

DELIVERABILITY STANDARD PRESSURE (*q.v.*).

DST

DRILL STEM TEST (*q.v.*).

DSU

DRILLING SPACING UNIT (*q.v.*).

DTPA

The Texas DECEPTIVE TRADE PRACTICES-CONSUMER PROTECTION ACT (DTPA) (*q.v.*).

Dual completion

The completion of a well into two separate producing formations at different depths. Petroleum from one formation is produced from one string of pipe, inside of which is a smaller string of pipe producing from the other formation. For a case involving the right of an operator to operate a dually completed well in a unitized field, see West Edmund Hunton Lime Unit v. Stanolind Oil & Gas Co., 193 F.2d 818, 1 *O.&G.R.* 462 (10th Cir. 1951).

See also MULTIPLE COMPLETION.

DUC

The DANSK UNDERGRUNDS CONSORTIUM (*q.v.*).

Due diligence clause

A provision of a drilling contract (or other agreement) requiring that the work to be performed will be conducted with due diligence.

See *e.g.*, W. E. Myers Drilling Corp. v. Elliott, 695 S.W.2d 809, 87 *O.&G.R.* 156 (Tex. App., El Paso, 1985, error ref'd n.r.e.) (holding that drilling contractor had not satisfied due diligence clause of a day work DRILLING CONTRACT (*q.v.*) and hence the contractor was entitled to recover only for the number of days reasonable and necessary to complete the well).

Due regard, doctrine of

See ACCOMMODATION DOCTRINE.

Duhig rule

The construction rule based on the case of Duhig v. Peavy-Moore Lumber Co., 135 Tex. 503, 144 S.W.2d 878 (1940), relating to reservations in deeds purporting to cover 100% interest in the premises. Under this rule the grantor is said to be estopped to deny the effectiveness of the instrument to convey the interest recited in the instrument's granting clause.

See TREATISE § 311 *et seq.*

Syn: ESTOPPEL BY DEED (*q.v.*).

DUMA

The Dubai Marine Areas. See Shwadran, *The Middle East, Oil and the Great Powers* 442 (3d ed. revised and enlarged, 1973).

Dump floods

A secondary recovery method by means of WATER-FLOODING (*q.v.*). In this method, as contrasted with more scientific methods, an opening in the casing is made to allow water to enter the hole from water-bearing sands. Dump floods are not favored because they will often trap large quantities of otherwise recoverable oil.

Dump gas

Gas disposed of under a so-called DUMP GAS CONTRACT (*q.v.*).

See also FIRM GAS; INTERRUPTIBLE GAS.

Dump gas contract

A gas purchase and sale contract which does not call for the delivery of a definite or fixed amount of gas but which calls for the delivery and purchase of gas remaining after satisfaction of the terms of a FIRM GAS CONTRACT (*q.v.*), which excess gas would otherwise be flared or vented. Dump gas contracts typically call for a lower price than do Firm gas contracts. See State of North Dakota v. Federal Power Comm'n, 247 F.2d 173 (8th Cir. 1957).

See also GAS PURCHASE CONTRACT.

Duster

A dry hole.

..E..

EA

Economic allowance (*q.v.*).

E & D expenses

Exploration and development expenses.

Earned depletion

In Canada (since May 6, 1974), the depletion allowance is calculated not on the basis of a percentage of income (percentage depletion) but as a percentage of "eligible expenditures." Hence, this form of depletion has come to be known as earned depletion. See Katchen and Bowhay, *Federal Oil and Gas Taxation* 47 (3d ed. 1979).

See also Frontier exploration allowance; Successor earned depletion.

Earned interest

As used in a joint venture agreement this term has been used to describe the right of a party to the agreement to acquire an interest in a well or area by timely payment of costs incurred by the other party or parties. Heritage Resources, Inc. v. Anschutz Corp., 689 S.W.2d 952, 86 *O.&G.R.* 613 (Tex. App., El Paso, 1985, error ref'd n.r.e.).

The interest in the drill site acreage (and perhaps in additional acreage) to which a farmee under a Farm-out agreement (*q.v.*) is entitled as soon as the initial well has been drilled. See Kuntz, Lowe, Anderson and Smith, *Cases on Oil and Gas Law* 641 (1986).

See also Drill and earn agreement.

Easements

Incorporeal rights of user of the surface. Upon the severance of minerals by lease or deed, so much of the surface as may reasonably be necessary for exploration for and the development of minerals may be used by the operator or lessee, absent express language in the creating instrument limiting the easements of the lessee or mineral owner. Stanolind Oil & Gas Co. v. Wimberly, 181 S.W.2d 942 (Tex. Civ. App. 1944).

Occasional cases have found an excessive user of surface easements by the owner of minerals or a lessee [Magnolia Petroleum Co. v. Norvell, 205 Okla. 645, 240 P.2d 80, 1 *O.&G.R.* 114 (1952) (excessive user by lessee as result of construction of system of roads to well locations found); Stradley v. Magnolia Petroleum Co., 155 S.W.2d 649 (Tex. Civ. App. 1941, error ref'd) (liability imposed on lessee for use and occupancy of six acres more than was reasonably necessary for its full enjoyment of the minerals, but no liability for the drilling of a water well and the taking of water necessary to drilling oil wells and developing an oil lease)], but such instances are relatively rare.

Some contemporary leases provide expressly for compensation to the lessor "for any damage done in said operation to the lands, trees, shrubs or to any structure, or to any livestock thereon." See *e.g.*, Meyer v. Cox, 252 S.W.2d 207, 1 *O.&G.R.* 1810 (Tex. Civ. App. 1952, error ref'd). Such a provision is of particular importance to a lessor who joins in a community lease or whose lease contains authority for pooling or unitization, inasmuch as he may otherwise be unfairly dealt with if the well drilled under the community lease or pooling or unitization agreement is upon his land, in which event he will suffer all the surface damage and yet be entitled only to a proportionate share of the royalties. See TREATISE §§ 218–218.14.

See also IMPLIED EASEMENTS.

Eastern overthrust belt (EOB)

An OVERTHRUST BELT (*q.v.*) in the eastern part of the United States.

Economic allowance

An allowance for a well measured in barrels per day based on the depth of mid-point of perforations or open hole, in feet. See Provisions Governing the Limitation and Allocation of Production of Oil, Saskatchewan MRO 118/68 A 62, 5 Lewis and Thompson, *Canadian Oil and Gas* Division D, Part X [5] (1971).

In Alberta, the economic allowance of injection and observation wells may be transferred with approval of the Oil and Gas Conservation Board to other wells in the unit or project. See Oil and Gas Conservation Board, Economic Allowance Allocation Unit and Project Area and all Fluid Injection Schemes (Sept. 12, 1961).

See also ALLOWABLE; GAS-OIL RATIO PENALTY FACTOR; WATER-OIL RATIO PENALTY FACTOR.

Economic connection clause

A provision of a GAS PURCHASE CONTRACT (*q.v.*) under which the seller is excused from connecting a well to the pipeline if such connection would be unprofitable. Coastal Oil & Gas Corp. v. Federal Energy Regulatory Comm'n, 782 F.2d 1249, 90 *O.&G.R.* 402 (5th Cir. 1986).

Economic depletion

See DEPLETION.

Economic Development Agreement (EDA)

A term commonly used for the type of agreement formerly known as a CONCESSION (*q.v.*). See Flint, "Foreign Investment and the New International Economic Order," in Hossain and Chowdhury, *Permanent Sovereignty Over Natural Resources in International Law* 144 at 145 (1984).

Economic force majeure clause

See FORCE MAJEURE CLAUSE.

Economic integration clause

A clause in a concession agreement designed to effect an integration of a mineral development operation and the economic development of the host country. Among such clauses are those relating to preference to local contractors and local goods and priority for the employment and training of local skills. See Mughraby, *Permanent Sovereignty Over Oil Resources* 100 (1966).

See also CONCESSION.

Economic interest

This term is defined by Federal Power Commission Order No. 441, 46 F.P.C. 1178 at 1179 (1971), as any interest [in production or revenues from a producing venture] other than a working interest.

Economic interest for tax purposes

(1) The *sine qua non* for securing the federal income tax depletion allowance in income derived from the production of petroleum. The concept is not well defined, and faint distinctions have been drawn in

the cases. One definition appears in Treas.Reg. § 1.611–1 (b)(1) (1980), taken from Palmer v. Bender, 287 U.S. 551 (1933):

"An economic interest is possessed in every case in which the taxpayer has acquired, by investment, any interest in mineral in place or standing timber and secures, by any form of legal relationship, income derived from the extraction of the mineral or severance of the timber to which he must look for a return of his capital."

Each of the usual types of oil and gas interests is treated as constituting an economic interest entitled to depletion: mineral interest, royalty interest, overriding royalty, production payment, net profits interest, working interest. See the cases cited for each of these interests in Anderson v. Helvering, 310 U.S. 404 (1940); Kirby Petroleum Co. v. Comm'r, 326 U.S. 599 (1946). See also Comm'r v. Southwest Exploration Co. 350 U.S. 308, 5 *O.&G.R.* 839 (1956).

Freede v. Comm'r, 86 T.C. 340, 88 *O.&G.R.* 640 (1986), concluded that the purchaser of gas under a TAKE-OR-PAY CONTRACT (*q.v.*) had an economic interest in the gas in place.

For detailed discussions of the economic interest concept, see the following:

Pasewark, "Determining Economic Interest in Oil and Gas," 34 *O.&G. Tax Q.* 707 (1986);

McMahon, "Defining the 'Economic Interest' in Minerals After *United States v. Swank*," 70 *Ky. L.J.* 23 (1981–82);

D. Williams, "The 'Economic Interest' Concept," *P.H. Oil and Gas Taxes* ¶ 1010 (1978);

Hambrick, "Economic Interest Revisited—A Stock Taking 1965–1975," *P.H. Oil Taxes* ¶ 1002 (1976);

Sneed, "Another Look at the Economic Interest Concept," 10 *Sw. Legal Fdn. Oil & Gas Inst.* 353 (1959);

Sneed, "Trends in the Economic Interest Concept of Oil and Gas and Mining Tax Law," 6 *Rocky Mt. Min. L. Inst.* 35 (1961).

See also DEPLETION PERCENTAGE.

(2) The CRUDE OIL WINDFALL PROFIT TAX ACT OF 1980 (*q.v.*) contains provision for an exemption from the tax when an "economic interest" in crude oil is held by a state or political subdivision (including an educational institution), and all the net income received is dedicated to a public purpose. Section 35 of the Mineral Leasing Act of 1920, as amended, 30 U.S.C. § 191, provides a formula for distributing a share of royalty revenues to the states in which the federal government realizes such revenues. A Solicitor's opinion has ruled that the states do not have an "economic interest" in federal royalty revenues for purposes of the exemption provided by the windfall

profit tax. Effect of the Crude Oil Windfall Profit Tax Act of 1980 on the States' Share of Federal Oil Royalties, M–36929, 87 I.D. 661 (Dec. 30, 1980).

Economic-out clause

The term applied to the provision sometimes included in a GAS PURCHASE CONTRACT (*q.v.*) which permits the purchaser to rescind contracts for deregulated natural gas if prices of competitive fuels drop to the extent that the distributors of the gas cannot compete in selling the gas. A typical provision of this kind permits the purchaser to fix a ceiling price for the contracted gas whereupon the seller is permitted to reject that price and to contract with another pipeline company for the gas, if a higher price is offered. See *The Wall Street Journal,* Aug. 25, 1982, p. 19, col. 1 (reporting the exercise of such a clause by the United Gas Pipe Line Co., under high-priced contracts at a range of $8–$9 per Mcf for "deep" natural gas and "tight-sands" gas, by setting a ceiling price for the contracted gas of $5.73 per Mcf).

See Johnson, "Natural Gas Sales Contracts," 34 *Sw. Legal Fdn. Oil & Gas Inst.* 83 at 104 (1983).

See also FERC-OUT CLAUSE: MARKET-OUT CLAUSE.

Economic Recovery Tax Act of 1981

Public Law 97-34 (Aug. 13, 1981). Among other matters, this Act made a number of changes in the CRUDE OIL WINDFALL PROFIT TAX ACT OF 1980 (*q.v.*): providing for a $2,500 royalty credit for 1981 and an exemption for subsequent years; reducing the tax on newly discovered oil; exempting independent producer stripper oil; and enacting a credit for producing natural gas from unconventional sources.

Economic Regulatory Administration (ERA)

The agency in the Department of Energy charged with responsibility for the allocation and pricing of crude oil, residual fuel oil, and refined petroleum products. See Department of Energy Delegation Order No. 0204–4, 42 Fed. Reg. 60726 (Nov. 29, 1977).

See also MANDATORY CANADIAN CRUDE OIL REGULATIONS; MANDATORY PETROLEUM PRODUCTS ALLOCATION REGULATIONS; MANDATORY REFINERY YIELD CONTROL PROGRAM; NOTICE OF PROBABLE VIOLATION; OFFICE OF HEARINGS AND APPEALS; OFFICE OF PRIVATE GRIEVANCE AND REDRESS; PRICE CONTROL OF OIL, GAS AND PETRO-

LEUM PRODUCTS; PROPOSED REMEDIAL ORDER; REMEDIAL ORDER; STANDBY MANDATORY INTERNATIONAL OIL ALLOCATION; STATEMENT OF OBJECTIONS.

Economic rent

A term in usage among economists to describe any surplus in the income of a factor of production—land, labor, or capital—in excess of the minimum amount necessary to call forth that factor's productive services. In the devising of policies for leasing lands for oil and gas or other mineral development (or the negotiation of concessions, profit sharing, participation or similar agreements by a host government with a production company), the lessor or government seeks to extract the maximum amount of this economic rent in the form of bonus, rental, and royalty under a lease or in the GOVERNMENT TAKE (*q.v.*) of the host country. See generally McDonald, *The Leasing of Federal Lands for Fossil Fuels Production* (1979).

See also LEASE BIDDING SYSTEMS.

Economic Stabilization Act of 1970 (ESA)

Pub. L. No. 91–379, 84 Stat. 799, as amended, establishing mandatory wage and price controls. These controls, while soon lifted for the economy in general, were continued on the petroleum industry until 1981. See Aman, "Institutionalizing the Energy Crisis: Some Structural and Procedural Lessons," 65 *Cornell L. Rev.* 491 (1980).

Economic waste

(1) The use of natural gas in any manner or process except for efficient light, fuel, carbon black manufacturing and repressuring, or for chemical or other processes by which such gas is efficiently converted into a solid or a liquid substance. Kan. Stat. Ann. § 55–702 (1976).

(2) The drilling of wells in excess of the number necessary for the efficient recovery of the oil and gas in place. See WASTE.

For a case in which the court considered economic waste in determining whether to permit increased density of drilling instead of despacing an existing 640-acre drilling and spacing unit and creating 80-acre units, see Winter v. Corporation Commission, 660 P.2d 145, 75 *O.&G.R.* 543 (Okla. App. 1983).

For a discussion of the economic waste concept in Oklahoma see Haymaker v. Oklahoma Corporation Comm'n, 731 P.2d 1008, ___ *O.&G.R.* ___ (Okla. App. 1986) (holding that Commission order denying application for additional well in 80-acre spacing unit was not supported by substantial evidence).

Economy energy transaction

A sale in which the purchaser pays only an "energy charge" (*i.e.*, an amount intended to cover the utility's costs of generating electricity) but not a "demand charge" (*i.e.*, an amount intended to cover the generating utility's capital costs). Village of Winnetka v. Federal Energy Regulatory Commission, 678 F.2d 354, 23 FPS 6-125 (D.C. Cir. 1982).

ECOPETROL

EMPRESA COLUMBIANA DE PETRÓLEOS (ECOPETROL) (*q.v.*).

ECPA

The Energy Conservation and Production Act of 1976, Pub. L. No. 94–385.

EDA

ECONOMIC DEVELOPMENT AGREEMENT (*q.v.*).

Edge lease

An oil and gas lease on the edge of the field, that is, so located on the reservoir that it is over the line that separates the water zone from the oil zone.

Edge tract

A tract or lease on the edge of a reservoir normally having limited production potential because it borders on the oil-water contact line. Romanov, "Statutory Unitization: Significant Legal Issues," *Inst. on Oil and Gas Conservation Law and Practice* 12-1 at 12-83 (Rocky Mt. Min. L. Fdn. 1985).

Edge unit system

A system employed in Louisiana "which enables the owner of a drilling unit on the edge of a pool to obtain his fair and equitable share of the oil and gas in the pool without unnecessary cost or the drilling of unnecessary wells. Upon application, notice and hearing, the Department [of Conservation] determines the amount of productive acreage in the edge spacing unit, then adds this acreage to the adjoining spacing unit which is presumably already producing. The owners of the edge tract are permitted to share in the cost of the well on the adjoining tract in the proportion of the number of productive acres in the edge tract to the number of acres in the consolidated tract, the productive unit is enlarged by adding such adjoining productive acreage with an appropriate allowable adjustment." IOCC, *General Rules and Regulations for the Conservation of Oil and Gas* 7 (1969).

Edge water

Water contained in a petroleum reservoir. In nearly all petroleum reservoirs there are two and often three fluids that appear: salt water, oil and (sometimes) natural gas. Lowest in the formation is water. The point of contact of oil and water in the reservoir is called the oil-water contact line. Wells located near this line will produce the edge water as well as petroleum.

See also BOTTOM WATER; CONNATE WATER.

Edge well

(1) A well located on or near the boundaries of an oil or gas field. Such a well will normally be a poor producer because it is bottomed on the formation where little petroleum occurs.

(2) A well penetrating a producing formation at the oil-water contact line. See Ball, Ball, and Turner, *This Fascinating Oil Business* 45 (2d ed. 1965).

Edwards balance

"An instrument for determining the specific gravity of gases." American Gas Ass'n, *Glossary for the Gas Industry* (3d ed. 1981).

EEPA

The ENERGY EMERGENCY PREPAREDNESS ACT OF 1982 (*q.v.*).

Effective pay

A factor sometimes used in a unitization agreement to determine the participation of lessor and/or lessee in the proceeds from production. Effective pay is multiplied by the number of acres over the pool to derive acre feet of sand. The parties then share according to the percentage of total acre feet of sand each owns.

The effective pay factor is a calculated figure which takes into consideration depth, potential productivity, saturation and perhaps other factors, depending on the wording of the unitization agreement.

See also UNIT AGREEMENT.

Effective tariff

The tariff filed by a natural-gas company with the Federal Power Commission or its successor, the Federal Energy Regulatory Commission, and permitted by the Commission to become effective. 18 C.F.R. § 154.21 (1980).

Efficient operation covenant

The phrase employed by D. Pierce, *Kansas Oil and Gas Handbook* § 10.10 (1986) to describe the obligation discussed in this Treatise under the name Covenant to use reasonable care and diligence. See TREATISE § 861 *et seq.*

EGPC

The Egyptian General Petroleum Corporation. See Shwadran, *The Middle East, Oil and the Great Powers* 484 (3d ed. revised and enlarged 1973).

EIA

The Energy Information Administration of the Office of Oil and Gas in the Department of Energy.

See also OIL AND GAS FIELD CODE MASTER LIST—1982.

Eight-times area rule

A policy followed by the Texas Railroad Commission in administering RULE 37 (*q.v.*), the oil well spacing regulation in Texas. This policy, which was applied primarily in the East Texas field, permits the drilling of wells on a tract of land, as an exception to the uniform spacing pattern, to that degree of density which obtains in an area surrounding the tract eight times its size. See Thomas v. Stanolind Oil & Gas Co., 145 Tex. 270, 198 S.W.2d 420 (1946); Sullivan (ed.), *Conservation of Oil and Gas, A Legal History* 1958 (1960), Chapter on Texas.

86 lease

An "Or form" lease employed in California. See Williams, Maxwell, Meyers and Williams, *Cases on Oil and Gas* Appendix 2 (5th ed. 1987); OIL AGE 86-C FORM.

88 lease

An UNLESS LEASE (*q.v.*). Also known as Producers 88 lease or Producers 88 lease—revised.

This does not describe a specific instrument or indicate the interests created thereby. Apparently every landowner in the mid-continent area leasing his land for oil and gas wants a "Producers 88" lease, and the landman or other person seeking to obtain a lease obligingly provides a "Producers 88" lease for his signature. In Fagg v. Texas Co., 57 S.W.2d 87 (Tex. Com. App. 1933), specific performance of a contract in writing to execute "an 88 form lease" on certain land was denied, the court declaring:

> "The particular character of the rights which were to be acquired by the proposed lessee, or the extent or duration of such rights, is not in any wise disclosed or made ascertainable. The provision relative to 'an 88 form lease' can shed no light on these matters, for the reason that the character of printed matter contained in any designated class of oil and gas lease forms depends on what matter various designers of such forms may deem appropriate—and may vary accordingly. As we see it the reference to 'an 88 form lease' is as incapable of definite application as if the term 'oil and gas lease form' had been used instead."

Generally speaking Producers 88 lease forms contain an "unless" clause rather than an "or" clause and are executed for a term of years "and so long thereafter" as oil or gas is produced. In other words, a certain structural pattern is usually indicated by the phrase "Producers 88 lease"—even this may not be true—but the phrase in no way indicates the details of the leasing arrangement. For a brief history of the origin of the "Producers 88 lease," see Walker, "Defects and Ambiguities in Oil and Gas Leases," 28 *Tex. L. Rev.* 895 (1950).

EIR

ENVIRONMENTAL IMPACT REPORT (*q.v.*).

EIS

ENVIRONMENTAL IMPACT STATEMENT (*q.v.*).

Elbow

See CROOKED WELL.

Election to participate

A means of choosing between options open to owners of pooled interests by the terms of a compulsory pooling or unitization statute. See Tenneco Oil Co. v. El Paso Natural Gas Co., 53 *Okla. B.J.* 2476 (Okla. 1982), *on rehearing,* 687 P.2d 1049, 82 *O.&G.R.* 322 (Okla. 1984). In its original opinion the court held that the Corporation Commission had jurisdiction to determine the validity of an election made by the owner of an operating interest to participate in a gas well. On rehearing the prior opinion of the court was vacated and the judgment of the trial court (finding the operating agreement modified the forced-pooling order of the Corporation Commission and that Tenneco's election to participate was effective) was affirmed. Two dissenters argued that the action should be dismissed for want of subject-matter jurisdiction on the ground that the Corporation Commission was the proper tribunal to resolve election-related contests.

See also COMPULSORY POOLING; COMPULSORY UNITIZATION; NEGATIVE ELECTION.

Electrical survey

See ELECTRICAL WELL LOG; GEOPHYSICAL SURVEY.

Electrical well log

"[A] continuous graphic record of the electrical properties of rock strata that is made by inserting electrodes into the uncased well bore and making a traverse of the strata penetrated by the drilling bit. It permits a determination of the characteristics of the rock, the thickness, and the fluid content of the strata penetrated by the drilling bit, and is also useful in correlating strata from well to well." Rev. Rul. 82-9.

An electrical survey of an uncased hole which reflects the resistivity of rock strata to electrical current and the spontaneous potential (S.P.) of the rock. From the resistivity curve, geologists can determine the nature of the rock strata penetrated; from the S.P. curve, some indication of the permeability of the rocks can be obtained. By correlating well logs from a number of wells in an area, a contour map of the subsurface structure can be drawn. *E.g.,* if a certain rock stratum is found in Well *A* at 3,000 feet and in Well *B,* one-half mile to the west, at 3,500 feet, the geologist can conclude that the stratum dips to the west between the two wells.

Electrical well logs are often called Schlumbergers (pronounced Slum-ber-jays) after the name of a prominent company in the business.

See Hilchie, "Well Logging," in *Rocky Mt. Min. L. Fdn. Basic Oil and Gas Technology for Lawyers and Landmen* (1979).

See also WELL LOG.

Electric logging

The procedure of lowering certain instruments into a well, and shooting electric currents through such instruments for the purpose of testing formations. In Steeger v. Beard Drilling Co., 371 S.W.2d 684, 19 *O.&G.R.* 391 (Tex. 1963), the court was concerned with the question whether such term, as employed in a contract, included the work of circulating mud and removing the drill stem preliminary thereto.

Elf Aquitaine

Societe Nationale Elf Aquitaine, a French state oil company.

Elf-ERAP

A French state oil corporation.

See also ERAP.

Elimination clause

See AUTOMATIC ELIMINATION CLAUSE.

El Loophole

Syn. for BROWNSVILLE LOOP (*q.v.*).

Emergency Petroleum Allocation Act of 1973 (EPAA)

The Act, 15 U.S.C.A. § 751 (1973), which established a federal program of regulation of price and allocation of supplies of petroleum products. See Cockrell, "Exceptions to Federal Regulations for Management of the Energy Crisis: The Emerging Agency Case Law," 28 *Okla. L. Rev.* 530 (1975).

Regulations issued under this Act are contained in 10 C.F.R. §§ 210–212 (1980).

Mobil Oil Corp. v. Dubno, 492 F. Supp. 1004 (D. Conn. 1980), invalidated a provision in a Connecticut statute forbidding integrated petroleum companies from raising wholesale prices in Connecticut for certain products by any amount higher than the average amount by which prices were raised "in all ports on the eastern coast of the United States," finding that the act was preempted by the EPAA and was unconstitutional as violative of the supremacy clause, *dism'd in part and aff'd in part,* 639 F.2d 919 (2d. Cir. 1981), *cert. denied,* 452 U.S. 967 (1981).

Mobil Oil Corp. v. Tully, 653 F.2d 497 (Temp. Emer. Ct. App. 1981), likewise invalidated a PASS-THROUGH PROHIBITION (*q.v.*) in a New York gross receipts tax. The judgment was vacated and remanded in the light of the expiration of federal price control authority, 455 U.S. 245 (1982), *remanded to District Court,* 689 F.2d 186 (Temp. Emer. Ct. App. 1982).

See also PRICE CONTROL OF OIL, GAS AND PETROLEUM PRODUCTS.

Emergency sales

See ONE HUNDRED AND EIGHTY DAYS EMERGENCY SALES; SIXTY-DAY EMERGENCY SALES.

Empresa Columbiana de Petróleos (Ecopetrol)

A Columbian national company established in 1948 that in time became involved in every phase of the petroleum industry. See Chester, *United States Oil Policy and Diplomacy* 164 (1983); Bernate-Rodriguez and Torres-Peña, "History and Developments of the Legislation and Policies Concerning Exploration and Exploitation of Oil and Gas in Columbia," International Bar Ass'n Section on Energy and Natural Resources, *International Energy Law* (1984) (Topic 2).

Emulsion

Accumulation of basic sediment and water in the bottom of collecting tanks. The emulsion is scraped out of the tanks periodically and disposed of as waste matter or treated for recovery of additional hydrocarbons.

ENAP

Empresa Nacional des Petroleo of Chile.

Encroachment

Entry of water or gas by gradual steps into an oil bearing formation as the oil is withdrawn. The term is usually used with reference to water in a WATER-DRIVE FIELD (*q.v.*). Such a field derives its energy mainly from edge- or bottom-water in the formation. Water is only slightly compressible but when tremendous volumes of it are present, as is frequently true in reservoir traps, the effect of the slight compression is greatly magnified. With a reduction of pressure as the result of the drilling of a well and the removal of oil, the water expands pushing the oil ahead of it.

End use control

Prohibition or regulation of the use of natural gas or oil for particular purposes, *e.g.*, the regulation of the use of natural gas for the manufacture of carbon black. Such controls are designed, not to maximize recovery, but to stretch the available supply of gas or oil over a longer period of time by prohibition of its use for relatively less beneficial or important uses. Typical carbon black legislation or regulation prohibits the use of sweet gas for the manufacture of carbon black where sour gas is available, or prohibits certain manufacturing processes which are less efficient in terms of total recovery of carbon black or in terms of utilization of the energy generated in the process. See Moses, "Statutory Regulations in the Carbon Black Industry," 20 *Tulane L. Rev.* 83 (1945). The authority of the states in this area has regularly been sustained. Walls v. Midland Carbon Co., 254 U.S. 300 (1920); Henderson Co. v. Thompson, 300 U.S. 258 (1937).

The Federal Power Commission and its successor, the Federal Energy Regulatory Commission, through pipeline certification jurisdiction as well as jurisdiction over sales of gas in interstate commerce for resale, imposed end use controls. Federal Power Comm'n v. Transcontinental Gas Pipe Line Corp., 365 U.S. 1 (1961); State of Louisiana v. Federal Power Comm'n, 503 F.2d 844 (5th Cir. 1974).

See also CURTAILMENT PLAN; 467 PLAN; INFERIOR USE; SUPERIOR USE.

End use plan

The name given a form of gas CURTAILMENT PLAN (*q.v.*) under which gas is allocated according to the use to which that gas would ultimately be put. Under this type of plan, contracts providing gas to the highest priority end users must be performed before any gas is allocated to the next highest user. See Consolidated Edison Co. of New York v. Federal Energy Regulatory Comm'n, 676 F.2d 763 (D.C. Cir. 1982).

See also PRO RATA PLAN.

End use rate schedule

A rate schedule for natural gas designed to discourage utilization of natural gas for "inferior" uses by imposing a higher charge for gas used for "inferior" uses than for gas used for "superior" uses. See Federal Power Commission Docket No. RM75–19, Proposal to Revise End Use Rate Schedules.

End user program

A program entered into by companies in petroleum-intensive industries designed to ensure adequate fuel supplies at reasonable costs. The nonenergy industry participant in the joint venture contributes all or most of the capital to finance the venture, and an independent oil company supplies the exploration, production, and marketing know-how. See Baggett, Dole, and Short, *Coopers & Lybrand Anatomy of a Drilling Fund* 8 (1980).

Energy charge

See ECONOMY ENERGY TRANSACTION.

Energy company

A term applied to a firm with substantial reserve and/or production positions in the various primary fuels areas. See Duchesneau, *Competition in the U.S. Energy Industry* 7 (1975).

Energy Emergency Preparedness Act of 1982 (EEPA)

Public Law 97–229, 42 U.S.C. §§ 6202–6245, enacted in 1982. The Act required the Department of Energy to prepare a plan on how it would react to a shortage situation. The Act further set a minimum fill rate for the STRATEGIC PETROLEUM RESERVE (*q.v.*) of 220,000 barrels a day for fiscal 1983.

Energy futures market

See FUTURES MARKET.

Energy Impact Money

See FEDERAL ENERGY IMPACT MONEY.

Energy Policy Office

The agency established in the Executive Office of the President by Executive Order on June 29, 1970 to advise the President and formulate policies on energy matters. In turn this agency was succeeded by the Federal Energy Office (FEO) and then by the Federal Energy Administration (FEA).

Energy Pricing and Taxation Agreement of September 1, 1981

An agreement entered into between Alberta and the federal government with respect to pricing and revenue-sharing for petroleum and natural gas. See Cumming, "Provincial and Federal Legislation Affecting Exploration, Development, Transmission and Marketing of Petroleum and Natural Gas in Canada: An Overview and Comment," 1 *Canadian-American L.J.* 17 at 34 (1982).

Energy Resources Conservation Act

An Oklahoma Act, 1985 Okla. Laws, ch. 2, codified as 52 O.S. § 601 *et seq.* (1985), designed to permit the state Corporation Commission to prevent certain transfers of energy resource assets by unfriendly corporate take-overs. Mesa Partners II v. Unocal Corp., 607 F.Supp. 624 (W.D. Okla. 1985), held that the Act was invalid under the Commerce Clause of the Constitution of the United States.

Energy Resources Conservation Board of Alberta (ERCB)

The board established by R.S. Alta. 1980, c. E–11, and charged with the regulation of the energy industry in the province. See Bruni and Miller, "Practice and Procedure Before the Energy Resources Conservation Board," 20 *Alta. L. Rev.* 78 (1982); Hollingsworth and Snider, "Some Aspects of 1985 Deregulation of Petroleum," 25 *Alta. L. Rev.* 36 at 42 (1986).

Energy Security Act

Pub. L. No. 96–294 (June 30, 1980) dealing with synthetic fuel, biomass energy, alcoholic fuels, solar energy, energy conservation, and geothermal energy.

Energy Tax Act of 1978

Pub. L. No. 95–618 (Nov. 9, 1978). The major provisions of this Act related to:

(1) a residential energy tax credit;

(2) a gas guzzler tax for fuel inefficient automobiles;

(3) an exemption from motor fuels excise taxes for certain alcohol fuels;

(4) the removal of certain excise taxes from buses;

(5) incentives for van pooling;

(6) changes in business investment credits to encourage conservation of, or conversion from, oil and gas or to encourage new energy technology; and

(7) miscellaneous changes affecting intangible drilling costs and percentage depletion.

Engineering committee

A committee formed to do preliminary work in gathering and compiling data preliminary to working out a pooling or unitization plan. See Myers, *The Law of Pooling and Unitization* § 4.01 (2d ed. 1967).

English ton

A unit of mass equal to 2,240 pounds. Also called the long ton as opposed to the short ton and the metric ton.

See Ton.

Enhanced recovery

"[T]he increased recovery from a pool achieved by artificial means or by the application of energy extrinsic to the pool, which artificial means or application includes pressuring, cycling, pressure maintenance or injection to the pool of a substance or form of energy but does not include the injection in a well of a substance or form of energy for the sole purpose of (i) aiding in the lifting of fluids in the well, or (ii) stimulation of the reservoir at or near the well by mechanical, chemical, thermal or explosive means." The Alberta Oil and Gas Conservation Act, R.S.A. 1970, c. 267, § 2(1)(15).

For studies of enhanced recovery see the following:

Symposium sponsored by the Enhanced Recovery and Research Committees of the Interstate Oil Compact Commission, 26 *IOCC Comm. Bull.* 7 (June 1984);

Office of Technology Assessment, Congress of the United States, *Enhanced Oil Recovery Potential in the United States* (1978).

See also SECONDARY RECOVERY; TERTIARY RECOVERY.

Enhanced recovery project

A pool or part thereof in which operations in accordance with a scheme for ENHANCED RECOVERY (*q.v.*) of oil are conducted or, where the scheme provides for the application of more than one recovery mechanism, the part of the area subject to the scheme which is subject to one such recovery mechanism. Alberta Oil and Gas Conservation Act, R.S.A. 1970, c. 267, § 2.(1)37.

ENI

The ENTE NAZIONALE IDROCARBURI (*q.v.*).

Enriched gas injection

A secondary recovery method involving the injection of gas rich in intermediate hydrocarbons in its natural state or enriched by addition of propane, butanes, or pentanes to the gas stream on the surface or in the well bore as gas is injected. See Smith, "The Engineering Aspects of Pressure Maintenance and Secondary Recovery Operations," 6 *Rocky Mt. Min. L. Inst.* 211 at 229 (1961).

See also SECONDARY RECOVERY.

Enriching gas

Increasing the heat content of gas by mixing it with a gas of higher Btu content.

Ente Nazionale Idrocarburi (ENI)

An Italian state-owned oil corporation. See Mughbraby, *Permanent Sovereignty Over Oil Resources* 62 (1966); Krueger, *The United States and International Oil* § A.14 (1975).

Entirety clause

A lease clause inserted primarily for the benefit of the lessee to make it clear to lessors or subsequent transferees of the lessor or lessors that inside property lines created by later divisions of the fee ownership or by royalty conveyances shall not affect the lessee's duties of development and operation. There appears to be a growing tendency to include such a clause in contemporary leases in form such as the following:

"If the leased premises are hereafter owned in severalty or in separate tracts, the premises, nevertheless, shall be developed and operated as an entirety, and royalties shall be paid to each separate owner in the proportion that the acreage owned by him bears to the entire leased acreage."

Even absent such a clause, however, it is clear that the duties of the lessee may not be increased as a result of subsequent transfers by the lessor or lessors. By virtue of an entirety clause in the lease, royalties from production under the lease are usually apportioned among mineral and royalty owners in accordance with their interest, wherever the well or wells may be located on the leased premises. There is a division of authority on the question of whether the presence of an entirety clause in the lease requires apportionment when the later executed mineral or royalty deed makes no reference to apportionment or non-apportionment. See TREATISE §§ 521.3, 678–678.2; Hardwicke and Hardwicke, "Apportionment of Royalty to Separate Tracts; The Entirety Clause and the Community Lease," 32 *Texas L. Rev.* 660 (1954).

Huie, Woodward and Smith, *Cases on Oil and Gas* 811 n. 51 (2d ed. 1972), suggest that

"Perhaps the kind of clause generally referred to as an *entirety clause* would be better described as a *royalty apportionment clause.* Professor Williams uses the term *entirety clause* in a wider sense, which includes clauses declaring that the lease is to be developed as an entirety even though there is no provision for apportionment of royalties, but most writers clearly have in mind a clause providing for apportionment of royalties and confining the use of the term to a clause of that kind would help to avoid confusion."

See also APPORTIONMENT.

Entitlement

(1) The amount of gas to which a purchaser is entitled under a curtailment program. See ANNUAL QUANTITY ENTITLEMENT; CURTAILMENT PLAN.

(2) A ticket issued under the ENTITLEMENT PROGRAM (*q.v.*).

(3) In Australia, the right of a permit holder who has discovered petroleum within the permit area to apply for a production license. See Land and Crommelin, *Australian Mining and Petroleum Laws* 248 (1979).

See also NATIVE GAS ENTITLEMENT.

Entitlement program

A program designed to equalize raw material costs for refineries when price for so-called "old oil" was fixed under price control regulations at a lower level than price for so-called "new oil" or imported oil. 39 Fed. Reg. 44246 (1974), 10 C.F.R. § 211.67 (1980). Refineries heavily dependent upon new oil or imported oil received entitlement tickets and those supplied with old oil purchased such tickets. The resulting transfer of cash was designed to equalize their costs.

For discussions of this program see the following:

Texaco, Inc. v. Department of Energy, 663 F.2d 158, 21 FPS 6–184 (D.C. Cir. 1980);

Exxon Corp. v. Department of Energy, 601 F.Supp. 1395 (D. Dela. 1985) (summarizing the history of much of the entitlement program), *aff'd in past and rev'd in part,* 802 F.2d 1400 (Temp. Emer. Ct. of App. 1986);

Mobil Oil Corp. v. Department of Energy, 520 F. Supp. 420 (N.D.N.Y.), *rev'd,* 659 F.2d 150 (Temp. Emer. Ct. of App. 1981), *cert denied,* 454 U.S. 1110 (1981);

Texaco, Inc. v. Department of Energy, 460 F. Supp. 339 (D.D.C. 1978), *appeal dism'd for lack of jurisdiction,* 616 F.2d 1193 (Temp. Emer. Ct. of App. 1979), rev'd, 663 F.2d 158 (D.C. Cir. 1980);

MacAvoy (Ed.), *Federal Energy Administration Regulation* 12 (Task Force on Reform of Federal Energy Administration 1977);

De Marchi, "Energy Policy Under Nixon," in Goodwin (Ed.), *Energy Policy In Perspective* 395 at 466 (1981);

Copp, *Regulating Competition in Oil* 98–102 (1976);

Baker, "The Entitlements Program: Emergency Oil Regulation and Private Proprietary Rights," 25 *Catholic U. L. Rev.* 601 (1976);

Statement of Frank G. Zarb, Administrator of the Federal Energy Administration, "Oversight—Federal Energy Administration Programs," Hearings before the Senate Committee on Interior and Insular Affairs, 94th Cong., 1st Sess., Serial No. 94–16 (92–106), 471 at 525;

Krueger, *The United States and International Oil* 135 (1975);

"Oil Decontrol: Who Would be Helped, Who Hurt?," *Forbes* (Sept. 1, 1975);

Langdon, "FEA Price Controls for Crude Oil and Refined Petroleum Products," 26 *Sw. Legal Fdn. Oil & Gas Inst.* 55 at 88 (1975);

Summers, "The Case for Decontrolling the Price and Allocation of Crude Oil," 53 *Texas L. Rev.* 1275 at 1290 (1975);

Note, "National Energy Costs and FEA's Mandatory Crude Oil Allocation Program," 61 *Va. L. Rev.* 903 at 922 (1975).

Kalt, *The Economics and Politics of Oil Price Regulation* (1981); Lane, *The Mandatory Petroleum Price and Allocation Regulations: A History and Analysis* (1981).

See also LAYERING; PRICE CONTROL OF OIL, GAS AND PETROLEUM PRODUCTS; REFINED PRODUCT ENTITLEMENT; SMALL REFINER BIAS.

Environmental impact report (EIR)

A report required by the California Environmental Quality Act (CEQA), Cal. Pub. Res. Code (1977) § 21050 *et seq.* under specified circumstances before certain projects may be commenced. No Oil, Inc. v. City of Los Angeles, 13 Cal.3d 68, 118 Cal. Rptr. 34, 529 P.2d 66, 50 *O.&G.R.* 293 (1974), held that the CEQA had been violated by the approval of an oil drilling project without a written determination concerning the environmental impact of that project.

Environmental impact statement (EIS)

The statement required of federal agencies by Section 102(C) of the National Environmental Policy Act of 1969, 42 U.S.C.A. § 4332(C), in every recommendation or report on proposals for legislation and other major Federal actions significantly affecting the quality of the human environment. The statement deals with (i) the environmental impact of the proposed action, (ii) any adverse environmental effects which cannot be avoided should the proposal be implemented, (iii) alternatives to the proposed action, (iv) the relationship between local short-term uses of man's environment and the maintenance and enhancement of long-term productivity, and (v) any irreversible and irretrivable commitments of resources which would be involved in the proposed action should it be implemented.

For a discussion of the requirement of an impact statement for Federal Power Commission gas curtailment orders see State of Louisiana v. Federal Power Comm'n, 503 F.2d 844 (5th Cir. 1974).

Environmental Protection Agency (EPA)

A federal agency created in 1970 to permit coordinated and effective governmental action for protection of the environment by the systematic abatement and control of pollution through integration of research, monitoring, standard setting and enforcement activities. Reorganization Plan No. 3 of 1970, Effective Dec. 2, 1970, 35 F.R. 15623, 84 Stat. 2086.

See also UNDERGROUND INJECTION CONTROL PROGRAM (UIC).

EOB

EASTERN OVERTHRUST BELT (EOB) (*q.v.*).

EOR

Enhanced oil recovery. See ENHANCED RECOVERY.

EOR technique

Enhanced oil recovery technique.

EPA

The ENVIRONMENTAL PROTECTION AGENCY (*q.v.*).

EPAA

The EMERGENCY PETROLEUM ALLOCATION ACT of 1973 (*q.v.*).

EPCA

The Energy Policy and Conservation Act, of 1975, Pub. L. No. 94–163.

Equalization point

A location employed for the purpose of determining the transportation charge ingredient in the price of oil. A hypothetical competition in the consuming areas between Middle East oil and U.S. oil was assumed at the equalization point, *e.g.*, Naples, Italy.

> "Under this system, the price of the Middle East oil exports from the Gulf plus transportation costs from the Gulf to Naples should be equivalent to the price of US oil in the Gulf of Mexico plus its transportation costs to the port of Naples. This led to a reduction in the posted price of Middle East oil by an amount equivalent to these transportation charges from the Gulf point in the Middle East to Naples. By shifting this hypothetical competitive Equalization Point westward to London, the price of Middle East oil was once more reduced by an amount equivalent to the transportation costs from Naples to London." Al-Chalabi, *OPEC and the International Oil Industry: A Changing Structure* 63 (1980).

See also BASE-POINT PRICING; BASING POINT; GULF-PLUS PRICING STRUCTURE; MULTIPLE BASE-POINT SYSTEM; PERSIAN GULF PRICING SYSTEM; PHANTOM FREIGHT; SINGLE BASE-POINT SYSTEM.

Equidistant offset rule

A rule adopted by the Texas Railroad Commission for the East Texas field under which a producer could have a permit to drill a well as close to that producer's property line as a neighboring tract's well. Prindle, *Petroleum Politics and the Texas Railroad Commission* 51 (1981), declared that under this rule:

> "A large lease touching several small tracts was therefore likely to be permitted more than its 'correct' density of drilling, according to the spacing rule."

See also OFFSET WELL.

Equipment costs

Cost of the equipment installed in a well prior to commencement of production. Such costs must be capitalized for federal income tax purposes. See CAPITAL EXPENDITURES.

Equipment production payment

A PRODUCTION PAYMENT (*q.v.*) created by the owner of a working interest for the purpose of equipping wells being drilled or to be drilled. If the purchaser pays the seller a sum of money for such production payment, the proceeds are pledged for the specific purpose and used only to pay the equipment costs. In many cases the assignee of the production payment pays the specified bills directly to the equipment supplier in accordance with the assignee's prior contract to do so, and no money is ever paid by the assignee to the party assigning the production payment. See Johnson, "Legal Aspects of Oil and Gas Financing," 9 *Sw. Legal Fdn. Oil & Gas Inst.* 141 at 149 (1958).

Syn.: Pledged production payment.

See also OIL PAYMENT.

Equitable estoppel

(1) A term sometimes used to refer to laches. Jordan v. Sutton, 424 So. 2d 305 at 307, 77 *O.&G.R.* 89 at 90 (La. App. 1982).

(2) This term is also used to refer to the doctrine precluding a tenant from denying his landlord's title. See ESTOPPEL IN PAIS.

The application of the doctrine of equitable estoppel to the government is discussed in Tosco Corp. v. Hodel, 611 F.Supp. 1130 at 1198 *et seq.* (D. Colo. 1985). This case was settled by an Aug. 4, 1986 agreement. See 2 *Nat. Res. & Environment* 74 (Fall 1986), 804 F.2d 590 (10th Cir. 1986).

Lohse v. Atlantic Richfield Co., 389 N.W.2d 352, 89 *O.&G.R.* 535 (N.D. 1986), concluded that: "The purpose of equitable estoppel is to preserve rights already acquired and not to create new ones; equitable estoppel does not itself give rise to a cause of action."

See also ESTOPPEL BY DEED.

Equitable partition

(1) Partition based on implied intent of concurrent owners. By virtue of this doctrine, if a cotenant purports to convey the full fee title in severalty to a portion of a tract held concurrently, the court may protect the interest of the purchaser by setting aside to him the particular tract purchased and by setting aside to the non-joining cotenants the equivalent of their interest in all of the tract out of the unsold portion of the tract, if it suffices for the purpose. The doctrine is equally applicable to oil and gas leases or mineral conveyances and other types of conveyances. From the limited number of reported cases involving mineral interests and equitable partition, two generalizations may perhaps be derived: (a) the probability of a judicial finding of equitable partition is increased where there is evidence of conduct of the non-conveying cotenant constituting ratification of the conveyances by the other cotenant; and (b) the courts are less willing to find an equitable partition where the person conveying erroneously believes himself to hold the entire fee simple interest than they are where the person conveying knew himself to be a cotenant. See TREATISE § 507.

(2) Partition obtained in a court of equity, or upon equitable grounds, rather than as a matter of right.

See also LICITATION; PARTITION.

Equitable pooling

A term, probably originating in Hoffman, *Voluntary Pooling and Unitization,* Ch. 5 (1954), describing the consequences of a series of Mississippi cases, which held that spacing regulations based on general conservation statutes, lacking compulsory pooling provisions, had the legal effect of pooling the land included in a drilling unit. The leading Mississippi cases are: Superior Oil Co. v. Berry, 216 Miss. 664, 63 So. 2d 115, 64 So. 2d 357, 2 *O.&G.R.* 193, 1094 (1953); Humble Oil & Ref. Co. v. Hutchins, 217 Miss. 636, 64 So. 2d 733, 65 So. 2d 824, 2 *O.&G.R.* 337 (1953); Superior Oil Co. v. Foote, 216 Miss. 728, 63 So. 2d 137, 64 So. 2d 355, 2 *O.&G.R.* 222 (1953).

The term "equitable" may have been applied to this kind of pooling because it is neither voluntary (by agreement) nor compulsory under a specific provision of a statute. "Judicial pooling" might be more appropriate, since the Mississippi court effected pooling probably not contemplated by the parties, nor by the legislature that passed the conservation statute. See TREATISE §§ 906–906.3.

Equity joint venture

A form of agreement in which a host government (or its national oil company) and a foreign oil company form an operating company in which each owns a specified percent of the shares. See Hossain, *Law and Policy in Petroleum Development* 121 (1979).

See also CONCESSION; JOINT ADVENTURE.

Equity kicker

A NONOPERATING INTEREST or CONVERTIBLE INTEREST (*q.v.*) in production, contingent upon and measured by production from properties in which borrowed funds are invested, given a lender as additional consideration for a loan.

See the following discussions:

Gelinas, "Federal Tax Consequences in Structuring Oil and Gas Investments for Institutional Investors," 31 *O.&G. Tax Q.* 579 at 583 (1983);

Barnett and Coffin, "New Financing Techniques in the Oil and Gas Industry," 34 *Sw. Legal Fdn. Oil & Gas Inst.* 431 at 432 (1983);

Maultsby, "Overview of Mineral Financing," *Rocky Mt. Min. L. Inst. on Mineral Financing* I-1 at I-14 (1982);

Wilson, "Tax Considerations in Selecting a Mineral Financing Vehicle," *Rocky Mt. Min. L. Inst. on Mineral Financing* 7-1 at 7-95 (1982).

See also DRILLING FUND.

Equity oil

Under participation agreements between host countries and producing oil companies, that portion of the oil produced accruing to the producing company is known as equity oil.

See also BUYBACK OIL; CONCESSION.

Equity production payment

A right to a share of production proceeds which will by its terms necessarily terminate substantially before the exhaustion of the burdened properties, usually because of a RESIDUAL RESERVE CLAUSE (*q.v.*), but the quantity of production attributable to it may vary significantly depending upon future discoveries or other events concerning the burdened properties. Griffith, "Current Developments in Oil and Gas Taxation Other than Legislative and Regulatory," 36 *Sw. Legal Fdn. Oil & Gas Inst.* 8-1 at 8-15 (1985).

ERA

The ECONOMIC REGULATORY ADMINISTRATION (*q.v.*).

ERAP

Enterprise de Recherches et d'Activities Petrolieres of France. See Krueger, *The United States International Oil* § A.15 (1975).

ERCB

The ENERGY RESOURCES CONSERVATION BOARD OF ALBERTA (ERCB) (*q.v.*).

ERDA

The Energy Research and Development Administration established by the Energy Reorganization Act of 1974, Pub. L. No. 93–438; 88 Stat. 1233; 42 U.S.C. § 5801 *et seq.*

ERTA

ECONOMIC RECOVERY TAX ACT OF 1981 (*q.v.*).

ESA

The ECONOMIC STABILIZATION ACT OF 1970 (*q.v.*).

Escalator clause

A clause in a GAS PURCHASE CONTRACT (*q.v.*) providing for progressive increases in the price to be paid or gas during the term of the contract.

The six types of escalator or escalation clauses in common use are:

1. The "two-party favored nation clause" provides that, if the pipeline company buying gas from producer *A* in the same field or area, contracts to buy gas from *B* in the same field or area at a price higher than it is already paying producer *A* it must thereafter pay producer *A* the same price it agrees to pay producer *B*.

2. Under a "third-party favored national clause," the pipeline buyer agrees to pay its suppliers from a certain field or area, the

highest price paid by *any* other buyer to producers in the same field or area.

3. The "renegotiation," "redetermination," or "better-market" clause generally provides that at stated intervals—two, three, four or five years—there shall be a renegotiation or redetermination of the contract price based upon the current prices then being paid in the field. If the buyer and seller cannot agree, then the price is fixed by arbitration. However, the arbitrators are bound to take the average of the two or three highest prices being paid by pipeline companies in the field or area, as the basis of the renegotiated price.

4. Under a wholesale price or spiral escalation clause, the producers' price is automatically increased when the pipeline is permitted to increase its wholesale rates, *i.e.*, to its distributor customers.

5. The so-called periodic or step-price increase clauses provide for an increase in the base price to be paid for gas at periodic intervals; for example, by one per cent per Mcf. at the end of each five years.

6. Most contracts also have a tax-increase clause by which the buyer pays a fraction, usually 2/3 or 3/4, of any increased severance or gross production taxes levied against the seller after the effective date of the contract.

See TREATISE § 726.

See also AREA RATE CLAUSE; BONA FIDE OFFER PROVISION; BTU ADJUSTMENT CLAUSE; DEFINITE ESCALATION CLAUSE; FERC-OUT CLAUSE; FPC CLAUSE; FPC PRICE PROTECTION CLAUSE; GOVERNMENTAL PRICE ESCALATOR CLAUSE; INDEFINITE ESCALATION CLAUSE; MOST FAVORED NATION CLAUSE; NATURAL GAS PRICE PROTECTION ACT; OIL EQUIVALENCY CLAUSE.

Escape clause

See JURISDICTIONAL ESCAPE CLAUSE.

Escrow money

Syn. for SUSPENSE MONEY (*q.v.*).

Escrow well

A term suggested by one writer for application to an offshore well being drilled with a floating rig since it is not known at the time the well is being drilled whether it will be plugged and abandoned even if capable of production. It is argued that such a well should qualify for the intangible drilling costs deduction. See Linden, "Review of Offshore Drilling—What are Intangibles?" 26 *Sw. Legal Fdn. Oil &*

Gas Inst. 441 at 445 (1975). Gates Rubber Co. & Subsidiaries v. Commissioner, 74 T.C. 1456, 67 *O.&G.R.* 647 (1980), *aff'd,* 694 F.2d 648 (10th Cir. 1982), and Sun Oil Co. v. Commissioner, 74 T.C. 1481, 68 *O.&G.R* 353 (1980), *aff'd,* 677 F.2d 294, 76 *O.&G.R.* 619 (3d Cir. 1982), *acq.,* I.R.B. 1983-26 (1983), held that the deduction for INTANGIBLE DRILLING AND DEVELOPMENT COSTS (*q.v.*) is available for preplatform wells.

See also Bullion, "Special Tax Considerations in Relation to Offshore Operations and Financing," *Rocky Mt. Min. L. Fdn. Offshore Exploration, Drilling and Development Institute* (1975).

Syn.: BORE HOLE; EXPENDABLE WELL; LINE TEST WELL; PRE-PLATFORM WELL.

ESECA

The Energy Supply and Environmental Coordination Act of 1974, Pub. L. No. 93–319. Regulations concerning the collection of information under this Act are contained in 10 C.F.R. § 207 (1980).

Established reserves

RESERVES (*q.v.*) which can be considered established in the sense that their existence and estimated amounts can reasonably be counted upon. Established reserves may be determined by crediting 100 per cent of proven reserves plus a varying percentage of probable reserves. National Energy Board, Report to The Governor in Council, *In the Matter of the Applications Under The National Energy Board Act of Trans-Canada Pipe Lines Ltd., et al.* page 3–2 (March 1960).

Estate

See CONVENTIONAL LIFE ESTATE; CORPOREAL ESTATE; DOMINANT ESTATE; EXTENDED TERM ESTATE; FREEHOLD INTEREST (OR ESTATE); FREEHOLD LAND; INCORPOREAL INTEREST; LEGAL LIFE ESTATE; NON-FREEHOLD INTEREST (OR ESTATE); SERVIENT ESTATE; SUBSURFACE ESTATE.

Estoppel

See COLLATERAL ESTOPPEL; EQUITABLE ESTOPPEL; ESTOPPEL BY DEED; ESTOPPEL IN PAIS.

Estoppel by deed

Estoppel arising from joinder in a deed to deny the effectiveness of the deed to convey the interest purported to be conveyed. See TREATISE § 311.

See also AFTER-ACQUIRED TITLE DOCTRINE; DUHIG RULE; EQUITABLE ESTOPPEL.

Estoppel in pais

Estoppel which arises from an act, conduct, or from silence when there is a duty to speak which will preclude a party from asserting a right which otherwise could have been claimed. Under this doctrine a tenant may be precluded from denying his landlord's title. See "Estoppel of a Tenant to Deny His Landlord's Title: An Overlooked Distinction in Oil and Gas Leases," 34 *Ala. L. Rev.* 585 (1983).

Syn. Equitable estoppel.

Ethane (C_2H_6)

A simple hydrocarbon associated with petroleum. It is gaseous at ordinary atmospheric conditions. See Interstate Oil Compact Commission, *Oil and Gas Production* 26 (1951).

Ethylene (C_2H_4)

A colorless hydrocarbon gas of slight odor having a heating value of 1,604 Btu per cubic foot and a specific gravity of O.9740. It is usually present in manufactured gas, constituting one of its illuminants. American Gas Association Bureau of Statistics, *Glossary for the Gas Industry* 20. Ethylene is an extremely versatile petrochemical, serving as a feedstock for producing fibres, insecticides, antifreeze, paint, plastics, and anti-knock additives for gasoline.

Evaluation well

In Alberta, a well which when being drilled is expected by the Energy Resources Conservation Board to penetrate a pool or oil sands deposit and which is drilled for the sole purpose of evaluation. Alberta Oil and Gas Conservation Act, R.S.A. 1970, c. 267, § 2(1)(17).

Evaporation pit

A pit utilized for the disposal of oilfield brine by evaporation.

Evergreen clause

A contract provision that the term of the contract will be extended for some specified period beginning with the date of the expiration of the primary term and that the contract shall remain in effect until terminated by action of one of the parties after giving the required notice prior to the anniversary date. Other variations of this type of clause also prevail in the industry. Final Regulations Under Sections 105 and 105(b) of the Natural Gas Policy Act of 1978, FERC Order No. 68 (Jan. 18, 1980), 20 FPS 5–12.

For a discussion of the employment of an Evergreen clause in drilling contracts, see Hancock, "The Offshore Drilling Contract," *Rocky Mt. Min. L. Fdn. Offshore Exploration, Drilling and Development Institute* 7–16 (1975).

Superior Oil Co. v. Pioneer Corp. 532 F. Supp. 731, 73 *O.&G.R.* 412 (N.D. Tex. 1982), held that a provision of a gas purchase contract giving the purchaser an option to extend the term of the contract was not an Evergreen Clause because the purchaser had to take affirmative action to exercise the option. As a consequence, the new contract arising by exercise of the option was not an EXISTING CONTRACT (*q.v.*) for purposes of the NATURAL GAS POLICY ACT OF 1978 (*q.v.*) but was either a ROLLOVER CONTRACT (*q.v.*) or a SUCCESSOR TO AN EXISTING CONTRACT (*q.v.*). The judgment was vacated and dismissed for want of jurisdiction, 706 F.2d 603 (5th Cir. 1983), *cert. denied,* 464 U.S. 1041, 104 S. Ct. 706 (1984).

Everything is A.P.I.

A phrase which has been used to indicate that operations are carried out in a proper and workmanlike manner. The reference is to the American Petroleum Institute's set of standards covering aspects of petroleum operations. See The Parliament of the Commonwealth of Australia, *Report from the Senate Select Committee on Off-Shore Petroleum Resources* 612 (1971).

Exception

(1) That which is excepted from a grant.

At common law, a distinction was drawn between "exceptions" and "reservations," the former being a part of the thing granted and of a thing *in esse,* and the latter being a thing not *in esse,* but newly created or reserved out of the land or tenement demised. See 1 *Coke on Littleton,* 47a. It was said, for example, that words of inheritance were essential if a reservation were to be in fee since the reservation resulted in a new interest, but such words were unnecessary in the case of an exception which merely involved excluding a particular part from the general thing granted. The distinction has lost most of its importance in contemporary law, largely because of the judicial policy of disregarding the technical distinctions and of construing the language used so as to effectuate the intention of the parties. See Bigelow and Madden, "Exception and Reservation of Easements," 38 *Harv. L. Rev.* 180 (1924).

The distinction continues to find significance in an occasional contemporary case. Early cases in Arkansas, for example, distinguished between the effect of exceptions and reservations of minerals, and further held that they were void as repugnant to the grant unless contained in the granting clause of a deed. In Bodcaw Lumber Co. v. Goode, 160 Ark. 48, 254 S.W. 345, 29 A.L.R. 578 (1923), the court gave effect to the intention of the parties by construing as an "exception" that which had been phrased in terms of a "reservation." The rule that a mineral reservation or exception must be contained in the granting clause if it is to have validity was repudiated in later cases. Beasley v. Shinn, 201 Ark. 31, 144 S.W.2d 710, 131 A.L.R. 1234 (1940); Carter Co. v. Weil, 209 Ark. 653, 192 S.W.2d 215 (1946). See the annotation, Validity of reservation of oil and gas or other mineral rights in deed of land, as against objection of repugnancy to the grant, 157 A.L.R. 485 (1945). Historically it has been impossible to make an exception or reservation in favor of a third person. See Joiner v. Sullivan, 260 S.W.2d 439 (Tex. Civ. App. 1953, error ref'd), criticized in 3 *O.&G.R.* 76 (1954). See also Freeport Coal Co. v. Valley Point Mining Co., 90 S.E.2d 296, 5 *O.&G.R.* 789 (W. Va. 1955). See TREATISE § 310.

(2) A well permit granted to a person although the area for which it is granted does not satisfy the requirements of the applicable well spacing rule. See RULE 37; SISTRUNK FORMULA; WELL SPACING.

For a case denying a request for exceptions under applicable Florida statutes and regulations, see Smacko, Ltd. v. Jordan, 469 So.2d 860, 85 *O.&G.R.* 461 (Fla. App. 1985).

Exception well

A well authorized or drilled as an exception under the applicable well spacing rule. See RULE 37; WELL SPACING.

Excess cash

A term used by the authors of a tax treatise to describe the additional consideration passing between the grantor and grantee in a sharing arrangement. Such additional consideration may be in form of cash not pledged to development, or cash pledged to development but in excess of the cost thereof, or property of unlike kind not related to the development project. Burke and Bowhay, *Income Taxation of Natural Resources* ¶ 7.15 (1980).

See also DIVISIBLE SHARING ARRANGEMENT; SHARING ARRANGEMENT.

Excessive production

(1) Production in excess of market demand

(2) Production in excess of ALLOWABLE (*q.v.*), *viz.*, hot oil, illegal oil.

Excess lands

In Texas public lands law, land incorrectly surveyed to include within the patent or other source of title more land than the patentee was entitled to. Such patentee, his heirs or assigns, has a preferential right to purchase the excess land and thereby perfect his title thereto. Excess lands are not vacant lands [see VACANCY] but are sold lands which have been segregated from the public domain and are owned by the patentee or his successors in interest in the sense that anyone owns lands contracted for but not yet paid for. See Vernon's Ann. Tex. Nat. Res. Code § 51.246 (1978); Foster v. Duval County Ranch Co., 260 S.W.2d 103 (Tex. Civ. App. 1953, error ref'd, n.r.e.).

Excess oil

A term sometimes used to describe illegal oil or oil produced in excess of ALLOWABLE (*q.v.*). See Turnbow v. Lamb, 95 F.2d 29 (5th Cir. 1938).

Excess royalty

A term occasionally used to describe a royalty in excess of the usual one-eighth royalty or to describe an OVERRIDING ROYALTY (*q.v.*). See Waller v. Mid-states Oil Corp., 218 La. 179, 48 So. 2d 648 (1950).

Exchange

See EXCHANGE AGREEMENT; EXCHANGE GAS; EXCHANGE OFFER; TRANSPORTATION BY EXCHANGE.

Exchange agreement

An agreement by one company to deliver oil or gas to another company at a specified location in exchange for oil or gas to be delivered by the latter to the former company at another location. In the case of crude oil, the agreement may be made because each has crude production closer to the other company's refinery than to its own refinery. In the case of gas, the agreement may be made because of proximity of gas production by one company to a gathering pipeline of another company.

For a case dealing with the impact of price control regulations upon a crude oil exchange agreement, see Getty Oil Co. v. Department of Energy, 569 F. Supp. 1204 (D. Dela. 1983), *aff'd as modified,* 749 F.2d 734 (Temp. Emer. Ct. App. 1984), *cert. denied,* 469 U.S. 1209, 105 S. Ct. 1176 (1985).

For an argument that exchange agreements are not anticompetitive, see Ritchie, "Petroleum Dismemberment," 29 *Vanderbilt L. Rev.* 1131 at 1144 (1976).

Exchange and renewal lease

A new lease issued in exchange for or in renewal of a prior lease. 43 C.F.R. § 3107 (1978). Under Section 14 of the Mineral Leasing Act of 1920, oil and gas leases were issued for a fixed term of twenty years. Holders of such leases were given the preferential right to renew the leases for successive terms of ten years. The twenty-year leases are no longer issued but the right to successive renewals of existing leases continues. An exchange lease may be issued to replace certain older leases on public domain lands or acquired lands. See *Rocky Mt. Min. L. Fdn., Law of Federal Oil and Gas Leases* ch. 12 (1985).

Exchange gas

Gas that is received from (or delivered to) another party in exchange for gas delivered to (or received from) such other party. American Gas Association Bureau of Statistics, *Glossary for the Gas Industry* 21.

Exchange offer

An offer (also known as a "roll-up" or "put-together") used by oil and gas companies to form a publicly held company, to take an existing private company public, or to increase the size of an existing publicly held company.

"There are three major types of roll-ups. In the 'true roll-up,' a company which has been a general partner of prior drilling programs offers to exchange company stock for the limited partners' interest in the prior partnerships. In the 'wide-open roll-up,' a newly formed company offers to trade its new stock for interests in partnerships organized by a specific sponsor or any sponsor. Finally, in the 'partnership-for-partnership roll-up,' a newly formed 'super' partnership (to be listed on an exchange) offers to exchange its interests for those in partnerships organized previously." Rakay, "Securities Laws Affecting Oil, Gas and Hard Mineral Financing in 1985," 6 *Eastern Min. L. Inst.* 11-1 at 11-19 (1985).

Excluded interest

A term employed in a unit operating agreement to refer to a COMMITTED WORKING INTEREST (*q.v.*) in land excluded from a participating area by contraction. See Rocky Mountain Unit Operating Agreement Form 2 (Divided Interest) January, 1955, Section 13.4, TREATISE § 920.4.

Excluded oil

Natural gas excluded from the definition of oil for purposes of the Petroleum Revenue Tax. See Daintith and Willoughby, *A Manual of United Kingdom Oil and Gas Law* 109–110 (1977).

Exclusive leasing power

The power to execute an oil and gas lease on an interest in land from which the lessor will not derive some or all of the usual lease benefits, *viz.*, bonus, rental, and royalty. This power has also been called EXECUTIVE RIGHT (*q.v.*), and its holder the EXECUTIVE (*q.v.*). The interest subject to the power is called either a non-participating royalty if the benefit to accrue under the lease is royalty only, or a non-executive mineral interest if the benefits to accrue under the lease include bonus or delay rental with or without a further interest in royalty.

The creation of an exclusive leasing power has been held void under the Rule against Perpetuities in Dallapi v. Campbell, 45 Cal. App. 2d 541, 114 P.2d 646 (1941). In Lathrop v. Eyestone, 170 Kan. 419, 227 Pac. 136 (1951), the creation of a perpetual interest (a non-participating royalty) subject to an exclusive leasing power was held void under the Rule against Perpetuities. However, separation of the exclusive leasing power from a nonparticipating royalty was expressly upheld under the perpetuities rule in Hanson, v. Ware, 224 Ark. 430, 274 S.W.2d 359, 4 *O.&G.R.* 325 (1955). See also Price v. Atlantic Ref. Co. 79 N.M. 629, 447 P.2d 509, 31 *O.&G.R.* 226 (1968). Other cases sustain the separation *sub silentio:* See, *e.g.*, Armstrong v. Bell, 199 Miss. 29, 24 So. 2d 10 (1945); Meeks v. Harmon, 207 Okla. 459, 250 P.2d 203, 1 *O.&G.R.* 1698 (1952); Watkins v. Slaughter, 144 Tex. 179, 189 S.W.2d 699 (1945); Schlittler v. Smith, 128 Tex. 628, 101 S.W.2d 543 (1937). See TREATISE §§ 323–326.

The nature of the exclusive leasing power has not been finally settled. Several Texas cases describe it as an agency "power coupled with an interest." Superior Oil Co. v. Stanolind Oil Co., 230 S.W.2d 346 (Tex. Civ. App. 1950), *aff'd*, 150 Tex. 317, 240 S.W.2d 281 (1951); Odstrcil v. McGlaun, 230 S.W.2d 353 (Tex. Civ. App. 1950); Allison v. Smith, 278 S.W.2d 940, 4 *O.&G.R.* 1136 (Tex. Civ. App. 1955). Such characterization has been criticized. Jones, "Separation of the Exclusive Leasing Power from Ownership of Minerals," 2 *Sw. Legal Fdn. Oil & Gas Inst.* 271 (1951); Meyers, "Effect of the Rule against Perpetuities on Perpetual Non-Participating Royalty," 32 *Texas L. Rev.* 369 (1954). The latter suggests that any interest subject to an exclusive leasing power should be considered in the nature of an incorporeal hereditament, vested and hence valid under the Rule against Perpetuities.

Elick v. Champlin Petroleum Co., 697 S.W.2d 1, 88 *O.&G.R.* 396 (Tex. App., Houston, 1985, error ref'd n.r.e.), held (one dissenting) that the executive right may be appurtenant to a royalty interest.

On the relationship between the holder of the exclusive leasing power and the mineral owner subject to it, see TREATISE §§ 339–339.3. See also UTMOST FAIR DEALING, DUTY OF.

Exclusive right doctrine

Synonym for the NONOWNERSHIP THEORY (*q.v.*) as to the nature of the landowner's interest in oil and gas. See Andrews, "The Correlative Rights Doctrine in the Law of Oil and Gas," 13 *So. Calif. L. Rev.* 185, 190 (1940).

Executive

The person holding the EXECUTIVE RIGHT (*q.v.*) or the EXCLUSIVE LEASING POWER (*q.v.*) over the minerals in a tract of land.

Exculpatory clause

A clause in a contract designed to relieve one party of liability to the other for specified injury or loss incurred in the performance of the contract. See e.g., ANR Production Co. v. Westburne Drilling, Inc., 581 F. Supp. 542, 80 *O.&.G.R.* 14 (D. Colo. 1984), construing an exculpatory clause in a Day Work DRILLING CONTRACT (*q.v.*) and giving effect to the clause as to certain (but not all) claims made for relief:

> "Although exculpatory agreements are strictly construed, they are enforceable where the parties are of equal bargaining power and the agreement is express and unequivocal."

Excuse rule

A term which has been applied to excuses for nonpayment or tardy, inadequate, or improper payment of delay rentals. D. Pierce, *Kansas Oil and Gas Handbook* § 6.04 (1986). See TREATISE § 606.6.

Executive interest

Article 108 of the Louisiana Mineral Code [R.S. 31:108 (1975)] defines executive interest as "a mineral right that includes an executive right." For a discussion of the nature and characteristics of the executive interest in Louisiana, see TREATISE § 339.4.

Executive right

Another name for EXCLUSIVE LEASING POWER (*q.v.*).

Article 105 of the Louisiana Mineral Code [R.S. 31:105 (1975)] defined the executive right as "the exclusive right to grant mineral leases of specified land or mineral rights. Unless restricted by contract it includes the right to retain bonuses and rentals. The owner of the executive right may lease the land or mineral rights over which he has power to the same extent and on such terms and conditions as if he were the owner of a mineral servitude." The nature and characteristics of the executive right in Louisiana are discussed in TREATISE § 339.4.

The definition in this MANUAL was cited in Whitehall Oil Co. v. Eckart, 197 So. 2d 664, 26 *O.&G.R.* 778 (La. App. 1966), *rev'd sub nom.* Gardner v. Goagni, 252 La. 30, 209 So. 2d 11, 29 *O.&G.R.* 229 (1968).

Exempt Alaskan oil

For purpose of the CRUDE OIL WINDFALL PROFIT TAX ACT OF 1980 (*q.v.*), this term means any crude oil (other than SADLEROCHIT OIL (*q.v.*)) which is produced: (1) from a reservoir from which oil has been produced in commercial quantities through a well located north of the Arctic Circle, or (2) from a well located on the northerly side of the divide of the Alaska-Aleutian Range and at least 75 miles from the nearest point on the Trans-Alaska Pipeline System. Internal Revenue Code § 4994.

Exempt allowables

Per well allowables not subject to reduction by the regulatory commission charged with responsibilities for fixing allowables. Thus, in Texas there are exempt allowables for discovery, marginal and special situation wells, and for county-regular, salt-dome, and certain waterflood fields. See Governors' Special Study Committee of the Interstate Oil Compact Commission, *A Study of Conservation of Oil and Gas in the United States* 105–107 (1964).

See also ALLOWABLE.

Exempt crude oil

Domestic crude oil which is exempt from price controls under the Emergency Petroleum Allocation Act of 1973 (EPAA), as amended by the Energy Policy and Conservation Act of 1975 (EPCA) and the Energy Conservation and Production Act of 1976 (ECPA).

See also COMPOSITE PRICE CEILING; PRICE CONTROL OF OIL, GAS AND PETROLEUM PRODUCTS.

Exempt front-end oil

For purposes of the CRUDE OIL WINDFALL PROFIT TAX ACT OF 1980 (*q.v.*), this term means any domestic crude oil: (A) which is removed from the premises before October 1, 1981, and (B) which is treated as front-end oil by reason of a front-end tertiary project on one or more properties each of which is a qualified property. Internal Revenue Code § 4994.

Exempt Indian Oil

For purposes of the CRUDE OIL WINDFALL PROFIT TAX ACT OF 1980 (*q.v.*), this term means any domestic crude oil—

(1) the producer of which is an Indian tribe, an individual member of an Indian tribe, or an Indian tribal organization under an economic interest held by such a tribe, member, or organization on January 21, 1980, and which is produced from mineral interests which are—

(A) held in trust by the United States for the tribe, member, or organization, or

(B) held by the tribe, member, or organization subject to a restriction on alienation imposed by the United States because it is held by an Indian tribe, an individual member of an Indian tribe, or an Indian tribal organization,

(2) the producer of which is a native corporation organized under the Alaska Native Claims Settlement Act (as in effect on January 21, 1980), and which—

(A) is produced from mineral interests held by the corporation which were received under that Act, and

(B) is removed from the premises before 1992, or

(3) the proceeds from the sale of which are deposited in the Treasury of the United States to the credit of tribal or native trust funds pursuant to a provision of law in effect on January 21, 1980. Internal Revenue Code § 4994.

Exempt oil

For purposes of the CRUDE OIL WINDFALL PROFIT TAX ACT OF 1980 (*q.v.*), this term means: (1) any crude oil from a qualified governmental interest or a qualified charitable interest, (2) any exempt Indian oil, (3) any exempt Alaskan oil, and (4) any exempt front-end oil. Internal Revenue Code § 4991.

The ECONOMIC RECOVERY TAX ACT OF 1981 (*q.v.*), P.L. 97–34 (Aug. 13, 1981), amended Section 4994 of the CRUDE OIL WINDFALL PROFIT TAX ACT OF 1980 (*q.v.*) by adding a category of exempt royalty oil. The term is defined as that portion of the qualified royalty owner's qualified royalty production for the quarter which does not exceed the royalty limit for such quarter. The royalty limit for any quarter is the production of (i) the number of days in such quarter, multiplied by (ii) the limitation in barrels specified, namely two barrels during 1982 through 1984 and three barrels in 1985 and thereafter.

Exempt royalty oil

Under the ECONOMIC RECOVERY TAX ACT OF 1981 (*q.v.*), this term is defined as that portion of the qualified royalty owner's qualified production for the quarter which does not exceed the royalty limit for such quarter. The royalty limit for any quarter is the production of the number of days in such quarter, multiplied by the limitation in barrels specified, namely two barrels during 1982 through 1984 and three barrels in 1985 and thereafter. I.R.C. § 6429(d)(2).

Exempt stripper well oil

Under the ECONOMIC RECOVERY TAX ACT OF 1981 (*q.v.*), this term includes oil removed from a STRIPPER WELL (*q.v.*) property which is exempted, effective Jan. 1, 1983, from the CRUDE OIL WINDFALL PROFIT TAX ACT OF 1980 (*q.v.*). I.R.C. § 4994(g).

See Mark and Wilson, "The Stripper Well Regulations: An Examination of the IRS Proposals," 32 *O.&G. Tax Q.* 31 (1983).

See also STRIPPER WELL EXEMPTION.

Exempt transportation

That transportation of oil by pipe line which was exempt from the petroleum transportation tax under § 3460 of the 1939 Internal Revenue Code. See Port Fuel Co. v. United States, 136 F. Supp. 89, 4 *O.&G.R.* 1664 (S. D. Tex. 1955).

Existing contract

This term is defined in § 2 of the NATURAL GAS POLICY ACT OF 1978 (*q.v.*) (Pub. L. No. 95–621) as any contract for the first sale of natural gas in effect on the day before the date of the enactment of this Act.

In Superior Oil Co. v. Pioneer Corp., 532 F. Supp. 731, 73 *O.&G.R.* 412 (N.D. Tex. 1982), the court concluded that since the exercise of an option was required to extend the term of a gas purchase and sale contract, a NEW CONTRACT (*q.v.*) was created by exercise of the option and that contract was not an EXISTING CONTRACT as defined by the Natural Gas Policy Act of 1978. The judgment was vacated and dismissed for want of jurisdiction, 706 F.2d 603 (5th Cir. 1983), *cert. denied,* 464 U.S. 1041, 104 S.Ct. 706 (1984).

EXL

An EXPLORATION LICENSE (*q.v.*) issued under the December, 1984, United Kingdom regulations [The Petroleum (Production) (Landward Areas) Regulations (1984)].

Expected third party price

The price at which it is anticipated by the parties to a concession agreement that crude oil from the Concession Area can be sold by the operating party consistent with its obligations as to the amount of oil to be offtaken and the amount to be sold to independent third parties, and taking into account the then foreseeable market position and prices obtained from independent third parties in recent past yearly periods for crude oil from the Concession Area. Paragraph 14.8 of the PETROMIN contract in OPEC, *Selected Documents of the International Petroleum Industry 1967* at p. 190.

See also CONCESSION; POSTED PRICE.

Expendable well

A term applied by the Internal Revenue Service to an exploratory well considered to have been drilled to obtain geological information rather than for the production of minerals. The costs of such a well were required to be capitalized rather than deducted as intangible drilling costs. See Linden, "Review of Offshore Drilling—What are Intangibles?" 26 *Sw. Legal Fdn. Oil & Gas Inst.* 441 at 445 (1975). Gates Rubber Co. & Subsidiaries v. Commissioner, 74 T.C. 1456, 67 *O.&G.R.* 647 (1980), *aff'd,* 694 F.2d 648 (10th Cir. 1982), and Sun Oil Co. v. Commissioner, 74 T.C. 1481, 68 *O.&G.R.* 353 (1980), *aff'd,* 677 F.2d 294, 76 *O.&G.R.* 619 (3d Cir. 1982), *acq.* I.R.B. 1983-26 (1983), held, however, that the deduction for INTANGIBLE DRILLING AND DEVELOPMENT COSTS (*q.v.*) is available for pre-platform wells. Since 1970 the percent of wells classified as dry holes has been greater offshore than onshore because of the greater number of expendable wells drilled offshore. Sincc these wells are not completed for production even though commercial quantities of oil and gas are found, they are classified as dry holes. See Report to the Federal Trade Commission on Federal Energy Land Policy: Efficiency, Revenue, and Competition. Committee Print for the Use of the Senate Committee on Interior and Insular Affairs, 94th Cong., 2d Sess. Serial No. 94–28 (92–118), at p. 341.

See also Bullion, "Special Tax Considerations in Relation to Offshore Operations and Financing," *Rocky Mt. Min. L. Fdn. Offshore Exploration, Drilling and Development Institute* (1975).

Syn.: BORE HOLE; ESCROW WELL; LINE TEST WELL; PRE-PLATFORM WELL.

Expense-bearing interest

A property interest in oil and gas that is subject to the expense of production. Thus a mineral fee interest and a working interest are expense bearing interests. It has been suggested that the distinction between a mineral interest and a royalty interest rests primarily on whether the interest bears expense of production or is expense free. See Maxwell, "The Mineral-Royalty Distinction and the Expense of Production," 33 *Texas L. Rev.* 463 (1955); Maxwell, "A Primer of Mineral and Royalty Conveyancing," 3 *U.C.L.A. L. Rev.* 449 (1956).

Expensed royalty system

A term applied to the system of international petroleum exploration and exploitation agreements under which royalties are not considered an advance on the income tax to be paid but simply a payment to the host country. The payment is deemed to be—like an expense—an allowable deduction for the determination of taxable income. Blinn, Duval, Le Leuch and Pertuzio, *International Petroleum Exploration & Exploitation Agreements* 231 (Barrows 1986).

See also CONCESSION; CREDITED ROYALTY.

Expense-free interest

A property interest in oil and gas that does not share in the burden of production expense. Thus, royalty, overriding royalty, oil payments, and net profits interests are expense free interests. See EXPENSE-BEARING INTEREST for further discussion and citation.

Experimental well

In Alberta, a well drilled, being drilled or operated pursuant to an experimental scheme approved by the Energy Resources Conservation Board. Alberta Oil and Gas Conservation Act, R.S.A. 1970, c. 267, § 2 (1) (18).

Exploitation well

A well located within the proven area of a reservoir which is drilled for the purpose of further developing said reservoir.

Syn.: DEVELOPMENT WELL.

Exploration

The search for oil and gas. Exploration operations include: aerial surveys, geophysical surveys, geological studies, core testing, and the drilling of test wells (wildcat wells). The cost of exploration, especially for deep production, often leads to cooperative arrangements between operators to divide the expense.

Gorenflo v. Texaco, Inc., 566 F. Supp. 722 at 727 (M.D. La. 1983), *aff'd,* 735 F.2d 835, 81 *O.&.G.R.* 284 (5th Cir. 1984), concluded that the word "develop" as used in the oil and gas industry contemplates and includes exploration.

See also GEOPHYSICAL EXPLORATION

Exploration and development costs

See COST OF EXPLORATION AND DEVELOPMENT.

Exploration covenant

In addition to the covenant of further exploration, there was formerly recognized a duty to drill an initial exploratory (or test) well, implied in oil and gas leases. See TREATISE §§ 811–813. Under modern oil and gas lease forms with a thereafter habendum clause and an unless delay rental clause, this covenant is no longer implied because it is contrary to express provisions of the lease.

See also FURTHER EXPLORATION COVENANT; IMPLIED COVENANTS.

Exploration license (EXL)

A license which may or may not be exclusive permitting the holder to search for hydrocarbons in a general area not covered by a production license. The holder of the license may usually engage in surveying operations and the drilling of shallow holes but he is not entitled to recover any petroleum discovered. *Syn.:* PROSPECTING LICENSE; RECONNAISSANCE LICENSE.

In the United Kingdom, the authorization by the Secretary of State for Energy to engage in prospecting and carrying out geological survey by physical or chemical means and drilling to specified depths for the purpose of obtaining geological information about strata in the exploration area, but not including any right to get petroleum. The license is for an initial term of three years which may be extended by the Secretary of State for Energy for an additional term of three years. Specified data (records, returns, plans, maps, samples, accounts and information) are required to be furnished the Minister on a confidential basis.

Under the December, 1984, United Kingdom regulations [The Petroleum (Production) (Landward Areas) Regulations (1984)], an exploration license (EXL) is for a six-year term and it allows the licensee to search for and drill for petroleum (subject to all necessary permissions from land owners and occupiers and planning permission). The licensee will also be allowed a short period in which to test any discovery, but for prolonged testing and further field appraisal an APPRAISAL LICENSE (*q.v.*) will be necessary. Case Digest and National News, [1984/85] 12 *OGTLR* D-129; J. Salter, *U.K. Onshore Oil and Gas Law* (1986).

See also APPRAISAL LICENSE (AL); DEVELOPMENT LICENSE (DL); EXPLORATION RETENTION LEASE; PRODUCTION LICENSE.

Exploration retention lease

An innovation in Australian mining law designed to provide a basis for protection of discoveries made by the holder of an EXPLORATION LICENSE (*q.v.*) prior to mining development proposals being approved by the government. The lease is designed to confer on the holder the right to execute such works and perform such operations as are necessary to evaluate the development potential of mineral discoveries made during exploration license activities; the lease does not authorize the recovery of any minerals. The exploration retention lease can be applied for and granted only where the minister is satisfied that there exists on the subject land an ore body or anomalous zone of possible economic potential. Le Messurier, "Comments on the Mining Act 1980 of the Northern Territory," 3 *Australian Mining and Petroleum L.J.* 131 at 132 (1981); [1986/87] 9 *OGLTR* D-99.

See also CONCESSION; RETENTION LEASE.

Exploratory drilling program

A DRILLING FUND (*q.v.*) in which the drilling program is composed of a relatively high percentage of properties which are unproven. Other types of program with a larger percentage of developmental wells offer less of a gamble for investors.

Exploratory license (Canada)

A license to explore for oil and gas. See 4 *O.&G.R.* 562 (1955).

See also PRODUCTION LICENSE.

Exploratory period

The period of time provided for in an oil and gas lease during which the lessee may retain the lease by drilling wells or by paying delay rental. In case of the UNLESS LEASE (*q.v.*), this period coincides with the primary term. At the end of the period, unless the lease contains one of several some type of DRILLING OPERATIONS CLAUSE (*q.v.*), the lease will terminate if production in paying quantities has not been obtained.

Exploratory permit

A permit authorizing exploration of Crown lands for petroleum. See *e.g.*, the Saskatchewan Regulations, 2 *O.&G.R.* 1193 at 1195 (1953).

Exploratory stage

The period of time specified by a concession, license, development contract or similar agreement during which an oil company agrees to complete specified activities in search of petroleum by means of geological and geophysical investigations, well drilling and other operations in order to fully explore the area and evaluate the existing structural or stratigraphic traps.

Exploratory term

Syn. for PRIMARY TERM (*q.v.*).

Exploratory title

In Australia, the exclusive right over an area to conduct petroleum exploration, including the drilling and testing of wells. See Lang and Crommelin, *Australian Mining and Petroleum Laws* 230 (1979).

See also PRODUCTION LICENSE.

Exploratory well

A well drilled in unproven or semi-proven territory for the purpose of ascertaining the presence underground of a commercial petroleum deposit. To be contrasted is the term DEVELOPMENT WELL (*q.v.*), which refers to a well drilled with the expectation of producing from a known productive formation, and which is located in accordance with spacing regulations and field development requirements.

As defined by the American Geological Institute, *Glossary of Geology and Related Sciences* 102, a well drilled either (a) in search of a new and as yet undiscovered pool (of oil or gas), or (b) with the hope of greatly extending the limits of a pool already developed.

On-Structure Deep Stratigraphic Test Wells, 87 I.D. 517 (Oct. 29, 1980), ruled that deep stratigraphic tests, on or off structures potentially holding oil or gas, are "geological explorations" authorized by the OUTER CONTINENTAL SHELF LANDS ACT OF 1953 (*q.v.*), and that the Secretary of the Interior could authorize permittees to conduct such tests on a structure before it was leased.

Sun Exploration & Production Co. v. Jackson, 715 S.W.2d 199, ____ *O.&G.R.* ____ (Tex. App., Houston, 1986), distinguished exploratory development wells from exploratory wildcat wells. An exploratory development well was described as one drilled to test potentially producing formations based on data obtained during earlier drilling and seismic operations. The decision to drill such a well "would necessary be based on a 'reasonable expectation of profit to the lessor and the lessee.'" An exploratory wildcat well was described as a speculative well "that did not offer a reasonable expectation of profit to a reasonably prudent operator under the same or similar facts and circumstances." The court sustained in part a trial court decree unconditionally canceling a lease as to a portion of the leased acreage and conditionally canceling other portions of the lease for prolonged failure of the lessee to drill exploratory development wells.

See FURTHER EXPLORATION COVENANT.

Exploratory work

Geological examinations, geophysical examinations, aerial mapping, investigations relating to the subsurface geology, test drilling, bulldozing, road building, surveying and all work necessarily connected therewith. See 4 *O.&G.R.* 560 (1955).

Exploratory work bonus

A deposit in money or bonds of a value equal to the amount that an exploratory permittee upon tender for certain Canada lands undertakes to expend for exploratory work within the first term of the permit. Territorial Lands Act, Public Lands Grant Act, Oil and Gas Land Order No. 1–1962, SOR/62–376 (Sept. 17, 1962).

See also BONUS.

Explosive

A substance, *e.g.*, trinitrotoluene or T.N.T., used to create an explosion. An explosive may be used in the well bore at the producing formation to shatter the formation and thereby increase the flow of oil, and may be used in an effort to regain control of a well which has blown out and caught fire.

Express covenant

As used in the oil industry, a written promise in a lease, an assignment, or other instrument. Such express covenants relate to a variety of subjects: *e.g.*, in the lease, to the payment of royalty, the furnishing of free gas to the lessor, the burial of pipelines, the restoration of cultivated fields, the lessee's right to remove casing and equipment, *etc.;* in assignments, one typical express covenant is that of the assignee to reassign the lease prior to its termination.

See also IMPLIED COVENANTS.

Express drilling clause

A provision in a lease or assignment requiring one of the parties to drill a well. The provision may be expressed as a covenant, for breach of which damages may be recovered. Fite v. Miller, 192 La. 229, 187 So. 650, 122 A.L.R. 446 (1939); 196 La. 876, 200 So. 285 (1941); R. Olsen Oil Co. v. Fidler, 199 F.2d 868, 2 *O.&G.R.* 58 (10th Cir. 1952). But such recovery has been limited to nominal damages. Guardian Trust Co. v. Brothers, 59 S.W.2d 343 (Tex. Civ. App. 1933, error ref'd). In other cases, the remedy for failure to comply with the express drilling clause has been automatic termination of the lease, the clause having been construed as a special limitation. Fogle v. Feazel, 201 La. 899, 10 So. 2d 695 (1942); Brightwell v. Norris, 242 S.W.2d 201 (Tex. Civ. App. 1951); Joycc v. Wyant, 202 F.2d 863, 2 *O.&G.R.* 693 (6th Cir. 1953).

Some care must be taken in adding an express drilling covenant to the standard form oil and gas lease to see that it is not nullified by other lease provisions. In Superior Oil Co. v. Dabney, 147 Tex. 51, 211 S.W.2d 563 (1948), the court held the express drilling obligations were extinguished by surrender of a portion of the leasehold and unitization of the balance under express surrender and unitization lease clauses.

See TREATISE §§ 883–885.5.

Expropriation

The taking by a national state of rights of property of individuals. In some instances the individuals are compensated for the rights taken and in other instances compensation may be denied. The term is frequently viewed as being synonymous with NATIONALIZATION (*q.v.*).

For an argument that the back-in provision of the Crown under Canada's National Energy Program constitutes an expropriation under international law and is therefore subject to the principle of customary international law requiring prompt, adequate and effective compensation, see Olmstead, Krauland and Orentlicher, "Expropriation in the Energy Industry: Canada's Crown Share Provision as a Violation of International Law," 29 *McGill L.J.* 439 (1984).

See also CONFISCATION; DIVESTMENT.

Extended primary term

Syn.: SECONDARY PRIMARY TERM (*q.v.*).

Extended-term estate

The term employed in Stewart v. Amerada Hess Corp., 604 P.2d 854 at 858, 65 *O.&G.R.* 530 at 535 (Okla. 1979), to describe the lessee's estate during the secondary term of an oil and gas lease.

Extension

(1) The reserves credited to a reservoir because of enlargement of its proved area. American Petroleum Institute Division of Statistics, *Organization and Definitions for the Estimation of Reserves and Productive Capacity of Crude Oil* 17 (Technical Report No. 2, June 1970).

(2) In Louisiana, a method by which a mineral servitude or a mineral royalty may be preserved beyond the prescription date for a period less than that which would result from an interruption by an acknowledgment. See Articles 56–57, 93 of the Louisiana Mineral Code [R.S. 31:56–57, 93 (1975)]; TREATISE § 216.3(c).

(3) The adjustment of previously estimated boundaries of known gas fields. Northern Natural Gas Co. v. O'Malley, 174 F. Supp. 176, 10 *O.&G.R.* 423 (D. Neb. 1959), *rev'd,* 277 F.2d 128, 12 *O.&G.R.* 335 (8th Cir. 1960).

Extension agreement

An agreement, usually between lessor and lessee, providing for the continued life of a lease which, but for the agreement, would have terminated.

Extension and renewal clause

A clause included in an instrument which creates an overriding royalty or oil payment out of a working interest to protect against a WASHOUT (*q.v.*). In effect, the clause provides that the interest shall apply and be a part of all future renewals or extensions of the lease. See TREATISE § 428.1.

Syn.: ANTI-WASHOUT PROVISION (*q.v.*).

Extension well

A well which enlarges the productive area of a proven reservoir.

Extraction plant

A plant for the extraction of the liquid constituents in casinghead gas or wet gas.

Extraneous gas

(1) Gas not produced from the area covered by a pooling or unitization agreement. Such gas may be purchased for reinjection or for processing. The pooling or unit agreement must in these instances contain specific provisions concerning accounting to owners of interests in the unit in such instances. See a typical provision in TREATISE § 921.14, note 5.

Syn.: Outside gas.

(2) This term is also used with reference to gas injected into underground gas storage to distinguish the injected gas from native gas.

Exxon formula

A term applied to a form of agreement in which one party advances delay rental payments in return for an assignment of the lease, the assignor reserving an overriding royalty and the right to reacquire its entire original interest by paying the former party its share of the rental within six months. Ginther v. Taub, 570 S.W.2d 516 at 521–522 (Tex. Civ. App. 1978, error ref'd n.r.e.). On subsequent appeal of Ginther v. Taub, 675 S.W.2d 724, 82 *O.&G.R.* 400 (Tex. 1984), a constructive trust was imposed on a knowing beneficiary of fraud.

. . F . .

Fade-out policy

A policy adopted by many host governments which have permitted their nationals to participate in joint ventures with foreigners, aimed at ensuring that the transition to full national ownership will ultimately take place. In the interest of maintaining a favorable investment in other sectors of the economy, such transfer of ownership should be planned and anticipated in agreement with the foreign interests concerned. The planned divestment may make provision for continuing foreign participation, *e.g.*, provision of information about technical progress, without continuing foreign ownership or control.

See also CONCESSION.

Fair dealing, duty of

See UTMOST FAIR DEALING, DUTY OF.

Fair field price method

A method of determining the value of company produced gas for rate purposes. Under this method all the expenditures and costs relating to the exploration, development and production of natural gas by the company up to the well mouth are excluded from operating expenses, and its production properties are excluded from its rate base. See Matter of Arkansas Louisiana Gas Co., 5 *O.&G.R.* 127 (Ark. Pub. Serv. Comm'n 1955), *rev'd sub nom.* Acme Brick Co. v. Arkansas Public Service Comm'n, 227 Ark. 436, 229 S.W.2d 208, 6 *O.&G.R.* 1395 (1957) [reversed by Ark. Act 175 of 1957, 7 *O.&G.R.* 371 (1957)].

See also City of Detroit, Mich. v. Federal Power Comm'n, 230 F.2d 810, 5 *O.&G.R.* 279 (D.C. Cir. 1955); *cert. denied,* 352 U.S. 829, 6 *O.&G.R.* 897 (1956).

The fair field price method of determining the cost of gas produced by pipeline companies is discussed in Davis, "General Principles Applicable to Utility Rates," American Gas Ass'n, *Regulation of the Gas Industry* 25-1 at 25-7 (1981).

See also ACCOUNTING METHODS; COST OF PRODUCTION METHOD; RATE BASE APPROACH.

Fair share of oil or gas in place

In a number of contexts it is asserted that a landowner has the right to recover a fair share of the oil and gas in place beneath his land. See *e.g.*, Billeaud Planters, Inc. v. Union Oil Co., 114 F. Supp. 564 at 570, 6 *O.&G.R.* 803 at 809 (W.D. La. 1956) ("We believe that a fair share of any land owner is that which he may recover from his land while complying with all the laws which control his operations. In other words, each land owner is entitled to 'an opportunity' to capture oil and gas underlying his land. That opportunity arises when it becomes evident, as in this case, that the land is productive."), *aff'd*, 245 F.2d 14, 7 *O.&G.R.* 798 (5th Cir. 1957).

For a discussion of this principle, said to modify the rule of capture, see Wronski v. Sun Oil Co., 89 Mich. App. 11, 279 N.W.2d 564, 63 *O.&G.R.* 182 (1979), *application for leave to appeal denied*, 407 Mich. 863 (1979).

Northern Michigan Exploration Co. v. Public Service Comm'n, 153 Mich. App. 635, 396 N.W.2d 487 at 488, ____ *O.&G.R.* ____ (1986), observed that the rule of capture has been modified by the "fair share" or "ownership-in-place" rule.

> "Under the rule, 'each owner of the surface is entitled only to his equitable and ratable share of the recoverable oil and gas energy in the common pool in the proportion which the recoverable reserves underlying his land bears to the recoverable reserves in the pool.' [Citing *Wronski v. Sun Oil Co.*] 'Fair share' is implemented by a number of procedures, including balancing, retroactive adjusting and proration. 8 **Williams & Meyers, [Oil and Gas Law]** *supra*, pp. 62, 695–696, 757."

The court sustained the 90-10 net pay proration formula adopted to allocate total production of gas from a common reservoir among the wells drilled into the reservoir.

In Texaco, Inc. v. Railroad Comm'n, 583 S.W.2d 307, 63 *O.&G.R.* 346 (Tex. 1979), the court observed that the "elementary rule of property that a landowner is entitled to an opportunity to produce his fair share of oil from a common reservoir" was qualified by both the rule of capture and the Commission's authority to prevent waste. In the instant case the court sustained the validity of a bonus allowable for water injection under a program which would increase the ultimate recovery of oil from a reservoir while causing net uncompensated drainage from some tracts.

For a detailed discussion of the fair share principle and methods available for calculation of fair share, see Graham, "Fair Share of Fair Game?" 8 *Nat. Res. Law.* 61 (1975).

See also CORRELATIVE RIGHTS; RULE OF CAPTURE.

Fairway

The name given to that portion of the East Texas field (the eastern part of the center of the field) with the thickest sands. See Hart, "Oil, the Courts, and the Railroad Commission," 44 *Southwestern Historical Q.* 303 at 313 (1941).

Farmee

The term applied to the person to whom a transfer described as a FARM OUT AGREEMENT (*q.v.*) has been made.

Farmers' oil

Syn. for royalty. Securities and Exchange Comm'n v. Crude Oil Corp., 93 F.2d 844 (7th Cir. 1937).

Farmer's sand

A colloquialism for the elusive oil bearing stratum which many landowners are convinced underlies their land regardless of the results of exploratory wells. Discussion Notes, 4 *O.&G.R.* 888 (1955).

Farm-in

(1) A term used in several countries to describe the person to whom a transfer described as a FARM-OUT AGREEMENT (*q.v.*) has been made, *viz.*, a FARMEE. See *Oil and Gas in Australia* (Australia and New Zealand Banking Group, 3d ed. 1976).

(2) The term is also used to describe the agreement itself, *viz.*, from the viewpoint of the farmee rather than from that of the farmor.

Farminee

A FARMEE (*q.v.*). See H.P. Williams, "Matters To Be Taken Into Consideration in the Negotiation of Farmouts and Operating Agreements," 1 *Austl. Mining & Petroleum L.J.* 509 at 511 (1978).

Farminor

A FARMOR (*q.v.*).

Farmor

The term applied to one who has made a transfer described as a FARM-OUT AGREEMENT (*q.v.*).

Farm-out

(1) The name given to a leasehold held by the owner thereof under a FARM-OUT AGREEMENT (*q.v.*).

(2) (Verb) To make a farm-out agreement.

Farm-out agreement

A very common form of agreement between operators, whereby a lease owner not desirous of drilling at the time agrees to assign the lease, or some portion of it (in common or in severalty) to another operator who is desirous of drilling the tract. The assignor in such a deal may or may not retain an overriding royalty or production payment. The primary characteristic of the farm-out is the obligation of the assignee to drill one or more wells on the assigned acreage as a prerequisite to completion of the transfer to him. See Rex Oil & Gas Co. v. Busk, 335 Mich. 368, 56 N.W.2d 221, 2 *O.&G.R.* 45 (1953). See TREATISE §§ 432–432.2.

The definition in this MANUAL was quoted in Sylvania Corp. v. Kilborne, 28 N.Y.2d 427 at 430, 322 N.Y.S.2d 678 at 679, 271 N.E.2d 524 at 525, 39 *O.&G.R.* 438 at 439 (1971).

For a discussion of the special problems of negotiating a farm-out agreement for operations in the Arctic, see Holt, "Problems Relating to Arctic Farmout and Joint Operating Agreements," 10 *Alberta L. Rev.* 450 (1972).

For a discussion of the negotiation and terms of farm-out agreements see Hemingway, "The Farmout Agreement: A Story Short But Not Always Sweet," 1 *Nat. Res. & Environment* 3 (Issue Number 2, Spring 1985).

For a discussion of the tax consequences of a farm-out agreement see the following:

Chapoton, "Income Tax on Transactions Commonly Handled by Natural Resource Practitioners," 27 *O.&G.R. Tax Q.* 209 at 223 (1978);

Gregg, "Oil and Gas Farmouts—Implications of Revenue Ruling 77–176," 29 *Sw. Legal Fdn. Oil & Gas Inst.* 601 (1978);

Wegher, "Taxation of Earned Interests—The Impact of Revenue Ruling 77–176," 24 *Rocky Mt. Min. L. Inst.* 521 (1978).

The negotiation and terms of farm-out agreements are discussed in the following:

Himebaugh, "An Overview of Oil and Gas Contracts in the Williston Basin," 59 *No. Dak. L. Rev.* 7 (1983);

Roberts, "Contracts and the Legal Framework of Petroleum Interests in the United Kingdom in the Context of Farm-ins," [1983] 2 *OGLTR* 21;

Scott, "How to Prepare an Oil and Gas Farmout Agreement," 33 *Baylor L.Rev.* 63 (1981);

Adams, "Farmout Agreements," *Rocky Mt. Min. L. Fdn. Mining Agreements Inst.* 2–1 (1979);

H. P. Williams, "Matters To Be Taken Into Consideration in the Negotiation of Farmouts and Operating Agreements," 1 *Austl. Mining & Petroleum L.J.* 509 (1978);

Klein and Burke, "The Farmout Agreement: Its Form and Substance," 24 *Rocky Mt. Min. L. Inst.* 479 (1978).

For a typical form of farm-out agreement, see Williams, Maxwell, Meyers, and Williams, *Cases on Oil and Gas* 994 (5th ed. 1987).

For other forms or letter agreements, see LETTER.

See also AFTER ACQUIRED RIGHTS CLAUSE; AREA OF MUTUAL INTEREST AGREEMENT; BACK-IN RIGHT; CALL; CHECKERBOARD FARM-OUT; CONVERTIBLE INTEREST; CONVERTIBLE OVERRIDE FARM-OUT; DEFERRED WORKING INTEREST FARM-OUT; DRILL AND EARN AGREEMENT; DRILL SITE ARRANGEMENT; "DRILL TO EARN" FARM-OUT; EARNED INTEREST; FARMOUT; FREE WELL; FREE WELL FARM-OUT; OBLIGATION WELL FARM-OUT; OPTION FARM-OUT; "PRODUCE TO EARN" FARM-OUT; SEISMIC FARM-OUT; SUBSTITUTE WELL CLAUSE; TAX PARTNERSHIP AGREEMENT; UNDIVIDED INTEREST FARM-OUT.

Farmoutee

A FARMEE (*q.v.*).

Farmoutor

A FARMOR (*q.v.*).

FASB

The Financial Accounting Standards Board of the American Institute of Certified Public Accountants.

FAS pricing

The pricing provision of an oil purchase and sale contract which locates the burden of shipping costs by specifying that the oil shall be "free alongside ship" (FAS) at the loading port. This pricing method is comparable to FOB (free on board) pricing. See Danielsen, *The Evolution of OPEC* 56 (1982); Daniel, "Carriage of Oil by Sea Crude Oil Sale Agreements," [1982] 5 *OGLTR* 163.

See also CIF PRICING; FOB PRICING.

Fault trap

A structural trap, favorable for the retention of petroleum, formed by the cracking and breaking of a rock plane. It is essential to the formation of the trap that the facing of the rock plane, up dip, be sealed off by an impervious formation.

See also GEOLOGICAL STRUCTURE; OVERTHRUST BELT; RESERVOIR; TRAP.

Favorable Petroleum Geological Province (FPGP)

An area favorable for the discovery of oil and gas. Under the provisions of the ALASKA NATIONAL INTEREST LANDS CONSERVATION ACT (ANILCA) (*q.v.*), land in an FPGP may be leased only by competitive bidding. See Asamera Oil, Inc., IBLA 82-1175, 82-1178, 82-1236, GFS(O&G) 1984-32 (Nov. 18, 1983). The FPGP classification applies to a total GEOLOGIC PROVINCE (*q.v.*) encompassing many possible specific structures or traps, and does not necessarily require the past or present existence of a producing or producible well.

See also KNOWN GEOLOGICAL STRUCTURE (KGS); PROVINCE.

Favored nation clause

See MOST FAVORED NATION CLAUSE.

FEA

The FEDERAL ENERGY ADMINISTRATION (*q.v.*).

Federal crude oil market

A proposed market to be operated by the federal government to accomplish the following objectives: (1) provide access to (FEA) refinery feedstocks for independent refiners; (2) provide an outlet for independent producers electing to use the market; and (3) provide a mechanism for determining a crude price upon which antitrust remedies could be based to prevent unfair competition by major integrated companies through subsidization of refining and marketing components out of crude oil profits. Under this proposal, refiners owning or controlling more than a designated percentage (*e.g.*, 30%) of their refinery feedstock requirements would be required to sell on the federal market, at a minimum, a prescribed percentage of their domestic crude oil production. See The Petroleum Industry, Hearings before the Subcommittee on Antitrust and Monopoly of the Committee on the Judiciary, U.S. Senate, 94th Cong., 1st Sess. on S. 2387 and Related Bills at p. 770.

Federal Energy Administration (FEA)

The administrative regulatory agency established as the successor to the Federal Energy Office by the Federal Energy Administration Act of 1974, Pub. L. No. 93–275, 15 U.S.C.A. § 763 *et seq.* For a detailed discussion of the activities of this agency see the statement by the administrator in "Oversight—Federal Energy Administration Programs," Hearings before the Senate Committee on Interior and Insular Affairs, 94th Cong., 1st Sess. Serial No. 94–16 (92–106), at p. 471. See also Aman, "Institutionalizing the Energy Crisis: Some Structural and Procedural Lessons," 65 *Cornell L. Rev.* 491 (1980).

The functions of the Federal Energy Administration were transferred to the Secretary of Energy by Pub. L. No. 95–91 (Aug. 4, 1977), 42 U.S.C. § 7151.

Federal Energy Impact Money

Money received by the federal government from sales, bonuses, royalties and rentals of public lands and paid over to a state. 30 U.S.C. § 191 (1982), provides that 50 percent of all money received from such sources shall be paid by the Secretary of the Treasury to each of the states within the boundaries of which the leased lands or deposits are located. See Israel, "Reducing the Impact of State, Local, and Indian Taxes on Western Mineral Development," 30 *Rocky Mt. Min. L. Inst.* 3-1 at 3-27 (1984) (discussing the use made of such money by various states).

Federal Energy Office (FEO)

The office established by Executive Order 11748, 38 Fed. Reg. 33575 (Dec. 6, 1973) and assigned responsibilities under the Emergency Petroleum Allocation Act of 1973, Pub. L. No. 93–159, 15 U.S.C.A. § 751 *et seq.*

Federal Energy Regulatory Commission (FERC)

The five member regulatory commission within the Department of Energy which replaced the FEDERAL POWER COMMISSION (*q.v.*) in 1977 when the Department of Energy was created by Pub. L. No. 95–91 (Aug. 4, 1977), 42 U.S.C. § 7101 *et seq.* The new commission has substantially the same regulatory powers as the predecessor commission and has been given additional responsibility for regulating oil pipelines, a function previously allocated to the Interstate Commerce Commission.

See Aman, "Institutionalizating the Energy Crisis: Some Structural and Procedural Lessons," 65 *Cornell L. Rev.* 491 (1980), and the symposium papers in 16 *Hous. L. Rev.* 1025–1302 (1979).

See also the entries under the heading FEDERAL POWER COMMISSION; PRICE CONTROL OF OIL, GAS AND PETROLEUM PRODUCTS.

Federal-floor provision

The term applied by State of Wyoming v. Moncrief, 720 P.2d 470, ___ *O.&G.R.* ___ (Wyo. 1986), to a gas royalty provision stating that "in no event shall the price for gas, or natural gasoline, be less than that received by the United States of America for its royalties from the same field." In this case the court found consistency between this provision, a MARKET-VALUE/AMOUNT-REALIZED PROVISION (*q.v.*), and a LESSOR-APPROVAL PROVISION (*q.v.*).

Federal land exchange

An exchange of land with the federal government designed to achieve land consolidation and mineral access objectives. See Quarles and Lundquist, "Federal Land Exchanges and Mineral Development," 29 *Rocky Mt. Min. L. Inst.* 367 (1983).

Federal Land Policy and Management Act of 1976 (FLPMA)

A statute, 43 U.S.C. § 1701 *et seq.* designed to modernize the law governing the use and disposition of publicly owned resources and lands.

A provision of this Act designed to rid federal lands of stale mining claims through a federal recording system was sustained in United States v. Locke, ___ U.S. ___, 105 S.Ct. 1785, 84 *O.&G.R.* 299 (1985).

For discussions of the Act see the following:

Holtkamp, "The Effect of FLPMA on the Mining Law: A Decade of Change," 32 *Rocky Mt. Min. L. Inst.* 11-1 (1986);

Short, "Wilderness Policies and Mineral Potential on the Public Lands," 26 *Rocky Mt. Min. L. Inst.* 39 (1980).

See also CHERRYSTEMMING PRACTICE; NATIONAL WILDERNESS PRESERVATION SYSTEM (NWPS); ROADLESS AREA REVIEW AND EVALUATION; WILDERNESS ACT OF 1964.

Federal lease

An oil and gas lease on federal land issued under the act of February 25, 1920, as amended (41 Stat. 437, as amended; 30 U.S.C. § 181, *et seq.*), or the Act of August 7, 1947 (61 Stat. 913, 30 U.S.C. § 351, *et seq.*). See *Rocky Mt. Min. L. Fdn. Law of Federal Oil and Gas Leases* ch. 3 (1985).

For a discussion of stipulations which may be included in federal leases, see *Rocky Mt. Min. L. Fdn. Law of Federal Oil and Gas Leases* ch. 15 (1985); Burton, "Federal Leasing—Restrictions and Extensions," 28 *Rocky Mt. Min. L. Inst.* 1133 (1982).

The conditions under which specially managed federal lands may be open to mineral and oil and gas development are discussed in Watson, "Mineral and Oil and Gas Development in Wilderness Areas and Other Specially Managed Federal Lands in the United States," 29 *Rocky Mt. Min. L. Inst.* 37 (1983).

See also ALASKA NATIONAL INTEREST LANDS CONSERVATION ACT (ANILCA); ALIEN LAND OR MINERAL OWNERSHIP RESTRICTIONS; AVERAGE EVALUATION OF TRACT (AEOT); BID FILES; BOARD OF LAND APPEALS; BUREAU OF LAND MANAGEMENT; BUY-BACK AGREEMEMT; CASE FILE; CHARGEABILITY; COMBINED HYDROCARBON LEASE; COMPETITIVE LEASE; DEPARTMENTAL LEASE; DEVELOPMENT CONTRACT; DISCOUNTED MROV (DMROV); DRAWING ENTRY CARD; EXCHANGE AND RENEWAL LEASE; FAVORABLE PETROLEUM GEOLOGICAL PROVINCE (FPGP); FEDERAL LEASING ACT; FILING SERVICES; 555 TERMINATION; FRACTIONAL OR FUTURE INTEREST LEASE; GEOMETRIC AVERAGE EVALUATION OF TRACT (GAEOT); KNOWN GEOLOGICAL STRUCTURE (KGS); LAND STATUS BOOK; LEASE CASE FILE; MEAN OF THE RANGE OF VALUES (MROV); MINERALS MANAGEMENT SERVICE (MMS); MINIMUM ACCEPTABLE BID; MINIMUM ROYALTY; MINIMUM ROYALTY STATUS; NOMINATION OF TRACT FOR LEASING; NON-COMPETITIVE LEASE; NON-CONVENTIONAL OIL RECOVERY STIPULATION; NON-PARTICIPATING AREA; NOTATION RULE; OCS ROYALTY OIL; 1/8 RULE; OFFICE OF APPEALS AND HEARINGS; OFFICE OF HEARINGS AND APPEALS; OPEN BONUS BID; OPEN LEASE AREA; OPEN LEASE AREA SUBJECT TO NO SURFACE

OCCUPANCY; OPEN LEASE AREA SUBJECT TO SPECIAL STIPULATIONS; OPEN PARCEL LEASE; OUTER CONTINENTAL SHELF LANDS ACT OF 1953; OVER-THE-COUNTER LEASE; OVER-THE-COUNTER LEASE OFFER; PARTICIPATING AREA; PARTY-IN-INTEREST STATEMENT; PERFORMANCE-TYPE LEASING; PETROLEUM TAR SANDS; PLAT BOOK; POST SALE ANALYSIS CHART; PREFERENCE RIGHT; PROTECTIVE LEASING; PROVEN OR SEMI-PROVEN ("DRAINAGE") METHOD OF EVALUATION; PUBLIC LANDS; PUT OPTION; QUALIFIED APPLICANT; RANGE OF VALUES METHOD; REDUCTION OF ROYALTIES; REDUCTION WORKS; RELINQUISHMENT OF LEASE; RESERVATION PRICE; RISK-FREE VALUE; ROYALTY REDUCTION; RULE OF APPROXIMATION; SECTION 6 LEASE; SECTION 8 LEASE; SERIAL REGISTER; SIMULTANEOUS FILINGS; 640-ACRE RULE; SIX-MILE-SQUARE RULE; SPLIT LEASE; SUSPENDED OR NO LEASE AREA; SUSPENSION OF OPERATIONS AND PRODUCTION; TEN PER CENT EXCESSIVE ACREAGE RULE; TEN PER CENT (RENTAL) RULE; TOP-FILED APPLICATION; TRACT BOOK; WILDCAT ACREAGE METHOD OF EVALUATION; WITHDRAWAL; WORKING INTEREST BIDDING.

Federal leasing act

The statute under which government land is leased for oil and gas purposes by the United States. The statute is called The Mineral Leasing Act of Feb. 25, 1920, 41 Stat. 437, 30 U.S.C. § 181 *et seq.* Similar in general is the Acquired Lands Leasing Act of 1947, 61 Stat. 913, 30 U.S.C. §§ 351–359. See Hoffman, *Oil and Gas Leasing on Federal Lands* (1957); *Rocky Mt. Min. L. Fdn. Law of Federal Oil and Gas Leases* ch. 3 (1985).

Federal Oil & Gas Royalty Management Act of 1982 (FOGRMA)

30 U.S.C. §§ 1701–1757 (1982), an Act designed to ensure that oil and gas royalties are accurately and promptly assessed and collected. See Marathon Oil Co. v. United States, 604 F.Supp. 1375, 87 *O.&G.R.* 455 (D. Alaska 1985), *aff'd,* 807 F.2d 759, 90 *O.&G.R.* 6 (9th Cir. 1986).

See also Day, "Valuing Federal Oil and Gas Royalties," 1 *Nat. Res. & Environment* 10 (Vol. 1, No. 2, Spring 1985).

Federal Petroleum Board

The agency charged with administration of the CONNALLY ACT (*q.v.*).

Federal Power Commission

The federal regulatory agency charged with administration of the Natural Gas Act, 52 Stat. 821, as amended, 15 U.S.C.A. §§ 717–717(w), regulating the transportation and sale of natural gas in interstate commerce.

The functions of the Federal Power Commission were transferred to the Secretary of Energy by Pub. L. No. 95–91 (Aug. 4, 1977), 42 U.S.C. § 7151. The major functions of the Commission are now exercised within the Department of Energy by the Federal Energy Regulatory Commission.

See also ABANDONMENT OF FACILITIES OR SERVICE; ABBREVIATED APPLICATION; ABRIDGED HEARING PROCEDURE; ADVANCE PAYMENT ORDER; ANETH LETTER; AREA PRICING POLICY; ASSOCIATED COMPANIES; ATLANTIC SEABOARD CLASSIFICATION METHOD; BUDGET-TYPE CERTIFICATE APPLICATION; CERTIFICATE CONDITION; CERTIFICATED CAPACITY; CERTIFICATE OF PUBLIC CONVENIENCE AND NECESSITY; CHANDELEUR INCENTIVE DOCTRINE; COMMODITY CHARGE THEORY; CONVENTIONALIZATION OF LEASE-SALE; CONVERTIBLE INTEREST; COST ALLOCATION METHODS; CURTAILMENT PLAN; DEDICATION OF RESERVES; DEEPER DRILLING EXCEPTION; EFFECTIVE TARIFF; END USE CONTROL; END USE RATE SCHEDULE; FILED RATE DOCTRINE; 533 PROGRAM; 467 PLAN; GOOD FAITH NEGOTIATION RULE; GRANDFATHER CERTIFICATE; GRANDFATHER CLAUSE; GRANDFATHER PRICE; INCREMENTAL COST METHOD; INCREMENTAL PRICING; INFERIOR USE; IN LINE PRICE; INTERDEPENDENT APPLICATION; JURISDICTIONAL ESCAPE CLAUSE; JURISDICTIONAL SALES; LIMITED TERM CERTIFICATE; MANUFACTURED GAS; MINIMUM RATE; MOLECULAR THEORY; NATIONAL RATE; NATIONAL RATE CASE; NATURAL GAS ACT; NATURAL GAS COMPANY; NATURAL GAS PRODUCER; NEW GAS; NON-JURISDICTIONAL SALES; OFFICE OF PIPELINE AND PRODUCER REGULATION (OPPR); OLD GAS; ONE HUNDRED AND EIGHTY DAY EMERGENCY SALES; ONE PRICE SYSTEM; OPTIONAL CERTIFICATING PROCEDURE; PAYBACK ORDER; POSTING; PREGRANTED ABANDONMENT; PRICE CONTROL OF OIL, GAS AND PETROLEUM PRODUCT; PRODUCTION ENHANCEMENT PROCEDURES; PRODUCTION OR GATHERING EXCLUSION; PRODUCTIVITY FACTOR; PROTEST CLAUSE; PRUDENT PIPELINE STANDARD; RATE SCHEDULE; RATE TILTING; RAYNE FIELD CASE; REDUCED PGA METHOD; REFUNDS INTEREST RATE (RIR) PROCEDURES; RELATIVE COST METHOD OF ALLOCATION; RELATIVE MARKET VALUE METHOD; REPLACEMENT CONTRACT POLICY; ROLLED-IN ALLOCATION METHOD; SALES REALIZATION METHOD; SANCTITY OF CONTRACT LEGISLATION; SEABOARD INTERESTS; SERVICE AGREEMENT; SIXTY-DAY EMERGENCY SALES; SMALL PRODUCER; SMALL PRODUCER SALES; SPECIAL RE-

LIEF APPLICATIONS; STORAGE SPRINKLING; SUSPECT PRICE; SUSPENDED ROYALTY; SUSPENSE MONEY; TARIFF; TARIFF-AND-SERVICE AGREEMENT; TIGHT FORMATION; TRACKING RATE CHANGE; TWO-PRICE SYSTEM; UNIFORM SYSTEM OF ACCOUNTS; VINTAGE; VOLUMETRIC METHOD OF ALLOCATION.

Feeder line

See PIPELINE.

Feedstock gas

Gas used as raw material for its chemical properties in creating an end product. Statement of Chairman John N. Nassikas, Federal Power Commission, "Federal Power Commission Oversight—Natural Gas Curtailment Priorities," Hearing before the Senate Committee on Commerce, 93rd Cong., 2d Sess., June 20, 1974, at p. 83; F.P.C. Order No. 493 (Sept. 21, 1973).

Fee royalty

The lessor's share of production.
Syn.: LANDOWNER ROYALTY.

FEO

The FEDERAL ENERGY OFFICE (*q.v.*)

Ferae naturae

Of a wild nature. By virtue of misapprehension of the nature of a producing formation, many courts formerly believed that oil was as migratory as the birds in the air, or at least as migratory in character as underground waters, from which ideas developed the so-called NON-OWNERSHIP THEORY (*q.v.*) that no person owned the oil and gas until produced but that the right to produce was limited to those persons who owned land upon which a well might be drilled. The former concept enabled some of the courts to adopt by analogy the rules governing the capture of wild animals; from the latter concept came the idea that the rights of a landowner to oil and gas were the same as his rights to underground waters. Under the wild animal analogy, the oil and gas belonged to the person who "captured" it, but the state, as in the case of wild animals, had the power to prohibit or regulate the capture. Under the underground water analogy, a landowner was permitted to take oil and gas from his land even though the result was to drain his neighbor's lands, since such right was given a landowner in the case of underground water. See TREATISE §§ 203, 203.2; RULE OF CAPTURE.

FERC

The FEDERAL ENERGY REGULATORY COMMISSION (*q.v.*).

FERC-out clause

An ESCALATOR CLAUSE (*q.v.*) in a GAS PURCHASE CONTRACT (*q.v.*) providing in essence that if the Federal Energy Regulatory Commission (FERC) or other appropriate governmental agency does not permit the pipeline purchase to "flow through" the price provided in the gas sales contract to *its* customers, that the price paid the producer will be reduced by the amount not permitted to be taken into the pipelines' cost basis. Johnson, "Natural Gas Sales Contracts," 34 *Sw. Legal Fdn. Oil & Gas Inst.* 83 at 103 (1983).

Syn.: Flow-through clause.

See also ECONOMIC-OUT CLAUSE; MARKET-OUT CLAUSE.

FES

The final environment statement required by the National Environmental Policy Act. See National Helium Corp. v. Morton, 486 F.2d 995, 47 *O.&G.R.* 1 (10th Cir. 1973), *cert. denied,* 416 U.S. 993 (1974).

Field

The general area underlaid by one or more pools. Ore Rev. Stat. § 520.005(4) (1979 Ed.). The words "field" and "pool" mean the same thing when only one underground reservoir is involved; however, "field," unlike "pool," may relate to two or more pools.

The Supreme Court of Texas has observed that "The word 'field' as used in the oil industry has a meaning which is usually determined from the context in which it is used. It may refer to a certain geographical area from which oil is produced or it may be restricted to a particular reservoir." Railroad Comm'n v. Rio Grande Valley Gas Co., 405 S.W.2d 304 at 309, 24 *O.&G.R.* 818 at 822–823 (Tex. 1966). In the instant case the court found that the term "field" as used in the Common Purchaser Act had the former definition.

In Bolton v. Coats, 533 S.W.2d 914 at 917, 53 *O.&G.R.* 379 at 384 (Tex. 1975), the court applied the word "field" to each physically separate productive stratum under a single well, lease or unit.

"The definition of a field is blurred at best. One writer says simply: 'I use the term "field" to describe an aggregate of overlapping, contiguous, or superimposed pools.' Pools and fields result from some set of geographical disturbances which may extend over a wide area, or form what is often called a 'trend' or 'basin,' which may be thought of as being to a field what a field is to a pool." Adelman, Bradley, and Norman, *Alaskan Oil: Costs and Supply* 18 (1971).

A number of writers apparently employ the words "field" and "pool" as synonymous terms. See *e.g.*, Miller, "Some Implications of Land Ownership Patterns for Petroleum Policy," 49 *Land Economics* 414 (1973); Abt Associates, *Energy Fuel Mineral Resources of the Public Lands* 115 (A Study Prepared for the Public Land Law Review Commission, 1970).

See also the discussion of the meaning of the term "field" in Palmer Oil Corp. v. Phillips Petroleum Co., 204 Okla. 543, 231 P.2d 997 at 1011 (1951), *appeal dism'd sub nom.* Palmer Oil Corp. v. Amerada Petroleum Corp., 343 U.S. 390, 1 *O.&G.R.* 876 (1952); Wotton v. Bush, 251 P.2d 376, 2 *O.&G.R.* 6 (Cal. App. 1952); 41 Cal. 2d 460, 261 P.2d 256, 3 *O.&G.R.* 12 (1953).

See also GAS CAP FIELD; GEOLOGICAL FIELD; GIANT FIELD; NON-ASSOCIATED GAS RESERVOIRS; OIL AND GAS FIELD CODE MASTER LIST—1982; OIL FIELD; OIL POOL; PROSPECT; RESERVOIR; SOLUTION GAS FIELD; STRIPPER WELL FIELD.

Field allowable

See ALLOWABLE; PRORATIONING.

Field compression test

A test to determine the gasoline content of casinghead gas or wet gas. Bosworth v. Eason Oil Co., 202 Okla. 359, 213 P.2d 548 (1949).

See also CHARCOAL TEST.

Field development well

As defined by the American Geological Institute, *Glossary of Geology and Related Sciences* 108, any well drilled within the presently known or proved productive area of a pool (reservoir) as indicated by reasonable interpretation of subsurface data, with the objective of obtaining oil or gas from that pool.

Syn.: DEVELOPMENT WELL.

Field drainage

Regional migration of oil or gas. This field wide movement in one direction results from removal of petroleum at any point in the reservoir. In contrast, local drainage results from unequal removal of petroleum from one well as compared to the removal from surrounding wells. Thus it could very well happen in a field in which the regional migration was to the east that local drainage over a fifty or hundred acre area was to the west.

One well known example of field drainage is in the East Texas Field, which is a truncated monocline dipping to the west, produced by water drive. The movement of the oil in the reservoir is up-dip, to the east. Thus landowners in the eastern part of the field will produce oil so long as any remains in the reservoir, and long after the western landowners' wells have gone to salt water. This is true without regard to the amount of oil originally in place beneath the respective owners' land. Efforts to increase the production of western landowners in the East Texas Field, by drilling of more wells as exceptions to the spacing rule have been rebuffed by the courts. See Byrd v. Shell Oil Co., 178 S.W.2d 573 (Tex. Civ. App. 1944); Woolley v. Railroad Comm'n, 242 S.W.2d 811 (Tex. Civ. App. 1951). One solution is compulsory unitization of the field, with participation factors based on recoverable oil originally in place.

Amoco Production Co. v. Alexander, 622 S.W.2d 563, 72 *O.&G.R.* 125 (Tex. 1981), held that the covenant to protect against drainage is not limited to local drainage but extends to field-wide drainage as well. The duty "may include (1) drilling replacement wells, (2) re-working existing wells, (3) drilling additional wells, (4) seeking field-wide regulatory action, (5) seeking Rule 37 exceptions from the Railroad Commission, (6) seeking voluntary unitization, and (7) seeking other available administrative relief."

See also DRAINAGE; STRUCTURAL ADVANTAGE.

Field hearing

A hearing held by the Texas Railroad Commission to gather information required to set the spacing and allocation rules for a given field, as distinguished from a STATEWIDE HEARING at which the Commission decided the overall level of Texas production for a given month. See Prindle, *Petroleum Politics and the Texas Railroad Commission* 71 (1981).

Field plant

See STRADDLE PLANT.

Field potential

The producing capacity of a field during a period of twenty-four hours.

See also WELL POTENTIAL.

Field pressure

"The pressure of natural gas as it is found in the underground formations from which it is produced." American Gas Ass'n, *Glossary for the Gas Industry* (3d ed. 1981).

Field price

The term "field price" has been used with various meanings in the natural gas industry. Comment, "Federal Price Control of Natural Gas Sold to Interstate Pipelines," 59 *Yale L.J.* 1468 at 1484 (1950), lists the following definitions of the term in this industry:

(1) the "going" price that a buyer must offer to get a contract for additional gas;

(2) the average weighted contract price at which gas is being delivered to (a) interstate pipelines or to (b) all buyers in the field, including intra state pipelines, local industrial users, and other producers.

See also POSTED FIELD PRICE.

Field price method

See FAIR FIELD PRICE METHOD.

Field separator

An installation for the removal of casinghead gas from the oil with which it is produced. Saturn Oil & Gas Co. v. Federal Power Comm'n, 250 F.2d 61, 8 *O.&G.R.* 365 (10th Cir. 1957), *cert. denied,* 355 U.S. 956, 8 *O.&G.R.* 843 (1958).

See SEPARATOR.

Field tank

See TANK.

Field value of natural gas

The Alberta Arbitration Act, R.S.A. 1970, c. 21, § 16.1 defines this term as "the commodity value of gas less just and reasonable costs, charges and deductions that are or may be fixed, determined or allowed for the transportation and distribution of that gas from the point of sale under the gas purchase contract to the point of end use." See Re Canadian Western Natural Gas Co., Ltd. and Shell Canada Resources, Ltd., 108 D.L.R.3d 431 (Alta. Q.B. 1979), *appeal allowed,* 118 D.L.R.3d 607 (Alta. Ct of App. 1980).

See also COMMODITY VALUE OF NATURAL GAS.

50–50 allowable formula

Under this formula, 50% of the field ALLOWABLE (*q.v.*) is prorated to the wells individually and the remaining 50% is prorated to acreage. The formula has been frequently applied in Texas. For a detailed explanation of how it works, and a criticism of its operation, see Hardwicke, "Oil Well Spacing Regulations," 31 *Texas L. Rev.* 99 at 113–116 (1952). This formula may not be applied to new oil and gas fields in Texas. Halbouty v. Railroad Comm'n, 163 Tex. 417, 357 S.W.2d 364, 16 *O.&G.R.* 788, *cert. denied,* 371 U.S. 888 (1962).

50–50 transaction

An agreement between concurrent owners whereby both parties bear all expenses equally. Krystal, "Income Tax Problems in Oil Transactions—The 'Carried Interest,'" *1948 Proceedings of the U.S.C. Tax Institute* 313 (1949).

Filed rate doctrine

The term applied to the rule that when a determination is made under Section 5 of the NATURAL GAS ACT (*q.v.*) that rates charged for natural gas are unjust and unreasonable, new rates are effective prospectively only, and the natural gas company has no refund liability for rates previously collected. Marston and Hollis, "A Review and Assessment of the FERC Natural Gas Enforcement Program," 16 *Houston L. Rev.* 1105 at 1106 note 10 (1979). See Atlantic Ref. Co. v. Public Service Comm'n of New York, 360 U.S. 378 at 389 (1959).

In Arkansas Louisiana Gas Co. v. Hall, 453 U.S. 571, 70 *O.&G.R.* 119 at 127 (1981), *motion for clarification denied,* 454 U.S. 809 (1981), the doctrine was said to prohibit "a federally regulated seller of natural gas from charging rates higher than those filed with the

Federal Energy Regulatory Commission pursuant to the Natural Gas Act." For subsequent appeal in this case see Hall v. Federal Energy Regulatory Commission, 691 F.2d 1184, 78 *O.&G.R.* 571 (5th Cir. 1982), *cert. denied,* 464 U.S. 822, 104 S.Ct. 88 (1983).

See also Public Service Co. of Colo. v. Public Utilities Comm'n of the State of Colo., 644 P.2d 933 (Colo. 1982).

Filing services

"Enterprises . . . which sign, formulate, prepare, offer advice on formulation or preparation, mail, deliver, receive mail or otherwise complete or file lease applications or offers for consideration." 43 C.F.R. § 3100.0–5(d) (1981). See Hawley, "Federal Oil and Gas Leases—The Sole Party in Interest Debacle," 27 *Rocky Mt. Min. L. Inst.* 987 (1982).

Syn.: LEASING SERVICE COMPANY (*q.v.*).

Filter cake

A synonym for WALL CAKE (*q.v.*).

Financing royalty trust

A ROYALTY TRUST (*q.v.*) created by a corporation seeking to generate funds through the sale of royalty interests in its natural resource properties.

Finder

A person serving as an intermediary to introduce and bring together parties to a business opportunity, leaving the ultimate negotiation of the business transaction to the principals. For a discussion of the role of a finder in mineral transactions and his right to compensation see Morgan, "Dealing with the Hungry Finder and Disclosures on Mineral Properties," 20 *Rocky Mt. Min. L. Inst.* 651 (1975).

Fingering

Finger-like infiltration of water or gas into an oil bearing formation as a result of failure to maintain reservoir pressure or as a result of taking oil in excess of the MAXIMUM EFFICIENT RATE (*q.v.*). Fingering renders the oil in the portions of the structure bypassed by the fingers unrecoverable by normal production methods.

See also BY-PASSING; CHANNELING.

Finished drilling date

The date at which the total depth of a well is reached without regard for any deepening that may be made after substantially continuous drilling has once ceased. Alberta Oil and Gas Conservation Regulations (Alta. Reg. 151/71) § 1–020(2)(7).

FIRA

The FOREIGN INVESTMENT REVIEW ACT (*q.v.*) of Canada.

FIRB

The FOREIGN INVESTMENT REVIEW BOARD (*q.v.*) of Australia.

Firedamp

Methane found in coalbeds. J. Salter, *U.K. Onshore Oil and Gas Law* 1-302 (1986).

See also COALBED GAS; METHANE; METHANE DRAINAGE LICENSE.

Fire flooding

Syn. for IN-SITU COMBUSTION (*q.v.*).

Firm customer

(1) A person entitled by contract to the delivery of a stated amount of gas. For Pierce Utility Authority v. Federal Power Comm'n, 526 F.2d 993 at 955 (5th Cir. 1976).

(2) A gas customer whose demand for gas is approximately the same every day of the year as opposed to a customer whose demand for gas may vary on a seasonal or other basis.

See also INTERRUPTIBLE CUSTOMER; SPACE HEATING CUSTOMER.

Firm gas

Gas required to be delivered and required to be taken under the terms of a gas purchase contract. Firm gas commands a higher price than DUMP GAS (*q.v.*).

See also INTERRUPTIBLE GAS.

Firm gas contract

A gas purchase contract calling for the delivery and purchase of fixed amounts of gas over a period of time. See State of North Dakota v. Federal Power Comm'n, 247 F.2d 173 (8th Cir. 1957).

See also Dump gas contract.

Firm service

A higher priced service for gas which is continuous without curtailment except under occasional, extraordinary circumstances. See Granite City Steel Co. v. Federal Power Comm'n, 320 F.2d 711 (D.C. Cir. 1963); Arkansas Power & Light Co. v. Federal Power Comm'n, 517 F.2d 1223 (D.C. Cir. 1975), *cert. denied,* 423 U.S. 933 (1976).

First marketable product

For purposes of the depletion deduction taken under § 611 of the Internal Revenue Code, the taxpayer's gross income from the property must be calculated, and in this determination it is necessary to determine the first marketable product when the taxpayer engages in an integrated mining-manufacturing process. The term is defined in Treasury Regulations § 1.613.4(d)(4)(iv). See Commissioner of Internal Revenue v. Portland Cement Co. of Utah, 450 U.S. 156 (1981).

First money

Syn. for Front end of oil payment. (*q.v.*)

First party favored nations clause

Syn. for Two party favored nations clause. (*q.v.*) See Escalator clause; Most favored nation clause.

First refusal clause

Syn. for Preferential right of purchase (*q.v.*).

First sale

In the Natural Gas Policy Act of 1978 (NGPA), 15 U.S.C. § 3301(21)(A), first sale was defined as "any sale of any volume of natural gas" to a specified purchaser. In Mid-Louisiana Gas Co. v. Federal Energy Regulatory Commission, 664 F.2d 530, 73 *O.&G.R.* 179 (5th Cir. Unit A, 1981), *reh. denied,* 669 F.2d 729 (5th Cir. Unit A, 1982), the court concluded that the transfer of production by a pipeline producer of gas to the transportation division of the pipeline was to be treated as a first sale under the Act, *vacated and remanded sub nom.* Public Service Comm'n of State of New York v. Mid-Louisiana Gas Co., 463 U.S. 319, 103 S. Ct. 3024, 79 *O.&G.R.* 149 (1983) (agreeing with the court of appeals that the Commission's exclusion of pipeline production was inconsistent with the statutory mandate and would frustrate the policy Congress sought to implement, but concluding—contrary to the view of the court of appeals—that Congress intended to give the Commission discretion in deciding whether the first sale treatment should be provided at the intracorporate transfer or at the downstream transfer), *remanded to the commission,* 24 FPS 6-117 (5th Cir. 1983). On a later appeal of Mid Louisiana Gas Co. v. Federal Energy Regulatory Comm'n, 780 F.2d 1238 (5th Cir. 1986), the court concluded that the pipeline-producer was not prohibited from pricing part of its company-owned production in accordance with the rate structure in the NGPA.

See also the following:

National Fuel Gas Supply Corp. v. Federal Energy Regulatory Comm'n, 811 F.2d 1563, ____ *O.&G.R.* ____ (D.C. Cir. 1987);

Gulf Oil Corp. v. Department of Energy, 671 F.2d 485 (Temp. Emer. Ct. App. 1982) (finding that transfer of natural gas liquids and natural gas liquid products by processor-refiners and gas processors to affiliated marketers constituted "first sales" within the meaning of mandatory petroleum price regulations), motion for summary judgment granted *sub nom.* Internorth Inc. v. Department of Energy, 548 F. Supp. 987 (D. Del. 1982).

See also Hollis, "Notable Recent Developments in Federal Natural Gas Regulation," 34 *Sw. Legal Fdn. Oil & Gas Inst.* 31 at 62 (1983).

First tier oil

Domestic crude oil subject to price controls under the provisions of the Emergency Petroleum Allocation Act of 1973 (EPAA) as amended by the Energy Policy and Conservation Act of 1975 (EPCA). Under EPAA the price of OLD OIL (*q.v.*) was fixed at the price prevailing in the field on May 15, 1973, plus $1.35 per barrel, resulting in a ceiling price of old oil which averaged approximately $5.25 a barrel. NEW OIL (*q.v.*), RELEASED OIL (*q.v.*), and STRIPPER WELL OIL (*q.v.*) could be sold at market price. Following the enactment of EPCA in December of 1975 ceilings were imposed on new oil, released oil, and stripper well oil (which came to be known as upper tier or second tier oil). Old oil, subject to a lower price ceiling, came to be known as first tier oil or lower tier oil.

See also COMPOSITE PRICE CEILING; PRICE CONTROL OF OIL, GAS AND PETROLEUM PRODUCTS.

First use tax

A tax imposed by statute in Louisiana in 1978 [codified as La. Rev. Stat. §§ 47:1301–47:1307] on certain gas destined for interstate commerce which passes through the State of Louisiana. Pending adjudication of a challenge to the Act, FERC Orders No. 10, 10–A, 10–B, and 10–C established procedures governing pipeline recovery of the tax. 16 FPS 5–836 (Aug. 28, 1978), 16 FPS 5–838 (Dec. 20, 1978), amended 17 FPS 5–243 (March 9, 1979), 20 FPS 5–478 (Apr. 24, 1980). The tax was held to be unconstitutional in Maryland v. Louisiana, 451 U.S. 725, 69 *O.&G.R.* 553 (1981).

Fishing

To seek to recover and draw forth from the well bore tools, cables, pipe, casing and rods which have become detached while in the well or which have been accidentally dropped into the well.

Fishing bid

A term applied to a small bonus bid in a competitive lease sale. The bid may be made on the basis of very limited geologic and seismic data with no expectation of success if other bids are filed but with the hope of "catching" a lease for a modest bid if no other bids should be filed.

See also BONUS BIDDING.

Fishing job

The attempt to fish out or recover from the well bore drilling tools, pipe or casing which have broken off or otherwise become disattached from the drill stem.

Fishing operation

"[A]n attempt to remove all of the pieces of pipe and equipment in the drilling hole when the string of drill pipe breaks into two or more lengths at a then unknown depth somewhere down the hole." Burger Drilling Co. v. Bauman, 643 F.2d 240 at 241, 69 *O.&G.R.* 511 at 513 (5th Cir., Unit A., 1981).

Fishing tools

Special instruments used in a fishing job. Many of these tools are specially prepared for a particular job.

Fishtail bit

See BIT, FISHTAIL.

Fiske formula

A formula applied by the Internal Revenue Service for determining what percentage of the proceeds from the sale of liquids realized by a CYCLING (*q.v.*) operation is from manufacturing and production respectively. From the sale price of plant products is deducted the cost of operating the manufacturing portion of the plant, depreciation on this portion, and a return on the investment in this portion of 10 percent per year. The remainder represents the fraction of the plant product sales attributable to production and hence subject to depletion. Fiske, "Tax Aspects of Secondary Recovery Operations," 6 *Rocky Mt. Min. L. Inst.* 195 at 208 (1961); Randolph, "Problems of the Oil and Gas Industry," 9 *N.Y.U. Inst. on Federal Taxation* 491 at 495 (1950); Myers, *The Law of Pooling and Unitization* § 10.08 (2d ed. 1967).

500 Mcf clause

A clause in a GAS LEASE-SALES AGREEMENT (GLA) (*q.v.*) designed to meet the problem which might be created by application of Interior Department regulation 43 C.F.R. § 192.83 (1952–1953), dealing with the suspension of an obligation to pay overriding royalties when production per day was at a low level. Under this clause the overriding royalty was converted into a portion of the working interest if the regulation became applicable. El Paso Natural Gas Co. v. American Petrofina Co. of Texas, 715 S.W.2d 177, ____ *O.&G.R.* ____ (Tex. App., Houston, 1986) (holding that by this clause the purchaser agreed to indemnify the overriding royalty owner from any loss in the event the payment of such royalty was suspended).

533 program

A program established by Federal Power Commission Order Nos. 533 and 533–A, 54 FPC 821, 2058 (1975), and reviewed in Federal Energy Regulatory Commission Order No. 2, 14 FPS 5–60 (Feb. 1, 1978), with respect to certificating pipeline transportation agreements by jurisdictional pipelines of certain gas sold by producers to nonresale industrial and commercial customers for high priority use. The legality of the policy announced in Order No. 533 was sustained in American Public Gas Ass'n v. Federal Energy Regulatory Comm'n, 587 F.2d 1089 (D.C. Cir. 1978).

555 termination

Automatic termination of lease for failure to pay the rent on time if there is no well capable of production on the leasehold. The name comes from Public Law 555, 83rd Cong., 68 Stat. 583 (1954), 30 U.S.C. § 226. Before this Act became effective, rental defaults required lease cancellation proceedings. See Decker, "Land Office Processing of Oil and Gas Lease Offers and Mineral Applications Including Delegation of Authority to Managers," 5 *Rocky Mt. Min. L. Inst.* 77 at 86 (1960).

Five-spot water flood program

A secondary recovery operation utilized in fields where permeability is low and/or viscosity is high. Four input or INJECTION WELLS (*q.v.*) are located in a pattern forming a square; the production well is in the center of the square. Water is introduced into the input wells, which moves through the reservoir toward the producing well, washing the oil before it.

The five-spot pattern may also be described in terms of equally spaced, parallel, alternating rows of staggered input and producing wells—that is, a series of line floods which permits a more rapid secondary depletion of a property. See Lytle, "History, Present Status, and Future Possibilities of Secondary Recovery Operations in Pennsylvania," 1 *IOCC Comm. Bull.* 29 at 33 (Dec. 1959).

See also SECONDARY RECOVERY; SWEEP; WATER FLOODING.

Fixed price royalty clause

A lease royalty clause providing for payment of a fraction of a fixed price per unit of production rather than a fraction of proceeds or market value or market price. Taylor v. Arkansas Louisiana Gas Co., 604 F.Supp. 779, 85 *O.&G.R.* 1 (W.D. Ark. 1985), *aff'd,* 793 F.2d 189, 90 *O.&G.R.* 201 (8th Cir. 1986) (sustaining the validity of the provision against a claim by lessors for a fraction of market value or market price).

Syn.: Fixed rate royalty clause.

Fixed term interest

A term interest that endures for a fixed number of years only (*e.g.* 20 years). Since the creating instrument contains no thereafter clause, the interest expires at the end of the fixed period, although there is a producing well on the land at such time. See TREATISE §§ 331–332.

See also TERM MINERAL OR ROYALTY INTEREST.

Fixed term royalty

A royalty interest created independent of a lease and characterized by a definite period of duration, such as twenty years. So called "term royalty" is generally used to designate a royalty interest for a fixed term and so long thereafter as production continues.

See also TERM MINERAL OR ROYALTY INTEREST.

Flambeau lights

A flaming torch used for the disposal in the field of casinghead gas produced with oil when such gas is without a market and is not used by the producer for some nonwasteful purpose. The use of flambeau lights is now generally regulated under state conservation laws.

Flaring of gas

The burning of gas in the field as a means of disposal when there is no market for the gas and the operator does not elect (or cannot) use the gas for a nonwasteful purpose. Flaring of gas is now generally regulated under state conservation laws.

Under some leases, royalty is payable on gas which is lost, flared or vented. See TREATISE § 644.5.

See also POPPING; STRIPPING LAW.

Flash point

The temperature and other conditions at which a given substance will ignite.

Flat sale of crude oil

In certain development contracts this term is used to mean a transaction in which there is no advantage (such as loans or lifting of products deriving or not deriving from the sale concerned) which might possibly be set off against the sale apart from the price. See *e.g.*, Article 28 of the INOC-ERAP contract in OPEC, *Selected Documents of the International Petroleum Industry*, 1968 at p. 107.

See also CONCESSION; POSTED PRICE.

Fleming assignment

A term occasionally used to describe a transaction involving the assignment of a working interest for cash in which assignment an oil payment is reserved by the assignor. See Appleman, "Sales and Assignments of Leases and Other Interests in Oil and Gas," 1 *Sw. Legal Fdn. Oil & Gas Inst.* 427 at 441 (1949).

See also ASSIGNMENT.

Flip

A term employed to describe the passage of a share of the working interest to a CARRIED PARTY (*q.v.*) after the CARRYING PARTY (*q.v.*) has recouped the costs of exploration and development. See Close, "Special Allocations in Oil and Gas Ventures," 33 *Sw. Legal Fdn. Oil & Gas Inst.* 437 at 460 (1982).

Flip-flop provision

The provision in a DRILLING FUND (*q.v.*) giving the limited partners a large percentage of the production until payout, under which the share of the limited partners is decreased and the share of the general partner is increased on payout. Emery, "Current Development in Oil and Gas Taxation," 32 *Sw. Legal Fdn. Oil & Gas Inst.* 335 at 336 (1981).

Flood

See WATER FLOODING.

Flow back procedures

Procedures performed after SANDFRACING (*q.v.*) to permit material, injected into a formation for purposes of widening passages through which oil can flow in the process of its extraction, to flow back out of the formation through a pipe known as a flow line. Remuda Oil & Gas Co. v. Nobles, 613 S.W.2d 312, 70 *O.&G.R.* 338 (Tex. Civ. App. 1981).

Flow bean

A construction in the lead line provided for the purpose of restricting flow or maintaining any desired amount of back pressure on the well.

Syn.: CHOKE.

Flow by heads

See HEADING; INTERMITTENT FLOW.

Flow diagram

An exhibit showing daily design capacity and reflecting operating conditions with proposed facilities and existing facilities in operation. 18 C.F.R. § 157.14(a)(7) (1980).

Flowing gas

A term used in the Permian Basin Area Rate Proceeding as including all gas other than new gas-well gas or residue gas derived therefrom, *viz.*, as including old gas-well gas, all casinghead gas, and residue gas derived from old gas-well gas or casinghead gas. Permian Basin Area Rate Proceeding, 34 F.P.C. 159 at 212, 23 *O.&G.R.* 103 at 161 (Opinion No. 468, Aug. 5, 1965), *remanded,* Skelly Oil Co. v. Federal Power Comm'n, 375 F.2d 6, 26 *O.&G.R.* 237 (10th Cir. 1967), *aff'd in part and rev'd in part sub nom. In re* Permian Basin Area Rate Cases, 390 U.S. 747, 28 *O.&G.R.* 689 (1968).

See also CROSS-FLOW.

Flowing tubing pressure (FTP)

The pressure measured upstream from a choke mechanism on the well-head while the well is flowing. This pressure, measured at a known flow rate, is useful in predicting future delivery capacities of oil and gas wells.

Flowing well

A well that produces oil by its own reservoir pressure. See Ferguson v. Housh, 227 S.W.2d 590 (Tex. Civ. App. 1950). In most newly discovered fields, the pressure differential between the reservoir fluids and the well-bore is enough to force the oil-gas solution into the well. If the pressure at the bottom of the well is sufficient to lift the oil to the surface the well will flow a mixture of oil and gas. Most wells flow through tubing and the flow is restricted by devices such as flow beans and adjustable chokes at the surface, or "bottom hole" chokes placed at the bottom of the tubing. These are adjusted as to size of opening to obtain desirable gas-oil ratios and flow the allowable daily production.

Flow line

A pipeline from a flowing well to a storage tank.

The Alberta Energy Resources Conservation Board Interim Directive ID–OG–PL 78–2, dealing with licensing of flow lines, defines this term as "a pipe for (i) the transmission of fluids from an oil well or wells to a tank, battery or common pipeline manifold, or (ii) the transmission of water obtained from oil or gas for disposal to other than an underground formation, and includes installations in connection therewith."

The Saskatchewan Surface Rights Acquisition and Compensation Act, 1968 § 2(c) defines a flow line as "a pipe or conduit of pipes used for the transportation, gathering or conduct of a mineral from a well head to a separator, treater, dehydrator, tank or tank battery or surface reservoir."

See PIPELINE.

Flow meter

A device designed to measure the quantity of a fluid passing through the meter.

See also DIFFERENTIAL PRESSURE FLOW METER.

Flow nipple

See CHOKE.

Flow plug

See CHOKE.

Flow schedule

The schedule of production from a well.

Flow string

The string of casing or tubing through which oil flows to the surface.

Syn.: CAPITAL STRING; OIL STRING; PAY STRING; PRODUCTION STRING.

Flow tank

The field tank into which oil is run as it is discharged from the wellhead. When the pressure of the crude oil at the surface is not too great and when the gas content of the oil is low, a simple flow tank may be used to separate the gas from the oil at atmospheric pressure. If pressure is high or the gas content is substantial, a series of flow tanks may be employed. OPEC, *Basic Oil Industry Information* 18 (1983).

Flow test

A test on initial completion of an oil and gas well and periodically thereafter to measure the flow of oil and gas, the percentage or volume of water, if any, flowing tubing pressure, liquid and gas gravities, established shut-in pressure prior to testing, and other technical data. Such tests are useful in diagnosing well problems and their causes and predicting future delivery capacities and ultimate oil and gas recoveries.

Flow-through clause

Syn. for FERC-OUT CLAUSE (*q.v.*).

FLPMA

The FEDERAL LAND POLICY AND MANAGEMENT ACT OF 1976 (*q.v.*).

Fluid injection

Injection under pressure through an input well of a fluid (liquid or gaseous) into a producing formation as part of a secondary recovery or pressure maintenance operation; a method of recovery of hydrocarbons in which part of the energy employed to move the hydrocarbons through a reservoir is applied from extraneous sources by the injection of liquids or gases into the reservoir. The fluids injected may be gas, air or water. The character and properties of the reservoir and the availability of the fluids dictate the choice of the fluid to be used for injection. See Williams, "Problems in the Conservation of Gas," 2 *Rocky Mt. Min. L. Inst.* 295 (1956); 16 Tex. Admin. Code § 3.46.

See also PRESSURE MAINTENANCE; SECONDARY RECOVERY; WATER FLOODING.

Fluid injection well

A well utilized for the injection of fluids into a producing formation. In Alberta the Oil and Gas Conservation Board may authorize the transfer of the allowable of a well used for injection purposes to another well or wells. See Oil and Gas Conservation Board, Transfer of Oil Allowable (Sept. 30, 1957); TRANSFERRED ALLOWABLE.

Flush production

Production resulting from natural reservoir pressures without the employment of extrinsic energy, *e.g.*, by pumping. The early productive life of a well or a field when gas pressure is the dominant expulsive force.

State *ex rel.* Stephan v. Martin, 230 Kan. 747, 641 P.2d 1011, 73 *O.&G.R.* 419 (1982), sustained the validity of an amendment to the ad valorem taxing statute providing for reduction of the valuation of flush production wells by 40 percent. The statute was based on the fact that:

"when a new well is completed it will ordinarily produce at a far greater rate than will be customary for that particular well after only a few weeks or months have elapsed. This initial excessive production is referred to as 'flush production' and, if used as one of the factors for determining value, is misleading and often results in excessive valuation and assessment for the initial year of taxation."

See also SETTLED PRODUCTION; STRIPPER PRODUCTION.

FOB pricing

The pricing provision of an oil purchase and sale contract which locates the burden of shipping costs by specifying that the oil shall be "free on board" (FOB) at the shipping point. This pricing method is comparable to FAS ("free alongside ship") pricing. See Danielsen, *The Evolution of OPEC* 56 (1982); Daniel, "Carriage of Oil by Sea Crude Oil Sale Agreements," [1982] 5 *OGLTR* 163.

See also CIF PRICING; FAS PRICING.

FOGEI

Foreign oil and gas extraction income. See 30 *O.&G. Tax Q.* 377 (1981).

FOGRMA

The FEDERAL OIL & GAS ROYALTY MANAGEMENT ACT OF 1982 (FOGRMA) (*q.v.*).

Footage contract

A contract between an operator and an independent drilling contractor, providing for payment to be made on the basis of an agreed sum per foot of hole drilled, from the surface to the agreed maximum depth.

"On a 'footage basis,' the drilling contractor furnishes the drilling crew, drilling equipment and certain specified services, materials and supplies; he is paid an agreed sum of money for each foot actually drilled, irrespective of whether the proposed depth is reached or not; all other materials, supplies and equipment are furnished by the well owner." Haas v. Gulf Coast Natural Gas Co., 484 S.W.2d 127 at 131, 43 *O.&G.R.* 381 at 389 (Tex. Civ. App. 1972).

Prior to December 31, 1942, an operator could, upon proper election, deduct footage contract expense from income as intangible drilling cost but could not deduct TURNKEY CONTRACT (*q.v.*) expense. However, since that date expenses under either type of contract are deductible. With this change in tax consequences the footage rate basis of paying for wells has become just one of three bases provided in the usual drilling contract. The other two are: DAY WORK (*q.v.*) and SHUT-DOWN TIME (*q.v.*).

For a discussion of the circumstances under which a day rate rather than a footage rate is charged, see Startex Drilling Co. v. Sohio Petroleum Co., 680 F.2d 412, 74 *O.&G.R.* 384 (5th Cir. 1982).

See also COMPLETION CONTRACT; DRILLING CONTRACT; GULF COAST CLAUSE.

Forced pooling

See COMPULSORY POOLING.

Forced-take payment

A payment required to be made to the surface owner under the provisions of the Alberta Surface Rights Act, S.A. 1983, c.S-27.1 (1983), by a mineral owner using the surface to develop his minerals.

Force majeure clause

(1) A lease clause providing that failure of production shall not cause automatic termination of the leasehold estate and that the performance of the lessee's covenants shall be excused when such failure of production or performance of covenants is due to causes specified in such clause. A typical force majeure clause in an Unless lease provides as follows:

> "All of lessee's obligations and covenants hereunder, whether express or implied, shall be suspended at the time or from time to time as compliance with any thereof is prevented or hindered by

or is in conflict with Federal, State, County, or municipal laws, rules, regulations or Executive Orders asserted as official by or under public authority claiming jurisdiction, or Act of God, adverse field, weather, or market conditions, inability to obtain materials in the open market or transportation thereof, war, strikes, lockouts, riots, or other conditions or circumstances not wholly controlled by lessee, and this lease shall not be terminated in whole or in part, nor lessee held liable in damages for failure to comply with any such obligations or covenants if compliance therewith is prevented or hindered by or is in conflict with any of the foregoing eventualities. The time during which lessee shall be prevented from conducting drilling or reworking operations during the primary term of this lease, under the contingencies above stated, shall be added to the primary term of the lease; provided, however, that delay rentals as herein provided shall not be suspended by reason of the suspension of operations and if this lease is extended beyond the primary term above stated by reason of such suspension, lessee shall pay an annual delay rental on the anniversary dates hereof in the manner and in the amount above provided."

See TREATISE §§ 683–683.4.

(2) Also a clause in any other contract excusing performance by a party under specified circumstances. See, *e.g.*, Transcanada Pipelines Ltd. v. Northern & Central Gas Corp. Ltd., 128 D.L.R.3d 633 (Ontario High Court of Justice 1981), *appeal dism'd,* 146 D.L.R.3d 293 (Ont. C.A. 1983) (construing the force majeure clause of a natural gas purchase contract); Gulf Oil Corp. v. Federal Energy Regulatory Comm'n, 706 F.2d 444 (3d Cir. 1983), *cert. denied,* 464 U.S. 1038, 104 S. Ct. 698 (1984) (adopting a strict construction of the force majeure clause of a gas purchase and sale contract); Nissho-Iwai Co., Ltd. v. Occidental Crude Sales, Inc., 729 F.2d 1530 (5th Cir. 1984) (discussing the operation of a force majeure clause in a crude oil sales agreement); Langham-Hill Petroleum Inc. v. Southern Fuels Co., 813 F.2d 1327 (4th Cir. 1987) (force majeure clause of contract for purchase of oil not triggered by action of Saudia Arabia leading to a dramatic drop in world oil prices).

Interpetrol Bermuda Ltd. v. Kaiser Aluminum International Corp., 719 F.2d 992 (9th Cir. 1983), gave effect to what was called an "economic force majeure clause" (as distinguished from a "standard force majeure clause") under which the seller of oil was excused from performance when its supplier defaulted for economic reasons.

For a discussion of the employment of force majeure clauses in a PETROLEUM INTERNATIONAL AGREEMENT (PIA) (*q.v.*) or CONCESSION (*q.v.*) see Blinn, Duval, Le Leuch, and Pertuzio, *International Petroleum Exploration & Exploitation Agreements* ch. 16 (1986).

See also ADAPTATION CLAUSE.

Foreign Investment Review Act (FIRA)

A Canadian statute [S.C. 1973–74, c. 46] providing legal authority to the government to review: (1) acquisition of control of existing Canadian businesses by foreigners or deemed foreigners who are defined as noneligible persons; (2) creation of new businesses in Canada by such noneligible persons; and (3) expansion of existing businesses in Canada of such noneligible persons into unrelated businesses. The application of the statute to the oil industry is discussed in Bonney, "Foreign Investment Review Act," 13 *Alberta L. Rev.* 83 (1975).

See also Atkey, "Foreign Investment Review Act—Paper Tiger or Sleeping Giant?" 30 *Rocky Mt. Min. L. Inst.* 22-1 (1984).

Under the INVESTMENT CANADA BILL (*q.v.*) (Bill C-15, first reading, December 7, 1984), major changes in this Act were made. See Lucas, "Investment Canada and the Resource Sector," 10 *Resources* (Feb. 1985); Arnett, "From FIRA to Investment Canada," 24 *Alberta L. Rev.* 1 (1985).

Foreign Investment Review Agency

An agency established under the FOREIGN INVESTMENT REVIEW ACT (FIRA) (*q.v.*) with oversight over implementation of the Act. Under the provisions of the INVESTMENT CANADA BILL (*q.v.*) the Agency is renamed INVESTMENT CANADA (*q.v.*).

Foreign Investment Review Board (FIRB)

An agency of the Commonwealth of Australia charged by the FOREIGN TAKEOVERS ACT (*q.v.*) with the administration of the Commonwealth's foreign investment policy. The Board does not have power to take decisions on foreign investment proposals, which rests with the Treasurer, but it consults with the States and renders advice to the Treasurer. See Pooley, "Foreign Investment Controls," 2 *Austl. Mining & Petroleum L.J.* 115 (1980).

Foreign Takeovers Act

The Australian Act of 1975 which came into operation on January 1, 1976, regulating foreign investments in Australia. The categories of foreign takeovers covered by the Act are: a proposed acquisition of voting and nonvoting shares by foreign persons; a proposed acquisition of assets by foreign persons; a proposed arrangement relating to directorates of Australian corporations leading to increased foreign representation; and a proposed arrangement relating to the lease or grant of other rights to a foreign person to use the assets of an Australian business. For a detailed discussion of the Act and of the Government's policy of foreign investment, see Chambers, "Government Regulation of Foreign Investment in the Australian Mineral Industry," 1 *Austl. Mining & Petroleum L.J.* 221 (1978).

Foreign tax credit

The credit available under Internal Revenue Code § 901 *et seq.* for foreign taxes paid. The availability of this credit to U.S.-based oil companies has been the subject of considerable controversy.

For discussions of the foreign tax credit, see the following:

Blinn, Duval, Le Leuch, and Pertuzio, *International Petroleum Exploration & Exploitation Agreements* 255 (1986);

Mikesell, *Petroleum Company Operations & Agreements in the Developing Countries* 121 (1984);

Taylor, "The Foreign Tax Credit, Deferral, and the DISC Provisions: Casualties in a Holy War of Protectionalism?" 16 *Hous. L. Rev.* 63 (1978);

Schmidt, "Operation of the Foreign Tax Credit in the Petroleum Industry: A 'Dry Hole'?" 15 *Va. J. Int. Law* 421 (1975).

Forfeiture clause

A clause in an oil and gas lease framed as a condition subsequent, giving the lessor a right of reentry (or power of termination) for breach of the condition. The typical OR LEASE (*q.v.*) form provides that the lessee is to drill a well or pay rentals or forfeit the lease. This has been interpreted to give the lessor an option to recover the rentals as damages or to declare a forfeiture and cancel the lease when no well has been commenced prior to the ANNIVERSARY DATE (*q.v.*) during the PRIMARY TERM (*q.v.*). Cohn v. Clark, 48 Okla. 500, 150 Pac. 467 (1915).

Other Or lease forms require the lessee to drill a well or forfeit the lease. See Welport Oil Co. v. Fairfield, 51 Cal.App.2d 533, 125 P. 2d 97 (1942); Hughes v. Ford, 406 Ill. 171, 92 N.E.2d 747 (1950); Elligson v. Shaw, 114 Mont. 550, 138 P.2d 947 (1943).

Forfeiture of lease

A loose term often used to mean any form of termination of the lease. Strictly, forfeiture is a remedy given by the lease expressly or by the courts to extinguish the life of a lease otherwise in force. Termination refers to the expiration of the lease by its own terms, or under the "unless clause," the "thereafter clause," etc. Although it is said that forfeitures are not favored, the courts have regularly cancelled oil and gas leases for breach of implied covenant where monetary damages were inadequate or unascertainable. See TREATISE §§ 825.1, 834, 844–844.3.

See also TERMINATION OF LEASE.

FORI

Foreign oil related income. See 30 *O.&G. Tax Q.* 377 (1981); Stevens, "TEFRA Amendments to I.R.C. Section 907 Create New Problems and Opportunities for Corporate Taxpayers," 31 *O.&G. Tax Q.* 546 (1983).

Formation

A succession of sedimentary beds that were deposited continuously and under the same general conditions. It may consist of one type of rock or of alterations of types. An individual bed or group of beds distinct in character from the rest of the formation and persisting over a large area is called a "member" of the formation. Formations are usually named for the town or area in which they were first recognized and described, often at a place where the formation outcrops. For example, the Austin chalk formation outcrops at Austin, Texas.

See also TARGET FORMATION; THIEF FORMATION; TIGHT FORMATION.

Formation pressure

See RESERVOIR PRESSURE

Formation water

Waste water produced by oil wells while drilling for oil. Formation water contains oil, gas and high concentrations of salt and chemicals, making it unfit for culinary or agricultural uses. Branch v. Western Petroleum, Inc., 657 P.2d 267, 76 *O.&G.R.* 144 (Utah 1982).

Forties

The first substantial oil field in the British sector of the North Sea discovered in October, 1970. The field is about 200 km from Aberdeen, Scotland.

Forum selection clause

A provision of a contract or other agreement specifying the forum in which any action at law concerning the contract or agreement shall be brought. See Prudential Resources Corp. v. Plunkett, 583 S.W.2d 97, 63 *O.&G.R.* 486 (Ky. 1978).

For a discussion of the application of a forum selection clause in a deed to a contract between the parties, see Phoenix Canada Oil Co. Ltd. v. Texaco, Inc., 560 F. Supp. 1372 (D. Del. 1983).

See also Wertz and Eisen, "Forum Selection and Governing Law Provisions in Multi-Jurisdictional Agreements—Preparation and Implementation," 32 *Rocky Mt. Min. L. Inst.* 4-1 (1986).

Forward combustion

Syn. for IN-SITU COMBUSTION. See Morse, "Trends in Oil Recovery Methods," 1 *IOCC Comm. Bull.* 1 at 7 (Dec. 1959).

Forward contract

A contract made for the delivery of a commodity sometime in the future. See FUTURES MARKET.

Forward oil purchase

A means of providing finance for the development of offshore oil and gas fields. Although the oil purchase resembles a loan it is clothed as a trading transaction and thus it can appear on the borrower's balance sheet otherwise than as a borrowing. Daintith and Willoughby, *A Manual of United Kingdom Oil and Gas Law* 38 (1977).

See also ADVANCE PAYMENT FINANCING; PROJECT FINANCING.

Forward sale

Syn. for ADVANCE PAYMENT FINANCING (*q.v.*).

Forward sales of strategic petroleum reserve oil

A procedure to implement the STRATEGIC PETROLEUM RESERVE DRAWDOWN PLAN (*q.v.*) involving forward sales of rights to oil stored in the STRATEGIC PETROLEUM RESERVE (*q.v.*). See *CCH Federal Energy Guidelines* ¶ 30,504 (April 11, 1983).

Fossil fuels

Fuels occurring naturally in the earth, such as coal, oil, or natural gas.

Foundation pile

Syn. for OUTER CONDUCTOR (*q.v.*).

Four heads approach

A method employed by the Surface Rights Board of Alberta in calculating compensation payable by the operator for the right of entry on the lands of another. Basically under this approach the landmen and the Board have looked at s. 23 of the Surface Rights Act, R.S.A. 1980, c. S-27 and have concentrated upon the first four or five items mentioned therein. See Markovich Bros. Farming Co. Ltd. v. PanCanadian Petroleum Ltd. [1984] 3 W.W.R. 416 (Alta. Q.B. 1984), in which the court rejected this approach for the GLOBAL APPROACH (*q.v.*).

See also Barton, "Controversy in Surface Rights Compensation: Pattern of Dealings Evidence and Global Awards," 24 *Alberta L. Rev.* 34 (1985).

467 plan

A pipeline's plan for curtailment of deliveries of natural gas on the basis of end use formulated in accordance with Federal Power Commission Orders No. 467, 467–A and 467–B. See Consolidated Edison Co. v. Federal Power Comm'n, 512 F.2d 1332, *petition for clarification granted and petition for rehearing denied,* 518 F.2d 448 (D.C.Cir. 1975).

See also CURTAILMENT PLAN; END USE CONTROL.

FPC

FEDERAL POWER COMMISSION (*q.v.*).

FPC clause

A price escalation clause in a gas sales contract. See ESCALATOR CLAUSE.

FPC clauses in gas sales contracts took many forms. With the adoption of a NATIONAL RATE (*q.v.*) in 1976 and the later adoption of the NATURAL GAS POLICY ACT OF 1978 (*q.v.*), substantial litigation was generated over the construction of these clauses. See, *e.g.*, Premier Resources, Ltd. v. Northern Natural Gas Co., 616 F.2d 1171, 66 *O.&G.R.* 91 (10th Cir. 1980), *cert. denied,* 449 U.S. 827, (1980); Mesa Petroleum Co. v. Kansas Power & Light Co., 229 Kan. 631, 629 P.2d 190 (1981), *reh. denied,* 230 Kan. 166, 630 P.2d 1129, 71 *O.&G.R.* 262 (1981), *cert. denied,* 455 U.S. 928 (1982); Amoco Production Co. v. Kansas Power & Light Co., 505 F. Supp. 628, 68 *O.&G.R.* 1 (D. Kan. 1980) (holding that the FPC clause was not unconscionable nor against public policy).

Oxley v. Oklahoma Gas & Electric Co., 53 *Okla. B.A.J.* 1161 (Okla. App. 1982), gave effect to an FPC price escalation clause, holding that it was triggered by an increase in gas prices under the NATURAL GAS POLICY ACT (NGPA) (*q.v.*). Certiorari was granted in *Oxley v. Oklahoma Gas & Electric Co.,* the Oklahoma Supreme Court adopted as its opinion the dissenting views of Bacon, J. in the court of appeals (*viz.,* the escalation clause was ambiguous and parol evidence should be admitted to determine the parties' intent), the opinion of the court of appeals was vacated and withdrawn, the trial court's judgment was reversed, and the cause was remanded for further proceedings not inconsistent with the views of Bacon, J. 53 *Okla. B.J.* 2383 (Okla. 1982).

See also GOVERNMENTAL PRICE ESCALATOR CLAUSE.

FPC escape clause

See JURISDICTIONAL ESCAPE CLAUSE.

FPC gas tariff

See TARIFF.

FPC price protection clause

A clause in a nonjurisdictional gas sales contract [see NONJURISDICTIONAL SALES] providing that the price established from time to time by the Federal Power Commission (or any successor agency) as the area ceiling price or rate shall be paid by the purchaser if higher than the contract price. Superior Oil Co. v. Western Slope Gas Co.,

604 F.2d 1281 at 1284, 66 *O.&G.R.* 312 at 316 (10th Cir. 1979), *on remand,* 549 F. Supp. 463, 74 *O.&G.R.* 593 (D. Colo. 1982).

In Amoco Production Co. v. Kansas Power & Light Co., 505 F. Supp. 628 at 630, *68 O.&G.R.* 1 at 3 (D. Kan. 1980), an FPC CLAUSE (*q.v.*) was described as an F.P.C. price protection clause.

See also PRICE CONTROL OF OIL, GAS AND PETROLEUM PRODUCTS.

FPGP

FAVORABLE PETROLEUM GEOLOGICAL PROVINCE (*q.v.*).

FPPU

Fixed price per unit of production. See Maxfield and Houghton, *Taxation of Mining Operations* § 8.03[2][f]

F/P ratio

The ratio of findings (discovery) of new gas to the production of gas. See Southern Louisiana Area Rate Cases v. Federal Power Comm'n, 428 F.2d 407 at 437, 37 *O.&G.R.* 311 at 352 (5th Cir. 1970), *cert. denied,* 400 U. S. 950 (1970).

FPS

Abbreviation for *Federal Power Service,* a set of reports of decisions, regulations, and other actions of the Federal Power Commission and of its successor, the Federal Energy Regulatory Commission.

Frac

A term used to refer to the method used to increase the deliverability of a production or underground storage well by pumping a liquid or other substance into a well under pressure to crack (fracture) and prop open the hydrocarbon bearing formation. American Gas Ass'n, *Glossary for the Gas Industry* (3d ed. 1981).

See also FRACTURING.

Frack head

See SANDFRACING.

Frac oil

Oil introduced into a well bore in order to fracture the producing formation so as to increase production flow. See " 'Wash' or 'Frac' Oil Not Subject to Windfall Profit Tax," 31 *O.&G. Tax Q.* 187 (1982); Rev. Rul. 82-41, 1982-11 I.R.B. 16, 72 *O.&G.R.* 196 (March 22, 1982).

See also FRACTURING.

Frac tank

"[A]ny portable or stationary, high volume holding vessel designed and constructed for use in separating, storing or temporarily holding materials used in or resulting from fracturing techniques in oil and gas exploration." 17 Okla. Stat. Ann. § 54 (enacted in 1981).

See also FRACTURING.

Fractional mineral or royalty deed

A deed conveying a fractional or undivided interest in minerals or royalties rather than the entire interest therein. See MINERAL DEED; ROYALTY DEED.

Fractional or future interest lease

A lease for lands in which the United States owns an undivided fractional interest or a future interest. See 43 C.F.R. §§ 3130, 3550 (1978).

See also FUTURE INTEREST LEASE.

Fractional undivided interests in oil or gas rights

As used in Regulation B of the Securities and Exchange Comm'n, the term includes landowners' royalty interests, overriding royalty interests, working interests, participating interests, and oil or gas payments. 17 C.F.R. § 230.300 (a)(1) (1980).

Fractionation

A process of separating various hydrocarbons from natural gas or oil as produced from the ground. See SEPARATION.

Fractionator

A device in which, by means of changes in temperature and pressure, various hydrocarbons are separated. See La Gloria Oil & Gas

Co. v. Scofield, 171 F. Supp. 614, 8 *O.&G.R.* 495 (W.D. Tex. 1957), *rev'd,* 268 F.2d 699, 10 *O.&G.R.* 681 (5th Cir. 1959), *cert. denied,* 361 U.S. 933, 11 *O.&G.R.* 718, *rehearing denied,* 361 U.S. 973 (1960).

See also SEPARATOR.

Fracturing

"A process of opening up underground channels in hydrocarbon-bearing formations, by force, rather than by chemical action such as acidizing. High pressure is hydraulically or explosively directed at the rock causing it to fracture." American Gas Ass'n, *Glossary for the Gas Industry* (3d ed. 1981).

"[A]ny processes, chemicals or other materials used to enhance an oil and gas well recovery operation." 17 Okla. Stat. Ann. § 54 (enacted in 1981).

See also ACID FRACTURING; BIG FRAC; FRAC OIL; FRAC TANK; HIGH-ENERGY GAS FRACTURING; HYDRAULIC FRACTURING; LITTLE FRAC; LOAD OIL; PETROFRACTURING; SANDFRACING; TIGHT FORMATION.

Fraudulent drainage

A term occasionally used to describe drainage from one tract to another tract by reason of wells on the latter tract drilled by a common lessee of the two tracts. There is some indication that the burden or liability of the common lessee is greater for so-called fraudulent drainage than for drainage caused by the wells of another person. See Seed, "The Implied Covenant in Oil and Gas Leases to Refrain from Depletory Acts," 3 *U.C.L.A. L. Rev.* 508 (1956); TREATISE §§ 824–824.3.

See also DEPLETORY COVENANT; DRAINAGE; OFFSET WELL COVENANT.

Free gas clause

A lease clause providing in substance as follows:

"Lessor shall have the privilege at his risk and expense of using gas from any gas well on said land for stoves and inside lights in the principal dwelling thereon out of any surplus gas not needed for operations hereunder."

Although the economic importance of this clause is relatively slight as compared to the economic importance of the other royalty provisions of an oil and gas lease, there has been a substantial crop of litigation over the construction and application of free gas clauses in leases, particularly in Kentucky. Among the commonly litigated issues over this type of clause are: (1) whether this royalty clause is an element in calculating damages for failure of a lessee to drill a well; (2) the quantity of gas to which the lessor is entitled; (3) whether the covenant to provide free gas to the lessor "runs with the land"; (4) what premises are entitled to the benefit of the free gas; (5) the right of the lessee to remove casing and plug a well from which free gas has been provided; (6) the apportionment of the benefit of the free gas clause; (7) whether the right to free gas is extinguished by an attempt to sever it from the dominant premises; (8) the right of the lessee to use compressors to accelerate the flow of gas from the wells if such use interferes with the taking of free gas; (9) whether gas must be furnished the lessor even though there is no production from the leased premises; and (10) whether the lessor is entitled to gas produced from an oil well. See TREATISE §§ 661–661.10.

Freehold interest (or estate)

An estate for life or in fee.

See also NONFREEHOLD INTEREST.

Freehold land

Land held by a person in a freehold estate. In Canada the term is used to describe land in which a private owner holds the mineral rights.

Freehold well

"[A] well that produces petroleum or natural gas from a spacing unit, the petroleum or natural gas in which is not owned by the Crown in right of Alberta." The Alberta Mines and Minerals Act, 1962, R.S.A. 1970, c. 238, § 134.

Free ride

An interest in production free of the expenses of production, *e.g.*, a royalty interest.

Freestone clause

Syn. for PUGH CLAUSE (*q.v.*), according to Roberts, "Administration of Oil Properties," 102 *T. & E.* 702 (1963).

See also SMK Energy Corp. v. Westchester Gas Co., 705 S.W.2d 174 (Tex. App., Texarkana, 1985, error ref'd n.r.e.), treating as synonymous the terms "Pugh clause" and "Freestone rider."

Freewater knockout

An installation for the removal of water from gas. Saturn Oil & Gas Co., Inc. v. Federal Power Comm'n, 250 F.2d 61, 8 *O.&G.R.* 365 (10th Cir. 1957), *cert. denied,* 355 U. S. 956, 8 *O.&G.R.* 843 (1958).

Free well

A term sometimes employed to describe the well which is drilled by an assignee as consideration for the assignment of an interest under a FARM-OUT AGREEMENT (*q.v.*). Seaman, "Financial Aspects of Oil Transactions," 3 *U.C.L.A. L. Rev.* 550 at 555 (1956); Appleman, "Tax Problems Involved in Sales and Assignments of Leases and Other Interests in Oil and Gas," 1 *Sw. Legal Fdn. Oil & Gas Inst.* 427 at 435 (1949).

Syn.: OBLIGATION WELL (*q.v.*).

Free well farm-out

A transaction in which "the farmee agrees to pay a share of the cost of a well or wells on the property which is disproportionately greater than the sahre of the working interest he acquires in the transaction. Production revenue is shared by the farmor and the farmee in accordance with their respective shares of the working interest. Under the fractional interest rules of the regulations, the farmee may not deduct (and must capitalize as a part of his depletable basis) the portion of the IDCs he pays which are attributable to the farmor's retained working interest. The farmor may not deduct the IDCs attributable to his share of the working interest (which the farmee must capitalize) because he has not paid or incurred such costs." Crichton, "Recapture of Intangibles Under Section 1254," 30 *Sw. Legal Fdn. Oil & Gas Inst.* 509 at 537 (1979).

See also FARMOUT AGREEMENT.

FRIC

For resale in interstate commerce. See Weymouth v. Colorado Interstate Gas Co., 367 F.2d 84 at 89, 25 *O.&G.R.* 371 at 377 (5th Cir. 1966).

Frigg field

A gas field straddling the median line between the British and the Norwegian sectors and believed to be the largest gas field in the North Sea. The first discovery was in the Norwegian sector in July, 1971.

Frigg field reservoir agreement

An agreement between the United Kingdom and the Kingdom of Norway relating to the exploitation of the Frigg field reservoir and the transmission of gas therefrom to the United Kingdom. For detailed discussion of this agreement see Outhit, "Unitisation As Between Companies—Of Fields Between States (International)," in International Bar Ass'n, *Proceedings of the Petroleum Law Seminar* (organized by the Committee on Energy and Natural Resources, Section on Business Law) (1978), and Outhit, "The Frigg Gas Field Unit," in International Bar Ass'n, *Proceedings of the Energy Law Seminar* (organized by the Committee on Energy and Natural Resources, Section on Business Law) Topic F, Paper 1 (1979).

See also Lagoni, "Oil and Gas Deposits Across National Frontiers," 73 *Am. J. Int. L.* 215 (1979).

Front end of oil payment

The oil payment assigned by a HORIZONTAL CUT OIL PAYMENT (*q.v.*). See PRIMARY PRODUCTION PAYMENT.

Front-end tertiary oil

Price controlled oil which has been deregulated to finance investments in enhanced oil recovery projects. See Department of Energy Petroleum Price Regulations § 212.78. Under prescribed circumstances, the first sales of crude oil by, or on the behalf of, a producer are not subject to ceiling price limitations until the additional revenue received by the producer equals the lesser of 75 percent of specified tertiary expenses actually incurred or $20 million per project or property.

Front-end tertiary oil removed from the premises before October 1, 1981, is exempted from the CRUDE OIL WINDFALL PROFIT TAX ACT OF 1980 (*q.v.*). Internal Revenue Code § 4994.

See also PRICE CONTROL OF OIL, GAS, AND PETROLEUM PRODUCTS.

Front-end tertiary provisions

For purposes of the CRUDE OIL WINDFALL PROFIT TAX ACT OF 1980 (*q.v.*), this term means: (i) the provisions of section 212.78 of the energy regulations which exempt crude oil from ceiling price limitations to provide financing for tertiary projects (as such provisions took effect on October 1, 1979), and (ii) any modifications of such provisions, but only to the extent that such modification is for purposes of coordinating such provisions with the tax imposed by this Act. Internal Revenue Code § 4994.

Frontier environment

An area where there has been no prior commercial activity, even though the area may lie an a KNOWN GEOTHERMAL RESOURCES AREA (KGRA) (*q.v.*) and has undergone research. California Energy Co. (On reconsideration), 85 IBLA 254, 92 I.D. 125 at note 15 (March 6, 1985).

Frontier exploration allowance

In Canada, an additional allowance for expenses in drilling an exploratory well under specified circumstances. Unlike EARNED DEPLETION (*q.v.*), this allowance is deductible against the taxpayer's income from any source. See Katchen and Bowhay, *Federal Oil and Gas Taxation* 56 (3d ed. 1979).

FTP

FLOWING TUBING PRESSURE (*q.v.*).

FUA

Fuel Use Act, *viz.*, the POWERPLANT AND USE ACT OF 1978 (*q.v.*).

Fuel oil

See BUNKER "C" FUEL OIL; DISTILLATE FUEL OIL; HEATING OIL; HEAVY FUEL OIL; MIDDLE DISTILLATES; RESIDUAL FUEL OILS.

Fuel use act

See POWERPLANT AND INDUSTRIAL FUEL USE ACT OF 1978.

Full cost accounting

An accounting method employed by about 60 percent of oil and gas companies in the United States under which all exploration expenses are capitalized. See Durand, "Financial Reporting Effect of Changes in Percentage Depletion Allowance in Oil and Gas Industry," 24 *O.&G. Tax Q.* 65 (1975). In the mid and late 1980s a number of companies shifted from this accounting method to SUCCESSFUL EFFORTS ACCOUNTING (*q.v.*). *The Wall Street Journal,* July 24, 1986, p. 6, col. 3. All of the so-called majors employ the latter accounting method. Concluding that harm to struggling producers would outweigh any benefits by investors, the Securities and Exchange Commission rejected a staff recommendation directed toward requiring that all companies use the latter method. *The Wall Street Journal,* October 31, 1986, p. 4, col. 2.

See also ACCOUNTING METHODS.

Full-hole core

See CORING.

Full-interest lease

A lease purporting to cover all, rather than an undivided interest in, the minerals in described premises.

Full stream gas

Syn. for WET GAS, (*q.v.*), or gas from a distillate well, as distinguished from casinghead gas. Matters of Deep South Oil Co. of Texas (Opinion No. 284), 14 F.P.C. 83, 4 *O.&G.R.* 1815 at 1834 (1955); Deep South Oil Co. of Texas v. Federal Power Comm'n, 247 F.2d 882, 7 *O.&G.R.* 1539 (5th Cir. 1957), *cert. denied in companion case,* 355 U. S. 930 (1958).

Full stream test

A test to determine the distillate content of gas. See Texas Gas Corp. v. Hankamer, 326 S.W.2d 944, 11 *O.&G.R.* 669 (Tex. Civ. App. 1959, error ref'd n.r.e.).

Full term working interest

A WORKING INTEREST (*q.v.*) which lasts so long as oil and gas is produced, as distinguished from a LIMITED WORKING INTEREST (*q.v.*) which is expected to terminate prior to the economic exhaustion of the mineral reserves upon the happening of a future event, such as the passage of time, the production of a specified quantity of mineral, or the realization from production of a determinable sum of money. See Griffith, "Current Developments in Oil and Gas Taxation," 25 *Sw. Legal Fdn. Oil & Gas Inst.* 323 at 325 (1974).

Functional allocation sharing arrangement

A method employed by drilling funds to maximize tax savings of investors by charging the investor with all expenditures made for currently deductible items while charging the sponsor with expenditures for nondeductible items. The intangible development costs then flowed through to the investor to be deducted on his personal tax return. The "at risk" provision of the Internal Revenue Code § 465 added in 1976 limits the amount of the deduction which may be claimed by the investor, and the recapture provision of § 1254 added at the same time reduced the investor's opportunity to convert ordinary income into capital gains by selling a developed property after claiming the deduction for intangibles. See *Forbes,* July 20, 1981, p. 84; Bruen and Taylor, *Federal Income Taxation of Oil and Gas Investments* ¶ 1.05[2] (1980); Close, "Special Allocations in Oil and Gas Ventures," 33 *Sw. Legal Fdn. Oil & Gas Inst.* 437 at 456 (1982).

See also DRILLING FUND; SHARING ARRANGEMENT.

Functional cost benefit method

A method of allocating costs between dry gas and liquid hydrocarbons, helium or other products extracted from gas as produced from the ground. See Ashland Oil, Inc. v. Phillips Petroleum Co., 463 F. Supp. 619 at 634 (N.D. Okla. 1978).

See also ACCOUNTING METHODS.

Further exploration covenant

The duty implied in oil and gas leases requiring the lessee to use due diligence in conducting further exploration operations on the leasehold after production is initially secured. The covenant seemed well established in Oklahoma by a number of cases until, in 1981, a divided Oklahoma Supreme Court in Mitchell v. Amerada Hess Corp., 638 P.2d 441, 72 *O.&G.R.* 104 (Okla. 1981), declared that "there is no implied covenant to further explore after paying production is obtained, as distinguished from an implied covenant to further develop." As indicated in TREATISE § 845.5, the full significance of this case remains unclear. A Texas decision, Clifton v. Koontz,

160 Tex. 82, 325 S.W.2d 684, 10 *O.&G.R.* 1109, 79 A.L.R.2d 774 (1959), also declared that there was no such implied covenant in Texas. As discussed in Treatise § 845.6, an exploration covenant may exist in Texas but it must not be labeled a covenant to explore further. See Sun Exploration & Production Co. v. Jackson, 715 S.W.2d 199, ____ *O.&G.R.* ____ (Tex. App., Houston, 1986), which distinguished exploratory development wells from exploratory wildcat wells and sustained in part a trial court decree unconditionally canceling a lease as to a portion of the leased acreage and conditionally canceling other portions of the lease for prolonged failure of the lessee to drill exploratory development wells.

The duty of further exploration has been recognized and enforced in other jurisdictions: Sauder v. Mid-Continent Petroleum Corp., 292 U.S. 272 (1934); Sinclair Oil & Gas Co. v. Masterson, 271 F.2d 310, 11 *O.&G.R.* 632 (5th Cir. 1959), *cert. denied,* 362 U.S. 952 (1960); Humble Oil & Ref. Co. v. Romero, 194 F.2d 383, 1 *O.&G.R.* 358 (5th Cir. 1952); Smith v. Moody, 192 Ark. 704, 94 S.W.2d 357 (1936); Carter v. Arkansas Louisiana Gas Co., 213 La. 1028, 36 So. 2d 26 (1948).

In general, the cases agree that in an action for breach of the covenant of further exploration, the lessor does not have the burden of showing that further drilling would probably result in profitable production. Rather, determination of breach seems to depend upon a number of factors, given varying weight by different opinions: (1) length of time elapsed since last drilling operations were conducted, (2) size of the tract, (3) number of wells drilled, (4) location of wells, (5) depth of horizons tested, (6) cost of exploration and amount of money already spent by the lessee, (7) degree of probability of success in exploring, (8) activities by the operator in the area relating to exploration, (9) willingness of another operator to drill if he can get a lease.

The cases are analyzed in TREATISE §§ 841–847.

See also the following:

Meyers and Crafton, "The Covenant of Further Exploration—Thirty Years Later," 32 *Rocky Mt. Min. L. Inst.* 1-1 (1986);

Merrill, "The Implied Covenant for Further Exploration," 4 *Rocky Mt. Min. L. Inst.* 205 (1958);

Brown, "The Proposed New Covenant of Further Exploration: Reply to Comment," 37 *Tex. L. Rev.* 303 (1959).

See also IMPLIED COVENANTS.

Futility excuse rule

A term which has been applied to an excuse for payment of rentals or commencement of operations under an "unless" lease when the lessee's title has been attacked by the lessor. See D. Pierce, *Kansas Oil and Gas Handbook* § 9.39 (1986); TREATISE § 606.6.

Future interest lease

A term occasionally used to describe a TOP LEASE (*q.v.*). See Ernest, "Top Leasing—Legality v. Morality," 26 *Rocky Mt. Min. L. Inst.* 957 at 969 (1980).

See also FRACTIONAL OR FUTURE INTEREST LEASE.

Future lease clause

The term applied in Alford v. Crum, 671 S.W.2d 870, 81 *O.&.G.R.* 189 (Tex. 1984), to the clause in a mineral deed reciting the ownership by each party of lease interest and future rentals in the event of termination of the lease in effect at the time of the mineral deed. See TREATISE § 340.2.

See also SUBJECT-TO CLAUSE; TWO-GRANT THEORY.

Futures market

A market trading in contracts to buy or sell oil at a fixed price by a certain date. Such markets exist in London [the INTERNATIONAL PETROLEUM EXCHANGE (*q.v.*)], New York [the New York Mercantile Exchange] and Chicago. For a report of the effect of futures trading on SPOT MARKET (*q.v.*) prices, see *The Wall Street Journal,* Feb. 29, 1984, p. 29; Editorial, "Crude Oil Futures: A Natural Development," [1983] 5 *OGLTR* 87.

For discussion of futures markets see the following:

Peck (ed.), *Futures Markets: Their Economic Role* (1985);

Ottino, "Oil Futures: The International Petroleum Exchange of London," 3 *J. of Energy & Nat. Res. Law* 1 (1985);

Roeber and Kennington, "Futures Trading and the Oil Industry: A Slow Revolution," 3 *J. of Energy & Nat. Res. Law* 21 (1984);

Elting Treat (ed.), *Energy Futures: Trading Opportunities for the 1980's* (1984).

See also BRENT BLEND; DAISY CHAIN; NETBACK; PAPER BARREL.

FWPCA

The Federal Water Pollution Control Act, 33 U.S.C. § 1251.

. . G . .

GAEOT

The GEOMETRIC AVERAGE EVALUATION OF TRACT (*q.v.*).

Gage tank

A tank used for the measurement of crude petroleum produced. Ark. Stat. Ann. 1947 § 53–501.

Gain charge back provision

A provision in a partnership agreement under which any gain realized upon the sale of a property will be charged back to the party to whom INTANGIBLE DRILLING AND DEVELOPMENT COSTS (*q.v.*) had been allocated until such party has recouped the losses previously allocated to it. Allison v. United States, 701 F.2d 933, 76 *O.&G.R.* 379 (Fed. Cir. 1983).

See also PROJECT FINANCING.

Gallon

A unit of volume. In the United States, the gallon is the space occupied by 8.3359 pounds of distilled water. The Imperial gallon in the United Kingdom is the space occupied by ten pounds of distilled water. Slightly different methods are used to assess the weight of the water involved. The U.S. gallon is equivalent to O.833 Imperial gallon, and the latter is equivalent to 1.201 U.S. gallons.

Gamma-gamma log

See GAMMA RAY-GAMMA RAY LOGGING.

Gamma ray-gamma ray logging

The process whereby gamma rays emitted by the subsurface formation as a result of gamma ray bombardment thereof are measured. Gamma ray-gamma ray logging is performed by the parties by lowering into the bore hole a tool containing a gamma ray emitting source and a gamma ray detector which produces output signals indicative of the gamma rays impinging thereon as a result of said bombardment, transmitting said output signals to the earth's surface, and utilizing said signals to produce a record of gamma ray detected in correlation with the depth of said detector in the bore hole. The record thus obtained by the parties in the form of a curve indicating relative number per unit of time of gamma rays emitted at different depths by the subsurface formations as a result of the gamma ray bombardment is a conventional gamma ray-gamma ray log, sometimes called a gamma-gamma log, or a scattered gamma ray log. Gamma ray-gamma ray logging may be used to indicate density and when so used is usually called density logging. See Well Surveys, Inc. v. McCullough Tool Co., 199 F. Supp. 37 (N.D. Okla. 1961).

See also CEMOTRON LOG; WELL LOG.

Gamma ray log

See NATURAL GAMMA RAY LOGGING.

G and G expenditures

Expenditures for GEOPHYSICAL AND GEOLOGICAL COSTS (*q.v.*).

Gas

"Any fluid, either combustible or noncombustible, which is produced in a natural state from the earth and which maintains a gaseous or rarefied state at ordinary temperature and pressure conditions." 30 C.F.R. § 221.2(o)(1980). In the oil and gas industries, it means natural gas (*q.v.*).

"Twenty-three states define gas as all natural gas, including casinghead gas, and all hydrocarbons not defined as oil. Generally, the remaining states describe the definition of a gas well, but do not specifically define natural gas." 26 *Oil & Gas Compact Bull.* 55 (June 1967).

Gas is defined by Ariz. Rev. Stat. § 27–501(9)(1976)(1979 Supp.) as "natural gas, casinghead gas, all other hydrocarbons not defined as oil and helium or other substances of a gaseous nature."

"Gas rights" were held to include liquid hydrocarbons produced from a gas well for purposes of a lease clause authorizing pooling "only as to the gas rights hereunder (excluding casinghead gas produced from oil wells) to form one or more gas operating units" in Skelly Oil Co. v. Savage, 202 Kan. 239, 447 P.2d 395, 33 *O.&G.R.* 231 (1968).

Northern Natural Gas Co. v. Grounds, 441 F.2d 704, 39 *O.&G.R.* 574 (10th Cir. 1971), *cert. denied,* 404 U.S. 951 (1971), held that references in leases and gas purchase contracts to gas or natural gas applied to the entire gas stream absent express reservation of any constituent elements, and helium passed thereunder unless expressly reserved. *Grounds* is discussed in Stucky, "Current Developments and Views Concerning Rights and Status of Landowner-Lessors," 21 *Sw. Legal Fdn. & Gas Inst.* 83 at 102 (1970).

Scott Paper Co. v. Taslog, Inc., 638 F.2d 790, 69 *O.&G.R.* 1 (5th Cir., Unit B, 1981), held that hydrogen sulphide gas was subject to the gas royalty provision of a lease rather than to the royalty provision applicable to "sulphur produced and marketed from the land."

Robert D. Lanier, 93 I.D. 66, 90 IBLA 293, GFS (O&G) 1986-14 (1986), held that a reservation of oil and gas properly included carbon dioxide.

Geothermal steam was viewed as "gas" in Reich v. Commissioner, 52 T.C. 700, 34 *O.&G.R.* 167 (1969), *aff'd*, 454 F.2d 1157, 41 *O.&G.R.* 612 (9th Cir. 1972), and taxpayer was permitted to deduct percentage depletion at the rate of 27½% against gross income received from geothermal steam wells and to deduct intangible costs of drilling and developing steam wells.

In a number of contexts it may become necessary to determine whether the term "gas" as used in a particular instrument includes condensate or other liquid constituents. See *e.g.*, Vernon v. Union Oil Co., 270 F.2d 441, 11 *O.&G.R.* 688 (5th Cir. 1959), *rehearing denied*, 273 F.2d 178, 11 *O.&G.R.* 697 (5th Cir. 1960). See TREATISE § 632.2.

See also ACID GAS; ARGON; ASSOCIATED GAS; BANKING OF GAS; BORROWED GAS; BRADENHEAD GAS; BROKERAGE OF GAS; CASINGHEAD GAS; COALBED GAS; COAL GAS; COMBINATION GAS; CONSUMER GAS; CUSHION GAS; DEEP GAS; DEVONIAN SHALE; DIRECT SALE GAS; DISPLACED GAS; DISTILLATE; DRY GAS; DUMP GAS; ENRICHING GAS; ETHANE; ETHYLENE; EXCHANGE GAS; EXTRANEOUS GAS; FEEDSTOCK GAS; FIREDAMP; FIRM GAS; FLARING OF GAS; FLOWING GAS; FULL STREAM GAS; GATHERING GAS; GEOPRESSURED BRINE; HELIUM; HIGH COST NATURAL GAS; ILLEGAL OIL OR GAS; INCENTIVE PRICE GAS; INDUSTRIAL GAS; INERT GAS INJECTION; INJECTED GAS; INTERRUPTIBLE GAS; INTERSTATE GAS; INTRASTATE GAS; LEAN GAS; LEGAL OIL OR GAS; LINE PACK GAS; LIQUEFIED ENERGY GAS; LIQUEFIED NATURAL GAS (LNG); LIQUEFIED PETROLEUM GAS; MAKE-UP GAS; MANUFACTURED GAS; MARKETABLE OIL OR GAS; METHANE; NATIVE GAS; NATIVE GAS ENTITLEMENT; NATURAL GAS; NATURAL GAS LIQUIDS; NATURAL GAS POLICY ACT OF 1978; NATURAL GAS PRICE PROTECTION ACT; NATURAL GAS PRICE REGULATION; NEW GAS; NEW NATURAL GAS; NONASSOCIATED GAS; NONFIRM GAS; NONPROCESSED GAS; NON-RECOVERABLE GAS; OFF-LEASE GAS; OFF-PEAK GAS; OFF-SYSTEM GAS; OLD GAS; OLD NATURAL GAS; 102 GAS; 103 GAS; 104 GAS; 105 GAS; 106 GAS; 107 GAS; 108

GAS; 109 GAS; ON-LEASE GAS; ON-SYSTEM GAS; PENALTY GAS; PIPELINE GAS; PIPELINE QUALITY GAS; PLANT PROTECTION GAS; POWER GAS; PROCESS GAS; PROCESSED GAS; PRODUCER GAS; PRODUCER RESERVATION GAS; PROVEN OIL OR GAS PROPERTY TRANSFER; PURCHASED GAS ADJUSTMENT CLAUSE; QUALIFIED PRODUCTION ENHANCEMENT GAS; QUALITY STANDARDS; RAW GAS; REFINERY GAS; REFINERY TAIL GAS; REPRESSURE GAS; RESALE GAS; RESIDUE GAS; RESTITUTION GAS; RICH GAS; ROLLOVER GAS; ROYALTY OIL OR GAS; SEASONAL GAS; SNG; SOLUTION GAS; SOUR GAS; STANDARD CUBIC FOOT; STORAGE GAS; STORED GAS; STRIPPER WELL NATURAL GAS; SWEET GAS; SYNGAS; SYNTHESIS GAS; SYNTHETIC NATURAL GAS (SNG); TAIL GAS; TIGHT FORMATION; TOP GAS; TOWN GAS; TRANSPORTATION GAS; WATER GAS; WET GAS; WORKING GAS.

Gas accounting agreement

An agreement between the lessee or operator and the landowner or other persons having an interest in a share of production providing for the method of measuring gas and products manufactured therefrom, expenses of processing and the allocation of proceeds among parties in interest. The landowner and other parties having an interest in a share of production warrant their interests and the agreement then provides for the method of accounting for and allocating all income from gas or liquid products sold or utilized by the lessee and all cost and expense of gathering, processing and delivering the gas. For a form of a Gas accounting agreement, see Williams, Maxwell and Meyers, *Cases on Oil and Gas* 961–965 (2d ed. 1964).

Gas balancing agreement

Syn. for DEFERRED PRODUCTION AGREEMENT (*q.v.*).

Gas bank agreement

A term used to describe an agreement between concurrent owners of interests in gas production where fewer than all such owners have entered into a contract of purchase and sale of the gas produced. Under the agreement, the producers agree that the gas sold belongs to the selling parties and that the nonselling parties shall have the right to produce sufficient volumes in the future to recover their share of the reserves. See Gregg, "Negotiating and Drafting Gas Purchase Contracts on Behalf of the Seller," 13 *Sw. Legal Fdn. Oil & Gas Inst.* 87 at 120 (1962).

Andrau v. Michigan Wisconsin Pipe Line, 712 P.2d 372, 90 *O.&G.R.* 616 (Wyo. 1986), concluded that a gas bank agreement did not require the overlifting unit operator to accept the underlifter's "gas in the bank" as payment for the underlifter's share of expenses at the favorable price realized by the overlifting unit operator for his gas sales:

> "Appellant, in seeking to pay his share of the cost from production of the well, is attempting to avoid both the risk consenters take and the penalty imposed upon nonconsenters. This would obviously remove any incentive for working interest owners to consent and provide the needed cash for drilling additional wells.
>
> "We note that appellant contends that allowing foreclosure on his entire interest produces an unfair result because his interest is worth three to five times the debt owed. Appellant is not prevented from bidding at the foreclosure sale, or from convincing others of the high value he places upon his interest so that they are encouraged to bid. In dealing with this claim of unjust results, we query whether appellant would assert his 'right' to sell his production under Moncrief's contract if the market value of gas had instead increased dramatically from the time of Moncrief's contract. It seems clear that if we were to accept appellant's argument, then those in his position would have the enviable choice of selling their share of production under the operator's contract, or under their own contract if the market value increases."

See also BALANCING; BANKING OF GAS; CANCELLED UNDERAGE; DEEMED PURCHASE FORMULA; DEFERRED PRODUCTION AGREEMENT; LIFTING; LIFTING TOLERANCE; "OUT OF BALANCE" PRODUCTION PLAN; OVERLIFT; SPLIT CONNECTION; UNDERAGE; UNDERLIFT/OVERLIFT PROVISION.

Gas behind the pipe

Gas in a potentially producing horizon penetrated by a well bore the production of which has been postponed pending the production of gas from another formation penetrated by the well bore. This gas is classified as proven but nonproducing reserves.

See the following discussions:

" 'Behind-the-Pipe' Natural Gas Reserves," Hearings before the Subcommittee on Oversight and Investigations of the House Committee on Interstate and Foreign Commerce, 95th Cong., 1st Sess., Feb. 22 and 23, 1977 (Serial No. 95–12);

"Natural Gas Shortages," Hearings before the Subcommittee on Energy and Power of the Committee on Interstate and Foreign

Commerce, House of Representatives, 94th Cong., 1st Sess. on H.R. 2418 [Serial No. 94–58] (1975) at pp. 256, 258, 647.

See also RESERVOIR "BEHIND THE PIPE."

Gas bubble

The term applied to the release to the market, following partial deregulation of gas sales, and the authorized increase in the price of regulated gas, of substantial quantities of gas previously withheld from the market by owners anticipating deregulation. As a result, the supply of gas exceeded demand under the then existing price structure in the early 1980s.

See also ILLINOIS OIL BUBBLE; PRICE CONTROL OF OIL, GAS, AND PETROLEUM PRODUCTS.

Gasbuggy

An experiment for commercial gas stimulation by an underground nuclear explosion designed to create a chimney and a fracture system that surrounds and is connected to the chimney, thus stimulating the flow of gas through "tight" reservoirs characterized by low permeability. See Rubin, Schwartz, and Montan, *An Analysis of Gas Stimulation Using Nuclear Explosives* (May 15, 1972).

Gas cap

The portion of a reservoir occupied by free gas.

Big Piney Oil & Gas Co. v. Wyoming Oil and Gas Conservation Comm'n. 715 P.2d 557, ____ *O.&G.R.* ____ (Wyo. 1986), concluded that the Commission had power to restrict gas cap production from a lease when such production caused migration of oil from adjoining premises, which oil became nonrecoverable after migration, and when the gas cap producer had produced more gas from the common pool than was estimated to have been under its lease originally.

See also OIL ZONE; SECONDARY GAS CAP; WATER ZONE.

Gas cap allowable

An ALLOWABLE (*q.v.*) granted an operator who shuts in a well producing from the gas cap of an oil producing reservoir. The allowable is transferable to another well in the same field. See "Transferred Allowables and Substitute Royalties," 5 *Oil & Gas Tax Q.* 59 at 70 (1956).

See also TRANSFERRED ALLOWABLE.

Gas cap drive

The energy derived from the expansion of excess gas in a free state as a gas cap above the oil zone, used in the production of oil. During the time that no gas is being produced from the gas cap, wells drilled into the oil zone of the reservoir constitute the only points for release of pressure. This pressure reduction is transmitted through the oil zone to the gas cap and allows the compressed gas in the gas cap to expand and move downward, forcing the oil ahead, as a piston sweeping downward. See Interstate Oil Compact Commission, *Oil for Today and for Tomorrow* 20 (1953).

See also RESERVOIR ENERGY.

Gas cap field

A gas expansion reservoir in which some of the gas occurs as free gas, rather than in solution. The free gas will occupy the highest portion of the reservoir, and when wells are bored to lower points on the structure, the gas will expand forcing the oil down-dip and into the well bore. One problem in producing from a gas cap field is to insure that production from the cap itself does not dissipate the pressure and thus deprive the reservoir of energy for primary production.

See also CONDENSATE GAS RESERVOIR; FIELD; RESERVOIR; WETTING THE GAS CAP.

Gas chromatography method

A method of testing gas for its gasoline content, described in Natural Gasoline Association of America Publication 2261.61.

Gas condensate

Syn. for CONDENSATE (*q.v.*). Also called distillate, drips, white oil, *etc.*

See also ALBINO OIL; LOW TEMPERATURE EXTRACTION (LTX); NATURAL GASOLINE; WATER-WHITE OIL; WHITE OIL.

Gas condensate reservoir

See CONDENSATE GAS RESERVOIR.

Gas distillate

See DISTILLATE.

Gas drive field

A petroleum reservoir produced by energy furnished by gas expansion. See GAS EXPANSION RESERVOIR.

Gas expansion reservoir

A petroleum reservoir produced by energy furnished by gas expansion. Such reservoirs may be either gas-cap fields or solution gas fields. In either event, the reduction in pressure that accompanies the boring of a well into the reservoir permits the expansion of the gas, which drives the oil to the well bore. Good conservation practice requires the careful regulation of gas-oil ratios in order to preserve reservoir energy.

See also RESERVOIR ENERGY.

Gas exploration and development incentive agreement

Syn. for ADVANCE PAYMENT AGREEMENT (*q.v.*).

Gas flaring

See FLARING OF GAS.

Gas fly-up

See PRICE SPIKE.

Gas gatherer

A person who gathers gas other than his own in a field or fields for delivery to a transporter or gas processing plant. La. State-wide Order No. 31–a–1 (1955), Interstate Oil Compact Commission, *A Legal Report of Oil and Gas Conservation Activities* 15 (1955). Other statutory definitions may vary.

Gas injection

Introduction of gas under high pressure into a producing reservoir through an input or injection well as part of a PRESSURE MAINTENANCE (*q.v.*), SECONDARY RECOVERY (*q.v.*), or RECYCLING (*q.v.*) operation.

Gas injection well

A well utilized to introduce gas under high pressure into a producing formation as part of a PRESSURE MAINTENANCE (*q.v.*), SECONDARY RECOVERY (*q.v.*), or RECYCLING OPERATION (*q.v.*).

Syn.: INPUT WELL.

Gas in storage

A term referring collectively to CUSHION GAS (*q.v.*) and WORKING GAS (*q.v.*). United Gas Pipe Line Co. v. Whitman, 390 So. 2d 913 (La. App. 1980), *writs denied,* 396 So. 2d 928, 929 (La. 1981).

Gas lease agreement

A form of agreement entered into by El Paso Natural Gas Co. in the San Juan Basin for the acquisition of substantial leasehold interests. In United Gas Improvement Co. v. Continental Oil Co. (the R AYNE FIELD CASE), 381 U.S. 392, 22 *O.&G.R.* 243 (1965), the court ruled that sales of leases covering proven and substantially developed gas reserves to an interstate pipeline company were subject to Federal Power Commission jurisdiction.

The gas lease agreement form considered in El Paso Natural Gas Co. v. Sun Oil Co., 426 F. Supp. 963, 57 *O.&G.R.* 93 (W.D. Texas 1977), was held to be distinguishable (and hence not subject to Federal Power Commission jurisdiction) because the leases transferred were neither proven nor substantially developed at the time of the execution of the agreement. Under those circumstances the defendants who sold working interests for a reserved overriding royalty were not "natural gas companies" within the meaning of the Natural Gas Act and were not required to seek certification from the Commission to collect overrides. Decision on appeal was withheld pending decision by the Federal Energy Regulatory Commission, 580 F.2d 722 (5th Cir. (1978). The Commission ruled that the lease agreements were within its jurisdiction (12 F.E.R.C. ¶ 61297 (1980), but on review it was held that the agreements were not within the regulatory jurisdiction of the Commission. El Paso Natural Gas Co. v. Sun Oil Co., 708 F.2d 1011 (5th Cir. 1983), *rehearing en banc denied,* 721 F.2d 818 (5th Cir. 1983), *cert. denied,* ____ U.S. ____, 104 S. Ct. 3589, 3590 (1984), *reh. denied,* ____ U.S. ____, 105 S. Ct. 52, 53 (1984).

See also GAS LEASE-SALES AGREEMENT (GLA).

Gas Lease-Sales Agreement (GLA)

An agreement to sell leasehold interests covering the production of gas from specified properties. See El Paso Natural Gas Co. v. American Petrofina Co. of Texas, 715 S.W.2d 177, ____ *O.&G.R.* ____ (Tex. App., Houston, 1986).

See also 500 MCF CLAUSE; GAS LEASE AGREEMENT; PRODUCTION IN COMMERCIAL QUANTITIES; PRODUCTION IN PAYING QUANTITIES; PROFITABILITY; RAYNE FIELD CASE; UNDEVELOPED ACREAGE CLAUSE; UNPROFITABILITY CLAUSE.

Gas leg

In the RELATIVE COST METHOD OF ALLOCATION (*q.v.*), the gas leg is the unit cost of gas from leases producing gas only. See Permian Basin Area Rate Proceeding, 34 F.P.C. 159 at 215, 23 *O.&G.R.* 103 at 106 (Opinion No. 468, Aug. 5, 1965), *remanded,* Skelly Oil Co. v. Federal Power Comm'n, 375 F.2d 6, 26 *O.&G.R.* 237 (10th Cir. 1967), *aff'd in part and rev'd in part sub nom. In re* Permian Basin Area Rate Cases, 390 U.S. 747, 28 *O.&G.R.* 689 (1968).

Gas lift

A method of raising oil from the bottom of the hole to the surface and forestalling the installation of pumps on wells to maintain production. Part of the energy required for production of oil is provided by gas (or air) injected into the fluid in the casing. Compressed natural gas (or air) is pumped into the hole under pressure. At the lower end of the tubing it becomes a part of the stream of fluid in the well, intermixing with the oil. The gas (or air) lightens or "aerates" the oil column and, by its effort to expand, carries the oil with it to the surface. The gas may be pumped into the tubing, forcing the oil up the hole between the tubing and casing, or into the space between the tubing and casing, forcing the oil up the tubing. Either gas (gas lift) or air (air lift) may be used, but gas is better. Gas lift is not to be confused with secondary recovery or pressure maintenance, the purpose of which is to propel oil in the reservoir into the well bore. Air and gas lift propel oil already in the well bore up to the surface, as a substitute for pumping.

Gas mixing equipment

Apparatus used for mixing manufactured and natural gas, or mixing of other gases incident to delivery of such mixed gas to the distribution system. 18 C.F.R. § 201.319 (1980).

Gas, natural

See GAS; NATURAL GAS.

Gas-oil contact line

The line between the oil zone and the gas zone in a reservoir. Three fluids frequently appear in a reservoir: gas, oil, and salt water. If the gas is in a free state, the line of contact between the gas zone and the oil zone is called the gas-oil contact line. The line is not sharply defined. Rather, it is a zone containing some oil and gas, with the percentage of gas increasing as one goes up the structure.

See also OIL-WATER CONTACT LINE.

Gas-oil ratio (GOR)

The number of cubic feet of gas produced per barrel of oil produced. Gas-oil ratios are frequently the subject of conservation regulation, because production from a well with a high gas-oil ratio usually results in inefficient use of reservoir energy. An average gas-oil ratio is 1500 cubic feet of gas per barrel of oil; ratios of 300 to 700 cubic feet of gas per barrel of oil are viewed as low, and ratios in excess of 2000 cubic feet per barrel of oil are viewed as high. In some countries, cubic meters of both gas and oil are compared.

See also OIL-WATER RATIO.

Gas-oil ratio adjustment

The reduction in ALLOWABLE (*q.v.*) for a high gas-oil ratio unit to conform with the production permitted by the limiting gas-oil ratio for the particular pool during a particular proration period. New Mexico Oil Conservation Comm'n, *Rules and Regulations* 2 (1958); 16 Tex. Admin. Code § 3.49.

Gas-oil ratio penalty factor

"[A] variable penalty factor less than unity used to decrease an Authorized MPR [MAXIMUM PERMISSIVE RATE (*q.v.*)] or Authorized EA [ECONOMIC ALLOWANCE (*q.v.*)] of a well, whichever is applicable, where the gas-oil ratio plus the average separator pressure for the last producing month for the well is in excess of 1,005." Provisions Governing the Limitation and Allocation of Production of Oil, Saskatchewan MRO 118/68 A 62, 5 Lewis and Thompson, *Canadian Oil and Gas* Division D, Part X [5] (1971).

See also ALLOWABLE.

Gas oils

(1) Petroleum fractions made up predominantely of material which boils at or above 430 degrees F., including heavy aromatic gas oil used as carbon black feedstock, but excluding process oils and refined lubricating oils. Regulations concerning mandatory allocation of certain naphthas and gas oils are contained in 10 C.F.R. § 211.181 *et seq.* (1980).

(2) The term applied on the INTERNATIONAL PETROLEUM EXCHANGE (*q.v.*) for heating-oil. *The Wall Street Journal,* April 7, 1981, p. 38, col. 1.

Gasoline

A volatile, inflammable, liquid hydrocarbon mixture.

See also CASINGHEAD GASOLINE; CONDENSATE; CRACKING; DRIP GASOLINE; NATURAL GASOLINE; UNFINISHED GASOLINE.

Gasoline marketing divestiture statute

A statute designed to exclude major oil companies from competing at the retail level with independent marketers.

> "The statutes are essentially of two types: those prohibiting the owning or leasing of marketing outlets by vertically integrated oil companies and those prohibiting or limiting the operation of retail outlets with company employees. Both types of statutes, however, have as their primary aim the exclusion of the majors as competitors at the retail level. This is thought to be necessary to prevent anticompetitive behavior that results from the majors' vertical integration combined with their oligopolistic control of crude oil producing, transporting, and refining." Meriwether and Smith, "Gasoline Marketing Divestiture Statutes: Preliminary Constitutional and Economic Assessment," 28 *Vanderbilt L. Rev.* 1277 at 1334 (1975).

Gas pool

See OIL FIELD; OIL POOL; POOL.

Gas pressure

The force of gas under compression, as in an underground formation.

Gas proration unit

The acreage assigned an individual well for the purpose of allocating allowable gas production. Railroad Comm'n of Texas v. Permian Basin Pipeline Co., 302 S.W.2d 238, 7 *O.&G.R.* 525, 529 (Tex. Civ. App. 1957, error ref'd n.r.e.), *appeal dism'd and cert. denied,* 358 U. S. 37, 9 *O.&G.R.* 830 (1958).

See also HIGH GAS-OIL PRORATION UNIT; PRORATION UNIT.

Gas purchase contract

A contract for the sale and purchase of gas entered into by the purchaser and the owners of interests in the gas as produced. Contracts of this type are usually for a long term inasmuch as the purchaser must have a substantial guaranty of an available supply to justify its expenditures for the construction of gathering, treatment and pipeline facilities and because dedication of large reserves was required before the Federal Power Commission, and its successor, the Federal Energy Regulatory Commission, would issue a certificate of public convenience and necessity to pipeline companies. In some cases, only the lessee is a party to the contract as "seller," and in such instances the contract will usually contain a provision for payment of royalties by the lessee. In other instances the lessors or royalty owners may be parties to the contract and be entitled to receive a share of the payments made by the "purchaser."

Gas purchase contracts are usually quite detailed and lengthy as it is essential that provision be made concerning the place of delivery, the quality and quantity of the gas, the right of the seller to use gas for operations on the premises, including repressuring, the methods of measurement of quality and quantity, the methods of operation, a schedule of payment in terms of quality and quantity, division of the burden of taxation, rights of assignment, the effect of force majeure, procedures for accounting, and remedies in the event of breach by either party. See TREATISE §§ 720–741.2.

On the authority of a bankruptcy court to reject contracts made by a bankrupt for the sale of gas, see Matter of Tilco, Inc., 408 F. Supp. 389 (D. Kan. 1976), *rev'd and remanded,* 558 F.2d 1369 (10th Cir. 1977).

For a gas purchase contract form and a discussion of its principal features, see American Gas Ass'n, *Regulation of the Gas Industry* ch. 15 (1981).

The definition in this MANUAL was quoted in Nordan-Lawton Oil & Gas Corp. of Texas v. Miller, 272 F. Supp. 125 at 136, 27

O.&G.R. 583 at 606 (W.D. La. 1967), *aff'd,* 403 F.2d 946, 31 *O.&G.R.* 526 (5th Cir. 1968) (citing this MANUAL).

See also ADAPTATION CLAUSE; ADD-ONS; ADVANCE PAYMENT AGREEMENT; ASSIGNMENT OF RESERVES; BANKING OF GAS; BONA FIDE OFFER PROVISION; BROKERAGE OF GAS; BTU ADJUSTMENT CLAUSE; BTU REJECTION CLAUSE; BUYER PROTECTION CLAUSE; CASINGHEAD GAS CONTRACT; COMMODITY CHARGE; COMMODITY VALUE OF NATURAL GAS; COMPENSATION PAYMENT; CONTRACTUAL CAP; CONVENTIONALIZATION OF LEASE-SALE; CONVENTIONAL SALES CONTRACT; DAILY CONTRACT QUANTITY; DAILY TAKE; DCQ; DEDICATION CONTRACT; DEDICATION OF RESERVES; DELIVERY PRESSURE; DEMAND RATE; DIRECT CUSTOMER; DIRECT SALE CUSTOMER; DIVISION ORDER; DUMP GAS CONTRACT; ECONOMIC CONNECTION CLAUSE; ECONOMIC-OUT CLAUSE; ESCALATOR CLAUSE; EXCHANGE AGREEMENT; EXISTING CONTRACT; FERC-OUT CLAUSE; FIELD VALUE OF NATURAL GAS; FIRM GAS CONTRACT; FLOW-THROUGH CLAUSE; FORCE MAJEURE CLAUSE; FPC PRICE PROTECTION CLAUSE; GOOD FAITH NEGOTIATION CLAUSE; GOVERNMENTAL PRICE ESCALATION CLAUSE; INDIRECT CUSTOMER; INTERRUPTIBLE GAS; INTRASTATE CLAUSE; INTRASTATE UTILIZATION CLAUSE; JURISDICTIONAL ESCAPE CLAUSE; KICKOUT CLAUSE; LIFE OF LEASE CONTRACT; MAKE-UP GAS; MARKET-OUT CLAUSE; MINIMUM COMMODITY BILL; MINIMUM TAKE PROVISION; MOST FAVORED NATION CLAUSE; NEW GAS; NONFIRM GAS; OFF-SYSTEM SALE; OIL EQUIVALENCY CLAUSE; OLD GAS; PARTICIPATION TYPE CONTRACT; PERCENTAGE OF PROCEEDS CONTRACT; PRE-INITIAL DELIVERY PAYMENT; PREPAYMENT PROVISION; PRESSURE CLAUSE; PRICE REDETERMINATION CLAUSE; PROPORTIONAL BTU ADJUSTMENT PROVISION; PROTEST CLAUSE; RATABLE TAKING; RATE OF TAKE PROVISION; RESALE CUSTOMER; ROLLOVER CONTRACT; SPECIAL MARKETING PROGRAM; SPLIT SALES; SPOT PURCHASES (OR SALES) OF GAS; SPRABERRY TYPE CONTRACT; STAND-BY REQUIREMENT; SUBSTITUTE FUEL CLAUSE; SUBSTANTIAL HARDSHIP CLAUSE; SUCCESSOR TO AN EXISTING CONTRACT; SURPLUS GAS CLAUSE; SWING; TAKE-AND-PAY CLAUSE; TAKE-AWAYS; TAKE-OR-PAY CLAUSE; TAKE-OR-PAY CONTRACT; TARIFF-AND-SERVICE AGREEMENT; TAX-REIMBURSEMENT CLAUSE; VINTAGE; WARRANTY CONTRACT.

Gas reforming equipment

Equipment used primarily for reforming gas with resultant changes in its chemical composition and calorific value. 18 C.F.R. § 201.316 (1980).

Gas Research Institute (GRI)

A nonprofit organization incorporated in 1976 to establish a national program of natural gas related research and development. Its role is to complement and enlarge the research and development work of individual gas service companies. Its projects are carried out through contracts with laboratories, universities, and other organizations which perform research and development work for outside sponsors. See Public Service Co. of Colo. v. Public Utilities Comm'n of the State of Colo., 644 P.2d 933 (Colo. 1982).

Gas royalty

The ROYALTY (*q.v.*) paid on gas produced and saved, often one-eighth of the market price, or the market value, or the proceeds of the sale of the gas at the well head. The royalty usually is not payable for gas used in the leasehold operations or reinjected into the producing stratum.

When gas contains liquefiable hydrocarbons in solution, considerable controversy has arisen over sharing the expenses of extraction of the gasoline content of the natural gas. Contemporary leases usually specifically provide for this matter.

Unlike the oil royalty clause, the gas royalty clause frequently calls for payment of the royalty in money rather than in kind. A typical royalty clause is as follows:

> "The said lessee covenants and agrees to pay lessor for gas of whatsoever nature or kind produced and sold, or used off the premises, or used in the manufacture of any products therefrom, one-eighth, at the market price at the well for the gas sold, used off the premises, or in the manufacture of products therefrom, said payments to be made monthly."

For an excellent discussion of some of the problems of determining the "Value of Lessor's Share of Production Where Gas Only Is Produced," see the paper of that title by J. T. Sneed, 25 *Tex. L. Rev.* 641 (1947). The author concludes his discussion with the comment that "the ordinary royalty clause pertaining to gas is one of the most ambiguous and incomplete provisions of an oil and gas lease ever to be brought before the courts." See TREATISE §§ 643.2, 643.6

See also CASINGHEAD GAS ROYALTY; FEDERAL-FLOOR PROVISION; FIXED PRICE ROYALTY CLAUSE; FREE GAS CLAUSE; LESSOR-APPROVAL PROVISION; MARKET-VALUE/AMOUNT REALIZED PROVISION; OPEN-END GAS ROYALTY CLAUSE.

Gas sales contract

See GAS PURCHASE CONTRACT.

Gas separation

The removal of dissolved gas from crude oil.

See also ABSORPTION PLANT; COMBINATION PLANT; COMPRESSION PLANT; PROCESSING PLANT; SEPARATOR.

Gas shrinkage

Gas lost or absorbed in the process of extraction of salable products from natural gas, exclusive of gas used as fuel. 18 C.F.R. § 201.772 (1980).

Gas, sour

See SOUR GAS.

Gas storage and balancing agreement

An agreement among parties having interests in production from a pooled or unitized area relating to adjustments to be made during the time any party does not take or market its full share of gas. For a form of such an agreement see Upchurch, "Split Stream Gas Sales and the Gas Storage and Balancing Agreement," 24 *Rocky Mt. Min. L. Inst.* 665 at 689 (1978).

See also BALANCING; UNIT AGREEMENT.

Gas storage, subsurface

Use of a depleted formation or an aquifer near a market to store gas brought in from another field. In Kentucky it has been held that a landowner has no cause of action when his land is used for this purpose on the ground that title to the gas is lost when it is returned to the formation. Hammonds v. Central Kentucky Natural Gas Co., 255 Ky. 685, 75 S.W.2d 204 (1934). Thus, while the landowner cannot complain of trespass, he can acquire title to the gas by producing it, under the law of capture. Where a severance has occurred, the Kentucky court has said that the power to execute a gas storage lease belongs to the owner of the mineral estate, who would be entitled to drill for and produce the gas in the absence of a contract. Central Kentucky Natural Gas Co. v. Smallwood, 252 S.W.2d 866, 2 *O.&G.R.* 19 (Ky. 1952). West Virginia rejects both positions of the Kentucky court, and holds that the landowner is entitled to damages for unauthorized storing of gas below the surface. The court also held that as between the owner of oil and gas rights in the land and the owner of the remaining interests, the latter held the property rights in depleted formations under the land and therefore had the exclusive right to make gas storage agreements. Tate v. United Fuel Gas Co., 137 W.Va. 272, 71 S.E.2d 65 (1952). Since there is doubt about the right of an oil and gas lessee to use the premises for gas storage, wise draftsmen will broaden the lease purposes to include this use of the land. In a number of states today, statutes authorize the condemnation of depleted formations for gas storage purposes. See TREATISE § 222.

West Bay Exploration Co. v. Amoco Production Co., 148 Mich. App. 197, 384 N.W.2d 407, ___ *O.&G.R.* ___ (1986), cited definitions in this MANUAL and concluded that leaving gas in place did not constitute "storage" as that word was used by the oil and gas industry and in the instrument construed. The judgment was vacated and the case remanded, 425 Mich. 878, 389 N.W.2d 865 (1986), but on remand, 155 Mich. App. 429, 399 N.W.2d 549 (1986), the court adhered to its prior decision.

See also CUSHION GAS; NATIVE GAS; NATIVE GAS ENTITLEMENT; WORKING GAS.

Gas, sweet

See SWEET GAS.

Gas well

A well capable of producing natural gas. Some statutes define the term on the basis of the gas-oil ratio. See *e.g.*, Texas Nat. Res. Code § 86.002 (5) (1978):

" 'Gas well' means a well that:

(A) produces gas not associated or blended with oil at the time of production;

(B) produces more than 100,000 cubic feet of gas to each barrel of oil from the same producing horizon; or

(C) produces gas from a formation or producing horizon productive of gas only encountered in a well bore through which oil also is produced through the inside of another string of casing."

Colorado Interstate Gas Co. v. HUFO Oils, 626 F.Supp. 38, ___ *O.&G.R.* ___ (W.D. Tex. 1985), *aff'd*, 802 F.2d 133, ___ *O.&G.R.* ___ (5th Cir. 1986), *reh. en banc denied*, 806 F.2d 261 (5th Cir. 1986), and HUFO Oils v. Railroad Commission, 717 S.W.2d 405, ___ *O.&G.R.* ___ (Tex. App., Austin, 1986), held that WHITE OIL (*q.v.*) extracted from natural gas by LOW TEMPERATURE EXTRACTION (*q.v.*) could not be counted as "oil" for purposes of classification of a well as an oil well or gas well.

For discussions of problems arising from classification of a well as a gas well or as an oil well when gas and oil are separately owned, see TREATISE § 219.7; Midkiff, "Phase Severance of Gas Rights from Oil Rights," 63 *Tex. L. Rev.* 133 (1984); "Big, Small Energy Firms Fight Over Texas Gas," *The Wall Street Journal,* Sept. 21, 1984, p. 33.

See also ALBINO OIL; LOW TEMPERATURE EXTRACTION (*LTX*).

In Oklahoma, a well which produces liquid hydrocarbons of 50 degree or higher API gravity. See Diggs v. Cities Service Oil Co., 241 F.2d 425, 7 *O.&G.R.* 827 (10th Cir. 1957).

In Kilpatrick Oil & Gas Co., 15 IBLA 216, GFS(O&G) 1974–37, although a 640-acre spacing pattern had been established by the Oklahoma Corporation Commission on the ground that natural gas would be the hydrocarbon encountered as a result of drilling a well, it was concluded that the well in question was an oil well. The opinion noted that "There is no federal definition of what constitutes an oil well as opposed to a gas well. This lack of a ready-made formula does not, however, bar intelligent classification." The well in question had a gas-oil ratio between 6,000:1 and 7,000:1, and the oil had a corrected gravity of 36.9 degree to 37.1 degree API.

Bolton v. Coats, 514 S.W.2d 482, 50 *O.&G.R.* 79 (Tex. Civ. App. 1974), *rev'd and remanded on other grounds,* 533 S.W.2d 914, 53 *O.&G.R.* 379 (Tex. 1975), held that a Railroad Commission finding that a well is a gas rather than an oil well is not subject to collateral attack.

A dry hole is generally not viewed as a "gas well" or as an "oil well" as those terms are customarily used in contracts unless required by express wording of the contract or necessary implication. See Nafco Oil & Gas, Inc. v. Tartan Resources Corp., 522 S.W.2d 703, 52 *O.&G.R.* 273 (Tex. Civ. App. 1975, error ref'd n.r.e.).

See also SPLIT-STREAM GAS WELL; TIGHT GAS WELL.

Gas well gas

A term used to distinguish gas produced other than in association with the production of oil from an oil well (*viz.,* casinghead gas). Deep South Oil Co. v. Federal Power Comm'n, 247 F.2d 882, 7 *O.&G.R.* 1539 (5th Cir. 1957), *cert. denied in companion case,* 355 U. S. 930 (1958).

This term was defined in the Permian Basin Area Rate Proceeding as "so-called non-associated gas, that is, gas from dry gas reservoirs and gas condensate reservoirs, and gas from gas-cap wells." Permian Basin Area Rate Proceeding, 34 F.P.C. 159 at 189, 23 *O.&G.R.* 103 at 130 (Opinion No. 468, Aug. 5, 1965), *remanded,* Skelly Oil Co. v. Federal Power Comm'n, 375 F.2d 6, 26 *O.&G.R.* 237 (10th Cir. 1967), *aff'd in part and rev'd in part sub nom. In re* Permian Basin Area Rate Cases, 390 U.S. 747, 28 *O.&G.R.* 689 (1968).

Gate station

A location at which gas changes ownership, from one party to another, neither of which is the ultimate consumer. Also referred to as CITY GATE (*q.v.*) station, town border station. American Gas Association Bureau of Statistics. *Glossary for the Gas Industry* 26.

Gathering facilities

Pipe lines and other facilities used to collect gas from various wells and bring it by separate and individual lines to a central point where it is delivered into a single line. In the Matter of Barnes Transportation Co., 18 F.P.C. 369, 7 *O.&G.R.* 1527 (1957).

Gathering gas

The first taking or the first retaining of possession of gas for transmission through a pipe line, after the severance of such gas, and after the passage of such gas through any separator, drip, trap or meter that may be located at or near the well. In the case of gas containing gasoline or liquid hydrocarbons that are removed or extracted in commercial quantities at a plant by scrubbing, absorption, compression, or any similar process, the term means the first taking or the first retaining of possession of such gas for transmission through a pipe line after such gas has passed through the outlet of such plant. The act of collecting gas after it has been brought from the earth. Saturn Oil & Gas Co. v. Federal Power Comm'n, 250 F.2d 61, 8 *O.&G.R.* 365 (10th Cir. 1957), *cert. denied,* 355 U.S. 956, 8 *O.&G.R.* 843 (1958).

Gathering line

Pipes used to transport oil or gas from the lease to the main pipeline in the area. In the case of oil, the lines run from lease tanks to a central pump station at the beginning of the main pipeline. In the case of gas, the flow is continuous from the well head to the ultimate consumer, since gas cannot be stored.

Gathering lines collect gas under fluctuating pressures which are then regulated by regulating stations before the gas is introduced into trunk or transmission lines. Smith v. Inland Gas & Oil Co., 14 W.W. R. 558, 4 *O.&G.R.* 937 (Sup. Ct. of Alberta 1955).

For purposes of regulation of a pipeline under the Natural Gas Pipeline Safety Act, classification of the line as a gathering line, DISTRIBUTION LINE (*q.v.*) or TRANSMISSION LINE (*q.v.*) may be of significance. See Hamman v. Southwestern Gas Pipeline, Inc., 721 F.2d 140 (5th Cir. 1983) (holding that the gathering line exception in the Act must be restricted to those pipelines that connect a transmission line to a gas well).

See also PIPELINE.

Gathering station

A compressor station at which gas is gathered from wells by means of suction because pressure is not sufficient to produce the desired rate of flow into a transmission or distribution system. American Gas Association Bureau of Statistics, *Glossary for the Gas Industry* 26.

Gathering system

The GATHERING LINES (*q.v.*), pumps, auxiliary tanks (in the case of oil), and other equipment used to move oil or gas from the well site to the main pipeline for eventual delivery to the refinery or consumer, as the case may be. In the case of gas, the gathering system includes the processing plant (if any) in which the gas is prepared for the market.

See also COLLECTING SYSTEM; DISTRIBUTION SYSTEM.

Gathering tax

A tax laid on the process of gathering gas. The Gas Gathering Tax of the State of Texas was declared unconstitutional in Michigan-Wisconsin Pipe Line Co. v. Calvert, 347 U.S. 157 (1954), as a tax on interstate commerce.

Gauge pressure

See PSIG.

Gauger

A person who measures the quantity and quality of oil and/or gas produced.

Gauging a well

Measurement of such characteristics of a well as potential for purposes of prorationing.

GCC

The GULF COOPERATION COUNCIL (GCC)(*q.v.*).

Gelation

A phenomenon whereby cement goes through a transformation into a gelatinous stage and loses its normal gradient and assumes the lesser gradient of water. This results in a loss of the hydrostatic head (pressure) which allows the pressure of a formation to overcome the pressure of the fluids in the hole, thus causing a blowout. Lancaster v. Petroleum Corp. of Delaware, 491 So.2d 768, ____ *O.&G.R.* ____ (La. App. 1986).

General Land Office Survey

The government survey which, except for lands embraced in grants made by foreign governments prior to the time it became territory of the United States, embraces the lands of Alabama, Florida, Mississippi, all states north of the Ohio River, and all states west of the Mississippi River except Texas. Under this survey:

> "the public lands of the United States are first surveyed into rectangular tracts, by running parallel lines north and south and crossing them at right angles with other parallel lines, so as to form rectangles six miles square, called townships. The first north and south line is a true meridian, and is called a principal or prime meridian. The north and south lines parallel to it are called range lines. The six-mile strips bounded by these lines are called ranges. The first east and west line is called a base line. The other east and west lines drawn parallel to it are called township lines. The six-mile strips bounded by these lines are called townships. The rectangles formed by the two sets of lines are also called townships. They are the largest subdivisions of the survey. . . .
>
> "The townships are subdivided into 36 tracts, each a mile square, called sections, and containing, as near as may be, 640

acres each. They are numbered consecutively, commencing with section 1 at the northeast corner, and proceeding west to section 6; thence in the next tier numbering east from section 7 to section 12; and so back and forth till section 36 is reached in the southeast corner." Patton and Patton, *Land Titles* § 65 (1938).

A Congressional Township is identified by its Township number and its Range number, *e.g.*, Township 5N (from the base line) Range 5W of the—meridian, and within the township the sections are identified by number. The diagram which follows shows a Congressional Township of thirty-six sections and the plan of numbering same:

6	5	4	3	2	1
7	8	9	10	11	12
18	17	16	15	14	13
19	20	21	22	23	24
30	29	28	27	26	25
31	32	33	34	35	36

See also the following:

Piccone, "History, The Government Survey, and Basic Oil and Gas Leasing Legislation," *Rocky Mt. Min. L. Fdn. Law of Federal Oil and Gas Leases* ch. 2 (1984);

Piccone, "Resurveys of Public Lands," 30 *Rocky Mt. Min. L. Inst.* 20-1 (1984).

General limitation clause

See LIMITATION CLAUSE.

General Shut-Down Order

An order issued by a regulatory commission setting forth the number of days oil wells must be shut down and the number of producing days for the month in question. Dutton, "Proration in Texas: Conservation or Confiscation?," 11 *Sw. L.J.* 186 (1957).

General warranty

A covenant of title in a deed, lease or assignment, the effect of which is to guarantee title against all defects, whether arising by virtue of acts of the grantor or by acts of his predecessors in title. A short form general warranty clause reads: "Grantor agrees to warrant and defend title forever."

See also SPECIAL WARRANTY; WARRANTY.

Geochemical prospecting

Exploratory methods that involve the use of chemical techniques. See Horvitz, "How Geochemical Analysis Helps the Geologist Find Oil," 55 *Oil and Gas Journal* 234 (Nov. 11, 1957).

A method of prospecting for oil and gas, predicated on the axiom that in nature there is no such thing as a perfect seal, involving the search for evidence of oil and gas leaks from underground reservoirs. See Donovan, "Geochemical Prospecting for Oil and Gas from Orbital and Suborbital Altitudes," 25 *IOCC Comm. Bull.* 36 (June 1983).

See also GEOPHYSICAL SURVEY.

Geochemical survey

See GEOPHYSICAL SURVEY.

Geographical unit

A UNIT (*q.v.*) whose boundaries are established on the basis of regular surface geographical lines (*e.g.*, lines bounding sections or regular subdivisions thereof) as distinguished from a GEOLOGICAL UNIT (*q.v.*) whose boundaries are established on the basis of geological evidence. See Superior Oil Co. v. Cox, 307 So. 2d 350 at 354, 50 *O.&G.R.* 323 at 330 (La. 1975).

Geological and geophysical costs

See GEOPHYSICAL AND GEOLOGICAL COSTS.

Geological field

As defined in Form EIA-23 of the Energy Information administration of the Office of Oil and Gas in the Department of Energy, a geological field is:

> "An area consisting of a single reservoir or multiple reservoirs all grouped on, or related to, the same individual geological structural feature and/or stratigraphic condition. There may be two or

more reservoirs in a field which are separated vertically by intervening impervious strata, or laterally by local geologic barriers or by both."

Some states, *e.g.*, Texas, regard reservoirs as fields and keep their records on that basis.

See also FIELD; OIL AND GAS FIELD CODE MASTER LIST—1982.

Geological survey

The principal types are: (1) surface—study, classification and measurement of outcrops of rock formations, and the mapping and correlation of data with other observations to produce a geological picture of underground formations; (2) subsurface—study, analysis and correlation of samples of rock extracted from wells drilled into the earth; and (3) core drilling—a modified form of subsurface geology which involves the drilling of shallow slim holes into the top layers of the earth's crust for the purpose of extracting rock samples for study and analysis. Yarbro, "Geological and Geophysical Exploration," *P–H Oil and Gas Taxes* ¶ 2009.1 (1978).

On-Structure Deep Stratigraphic Test Wells, 87 I.D. 517 (Oct. 29, 1980), ruled that deep stratigraphic tests, on or off structure potentially holding oil or gas, are "geological explorations" authorized by the OUTER CONTINENTAL SHELF LANDS ACT OF 1953 (*q.v.*), and that the Secretary of the Interior could authorize permittees to conduct such tests on a structure before it was leased.

Geological unit

A UNIT (*q.v.*) whose boundaries are established on the basis of geological evidence as distinguished from a GEOGRAPHICAL UNIT (*q.v.*) whose boundaries are established on the basis of regular surface geographical lines (*e.g.*, lines bounding sections or regular subdivisions thereof). See Superior Oil Co. v. Cox, 307 So. 2d 350 at 354, 50 *O.&G.R.* 323 at 330 (La. 1975).

Geologic province

Any large area or region considered as a whole, all parts of which are characterized by similar features or by a history differing significantly from that of adjacent areas. American Geologic Institute, *Glossary of Geology* (2d ed.).

See also FAVORABLE PETROLEUM GEOLOGICAL PROVINCE (FPGP); PROVINCE.

Geologic structure

Layers of sedimentary rock which have been displaced from the horizontal by various forces of nature. Five general categories of structures are recognized: (1) fault [see FAULT TRAP], (2) ANTICLINE (*q.v.*), (3) MONOCLINE (*q.v.*), (4) SYNCLINE (*q.v.*), and (5) dome [see SALT DOME].

See also RESERVOIR; STRUCTURE.

Geologist

A person trained in the study of the crust of the earth. A petroleum geologist (in contrast to a hard rock geologist) is primarily concerned with sedimentary rocks, which produce most of the world's oil. In general, the work of a petroleum geologist consists of the search for traps (structural and stratigraphic) favorable to the accumulation of oil or gas. In addition to determining favorable locations for drilling, the geologist may supervise the drilling of the well, particularly with regard to coring, making electrical well logs, and performing drill stem tests. The geologist also may formulate the development program of a newly discovered oil field.

Geometric average evaluation of tract (GAEOT)

A calculation made by the MINERALS MANAGEMENT SERVICE (MMS)(*q.v.*) in evaluating competitive lease bids on submerged lands of the OUTER CONTINENTAL SHELF (OCS)(*q.v.*). It is the geometric mean of the bids received on the tract and the MROV (*q.v.*). See Mead, Moseidjord, Muraoka and Sorensen, *Offshore Lands: Oil and Gas Leasing and Conservation on the Outer Continental Shelf* 124 (1985).

See also FEDERAL LEASE.

Geometry of a reservoir

A phrase used by petroleum engineers as a synonym for the shape of a RESERVOIR (*q.v.*).

Geophone

See SEISMOMETER; WAVE VIBRATOR.

Geophysical and geological costs

In federal income taxation law, the expenditures incurred by an operator in making geophysical surveys and geological studies of an area of interest. In I.T. 4006, 1950–1 C.B. 48, the Revenue Service takes the position that these costs must be capitalized. Rev. Rul. 83-105, 1983-30 I.R.B. 7, 76 *O.&G.R.* 653 (July 25, 1983), amplified and explained the tax treatment of these costs under Rev. Rul. 77-188.

See Burke, "Current Expensing of Geological and Geophysical Costs: A Need for Legislative Clarification," 34 *Okla. L. Rev.* 778 (1981).

See also AREA OF INTEREST; CAPITAL EXPENDITURES.

Geophysical and geological survey

Defined in La. Rev. Stat. LSA–R.S. § 30–211 (1975), as "magnetometer surveys, gravitymeter surveys, torsion balance surveys, seismograph surveys, using either the reflection or the refraction method, soil analysis surveys which tend to show the presence or absence of hydrocarbons, electrical surveys, using either the Eltran or some similar method and any method utilizing short wave radio."

See also GEOPHYSICAL EXPLORATION.

Geophysical exploration

The search for geologic structures favorable to the accumulation of petroleums by means of geophysical devices. By use of one or more of such devices, geophysicists seek to arrive at a picture of subsurface conditions. The gravity meter measures the gravitational pull of subsurface rocks, revealing on occasion disconformities and structural traps. The magnetometer measures the magnetic attraction of iron contained in various types of rock, from which it is sometimes possible to locate a subsurface structure. Perhaps the most commonly used geophysical device is the seismograph, which measures shock waves reflected and refracted by subterranean rock layers. From this data is plotted a contour map indicating the presence (if any) of structural traps. Today, in any new area, geophysical investigation is the almost universal preliminary to exploratory drilling.

For a discussion of the technology of geophysical exploration, see Green and Wilson, "Trends in Geophysical Prospecting for Petroleum," 1 *Sw. Legal Fdn. Inst. on Economics of the Petroleum Industry* (1963).

See also GROUP SHOOT; SEISMOGRAPH; SPEC SHOOT; WAVE VIBRATOR.

Geophysical exploration permit

A permit executed by the owner authorizing mineral exploration by the use of a seismograph and other geophysical and geological methods upon certain described land. Also, a permit issued by a governmental agency (where required) authorizing use of public roads in conducting geophysical exploration.

Geophysical survey

The accurate measurement and recording of certain physical quantities in the outer rock shell of the earth, the object being to learn the nature and contour of underground geological structures. The principal methods are:

(1) Seismic, in which the rate of transmission of shock waves through the earth is measured and recorded by a seismograph. The waves are produced by exploding charges of dynamite in shallow holes drilled for this purpose. Upon striking rock formations, the waves are reflected back to the seismograph. The time lapse is a measure of the depth of the formation. The rate at which the waves are transmitted varies with the medium through which they pass. Seismic surveys may be either reflection or refraction surveys, the former type generally giving a better detail picture and the latter a better overall picture.

(2) Gravity, which measures the intensity of gravity at different points on the earth's surface. Gravity-meters can detect variations of one-one hundred millionth of the total force of gravity. Since salt is lighter than the rocks above it, the force of gravity is slightly less over a salt dome. In anticlines, the force of gravity is slightly greater over the top of the anticline because the denser basement rocks are nearer the surface. Faults may be detected because the force of gravity is slightly greater on one side of a fault, the denser rocks being closer to the surface there.

(3) Magnetic, which measures the magnetic intensity of the earth's field at different points by use of a magnetometer to obtain data regarding the structure of the earth's crust. This method is employed principally in conjunction with other more precise methods of prospecting.

(4) Electrical, which measures the electrical resistance of the earth from place to place. Since oil is a nonconductor of electricity, an abnormally high resistance may indicate its presence. This method is effective only in the instance of relatively shallow pools of oil.

(5) Geochemical or "halo" method, which analyzes a series of soil samples gathered with an auger for their hydrocarbon and mineral

content. Plotting the high values in such samples reveals possible petroleum deposits if lines connecting the points form a pattern such as an aureole or halo.

See Yarbro, "Geological and Geophysical Exploration," *P–H Oil and Gas Taxes* ¶ 2009.1 (1978).

See also VIBROSIS.

Geophysical trespass

The wrongful entry on land for the purposes of making a geophysical survey on the land.

Liability for entry poses no special legal problem, but the measure of damages does. Clearly the landowner can recover for injury done to the surface. But what can he recover for the unauthorized survey of the subsurface? Angelloz v. Humble Oil & Ref. Co., 196 La. 604, 199 So. 656 (1940), sustained a damage award under two theories of recovery: (1) value of the right to enter for geophysical survey purposes, and (2) loss of lease value from dissemination by the trespasser of unfavorable geophysical survey results. See Rice, "Wrongful Geophysical Exploration," 44 *Mont. L. Rev.* 53 (1983); Warner, "Oil and Gas: Recovery for Wrongful Geophysical Exploration—Catching Up With Technology," 23 *Washburn L.J.* 107 (1983) (arguing that liability should not depend upon physical trespass); Malone, "Ruminations on a New Tort," 4 *La. L. Rev.* 309 (1942); Hawkins, "The Geophysical Trespasser," 29 *Tex. L. Rev.* 310 (1951); Shine, "Measure of Damages in Suits Relating to Geophysical Operations," 29 *Notre Dame Law.* 49 (1953); TREATISE § 230.

Geopressured brine

Formation water, unusually hot and in some instances saturated with methane, contained under abnormally high pressure in some sedimentary rocks.

Georges Bank

An area of about 20,000 square miles of sea, well off Cape Cod, which has been the subject of considerable controversy among environmentalists, persons involved in the rich fishing industry of the area, oil companies interested in exploring for oil in the area, and governmental agencies charged with decisions on leasing of the OUTER CONTINENTAL SHELF (OCS) (*q.v.*). See MacLeish, *The Struggle for Georges Bank* (1985).

Geothermal energy

Energy derived from underground heat reservoirs.

Geothermal gradient

The change in temperature of the earth with depth, expressed either in degrees per unit depth, or in units of depth per degree. The mean rate of increase in temperature with depths in areas that are not adjacent to volcanic regions is about 1 degree F in about 55 feet corresponding to about 100 degrees F per mile of depth.

Geothermal resources

This term is defined by Cal. Pub. Resources Code § 6903 (1977) as "the natural heat of the earth, the energy, in whatever form, below the surface of the earth present in, resulting from, or created by, or which may be extracted from, such natural heat, and all minerals in solution or other products obtained from naturally heated fluids, brines, associated gases, and steam, in whatever form, found below the surface of the earth, but excluding oil, hydrocarbon gas or other hydrocarbon substances."

For discussions of these resources, see the following:

Lindsey and Supton, *Geothermal Energy—Legal Problems of Resource Development* (1976);

Kruger and Otte, *Geothermal Energy* (1973);

Martin, "The Geothermal Resources Act: A Case Study in Resource Management," 19 *U. of Brit. Col. L. Rev.* 1 (1985);

"Symposium on Development of Geothermal Resources,"14 *Nat. Res. L.* 589 (1982);

Sato and Crocker, "Property Rights to Geothermal Resources," 6 *Ecology L.Q.* 247 (1977);

Schlauch and Worcester, "Geothermal Resources: A Primer for the Practitioner," 9 *Land & Water L. Rev.* 327 (1974);

Geothermal Energy Research, Development, and Commercial Demonstration Act of 1973, Hearings before the House Committee on Energy of the Committee on Science and Astronautics, 93rd Cong., 2d Sess., on H.R. 11212 (1974);

Bjorge, "The Development of Geothermal Resources and the 1970 Geothermal Steam Act—Law in Search of Definition," 46 *U. Colo. L. Rev.* 1 (1974);

Eisenstat, "Tax Treatment of Exploring and Developing Geothermal Resources," 22 *Oil & Gas Tax Q.* 76 (1973);

Geothermal Resources, Hearing before the Subcommittee on Water and Power Resources of the Committee on Interior and Insular Affairs, U.S. Senate, 93rd Cong., 1st Sess., on The Potential for the Production of Power from Geothermal Resources (June 13, 1973);

Aidlin, "Representing the Geothermal Resources Client," 19 *Rocky Mt. Min. L. Inst.* 27 (1974);

Tompkins, *Power From the Earth: Geothermal Energy* (Institute of Governmental Studies, University of California, Berkeley, Public Policy Bibliographies, 1972);

"Legal Study of Geothermal Resources on Public Lands," in U.S. Public Land Law Review Commission, *Energy Fuel Mineral Resources of the Public Lands* (1970);

Bible, "The Geothermal Steam Act of 1970," 8 *Idaho L. Rev.* 86 (1971);

Olpin, "The Law of Geothermal Resources," 14 *Rocky Mt. Min. L. Inst.* 123 (1968);

Brooks, "Legal Problems of the Geothermal Industry," 6 *Nat. Res. J.* 511 (1966).

Geothermal steam

Steam produced by underground heat sources. For tax purposes it has been held that such steam is gas and is entitled to percentage depletion under the provision relating to "oil and gas well." Reich v. Commissioner, 454 F.2d 1157, 41 *O.&G.R.* 612 (9th Cir. 1972).

United States v. Union Oil Co. of Cal., 549 F.2d 1271; 55 *O.&G.R.* 425 (9th Cir. 1977), *cert. denied,* 434 U.S. 930 (1977), held that a reservation of "all coal and other minerals" in a patent under the Stock-Raising Homestead Act included geothermal steam and associated resources.

Geothermal Kinetics, Inc. v. Union Oil Co. of Cal., 75 Cal.App. 3d 56, 141 Cal. Rptr. 879, 58 *O.&G.R.* 22 (1977), held that a grant of minerals included geothermal resources, including steam therefrom.

Renewable Energy, Inc., 89 I.D. 496, 67 IBLA 304 (Sept. 30, 1982), held that a reservation of "all minerals" in a patent under section 8 of the Taylor Grazing Act embraced geothermal resources.

Pariani v. State, 105 Cal.App.3d 923, 164 Cal. Rptr. 683, 66 *O.&G.R.* 169 (1980), held that a reservation of "mineral deposits" included geothermal resources.

An opinion of the Solicitor of the Department of the Interior has ruled that (1) geothermal steam as defined in the Geothermal Steam Act of 1970 is not a "mineral" as that term is used in the mineral leasing laws, and (2) only lands in wilderness areas designated subsequent to the passage of the Steam Act of 1970 were available for geothermal leasing. Geothermal Leasing in Designated Wilderness Areas, 88 I.D. 813 (1981).

GFS(O&G)

Abbreviation of *Gower Federal Service - Oil and Gas,* a set of reports published by the Rocky Mountain Mineral Law Foundation containing decisions and opinions of the Interior Department relating to public lands.

GFS(OCS)

Abbreviation of *Gower Federal Service - Outer Continental Shelf,* a set of reports published by the Rocky Mountain Mineral Law Foundation containing decisions relating to the leasing and development of Outer Continental Shelf lands.

Ghost training

A term applied to a requirement imposed by a PETROLEUM INTERNATIONAL AGREEMENT (PIA) (*q.v.*) or CONCESSION (*q.v.*) that a national of the host country be assigned as a counterpart to each of certain expatriates employed by the international oil company. Blinn, Duval, Le Leuch, and Pertuzio, *International Petroleum Exploration & Exploitation Agreements* 155 (1986).

Giant field

A field having more than 100 million bbl. of recoverable oil or more than 1 Tcf of recoverable gas. Halbouty, "Giant Oil and Gas Fields in the United States," 52 *A.A.P.G. Bull.,* No. 7, pp. 1115–1151 (1978).

Gigajoule

One billion JOULE (*q.v.*)

Gilsonite

A trademark used to describe ASPHALTUM (*q.v.*) which is mined, marketed, or manufactured by or for American Gilsonite Company.

Gin pole

The top part of a derrick, containing four gin pole legs. The legs are lengths of angle iron welded to plates by which they are bolted to horizontal iron beams. When a derrick is complete the gin pole legs are interconnected with other parts of the structure and surmounted by a pyramid-shaped device which forms the top of the derrick. See International Derrick & Equipment Co. v. Croix, 241 F.2d 216, 7 *O.&G.R.* 1086 (5th Cir. 1957), *cert. denied,* 354 U.S. 910 (1957).

Girbitol process

A process by which sour gas is sweetened by the removal of hydrogen sulphide so that the gas may be taken by pipelines. See Shamrock Oil & Gas Corp. v. Comm'r, 35 T.C. 979, 13 *O.&G.R.* 1090 at 1130 (1961).

GLA

GAS LEASE AGREEMENT (*q.v.*); GAS LEASE-SALES AGREEMENT (GLA) (*q.v.*).

Global approach

A method employed by the Surface Rights Board of Alberta in calculating compensation payable by an operator for the right of entry on the lands of another. Under this approach the Board looks at *many* factors that must be considered, all of them interrelated. See Markovich Bros. Farming Co. Ltd. v. PanCanadian Petroleum Ltd., [1984] 3 W.W.R. 416 (Alta. Q.B. 1984), in which the court adopted this approach rather than the so-called FOUR HEADS APPROACH (*q.v.*).

See also Barton, "Controversy in Surface Rights Compensation: Pattern of Dealings Evidence and Global Awards," 24 *Alberta L. Rev.* 34 (1985).

Global settlement

The term applied to a settlement by a major refiner with the Department of Energy designed to dispose of all federal oil price control-related allegations outstanding against the refiner. See *CCH, Energy Management* ¶ 0291 (Nov. 23, 1981), reporting certain details of the settlement made by DOE with Chevron, the fifteenth major refiner (out of the top 35) to enter into such a settlement.

Glycol dehydrator

A facility for the removal of small particles of water called "mist" which may not have been previously removed from natural gas by separators. The removal of mist prevents water collecting in low points downstream between the dehydrator and the compressor station. Continental Oil Co. v. Federal Power Comm'n, 247 F.2d 904, 7 *O.&G.R.* 1534 (5th Cir. 1957).

See also DEHYDRATION PLANT.

GMOR

A guaranteed minimum overriding royalty. See True v. United States, 629 F.Supp. 881, 89 *O.&G.R.* 215 (D. Wyo. 1986).

GNP implicit price deflator

This term is defined by Section 101 of the NATURAL GAS POLICY ACT OF 1978 (*q.v.*), Pub. L. No. 95–621, as the implicit price deflator, seasonally adjusted, for the gross national product, as computed and published by the Department of Commerce for the calendar quarter involved.

GOCO

The acronym for a government-owned, contractor-operated commercial demonstration project.

Go-devil

(1) A PIG (*q.v.*) used to clean a pipeline.

(2) A ball or other missile dropped down a well to detonate an explosive device or to initiate the operation of a down hole tool.

Gold standard adjustment

An adjustment made by the examiner and rejected by the Commission in the Permian Basin Area Rate Proceeding, reflecting the fact that much of the gas in the Basin was of less than pipeline quality, to give a premium for pipeline quality gas. Permian Basin Area Rate Proceeding, 34 F.P.C. 159 at 207, 23 *O.&G.R.* 103 at 155 (Opinion No. 468, Aug. 5, 1965), *remanded,* Skelly Oil Co. v. Federal Power Comm'n, 375 F.2d 6, 26 *O.&G.R.* 237 (10th Cir. 1967), *aff'd in part and rev'd in part sub nom. In re* Permian Basin Area Rate Cases, 390 U.S. 747, 28 *O.&G.R.* 689 (1968).

Go-no-go decision

A colloquialism for the right of a nonoperating working interest owner to elect whether to join in a particular phase of exploration/development. Frontier Exploration, Inc. v. Blocker Exploration Co., 14 *Colo. Law.* 1448 (Colo. App. 1985).

Good faith claimant

As defined by Texas Nat. Res. Code § 51.172 (1978) for purposes of the statute dealing with sale or leases of a VACANCY (*q.v.*), the terms "good faith claimant" and "claimant" mean any person:

"(A) who occupies or uses or has previously occupied or used or whose predecessors in interest have occupied or used a vacancy for purposes other than exploring for or removing oil, gas, sulphur, or other minerals from the vacancy; and

"(B) who has himself or whose predecessors in interest had the vacancy enclosed or within definite recognized boundaries and in possession for a period of 10 years with a good faith belief that the vacancy was included inside the boundaries of the survey or surveys that were previously titled, awarded, or sold under circumstances that would have vested title in the vacancy if it were actually located within the boundaries of the survey or surveys whose boundaries are recognized boundaries in the community."

Good faith clause

(1) A lease clause providing that the judgment of the lessee, when not fraudulently exercised, in carrying out the purposes of the lease shall be conclusive. The purpose of the clause is to substitute good faith of the lessee for the standard of the reasonably prudent operator in the adjudication of controversies concerning the performance of the express and implied duties of the lessee. See Merrill, "Lease Clauses Affecting Implied Covenants," 2 *Sw. Legal Fdn. Oil & Gas Inst.* 141 at 187 (1951).

(2) Also, a lease clause providing in substance as follows:

"If lessee shall, in good faith and with reasonable diligence, attempt to pay any rental, but shall fail to pay or incorrectly pay some portion thereof, this lease shall not terminate unless lessee, within thirty days after written notice of its error or failure, shall fail to rectify the same."

This clause was held to be valid and effective in Woolley v. Standard Oil Co., 230 F.2d 97, 5 *O.&G.R.* 1394 (5th Cir. 1956). It has been urged, however, that the clause is invalid because it is repugnant to and inconsistent with the provisions of the delay rental clause of an Unless lease. The limited authority on the question is collected in Discussion Notes, 5 *O.&G.R.* 1402 (1956). See TREATISE §§ 605.2, 605.6, 606.6, 682.1.

See also DEFAULT CLAUSE; JUDICIAL ASCERTAINMENT CLAUSE; NOTICE AND DEMAND CLAUSE.

Good faith negotiation rule

A rule adopted by the Federal Energy Regulatory Commission (FERC) granting producers the right to abandon a gas purchase and sale contract if the producer seeks a higher price for its gas, is unable to reach an agreement with the purchaser on a price, and can find another purchaser. 18 CFR § 270.201 (1986). 14 *BNA's Energy Report* 465 at 514 (1986).

See also FEDERAL POWER COMMISSION.

Good faith pooling

The exercise of the right to pool given by a pooling clause of an oil and gas lease in good faith and for the purpose of promoting mineral development and not for some ulterior purpose beneficial solely to the lessee. See Diggs v. Cities Service Oil Co., 241 F.2d 425, 7 *O.&G.R.* 827 (10th Cir. 1957).

Good faith trespasser

An operator who enters upon the land of another without authority but in good faith. If such a person drills and secures production, he is liable to the true owner for the value of the oil produced, less reasonable drilling and operating costs. The allowance of this credit is usually determined by the benefit conferred upon the true owner, not the expenses incurred by the operator. For some of the factors that influence the determination of the good or bad faith of a trespasser, see BAD FAITH TRESPASSER. See TREATISE §§ 226–226.3.

See also SUBSURFACE TRESPASS.

Good oil field practice

A term occasionally used to indicate that operations are carried out in a proper and workmanlike manner. It has been used in the same way as the phrase "everything is A.P.I.," which refers to the American Petroleum Institute's set of standards covering aspects of petroleum operations. See The Parliament of the Commonwealth of

Australia, *Report from the Senate Select Committee on Off-Shore Petroleum Resources* 613 (1971).

Good production practice (GPP)

Production of crude oil or raw gas at a rate not governed by a base allowable, but limited to what can be produced without adversely and significantly affecting conservation, the prevention of waste, or the opportunity of each owner in the pool to obtain his share of production. Alberta Oil and Gas Conservation Regulations (Alta. Reg. 151/71) § 1–120 (2) 9.

See also MAXIMUM RATE LIMITATION.

GOR

GAS-OIL RATIO.

Governing law clause

CHOICE OF LAW CLAUSE (*q.v.*).

Governmental interest

See QUALIFIED GOVERNMENTAL INTEREST.

Governmental price escalator clause

An ESCALATOR CLAUSE (*q.v.*) in a GAS PURCHASE CONTRACT (*q.v.*) providing that if a governmental authority fixes a price for any natural gas that is higher than the price specified in the contract, the contract price shall be increased to that level. Energy Reserves Group, Inc. v. Kansas Power & Light Co., 459 U.S. 400, 103 S. Ct. 697 at 701, 76 *O.&G.R.* 593 at 598 (1983).

See also FPC CLAUSE.

Government take

This term is used to encompass the total revenue (including royalties, taxation, and government participation) generated for the government from oil production. See Dam, *Oil Resources* 131 (1976).

See also CONCESSION.

GPM

Gallons of gasoline per thousand cubic feet of gas.

GPP

GOOD PRODUCTION PRACTICE (*q.v.*).

Grandfather certificate

A certificate of convenience and necessity issued by virtue of the GRANDFATHER CLAUSE (*q.v.*) of the Natural Gas Act.

Grandfather clause

(1) The clause added to the Natural Gas Act, 15 U.S.C. § 717 *et seq.* in 1942 relating to the issuance of certificates of convenience and necessity to companies engaged on the effective date of the amendment in the transportation of gas subject to the jurisdiction of the Commission. The amendment to Section 7 (c) prohibited all gas companies from engaging in the transportation or sale of natural gas subject to the jurisdiction of the Commission "unless there is in force with respect to such natural gas companies a certificate of public convenience and necessity issued by the Commission authorizing such acts or operations." The grandfather clause of the amendment provided that as to companies so engaged on the effective date of the amendment the Commission would issue certificates for the particular route or routes without further proof of public convenience and necessity if applied for within ninety days after the effective date of the amendatory Act. J. M. Huber Corp. v. Federal Power Comm'n, 236 F.2d 550, 6 *O.&G.R.* 519 (3d Cir. 1956), *cert. denied,* 352 U.S. 971, 6 *O.&G.R.* 1407 (1957).

See also FEDERAL POWER COMMISSION.

(2) "The continuation of a former rule, clause or policy (usually in a contractual agreement) where a change to a new rule or policy would be patently unfair to those covered by the former." American Gas Ass'n, *Glossary for the Gas Industry* (3d ed. 1981).

Grandfather price

The price being charged on June 7, 1954 under a contract for the sale of gas which by virtue of Phillips Petroleum Co. v. Wisconsin, 347 U.S. 672, 3 *O.&G.R.* 745 (1945), was subjected to Federal Power Comm'n jurisdiction. By its Order 174, the FPC treated operations existing on that date on a "grandfather" basis; producers were authorized to continue operations existing on that date. See Shannon, "Recent Developments Affecting Production, Transportation and Sale of Gas," 8 *Sw. Legal Fdn. Oil & Gas Inst.* 219 at 225 *et seq.* (1957).

Granting clause, lease

The lease clause containing the required words of grant to create an interest in the lessee. A typical granting clause provides as follows:

"Witnesseth: That the lessor, for and in consideration of $______ cash in hand paid, receipt of which is hereby acknowledged, and of the covenants and agreements hereinafter contained on the part of the lessee to be paid, kept and performed, has granted, demised, leased and let and by these presents does grant, demise, lease and let exclusively unto said lessee, with the exclusive right of mining, exploring by geophysical and other methods and operating for and producing therefrom oil and all gas of whatsoever nature or kind, and laying pipe lines, telephone and telegraph lines, housing and boarding employees, building tanks, power stations, gasoline plants, ponds, roadways, and structures thereon to produce, save, market and take care of said products and the exclusive surface and sub-surface rights and privileges related in any manner to any and all such operations and any and all other rights and privileges necessary, incident to, or convenient for the economical operation alone or conjointly with neighboring land for such purposes, all that certain tract or tracts of land situated in the County of ________, State of ________, described as follows, to wit: . . ."

See McRae, "Granting Clauses in Oil and Gas Leases: Including Mother Hubbard Clauses," 2 *Sw. Legal Fdn. Oil & Gas Inst.* 43 (1951); TREATISE §§ 665–666.2

Gravel packing

Creating a cavity about a well bore where it passes through reservoir rock and surrounding the perforated liner of the well with a body of gravel or corase sand. This helps to prevent sand incursion or caving, and to reduce resistance offered to the flow of fluid into the well.

Graveyard tour

The midnight to 8:00 a.m. work shift in the oil fields. ("Tour" is pronounced to rhyme with "hour" or "tower.") *API Quarterly* 3 (Spring 1957). See DRILLER; TOUR.

Gravitational force

Energy derived from the force of gravity for production of oil. Only where the permeability of the reservoir rock is high and the structure dips sufficiently, or the reservoir rock is thick, does gravity become active enough to furnish the dominant driving force for production. See Interstate Oil Compact Commission, *Oil for Today and for Tomorrow* 21 (1953).

See also RESERVOIR ENERGY.

Gravitational segregation

Separation of water from oil and of heavier hydrocarbons from lighter hydrocarbons by the force of gravity, either in the producing horizon or by gravity separators after production. The stratification of gas, oil and water according to their densities.

Gravity, API

See API GRAVITY; TRAP TEST.

Gravity differential

A DIFFERENTIAL (*q.v.*) in the price of oil from a given source from the MARKER PRICE (*q.v.*) of BENCHMARK CRUDE (*q.v.*) based upon the relative gravity of the crude in question and that of benchmark crude. "The 'gravity' differential is about 10 cents per barrel per degree of API gravity." Danielsen, *The Evolution of OPEC* 65 (1982).

Gravity meter

A geophysical device which measures the gravitational pull of rocks. The composition of rocks affects their gravitational pull—the less compacted the rock, the less its pull. From such data, geophysicists may be able to locate faults or other reservoir traps.

See also GEOPHYSICAL EXPLORATION; GEOPHYSICAL SURVEY; TORSION BALANCE.

Gravity structure

A deep water structure built of reinforced concrete, steel, or a combination thereof which relies on gravity for stability on the sea bed. These structures may be used for drilling, production and storage.

Gravity survey

A method, using a gravity instrument, to detect variations in the gravitational pull of rocks in the subsurface. Variations or anomalies are contoured on a map and give evidence of geologic structures. American Gas Association Bureau of Statistics, *Glossary for the Gas Industry* 27.

See also GEOPHYSICAL SURVEY.

Gravity temperature correction table

A table for conversion of the measured volume of crude oil of a known gravity and temperature to its volume at sixty degrees Fahrenheit. See Hardwicke, *The Oilman's Barrel* 95 (1958).

Green book

In the United Kingdom this term refers to the Memorandum on the Control of Mineral Working (2d ed. 1960). J. Salter, *U.K. Onshore Oil and Gas Law* 5-001 (1986).

Green oil

A PARAFFIN BASE OIL (*q.v.*), as distinguished from an ASPHALT BASE OIL (*q.v.*), known as black oil. See Ball, Ball, and Turner, *This Fascinating Oil Business* 210 (2d Ed. 1965).

GRI

GAS RESEARCH INSTITUTE (*q.v.*).

Griefstem

A heavy square pipe working through a square hole in the rotary table which rotates the drill stem in rotary drilling. Also called the Kelly bar or Kelly joint.

Gross production tax

See PRODUCTION TAX.

Gross products tax

See PRODUCTION TAX.

Gross royalty

A term sometimes used to describe LANDOWNER ROYALTY (*q.v.*).

Gross royalty trust agreement

A trust agreement, binding the royalty on minerals recovered from described premises, entered into to facilitate the sale of smaller components of the royalty, the recording of subsequent sales thereof, and the receipt and disbursement of proceeds resulting from production of the leased substances attributable to the royalty. The agreement may be entered into before or after leasing of the affected premises. See, *e.g.*, Voyager Petroleums Ltd. v. Vanguard Petroleums Ltd., [1982] 2 W.W.R. 36 (Alta. Q.B. 1982), *appeal dism'd*, 149 D.L.R. 3rd 417, [1983] 5 W.W.R. 622 (Alta. Ct. of App. 1983).

See also ROYALTY TRUST.

Gross value

"The value of petroleum at the well produced and saved, without deduction for expense of production." See Smith-Hurd Ill. Rev. Stat., chapter 96 1/2 § 5001(5)(1979); Burns Ind. Stat. § 14–4–3–1(5)(Code Ed. 1973).

Group shoot

Geophysical exploration on a cost sharing basis by several oil companies. Energy Data Requirements of the Federal Government (Part III—Federal Offshore Oil and Gas Leasing Policies), Hearings before the Subcommittee on Activities of Regulatory Agencies of the Permanent Select Committee on Small Business, House of Representatives, 93rd Cong., 2d Sess. (1974) at p. 363.

See also GEOPHYSICAL EXPLORATION; SPEC SHOOT.

Grub stake agreement

Agreement whereby one party undertakes to prospect for minerals and agrees to yield to the other, who furnishes money or supplies for the enterprise, a certain proportionate interest in any minerals discovered. These agreements are fairly common in the case of prospecting for solid minerals but are rarely used in prospecting for oil or gas. Occasionally an agreement is found to be a grub stake agreement rather than a MINING PARTNERSHIP (*q.v.*). See Gillespie v. Shufflin, 91 Okla. 72, 216 Pac. 132 (1923); TREATISE § 436.

GSA

Geological Society of America.

Guaranteed royalty payment

(1) A minimum cash payment to be made to the lessor by the lessee in the event of production when the fractional or percentage royalty payable under the lease does not equal a specified sum. See Cherokee Resources, Inc. v. Gold Energy Corp., 11 Kan. App.2d 436, 724 P.2d 695, 90 *O.&G.R.* 223 (1986) (holding that, where the leasehold interest had been divided by partial assignment, the burden of the obligation to pay the difference between the royalty on actual production and the guaranteed minimum royalty while the lease was held by production was apportioned among the leaseholders in proportion to their percentage of the total acreage in the lease); TREATISE § 644.10.

(2) The term applied to the payment to be made by working interest owners to owners of royalty interests in a fixed amount for a specified period of years in lieu of the otherwise payable fractional or percentage royalty based on value or proceeds of production. For an example of an agreement for a guaranteed royalty payment, see Schlipf v. Exxon Corp., 626 S.W.2d 74, (Tex. Civ. App. 1981), *error ref'd n.r.e.*, 644 S.W.2d 453 (Tex. 1982) (setting aside summary judgment of constructive trust for royalty owners based on unjust enrichment and, in effect, sustaining the validity of the agreement for the guaranteed royalty payment).

Guaranteed sales price

In certain development contracts the host country guarantees to the contracting oil company the right to purchase a specified percentage of the production of crude oil at a price (called guaranteed sales price) calculated in the manner specified in the contract. See *e.g.*, Articles 21 and 28 of the INOC-ERAP contract in OPEC, *Selected Documents of the International Petroleum Industry* 1968 at p. 107.

See also POSTED PRICE.

Gulf Coast clause

(1) A provision in a DRILLING CONTRACT (*q.v.*) providing for a change from a footage rate of pay to a day work scale under certain conditions which render drilling abnormally difficult or hazardous. See Buster Gardner Drilling Co. v. Associated Oil & Gas Explora-

tion, Inc., 214 So. 2d 267 at 270, 32 *O.&G.R.* 169 at 172 (La. App. 1968), *writ refused,* 253 La. 59, 216 So. 2d 306 (1968), for an example of this clause.

(2) A so-called standard TURNKEY CONTRACT (*q.v.*) contains a clause, "commonly called a Gulf Coast Clause, which allows the operator 'outs' to cease drilling if certain specified unfavorable conditions are reached. Among the conditions usually specified in a Gulf Coast Clause are high or low pressure, impenetrable subsurface formations, loss of mud circulation, and salt." Brountas v. Commissioner, 73 T.C. 491 at 497 (1979), 74 T.C. 1062, 67 *O.&G.R.* 477 (1980), *vacated and remanded,* 692 F.2d 152, 75 *O.&G.R.* 193 (1st Cir. 1982), *cert. denied,* 462 U.S. 1106, 103 S.Ct. 2453 (1983). A so-called "no-out" contract does not contain such a clause.

Gulf Cooperation Council (GCC)

An organization comprised of Saudi Arabia, the United Arab Emirates, Kuwait, Bahrain, Qater, and Oman. CCH, *Energy Management* (Issue No. 739, March 17, 1987). See also Yorke and Turner, *European Interests and Gulf Oil 42* (1986).

Gulf-plus pricing structure

A pricing structure which was employed when the United States Gulf and the Caribbean were the foreign world's primary sources of crude oil, "Crude oil produced in the Eastern Hemisphere was priced to meet U.S. crude oils delivered into foreign markets. At any given point in the Eastern Hemisphere, the price of oil approximated the price at the United States Gulf *plus* tanker rates from there to the point of delivery, irrespective of the actual origin of the oil." Jacoby, *Multinational Oil* 220 (1974); Chester, *United States Oil Policy and Diplomacy* 14 (1983).

See also BASE POINT PRICING; BASING POINT; EQUALIZATION POINT; MULTIPLE BASE-POINT SYSTEM; PERSIAN GULF PRICING SYSTEM; PHANTOM FREIGHT; SINGLE BASE-POINT SYSTEM.

Gun barrel

A settling tank in which oil floats to the top and salt water is removed from the bottom and diverted. Phoenix v. Graham, 349 Ill. App. 326, 110 N.E.2d 669, 2 *O.&G.R.* 325 (1953).

Gun perforation

PERFORATION (*q.v.*) of casing cemented in place in the well by a tool lowered into the hole to fire steel projectiles through the casing and into the formation in order to provide holes through which the well fluids may flow.

See also JET PERFORATION; PERFORATION.

GUPCO

Gulf of Suez Petroleum Co.

Gusher

An oil well that comes in with such great pressure that the oil flows out of the well head and into the air, somewhat like a geyser. Such wells used to be commonplace, but with improved drilling methods, notably the use of drilling mud, gushers are a rarity today. Gushers were particularly prevalent in gas cap fields, where enormous pressures are encountered.

Gusher letter

A colloquialism employed to describe a letter sent to participants in a drilling program to announce the discovery of oil or gas in paying quantities. See Heberer v. Commissioner, T.C. Memo. 1974–139, 48 *O.&G.R.* 403 (1974).

. . H . .

Habendum clause

The clause in a deed or lease setting forth the duration of the grantee's or lessee's interest in the premises. A typical habendum clause in an UNLESS LEASE (*q.v.*) provides as follows:

"It is agreed that this lease shall remain in force for a term of ten years from date and as long thereafter as oil, or gas, of whatsoever nature or kind, or either of them is produced from said land or drilling operations are continued as hereinafter provided."

The ten-year period specified in this clause is the so-called "primary term" of the lease. See TREATISE §§ 334–334.10, 603–604.12.

Hadlick's tripod theory

A theory that the petroleum industry is a monopoly which rests on a tripod, the legs of which are the proration laws of the oil producing states, the Federal government in the form of legislation, and the large companies and oil producers. See Zimmermann, *Conservation in the Production of Petroleum* 5 (1957).

Halbouty concept

The name given to a lease bidding proposal of Michel T. Halbouty under which a successful bonus bid would not be paid immediately but would become an obligation of the lessee to spend that sum on exploration and development of the lease. If less were spent for those purposes, the lessee would pay the difference to the lessor; if more were spent, the lessee would have no further obligation to the lessor except for royalties. Claimed advantages are encouragement of competition for leases, more thorough exploration and more discoveries, an ultimately larger yield to the lessor while saving interest on the delayed payment of the bonus. See McDonald, *The Leasing of Federal Lands for Fossil Fuels Production* 109 (1979) (arguing that these alleged advantages will not be realized).

See also LEASE BIDDING SYSTEMS.

Half and half plan

A plan devised by the Council on Environmental Quality to conserve energy and meet the needs of a growing economy. The program—half growth and half conservation—was based on growth in net per capita energy consumption of O.7 percent per year and on a continuing conservation effort which would, through improved efficiency and elimination of waste, save energy at a rate of O.7 percent per year. *The Fifth Annual Report of the Council on Environmental Quality* 475 (1974).

Hard rock minerals

Solid minerals, as distinguished from oil and gas, especially those solid minerals found in hard rocks.

Hardship clause

See ADAPTATION CLAUSE.

Hardship provision

A provision of a PETROLEUM INTERNATIONAL AGREEMENT (PIA) (*q.v.*) or CONCESSION (*q.v.*) dealing with the unexpected upsetting of circumstances causing a fundamental alteration in the economics of the agreement. Such a provision is extremely complex and deals with the determination of the events which may trigger the readjustment process and the establishment of an appropriate procedure for the adaptation of the relationship to new circumstances. See Blinn, Duval, Le Leuch, and Pertuzio, *International Petroleum Exploration & Exploitation Agreements* ch. 16 (1986).

Hawkins case

A term applied to Railroad Comm'n v. Humble Oil & Ref. Co., 193 S.W.2d 824 (Tex. Civ. App. 1946, error ref'd n.r.e.).

HBP

Abbreviation for "held by production," *viz,* acreage under lease which is continued in effect beyond the expiration of the primary term by production.

HC

Abbreviation for HOST COUNTRY.

Head

The differential of pressure causing flow in a fluid system, usually expressed in terms of the height of a liquid column that the pressure will support. Also, the differential across a primary measuring device in feet of flowing fluid. American Gas Association Bureau of Statistics, *Glossary for the Gas Industry* 28.

Headache post

A timber set under the walking beam to prevent it from falling on members of the drilling crew when it is disconnected. (Some say its purpose is to give the driller a place to rest his head when slow progress or other worries cause his head to ache.) *API Quarterly* 3 (Spring 1957). See DRILLING RIG.

Heading

An unsteady flow of oil from an oil well.

Heading may be due to a lack of gas which causes the well to "load up with fluid." It may be due to a lack of oil which causes gas to flow through, increasing the gas-oil ratio. When heading is due to a lack of gas, remedial work usually involves the installation of a packer on the tubing, and many operators install "kick-off" or differential flow valves on the tubing line at this time. By means of the packer, the well is restored to steady flow for a period after which gas lift begins, using the flow valves to attain economical use of input gas. Usually dry gas, the residue after extraction of casinghead gasoline, is compressed and introduced into the well at the casinghead so that the gas enters the annular space between the casing and tubing. The automatic differential valves permit the input gas to enter the tubing, thus lightening the oil column enough to permit the well to flow steadily. *Syn.:* Flow by heads.

See also INTERMITTENT FLOW.

Headright

(1) The term used to describe the right of a member of the Osage Tribe of Indians to a share of the distributable income from minerals plus a reversionary title to a like share of minerals on the expiration of the mineral trust established under the Osage Allotment Act of June 28, 1906, 34 Stat. 539. See Rev. Rul. 70-116 (headright income of a non-competent Osage Indian is not includible in his gross income); Rev. Rul. 77-78 (headright income received by competent Osage Indian is includible in gross income).

The right of a member of an Indian tribe to participate in the income derived from the production of oil and gas and other minerals from lands in which the tribe owns mineral rights. Bell v. Phillips Petroleum Co., 641 P.2d 1115, 72 *O.&G.R.* 314 (Okla. 1982):

"In defining a headright the court in *Globe Indemnity Co. v. Bruce,* 81 F.2d 143 [10th Cir. 1935] said that it is 'the right to receive the trust funds and mineral interest at the end of the trust period, and during that period to participate in the distribution of bonuses and royalties accruing from the mineral estates and the interest on the trust funds.' "

(2) A term which has been employed to describe an undivided interest in minerals transferred to a Royalty trust (*q.v.*). See Shaffer v. Kansas Farmers Union Royalty Co., 146 Kan. 84, 69 P.2d 4 at 6 (1937), *appeal dism'd,* 303 U.S. 623 (1938).

Head well

A well that makes its best production by intermittent pumping or flowing. 30 C.F.R. § 221.49 (e) (1980).

Heater

A piece of equipment often necessary on high pressure gas and distillate wells and especially in cold weather to prevent hydrates from forming which would hinder the operation of a separator. Matters of Continental Oil Co., 16 F.P.C. 1, 6 *O.&G.R.* 750 at 764 (1956).

See also Bottom hole heater.

Heater-treater

A tall, cylindrically shaped upright unit connected to a tank battery serving producing wells, commonly used in oilfield production processes in order to separate water and other foreign substances from the crude oil. At the bottom of the heater-treater is an automatic gas burner that heats the oil; as the temperature of the oil increases, the water and other contaminants separate from the oil and drop to the bottom of the heater. The contaminants are discharged from the heater-treater and the crude oil, without contaminants, is put into the production tank. Hartford Accident & Indemnity Co. v. Champion Chemicals, Inc., 420 So. 2d 1282 (La. App. 1982).

See also Basic sediment; Dehydration plant; Treatment plant.

Heating oil

Oil used for residential heating. See Distillate fuel oil.

Heavy fuel oil

A refinery residue after the desirable marketable products such as gasoline, kerosene, lubricating oils, wax and distillate fuel oil have been extracted from the crude. See Zimmermann, *Conservation in the Production of Petroleum* 355 (1957).

Heavy oil

For purposes of the CRUDE OIL WINDFALL PROFIT TAX ACT OF 1980 (*q.v.*.), this term "means all crude oil which is produced from a property if crude oil produced and sold from such property during—

"(A) the last month before July 1979 in which crude oil was produced and sold from the property, or

"(B) the taxable period, had a weighted average gravity of 17 degrees API or less (corrected to 60 degrees Fahrenheit)." Internal Revenue Code § 4991.

For purposes of price relief by the Department of Energy and its predecessors during the 1971–81 period of price controls, heavy oil was defined as any petroleum resource that is less than 20 degrees API gravity.

As API gravity approaches the range of 10 to 12 degrees, heavy oil deposits are frequently referred to as "tar sand" and "bitumen." See Trimble and Birdwell, "Potential and Future of Heavy Oil," 19 *Sw. Legal Fdn. Exploration and Economics of the Petroleum Industry* 387 (1980).

See also DILUENT; PETROLEUM TAR SANDS.

Hectare

In the metric system, a hectare is the land measure unit for ten thousand square meters. One hectare is the equivalent of 2.471 acres.

HEGF

HIGH-ENERGY GAS FRACTURING (*q.v.*).

Held by production

(1) A leasehold kept in force by virtue of production in paying quantities.

(2) Acreage which participates in the production upon a royalty basis and does not receive delay rentals.

Helex plant

A plant designed to extract crude helium from helium-rich natural gas. Leftwich, "The Workback Method of Valuing Raw Materials: The Helium Cases," 35 *O.&G. Tax Q.* 292 (1986).

Helium

A colorless, odorless, and inert gas. Northern Natural Gas Co. v. Grounds, 441 F.2d 704, 39 *O.&G.R.* 574 (10th Cir. 1971), *cert. denied,* 404 U.S. 951 (1971), held that references in leases and gas purchase contracts to gas or natural gas applied to the entire gas stream absent express reservation of any constituent elements, and helium passed thereunder unless expressly reserved. *Grounds* is discussed in Stucky, "Current Developments and Views Concerning Rights and Status of Landowner-Lessors," 21 *Sw. Legal Fdn. Oil & Gas Inst.* 83 at 102 (1970). See also TREATISE § 219 notes 1, 10.1.

In Northern Natural Gas Co. v. Grounds, 393 F.Supp. 949, 51 *O.&G.R.* 453 (D. Kan. 1974), the court determined the reasonable value of helium in the natural gas stream and held that a royalty of 50% was a reasonable measure of the landowners' contribution. The case contains a detailed discussion of the process by which "commingled helium" is extracted from "helium bearing natural gas" to produce "crude helium" from which, after further extraction of the nitrogen content of the mix, "Grade A helium" with a 99.995% to 99.997% helium content, may be produced for distribution and sale to the ultimate consumer.

The entitlement of royalty owners and sellers of natural gas to a share of the value of helium removed from gas delivered to a purchaser under a gas purchase contract has been the subject of substantial litigation. See Ashland Oil, Inc. v. Phillips Petroleum Co., 364 F.Supp. 6, 46 *O.&G.R.* 451 (N.D. Okla. 1973), *aff'd in part, rev'd and remanded in part,* 554 F.2d 381, 57 *O.&G.R.* 390 (10th Cir. 1977), *cert. denied,* 434 U.S. 921, *reh. denied,* 434 U.S. 988 (1977), *on remand,* 463 F.Supp. 619, 62 *O.&G.R.* 483 (N.D. Okla. 1978), *aff'd in part and rev'd in part,* 607 F.2d 335, 64 *O.&G.R.* 332 (10th Cir. 1979), *cert. denied,* 446 U.S. 936 (1980); Texaco Inc. v. Phillips Petroleum Co., 481 F.2d 70, 46 *O.&G.R.* 339 (10th Cir. 1973), *rev'd and remanded,* 415 U.S. 125, 47 *O.&G.R.* 348 (1974).

After several trips back and forth from the district court to the Supreme Court via the Court of Appeals for the Tenth Circuit, appeals from the Northern District of Oklahoma in Ashland Oil, Inc. v. Phillips Petroleum Co., and from the District of Kansas in Northern Natural Gas Co. v. Grounds, were consolidated, and the Court of Appeals held that the district court had erred in failing to employ the "work back" method for computing the value of the helium content of processed natural gas. Northern Natural Gas Co. v. Grounds, 666 F.2d 1279, 72*O.&G.R.* 531 (10th Cir. 1981), *cert. denied,* 457 U.S. 1126 (1982).

See also Hood, "Oil and Gas: Helium—Is It Covered by an Oil and Gas Lease in Oklahoma?," 37 *Okla. L. Rev.* 809 (1984).

The requirement of an environmental impact statement prior to the cancellation of a contract for the purchase of helium is discussed in National Helium Corp. v. Morton, 486 F.2d 995, 47 *O.&G.R.* 1 (10th Cir. 1973), *cert. denied,* 416 U.S. 993 (1974).

Certain of the difficulties encountered in drafting appropriate royalty provisions relating to helium are illustrated by Cline v. Angle, 216 Kan. 328, 532 P.2d 1093, 53 *O.&G.R.* 263 (1975).

For discussions of certain of the contemporary uses of helium and aspects of its conservation, see the following:

Leftwich, "The Workback Method of Valuing Raw Materials: The Helium Cases," 35 *O.&G. Tax Q.* 292 (1986);

Laverick, "Helium—Its Storage and Use in Future Years," 16 *IOCC Comm. Bull.* 64 (June 1974);

Price, "The Helium Conservation Program of the Department of the Interior," 1 *Environmental Affairs* 333 (1971).

See also REDUCTION WORKS.

Henze type proration order

A type of proration order taking its name from the Henze Field in DeWitt County, Texas, in which the order was first applied. See 4 *O.&G.R.* 1846, 7 *O.&G.R.* 525, 15 *O.&G.R.* 174. The Henze type order does not fix express allowables for gas wells in terms of cubic feet of gas but each well is assigned a participation factor, *viz.*, a fraction representing the well's fair share of total production of gas from the field. See Stayton, "Proration of Gas," 14 *Sw. Legal Fdn. Oil & Gas Inst.* 1 at 16 (1963). This method of allocation was held invalid in Rudman v. Railroad Comm'n, 162 Tex. 579, 349 S.W.2d 717, 15 *O.&G.R.* 174 (1961).

See also ALLOWABLE; PRORATIONING.

Hepburn Act

An act regulating interstate oil pipe lines as common carriers. 49 U.S.C.A., ch. 1.

Heptane

An hydrocarbon of the paraffin series. It is liquid at ordinary atmospheric conditions, although small amounts may be present in the gas associated with petroleum. See Interstate Oil Compact Commission, *Oil and Gas Production* 26 (1951).

Herndon-type carried interest

A form of CARRIED INTEREST (*q.v.*), deriving its name from Herndon Drilling Co., 6 T.C. 628 (1946). In this type of carried interest A, the owner of a lease, assigns a fractional interest in the lease to B, an assignee, and in addition assigns from the retained interest in the lease an oil payment measured by the operating expenses incurred by the assignee on behalf of the assignor. See Burke and Boyhay, *Income Taxation of Natural Resources* ¶ 15.18 (1981); Fielder, "The Option to Deduct Intangible Drilling and Development Costs." 33 *Texas L. Rev.* 825 at 840 (1955); TREATISE §§ 424–424.4.

Hexagonal pattern

A water-flood pattern.

See also SEVEN-SPOT PATTERN; WATER FLOODING.

Hexane

An hydrocarbon of the paraffin series. It is liquid at ordinary atmospheric conditions, although small amounts may be present in the gas associated with petroleum. See Interstate Oil Compact Commission, *Oil and Gas Production* 26 (1951).

High

A geological colloquialism designating the uppermost part of a structure, where there exists the greatest likelihood of discovery of petroleum.

High cost natural gas

This term is defined by Section 107 of the NATURAL GAS POLICY ACT OF 1978 (*q.v.*) (Pub. L. No. 95–62) as natural gas determined to be—

(1) produced from any well the surface drilling of which began on or after February 19, 1977, if such production is from a completion location which is located at a depth of more than 15,000 feet;

(2) produced from geopressured brine;

(3) occluded natural gas produced from coal seams;

(4) produced from Devonian shale; and

(5) produced under such other conditions as the Commission determines to present extraordinary risks or costs.

The Federal Energy Regulatory Commission has proposed to limit the maximum lawful price of high cost natural gas to ensure that the ceiling prices do not go above the COMMODITY VALUE OF NATURAL GAS (*q.v.*). FERC Dkt. No. RM 82-32-000, 18 C.F.R. Part 271, 24 FPS 3-1113 (Feb. 10, 1983).

High-energy gas fracturing (HEGF)

A rock-fracturing technique to increase flow of natural gas in Devonian shales and other rocks containing natural fractures. The technique depends on tailoring a pulse of high pressure in a wellbore so that multiple fractures are created which intersect natural fractures in the surrounding gas-bearing formation. Conventional HYDRAULIC FRACTURING (*q.v.*) tends to produce a single long fracture, usually parallel to any natural fractures in the rock. Failure of the fracture to intersect these natural fractures reduces the number of pathways by which gas can flow into the borehole. The pressure pulse in the borehole is generated from a burning propellant which produces high pressure combustion gases in periods of several thousandths of a second. Department of Energy, *Energy Insider* (Vol. 4, No. 10, p. 3, May 25, 1981).

See also FRACTURING.

High gas-oil ratio proration unit

A PRORATION UNIT (*q.v.*) with at least one producing oil well with a gas-oil ratio in excess of the limiting gas-oil ratio for the pool in which the unit is located. New Mexico Oil Conservation Comm'n, *Rules and Regulations* 3 (1958).

High pressure area

A field in which extraordinary reservoir pressures are encountered; for example, a CONDENSATE-GAS RESERVOIR (*q.v.*) usually has very high pressure, in excess of 2,000 pounds per square inch. In drilling in such a field precautions must be taken against blowouts. Negligence in preventing blowouts in a high pressure area may subject the operator to liability for the value of the oil, gas, and condensate drained from under the land of others and dissipated into the air from the blowout well. See Elliff v. Texon Drilling Co., 146 Tex.

575, 210 S.W.2d 558, 4 A.L.R.2d 191 (1948), noted, 27 *Tex. L. Rev.* 349 (1949).

High pressure gas injection

Injection of gas in quantities exceeding the volumes produced, in order to maintain reservoir pressure at or above that level necessary to achieve miscibility, a single phase state, between injected gas and reservoir oil. Smith, "The Engineering Aspect of Pressure Maintenance and Secondary Recovery Operations," 6 *Rocky Mt. Min. L. Inst.* 211 at 227 (1961).

See also SECONDARY RECOVERY.

High-priority user

This term is defined in Section 401 of the NATURAL GAS POLICY ACT OF 1978 (*q.v.*)(Pub. L. No. 95–621) as any person who—

(A) uses natural gas in a residence;

(B) uses natural gas in a commercial establishment in amounts of less than 50 Mcf on a peak day;

(C) uses natural gas in any school, hospital, or similar institution; or

(D) uses natural gas in any other way the curtailment of which the Secretary of Energy determines would endanger life, health, or maintenance of physical property.

High-volume system

A liquid petroleum pipeline system or a segment of a system which transports volumes in excess of 1000 BPH on a regular basis. Alberta Energy Resources Conservation Board Information Letter IL–PL 76–1 (Jan. 9, 1976).

See also INTERMEDIATE-VOLUME SYSTEM; LOW-VOLUME SYSTEM.

Hinshaw pipeline

A pipeline whose facilities are excluded from Federal Energy Regulatory Commission jurisdiction pursuant to section 1(c) [68 Stat 36 (Mar. 27, 1954)] of the NATURAL GAS ACT (*q.v.*). See Federal Energy Regulatory Commission Final Rule, Docket No. RM79–24, Order No. 63, issued January 3, 1980, "Certain Transportation, Sales and Assignments by Pipeline Companies not Subject to Commission Jurisdiction Under Section 1(c) of the Natural Gas Act."

See also PIPELINE.

Hispanoil

A Spanish National Petroleum Company. For a study of the company see International Bar Ass'n, 1 *Energy Law 1981* at p. 69.

History of well

A systematic written account of the drilling and operation of a well. The maintenance of such a history is required by statute or regulation in some states. In California, for example, it is required that an operator shall keep a history of the drilling of a well which "shall show the location and amount of sidetracked casings, tools, or other material, the depth and quantity of cement in cement plugs, the shots of dynamite or other explosives, and the results of production and other tests during drilling operations." Cal. Pub. Res. Code § 3213 (1972).

Hoffman clause

The SUBJECT-TO CLAUSE (*q.v.*) of deeds affecting premises subject to a lease. See TREATISE § 340.1, note 4.

Hoisting drum

See DRAW WORKS

Homestead

By law in many states, the residence of the heady of a family. State laws frequently forbid the sale or lease of such without joinder of both husband and wife. Moreover, sale of the homestead under execution or other legal process is often forbidden. See 1 *Am. Law of Prop.* § 5.75–5.120 (1952).

Horizon

A plane of stratification assumed to have been once horizontal and continuous. In paleontology, a stratum characterized by particular fossils. Also, a zone of a particular FORMATION (*q.v.*), such as the reservoir horizon, being that portion of a formation of sufficient porosity and permeability to form a petroleum reservoir.

See also PAY HORIZON.

Horizontal assignment

An assignment of an interest in the minerals above or below or between specified depths, or in a given stratum or horizon, *e.g.*, an assignment of the miernals in the Ellenberger formation, or an assignment of all minerals at a depth greater (or less) than 4000 feet beneath the surface.

See also ASSIGNMENT.

Horizontal cut oil payment

The assignment of a part of an OIL PAYMENT (*q.v.*), providing for a payout first to the assignee before the assignor receives payment. Thus if *A* owns an oil payment for the first $100,000 out of 1/8 of the 7/8 working interest, he may assign a horizontal cut oil payment to *B* by transferring the first $50,000 out of 1/8 of 7/8. See Burke and Bowhay, *Income Taxation of Natural Resources* § 5.01 (1980).

See also VERTICAL CUT OIL PAYMENT.

Horizontal drilling

An experimental natural gas production process whereby a well is drilled horizontally, rather than vertically, to penetrate a gas bearing formation. This method of drilling is more expensive than a vertical bore by perhaps 400 percent but an experimental horizontal well in West Virginia realized a sevenfold increase in production. CCH, *Energy Management* 3 (Issue No. 735, Feb. 17, 1987).

Horizontal severance

A conveyance of all, or some portion, of the minerals above or below or between specified depths, or in a given stratum or horizon, *e.g.*, a conveyance of the mienrals in the Ellenberger formation, or a conveyance of all minerals at a depth greater (or less) than 4000 feet beneath the surface.

See also PHASE SEVERANCE; SEVERANCE; VERTICAL SEVERANCE.

Hot fluid injection

A THERMAL METHOD OF OIL RECOVERY (*q.v.*) involving the direct injection of a hot fluid (water, gas, or steam) with the objective of increasing the flow of low gravity crude oil. See Nelson and McNiel, "Oil Recovery by Thermal Methods," 17 *Interstate Oil Compact Bull.* 56 at 60 (Dec. 1958).

See also SECONDARY RECOVERY; TERTIARY RECOVERY.

"Hot-footing" a well

Installation of heater at the bottom of an input well for purpose of increasing the flow of heavy crude oil from production wells. See THERMAL METHOD OF OIL RECOVERY.

Hot oil

(1) Illegal oil or gas; oil or gas produced from any well in excess of the amount allowed by a rule, regulation or order of the regulatory board or commission (*e.g.*, a proration order), as distinguished from oil or gas produced not in excess of the amount so allowed by a rule, regulation, or order, which is "legal" oil. The CONNALLY ACT (*q.v.*) was enacted to supplement state conservation laws by regulating the interstate transportation of petroleum and petroleum products produced in violation of such conservation laws.

(2) This term has also been applied to oil produced by a host country after confiscation of the assets of a foreign oil company. A number of actions have been brought by such oil companies seeking title to oil when removed from the host country to another country. See Muir, "The Changing Legal Framework of International Energy Management," 9 *Int'l. Law.* 605 at 609 (1975).

Hot Oil Act

See CONNALLY ACT.

Hot oil truck

(1) A truck with a tank into which oil is pumped and then heated for the purpose of melting paraffin in the flow lines.

(2) A truck used to transport HOT OIL (*q.v.*).

HPV

HYDROCARBON PORE VOLUME (*q.v.*).

Huff and puff

A synonym for the thermal recovery method known as STEAM STIMULATION (*q.v.*).

Hybrid platform

A GRAVITY STRUCTURE (*q.v.*) for deep water operations in which steel and concrete are used in its construction in roughly equal proportions.

Hydrafrac treatment

A method of inducing fractures in reservoir rock about producing wells by means of high pressures and the introduction of sand into the fractures, preventing their closing after the pressure is released. The purpose of the treatment is to improve the flow of oil into the well.

See also FRACTURING.

Hydraulic fracturing

A mechanical method of increasing the permeability of rock, and thus increasing the amount of oil or gas produced from it. The method employs hydraulic pressure to fracture the rock. It is extensively employed on limestone formations.

The experience in one state with hydraulic fracturing is summarized in Lytle, "Results of Stimulating the Oil and Gas Sands by Hydraulic Fracturing in Pennsylvania," 7 *IOCC Comm. Bull.* 17 (June 1965).

See also ACID FRACTURING; FRAC OIL; FRAC TANK; FRACTURING; HIGH-ENERGY GAS FRACTURING; PETROFRACTURING; SANDFRACING; TIGHT FORMATION.

Hydrocarbon

An organic chemical compound of hydrogen and carbon, called petroleum. The molecular structure of hydrocarbon compounds varies from the simplest, methane (CH_4), a constituent of natural gas, to the very heavy and very complex. Octane, a constituent of crude oil, is one of the heavier, more complex molecules (C_8H_{18}).

Hydrocarbon pore volume

The volume of oil and gas contained underground in the pores of the rock. Mobil Oil Corp. v. Exxon Corp., 177 Cal. App.3d 942, 223 Cal. Rptr. 392, 88 *O.&G.R.* 443 (1986).

Hydrocarbon solvent slug injection

A secondary recovery method. Miscibility between reservoir oil and injected fluids is obtained by first injecting a slug of intermediate hydrocarbons, usually propane and/or butane, into injection wells, and following the slug with gas injected into the same wells. See Smith, "The Engineering Aspects of Pressure Maintenance and Secondary Recovery Operations." 6 *Rocky Mt. Min. L. Inst.* 211 at 230 (1961).

See also SECONDARY RECOVERY.

Hydrocracking

Catalytic cracking of heavy hydrocarbons in the presence of hydrogen to produce lighter distillates and of light oils to produce liquids and gases.

See also CATALYTIC CRACKING; CRACKING; REFINER; THERMAL CRACKING; TOPPING PROCESS.

Hydrodynamics

The branch of science that deals with the cause and effect of regional subsurface fluid migration. See Brown. "Hydrodynamics in the Management of Natural Fluid Resources," 5 *IOCC Comm. Bull.* 19 (June 1963).

Hydroforming

A process in which naphthas are passed over a catalyst at elevated temperatures and moderate pressures, in the presence of added hydrogen or hydrogen-containing gases, to form high-octane motor fuel or aromatics.

Hydrogen sulphide

An odorous compound found in SOUR GAS (*q.v.*).

Hydrostatic pressure

Pressure exerted by a fluid at rest. In a WATER-DRIVE FIELD (*q.v.*) hydrostatic pressure may furnish the primary energy for production; if a continuous reservoir horizon outcrops some distance from the reservoir, it will act as a conduit through which water under a hydraulic head encroaches into the oil and gas zone as pressures are released.

Hypothetical reserves or resources

Undiscovered resources that may reasonably be expected to exist in a known mining district under known geologic conditions. Exploration that confirms their existence and reveals quantity and quality will permit their reclassification as RESERVES (*q.v.*) or as IDENTIFIED-SUBECONOMIC RESERVES OR RESOURCES (*q.v.*). 2 *OCS Oil and Gas—An Environmental Assessment,* A Report to the President by the Council on Environmental Quality (April 1974), at p. 12.

. . I . .

IADC

The International Association of Drilling Contractors.

IADC form

A drilling contract form prepared by the International Association of Drilling Contractors. For an example and discussion of the form see Hancock, "The Offshore Drilling Contract," *Rocky Mt. Min. L. Fdn. Offshore Exploration, Drilling and Development Institute* (1975).

See also DRILLING CONTRACT.

IBLA

Abbreviation for the Department of *Interior Board of Land Appeals,* a set of decisions relating to the use and disposition of public lands and their resources and the use and disposition of mineral resources in certain acquired lands of the United States and in the submerged lands of the Outer Continental Shelf.

ICSID

The International Center for Settlement of Investment Disputes, established by an international convention. See Jackson, "Negotiations Between American Contractors and Foreign Host Country Governments," 8 *Nat. Res. Law.* 1 at 4 (1975).

ID

(1) Abbreviation for Inside diameter.

(2) Abbreviation of the *United States Department of the Interior Decisions,* a set of reports containing decisions and opinions of the Interior Department on disposition of public lands and other matters within the responsibility of that Department of the United States government.

IDC

Abbreviation for INTANGIBLE DRILLING AND DEVELOPMENT COSTS (*q.v.*).

Identified resources

Specific bodies of mineral-bearing material whose location, quality, and quantity are known from geologic evidence supported by engineering measurements with respect to the demonstrated category. 2 *OCS Oil and Gas—An Environmental Assessment,* A Report to the President by the Council on Environmental Quality (April 1974), at p. 10.

See also RESERVES.

Identified-subeconomic reserves or resources

Known resources that may become recoverable as a result of changes in technologic, economic, and legal conditions. *OCS Oil and Gas—An Environmental Assessment,* A Report to the President by the Council on Environmental Quality (April 1974) at p. 11.

See also RESERVES.

IEA

The INTERNATIONAL ENERGY AGENCY (*q.v.*).

IEP

INTERNATIONAL ENERGY PROGRAM (*q.v.*).

IFP

INSTITUT FRANCAIS DU PETROLE (*q.v.*).

IGS

INSTITUTE OF GEOLOGICAL SCIENCES (*q.v.*).

Illegal container

Any receptacle which contains illegal oil or illegal oil products. Comp. Laws Mich. § 319.2(q); Mich. Stat. Ann. § 13.139(2)(q) (1980 Supp.).

Illegal conveyance

Any conveyance by or through which illegal oil or illegal oil products are being transported. Comp. Laws Mich., § 319.2(p); Mich. Stat. Ann. § 13.139(2)(p) (1980 Supp.).

Illegal oil or gas

Oil or gas produced from any well in excess of the amount allowed by a rule, regulation or order of the regulatory board or commission, as distinguished from oil produced not in excess of the amount so allowed by any rule, regulation, or order, which is "legal" oil.

Article 6066a, Vernon's Civil Statutes of Texas, was amended in 1965 to provide that "When any oil has been retained in storage for a period of more than six (6) years without being used, consumed or moved into the regular channels of commerce, it shall be presumed that such oil is 'unlawful oil.' "

"A lessee or assignee who produces oil contrary to law or commission order is liable to the royalty owner for his share of what is actually, although illegally, produced." Bolton v. Coats, 533 S.W.2d 914 at 916, 53 *O.&G.R.* 379 at 381 (Tex. 1975).

See also CONNALLY ACT; HOT OIL.

Illegal product

Any product of oil or gas, any part of which was processed or derived, in whole or in part, from illegal oil or illegal gas or from any product thereof, as distinguished from "legal" product, which is a product processed or derived to no extent from illegal oil or illegal gas.

Illegal production

Production of illegal oil or gas.

Illinois oil bubble

A substantial increase in the supply of oil as a result of an unrestrained Illinois oil boom during the period 1937–1940. Cooperative prorationing by Oklahoma and Texas at the time restrained the fluctuations in price resulting from the boom. See Danielsen, *The Evolution of OPEC* 89 (1982).

See also GAS BUBBLE.

Imbalance

See BALANCING; TAKE IMBALANCE.

IMCO Conventions

Conventions drafted under the aegis of the INTER-GOVERNMENTAL MARITIME CONSULTATIVE ORGANIZATION (IMCO) (*q.v.*), a specialized agency of the United Nations. Among the conventions adopted by IMCO are several dealing with oil pollution of the sea, including the 1969 International Convention on Civil Liability for Oil Pollution Damage and the 1971 International Convention on the Establishment of an International Fund for Compensation for Oil Pollution Damage.

For discussions of the IMCO Conventions, see the following:

Juda, "IMCO and the Regulation of Ocean Pollution From Ships," 26 *Int. & Comp. L.Q.* 558 (1977);

Mensah, "International Environmental Law: International Conventions Concerning Oil Pollution at Sea," 8 *Case Western Reserve J. Int'l Law* 110 (1976);

Greenberg, "IMCO: An Environmentalist's Perspective," *Id.* at 131;

Wood, "Requiring Polluters to Pay for Aquatic Natural Resources Destroyed by Oil Pollution," 8 *Nat. Res. Law.* 545 (1976);

National Petroleum Council, "Protection of the Marine Environment," *Id.* at 511.

See also CRISTAL; TOVALOP.

IMDA

The INDIAN MINERAL DEVELOPMENT ACT of 1982 (IMDA) (*q.v.*).

IMINOCO

Iranian Marine International Oil Co.

Immutability clause

Syn. for LAW STABILIZING CLAUSE (*q.v.*).

IMP

Interim Management and Policy Guideline for Wilderness Review. See Rocky Mountain Oil & Gas Ass'n v. Watt, 696 F.2d 734, 78 *O.&G.R.* 152 (10th Cir. 1982).

Impact statement

See ENVIRONMENTAL IMPACT STATEMENT.

Impenetrable substance

A stratum that cannot be drilled through. The typical DRILLING CONTRACT (*q.v.*) will have a provision governing the rights of the operator and the independent drilling contractor in the event that an impenetrable substance is encountered in drilling.

Some such clauses appear to be primarily concerned with the problem of impossibility of performance by the drilling contractor. Others recognize this problem but seem to be designed also to meet the eventuality that BASEMENT ROCK (*q.v.*) is encountered above the depth sought to be tested. In this event, of course, the operator is as interested as the driller in suspending operations, as no oil will be discovered in the well. See R. Olsen Oil Co. v. Fidler, 199 F.2d 868, 2 *O.&G.R.* 58 (10th Cir. 1952).

The term "practically impenetrable substance" was defined in the jury instruction reviewed in Arkla Exploration Co. v. Boren, 411 F.2d 879 at 881 (8th Cir. 1969), as "any substance that is encountered which is not penetrable with reasonable cost and facilities as long as the driller has performed the drilling with due diligence and without negligence. In other words, a practically impenetrable substance is one in which with available equipment and at a reasonable cost the substance cannot be penetrated."

In Lerblance v. Continental Oil Co., 437 F.Supp. 223 at 228, 59 *O.&G.R.* 50 at 60 (E.D. Okla. 1976), the court ruled that a "practically impenetrable substance" within the meaning of the operating agreement in question had been encountered when the circumstances were as follows:

> ". . .[I]nordinate difficulties were encountered by the defendant in drilling the well. The formation in question had a tenden- cy to cave in. The beds which were being penetrated had relatively steep dip causing difficulty in maintaining vertical penetration by the drill bit. Deviation was abrupt and severe. 1200 feet of iron was in the hole. More than $600,000 had been expended to achieve a depth of approximately 7600 feet. The cost of sidetracking or drilling a window in the casing and drilling the well to the projected depth, even if mechanically possible, would have made the total cost of the well in excess of 1.2 million dollars."

Implied covenants

Obligations imposed by the courts on lessees, derived by implication from the lease. The courts usually state that these obligations are implied in fact, from the intent of the parties. Indian Territory Illuminating Oil Co. v. Rosamond, 190 Okla. 46, 120 P.2d 349 (1941); Danciger Oil & Ref. Co. v. Powell, 137 Tex. 484, 154 S.W.2d 632 (1941); Gulf Production Co. v. Kishi, 129 Tex. 487, 103 S.W.2d 965 (1937). See Walker, "The Nature of the Property Interests Created by an Oil and Gas Lease," 1 *Texas L. Rev.* 339 at 404–406 (1933). But a most eminent authority on the subject regards the covenants as implied in law to do justice. Merrill, *Covenants Implied in Oil and Gas Leases* § 220 (2d ed. 1940).

There is also disagreement regarding the classification of the various duties. See TREATISE § 804. Regardless of this disagreement, the courts generally recognize at present the following implied covenants:

(1) To protect the leasehold from drainage [see OFFSET WELL COVENANT];

(2) To reasonably develop the premises [see REASONABLE DEVELOPMENT COVENANT];

(3) To produce and market the product [see MARKETING COVENANT; PRODUCTION AND MARKETING COVENANT];

(4) To conduct surface and drilling operations with due care.

To this list might be added two more covenants, one old and one new:

(1) To drill an initial exploratory well [see EXPLORATION COVENANT]. This covenant is outmoded at present because of express lease provisions about the initial well.

(2) To explore further [see FURTHER EXPLORATION COVENANT]. This covenant is coming to be recognized by many states, which refuse to allow a lease to be kept alive indefinitely without exploration once any production has been obtained. See the discussion and cases cited in Meyers, "The Implied Covenant of Further Exploration," 34 *Tex. L. Rev.* 553 (1956); TREATISE §§ 841–847.

The obligation of the lessee is not absolute: liability is determined by reference to the PRUDENT OPERATOR STANDARD (*q.v.*). That is, the lessee has the duty of acting in the same manner as an ordinary, prudent operator would act under similar circumstances. Thus there is no breach of covenant to drill offset wells unless such wells will repay the cost of drilling, equipping and operating them, plus some profit. Stanolind Oil & Gas Co. v. Sellers, 174 F.23d 948 (10th Cir. 1949); Coyle v. North American Oil Consol., 201 La. 99, 9 So.2d 473 (1942); Ramsey Petroleum Corp. v. Davis, 184 Okla. 155, 85 P.2d 427 (1938); Texas Pacific Coal & Oil Co. v. Barker, 117 Tex. 418, 6 S.W. 2d 1031 (1928). Where the lessee is himself causing drainage by operation of adjacent wells, some courts have relaxed or abandoned the prudent operator standard and required offset drilling even though the well will not be profitable. See, *e.g.*, Bush Oil Co. v. Beverly Lincoln Land Co., 69 Cal.App.2d 246, 158 P.2d 754 (1945); Seed, "The Implied Covenant to Refrain from Depletory

Acts," 4 *U.C.L.A. L. Rev.* 508 (1956); TREATISE §§ 824–824.3; D EPLETORY COVENANT.

To summarize the problems associated with implied covenants: (1) What duties are implied? (2) What standard of conduct determines breach of the duties? (3) What effect do express covenants have on implied covenants? (4) How is breach of covenant or compliance with it proved? (5) What parties (*e.g.*, owners of nonparticipating royalty?) are entitled to enforce the covenants? (6) What are the remedies available for breach of covenant?

Meyers and Crafton, "The Covenant of Further Exploration—Thirty Years Later," 32 *Rocky Mt. Min. L. Inst.* 1-18 (1986), suggest that the judicial implication of covenants into oil and gas leases is nothing more than a response to the fact that the lease is archetypically a relational contract.

See also DIVISIBLE COVENANTS; EXPRESS COVENANT.

Implied easements

Easements created by implication rather than by express terms of an instrument. In the law of oil and gas, it has been held that absent express language creating easements of ingress and egress, the grant or reservation of minerals will carry with it the implication of such easements. Lemar v. Garner, 121 Tex. 502, 50 S.W.2d 769 (1932). It has also been held that in an oil and gas lease silent on the matter, there is an implied easement to enter and make geophysical tests on the leasehold. Yates v. Gulf Oil Corp., 182 F.2d 286 (5th Cir. 1950). See TREATIES §§ 218–218.2

See also EASEMENTS.

Import quota

See OIL IMPORT QUOTA.

Improved recovery techniques

"[A]ll methods of supplementing natural reservior forces and energy, or otherwise increasing ultimate recovery from a reservoir. Such techniques include: (1) pressure maintenance; (2) cycling; and (3) secondary recovery in its original sense (*i.e.*, fluid injection applied relatively late in the productive history of a reservior for the purpose of stimulating production after recovery by primary methods of flowing or artificial lift have approached an economic limit.) Improved recovery techniques also include thermal methods and the use of miscible displacement fluids." American Petroleum Institute

Division of Statisitcs, *Organization and Definitions for the Estimation of Reserves and Productive Capacity of Crude Oil* 18 (Technical Report No. 2, June 1970).

See also SECONDARY RECOVERY; TERTIARY RECOVERY.

Imputed Alberta border price

The price established under Alberta Natural Gas Canadian Pricing Orders for the transmission of Alberta gas outside the province. See Saskatchewan Power Corp. v. Transcanada Pipeline Ltd., [1981] 2 S.C.R. 688, 130 D.L.R.3d 1 (Sup. Ct. of Canada 1981).

Imputed stripped well crude oil exemption

An exemption from price controls applicable to the first sale of crude oil designed to minimize the possibility that stripper well properties would be withheld from unitizations because of the possible loss of their stripper well status when a unit base production control level was established for the utilized property. A fixed amount of crude oil production from the unitized property was treated as stripper well crude oil following the implementation of a unit base production control level. Domestic Crude Oil Composite Price Adjustment (Energy Action No. 11), Hearing before the Subcommittee on Energy and Power of the House Committee on Interstate and Foreign Commerce, 95th Cong., 1st Sess., March 29, 1977 (Serial No. 95–13) at 52–53.

Francis Oil Co. v. Exxon, 687 F.2d 484 (Temp. Emer. Ct. App. 1982), *cert. denied,* 459 U.S. 1010, 103 S. Ct. 365 (1982), concluded that when a stripper well property joined a unit, the individual tract's stripper well oil was automatically imputed to the unit as a whole and it was up to the participants in the agreement to decide how to allocate exempt oil among themselves.

See also PRICE CONTROL OF OIL, GAS AND PETROLEUM PRODUCTS; STRIPPER WELL OIL.

Imputed stripper well lease oil price

Under the provisions of the Emergency Petroleum Allocation Act of 1973 (EPAA) [Pub. L. No. 93–159], 15 U.S.C. §§ 751–760h, as amended by the Energy Policy and Conservation Act of 1975 (EPCA) [Pub. L. No. 94–163], and the Energy Conservation and Production Act of 1976 (ECPA) [Pub. L. No. 94–385], price ceilings for oil produced in the United States were established. Regulations issued under the 1973 EPAA established two-tier pricing. The price of OLD OIL (*q.v.*) was fixed at the price prevailing in the field on May 15, 1973, plus $1.35 per barrel, resulting in a ceiling price for old oil which averaged approximately $5.25 a barrel. NEW OIL, RELEASED OIL and STRIPPER WELL OIL (*q.v.*) could be sold at market price. Following the enactment of EPCA in December of 1975 ceilings were imposed on new oil, released oil and stripper well oil (described as upper tier or second tier oil to distinguish it from old oil, which came to be described as lower tier or first tier oil). Beginning in February 1976 upper tier oil came under a ceiling of $11.28 a barrel. The EPCA also imposed a COMPOSITE PRICE CEILING (*q.v.*) on all domestic oil of $7.66 a barrel for February, 1976, with provision for escalation of the composite or average price ceiling at an annual rate not exceeding ten percent. Under ECPA, effective September 1, 1976, stripper production was exempted from controls and there emerged a three-tier pricing system consisting of lower tier, upper tier, and exempt crude oil. Thereafter for purposes of determining compliance with the composite price ceiling there was attributed to stripper well production an imputed stripper well oil price of $11.63 per barrel (subject to an escalator provision).

See also PRICE CONTROL OF OIL, GAS, AND PETROLEUM PRODUCTS; STRIPPER WELL OIL.

Incentive allowable

An additional ALLOWABLE (*q.v.*) designed to provide encouragement for exploratory and development drilling in pools with low reserves per acre. See Crommelin, "Government Management of Oil and Gas in Alberta," 13 *Alta. L. Rev.* 146 at 181 (1975).

Incentive exploratory well

A well certified by the Alberta Energy Resources Conservation Board after January 1, 1974 under the Exploratory Drilling Incentive Regulations, 1975 (Alta. Reg. 18/74). The Board will certify a well drilled for oil or gas that is (a) located more than three miles from a completed well, or (b) located less than three miles from a completed well but expected to be drilled significantly deeper than the completed well. See Providence of Alberta Energy Resources Conservation Board, Informational Letter No. IL–OG 74–4 (Feb. 13, 1974). The incentive offered for the drilling of exploratory wells takes the form of a government contribution toward drilling cost or an exemption from Crown royalty upon oil and gas production. See Crommelin, "Government Management of Oil and Gas in Alberta," 13 *Alta. L. Rev.* 146 at 167 (1975).

Informational Letter IL 83-9 (25 Aug. 1983) of the Alberta Energy Resources Conservation Board describes the procedures employed by the Board when certifying and processing an incentive exploratory well.

See also INCENTIVE WILDCAT WELL.

Incentive oil

An additional allocation of crude oil by a host government to a multinational oil company as a reward for investment by the company in refining or other activities in the host country. *The Wall Street Journal,* May 4, 1981, p. 1, col. 7.

See also Quandt, *Saudi Arabia's Oil Policy* 33 (Brookings Institution 1982) (describing "incentive crude" as oil supplies made available in exchange for technology transfer or investment in the host country).

See also CONCESSION.

Incentive price gas

The term applied to certain gas [new natural gas, certain Outer Continental Shelf gas, new onshore production wells, certain high-cost gas, and stripper well gas] entitled to an incentive price under the provisions of the NATURAL GAS POLICY ACT OF 1978 (NGPA) (*q.v.*). See Haase, "The Federal Role in Implementing the Natural Gas Policy Act of 1978," 16 *Hous. L. Rev.* 1067 at 1068 (1979).

Incentive rate of return (IROR)

A rate of return including as a factor an incentive to engage in specified activities. See Incentive Rate of Return for the Alaska Natural Gas Transportation System, FERC Order No. 17, 16 FPS 5–553 (Dec. 1, 1978). The IROR is decreased as the Cost Performance Ratio (the ratio of deflated actual capital costs to projected capital costs) is increased in order to provide an incentive for project sponsors to keep construction costs as low as possible.

Incentive wildcat well

A well certified as a wildcat well for purposes of Alberta Exploratory Drilling Incentive Regulations. See Province of Alberta, Energy Resources Conservation Board, Informational Letter No. IL–OG 72–26 (Dec. 29, 1972). This Informational Letter was superseded by Informational Letter No. IL–OG 72–26 (Feb. 13, 1974).

See also INCENTIVE EXPLORATORY WELL.

Inch-mile allocation method

An allocation method for transportation costs of gas utilizing diameter of the pipe as a cost factor as well as the length of the portion of pipeline used. McCulloch Interstate Gas Corp., 16 FPS 5–15 (Sept. 5, 1978).

See also ACCOUNTING METHODS.

Inclination survey

A form of well survey. See Rule 54 of the Texas Railroad Commission, 17 *O.&G.R.* 109 (1963).

See also STRAIGHT HOLE CLAUSE.

Inclinometer

An instrument employed to determine whether a well bore is verticle. See ACID BOTTLE INCLINOMETER.

Income fund

Syn.: for INCOME PROGRAM (*q.v.*)

Income program

A PRODUCTION FUND (*q.v.*) formed to acquire and operate producing oil and gas wells. A variation of this is a fund that acquires overriding royalty interests in a combination of producing, proven, semiproven, or undeveloped properties, instead of producing properties. Baggett, Dole, and Short, *Coopers & Lybrand Anatomy of a Drilling Fund* 7 (1980). Income programs were popular investments in 1982 and 1983, raising more than $3 billion but problems encountered in the 1982-83 energy recession period by Petro Lewis, one of the major income programs, substantially reduced investments in income programs in 1984. See *The Wall Street Journal,* April 9, 1984, p. 1, col. 6 (reporting that Petro Lewis was seeking to sell $1 billion of the reserves held by it and its 183,000 limited-partner investors, that it had slashed payments to the limited partners, and that it had reduced the prices at which it was willing to buy interests tendered by its limited partners).

See also DRILLING FUND.

Incorporation by reference

The method of making one document become a part of another separate document by referring to the former in the latter, and declaring that the former shall be taken and considered as part of the latter the same as if it were fully set out therein.

See also REFERENTIAL INCORPORATION.

Incorporeal interest

A non-possessory interest in real property. The most familiar is an easement.

In oil and gas law, a number of interests are regarded as incorporeal. For example, a number of states regard severed interests in minerals, created by deed or lease, as incorporeal interests, often called *profits à prendre.* See, *e.g.*, Little v. Mountain View Dairies, 35 Cal.2d 232, 217 P.2d 416 (1950); Callahan v. Martin, 3 Cal.2d 110, 43 P.2d 788 (1935); Barker v. Campbell-Ratliff Land Co., 64 Okla. 249, 167 Pac. 468 (1917); TREATISE §§ 210–211. Some other states regard such interests as corporeal in character. See CORPOREAL ESTATE.

Increment accrual

In an A–B–C TRANSACTION (*q.v.*), this term has been employed in reference to that portion of the reserved oil payment representing the sums to be realized by *C*, the oil payment purchaser, and utilized to pay interest in his debt for the purchase price and his "squeeze" or profit. See Sack, "ABC's of the ABC Oil Transaction," 59 *Northwestern L. Rev.* 591 at 593 (1964).

Incremental cost method

A method of determining a rate base wherein costs of facilities which were added for the benefit of a particular customer are added to the particular customer's rate base rather than "rolled in" to become part of the rate base for all customers. See Battle Creek Gas Co. v. Federal Power Comm'n, 281 F.2d 42 (D.C. Cir. 1960).

See also ROLLED-IN ALLOCATION METHOD.

Incremental pricing

A system of allocating the low unit costs of "old gas" to "high priority" consumers (mainly residential consumers) and their distributor suppliers while allocating all of the much higher units costs of "new gas" to "low priority" consumers (mainly industrial consumers). Efforts by the Federal Power Commission to implement incremental pricing and the adoption of incremental pricing by the Natural Gas Policy Act are discussed in the following papers:

Mogel and Mapes, "Assessment of Incremental Pricing Under the Natural Gas Policy Act," 29 *Cath. U. L. Rev.* 763 (1980);

Cormie, "Incremental Pricing Under the Natural Gas Policy Act of 1978," 57 *Denver L.J.* 1 (1979);

Pierce, "Natural Gas Policy Act of 1978," 47 *J. Kan. B.A.* 259 at 270 (1978).

This term was defined in Consumer Energy Council of America v. Federal Energy Regulatory Commission, 673 F.2d 425 at 434 (D.C. Cir. 1982), *aff'd,* 463 U.S. 1216, 103 S.Ct. 3556, *reh. denied,* 463 U.S. 1250, 104 S.Ct. 40 (1983), as follows:

> "Incremental pricing is a 'mechanism for passing through to end users some of the increased prices for natural gas,' so that large industrial gas users will pay a disproportionate share of the increases in gas prices. The program's goals are 'to restrain the prices paid by pipelines for natural gas supplies, particularly after deregulation, and to protect residential consumers from higher prices resulting from deregulation.' "

See also ALTERNATIVE FUEL COST; MAXIMUM SURCHARGE ABSORPTION CAPABILITY (MASC); REDUCED PGA METHOD; ROLLED-IN PRICE.

Incremental tertiary oil

For purposes of the CRUDE OIL WINDFALL PROFIT TAX ACT OF 1980 (*q.v.*), this term means the excess of: (1) the amount of crude oil which is removed from a property during any month and which is produced on or after the project beginning date and during the period for which a qualified tertiary recovery project is in effect on the property, over (2) the base level of such property for such month. Internal Revenue Code § 4992.

Indefinite escalation clause

Any provision other than a DEFINITE ESCALATION CLAUSE (*q.v.*) under which the price in a contract for the sale or transportation of natural gas by an independent producer may be determined or changed.

See also ESCALATOR CLAUSE.

Indefinite pricing clause

Syn.: for ESCALATOR CLAUSE (*q.v.*). Johnson, "Natural Gas Sales Contracts," 34 *Sw. Legal Fdn. Oil & Gas. Inst.* 83 at 94 (1983).

Independent drilling contractor

A person or corporation engaged in drilling wells for hire. For a careful and complete discussion, see Masterson, "The Legal Position of the Drilling Contractor," 1 *Sw. Legal Fdn. Oil & Gas Inst.* 183 (1949).

See also Holdaway v. Gustanson, 632 F.Supp. 393, ____ *O.&G.R.* ____ (D. Wyo. 1986) (discussing the Wyoming law relating to the status of independent contractor).

See also DRILLING CONTRACT.

Independent pipeline

A pipeline not owned by the producers of the oil or gas transported therein.

Independent producer

A term loosely defined in varying ways:

(1) A purely domestic organization not dependent upon foreign oil.

(2) A company or individual whose actual management and financial source are substantially the same.

(3) A person who produces oil and gas and is not engaged in transportation, refining or marketing of such products.

(4) A company that is relatively small and largely unintegrated.

(5) "[A]ny person . . . who is engaged in the production or gathering of natural gas and who sells natural gas in interstate commerce for resale, but who is not engaged in the transportation of natural gas (other than gathering) by pipeline in interstate commerce." 18 C.F.R. § 154.91 (1980).

(6) A producer "without corporate affiliation with an interstate gas pipeline company." Oklahoma Natural Gas Co. v. Federal Power Comm'n, 257 F.2d 634 at 642, 9 *O.&G.R.* 804 at 813 (D.C. Cir. 1958) (dissenting opinion), *cert. dism'd,* 358 U.S. 948, 10 *O.&G.R.* 113 (1959).

(7) For purposes of the CRUDE OIL WINDFALL PROFIT TAX ACT OF 1980 (*q.v.*), an independent producer is any person other than a retailer as defined in Internal Revenue Code § 613A(d)(2) or a refiner as defined in § 613A(d)(4) of the Code. Internal Revenue Code § 4992(b). Thus the term "independent producer" excludes any taxpayer who directly, or through a related person, sells oil or natural gas (excluding bulk sales of such items to commercial or industrial users), or any derivative product through any retail outlet operated

by the taxpayer or a related person or to any person who, in effect, either (1) must use a trademark, trade name, service name, or name owned by the taxpayer or a related person in marketing oil or gas or (2) is given authority to use a retail outlet controlled by the taxpayer or a related person. A person is not a retailer if his combined gross receipts for the quarter from the sale of oil, natural gas or any derivative product from all includable retail outlets do not exceed $1,250,000. A refiner is a taxpayer having refinery runs (either individually or together with a related person) that exceed 50,000 barrels on any day during the canedar quarter.

The most general usage in the oil (as distinguished from the gas) industry is (3).

Independent producer oil

For purposes of the CRUDE OIL WINDFALL PROFIT TAX ACT OF 1980 (*q.v.*), this term refers to the portion of an independent producer's qualified production for the quarter which does not exceed such person's independent producer amount for such quarter. Internal Revenue Code § 4992.

See also TRANSFER RULE.

Independent refiner

As defined in the proposed MANDATORY PETROLEUM PRODUCTS ALLOCATION REGULATIONS (*q.v.*), a refiner who (a) in a prescribed period obtained more than 70 per centum of his refinery input of domestic crude oil (or 70 per centum of his refinery input of domestic and imported crude oil) from producers who do not control, are not controlled by, and are not under common control with, such refiner, and (b) marketed or distributed in such period and continues to market or distribute a substantial volume of gasoline refined by him through branded independent marketers or nonbranded independent marketers. 38 F.R. 34419 (Dec. 13, 1973).

See also REFINER.

Indeterminate pricing clause

Syn. for ESCALATOR CLAUSE (*q.v.*).

Indian allotment

"An allocation of a parcel of public lands or Indian reservation lands to an Indian for his individual use; also, the lands so allocated." United States Department of the Interior Bureau of Land Management, *Glossary of Public-Land Terms* 22 (1949).

See also INDIAN LANDS; PUBLIC LANDS.

Indian lands

Land set aside by the government for Indians. Indian lands constitute a type of property ownership different from all other types in the United States or at common law. In general there are two classes of Indian lands, tribal lands and allocated lands. Tribal lands are owned by a group or tribe of Indians collectively in common, and are not alienable, inheritable or devisable. The group or tribe has a right of perpetual occupancy. Allotted lands are held by an individual Indian with certain restrictions on alienation and with a tax exemption or held by the government in trust for the individual Indian. See McLane, *Oil and Gas Leasing on Indian Lands* (1956).

Although Department of the Interior approval of oil and gas leases affecting certain Indian land is required, it has been held that the Indian himself, without joinder of the Department, has capacity to maintain an action seeking damages for the alleged breach of the lease. Poafpybitty v. Skelly Oil Co., 390 U.S. 365, 32 *O.&G.R.* 55 (1968). On remand of *Poafpybitty* it was held that there was no breach of the lessee's duties under its lease. Poafpybitty v. Skelly Oil Co., 517 P.2d 432, 47 *O.&G.R.* 168 (Okla. 1973).

Montana v. Blackfeet Tribe of Indians, 471 U.S. 759, 85 L.Ed.2d 753, 105 S.Ct. 2399, 84 *O.&G.R.* 630 (1985), held that the state of Montana could not tax Indian royalty income from leases issued pursuant to the Indian Leasing Act of 1938.

See also the following:

Kerr-McGee Corp. v. Navajo Tribe of Indians, 471 U.S. 195, 105 S.Ct. 1900, 84 *O.&G.R.* 213 (1985) (holding that Navajo Tribe ordinances imposing taxes on the value of leasehold interests in tribal lands and on receipts from the sale of property produced or extracted or the sale of services within those lands were valid without the approval of the Secretary of the Interior);

Merrion v. Jicarilla Apache Tribe, 617 F.2d 537 (10th Cir. 1980), *aff'd,* 455 U.S. 130, 72 *O.&G.R.* 617 (1982), noted, 37 *Okla. L. Rev.* 369 (1984), held that the Jicarilla Apache Tribe had power to levy an oil and gas severance tax, the tax did not violate the commerce clause of the United States Constitution, and Congress had not preempted the tribal taxation.

For other cases sustaining the power of Indian Tribes on oil and gas leases see the following:

Southland Royalty Co. v. Navajo Tribe of Indians, 715 F.2d 486, 78 *O.&G.R.* 197 (10th Cir. 1983);

Conoco, Inc. v. Shoshone and Arapahoe Tribes, 569 F.Supp. 801, 78 *O.&G.R.* 181 (D. Wyo. 1983);

Blackfeet Tribe of Indians v. Montana, 507 F.Supp. 446, 68 *O.&G.R.* 725 (D. Mont. 1981).

On the taxability of mineral lessees of Indian lands, see Comment, "The Case for Exclusive Tribal Power to Tax Mineral Lessees of Indian Lands," 124 *U. Pa. L. Rev.* 491 (1975).

The development of the mineral resources of Indian lands is discussed in the following:

Getches, Rosenfelt and Wilkinson, *Federal Indian Law* (1979);

Maxfield, Dieterich and Trelease, *Natural Resources Law on American Indian Lands* (1977);

Price, *Law and the American Indian* (1973);

McLane, *Oil and Gas Leasing on Indian Lands* (1955);

Muys, "Gas Royalty Valuation Standards and Procedures Applicable to Federal and Indian Lands," 37 *Sw. Legal Fdn. Oil & Gas Inst.* 2-1 (1986);

Moore, "Indian Leasing," *Rocky Mt. Min. L. Fdn. Law of Federal Oil and Gas Leases* ch. 26 (1985);

Montgomery, "Tribal Sovereignty and Congressional Dominion: Rights-of-Way for Gas Pipelines on Indian Reservations," 38 *Stanford L. Rev.* 195 (1985);

Maxfield, "Tribal Control of Indian Mineral Development," 62 *Oregon L. Rev.* 49 (1983);

Moore, "Mineral Development on Indian Lands—Cooperation and Conflict," 28 *Rocky Mt. Min. L. Inst.* 1 (1982);

Berger, "Indian Lands—Minerals—Related Problems," 14 *Rocky Mt. Min. L. Inst.* 89 (1968);

Moore, "Title Examination of Indian Lands," *Rocky Mt. Min. L. Fdn. Mineral Title Examination Institute* Paper 6 (1977);

Burley, "Indian Lands—An Industry Dilemma," 27 *Rocky Mt. Min. L. Inst.* 1605 (1982);

Bell v. Phillips Petroleum Co., 641 P.2d 1115, 72 *O.&G.R.* 314 (Okla. 1982).

See also EXEMPT INDIAN OIL; HEAD RIGHT; INDIAN MINERAL DEVELOPMENT ACT OF 1982 (IMDA); OIL & GAS ROYALTY MANAGEMENT ACT OF 1982; PUBLIC LANDS.

Indian Mineral Development Act of 1982 (IMDA)

An Act, 25 U.S.C. §§ 2102–2108, designed to provide Indian tribes with flexibility in the development and sale of mineral resources. See Quantum Exploration, Inc. v. Clark, 780 F.2d 1457, 90 *O.&G.R.* 81 (9th Cir. 1986).

Indicated additional reserves

"With the present state of industry technology, certain quantities of crude oil (other than those defined and reported as proved reserves) may be economically recoverable from the following potential sources:

> Known productive reservoirs in existing fields expected to respond to improved recovery techniques such as fluid injection where (a) improved recovery technique has been installed but its effect cannot yet be fully evaluated; or (b) an improved technique has been installed but knowledge of reservoir characteristics and the results of a known technique installed in a similar situation are available for use in the estimating procedure.

"Crude oil potentially available from these sources is reported as 'indicated additional reserves.' The economic recoverability of these reserves is not considered to be established with sufficient conclusiveness to allow them to be included in proved reserves; however, if and when improved recovery techniques are successfully applied to known reservoirs, the corresponding indicated additional reserves will be reclassified and added to the inventory of 'proved' reserves.

"Indicated additional reserves do not include reserves associated with acreage that may be added to the area of a proved reservoir as the result of future drilling." American Petroleum Institute Division of Statistics, *Organization and Definitions for the Estimation of Reserves and Productive Capacity of Crude Oil* 14 (Technical Report No. 2, June 1970).

See also RESERVES.

Indicated reserves or resources

Reserves or resources for which tonnage and grade are computed partly from specific measurements, samples, or production data and partly from projection for a reasonable distance on geologic evidence. The sites available for inspection, measurement, and sampling are too widely or otherwise inappropriately spaced to permit the mineral bodies to be outlined completely or the grade established throughout. 21*OCS Oil and Gas—An Environmental Assessment,* A

Report to the President by the Council on Environmental Quality (April 1974) at p. 11.

See also RESERVES.

Indirect customer

A term used to designate a purchaser of gas from an intermediary, usually a pipeline or city gage, who in turn has bought from a gas pipeline company, as distinguished from a direct customer who purchases directly from the gas pipeline company. State of Louisiana v. Federal Power Comm'n, 503 F.2d 884, at 869 (5th Cir. 1974).

Indirect offsetting

Syn. for Diagonal offsetting. See OFFSET WELL.

Indispensable parties

Those persons whose interest in litigation is such that the court will not proceed without them although it may mean dismissing the suit. See TREATISE § 875 *et seq.*

See also NECESSARY PARTIES; PROPER PARTIES.

Individual loss provision

A provision in an operating agreement placing upon the individual contributor (rather than on all participants), the loss caused by failure of title to an interest included in the agreement. See Folks, "The Modern Form Operating Agreement," *1959 Sw. Legal Fdn. Nat'l Inst. for Petroleum Landmen* 69 at 70 (1960).

See also JOINT LOSS PROVISION; JOINT OPERATING AGREEMENT; OPERATING AGREEMENT.

Indivisibility, Rule of

See RULE OF INDIVISIBILITY.

Indivisible covenants

See DIVISIBLE COVENANTS.

Induced flow

Flow made possible by application of artificial methods, *e.g.*, by swabbing the well, or by injecting extraneous gas under pressure into the oil.

Industrial gas

Gas purchased for resale for industrial use only. See Pacific Natural Gas Co. v. Federal Power Comm'n, 276 F.2d 350 (9th Cir. 1960).

Industry deal

The term applied to a sales arrangement whereby companies engaged primarily in the exploration business and companies engaged primarily in the business of promoting oil and gas prospects are solicited to purchase an undivided fractional interest in an oil and gas lease, coupled with an operating agreement whereby the party proposing the prospect oversees or operates the drilling of a test well on the lease. Pezold and Richey, "The 'Industry Deal' Among Oil and Gas Companies and the Federal Securities Acts," 16 *Texas Tech L. Rev.* 827 (1985). The authors suggest that these deals involve a "security" although historically the industry has held as contrary view; the enactment of a definitional exemption into the federal securities laws is suggested.

See also JOINT OPERATING AGREEMENT; SECURITIES REGULATION.

Inert gas injection

The injection of an inert (*viz.* noncombustible) gas, such as nitrogen, into a reservoir to displace the hydrocarbon gas. Once injected into the reservoir the nitrogen expands, either forcing hydrocarbon gas from the reservoir or removing obstructions that prevented the flow of gas into the well bore.

See also INJECTION WELL; PRODUCTION ENHANCEMENT PROCEDURES.

Inferior use

A relatively uneconomic or less beneficial use of oil or gas.

Use of sweet gas for the manufacture of carbon black is inferior to the use of such gas for domestic or industrial heating and lighting. Some inferior uses of gas are regulated by state or federal law. For example, the use of sweet gas for the manufacture of carbon black is generally regulated in the producing states. Certain inferior uses of gas have been prohibited by the Federal Power Commission and its successor, the Federal Energy Regulatory Commission.

See also END USE CONTROL.

Inferred reserves or resources

Reserves or resources for which quantitiative estimates are based largely on broad knowledge of the geologic character of the deposit and for which there are few, if any, samples or measurements. The estimates are based on an assumed continuity or repetition, of which there is geologic evidence; this evidence may include comparison with deposits of similar type. Bodies that are completely concealed may be included if there is specific geologic evidence of their presence. Estimates of inferred reserves or resources should include a statement of the specific limits within which the inferred material may lie. 2 *OCS Oil and Gas—An Environmental Assessment,* A Report to the President by the Council on Environmental Quality (April 1974) at p. 11.

See also RESERVES.

Infill drilling

Drilling of an additional well or additional wells in excess of those provided for by a spacing order in order to more adequately drain a reservoir. Anderson, "New Directions in Oil and Gas Conservation Law," *Institute on Oil and Gas Conservation Law and Practice* 14-1 at 14-13 (Rocky Mt. Min. L. Fdn. 1985).

Infill well

(1) A well drilled on an irregular pattern disregarding normal target and spacing requirements. In an ENHANCED RECOVERY PROJECT (*q.v.*) developed on uniform spacing, the occurrence of unswept regions or the prevalence of coning may cause losses in oil recovery or unnecessary deferral of production. Under such circumstances the operator may apply for an infill drilling order to permit productivity or conservation improvement. The IW order [Infill well drilling order] will specify one minimum allowance for each developed drilling spacing unit irrespective of the number of wells that are drilled in it. Alberta Energy Resources Conservation Board. Informational Letter No. IL–OG–72–11 (June 16, 1972). The Board will not usually give the necessary permission for an infill well unless there is substantial agreement among operators that infill drilling is required. Crommelin, "Government Management of Oil and Gas in Alberta," 13 *Alberta L. Rev.* 146 at 174 (1975).

(2) A DEVELOPMENT WELL (*q.v.*).

For a discussion of the increased recovery which may be made possible in a number of fields by infill drilling, see Lopez & Parsley,

"Microbes, Simulators, and Satellites: The Prudent Operator Pursues Enhanced Recovery Under the Implied Covenants," 58 *N.D. L. Rev.* 501 at 524 (1982).

Infiltrating water

Water entering or penetrating an oil bearing formation as underground pressure is reduced by virtue of the drilling of a well and the production of oil.

Inflation adjustment

See ANNUAL INFLATION ADJUSTMENT FACTOR.

INGAA

INTERSTATE NATURAL GAS ASSOCIATION OF AMERICA (*q.v.*).

"In gross" provision

The term applied to the ACREAGE ESTIMATE PROVISION (*q.v.*) of a lease granting clause to the effect that for purposes of determining the amount of designated payments (*e.g.*, bonus, rental, shut-in royalty) the number of gross acres specified in the granting clause shall be deemed correct, whether actually more or less. Kuntz, Lowe, Anderson and Smith, *Oil and Gas Law* 128 (1986).

Initial development period

In the life of a field, that stage just succeeding the completion of the discovery well, in which DEVELOPMENT WELLS (*q.v.*) are drilled to exploit the field and to determine its boundaries. After the initial development period the field passes into the FLUSH PRODUCTION (*q.v.*) stage, then to the SETTLED PRODUCTION (*q.v.*) stage and then into the STRIPPER PRODUCTION (*q.v.*) stage.

Initial exploratory well covenant

An implied EXPLORATION COVENANT (*q.v.*) requiring the lessee to commence the drilling of an initial well on the leasehold within a reasonable time and to prosecute such drilling operations with due diligence until the well is completed. See TREATISE §§ 811–813.

Initial production

One of several stages of the life of an oil well or oil field. Initial production is the first state when the well or field is first put into production. The period of time for this stage varies, but it is the shortest of the stages. The other stages are (1) FLUSH PRODUCTION (*q.v.*), (2) SETTLED PRODUCTION (*q.v.*) and (3) STRIPPER PRODUCTION (*q.v.*).

Initial term

See PRODUCTION LICENSE.

Injected gas

Natural gas contained in a gas storage facility which has been injected into the facility from some outside source. Arkla, Inc. v. United States, 592 F.Supp. 502, 83 *O.&G.R.* 209 (W.D. La. 1984), *rev'd and remanded,* 765 F.2d 487, 85 *O.&G.R.* 431 (5th Cir. 1985), *reh. den.*, 772 F.2d 904 (5th cir. 1985), *cert denied,* 106 S.Ct. 1374 (1986).

Injection packer

See PRODUCTION INJECTION PACKER

Injection well

A well employed for the introduction into an underground stratum of water, gas or other fluid under pressure. Injection wells are employed for the disposal of salt water produced with oil or other waste. See WASTE INJECTION WELL. They are also employed for a variety of other purposes, including: (1) PRESSURE MAINTENANCE (*q.v.*), to introduce a fluid into a producing formation to maintain underground pressures which would otherwise be reduced by virtue of the production of oil and/or gas; (2) CYCLING (*q.v.*) or RECYCLING (*q.v.*), to introduce residue gas into a formation after liquefiable hydrocarbons have been extracted from gas produced from the formation; (3) SECONDARY RECOVERY (*q.v.*) operations, to introduce a fluid to decrease the viscosity of oil, reduce its surface tension, lighten its specific gravity, and/or to drive oil into producing wells, resulting in greater production of oil; and (4) TERTIARY RECOVERY (*q.v.*) operations to introduce chemicals or energy as required for displacement and for the control of flow rate and flow pattern in the reservoir.

Syn.: Input well.

Briggs v. Gaddis, 133 Ill. App.3d 704, 88 Ill. D. 737, 479 N.E.2d 350, 87 *O.&G.R.* 10 (1985), concluded that use of an injection well to dispose of salt water was not, under the circumstances of this case, a secondary recovery program.

An injection well is treated for Federal income tax purposes as part of production, and costs of drilling may be capitalized or deducted as intangibles. Burke and Bowhay, *Income Taxation of Natural Resources* ¶¶ 14.13, 15.21 (1981).

When a sliding scale (step-scale) royalty is based on average daily production per well, the lease or unit agreement involved should be specific as to which (if any) injection wells may be counted as producing wells for the purpose of determining average daily production per well. See Marathon Oil Co., 81 I.D. 447, 16 IBLA 298, GFS (O&G) 1974–62; Atlantic Richfield Co., Marathon Oil Co., 81. I.D. 457, 16 IBLA 329, GFS (O&G) 1974–63. The decisions in these cases were set aside in Marathon Oil Co. v. Kleppe, 407 F.Supp. 1301, 54 O.&G.R. 535 (D. Wyo. 1975), *aff'd,* 556 F.2d 982 (10th Cir. 1977).

A similar problem arose in connection with price control regulations, *viz.,* whether an injection well was to be counted for purposes of determining whether a field was a STRIPPER WELL FIELD (*q.v.*), production from which was entitled to a higher price. See *In re* Stripper Well Litigation, 520 F.Supp. 1232 (D. Kan. 1981) (holding that injection wells were to be counted for this purpose), *rev'd,* 690 F.2d 1375 (Temp. Emer. Ct. App. 1982), *cert. denied,* 459 U.S. 1127, 103 S.Ct. 763 (1983), *on remand,* 578 F.Supp. 586 (D. Kan. 1983), *on certified questions,* 744 F.2d 98 (Temp. Emer. Ct. App. 1984), *cert. denied,* ____ U.S. ____, 105 S. Ct. 576 (1984).

Wiggins Brothers, Inc. v. Department of Energy, 667 F.21d 77 (Temp. Emer. Ct. of App. 1981), *cert. denied,* 456 U.S. 90 (1982), concluded that an injection well was not to be counted as a well that produced crude oil for purposes of determining whether a property was within the MARGINAL PROPERTY RULE (*q.v.*) of the Department of Energy under which production from a marginal property was entitled to the upper tier price under price control regulations, *on remand,* 548 F.Supp. 547 (N.D. Tex. 1982).

See also Prosper Energy Corp. v. Department of Energy, 549 F. Supp. 300 (N.D. Tex. 1982).

See also INERT GAS INJECTION.

"In kind" or "In money" distinction

See ROYALTY.

In line price

A price for gas which is "in line" with other prices for gas produced and sold for resale in interstate commerce, satisfying the requirements imposed by the CATCO case, Atlantic Refining Co. v. Public Service Comm'n, 360 U.S. 378, 10 *O.&G.R.* 1021 (1959).

For a thorough discussion of CATCO and the meaning of "out of line," see Johnson, "Producer Rate Regulation In Natural Gas Certification Proceedings; CATCO in Context," 62 *Columbia L. Rev.* 773 (1962). The method used by the Federal Power Commission to determine "in line" price is discussed in Public Service Comm'n of State of N.Y. v. Federal Power Comm'n, 373 F.2d 816 at 824, 26 *O.&G.R.* 523 at 531 (D.C. Cir. 1967), *rev'd,* Federal Power Comm'n v. Sunray DX Oil Co., 391 U.S. 9, 29 *O.&G.R.* 305 (1968).

See also SUSPECT PRICE.

Innage gauge

A measure of the quantity of oil in a tank calculated on the basis of the depth of the oil in the tank. See Irving and Draper, *Accounting Practices in the Petroleum Industry* 58 (1958).

See also AUTOMATIC GAUGE; OUTAGE GAUGE.

INOC

The IRAQ NATIONAL OIL COMPANY (*q.v.*).

In-oil payment

See LONG OIL PAYMENT; OIL PAYMENT; SHORT-LIVED IN-OIL PAYMENT.

Input well

See INJECTION WELL.

In-situ combustion

An experimental means of recovery of oil of low gravity and high viscosity which is unrecoverable by other methods. The essence of the method is to heat the oil in the horizon to increase its mobility by decreasing its viscosity. Heat is applied by igniting the oil sand and keeping the fire alive by the injection of air. The heat breaks the oil down into coke and lighter oils and the coke catches fire. As the combustion front advances, the lighter oils move ahead of the fire into the bore of a producing well.

In Waseco Chem. & Supply Co. v. Bayou State Oil Corp., 371 So.2d 305, 65 *O.&G.R.* 351 (La. App. 1979), *writs denied,* 374 So.2d 656 (La. 1979), the court sustained a decree cancelling a lease under the reasonable development covenant for failure to engage in "fire flooding" or in-situ combustion on the lease. For discussions of this case see Frazier, "The Prudent Operator Standard: Does It Include a Duty to Use Enhanced Recovery?" 40 *La. L. Rev.* 974 (1980); Boyle, "Oil and Gas: The Implied Covenant for Reasonable Development Includes a Duty to Use Secondary Recovery Methods Under the Proper Circumstances," 15 *Tulsa L.J.* 597 (1980).

See also the following:

Myers, *The Law of Pooling and Unitization* § 2.05 (2d ed. 1967);

Mize, "Oil and Gas—Enhanced Recovery in Louisiana—Obligations and Liabilities," 56 *La. L. Rev.* 723 (1982).

Roark, "Engineering Aspects of Fluid Injection Into Oil Reservoirs Which Require Legal Action," A.B.A., Section of Mineral and Natural Resources Law, *1957 Proceedings* 230 at 234 (1957);

Nelson and McNeil, "Oil Recovery by Thermal Methods," 17 *Interstate Oil Compact Bull.* 56 at 62 (Dec. 1958);

Morse, "Trends in Oil Recovery Methods," 1 *IOCC Comm. Bull.* 1 at 7 (Dec. 1959).

See also SECONDARY RECOVERY; TERTIARY RECOVERY; THERMAL METHOD OF OIL RECOVERY.

Installment bonus

See DEFERRED BONUS.

Installment bonus payment with forgiveness option

A proposed bidding system for leases on federal lands whereunder bonus is to be paid in installments with unpaid installments forgiven in the event of surrender of the lease. McDonald, *The Leasing of Federal Lands for Fossil Fuels Production* 112 (1979).

See also LEASE BIDDING SYSTEMS.

Institute of Geological Sciences (IGS)

An organization responsible for geological mapping of Great Britain, investigating and reporting on mineral resources, and collecting information concerning wells and mines.

Institute of Petroleum (IP)

A British scientific society which provides a forum for discussion of problems of the petroleum industry, establishes codes of practice for safety and operations, and publishes standards for measuring and testing petroleum products.

Institut Francais du Petrole (IFP)

An organization, with headquarters in Paris, concerned with the interests of the petroleum sector of the French economy, energy conservation, and environmental protection.

Intangible drilling and development costs (IDC)

Expenditures incurred by an operator for labor, fuel, repairs, hauling and supplies used in drilling, shooting and cleaning of wells, in preparing the surface preparatory to drilling, and in the construction of derricks, tanks, pipelines and other structures erected in connection with drilling but not including the cost of the materials themselves. The fundamental test is, do the items have salvage value? If not, they qualify as intangibles.

Under Internal Revenue Code § 263(c), an option to deduct intangible drilling and development costs as expenses is recognized. The presently applicable regulations are Treas. Reg. § 1.612–4 (1980). In general the option is between (1) deducting all intangibles (incurred in drilling producing wells or dry holes) and capitalizing all such costs, or (2) deducting dry hole intangible costs and capitalizing other intangibles. Once the election is made, it is binding in future years. See Burke and Bowhay, *Income Taxation of Natural Resources* ¶ 14.04 (1981); Fielder, "The Option to Deduct Intangible Drilling and Development Costs," 33 *Tex. L. Rev.* 825 (1955).

Standard Oil Co. (Indiana) v. Comm'r, 77 T.C. 349, 70 *O.&G.R.* 371 (Tax Court 1981), held that costs of constructing offshore jacket-type drilling platforms were deductible as intangible drilling and development costs.

For a case dealing with deductibility of intangible drilling and development costs, see Keller v. Comm'r of Internal Revenue, 79 T.C. 7, 74 *O.&G.R.* 129 (1982), *aff'd,* 725 F.2d 1173, 80 *O.&G.R.* 639 (8th Cir. 1984).

The Tax Reform Act of 1976 (*q.v.*) provided for the recapture as ordinary income of previously deducted intangible drilling and development costs to the extent of any gains realized on disposition of the property. I.R.C. § 1254. See Burke & Bowhay, *Income Taxation of Natural Resources* ¶ 14.18 (1978).

See also CAPITAL COSTS; GAIN CHARGE BACK PROVISION; NON-RECOURSE NOTE; PREPAID IDC; PRE-PLATFORM WELL.

Integrated oil company

A company engaging in all phases of the oil industry, from exploration for oil deposits to retail sale of oil products (including gasoline). These phases, in outline, are: Exploration, production, transportation, manufacturing and refining, and retailing. Some well-known integrated oil companies are Exxon, Gulf Oil, Shell Petroleum, and Texaco.

The definition in this MANUAL was quoted in Saturn Oil & Gas Co. v. Federal Power Comm'n, 250 F.2d 61, 8 *O.&G.R.* 365, at 371 (10th Cir. 1957), *cert. denied,* 355 U.S. 956, 8 *O.&G.R.* 843 (1958).

Interdependent application

An application for a certificate of convenience and necessity which, considered alone, is incomplete and depends vitally upon information in another application. 18 C.F.R. § 157.13(c) (1980).

Inter-governmental Maritime Consultative Organization (IMCO)

A United Nations special agency "whose aim is to provide machinery for co-operation among governments on technical matters affecting international shipping and, with special responsibility for the safety of life at sea, to ensure that the highest possible standards of safety at sea and of efficient navigation are achieved." IMCO 1972–73, 8 *J. of World Trade Law* 122 (1974).

See also IMCO CONVENTIONS; MARINE ENVIRONMENT PROTECTION COMMITTEE (MEPC).

Interlockers

The term applied to Schedule 3 of the Scheme to transfer assets of the BRITISH NATIONAL OIL COMPANY (BNOC) (*q.v.*) to a new company, BRITOIL, LTD. (*q.v.*). The term refers to the fact that the rights of BNOC regarding participation and the rights of BNOC regarding equity were interlocked. See Baker and Daniel, "BNOC and Privitisation—The Past and the Future," 1 *J. of Energy & Nat. Resources Law* 149 at 153 (1983).

Intermediate base oil

See MIXED BASE OIL.

Intermediate string

See CASING.

Intermediate-volume system

A liquid petroleum pipeline system or a segment of a system which transports volumes in excess of 100 BPH but less than 1000 BPH on a regular basis. Alberta Energy Resources Conservation Board Informational Letter IL–PL 76–1 (Jan. 9, 1976).

See also HIGH-VOLUME SYSTEM; LOW-VOLUME SYSTEM.

Intermittent flow

Alternate flows of oil and of gas, with intervening periods of quiescence. Intermittent flow, or flowing "by heads," results when the reservoir pressure is not sufficient for continuous flow. See HEADING.

International Association of Drilling Contractors (IADC)

See IADC FORM.

International Energy Agency (IEA)

An autonomous agency established under the International Energy Program to implement that program.

For discussions of the organization and activities of this Agency, see the following:

Daintith and Hancher, *Energy Strategy in Europe: The Legal Framework* (1986);

Holley, "The IEA and EEC Emergency Oil Allocation Systems: Legal Problems," 1 *J. of Energy and Nat. Res. Law* 73 (1983);

Claudy, "The International Energy Agency," 14 *Nat. Res. L.* 457 (1982);

Mahaffie, "The International Energy Agency in Operation." 17 *Hous. L. Rev.* 961 (1980);

Hopkins, "The International Energy Agency and Its Emergency System," in International Bar Ass'n, *Proceedings of the Energy Law Seminar* (organized by the Committee on Energy and Natural Resources, Section on Business Law) Topic C, Paper 4 (1979);

Wright, "The Role of Industry in the IEA," *Id.* Topic C. Paper 4;

Willrich and Conant, "The International Energy Agency," 71 *Am. J. Int'l L.* 199 (1977);

"U.S. Policy and the International Energy Agency," Hearings before the Subcommittees on International Organizations and Movements and on Foreign Economic Policy of the House Committee on Foreign Affairs, 93rd Cong., 2d Sess. (Dec. 18 and 19, 1974).

International Energy Program (IEP)

An agreement entered into by the United States and other major oil consuming nations at Brussels in September, 1974, on a plan for sharing energy imports in time of emergency and cooperating on other energy programs such as research and development.

Regulations dealing with International Voluntary Agreements under this Program are contained in 10 C.F.R. § 209 (1980). Regulations for Standby Mandatory International Oil Allocation under this Program are contained in 10 C.F.R. § 218 (1980).

The International Energy Agency has not as yet resolved the problem of what price will be paid for oil shared among its members during periods of worldwide shortages. See General Accounting Office, *Determination of Oil Price in the International Sharing System—An Unresolved Issue* (1982) [Stock No. GAO/ID-83-15 (B-203093)]; *CCH, Energy Management* (Issue No. 516, Dec. 7, 1982).

For discussions of the Program, see the following:

Murphy, "The International Energy Program: An Assessment," 26 *DePaul L. Rev.* 595 (1977);

"International Energy Program," Hearing before the Senate Committee on Interior and Insular Affairs, 93rd Cong., 2d Sess. (Nov. 26, 1974);

Hurni, "The International Energy Programme," 9 *J. World Trade L.* 701 (1975).

International market price

In certain development contracts this term means the average realized price per barrel really obtained by the contracting oil company or the host country for arm's length transactions on world markets. See *e.g.*, Article 28 of the INOC-ERAP contract in OPEC, *Selected Documents of the International Petroleum Industry 1968* at p. 107.

See also POSTED PRICE.

International Petroleum Exchange

A London market for trading in heating-oil futures. *The Wall Street Journal,* April 7, 1981, p. 38, col. 1; *The New York Times,* April 23, 1981, p. 27, col. 3.

See also BRENT BLEND; FUTURES MARKET.

INTERTANKO

The International Association of Independent Tanker Owners. See "The Tonnage Contract," [1982] 1 *OGLTR* 32.

Interruptible customer

A customer for INTERRUPTIBLE GAS (*q.v.*).

See also FIRM CUSTOMER; SPACE HEATING CUSTOMER; STORAGE WITHDRAWAL INTERUPTION POLICY.

Interruptible gas

Gas which is not required by the terms of a GAS PURCHASE CONTRACT (*q.v.*) to be delivered on an uninterrupted basis. The seller may for specified reasons interrupt the delivery of this gas. Purchasers of interruptible gas (so-called interruptible customers) have alternate facilities to burn competing fuels, such as oil and coal. If gas is interrupted, the customer uses a competing fuel. The price of interruptible gas must be competitive with the price of such other fuels if the customer is to purchase gas on this basis.

See also DUMP GAS; FIRM GAS.

Interruptible rate schedule

A schedule of rates for natural gas the delivery of which may be interrupted from time to time. See Panhandle Eastern Pipe Line Co. v. Federal Power Comm'n, 232 F.2d 467, 5 *O.&G.R.* 1428 (3d Cir. 1956), *cert. denied,* 352 U.S. 891, 6 *O.&G.R.* 898 (1956).

Interruptible service

A lower priced service to utility customers which may be interrupted, *e.g.,* upon two hours' notice. This service is on a "when available" basis and may be interrupted frequently in winter periods when the demand for gas is greatest. See Granite City Steel Co. v. Federal Power Comm'n, 320 F. 2d 711 (D.C. Cir. 1963); Arkansas Power & Light Co. v. Federal Power Comm'n, 517 F.2d 1223 (D.C. Cir. 1975), *cert. denied,* 423 U.S. 933 (1976).

Interruptible transportation service rate (IT rate)

A rate for sales and transportation services of a pipeline which are interruptible at the pipeline's discretion. Public Service Comm'n of State of N.Y. v. Federal Energy Regulatory Comm'n, 813 F.2d 448 (D.C. Cir. 1987).

Interruption of prescription

See PRESCRIPTION.

Interstate gas

"Gas transported in interstate pipelines to be sold and consumed in states other than that state in which the gas was produced." American Gas Ass'n, *Glossary for the Gas Industry* (3d ed. 1981).

Interstate Natural Gas Association of America (INGAA)

A non-profit national trade association representing many of the major interstate natural gas transmission companies subject to the jurisdiction of the Federal Power Commission and its successor, the Federal Energy Regulatory Commission, under the Natural Gas Act of 1938.

Interstate Oil Compact

An interstate compact negotiated and first approved by Congress in 1935, the purpose of which is the conservation of oil and gas by the prevention of waste. The Compact provides no coercive powers, but relies on voluntary agreement to accomplish its objectives. The Compact originally had 6 member states and now has thirty members and six associate members. For a general discussion of its formation and operation, see Hardwicke, *Anti-Trust Laws, et al. vs. Unit Operation of Oil and Gas Pools* (1948). See also Ely, *Oil Conservation by Interstate Agreement* (1933); Murphy, "The Interstate Oil Compact to Conserve Oil and Gas," 17 *Miss. L.J.* 314 (1946).

Interstate Oil Compact Commission (IOCC)

The administrative agency of the Interstate Oil Compact. It has no compulsive powers, but provides a number of services to member states, the industry, and state regulatory agencies, among which are the collection and publication of data, the making of studies and recommendations in conservation problems, and the furnishing of an opportunity for exchange of information and discussion of industry problems.

Interstitial water

See CONNATE WATER

Intertract bidding

A proposed bidding system for leases of coal on federal lands, under which the government would put up a number of tracts for simultaneous bidding, but would not commit itself to granting leases on all of them. "With simultaneous bidding on all the tracts, there would be competition among bidders for each tract, but also competition among high bidders since eases would not be granted on all tracts. To obtain a lease a bidder would not only have to outbid others interested in the same tract, but would have to bid high enough to assure that a tract on which he had bid would be selected for the granting of a lease." McDonald, *The Leasing of Federal Lands for Fossil Fuels Production* 115 (1979).

See also LEASE BIDDING SYSTEMS.

Interval

(1) The vertical distance between strata.

(2) The distance between two points or depths in a bore hole. Bureau of Mines, *A Dictionary of Mining, Mineral and Related Terms* 586 (1968); Energy Resources Group, Inc., 92 IBLA 219, GFS(O&G) 1986-67.

See also STRATIGRAPHIC INTERVAL.

Intrastate clause

A clause of a GAS PURCHASE CONTRACT (*q.v.*) prohibiting transportation of the gas outside the state of sale or requiring that the purchaser give notice of any proposed out-of-state transmission and affording the seller the right to terminate the contract before such transportation begins. See Cassin, "Gas Purchase Contracts—Enticing a Shy Genie from an Invisible Lamp," 25 *Sw. Legal Fdn. Oil & Gas Inst.* 27 at 35 (1974).

Intrastate gas

"Gas sold and consumed in the state where it is produced and not transported in interstate pipelines." American Gas Ass'n, *Glossary for the Gas Industry* (3d ed. 1981).

Intrastate utilization clause

A provision of a GAS PURCHASE CONTRACT (*q.v.*) representing that the pipeline purchaser is engaged solely in intrastate transportation of natural gas and that the gas purchased shall be sold and used only in connection therewith. Superior Oil Co. v. Western Slope Gas Co., 549 F. Supp. 463 at 465, 74 *O.&G.R.* 593 at 595 (D. Colo. 1982).

Inventory committee

A committee appointed by an Operators Committee to make an inventory of the physical property taken over by a Unit Operator under a pooling or unitization agreement. See Myers, *The Law of Pooling and Unitization* 128 (1957).

Investment Canada

The proposed successor to the FOREIGN INVESTMENT REVIEW AGENCY (FIRA) (*q.v.*) under the provisions of the INVESTMENT CANADA BILL (*q.v.*).

Investment Canada Bill

Bill C-15 (first reading December 7, 1984), making major changes in the FOREIGN INVESTMENT REVIEW ACT (FIRA) (*q.v.*) and renaming the FOREIGN INVESTMENT REVIEW AGENCY (*q.v.*) as INVESTMENT CANADA. See Lucas, "Investment Canada and the Resource Sector," 10 *Resources* (Feb. 1985); Arnett, "From FIRA to Investment Canada," 24 *Alberta L. Rev.* 1 (1985).

Investment guarantee

A provision of a CONCESSION (*q.v.*) agreement designed: (1) to guarantee the operator against abrogation of the concession; (2) to guarantee a minimum net profit, or (3) to guarantee the convertibility of such profits into foreign exchange abroad. See Mughraby, *Permanent Sovereignty Over Oil Resources* 102 (1966).

Investment recovery oil

See COST RECOVERY OIL.

Invited application

An application in the United Kingdom for a PRODUCTION LICENSE (*q.v.*) in accordance with the provisions of Regulation 7 of The Petroleum (Production) Regulations 1976. See Henderson *et al., Oil and Gas Law: The North Sea Exploitation* 3.1015 (1979).

IOC

Abbreviation for International oil company.

IOCC

The Interstate Oil Compact Commission.

IP

(1) Abbreviation for INITIAL PRODUCTION (*q.v.*).
(2) The INSTITUTE OF PETROLEUM (*q.v.*).

IPAA

Independent Petroleum Association of America.

IPAC

Iran Pan American Oil Co.

IPAM

The Independent Petroleum Association of the Mountain States.

IPC

The IRAQ PETROLEUM COMPANY (*q.v.*).

IPRO

Independent producers and royalty owners.

IPRO exemption

The exemption given indpendent producers and royalty owners from the provisions of the Tax Reduction Act of 1975 designed to eliminate percentage depletion. See "Initial Proposed Section 613A Regulations," 24 *O.&G. Tax Q.* 218 at 222 (1975).

See also DEPLETION, PERCENTAGE; TRANSFER RULE.

IRAA

The Independent Refiners Association of America.

Iranian consortium

A 1954 organization of companies engaged in producing oil in Iran. See "Multinational Oil Corproations and U.S. Foreign Policy," Report to the Committee on Foreign Relations, United States Senate, by the Subcommittee on Multinational Corporations, 93rd Cong., 2d Sess. (Jan. 2, 1975) at p. 95.

See also APQ SYSTEM; CONCESSION; OSCO.

Iranian Oil Exploration and Producing Company

The predecessor to the OIL SERVICE COMPANY OF IRAN (OSCO) (*q.v.*).

Iraq National Oil Company (INOC)

For discussions of this national oil company see Shwadran, *The Middle East, Oil and the Great Powers* 279 *et seq.* (3d ed. revised and enlarged, 1973); OPEC, *Selected Documents of the International Petroleum Industry 1967* at p. 14; *Id. 1968* at p. 17

Iraq Petroleum Company (IPC)

For a discussion of the history of this company, see Shwadran, *The Middle East, Oil and the Great Powers* 237 *et seq.* (3d ed. revised and enlarged, 1973).

IROR

INCENTIVE RATE OF RETURN (*q.v.*).

Irrigation gas clause

A lease clause authorizing the lessor, at his option, to take in kind all or a part of his royalty on gas for use as fuel for irrigation wells located on the land from which the gas is being produced. Heare, "Effect of Gathering and Processing on Payment of Gas Royalties and Similar Interests," 10 *Sw. Legal Fdn. Oil & Gas Inst.* 153 at 1546 (1959). See TREATISE § 662.

Island acreage

Acreage so surrounded by drilling units that it cannot be produced. Bigland Operating Co. v. Brown, 347 So.2d 1310 at 1312, 57 *O.&G.R.* 561 at 565 (Miss. 1977).

Isobath

Lines connecting points of equal water depth.

Isolated tract

"A parcel of vacant public lands, not exceeding 1520 acres, which is surrounded by appropriated public lands." United States Department of the Interior Bureau of Land Management, *Glossary Public-Land Terms* 23 (1949).

See also PUBLIC LANDS.

Isopach lines

Lines on a map joining points of equal sand thickness. See Limes, "Geological Proof of Drainage," 11 *L.S.U. Min. Law Inst.* 33 at 43 (1964).

Isopachous map

A "map which represents the thickness of a formation by means of lines, similar to contour lines, drawn through points of equal thickness." Mobil Oil Corp. v. Gill, 194, So.2d 351, 26 *O.&G.R.* 768 at 770 (La. App. 1966), *writ ref'd,* 250 La. 174, 194 So.2d 738, 26 *O.&G.R.* 773 (1967).

Isopentane

A very high octane blending material for automotive gasolines.

IT rate

INTERRUPTIBLE TRANSPORTATION SERVICE RATE (*q.v.*).

"Ivy" option

A nickname for the option available under Subdivision (iv) of Sub-Paragraph (5) of Section 1.614–2(a)(4) of the 1956 proposed Treasury Regulations. Under this option, the taxpayer, instead of having all of his operating interests which he included in an invalid basic aggregation treated as separate properties for the years in which such an invalid basic aggregation was in effect, could have his tax liability recomputed on the basis of forming new aggregations within the proper operating unit. See Stroud, "Major Points of Impact of New Natural Resources Regulations on Oil and Gas," 8 *Sw. Legal Fdn. Oil & Gas Inst.* 393 at 439 (1957); French, "The Oil and Gas Property and Aggregation," 36 *Texas L. Rev.* 745 at 767 (1958). The "Ivy" option was abolished by the 1961 regulations. See McLane, "Recent Developments in Oil and Gas Taxation," 12 *Sw. Legal Fdn. Oil & Gas Inst.* 463 at 484 (1961).

See also AGGREGATION OF PROPERTIES.

IW

INFILL WELL (*q.v.*).

IW order

Infill well drilling order. See INFILL WELL.

. . J . .

Jack-up rig

A mobile drilling platform with extendible legs for support on the ocean floor. Kash, *et al.*, *Energy Under the Oceans* 39, 366 (1973).

See also MOBILE RIG.

Jactitory action (jactitation suit)

A SLANDER OF TITLE (*q.v.*) action in Louisiana, borrowed from Spanish procedure. Article 3655 of the Louisiana Code of Civil Procedure (1961), provides for a possessory action [*viz.*, "one brought by the possessor of immovable property or of a real right to be maintained in his possession of the property or enjoyment of the right when he has been disturbed, or to be restored to the possession or enjoyment thereof when he has been evicted"], which merges the former possessory action and the former jactitory action. Disturbances of possession, giving rise to the possessory action, include disturbance in fact and disturbance in law. The latter, which provided the basis for jactitory actions, was defined as "the execution, recordation, registry, or continuing existence of record of any instrument which asserts or implies a right of ownership or to the possession of immovable property or of a real right, or any claim or pretension of ownership or right to the possession thereof except in any action or proceeding, adversely to the possessor of such property or right." *Id.*, Art. 3659.

The nature of this action is discussed in Broussard v. Louisiana Land & Exploration Co., 164 So. 2d 84 (La. App. 1964), *writ denied,* 246 La. 603, 165 So. 2d 488 (1964).

See also Zengel, "The Real Actions—A Study in Code Revision" 29 *Tulane L. Rev.* 617 at 619 (1955).

JAS

The Joint Association Survey by three industry trade groups of the cost per foot of well drilling. See Permian Basin Area Rate Proceeding, 34 F.P.C. 159 at 197, 23 *O.&G.R.* 103 at 141 (Opinion No. 468, Aug. 5, 1965), *remanded,* Skelly Oil Co. v. Federal Power Comm'n, 375 F.2d 6, 26 *O.&G.R.* 237 (10th Cir. 1967), *aff'd in part and rev'd in part sub nom. In re* Permian Basin Area Rate Cases, 390 U.S. 747, 28 *O.&G.R.* 689 (1968).

JDPC

The Japan Petroleum Development Corporation.

Jet perforating

A method of perforating casing. A shaped charge of high explosives is used to burn a hole through the casing instead of using a gun to fire a projectile.

See also BULLET PERFORATION; GUN PERFORATION; PERFORATION.

Jetting

Injection of gas into a stratum for purpose of PRESSURE MAINTENANCE (*q.v.*), SECONDARY RECOVERY (*q.v.*), *etc.* Dunn v. Republic Natural Gas Co., 124 F.2d 128 (5th Cir. 1941), *cert. denied,* 315 U.S. 821 (1942).

Joinder of parties

See INDISPENSABLE PARTIES; NECESSARY PARTIES; PROPER PARTIES.

Joint

(1) A place where two things are joined together.

(2) A length of pipe or tubing. See Ball, Ball, and Turner, *This Fascinating Oil Business* 95 (2d ed. 1965).

Joint account well

A well drilled under the terms of a JOINT OPERATING AGREEMENT (*q.v.*) for the joint account of all participants. Hazlett, "Drafting of Joint Operating Agreements," 3 *Rocky Mt. Min. L. Inst.* 227 at 290 (1957).

See also NON-JOINT DRILLING.

Joint adventure

An association of persons for the prosecution of a single venture. The usual elements of a joint adventure (*Syn.:* Joint venture) are: (1) a community of interest in the object of the undertaking; (2) an equal right to direct and govern the conduct of each other with respect thereto; (3) share in the losses if any; and (4) a close and even fiduciary relationship between the parties. Beck v. Cagle, 46 Cal. App. 2d 152, 115 P.2d 613 (1941). See Crane, *Partnership* § 35 (2d ed. 1952); Grannell v. Wakefield, 172 Kan. 658, 242 P.2d 1075, 1

O.&G.R. 658 (1952); Maxwell, "Enforceability of Oral Agreements in Oil and Gas Transactions," 6 *Sw. Legal Fdn. Oil & Gas Inst.* 165 at 201–209 (1956).

Where minerals are acquired by co-owners for the purpose of resale and division of the profits, a joint adventure may arise, in which event either of the co-owners has power to convey or lease the concurrently owned interest except to the extent that such power is limited by the agreement creating the joint adventure. Taylor v. Brindley, 164 F.2d 235 (10th Cir. 1947).

For a distinction of a leasing transaction from a joint venture, see J.T. Williams II, "Assignment of Leasehold, Royalty and Oil Payment," 2 *Sw. Legal Fdn. Oil & Gas Inst.* 469 at 487 (1951).

See TREATISE §§ 437–437.2.

For a discussion of the joint venture and the modern concession agreement, see Mikesell, *Petroleum Company Operations & Agreements in the Developing Countries* 108 (1984).

For a discussion of the employment of joint venture agreements in Norwegian petroleum development, see Krohn, Kaasen, *et al.*, *Norwegian Petroleum Law* Part 3 (1978).

The effect of joint ventures on competitive bids for offshore oil is discussed in Klein, *The Impact of Joint Ventures on Bidding for Offshore Oil* (revised ed. 1981).

Antitrust Problems raised by joint ventures are discussed in Coyle, "Antitrust Considerations in Mineral Exploration and Exploitation Ventures," *Rocky Mt. Min. L. Fdn. Mining Agreements Institute* 4–1 (1979).

For detailed discussions of the law of joint adventure in Australia, see the papers presented at the 5th Annual Conference of the Australian Mining and Petroleum Law Association, 3 *Australian Mining and Petroleum L.J.* (1981); Ryan, "Joint Adventure Agreements," 4 *Australian Mining and Petroleum L.J.* 101 (1982), and Crommelin, "The Mineral and Petroleum Joint Venture in Australia," 4 *J. Energy & Nat. Res. L.* 65 (1986).

Joint adventure financing is discussed in several papers in International Bar Ass'n, *Energy Law 1981*.

See also AFTER ACQUIRED RIGHTS CLAUSE; BACK-IN RIGHT; CHILLING THE BID; CONSENT PARTY; CONSORTIUM; CROSS-CHARGE; EARNED INTEREST; EQUITY JOINT VENTURE; GROUP SHOOT; MONEY LEFT ON THE TABLE; PERMITTED CHARGING CLAUSE; PROJECT FINANCING; TAX SHIFTING CLAUSE; THIRD FOR A QUARTER DEAL; UNDERLIFT/OVERLIFT PROVISION.

Joint bid agreement

An agreement of two or more companies interested in acquiring oil and gas leases offered for sale through competitive bidding, under which a single bid is submitted on behalf of the group. Antitrust problems and governmental restrictions on participation of larger companies in joint bid agreements involving continental shelf leases are discussed in Burke and Oliver, "Current Antitrust Developments in Oil and Gas Exploration and Production," 30 *Sw. Legal Fdn. Oil & Gas Inst.* 271 (1979).

See also LEASE BIDDING SYSTEMS.

Joint exploration activities

A term used "to describe the situation of a jointly owned lease or block of acreage which contemplates the exploration and drilling of multiple wells, each party paying for its own costs and being entitled to its pro rata share of income and operating expenses. This joint form of oil and gas activity is primarily conducted via the form of a 'joint operating agreement' in which the various participants appoint an operator who controls the day-to-day operations and has authority to make decisions affecting the other interest owners in nonmajor areas of operations. In major areas of operations, for example, to commit substantial funds, to determine places of drilling, to conduct secondary or tertiary recovery operations, it usually takes more than a majority in interest to approve such operations." Bean, "Entity Selection—An Experience in Alchemy—A Comparison of Corporations, Partnerships, and Joint Ventures," 30 *Sw. Legal Fdn. Oil & Gas. Inst.* 363 at 367 (1979).

Joint lease

A COMMUNITY LEASE (*q.v.*). Also, any lease in which two or more mineral owners join, including concurrent owners. See Hoffman, *Voluntary Pooling and Unitization* 9 (1954).

Joint loss provision

A provision in an operating agreement placing upon all participants (rather than on the individual contributor) the loss caused by failure of title to an interest included in the agreement. See Folks, "The Model Form Operating Agreement," *1959 Sw. Legal Fdn. Nat'l Inst for Petroleum Landmen* 69 at 70 (1960).

See also INDIVIDUAL LOSS PROVISIONS; JOINT OPERATING AGREEMENT; OPERATING AGREEMENT.

Joint operating agreement

(1) An agreement between or among interested parties for the operation of a tract or leasehold for oil, gas and other minerals. This type of agreement is frequently entered into before there has been any development. Typically the agreement provides for the development of the premises by one of the parties for the joint account. The parties to the agreement share in the expenses of the operations and in the proceeds of development, but the agreement normally is not intended to affect the ownership of the minerals or the rights to produce, in which respects, among others, the joint operating agreement is to be distinguished from a unitization agreement and from a mining partnership. A joint operation may be carried on by a variety of means other than by a joint operating agreement, including the following: joint adventure, partnership, corporation or trust. See TREATISE § 503.2.

The joint operating agreement does not result, as do these other methods of conducting a joint operation, in the creation of a separate tax entity. If the agreement between the concurrent owners includes the sale or disposition of the products produced, however, it may result in the creation of a partnership for tax purposes. See Burke and Bowhay, *Income Taxation of Natural Resources* ¶¶ 10.02–10.08 (1981). The joint operating agreement must provide either that each co-owner has a right to take his share of production in kind or that the authority of the operator to market the production shall be revocable at the will of the other concurrent owners if taxability as an association is to be avoided.

Williams v. BP Alaska Exploration, Inc., 677 P.2d 236 (Alaska 1983), concluded that under the Alaska Business License Act all monies received from nonoperating co-owners of leases as reimbursement for their share of costs incurred by the operator under operating agreements were to be included within the operator's gross income for the year of receipt.

(2) An agreement between or among adjoining landowners or lessees concerning the development of a common pool.

For an example of a joint operating agreement, see TREATISE § 920.5.

See also the following:

Blinn, Duval, Le Leuch, and Pertuzio, *International Petroleum Exploration & Exploitation Agreements* ch. 10 (1986);

Lewis, "Comment: The Joint Operating Agreement: Partnership or Not?," 4 *J. of Energy & Nat. Res. L.* 80 (1986);

Conine, "Rights and Liabilities of Carried Interest and Nonconsent Parties in Oil and Gas Operation," 37 *Sw. Legal Fdn. Oil & Gas Inst.* 3-1 (1986);

Kutzschbach, "Operating Agreement Considerations in Acquisitions of Producing Properties," 36 *Sw. Legal Fdn. Oil & Gas Inst.* 7-1 (1985);

Willoughby, "Forfeiture of Interests in Joint Operating Agreements," 3 *J. of Energy & Nat. Res. L.* 256 (1985) (discussing the jurisdiction of courts to relieve against the forfeiture of interests in operating agreements);

Moore, "Joint Operating Agreements—Is There Really a Standard That Can Be Relied Upon?," 5 *Eastern Min. L. Inst.* 15-1 (1984);

Heaney, "The Joint Operating Agreement, the AFE and COPAS—What They Fail to Provide," 29 *Rocky Mt. Min. L. Inst.* 733 (1983);

David, "Pitfalls of Joint Operating Agreements," [1983] 8 *OGLTR* 1980;

Amman, "Accounting Procedures for Joint Mining Operations," *Rocky Mt. Min. L. Fdn. Mining Agreements Inst.* 5–1 (1979).

See also AFTER-ACQUIRED RIGHTS CLAUSE; BALANCING; CONSENT PARTY; CONTRACT AREA; CONTRIBUTION CLAUSE; DEEMED PURCHASE FORMULA; DRILLING FUND; INDIVIDUAL LOSS PROVISION; INDUSTRY DEAL; JOINT ACCOUNT WELL; JOINT LOSS PROVISION; MAINTENANCE OF UNIFORM INTEREST CLAUSE; NON-CONSENT PENALTY; NON-JOINT DRILLING; OPERATING AGREEMENT; PER WELL CHARGE; PROGRAM MANAGEMENT FEE; TAX SHIFTING CLAUSE; UNDERLIFT/OVERLIFT PROVISION; UNIT AGREEMENT; WITHERING CLAUSE.

Joint tenancy

A form of CONCURRENT OWNERSHIP (*q.v.*), the most important feature of which is a right of survivorship.

Joint unit well

A well drilled in an area that has been unitized. Gates Rubber Co. & Subsidiaries v. Commissioner, 74 T.C. 1456, 67 *O.&G.R.* 657 (1980), *aff'd,* 694 F.2d 648 (10th Cir. 1982); Sun Oil Co. v. Commissioner, 74 T.C. 1481, 68 *O.&G.R.* 353 (1980), *aff'd,* 677 F.2d 294, 76 *O.&G.R.* 619 (3d Cir. 1982), *acq.,* I.R.B. 1983-26 (1983).

Joint venture

See JOINT ADVENTURE.

Joule

A unit of energy, named after the British physicist James Prescott Joule (1818–1889):

(1) Under the International System of energy, a joule is equal to the work done when a current of one ampere is passed through a resistance of one ohm for one second.

(2) The energy equal to the work done when the point of application of a force of one newton is displaced one meter in the direction of the force.

Judicial ascertainment clause

An oil and gas lease clause providing that the lease shall not terminate, be cancelled or forfeited for failure to perform implied covenants, conditions or obligations until it is judicially determined that such failure exists. Some such clauses provide further that any judicial decree resulting from such failure shall be in the alternative, providing for reasonable time for compliance by the lessee after breach is established in court. See TREATISE §§ 682–682.5.

See also DEFAULT CLAUSE; GOOD FAITH CLAUSE; NOTICE AND DEMAND CLAUSE.

Jumbo burner

A flaming torch used for the disposal in the field of casinghead gas produced with oil when such gas is without a market and is not used by the producer for some non-wasteful purpose. The use of jumbo burners or flambeau lights is now generally regulated under state conservation laws.

Jumping Pound Decision

The July 29, 1954, and December 3, 1959, decisions of the Public Utilities Board of Alberta, pursuant to an application under Section 9 of The Gas Utilities Act, relating to charges and deductions to be allowed for processing costs in determining the value of gas for royalty purposes. See Rae, "Royalty Clauses in Oil and Gas Leases," 4 *Alberta L. Rev.* 323 at 340 (1965); Muir, "Utilization of Alberta Gas," 13 *Alberta L. Rev.* 64 (1975).

Jurisdictional escape clause

A clause in some contracts between independent producers and pipeline companies providing in substance that if a Federal agency asserts jurisdiction over the seller or over prices set forth in the contract, the seller has a right to cancel the contract or terminate the service. Wolf, "The Independent Producer and the Federal Power Commission," 6 *Sw. Legal Fdn. Oil & Gas Inst.* 1 at 21 (1955); Magnolia Petroleum Co. v. Texas Illinois Natural Gas Pipeline Co., 130 F. Supp. 890, 4 *O.&G.R.* 408 (S.D. Tex. 1954).

It has been held that a jurisdictional escape clause is not effective to give a seller of natural gas the right to abandon deliveries subject to Federal Power Commission or Federal Energy Regulatory Commission jurisdiction without the consent of the Commission. See TREATISE § 732.

Syn.: FERC-OUT CLAUSE; FPC ESCAPE CLAUSE.

Jurisdictional sales

A term used to describe sales of natural gas which were subject to the jurisdiction of the Federal Power Commission under the Natural Gas Act.

The NATURAL GAS POLICY ACT OF 1978 (NGPA) (*q.v.*), Pub. L. No. 95–621, provided for a single national market for gas sales, eliminating the jurisdictional sale-nonjurisdictional sale distinction.

See also AREA PRICING POLICY; MOLECULAR THEORY; VOLUMETRIC METHOD OF ALLOCATION.

Just and equitable share of the production

That part of the authorized production from the pool that is substantially in the proportion that the amount of recoverable oil or gas or both in the developed area of each person's tract or tracts in the pool bears to the recoverable oil or gas or both in the total developed area in the pool. IOCC, *A Suggested Form of General Rules and Regulation for the Conservation of Oil and Gas* (1960), Rule III.

. . K . .

Kelly

A long steel forging which makes connection with the top joint of drill stem in the drill string. See *A Primer of Oil Well Drilling* (Petroleum Extension Service, Univ. of Texas, Div. of Extension, 2d ed. 1957).

See also DRILLING RIG; GRIEFSTEM.

Kerogen

A hydrocarbon found in OIL SHALE (*q.v.*), which when extracted and treated yields oil. See 8 O.&G.R. 515 (1958).

For a discussion of the nature and characteristics of kerogen, see Brennan v. Udall, 251 F. Supp. 12, 25 *O.&G.R.* 629 (D. Colo. 1966).

Kerosine

The petroleum fraction containing hydrocarbons that are slightly heavier than those found in gasoline and naptha, with a boiling range of about 180 to 300 degree C. Prior to 1910, kerosine (also spelled kerosene) was the most important petroleum product because of its use for home and commercial lighting; in recent years demand has risen again as a result of kerosine's use in gas turbines and jet engines. See Hammond, Metz, and Maugh, *Energy and the Future* 162 (1973).

See also CASE OIL.

Key bed

The stratum selected for contouring. If, as is supposed, other strata are comformable to the key bed, then a correct contouring of the key bed will indicate the subsurface structure.

Key horizon

See KEY BED.

Key money

Syn. for BONUS (*q.v.*). See Beurbe v. Minister of National Revenue, 54 D.T.C. 289, 4 *O.&G.R.* 799 (Income Tax Appeal Board of Canada, 1954).

KGRA

KNOWN GEOTHERMAL RESOURCES AREA (*q.v.*).

KHS

KNOWN GEOLOGIC STRUCTURE (*q.v.*).

Kick

Loss of normal fluid circulation caused by pressure from below in excess of that exerted by the drilling fluid being pumped into the well. If efforts to control a kick are unsuccessful and the subsurface pressure increases to the point where the expulsion of drilling fluid is violent and uncontrolled, a blow-out can and often does develop. See Fidelity-Phenix Fire Insurance Co. of New York v. Dyer, 220 F.2d 697, 4 *O.&G.R.* 973 (5th Cir. 1955); MUD.

Kickout clause

A clause found in some purchase contracts for oil and gas that permits the purchaser, under certain conditions—usually relating to pricing or market availability—to renegotiate the contract. See Blinn, Duval, Le Leuch, and Pertuzio, *International Petroleum Exploration & Exploitation Agreements* 333 (1986).

Kill a well

To cease production from a well, usually for the purpose of converting it into an input or injection well.

This term is also used (1) to describe the act of bringing under control a well which is threatening to blow out, and (2) to describe the procedure of circulating water and mud into a completed well before starting well service operations.

Kill line

A line attached to the BLOW-OUT PREVENTER (*q.v.*) assembly through which drilling fluid, commonly mud, can be pumped into the hole to subdue well pressure caused by oil and gas. The connection to which the kill line is attached is the stand pipe. Walters v. Inexco Oil Co., 511 F. Supp. 21 (S.D. Miss. 1979), *rev'd and remanded,* 725 F.2d 1014 (5th Cir. 1984).

Knock-for-knock indemnity clause

A clause utilized in some offshore drilling contracts which makes each perty responsible for death or injury to its own employees and for loss of their property regardless of the negligence or fault of any party. The drilling contractor and the operator undertake to indemnify one another for any such claims or costs. These arrangements treat employees of subcontractors as though they were the employees of the party hiring them. Thus the operator accepts responsibility for individuals it brings to the work site, such as the employees of its service contractors. Hunt, "Private Risk Allocation in Offshore Projects," 14 *Resources* (The Newsletter of the Canadian Institute of Resources Law, Fed. 1986).

Knockout

"Fractionating system for removal of such heavy hydrocarbons as paraffins, hexanes, pentanes, and mercaptans." American Gas Ass'n, *Glossary for the Gas Industry* (3d ed. 1981).

Knowledge box

A driller's term for the place where he keeps his orders and reports. *API Quarterly* 3 (Spring 1957).

Known geological structure (KGS)

The trap in which an accumulation of oil or gas has been discovered by drilling and determined to be productive, the limits of which include acreage that is presumptively producing. 43 C.F.R. 3100.0–5(a) (1978). Whether or not federal lands include known geologic structures of producing oil and gas fields determines many of the distinctions and classifications of federal leases. In declaring land within an oil and gas lease to be within a known geologic structure, the Bureau of Land Management relies on the reports of the Geological Survey. A determination by the Geological Survey that land is within an undefined known geologic structure will not be disturbed in the absence of a clear showing that the determination was improperly made. Vernon and Rita Benson, IBLA 80–24, 48 IBLA 64, GFS (O&G) 1980–114 (May 29, 1980); See Duncan Miller, 19 IBLA 86, GFS (O&G) 1975–26 (1975) (March 3, 1975). See also *Rocky Mt. Min. L. Fdn. Law of Federal Oil and Gas Leases* ch. 3 (1985).

Robert L. Lyon, IBLA 82-566, GFS(O&G) 1982-205 (Aug. 10, 1982), sustained a determination of the Geological Survey that land within the so-called Austin Chalk formation was within a known geological structure.

For a discussion of the meaning of this term as employed by Congress and by the Secretary of the Interior, see Arkla Exploration Co. v. Watt, 562 F. Supp. 1214, 78 *O.&G.R.* 235 (W.D. Ark. 1983), *aff'd sub nom.* Arkla Exploration Co. v. Texas Oil & Gas Corp., 734 F.2d 347, 81 *O.&G.R.* 486 (8th Cir. 1984), *cert. denied,* 469 U.S. 1158, 105 S. Ct. 905 (1985).

See also FAVORABLE PETROLEUM GEOLOGICAL PROVINCE (FPGP); PROVINCE.

Known geothermal resources area (KGRA)

"[A]n area in which the geology, nearby discoveries, competitive interests, or other indicia would, in the opinion of the Secretary [of the Interior], engender a belief in men who are experienced in the subject matter that the prospects for extraction of geothermal steam or associated GEOTHERMAL RESOURCES (*q.v.*) are good enough to warrant expenditures of money for that purpose." 43 C.F.R. § 3200.0–5 (k) (1978).

As of 1973, about 1.8 million acres of land in the western United States had been classified as being within such a KGRA by the U. S. Geological Survey and an additional 96 million acres were listed as having prospective value for geothermal recourses.

California Energy Co. (On Reconsideration), 85 IBLA 254, 92 I.D. 125 (March 6, 1985), deals with the authority of the Secretary of the Interior to reject a bid for a lease in a KGRA. The government's reliance on oil and gas drilling data to calculate geothermal resource exploration costs was found to be in error.

See also FRONTIER ENVIRONMENT.

KNPC

The KUWAIT NATIONAL PETROLEUM COMPANY (*q.v.*).

KOC

The KUWAIT OIL COMPANY (*q.v.*).

KPC

KUWAIT PETROLEUM CORPORATION (KPC) (*q.v.*).

Kuwait National Petroleum Company (KNPC)

For a discussion of the history of this company, see Shwadran, *The Middle East, Oil and the Great Powers* 418 (3d ed. revised and enlarged, 1973).

Kuwait Oil Company (KOC)

For a discussion of the history of this company, see Shwadran, *The Middle East, Oil and the Great Powers* 414 *et seq.* (3d ed. revised and enlarged, 1973).

Kuwait Petroleum Corporation (KPC)

An entity established in 1980, wholly owned by the government of Kuwait, to which all government-owned shares of companies involved in the hydrocarbon industry were assigned. See Santa Fe International Corp. v. Watt, 591 F.Supp. 929, 84 *O.&G.R.* 221 (D. Dela. 1984).

. . L . .

Laches

Neglect, for an unreasonable and unexplained length of time, under circumstances permitting diligence, to do what in law should have been done; an inexcusable delay in asserting a right; an implied waiver arising from knowledge of existing conditions and an acquiescence in them; such delay in enforcing one's rights as works disadvantage to another.

For cases dealing with the effect of alleged laches on various claims, see the following:

Pope v. Pennzoil Producing Co., 288 Ark. 10, 701 S.W.2d 366, 87 *O.&G.R.* 488 (1986):

"Production commenced in December 1971. Appellant personally observed the drilling, the erection of the tanks, batteries, pumping units, and the laying of the pipelines. Still, he silently stood by and made no claim until December, 1981, thirteen years after the initial leases had been executed, ten years after production had begun, and ten years after the value of the leases had dramatically increased. The Chancellor sagaciously noted:

> Due to the risks involved in the exploration for and production of oil and gas, I find that the Plaintiff [appellant] should be barred by the doctrine of laches as to any claim at this time to his allegedly unleased mineral interest. No doubt had production ceased before the well paid out the Plaintiff certainly would make no claim to a working interest and share in the cost of drilling, but would only seek payment for his 1/8 royalty.

The Chancellor was correct. The appellant is barred by the doctrine of laches.";

Tosco Corp. v. Hodel, 611 F.Supp. 1130 at 1208 *et seq.* (D. Colo. 1985) (discussing application of laches to the government), settled by Aug. 4, 1986 agreement, see 2 *Nat. Res. & Environment* 74 (Fall 1986), 804 F.2d 590 (10th Cir. 1986);

Richardson v. Richland County, 711 P.2d 777, 89 *O.&G.R.* 317 (Mont. 1985), and Anderson v. Richland County, 711 P.2d 784, 89 *O.&G.R.* 306 (Mont. 1985) (holding that an action to quiet title against a royalty interest reserved by the county in a void tax sale was barred by laches);

Jordan v. Sutton, 424 So. 2d 305 at 310 (La. App. 1982), 77 *O.&G.R.* 89 at 98 (finding that in instant case the plaintiff was not barred by laches from seeking review of order of the Commissioner of Conservation but was barred by laches as to certain other claims);

Corbello v. Sutton, 442 So. 2d 610, 80 *O.&G.R.* 490 (La. App. 1983) (finding action to review order of the Commissioner of Conservation was barred by laches), *dismissal of appeal from Commissioner of Conservation aff'd on different grounds,* 446 So. 2d 301, 82 *O.&G.R.* 79 (La. 1984);

Morgan v. Morgan, 431 So. 2d 1119, 77 *O.&G.R.* 511 (Miss. 1983) (claimants who had knowledge that deed in chain of title was a forgery were estopped by laches to assert their claim against an oil and gas lessee who had drilled and obtained production under a lease executed by the grantee of forged deed).

Syn.: EQUITABLE ESTOPPEL (*q.v.*).

See also LYING BEHIND THE LOG.

LACT

See LEASE AUTOMATIC CUSTODY TRANSFER.

Lag

The time period between investment in a lease and first realization of revenue from the sale of gas. See Permian Basin Area Rate Proceeding, 34 F.P.C. 159 at 199, 23 *O.&G.R.* 103 at 144 (Opinion No. 468, Aug. 5, 1965), *remanded,* Skelly Oil Co. v. Federal Power Comm'n, 375 F.2d 6, 26 *O.&G.R.* 237 (10th Cir. 1967), *aff'd in part and rev'd in part sub nom. In re* Permian Basin Area Rate Cases, 390 U.S. 747, 28 *O.&G.R.* 689 (1968).

Land committee

A committee charged with securing signatures of royalty owners to a pooling or unitization agreement. See Myers, *The Law of Pooling and Unitization* § 4.06 (2d ed. 1967).

Landed cost of oil

Cost of imported oil at the dock, *viz.,* inclusive of transportation costs.

Landfill gas recovery project

See LFG RECOVERY PROJECT.

Landman

An employee of an oil company whose primary duties are the management of the company's relations with its landowners. Such duties include the securing of oil and gas leases, lease amendments, pooling and unitization agreements and instruments necessary for curing title defects from landowners.

See the following:

McDavid, "Legal and Ethical Obligations of the Landman," 7 *Eastern Min. L. Inst.* ch. 20 (1986);

Knutson, "Legal and Ethical Obligations a Landman Owes His Employer," 31 *Rocky Mt. Min. L. Inst.* 19-1 (1985);

Harris, "Analyzing and Curing Title Opinions," 31 *Rocky Mt. Min. L. Inst.* 20-1 (1985);

Allott, "Unanticipated Liability of the Landman," 31 *Rocky Mt. Min. L. Inst.* 21-1 (1985).

See also CONTRACT LANDMAN; CONTRACT LEASEMAN; LEASE HOUND.

Landmen's Lease

An UNLESS LEASE (*q.v.*) form prepared by the Alberta Landmen's Ass'n (Form 1). Gordon v. Connors, 8 W.W.R. (N.S.) 145, [1953] 2 D.L.R. 137, 2 *O.&G.R.* 467 (Alberta Supreme Court, App. Div., 1953), *appeal dism'd,* [1953] 2 S.C.R. 127, [1953] 4 D.L.R. 513 (Supreme Court of Canada 1953).

Landowner interest

A generic name for a property interest in oil and gas granted or retained by a person not interested in carrying on exploration or development operations. Particular interests included within the term are: mineral interest, royalty interest, non-executive mineral interests, overriding royalty, production payments, and the variety of interests that arise upon execution of a lease, including bonus, rental, and royalty. A working interest in a lease is not referred to as a landowner interest.

Landowner royalty

A share of the gross production of minerals free of the costs of production. Occasionally the term is used to describe an interest in production created by a landowner independently of a lease as distinguished from a lessor's royalty, which arises under a lease. In this sense, the landowner royalty may have a perpetual or any other specified duration. In most instances the two terms, landowner royalty and lessor's royalty, are used synonymously.

Landowners' royalty pool

An arrangement whereby royalty or mineral interests, or both, are transferred by a landowner to a business trust or corporation in return for beneficial trust interests or corporate shares. The purpose of the transfer is to give the landowner a share in production from all land covered by the agreement. This device was popular in Kansas, Oklahoma and Texas in the 1920's and 1930's, with some pools covering hundreds of thousands of acres located in two or three states. See TREATISE §§ 907–907.11.

Land status book

A book maintained by the Bureau of Land Management which shows, by township and range, lease applications and issued leases. Comptroller General's Report to the Congress, *Actions Needed to Increase Federal Onshore Oil and Gas Exploration and Development* 70 (1981).

LAPCO

Lavan Petroleum Co.

LAPIDOTH

The Israel Oil Prospectors Corporation Ltd.

Late penalty

See CONTINENTAL OFFSHORE STRATIGRAPHIC TEST (COST).

Law stabilizing clause

A clause in a CONCESSION (*q.v.*) agreement designed to stabilize the law of the host country in one or another respect. Such a clause may be designed to preclude changes in the taxation law of the host country or to foreclose abrogation of the agreement by the host country.

For an argument that a clause of this kind runs counter to the fundamental concept of permanent sovereignty, see Hossain and Chowdhury, *Permanent Sovereignty Over Natural Resources in International Law* (1984).

Syn.: Immutability clause.

For discussions of this clause see the following:

Blinn, Duval, Le Leuch, and Pertuzio, *International Petroleum Exploration & Exploitation Agreements* ch. 16 (1986);

El Sheikh, *The Legal Regime of Foreign Private Investment in the Sudan and Saudi Arabia* 256 (1984);

Mughraby, *Permanent Sovereignty Over Oil Resources* 52 (1966).

Lay barge

A barge used to lay underwater pipelines.

Laydown drilling unit (Laydown spacing)

See STANDUP DRILLING UNIT (STANDUP SPACING).

Layering

A term applied to a practice which developed under the ENTITLEMENT PROGRAM (*q.v.*) involving the purchase and sale of oil through the books of a number of companies within a few days during which oil was miscertified so as to be entitled to a higher price. It was alleged that some domestic producers would sell old oil to resellers and, in effect, buy it back as new oil or stripper oil. In many cases, the oil never left the pipeline; the oil companies used the resellers to "launder" the oil. Congressional investigators contend that by the end of 1980 1.3 million barrels of stripper oil was being produced daily in the U.S., yet far more than that, 2 million barrels per day, were being reported as purchased by refiners. At the same time, 700,000 barrels of old oil, worth as much as $30 less, was disappearing every day between the production fields and the refiners. See Greenberg, "The rise and well-cushioned fall of Robert Sutton," *Forbes Magazine* (Aug. 1, 1983) page 34.

Lazy bench

A bench on which workers or visitors may rest; a bench from which drilling operations may be observed. See DRILLING RIG.

Lean gas

Gas containing little or no liquefiable hydrocarbons. *Syn.:* DRY GAS.

Lease

(1) The conveyance of a nonfreehold interest in land.

(2) The instrument by which a leasehold or working interest is created in minerals.

The oil and gas lease has passed through an evolutionary development. Early leases were generally for long terms without a THEREAFTER CLAUSE (*q.v.*). Another early form of the lease was the NO-TERM LEASE (*q. v.*). Most contemporary leases are of the Unless or Or types [See OR LEASE; UNLESS LEASE].

The very name, "lease," is unfortunate as it tends to give the impression to the uninformed that the "oil and gas lease" is of the same genus as the common law "lease" of land, whereas, except in Louisiana [see Dees v. Hunt Oil Co., 123 F. Supp. 58, 3 *O.&G.R.* 1860 (W. D. La. 1954); Gulf Ref. Co. v. Hayne, 138 La. 555, 70 So. 509 (1915)] the dissimilarities are more important than the similarities.

The most common oil and gas lease in the mid-continent area is the so-called "Producers 88" lease. [See 88 LEASE]. Even this does not describe a specific instrument or indicate the interests created thereby, although generally speaking Producers 88 lease forms contain an "unless" clause rather than an "or" clause and are executed for a term of years and so long thereafter as oil and gas is produced. The Or lease is commonly employed in California. See 86 LEASE.

The distinction between a lease and a deed is difficult to draw but it has importance in a number of legal contexts. See TREATISE §§ 205–207; Hoffman, "Determination of Whether an Instrument Is a Lease or an Absolute Conveyance of Oil and Gas," 25 *Texas L. Rev.* 157 (1946). The principal interests arising from an oil and gas lease are the working or leasehold interest of the lessee, and the royalty, delay rental, bonus, and possibility of reverter or power of termination interests of the lessor. See Masterson, "A Survey of Basic Oil and Gas Law," 4 *Sw. Legal Fdn. Oil & Gas Inst.* 219 at 258–277 (1953).

Taussig v. GoldKing Properties Co., 495 So.2d 1008 at 1016, ____ *O.&G.R.* ____ at ____ (La. App. 1986), reports testimony that "persons in different sections of the oil industry often use the term 'lease' loosely referring to a geographical location and the physical property, the wells, the tank battery, etc."

See also AUTOMATIC TERMINATION OF LEASE; BLOCK LEASE; BOTTOM LEASE; CANCELLATION DECREE; CHECKERBOARD LEASING; COMBINATION LEASE; COMBINED HYDROCARBON LEASE; "COMMENCE" LEASE; COMMUNITY LEASE; COMPETITIVE LEASE; "COMPLETION" LEASE; CONDITIONAL LEASE; CORRECTION LEASE; COUNTERPART LEASES; COVER LEASE; DEPARTMENTAL LEASE; DISCOVERY LEASE SELECTION; DRILL OR FORFEIT LEASE; DRILL OR PAY LEASE; DOWN-DIP LEASE; EDGE LEASE; 88 LEASE; EXCHANGE AND RENEWAL LEASE; EXPLORATION RETENTION

LEASE; FEDERAL LEASE; FRACTIONAL OR FUTURE INTEREST LEASE; FULL-INTEREST LEASE; FUTURE INTEREST LEASE; JOINT LEASE; LANDMEN'S LEASE; LEVERAGED LEASE; LIEU LEASE; LONG TERM LEASE; MARKET VALUE LEASE; MID-CONTINENT LEASE; MINERAL LEASE; MULTIPLE COMMUNITY LEASE; NET PROFIT SHARE LEASE (NPSL); NEW LEASE; NON-COMPETITIVE LEASE; NON-CONVENTIONAL OIL RECOVERY STIPULATION; NON-DRILLING LEASE; NO-PREJUDICE CLAUSE; OIL AGE 86–C FORM; OLD LEASE; OPEN-END LEASE; OPEN PARCEL LEASE; OVER-THE-COUNTER LEASE; PAID UP LEASE; PERPETUAL LEASE; POOLING LEASE; PREFERENCE RIGHT LEASE; PROCEEDS LEASE; PROTECTION LEASE; RATIFICATION OF LEASE; RETENTION LEASE; SECTION 6 LEASE; SECTION 8 LEASE; SECURITY LEASE; SELECTION LEASE; SHOOTING LEASE; SPLIT LEASE; STORE LEASE; STRIPPER WELL LEASE; SURFACE LEASE; TOP LEASE; UNITIZED LEASE; UP-DIP LEASE; WASTE WATER LEASE.

Lease acquisition costs

Bonus payments. In Canada such costs have in practice been treated as non-deductible capital expenditures. See Discussion Notes, 4 *O. & G. R.* 814 (1955); McDonald, *Canadian Income Tax* § 53.2 (a) (1955). In the United States prior to the Tax Reduction Act of 1974, cash bonus was treated as advance royalty which was depletable.

See also BONUS.

Lease acquisition fund

An alternative to a DRILLING FUND (*q.v.*) by which one may invest in varying combinations of exploratory, development, or wildcat oil and gas properties. The traditional fund of this type involves a limited partnership which the corporate general partner uses to carry its lease inventory or to purchase leases from third parties. Subscribers are usually called "participants." See Reiff, "Tax Perspectives of Lease Acquisition Funds Used as a Financing Vehicle in a Declining Market," 53 *Okla. B.A.J.* 2548 (1982), 32 *O.&G. Tax Q.* 367 (1983).

See also INCOME FUND; PRODUCTION FUND; ROYALTY TRUST.

Lease allowable

See ALLOWABLE; PRORATIONING.

Lease allowable system

The lease allowable system, permitting the combination of the allowables of all the wells on a lease into one total allowable for the entire lease, is discussed in Blazier, "The Lease Allowable System: New Method of Regulating Oil Production in Texas," 47 *Texas L. Rev.* 658 (1969).

See also ALLOWABLE.

Lease automatic custody transfer (LACT)

A completely automatic gauging system to take readings for volume, temperature, gravity, and amount of foreign matter when a new batch of oil leaves a tank and enters a pipeline. See *API Bulletin 2509A;* Hardwicke, *The Oilman's Barrel* 97 (1958).

Three surveys conducted among oil producers, pipeline companies, and suppliers of LACT equipment are discussed in Graham, "LACT Requirements Pose New Considerations of Oil Regulatory Authority," 7 *IOCC Comm. Bull.* 23 (Dec. 1965).

Lease bidding systems

See AD VALOREM CHARGE; AUCTION; BONUS BIDDING; CHILLING THE BID; DEFERRED BONUS BIDDING; ECONOMIC RENT; FISHING BID; HALBOUTY CONCEPT; INSTALLMENT BONUS PAYMENT WITH FORGIVENESS OPTION; INTERTRACT BIDDING; JOINT BID AGREEMENT; MONEY LEFT ON THE TABLE; NET PROFITS BIDDING; OPEN BONUS BID; PERFORMANCE TYPE LEASING; PRIVATIZATION; PROFIT SHARE BIDDING; ROYALTY BIDDING; TAPERED ROYALTY; VARIABLE NET PROFIT SHARE BIDDING SYSTEM; VARIABLE WORK COMMITMENT BIDDING SYSTEM; WINNER'S CURSE; WORK COMMITMENT BIDDING; WORKING INTEREST BIDDING.

Energy Action Educational Foundation v. Andrus, 631 F.2d 751 (D.C. Cir. 1979), *on subsequent appeal,* 654 F.2d 735 (D.C. Cir. 1980), *rev'd sub nom.* Watt v. Energy Action Educational Foundation, 454 U.S. 151, 72 *O.&G.R.* 1 (1981), dealt with the requirement imposed by Congress for the use of alternative bidding systems in the leasing of Outer Continental Shelf Lands. The Department of Energy has subsequently issued proposed rules dealing with a variable net profit share bidding system [46 Fed. Reg. 15, 484 (March 5, 1981)] and a variable work commitment bidding system [46 Fed. Reg. 20,522 (April 3, 1981)].

On second appeal of Andrus, 654 F.2d 735 (1980), the court ordered new regulations to be in place by May 1981. This judgment was reversed, Watt v. Energy Action Foundation, 102 S.Ct. 205 (1981). Pending Supreme Court review of *Andrus,* a final rule was issued by the Department of Energy establishing an Outer Continental Shelf Oil and Gas Variable Work Commitment Bidding system.

The rule summarizes the anticipated effect of various lease bidding systems. 46 F.R. 35614 (July 9, 1981).

For discussions of alternative bidding systems to maximize the capture of economic rent, see the following:

Mead, Moseidjord, Muraoka, and Sorensen, *Offshore Lands: Oil and Gas Leasing and Conservation on the Outer Continental Shelf* (1985);

Mikesell, *Petroleum Company Operations and Agreements in the Developing Countries* 38 *et seq.* (1984);

Ramsey, *Bidding and Oil Leases* (1980);

McDonald, *The Leasing of Federal Lands for Fossil Fuels Production* 95 (1979);

Reece, *Leasing Offshore Oil: An Analysis of Alternative Information and Bidding Systems* (1979);

Crommelin and Thompson, *Mineral Leasing as an Instrument of Public Policy* (1977);

Gaffney, *Oil and Gas Leasing Policy: Alternatives for Alaska in 1977* (1977);

Dam, *Oil Resources* (1976);

Mead, Moseidjord, and Sorensen, "Competition in Outer Shelf Oil and Gas Lease Auctions: A Statistical Analysis of Winning Bids," 26 *Nat. Res. J.* 95 (1986);

Burris & Robson, "Evaluation of Royalty Bid and Profit Share Bid Bidding Systems," 20 *Sw. Legal Fdn. Exploration and Economics of the Petroleum Industry* 123 (1982);

McDonald, "The Economics of Alternative Leasing Systems on the Outer Continental Shelf," 18 *Houston L. Rev.* 967 (1981);

Gilley, Karels and Lyon, "The Economics of Oil Lease Bidding," 18 *Houston L. Rev.* 1061 (1981);

Logue, Sweeney and Willett, "Optimal Leasing Policy for the Development of Outer Continental Shelf Hydrocarbon Resources" 51 *Land Economics* 191 (1975);

Crommelin, "Offshore Oil and Gas Rights; A Comparative Study," 14 *Nat. Res. J.* 457 (1974);

"Alaska's Petroleum Leasing Policy," in University of Alaska Institute of Social, Economic and Government Research, *Review of Business and Economic Conditions* (Vol. 7, No. 3, July 1970).

Lease bonus

See Bonus.

Lease broker

A person who seeks to secure leases for speculation and resale in areas where survey or exploration work is being done.

See also LANDMAN; LEASE HOUND; LEASEMAN.

Lease burdens

As defined in a Rocky Mountain unit operating agreement, the royalty reserved to the lessor in an oil and gas lease, an overriding royalty, a production payment and any similar burden, but not including a carried working interest, a net profits interest or any other interest which is payable out of profits. See Rocky Mountain Unit Operating Agreement Form 1 (Undivided Interest) May, 1954, Section 1.8, TREATISE § 920.3.

Lease case file

A file maintained by the BUREAU OF LAND MANAGEMENT (*q.v.*) for each mineral application and containing copies of the applications, issued leases, correspondence, etc. Comptroller General's Report to the Congress, *Actions Needed to Increase Federal Onshore Oil and Gas Exploration and Development* 70 (1981).

Lease clause

See ACREAGE ESTIMATE PROVISION; ACREAGE RETENTION CLAUSE; ACREAGE SELECTION CLAUSE; ALTERNATIVE FUEL CLAUSE; ASSIGNMENT CLAUSE; BURIED PIPE COVENANT; CASINGHEAD GAS CLAUSE; CASING, PULL; CESSATION OF PRODUCTION CLAUSE; CHANGE OF OWNERSHIP CLAUSE; COMMENCE DRILLING CLAUSE; COMPENSATORY ROYALTY CLAUSE; CONTINUOUS DRILLING OPERATIONS CLAUSE; COVER-ALL CLAUSE; DEFAULT CLAUSE; DELAY RENTAL CLAUSE; DEVELOPMENT CLAUSE; DILUENT CLAUSE; DIRECTIONAL DRILLING CLAUSE; DRILLING AND OPERATING RESTRICTIONS; DRILLING AND RENTAL CLAUSE; DRILLING CLAUSE; DRILLING OPERATIONS CLAUSE; DRY HOLE CLAUSE; ENTIRETY CLAUSE; EXPRESS COVENANT; EXPRESS DRILLING CLAUSE; FORCE MAJEURE CLAUSE; FORFEITURE CLAUSE; FREE GAS CLAUSE; GOOD FAITH CLAUSE; GRANTING CLAUSE, LEASE; HABENDUM CLAUSE; IMPLIED COVENANTS; IMPLIED EASEMENTS; "IN GROSS" PROVISION; INITIAL EXPLORATORY WELL COVENANT; IRRIGATION GAS CLAUSE; JUDICIAL ASCERTAINMENT CLAUSE; LESSOR'S SPECIAL INSPECTION CLAUSE; MISTAKE CLAUSE; MOST FAVORABLE LESSOR AGREEMENT; NO-PREJUDICE CLAUSE; NON-CONVENTIONAL OIL RECOVERY STIPULATION; NO-TERM LEASE; NOTICE AND DEMAND CLAUSE; OFFSET CLAUSE; OFFSET ROYALTY CLAUSE; OFF-

SET WELL COVENANT; OR LEASE; PAYMENT FOR SURFACE ACREAGE CLAUSE; POOLING CLAUSE; PRIMARY TERM; PRODUCTION AND MARKETING COVENANT; PRODUCTS ROYALTY CLAUSE; PROPORTIONATE INCREASE CLAUSE; PROPORTIONATE REDUCTION CLAUSE; PUGH CLAUSE; REASONABLE DEVELOPMENT COVENANT; RELEASE OF RECORD CLAUSE; REMOVAL OF FIXTURES CLAUSE; RETAINED ACREAGE CLAUSE; REWORKING CLAUSE; RIGHT -TO-CURE CLAUSE; RIPARIAN LEASE CLAUSE; ROYALTY CLAUSE; ROYALTY-FREE CLAUSE; SAVINGS CLAUSE; SHUT-IN GAS WELL CLAUSE; SUBROGATION CLAUSE; SUBSTITUTE FUEL CLAUSE; SURFACE AND SUBSURFACE USER PROVISIONS; SURFACE DAMAGE CLAUSE; SURRENDER CLAUSE; TAKE-OVER CLAUSE; TAX SHIFTING CLAUSE; TERM CLAUSE; THEREAFTER CLAUSE; THIRTY DAY-SIXTY DAY CLAUSE; TIME OF ESSENCE CLAUSE; UNDIVIDED INTEREST CLAUSE; UNLESS LEASE; WARRANTY.

Leasehold interest

The interest of one holding as a grantee or lessee under an oil and gas lease or lease of oil, gas and other minerals. Such interest includes the right on the part of the lessee to drill and produce, and is subject to the payment to the lessor of a ROYALTY (*q.v.*) of a stated fraction or percentage of the production, free of operating expense, either in kind or at the prevailing price at the time of production.

See also Miller v. Schwartz, 354 N.W.2d 685, 84 *O.&G.R.* 143 (N.D. 1984), citing this MANUAL for the proposition that "it appears that the term 'working interest,' as commonly used in the oil industry, is generally synonymous with the term 'leasehold interest.' "

Syn.: WORKING INTEREST.

Lease hound

A person engaged in securing oil and gas leases from landowners. A lease hound may be an employee of an oil company, in which case he is also called a LANDMAN (*q.v.*). But many lease hounds are self-employed; taking leases on their own account in an active area and then assigning them to an operator for exploration and development, usually retaining an OVERRIDING ROYALTY (*q.v.*) or other interest in production.

Lease interest

(1) A term sometimes used in mineral deeds executed at a time when the minerals are subject to a lease. Under this circumstance, the deed may provide for the conveyance of a given fraction or per-

centage of the "lease interest" after the termination of the existing lease as well as a given fraction or percentage of the interests arising under the existing lease. The words apparently have no technical or customary meaning according to a dissenting opinion in Garrett v. Dils Co., 157 Tex. 92, 299 S.W.2d 902 at 910, 7 *O.&G.R.* 322 at 329 (1957); in general, however, the words are used to include the right to join in any future lease and to receive a proportionate share of the lease proceeds, including bonus, rental and royalty.

(2) The term "lease interest" was said to mean "the right to execute oil and gas leases" in Delta Drilling Co. v. Simmons, 161 Tex. 122, 338 S.W.2d 143, 13 *O.&G.R.* 68 (1960).

Lease line

See PIPELINE.

Lease lottery

See NONCOMPETITIVE LEASE.

Leaseman

A person who engages in negotiating and acquiring oil and gas leases from various landowners. Aladdin Oil Corp. v. Perluss, 230 Cal. App. 2d 603, 41 Cal. Rptr 239 at 241 (1964). *Syn:* LEASE HOUND.

See also LANDMAN.

Lease selection

The selection for lease which a permittee may make from the lands subject to a permit to explore. See, *e.g.*, Saskatchewan Petroleum and Natural Gas Regulations, 1969 (O.C. 8/69) § 21.

Lease separation

A term used in the Permian Basin Area Rate Proceeding to refer to the separation of condensate liquids from gas on the lease property, rather than by later processing. 34 F.P.C. 159 at 215, 23 *O.&G.R.* 103 at 165 (Opinion No. 468, Aug. 5, 1965), *remanded,* Skelly Oil Co. v. Federal Power Comm'n, 375 F.2d 6, 26 *O.&G.R.* 237 (10th Cir. 1967), *aff'd in part and rev'd in part sub nom. In re* Permian Basin Area Rate Cases, 390 U.S. 747, 28 *O.&G.R.* 689 (1968).

Lease tank

See TANK.

Leasing service company

A company engaged in the business of filing for its clients a DRAWING ENTRY CARD (*q.v.*) in a federal NON-COMPETITIVE LEASE (*q.v.*). Lloyd Chemical Sales, Inc., IBLA 80–94, 49 IBLA 392, GFS (O&G) 1980–163 (Sept. 5, 1980).

A variant is a company engaged in the business of sending standardized form letters to second drawees under the simultaneous oil and gas leasing system, offering to search for any possible defects in the offer of the first drawee. Should a potential defect be discovered, the company protests the issuance of the lease and if the protest is successful and the lease is issued to the second drawee, the company retains a percentage of the lease. See Geosearch, Inc. v. Andrus, 508 F. Supp. 839 (D. Wyo. 1981); 517 F. Supp. 1245 (D. Wyo. 1981).

For a discussion of the activities of leasing service companies, see Allenbright, *$10 Wildcat* 119 (1979).

See also the following:

Lowey v. Watt, 684 F.2d 957, 73 *O.&G.R.* 480 (D.C. Cir. 1982) (giving effect to disclaimer by a leasing service company of a possibly illegal exclusive sales agency clause in standard agreements clients executed before filing applications for noncompetitive leases);

Geosearch, Inc. v. Watt, 721 F.2d 694, 71 *O.&G.R.* 416 (10th Cir. 1983), *cert. denied sub nom.* Geosearch, Inc. v. Clark, 104 S. Ct. 2437 (1984) (following rationales and conclusions of *Lowey v. Watt* and holding that second drawees or their assignee could not successfully contest issuance of a lease to qualified first drawees).

See also FILING SERVICES; PUT OPTION.

LEG

LIQUEFIED ENERGY GAS (LEG) (*q.v.*).

Legal committee

A committee charged with handling the legal problems arising in the negotiation of a pooling or unitization agreement, the drafting of necessary instruments, and advising on legal problems generally. See Myers, *The Law of Pooling and Unitization* § 4.03 (2d ed. 1967).

Legal life estate

A life estate arising by operation of law, *e.g.*, under local law creating a dower, curtesy or homestead interest, as distinguished from a CONVENTIONAL LIFE ESTATE (*q.v.*) which is created by a volitional act.

Legal oil or gas

Oil or gas produced from a well not in excess of the amount allowed by any rule, regulation, or order of the regulatory board or commission (*e.g.*, a proration order), as distinguished from oil or gas produced in excess of the amount allowed by any rule, regulation, or order, which is ILLEGAL OIL OR GAS (*q.v.*).

Legal subdivision

A quarter-quarter section of land (*viz.*, 1/16th of a section, or 40 acres).

In Robert P. Kunkel, 74 I.D. 373 at 376, GFS SO–1967–44 (Nov. 7, 1967), it was declared that a legal subdivision:

"can embrace a collection of smaller legal subdivisions. . . . Of course, the larger unit must be a 'legal subdivision,' a unit which is provided for by the public land surveys, such as a half-quarter section, quarter section, half section, etc. Thus, only two contiguous quarter-quarter sections located in the same quarter section can be designated as a half-quarter section, such as 'N ½ NE ¼,' 'E ½ NE ¼,' etc. but two contiguous quarter-quarter sections located in different quarter sections cannot be so designated. They must be separately described, such as 'SE ¼ NE ¼' and 'NE ¼ SE ¼.' Also, two cornering quarter-quarter sections located in the same quarter section must be separately described, *e.g.*, 'NE ¼ NE ¼' and 'SW ¼ NE ¼.'

"This is also true with respect to lots. . . .

"The position taken in the decisions below that 'legal subdivision' in the regulation means only combinations of perfectly regular subdivisions is not required by the language of the regulation or by any other authority that we know."

In Jacob N. Wasserman, 74 I.D. 392, GFS SO–1967–47 (Nov. 22, 1967), the description "E ¾ of SE ¼ NW ¼" was held not to be a proper description of a legal subdivision; to be sufficient, a description must be in terms of aliquot portions, *viz.*, in terms of halves, quarters, halves of quarters, and quarter-quarters.

For purposes of section 30(a) of the Mineral Leasing Act, the term "legal subdivision" refers to a quarter-quarter section. "Partial Assignments Under Section 30(a) of the Mineral Leasing Act," 76 I.D. 108, GFS SO–1969–23 (June 23, 1969).

See also GENERAL LAND OFFICE SURVEY; REGULAR SUBDIVISION; SURVEY.

Legal usufruct

A USUFRUCT (*q.v.*) arising by operation of law, as that of a surviving spouse in community.

Lens

A relatively porous, permeable, irregularly shaped, sedimentary deposit surrounded by impervious rock. The lens may serve as a local center of concentration of oil in the formation. A lenticular sedimentary bed that pinches out in all directions.

The definition of LENS in this TREATISE was quoted in Railroad Comm'n v. Graford Oil Corp., 557 S.W.2d 946, 59 *O.&G.R.* 338 at 344 (Tex. 1977).

Lenticular reservoir

A lens of porous and permeable sediments surrounded by strata of low permeability, often shale. There may be a number of such lens unconnected with each other in an area. Such reservoirs are often small, but completely saturated with oil or gas. The shoestring sands of the mid-continent region are notable examples of lenticular reservoirs.

See also RESERVOIR; SHOESTRING SANDS.

The definition of LENTICULAR RESERVOIR in this TREATISE was quoted in Railroad Comm'n v. Graford Oil Corp., 557 S.W.2d 946, 59 *O.&G.R.* 338 at 344 (Tex. 1977).

Lesion

A civil law concept enabling the vendor of immovable property to rescind a sale where it can be shown that the purchase price did not equal at least one half of the true value of the property. La. Civ. Code arts. 1860–62 (1970). Article 17 of the Louisiana Mineral Code (1975) provides that the sale of a mineral right, including a mineral servitude, cannot be rescinded on account of lesion. See McCollam, "A Primer for the Practice of Mineral Law Under the New Louisiana Mineral Code," 50 *Tulane L. Rev.* 729 at 740 (1976).

Lessee

(1) The person entitled under an oil and gas lease to drill and operate wells, paying the lessor a royalty and retaining the remainder, often 7/8ths of the production, known as the "working interest." The lessee pays all production costs out of his fraction, the lessor's fraction being free and clear of all such costs.

(2) The term "lessee" is defined by some statutes to include the lessee under an oil and gas lease, or the owner of any land or mineral rights who conducts or carries on any oil and gas development, exploration and operation thereon, or any person so operating for himself or others. Wash. Laws 1951, ch. 146, § 3 (6), R. C. W. 78.52.010(7) (1962).

Lesser estate clause

See PROPORTIONATE REDUCTION CLAUSE.

Lesser interest clause

See PROPORTIONATE REDUCTION CLAUSE.

Lessor

The owner of mineral rights who has executed a lease. He is normally entitled to the payment of a royalty (often 1/8th) on production, free and clear of the cost of developing or operating the property, except taxes on his share of the production. Other interests of a lessor arising from a lease include a possibility of reverter or power of termination, a right in many instances to a bonus and delay rentals, and the benefit of implied covenants.

Lessor-approval provision

The term applied by State of Wyoming v. Moncrief, 720 P.2d 470, ____ *O.&G.R.* ____ (Wyo. 1986), to a gas royalty provision stating that "the value [of gas and natural gasoline] shall be as approved by the lessor." In this case the court found consistency between this provision, a MARKET-VALUE/AMOUNT-REALIZED PROVISION (*q.v.*), and a FEDERAL-FLOOR PROVISION (*q.v.*).

Lessor's royalty

A share of the gross production of minerals free of the costs of production, arising under an oil and gas lease. For many years the usual lessor's royalty was one-eighth of the production but the interest is frequently greater or may be less than this amount. In California the royalty is usually expressed as a percentage rather than as a fraction of production. Occasionally the term is used to describe an interest in production arising under the terms of a lease as distinguished from a LANDOWNER ROYALTY, which term may be used to describe an interest in production created by a landowner independently of a lease. In most instances the two terms are used synonymously.

Lessor's special inspection clause

A clause reported to have been included in at least one lease under which, in lieu of being furnished an electrical log, the Lessor shall have the right to be lowered head first down the casing equipped with a two cell battery flashlight to a depth of 7,000 feet, or some lesser depth if heaving shales be encountered. The clause further provided that "Lessee agrees that Lessor will be lowered at a rate of speed not to exceed that rate which any prudent operator would lower his Lessor into a well bore. It is further understood that if lowering line should part, immediate fishing operations shall be commenced, and in no event shall Lessor be cemented, plugged or abandoned." Hemingway, *The Law of Oil and Gas* 409 (2d ed. 1983).

Letter

See ACREAGE CONTRIBUTION LETTER; ANETH LETTER; BOTTOM HOLE DONATION LETTER; BOTTOM HOLE LETTER; COMFORT LETTER; CONTRIBUTION AGREEMENT; COUNTER LETTER; DONATION LETTER; DRY HOLE AGREEMENT; GUSHER LETTER; PURCHASE LETTER; TAKE-OUT LETTER.

Leveraged drilling fund

A DRILLING FUND (*q.v.*) in which a portion of the capital subscribed is derived from nonrecourse borrowing. See Dauber, "Oil and Gas for the Passive Investor—Tax and Business Considerations," 25 *Sw. Legal Fdn. Oil & Gas Inst.* 419 at 449 (1974); Klein, "The State of Leverage," 24 *O.&G. Tax Q.* 282 (1975).

Leveraged lease

A transaction in which the lessor participants seek to obtain the taxation benefits associated with ownership of the property.

"In a leveraged lease, the equity parties separate the transaction from normal business by borrowing specifically to acquire the particular asset to be leased, rather than drawing upon their general funds. These borrowings are normally made by a partnership of equity parties. I use the word 'partnership' in the income tax sense since the joint financing arrangement in a leveraged lease will always constitute a partnership for income tax purposes. . . . The partnership may borrow between 60% and 95% of the cost of the asset to be leased. These borrowings are on a non-recourse basis so that the partners' personal liability to the lender is limited to what is generally described as a 'fraudulent or wilfull misconduct or gross neglect,' . . ." Blaikie, "Leveraged Leasing," 3 *Australian Mining & Petroleum L.J.* 70 at 71 (1981).

This arrangement was described as follows in CRC Corp. v. Comm'r of Internal Revenue, 693 F.2d 281, 75 *O.&G.R.* 429 (3d Cir. 1982), *cert. denied,* 462 U.S. 1106, 103 S.Ct. 2453 (1983):

"Under these arrangements an oil and gas operator assembles a package of leasehold interests which he conveys to a limited partnership, for a cash payment and a nonrecourse note secured by a mortgage on the leaseholds and equipment used in resulting wells. Simultaneously, the operator enters into a fixed price no-out turnkey contract to drill wells, at no further cost to the investors. The operator also simultaneously obtains a completion joint venture option under which the operator can recover an interest in a completed well by remitting to the limited partners a portion of the cash consideration which they paid."

See also NONRECOURSE FINANCING.

LFG recovery project

A project for the recovery of methane gas from landfills. See Kahn, "Methane from Landfills," 1 *Nat. Res. & Environment* 13 (Vol. 1, No. 2, Spring 1985).

Liberative prescription

Prescription *liberandi causa.* See PRESCRIPTION.

Libyan General Petroleum Corporation (LIPETCO)

A state oil company which was abolished in 1970 and was succeeded by the LIBYAN NATIONAL OIL CORPORATION (LINOCO) (*q.v.*).

Libyan National Oil Corporation (LINOCO)

A state oil company established in July, 1970, as the successor to the LIBYAN GENERAL PETROLEUM CORPORATION (LIPETCO) (*q.v.*). See OPEC, *Selected Documents of the International Petroleum Industry 1970* at p. 61.

Libyan premium

A premium paid at one time for Libyan crude oil based on the fact that the transportation costs of marketing such crude was less than the transportation costs of marketing crude produced in the Gulf States (Abu Dhabi, Iran, Iraq, Kuwait, Qatar and Saudia Arabia).

Libyan producers agreement

A 1971 agreement by producers of Libyan oil that if a party's crude oil production was cut back as a result of government action, all other parties would share in such cut back as provided in the Agreement. And if there was insufficient Libyan oil to meet the contractual obligations due to restrictions or shut down by the Libyan government, those parties with Persian Gulf production would supply the Libyan producers who were cut back with Persian Gulf oil at cost. See Hunt v. Mobil Oil Corp., 410 F. Supp. 10 (S.D. N.Y. 1975), *aff'd,* 550 F.2d 68 (2d Cir. 1977), *cert. denied,* 434 U.S. 984 (1977); 465 F. Supp. 195 (S.D. N.Y. 1978), *aff'd without opinion,* 610 F.2d 806 (2d Cir. 1979).

For discussions of the agreement see the following:

Jackson, "Negotiations between American Contractors and Foreign Host Governments," 8 *Nat. Res. Law.* 1 at 6 (1975);

Sampson, *The Seven Sisters* 217 (1975).

Syn.: Safety net; Sharing agreement.

See also BACK-UP CRUDE.

License

With the decline in the popularity of the term CONCESSION (*q.v.*) to describe the natural resources exploration and development agreements made by host nations with foreign oil companies, the term "license" has come to be applied to some such agreements. See Dam, *Oil Resources* 14 (1976).

The details of the license system employed in the United Kingdom for onshore and continental shelf exploration and production are set forth in Daintith and Willoughby, *A Manual of United Kingdom Oil and Gas Law* 20–70 (1977).

Licensing procedures and criteria are discussed in the following papers:

Cameron, "North Sea Oil Licensing: Comparisons and Contrasts," [1984/85] 4 *OGLTR* 99;

Cameron, "UK Licensing Criteria," [1984/85] 2 *OGLTR* 27.

See also APPRAISAL LICENSE (AL); CONVENTIONAL LICENSE; DEVELOPMENT LICENSE; EXPLORATION LICENSE (EXL); EXPLORATORY LICENSE (CANADA); METHANE DRAINAGE LICENSE; PETROLEUM LICENSE; PRODUCTION LICENSE; RECONNAISSANCE LICENSE.

License fee system

A system established in 1973 by Presidential Proclamation 4210 replacing the prior OIL IMPORT QUOTA (*q.v.*) program with a modified tariff system with potentially unlimited imports. See Preston, "National Security and Oil Import Regulation: The License Fee Approach," 15 *Va. J. Int. Law* 399 (1975).

Licitation

Partition by sale of property and division of the proceeds of the sale. See La. Civ. Code Art. 1339 (1952). The property to be partitioned is sold at public auction after the advertisements required by law. Where land is burdened by a mineral right created by fewer than all of the co-owners of the land, partition by licitation is favored over partition in kind. Patrick v. Johnstone, 361 So. 2d 894, 62 *O.&G.R.* 173 (La. App. 1978), *writ denied,* 364 So. 2d 600 (1978).

See also Gates, "Partition of Land and Mineral Rights," 43 *La. L. Rev.* 1119 (1983).

See also EQUITABLE PARTITION; PARTITION.

Lie-down drilling unit (Lie-down spacing)

See STANDUP DRILLING UNIT (STANDUP SPACING).

Lieu lease

A new lease given by a lessor to an assignee of the lessee "in lieu of" the original lease. An EXTENSION AND RENEWAL CLAUSE (*q.v.*) in the assignment may entitle the lessee-assignor to an interest in the new lease. See Seaman, "Financial Aspects of Oil Transactions," 3 *U.C.L.A. L. Rev.* 550 at 552 (1956).

Lieu royalty

Syn. for COMPENSATORY ROYALTY (*q.v.*) or SUBSTITUTE ROYALTY (*q.v.*) or SHUT-IN ROYALTY (*q.v.*).

In Alaska, where a storage lessee also holds the right to produce oil or gas not previously produced in conjunction with stored oil or gas, the storage lease may provide for a royalty upon stored oil or gas when produced. In lieu of a storage fee or rental on stored oil or gas or both, the storage lease may provide for a royalty upon stored oil or gas when produced, which royalty rate may be the same as or different from the royalty rate or rates provided for in any oil or gas leases involved. See the Alaska Mineral Leasing Regulations, 11 AAC 83.510.

Life index

A measure of remaining gas reserves based on current production obtained by dividing the known reserves by annual production.

Lifeline rate

A special low rate for a commodity (*e.g.*, gas, electricity, or telephone service) made available (1) for the consumption of a fixed "lifeline" quantity of the commodity, that low rate being uniformly available to all residential users, or (2) for a relatively small class of qualifying consumers (*e.g.*, the poor or elderly). Cal. Publ. Util. Code § 739, enacted in 1975, requires the California Public Utilities Commission to designate lifeline quantities for gas and electricity and to require gas and electric utilities to include lifeline rates in their schedules. See Sackett, "Lifeline Rates for Natural Gas Utilities—A Hit or a Myth?" 2 *J. Contemp. L.* 218 (1976).

Life of lease contract

A GAS PURCHASE CONTRACT (*q.v.*) having the duration of the life of the lease owned by seller.

Lifting

(1) The term utilized in a JOINT OPERATING AGREEMENT (*q.v.*), PRODUCTION SHARING CONTRACT (*q.v.*), SERVICE CONTRACT (*q.v.*), or other contract between or among two or more parties having an interest in production to indicate that a party has taken and removed some or all or more than its share of production for the period in question.

See also BALANCING; CANCELLED UNDERAGE; DEEMED PURCHASE FORMULA; DEFERRED PRODUCTION AGREEMENT; GAS BANK AGREEMENT; LIFTING TOLERANCE; "OUT OF BALANCE" PRODUCTION PLAN; OVERLIFT; SPLIT CONNECTION; UNDERAGE; UNDERLIFT; UNDERLIFT/OVERLIFT PROVISION.

(2) The process of bringing oil to the surface. See ARTIFICIAL LIFT; LIFTING COSTS.

Lifting costs

The expenses of lifting oil from a producing formation to the surface, being part of the current operating expenses of a working interest.

I.R.B. 1960–47, 11 declares that this term "as used in the oil and gas producing industry, is usually considered to be synonymous with 'operating costs' and consists of those deductible costs incurred in the production of oil and gas after completion of drilling and before its removal from the property for sale or transportation. Such costs consist of labor, superintendence, supplies, repairs and assets having a life not in excess of one year, maintenance, applicable overhead costs, as well as those items properly includible in the computation of gross income under the provisions of Revenue Ruling 141." 13 *O.&G.R.* 164 at 165 (1961).

Lifting sub

A SUB (*q.v.*) used with a drill collar to provide a shoulder to which to fit the drill-pipe elevators so that the drill collar can be raised or lowered into the hole.

Lifting tolerance

A provision of a JOINT OPERATING AGREEMENT (*q.v.*), PRODUCTION SHARING CONTRACT (*q.v.*), SERVICE CONTRACT (*q.v.*), or other contract between or among two or more parties having an interest in production under which a party's "lifting" (taking of production in kind as required by the contract) during the latter dates (*e.g.*, 21 days, 30 days) of an accounting period (*e.g.*, a quarter of a year, a year) may be counted as lifted in the next succeeding accounting period (thus avoiding or reducing the party's overlift in the prior period) or under which a party's "lifting" during the early dates of an accounting period may be counted as lifted in the prior accounting period (thus avoiding or reducing the party's underlift in the prior period.)

See also BALANCING; CANCELLED UNDERAGE; DEEMED PURCHASE FORMULA; DEFERRED PRODUCTION AGREEMENT; GAS BANK AGREEMENT; LIFTING; "OUT OF BALANCE" PRODUCTION PLAN; OVERLIFT; SPLIT CONNECTION; UNDERAGE; UNDERLIFT; UNDERLIFT/OVERLIFT PROVISION.

"Light end" products

Naphtha, kerosene, diesel fuel and lube oil produced by a refinery from crude oil. See Texas American Asphalt Corp. v. Walker, 177 F. Supp. 315 (S.D. Tex. 1959).

Light petroleum products (LPP)

A term including No. 2 fuel oil, diesel fuel, kerosine, jet fuel, and gasoline. Florida Gas Transmission Co., 23 FPS 5-421 (Opinion No. 144, Sept. 2, 1982).

Limitation clause

The clause of a deed or lease specifying the duration of the interest granted. Limitation clauses may be subdivided into clauses of general limitation (which state the maximum duration of the granted interest) and clauses of special limitation (which provide for earlier termination of the granted interest upon the happening of a specified event, *e.g.,* upon the cessation of specified drilling or production operations upon an oil and gas leasehold).

See also DEVOTIONAL LIMITATION DOCTRINE; POSSIBILITY OF REVERTER.

Limitation notice

A notice served on a licensee setting the limits within which rates of production may thereafter be required to be increased or reduced in the national interest. See Daintith and Willoughby, *A Manual of United Kingdom Oil and Gas Law* 49 (1977).

Limited capacity well

A well incapable of producing the ALLOWABLE (*q.v.*) that would normally be assigned to it. Railroad Comm'n v. Woods Exploration & Producing Co., 405 S.W.2d 313 at 315, 24 *O.&G.R.* 831 at 834 (Tex. 1966), *cert. denied sub nom.* Aluminum Co. of America v. Woods Exploration & Producing Co., 385 U.S. 991 (1966).

Limited carried interest

A CARRIED INTEREST (*q.v.*) which is to be carried for the initial development phase only of the operation. After the operator has recouped his advances to the carried interest, the carry terminates. See "Carried Interests Revisited by Tax Court." 8 *O.&G. Tax Q.* 159 at 161 (1959).

Limited liability company

A hybrid type of organization having characteristics of both a corporation and a LIMITED PARTNERSHIP (*q.v.*). The first such company was created in 1977 when Wyoming enacted the Wyoming Limited Liability Company Act, 1977 Wyo. Sess. Laws 537, codified at Wyo. Stat. Ann. §§ 17-15-101 to 17-15-136 (1977 & Supp. 1983). See Burke & Meyer, "Federal Income Tax Classification of Natural Resource Ventures: Co-Ownership, Partnership or Association?" 37 *Sw. L.J.* 859 at 887 (1984).

Limited offer exemption

An exemption under the BLUE SKY LAW (*q.v.*) of certain states to offerings to a limited number of persons or offerings of a given amount or offerings for particular purposes. See TREATISE § 441.4 at note 20. A Uniform Limited Offering Exemption has been drafted by a committee of the North American Securities Administrators Association, Inc. (NASAA) and approved at the 1981 annual meeting of the Association. 1 *CCH Blue Sky L. Rep.* ¶ 5294. See TREATISE § 441.4.

Limited overriding royalty

A term sometimes used to describe an OIL PAYMENT (*q.v.*). See, *e.g.*, Fleming v. Commissioner, 24 T.C. 818, 4 *O.&G.R.* 1609 (1955), *rev'd*, 241 F.2d 78, 6 *O.&G.R.* 1458 (5th Cir. 1957), *rev'd sub nom.* Commissioner v. P. G. Lake, Inc., 356 U.S. 260, 8 *O.&G.R.* 1153 (1958).

Limited partnership

A form of organization, frequently employed in financing oil and gas ventures, by which an investor of funds becomes a limited partner with limited liability. See the Uniform Limited Partnership Act (1969). Sixth Geostratic Energy Drilling Program 1980 v. Ancor Exploration Co., 544 F. Supp. 297, 74 *O.&G.R.* 89 (N.D. Okla. 1982), while concluding that certain limited partners were indispensable parties to an action where receivership of partnership assets was sought, held that the limited partners, like shareholders of a corporation, should not be considered in determining diversity of citizenship.

See also the following:

Keyser, "Publicly Traded Limited Partnerships: The Treasury Fights the Wrong War," 36 *Sw. Legal Fdn. Oil & Gas Inst.* 10-1 (1985);

Giannola, "Structuring Oil and Gas Limited Partnerships—an Update," 36 *Sw. Legal Fdn. Oil & Gas Inst.* 11-1 (1985);

McMillan, "Obtaining Equity Capital for Drilling Operations: The Securities Aspect," *Rocky Mt. Min. L. Inst. on Mineral Financing* 6-1 *et seq.* (1982) (containing examples of forms employed in limited partnership financing of oil and gas ventures);

"Investing in Oil and Gas Through Limited Partnerships," *P.H. Oil & Gas/Natural Resources Taxes* ¶ 3004 (1983).

See also DEVELOPMENTAL PROGRAM WELL; DRILLING FUND; LEASE ACQUISITION FUND; LIMITED LIABILITY COMPANY; LISTED DEPOSITORY RECEIPT; MASTER LIMITED PARTNERSHIP; PUBLIC LIMITED PARTNERSHIP (PLP); ROLL-UP.

Limited recourse financing

Financing of a project by a loan for which there is limited recourse to assets of the borrower other than funds generated by the project for which the loan is made. Limited recourse financing is distinguished from NONRECOURSE FINANCING (*q.v.*) inasmuch as under some but not all circumstances there may be access to other assets of the borrower, *e.g.*, for breach of a completion covenant, a covenant that the facilities will work, or a covenant to contribute the borrower's share of costs regardless of overruns. See Willoughby, "Limited Recourse Loans," in *Proceedings of the Petroleum Law Seminar* (Jan. 8–13, 1978), organized by the Committee on Energy and Natural Resources, Section on Business Law, International Bar Association; Ladbury, "Recent Trends in Limited Recourse Financing with Particular Reference to Limited Recourse Loans, Production Payments and Forward Sale and Purchase Agreements," 2 *Austl. Mining & Petroleum L.J.* 68 (1979); McCormick, "Legal Issues in Project Finance," 1 *J.E.R.L.* 21 (1983).

See also PROJECT FINANCING.

Limited term abandonment

Authorization by the Federal Energy Regulatory Commission permitting gas previously committed to interstate commerce to be sold in the spot market and transported by any means allowed under Order No. 436. See Griggs, "Restructuring the Natural Gas Industry: Order No. 436 and Other Regulatory Initiatives," 7 *Energy L. J.* 71 at 84 (1986).

See also ABANDONMENT OF FACILITIES OR SERVICE.

Limited term certificate

A certificate of public convenience and necessity issued by the Federal Power Commission or its successor, the Federal Energy Regulatory Commission, for the sale of natural gas for resale in interstate commerce for a specified limited term. 18 C.F.R. §§ 2.70, 159.29 (1980). In Moss v. Federal Power Comm'n, 424 U.S. 494, 54 *O.&G.R.* 247 (1976), the court made it clear that while the Commission could issue a certificate without term limitation despite the fact that a producer had applied for a limited term certificate, the Commission could also issue a certificate for a limited term or a certificate authorizing abandonment at a future date certain.

See also ONE HUNDRED AND EIGHTY DAY EMERGENCY SALES; SIXTY -DAY EMERGENCY SALES.

Limited term sale

See LIMITED TERM CERTIFICATE.

Limited term working interest

A LIMITED WORKING INTEREST (*q.v.*).

Limited working interest

A WORKING INTEREST (*q.v.*) which will terminate prior to the economic exhaustion of the reserves upon the happening of some event, *e.g.*, the passage of time, production of a specified quantum or realization of a predetermined sum of money. The tax treatment of such an interest is discussed in Griffith, "Current Developments in Oil and Gas Taxation," 25 *Sw. Legal Fdn. Oil & Gas Inst.* 323 (1974); *Miller's Oil and Gas Federal Income Taxation* § 13–5 (1980 edition).

Line flood

A system of water flood in which two rows of oil wells are staggered on both sides of an equally spaced line of water intake wells. When the oil wells reach their economic limit of production another row of oil wells is drilled ahead of the flood and the former oil wells are converted into water intake wells. See Lytle, "History, Present Status, and Future Possibilities of Secondary Recovery Operations in Pennsylvania," 1 *IOCC Comm. Bull.* 29 at 33 (Dec. 1959).

See also SECONDARY RECOVERY; WATER FLOODING.

Line loss

The amount of gas lost in a distribution system or pipeline.

Line pack gas

The volume of gas maintained in a pipeline at all times in order to maintain pressure and effect uninterrupted flow or transportation of natural gas through the pipeline. Revenue Ruling 68–620, 1968–49 I.R.B. 16, 30 *O.&G.R.* 319.

Transwestern Pipeline Co. v. United States, 639 F.2d 679 (Ct. Cl. 1980), held that for federal income tax purposes, the cost of line pack in a natural gas pipeline system constitutes a capital expenditure which is depreciable over the useful life of the system, rejecting the position long taken by the Internal Revenue Service that the cost of line pack is a nondepreciable inventory expense.

In Technical Advice Memorandum 8040005, dated June 17, 1980, the Internal Revenue Service ruled that a taxpayer must treat as inventory the volume of gas needed in a gas pipeline to maintain the uninterrupted flow of gas in the pipeline. 29 *O.&G. Tax Q.* 599 (1981).

Line test well

A test well drilled near the line between two separate properties designed to test the area (particularly in the Outer Continental Shelf) for a show of oil or gas. Typically the owner(s) of each of the properties contribute to the cost of the well. Frequently the well is a so-called ESCROW WELL, EXPENDABLE WELL, or PRE-PLATFORM WELL (*q.v.*) not expected to be completed as a producing well even if the test is favorable. The transaction may be structured as a pooling unit to which each of the properties contribute acreage or as a CONTRIBUTION AGREEMENT (*q.v.*).

LINOCO

The LIBYAN NATIONAL OIL CORPORATION (*q.v.*).

LIPETCO

The LYBIAN GENERALPETROLEUM CORPORATION (*q.v.*)

Liquefied energy gas (LEG)

A term inclusive of LIQUEFIED PETROLEUM GAS (LPG) (*q.v.*) and LIQUEFIED NATURAL GAS (LNG) (*q.v.*). See "Liquefied Energy Gases," Hearings before the Senate Committee on Commerce, Science and Transportation, 95th Cong., 2d Sess. Serial No. 95–134 (1978).

Liquefied natural gas (LNG)

Natural gas that has been cooled to about −160 degree Centigrade for storage or shipment as a liquid in high pressure cyrogenic containers. See Resor, "Revolution in the Natural Gas Industry," 102 *Trusts & Estates* 1092 (1963). For a discussion of certain of the problems of shipping this gas and common provisions of contracts of affreightment, see Mankabady, "The Affreightment of Liquefied Natural Gas," 9 *J. World Trade Law* 654 (1975); Greenwald, "Japanese LNG Contracts," [1983/84] 10 *OGLTR* 222 (1984).

Special problems of liquefied natural gas are discussed in several papers in International Bar Ass'n, 2 *Energy Law 1981.*

Problems of regulation of the price of imported liquefied natural gas are dealt with in West Virginia Public Services Comm'n v. U. S. Dept. of Energy, 681 F.2d 847 (D.C. Cir. 1982).

For discussions sales and shipping agreements for liquefied natural gas see the papers by McCarthy, Masuda, and Susuki in International Bar Association, *Energy Law in Asia and the Pacific* 651 *et seq.* (1982).

Liquefied petroleum gas (LPG)

Butane and propane separated from natural gasoline and sold in liquid form as fuel, commonly known as bottled gas, tank gas, or simply LPG. Domestic use of LPG is confined largely to those areas where other gaseous fuels are not available. Industrial uses of LPG are varied and many. Some plants use it as firm fuel or as stand-by fuel for natural gas, while others use it in special heat-treating processes or in steel cutting or in other special heating operations.

Natural gas liquids used as motor fuel blending stocks provide clean-burning characteristics, give volatility control, and impart other desirable qualities. Many of the liquids can be upgraded into a variety of chemicals: alkylates, disopropyl, butadiene, ethylene, cyclohexene, *etc.*

Liquid constituents

Hydrocarbons in solution in natural gas which are liquefiable at surface temperature and pressure or by treatment and processing.

Liquid hydrocarbons

Hydrocarbons which are liquid at surface temperature and pressure.

Listed depository receipt

A transferable receipt from a bank or trust company acknowledging that the institution holds the thing described in the receipt as agent for the receipt holder; the receipt is described as "listed" when listed for trading on a stock exchange. See Mann, "Financing Oil and Gas Operations—Recent Developments," 33 *Sw. Legal Fdn. Oil & Gas Inst.* 407 at 418 (1982):

> "In this context, an oil and gas limited partnership interest that cannot be listed for trading according to the rules of a stock exchange would be deposited with a bank for the account of the limited partner. The limited partner would hold the depository receipt which, under the rules of the stock exchange, would be eligible for listing. The Apache Corporation was the first to use this innovative idea for an oil and gas limited partnership."

Little big inch pipeline

A 20-inch products pipeline from east Texas to the east coast built during World War II to meet the problem caused by tanker losses at sea as a result of submarine warfare. After the war the pipeline was sold to Texas Eastern Transmission Corp. and converted to a gas pipeline. Subsequently, in 1958, the pipeline was returned to products service. See Johnson, *Petroleum Pipelines and Public Policy, 1906–1959*, 324, 341–348, 383 (1967).

Little frac

This term is defined by Stoltz, Wagner & Brown v. Cimarron Exploration Co., 564 F. Supp. 840 at n.5, 77 O.&G.R. 529 at n.5 (W.D. Okla, 1981), as follows:

> "A 'little frac' is a limited-entry type of technique with fewer perforations than the big frac and pumping the gel water into the hole at a rate not over twice the number of holes, i.e., if you had ten perforations then pump 20 gallons of water a minute."

See also BIG FRAC; FRACTURING.

Live oil

Crude oil before gas has been separated from the liquid.

Syn.; UNSTABILIZED CRUDE OIL.

LNG

LIQUEFIED NATURAL GAS (*q.v.*)

LNOC

The LIBYAN NATIONAL OIL CORPORATION (*q.v.*).

Load factor

Average daily requirement divided by maximum daily requirement, stated as a percentage.

In Lynchburg Gas Co. v. Federal Power Commission, 336 F.2d 942 at 944 note 1 (D.C. Cir. 1964), this term is defined as "the ratio between a buyer's average daily purchases and its contract demand, the maximum volume it has a right to take under its contract."

Load oil

(1) Any oil or liquid hydrocarbon which has been used in any remedial operation in an oil or gas well. New Mexico Oil Conservation Comm'n, *Rules and Regulations* 3 (1958).

(2) Oil injected into a well as part of a fracturing operation. See Whitaker v. Texaco, Inc., 283 F.2d 169, 13 *O.&G.R.* 502 (10th Cir. 1960); FRACTURING.

Load-on-top

A procedure adopted by major oil companies in 1964 designed to reduce pollution by deballasting and tank washing operations of tankers at sea. See Daintith and Willoughby, *A Manual of United Kingdom Oil and Gas Law* 66 (1977).

Loan participation

Division of a loan among several financial institutions as a means of enabling an originating lender to accommodate large customers which it could not otherwise handle. The institutions participating in the loan generally see it as a way to invest profitably with a minimum of cost, effort, and risk. See Fisher & Muratet, "The Aftermath of Penn Square Bank: Protecting Loan Participants from Setoffs," 18 *Tulsa L.J.* 261 (1982).

LOC

Louisiana Office of Conservation.

Local drainage

See DRAINAGE.

Location

(1) A well site. The usage varies somewhat according to context. For example, newspapers will announce the "location" of a wildcat well at a certain place. This means that it has been decided that a well will be drilled at that place. It is also proper to speak of spacing units as "locations," *e.g.*, the *X* well is two "locations" south of the *Y* well.

(2) "A claim to public lands which is established either by the surrender of scrip or by the initiation of a mining claim or a settlement claim." United States Department of the Interior Bureau of Land Management, *Glossary of Public-Land Terms* 27 (1949).

See also COMPLETION LOCATION.

Location damages

Compensation paid by an operator to the surface owner for injury to the surface or to growing crops in the drilling of a well. Such payment may be required by law for excessive user of surface easements, by statute, by a SURFACE DAMAGE CLAUSE (*q.v.*) in an oil and gas lease, by a TENANT'S CONSENT AGREEMENT (*q. v.*) or by other agreement.

Location exception

A well location authorized as an exception to the regular well spacing rule.

See also EXCEPTION WELL; RULE 37; SISTRUNK FORMULA; WELL SPACING.

Locked-in rate

A rate in which an "increased rate is later superseded by a further increase." It is thus "effective only for the limited intervening period, called the 'locked-in' period, and retains significance in § 4(e) proceedings only in respect of its unrefundability if found unlawful." Wisconsin v. Federal Power Comm'n, 373 U.S. 294 at 298, n. 5, 18 *O.&G.R.* 541 at 544, n. 5 (1963).

Lode or vein

A continuous zone or belt of mineral-bearing rock or other earthy matter in place in fissure or rock, or lying within well defined channels and having boundaries sharply defined by rocky walls; or a continuous body of mineral that is clearly distinguished from neighboring rock and the general mass of the mountain. Fuller v. Mountain Sculpture, Inc., 6 Utah 2d 385, 314 P.2d 842, 8 *O.&G.R.* 90 (1957).

For a discussion of the distinction between lode and placer deposits see Keller, "Lode or Placer?—Locating the Distinction," 31 *Rocky Mt. Min. L. Inst.* 12-1 (1985).

"Logging off"

The accumulation of liquids in the well bore of gas wells preventing gas from rising to the surface.

Log of well

See WELL LOG.

London dumping convention

The International Convention on the Prevention of Marine Pollution by Dumping of Wastes and Other Matter 1972 whereby the contracting States undertook to prevent pollution of the sea by the dumping of waste and other matter.

London Policy Group (LPG)

An organization created in 1971 in order to negotiate jointly as an industry with OPEC regarding increases in producer-government "take." It was composed of representatives from approximately twenty-four petroleum companies operating in the Persian Gulf and Libya. Krueger, *The United States and International Oil* 31, 65 (1975).

Long oil payment

An OIL PAYMENT (*q.v.*) with a long pay-out. See Discussion Notes, 4 *O.&G.R.* 1074 (1955).

See also SHORT-LIVED IN-OIL PAYMENT.

Long section

A section of land in the United States Governmental Survey which contains more than 640 acres. See Stevens v. State Corporation Comm'n, 185 Kan. 190, 341 P.2d 1021, 11 *O.&G.R.* 804 (1959).

See also GENERAL LAND OFFICE SURVEY; LOT; SHORT SECTION.

Long term lease

An oil and gas lease executed for a long primary term without a thereafter clause. This was an early form of oil and gas lease which has passed out of use because it was not found satisfactory by either lessors or lessees. The former desired some assurance of a periodic return from the land in the form of rentals or royalties, and the latter desired to insure that their interest would last so long as oil or gas was produced from the land. This lease form has been largely supplanted by the UNLESS LEASE (*q.v.*) and OR LEASE (*q.v.*) forms in which the habendum clause includes a THEREAFTER CLAUSE (*q.v.*). See TREATISE § 601.1.

Long ton

See TON.

Lookback

An agreement between the buyer and seller whereby the sale price of a property will be redetermined or adjusted at a time after the sale has been consummated. See "Lookbacks," 11 *O.&G. Tax Q.* 88 (1962).

Look-see assignment

The term applied by L. Skeen, *West Virginia Oil and Gas Law* 46 (1984), to a lease assignment form said to give the purchaser an interest for a fixed sum covering drilling and logging and which gives the purchaser a look at the well before deciding if he desires to pay an additional pro rata sum for his share of completion costs. Form 20 in this work, described as a Look-see assignment, appears to give the operator the right to complete a well after which the purchaser is to be notified of his share of completion expenses; if the purchaser fails to pay his share the *operator* is given the option to consider the assignment of a share of the working interest "null and void" or the option to sue the purchaser for his proportionate share of the completion expenses.

LOOP

The LOUISIANA OFFSHORE OIL PORT (*q.v.*).

Looping

The construction of a second pipe line parallel to another existing pipe line, thus increasing the carrying capacity of that part of the line. See Battle Creek Gas Co. v. Federal Power Comm'n, 281 F.2d 42 (D.C. Cir. 1960).

See also PARTIAL LOOPING.

Loop lines

Additional pipe lines on the original right-of-way paralleling the original pipe lines which are laid to increase capacity. Northern Natural Gas Co. v. O'Malley, 174 F. Supp. 176, 10 *O.&G.R.* 423 (D. Neb. 1959), *rev'd,* 277 F.2d 128, 12 *O.&G.R.* 335 (8th Cir. 1960).

Losing returns

Loss of drilling MUD (*q.v.*) used to control high pressure into underlying structure.

Heavy gas pressure may be encountered during drilling. In order to control the pressure it is necessary to use heavy drilling mud. The mud is normally returned to the surface by mud circulating pumps but sometimes the mud disappears into the reservoir down in the earth. This disappearance of mud into the underlying structure is known as "losing returns." When this occurs, the mud is forced into the underlying geological structure containing the gas and has a tendency to seal off the flow of gas into the hole. After casing is set, perforated and tubing run, it is necessary either to swab the tubing or flow the well to complete the well as a producer. When high pressures are encountered, swabbing may not be feasible as the pressure may blow the swab out of the well and possibly cause loss of control of the well. See Rogers v. Osborn, 152 Tex. 540, 261 S.W.2d 311, 2 *O.&G.R.* 304, 1439 (1953).

Lost circulation

The loss of drilling fluids to the formation, usually cavernous or very permeable, evidenced by the complete or partial loss of drilling fluid returns to the surface. See CIRCULATION.

" 'Lost circulation' is a very serious but not altogether uncommon event which usually occurs when in the drilling process a cavern or some extremely porous formation is encountered into which the drilling mud escapes without returning to the surface. Drilling mud is initially pumped under high pressure down inside the drill pipe and through holes in the rotating bit. Full circulation is essential to the rotary drilling process. The mud lubricates and cools the bit. It returns in suspension to the surface the cuttings which geologists study for the presence of hydrocarbons and which, if left in the hole, would clog the bit and stick the pipe; and, on its return journey, the mud cakes the well bore, sealing harmful formations while protecting valuable ones, and it creates support for the walls of the hole. In the case of lost circulation, cuttings and cave-ins will fall on top of the drill collars and bit, causing the pipe to get stuck in the hole." Burger Drilling Co. v. Bauman, 643 F.2d 240 at 241, 69 *O.&G.R.* 511 at 513 (5th Cir., Unit A, 1981).

Startex Drilling Co. v. Sohio Petroleum Co., 680 F.2d 412, 74 *O.&G.R.* 384 (5th Cir. 1982), was concerned with the question whether there had been loss of circulation in a well which, under the terms of a drilling contract, caused the day rate rather than the footage rate to be applicable. The court discusses in detail the controversy over the meaning of this somewhat ambiguous term, *viz.*, whether there was lost circulation when returns of drilling mud amounted to 80 percent.

Lot

"A subdivision of a section which is not described as an aliquot part of the section but which is designated by number, *e.g.*, Lot 2. A lot is ordinarily irregular in shape and its acreage varies from that of a regular subdivision." United States Department of the Interior Bureau of Land Management, *Glossary of Public-Land Terms* 27 (1949).

Louisiana Offshore Oil Port (LOOP)

An oil unloading facility located in the Gulf of Mexico 18 miles offshore adjacent to La Fourche Parish, in waters of sufficient depth (105 to 115 feet) to accommodate a Very Large Cargo Carrier (VLCC) (*q.v.*) which has a draft of up to 95 feet when fully loaded. See Wolbert, *U.S. Oil Pipe Lines* 68 (1979).

Lo-Vaca problem

The problem arising from the failure of the Lo-Vaca Gathering Company to meet its contractual obligations to supply natural gas to a large area of Texas in 1972. See Prindle, *Petroleum Politics and the Texas Railroad Commission* 108 *et seq.* (1981).

Lower tier crude oil

This term is defined by Section 4988 of the National Energy Act (H.R. 8444), as passed by the House of Representatives on August 5, 1977, as controlled crude oil which is certified by the producer as having been sold pursuant to the lower tier ceiling price rule in effect (at the time of the first purchase) under section 4(a) of the Emergency Petroleum Allocation Act of 1973.

See also EXEMPT CRUDE OIL, SECOND TIER OIL.
Syn: FIRST TIER OIL; OLD OIL.

Lower tier oil

Syn. for OLD OIL (*q.v.*).

Low-priority user

Any user other than a HIGH-PRIORITY USER (*q.v.*).

Low temperature extraction (LTX)

A process by which gaseous hydrocarbons are caused to condense or liquify in a gas stream by refrigeration to temperatures below zero degrees Fahrenheit. Colorado Interstate Gas Co. v. HUFO Oils, 626 F.Supp. 38 ___ *O.&G.R.* ___ (W.D.Tex. 1985), *aff'd,* 802 F.2d 133, ___ *O.&G.R.* ___ (5th Cir. 1986), *reh. en banc denied,* 806 F.2d 261 (5th Cir. 1986).

Colorado Interstate Gas Co. v. HUFO Oils, *supra,* and HUFO Oils v. Railroad Commission, 717 S.W.2d 405, ____ *O.&G.R.* ____ (Tex. App., Austin, 1986), held that white oil extracted from natural gas by low temperature extraction could not be counted as "oil" for purposes of classification of a well as an oil well or gas well.

See also ALBINO OIL; GAS CONDENSATE; GAS WELL; NATURAL GASOLINE; WATER-WHITE OIL; WHITE OIL.

Low-volume system

A liquid petroleum pipeline system or a segment of a system which transports less than 100 BPH on a regular basis. Alberta Energy Resources Conservation Board Informational Letter IL–PL 76–1 (Jan. 9, 1976).

See also HIGH-VOLUME SYSTEM; INTERMEDIATE-VOLUME SYSTEM.

LPG

(1) LIQUEFIED PETROLEUM GAS (*q.v.*), being liquefied propanes and butanes separately or in mixtures.

(2) LONDON POLICY GROUP (*q.v.*).

LPGA

LIQUEFIED PETROLEUM GAS ASSOCIATION.

LPG-gas drive

Use of high-pressure enriched gas or an LPG-slug to achieve the miscible or partly miscible displacement of oil by gas. See Morse, "Trends in Oil Recovery Methods," 1 *IOCC Comm. Bull.* 1 at 5 (Dec. 1959).

See also SECONDARY RECOVERY.

LPP

LIGHT PETROLEUM PRODUCTS (*q.v.*).

LSD

Abbreviation of LEGAL SUBDIVISION (*q.v.*).

LTA

LIMITED TERM ABANDONMENT (*q.v.*).

LTX

An acronym for LOW TEMPERATURE EXTRACTION (LTX) (*q.v.*).

Lubricating oil

An oil used for the lubrication of machinery.

The process of preparing such oil was described in Asiatic Petroleum Corp. v. United States, 183 F. Supp. 275, 12 *O.&G.R.* 841 (Customs Court, 1959), as follows:

> "The heavy distillate fraction of petroleum crude oil is further distilled under vacuum, which is then followed by a solvent extraction, which is followed by a solvent dewaxing, then occasionally is followed by acid treatment, and then clay filtration, which permits the basic stocks to be run down to separate storage tanks. . . . [T]hese basic stocks are later blended together in mixing tanks . . . to meet certain specifications of viscosity and flash and gravity, and then to this mixture is added a chemical or chemicals, which are known as additives. These are mainly used to enhance the properties of the lubricating oil."

Lurgi process

A commercial process, originated in Germany, for coal gasification. See Henry v. Federal Power Comm'n, 513 F.2d 395, 52 *O.&G.R.* 135 (D.C. Cir. 1975).

See also MANUFACTURED GAS.

Lying behind the log

A term applied to conduct of the lessor during drilling operations by the lessee which may cause the court to find a lease preserved by estoppel and laches despite the expiration of the primary term. For this argument to prevail, the lessee must show (1) a duty on the part of the lessor to speak or act in some manner, and (2) detrimental reliance on a failure to perform such duty. Kuykendall v. Helmerich & Payne, Inc., 54 *Okla. B.A.J.* 26 (Okla. App. 1982), noted, 19 *Tulsa L.J.* 271 (1983).

Duer v. Hoover & Bracken Energies, Inc., ____ P.2d ____, ____ *O.&G.R.* ____, 57 *Okla. B.J.* 1447 (Okla. App. 1986), rejected equitable defense of laches based upon allegation that lessee was prejudiced because lessor "laid behind the log" until the venture proved profitable and then asserted his claim that the lease had terminated automatically by reason of failure to make timely payment of rentals:

"Because Lessee commences drilling knowing Lessor never received his payment, it is evident any prejudice it suffered was the result of its own actions and not as a result of Lessor's 'delay' in instituting suit. He who seeks equity must do equity."

See also LACHES.

Syn.: Riding the well down.

. . M . .

MAB

MINIMUM ACCEPTABLE BID (*q.v.*).

Macaroni

Equipment for wells with a SLIM HOLE (*q.v.*), emphasizing its smallness. Waterbury v. Byron Jackson, Inc., 576 F.2d 1095 at 1096, 61 *O.&G.R.* 167 at 168 (5th Cir. 1978).

MAFLA area

The acronym for the offshore of Mississippi, Alabama and Florida in the Eastern Gulf of Mexico. See Sierra Club v. Morton, 510 F.2d 813 (5th Cir. 1975).

Magnetic survey

See GEOPHYSICAL SURVEY.

Magnetometer

A device that measures the relative intensity of the earth's magnetic effect. It is especially useful where salt or igneous or metamorphic rock is responsible for the subsurface structure, if any.

See also GEOPHYSICAL EXPLORATION; GEOPHYSICAL SURVEY.

Maintenance of uniform interest clause

A clause commonly included in standard operating agreements providing for the maintenance of uniform interests in the CONTRACT AREA (*q.v.*). The primary purpose of the clause appears to be preventing undue expense and burden on the operator in having to deal with multiple variations of ownership in each property contained within the Contract area. See Kutzschbach, "Operating Agreement Considerations in Acquisitions of Producing Properties," 36 *Sw. Legal Fdn. Oil & Gas Inst.* 7-1 at 7-27 (1985).

Major company

A company integrated to a substantial degree, that is, engaged in production, refining, transportation, and marketing.

For a journalistic exposé of alleged control of government policy by major oil companies, see Sherrill, *The Oil Follies of 1970-1980: How the Petroleum Industry Stole the Show (and Much More Besides)* (1983).

See also SEVEN SISTERS.

Make-up gas

(1) Gas that is taken in succeeding years having been paid for previously under a TAKE-OR-PAY CLAUSE (*q.v.*) in a GAS PURCHASE CONTRACT (*q.v.*). The contract will normally specify the number of years after payment in which the purchaser can take delivery of make-up gas without paying a second time. See TREATISE § 724.5.

In Lone Star Gas Co. v. McCarthy, 605 S.W.2d 653 at 656, 67 *O.&G.R.* 623 at 627 (Tex. Civ. App. 1980, error ref'd n.r.e.), the court quoted and adopted this definition of make-up gas, rejecting the contention that the term should be more broadly defined to embrace "setting an account in order":

> "In the gas sales industry 'make up' is a word of art. Both parties had substantial experience in the oil and gas industry. In construing the contract the courts give consideration to the meaning which is attributed to the term in the industry."

See also Universal Resources Corp. v. Panhandle Eastern Pipe Line Co., 813 F.2d 77, ____ *O.&G.R.* ____ (5th Cir. 1987) (citing this MANUAL).

For a discussion of the make-up clause of the take-or-pay provision of a gas sales contract, see Markette, "Oil and Gas: 'Take or Pay' Gas Contracts: Are They Subject to Royalty?" 35 *Okla. L. Rev.* 150 (1982).

See also MAXIMUM QUANTITY CLAUSE.

(2) Gas purchased from other reservoirs to supplement reservoir gas in gas-injection operations. Use of make up gas permits injection of a gas volume equal to 100% or more of the volume of gas produced.

Make-up payment

Under certain CONCESSION (*q.v.*) contracts, an additional payment required to be made to the host country when oil profits exceed a specified ratio to income tax and royalty payments to the host country. See Article 5 of the Oil Concession Agreement between Kuwait, the Kuwait National Petroleum Co. and Hispanica de Petroles [OPEC, *Selected Documents of the International Petroleum Industry 1968* at p. 156].

Make-up right

The right to make up an underlift out of the share of production taken by an overlifter. See UNDERLIFT/OVERLIFT PROVISION.

Make water, to

To produce water from a well, either alone or in conjunction with the production of oil.

Making hole

Actually drilling a well. Hamilton v. Stekoll Petroleum Co., 250 S.W.2d 645, 1 *O.&G.R.* 1362 at 1366 (Tex. Civ. App. 1952), *rev'd,* 152 Tex. 182, 255 S.W.2d 187, 2 *O.&G.R.* 102 (1953).

Manahan-type carried interest

A form of CARRIED INTEREST (*q. v.*), deriving its name from Manahan Oil Co., 8 T. C. 1159 (1947). In this type of carried interest, *A,* the owner of a lease, assigns all of the working interest to *B,* who undertakes the costs of specified drilling and development. *A* retains a reversionary interest in part of the working interest, which reversion occurs when *B* has recovered the specified costs during the pay out period. See Burke and Bowhay, *Income Taxation of Natural Resources* ¶ 15.17 (1981); Fielder, "The Option to Deduct Intangible Drilling and Development Costs," 33 *Tex. L. Rev.* 825 at 839–40 (1955); TREATISE §§ 424–424.4.

Railroad Comm'n v. Olin Corp., 690 S.W.2d 628, 88 *O.&G.R.* 579 (Tex. App., Austin, 1985), concluded that the interest of a NON-CONSENT PARTY (*q.v.*) is a Manahan-type carried interest. Error was ref'd n.r.e., 701 S.W.2d 641; 88 *O.&G.R.* 586 (Tex. 1985) (approving only the result reached by the court of appeals requiring Olin Corp. and Tenexplo to pay for the plugging of the well).

See also Rev. Rul 75–446, 1975–42 I.R.B. 8, 51 *O.&G.R.* 299 (carrying party holding entire working interest for complete payout period has option to deduct all intangible drilling and development costs incurred in drilling a well).

Mandatory Canadian Crude Oil Allocation Regulations

Regulations, providing for the allocation of crude oil imported from Canada among certain refineries and other consumers in the United States, designed to mitigate the adverse effect on dependent firms of reduction in export levels of Canadian crude oil. 10 C.F.R. § 214 (1980). For application of the regulations see Koch Refining Co. v. United States Department of Energy, 497 F. Supp. 879 (D. Minn. 1980), 504 F. Supp. 593 (D. Minn. 1980), *aff'd*, 658 F.2d 799 (Temp. Emer. Ct. App. 1981).

See also ECONOMIC REGULATORY ADMINISTRATION (ERA).

Mandatory contract carriage

The term applied to a proposed modification of federal natural gas regulations under which pipelines with extra capacity would be forced to haul gas for others at a fee. *Forbes,* Jan. 2, 1984, p. 82.

See also COMMON CARRIER LAW.

Mandatory oil import quota

See LICENSE FEE SYSTEM; OIL IMPORT QUOTA.

Mandatory petroleum price regulations (MPPR)

Federal regulations relating to petroleum prices. See State of Louisiana v. Department of Energy, 507 F. Supp. 1365 (W.D. La. 1981), 519 F. Supp. 351 (W.D. La. 1981), *aff'd in part, rev'd in part,* 690 F.2d 180 (Temp. Emer. Ct. App. 1982), *cert. denied,* 460 U.S. 1069, 103 S. Ct. 1522 (1983).

Mandatory Petroleum Products Allocation Regulations

Regulations for the allocation of petroleum products as issued under the authority of the Economic Stabilization Act of 1970, as amended, and the Emergency Petroleum Allocation Act of 1973. 10 C.F.R. Ch. II, Part 200 (1980). See Note, "National Energy Goals and FEA's Mandatory Crude Oil Allocation Program," 61 *Va. L. Rev.* 903 (1975).

See also ECONOMIC REGULATORY ADMINISTRATION (ERA).

Mandatory refinery yield control program

A program designed to require each refiner to utilize available supplies of crude oil in a manner best suited to ensure adequate production levels of refined petroleum products and residual fuel oil which are or may be in short supply. 10 C.F.R. § 211.71 (1980).

See also ECONOMIC REGULATORY ADMINISTRATION (ERA).

Mandatory work program

A provision of a PETROLEUM INTERNATIONAL AGREEMENT (PIA) (*q.v.*) or CONCESSION (*q.v.*) fixing minimum expenditures, number of seismic lines, specific number of exploratory wells, *etc.* See Blinn, Duval, Le Leuch, and Pertuzio, *International Petroleum Exploration & Exploitation Agreements* 124 (1986).

Syn.: Obligatory work program.

Manifest

A document issued by a shipper covering oil or products to be transported by truck or other motor vehicle.

Manifold pit

An open space into which all lines conveying oil to and from a pumping station enter, and which is designed to permit the escape of inflammable and explosive gases incident to the transportation of oil, so that the danger of explosions may be avoided.

Manufactured gas

Synthetic gas manufactured from coal (*e.g.*, by the LURGI PROCESS (*q.v.*)), or other products as distinguished from NATURAL GAS (*q.v.*). In Henry v. Federal Power Comm'n, 513 F.2d 395, 52 *O.&G.R.* 135 (D.C. Cir. 1975), the court affirmed the determination by the Federal Power Commission that it lacked jurisdiction over the production, sale or transportation of such gas prior to its mixture with natural gas produced from wells. See Status and Obstacles to Commercialization of Coal Liquefication and Gasification, Committee Print for the use of The National Fuels and Energy Policy Study Committee on Interior and Insular Affairs, U.S. Senate, pursuant to S. Res. 45, 94th Cong., 2d Sess. Serial No. 94–33 (92–123).

See also SYNTHESIS GAS; SYNTHETIC NATURAL GAS (SNG).

Mareva type injunction

A procedure enabling a creditor in a proper case to stop his debtor from parting with his assets pending trial. See B.P. Exploration Company (Libya) Ltd. v. Hunt, [1981] 1 W.W.R. 209 (N.W.T. Sup. Ct. 1980) (holding that the court had jurisdiction to grant this type of injunction).

Marginal cost pricing

A system of setting the price of natural gas (or other) service equal to the marginal cost of providing such service for various consumer classes. See Silverman, "Encouraging Conservation of Natural Gas Through the Price Mechanism," 57 *Denver L.J.* 545 (1980).

See also INCREMENTAL PRICING; ROLLED-IN PRICE.

Marginal property rule

The rule applicable under mandatory petroleum price regulations to a property whose average daily production of crude oil per well during calendar year 1978 did not exceed the number of barrels specified in 10 C.F.R. 212.72 (1981) for the corresponding average completion depth. In Wiggins Brothers, Inc. v. Department of Energy, 667 F.2d 77 (Temp. Emer. Ct. App. 1981), *cert. denied,* 456 U.S. 905 (1982), the court concluded that injection wells were not to be counted as "wells that produced crude oil" under this rule, *on remand,* 548 F. Supp. 547 (N.D. Tex. 1982).

See also Exxon Corp. v. Department of Energy, 601 F.Supp. 1395 (D. Dela. 1985) (discussing the history of the ENTITLEMENT PROGRAM (*q.v.*) and the marginal property rule), *aff'd in part and rev'd in part,* 802 F.2d 1400 (Temp. Emer. Ct. App. 1986).

Marginal unit

A PRORATION UNIT (*q.v.*) that will not produce at a rate equal to the top unit allowable for the proration period for the pool. New Mexico Oil Conservation Comm'n, *Rules and Regulations* 3 (1958).

Marginal well

A well incapable of production except by artificial lift (pumping, gas lift or other means of artificial lift) and when so equipped, capable of producing only a limited amount of oil. The term is defined in terms of depth of the well and capacity to produce in the Texas Marginal Well statute, Tex. Nat. Res. Code §§ 85.121, 85.122 (1978); 16 Tex. Admin. Code § 3.69. Sometimes the term is used as synonymous with STRIPPER WELL (*q.v.*).

Marginal well allowable

The ALLOWABLE (*q.v.*) granted a marginal well under the provisions of a marginal well statute.

Marginal well statute

A statute defining "marginal well" and making express provision concerning the allowable granted a marginal well. See, *e.g.*, Tex. Nat. Res. Code §§ 85.121 *et seq.* (1978). This statute defines a marginal well in terms both of production and depth of well, and declares that

> "to artificially curtail the production of a marginal well below the marginal limit as set out in Sections 85.121 through 85.122 of this code before the marginal well's ultimate plugging and abandonment is declared to be waste." [§ 85.123]
>
> "No rule or order of the commission or of any other constituted legal authority shall be adopted requiring the restriction of the production of a marginal well." [§ 85.124]

Statutes of this type are designed, in part at least, to discourage premature abandonment of low production wells, which abandonment might be hastened by a very low allowable for the wells. The statute may have the effect of making the "per well" factor a major factor in the fixing of well allowables. Regulatory commissions are reluctant to fix the allowable for a non-marginal well at a lower figure than the required allowable for a marginal well. Hence the allowable on a per well basis is equivalent, at least, to the marginal well allowable. If the total allowable for a field is relatively small, and the number of wells great, the per well allowable so calculated may largely consume the total field allowable, leaving little to be allocated on the basis of such factors as potential, acreage, etc. See Railroad Comm'n v. Rowan & Nichols Oil Co., 310 U.S. 573 (1940), *as amended,* 311 U.S. 614 (1940).

Marine Environment Protection Committee (MEPC)

A committee established in 1973 for the purpose of executing and coordinating the work of the Inter-Governmental Maritime Consultative Organization (IMCO), an agency of the United Nations, in the marine pollution field. See National Petroleum Council, "Protection of the Marine Environment," 8 *Nat. Res. Law.* 511 (1975).

Marine riser

A telescopic pipe running from a floating drilling rig to the ocean floor used to direct the drill stem and carry mud. Kash, *et al., Energy Under the Oceans* 39, 366 (1973).

Marker crude

See BENCHMARK CRUDE.

Marker price

A price fixed by the ORGANIZATION OF PETROLEUM EXPORTING COUNTRIES (OPEC) (*q.v.*) for so-called BENCHMARK CRUDE (*q.v.*). Each member of OPEC was expected to calibrate its price schedules around the marker price to reflect differences in quality (that is, gravity and sulfur content) and transportation costs. See Danielsen, *The Evolution of OPEC* 64 (1982).

See also OIL PURCHASE AND SALE CONTRACT.

Marker well

This term is defined in § 2 of the Natural Gas Policy Act of 1978 (Pub. L. No. 95–621) as any well from which natural gas was produced in commercial quantities at any time after January 1, 1970, and before April 20, 1977. Included is a NEW WELL (*q.v.*) which is drilled to a deeper completion location after February 19, 1977, but not a New well the surface drilling of which began on or after that date.

Market

See FEDERAL CRUDE OIL MARKET; FUTURES MARKET; SPOT MARKET.

Marketability test

A test applied in assessing the valuableness of mineral claims to determine whether a patent may be issued. "The claimant must show that a man of ordinary prudence could extract and market the claimed minerals at a profit. This requires that there exists, at the time of discovery rather than at some speculative future date, a market for the discovered minerals that is sufficient to attract the efforts of a person of ordinary prudence." Roberts v. Morton, 389 F. Supp. 87 at 91 (D. Colo. 1975), *aff'd,* 549 F.2d 158 (10th Cir. 1976), *cert. denied,* 434 U.S. 834 (1977).

See also Braunstein, "Natural Environments and Natural Resources: An Economic Analysis and New Interpretation of the General Mining Law," 32 *U.C.L.A. L. Rev.* 1133 (1985) (proposing that a discovery is not sufficient under the mining law unless the mining claimant can establish that the revenue reasonably anticipated from mining the claim equals or exceeds the full cost that will be incurred as a result of mining, including the social opportunity cost of consuming the *in situ* resources of the land on which the claim is located).

Marketable oil or gas

Oil or gas sufficiently free from impurities that it will be taken by a purchaser. See MERCHANTABLE OIL.

Market cap

See CONTRACTUAL CAP.

Market demand

"[T]he actual demand for oil from any particular pool or field for current requirements for current consumption and use within or without the state, together with the demand for such amounts as are necessary for building up or maintaining reasonable storage reserves of oil or the products thereof." Comp. Laws Mich., § 319.2(m); Mich. Stat. Ann. § 13.139(2)(m) (1973) (1980 Supp.).

For discussion of varied definitions of this term and of the calculation of market demand, see Hardwicke, "Market Demand as a Factor in the Conservation of Oil," 1 *Sw. Legal Fdn. Oil & Gas Inst.* 149 (1949).

For an argument that prorationing on the basis of market demand results in waste, see Vafai, "Market Demand Prorationing and Waste—A Statutory Confusion," 2 *Ecology L. Q.* 118 (1972).

See also PRORATIONING; REASONABLE MARKET DEMAND.

Market demand prorationing

PRORATIONING (*q.v.*) on the basis of market demand.

Marketing covenant

The express or implied covenant in an oil and gas lease to use due diligence to sell the product. The covenant is implied in order that the lessor will realize benefit from the retained royalty. See TREATISE §§ 853–858.3.

The most difficult problems in application of the covenant relate to gas. Among other problems are (1) the marketability of gas of the quality produced, (2) the availability of a market, (3) the responsibility of the lessee to install equipment to make the gas available to the pipeline purchaser, and (4) the question whether the lessee used good business judgment in executing one long-term gas sales contract rather than another.

See also IMPLIED COVENANTS.

Market-out clause

The term applied to a provision of a GAS PURCHASE CONTRACT (*q.v.*) permitting a pipeline purchaser to lower its price if market conditions dictate. The well owner is allowed to reject the lower price and have the pipeline transport the gas to another buyer. *Forbes Magazine*, Jan. 3, 1983, p. 99.

Take or Pay Provisions in Gas Purchase Contracs, F.E.R.C. Docket No. P. 83-1-000. 23 FPS 5-921 at 5-924, 47 Fed. Reg. 57268, 57270 (Statement of Policy issued Dec. 16, 1982), noted with favor "that a number of pipelines have recently exercised market-out provisions in gas purchase contracts for high cost gas or are renegotiating pricing and other contract terms."

See also the following:

Smith and Billings, "Taxation and Financial Reporting Regarding the Economic-Out Clause," 35 *O.&G. Tax Q.* 115 (1986);

Hollis, "Notable Recent Development in Federal Natural Gas Regulation," 34 *Sw. Legal Fdn. Oil & Gas Inst.* 31 at 39 (1983);

Johnson, "Natural Gas Sales Contracts," 34 *Sw. Legal Fdn. Oil & Gas Inst.* 83 at 104 (1983);

Turner, "Natural Gas—Impact of Deregulation or Regulation on Sales Contracts," 29 *Rocky Mt. Min. L. Inst.* 501 at 521 (1983).

See also ECONOMIC-OUT CLAUSE: FERC-OUT CLAUSE.

Market-Oriented Program Planning Study

A study undertaken by the Energy Research and Development Administration to help policy makers understand the relationship between costs and supplies of natural gas. See Wildavsky and Tenenbaum, *The Politics of Mistrust* 238 (1981) (a study of the problem of estimating American oil and gas resources).

Market price

The price at which oil or gas is purchased and sold. There is rarely dispute over the market price of oil but the market price of gas is sometimes more difficult of ascertainment. See Phillips Petroleum Co. v. Bynum, 155 F.2d 196 (5th Cir. 1946), *cert. denied,* 329 U.S. 714 (1946).

For a discussion of the factors relevant to the determination of market price of gas see Montana Power Co. v. Kravik, 179 Mont. 87, 586 P.2d 298, 62 *O.&G.R.* 472 (1978), *on subsequent appeal,* 616 P.2d 321, 68 *O.&G.R.* 269 (Mont. 1980).

Sowell v. Natural Gas Pipeline Co. of America, 604 F.Supp. 371 at 375, 84 *O.&G.R.* 407 at 414 (N.D. Tex. 1985), *aff'd,* 789 F.2d 1151, ___ *O.&G.R.* ___, *reh. denied;* 793 F.2d 1287 (5th Cir. 1986), notes that the terms "market price" and "market value" have on occasion been distinguished by some courts, whereas other courts have used the terms interchangeably. In the instant case the court found it unnecessary to determine whether the terms were equivalent.

See also Posted field price; Posted price.

Market value

The value of a product in the relevant market. Special difficulties may be found in determining the market value of gas under royalty clauses requiring an accounting by the lessee to the lessor on the basis of market value. See Treatise § 650.2. For the distinction between market value and proceeds see Proceeds.

See also Market price.

Market-value/amount-realized provision

The term applied by State of Wyoming v. Moncrief, 720 P.2d 470, ___ *O.&G.R.* ___ (Wyo. 1986), to a gas royalty provision stating that the amount of royalty to be paid should be "the market value at the well of one-eighth of the gas so sold or used, provided that on gas sold at the wells the royalty shall be one-eighth of the amount realized from such sale." In this case the court found consistency between this provision, a Lessor-approval provision (*q.v.*), and a Federal floor provision (*q.v.*).

Market value lease

A lease under which the royalty payment to the lessor is based on market value of the gas produced rather than the proceeds of sale of gas produced. See Continental Oil Co. v. Federal Power Comm'n, 519 F.2d 31 at 35, 52 *O.&G.R.* 445 at 451 (5th Cir. 1975), *cert. denied,* 425 U.S. 971 (1976).

See also Lightcap v. Mobil Oil Corp., 221 Kan. 448, 562 P.2d 1, 57 *O.&G.R.* 487 (1977), *cert. denied,* 434 U.S. 876 (1977), *reh. denied,* 440 U.S. 931 (1979), and Exxon Corp. v. Middleton, 613

S.W.2d 240, 67 *O.&G.R.* 431 (Tex. 1981) (distinguishing a "proceeds lease" (*viz.*, one providing for royalty of a portion of proceeds of sale of oil or gas) from a market value lease), *on remand, dism'd in part, rev'd and remanded in part on joint motion of parties,* 619 S.W.2d 477, 69 *O.&G.R.* 115 (Tex. Civ. App. 1981).

Matsen v. Cities Service Oil Co., 223 Kan. 846, 667 P.2d 337, 77 *O.&G.R.* 462 (1983), *cert. denied or dism'd as to various parties,* 468 U.S. 1222, 105 S. Ct. 17 (1984), 105 S. Ct. 3491, 3492 and 472 U.S. 1023, 106 S. Ct. 20 (1985), concluded that evidence of regulated natural gas prices is admissible on the issue of market value of natural gas and should be considered by the trial court in determining that issue. The court sustained a trial court finding that:

> "the most realistic guide to the market value of natural gas for the period in question was the maximum FPC regulated price, a price at which natural gas was actually being sold in interstate commerce from the Hugoton field. This approach disregards FPC vintaging for the purpose of fixing the market value upon which royalties are to be based."

In Oklahoma, the court has taken a position contrary to that of *Exxon Corp.* and has held that "market value" is measured by the price specified by the contract of sale of gas entered into by the lessee acting reasonably under his implied duty to market royalty gas. Tara Petroleum Corp. v. Hughey, 630 P.2d 1269, 71 *O.&G.R.* 386 (Okla. 1981).

For a discussion of the holdings of courts in these and other states on the problem of measuring market value of gas, see TREATISE § 650.4.

See also COMPARABLE SALES.

Market waste

The production of oil in any field or pool in excess of the market demand. Comp. Laws Mich., § 319.2(1)(3); Mich Stat. Ann. § 13.139(2)(*l*)(3) (1980 Supp.).

Massachusetts trust

A trust (as distinguished from a partnership or corporation) used to carry on a business. See TREATISE § 907.1; CERTIFICATE OF BENEFICIAL INTEREST.

Mass flow monitoring

A procedure for metering flow through pipelines for the purpose of early identification of leaks. Kash, *et al., Energy Under the Oceans* 366 (1973).

Master limited partnership

A LIMITED PARTNERSHIP (*q.v.*) which is itself a partner in smaller partnerships. This form of partnership was created in the 1980s by a number of oil companies and pipeline companies to highlight petroleum holdings and to pass on cash and certain tax benefits directly to holders. It is similar to a stock offering in that it may be publicly traded on a stock exchange and thus offers far greater liquidity than a standard partnership. *The Wall Street Journal,* July 1, 1986, page 29, col. 3 and page 32, col. 3.

For discussions of this form of partnership see the following:

Marich and McKee, "Sections 704(c) and 743(b): The Shortcomings of Existing Regulations and the Problems of Publicly Traded Partnerships," 37 *Sw. Legal Fdn. Oil & Gas Inst.* 11-1 (1986);

Bech, "Publicly Traded Oil and Gas Limited Partnerships—Opportunities and Limitations from a Nontax Perspective," 37 *Sw. Legal Fdn. Oil & Gas Inst.* 12-1 (1986).

Masterson clause

A term applied to a clause in a deed creating a DEFEASIBLE TERM INTEREST (*q.v.*) which incorporates all savings clauses from an existing lease into the term grant (or reservation) by providing that if at the end of the fixed term of the interest there is a valid recorded lease on the land the defeasible term interest will not terminate as long as the lease exists. Discussion Notes, 87 *O.&G.R.* 337 at 338 (1986).

Material balance

A method of estimating petroleum reserves. See Graham, "Fair Share or Fair Game?," 8 *Nat. Res. Law.* 61 at 75 (1975).

Mat supported jack-up

A self-elevating drilling rig used in offshore drilling which rests on a large steel frame on the sea bed rather than on independently adjustable legs. See Whitehead, *An A-Z of Offshore Oil & Gas* 151 (1976).

Maturity clause

An acceleration clause in a loan agreement pursuant to which the lender, under specified circumstances, may declare the loan matured and due. See Krohn, Kaasen, *et al.*, *Norwegian Petroleum Law* 4–34 (1978).

Maximum efficient rate (MER)

The maximum rate at which oil can be produced without excessive decline or loss of reservoir energy. For example, in a water drive field the rate of withdrawals of oil may be limited to about 3 to 5 percent per year of the ultimate yield so as to coincide with the rate of movement of water into the structure. If this were not done, pressure would drop, gas would come out of solution in the oil rendering it more viscious and in part nonrecoverable, and water would "finger" through the producing structure, segregating pockets of unrecoverable oil.

See also the following:

McDonald, *The Leasing of Federal Lands for Fossil Fuels Production* Ch. 7 (1979) (discussing the problem of giving economic content to the calculation of the MER);

Bruce, " 'Maximum Efficient Rate'—Its Use and Misuse in Production Regulation," 9 *Nat. Resources Law.* 441 (1976);

Hearings before Committee on Interstate and Foreign Commerce on H.R. 7372, 76th Cong., 3d Sess. 560 (1939);

Fanning, *Our Oil Resources* 129 (2d ed. 1950);

Culbertson, "Determination of MER in Texas," XI *Interstate Oil Compact Quarterly Bulletin* 23 (May, 1952);

Buckley, *Petroleum Conservation* 151–163 (1951).

For a discussion of the relationship between MER, MPR [Maximum production rate], and actual production see The Petroleum Industry, Hearings before the Subcommittee on Antitrust and Monopoly of the Committee of the Judiciary, U. S. Senate, 94th Cong., 1st Sess. on S. 2387, at p. 88, 270, 564 *et seq.*

Syn.: Optimum rate of flow (or production).

Maximum permissive rate (MPR)

The maximum rate of production permitted under Provisions Governing the Limitation and Allocation of Production of Oil, Saskatchewan MRO 118/68 A 62, 5 Lewis & Thompson, *Canadian Oil and Gas* Division D, Part X [5] (1971).

See also Water-oil ratio penalty factor.

Maximum quantity clause

A provision of a TAKE-OR-PAY CONTRACT (*q.v.*) establishing a maximum quantity of MAKE-UP GAS (*q.v.*) which may be taken by the purchaser in a given period of time. See Markette, "Oil and Gas: 'Take or Pay' Gas Contracts: Are They Subject to Royalty?," 35 *Okla. L. Rev.* 150 (1982).

Maximum rate limitation

"[T]he maximum rate of production prescribed for the avoidance of waste." The Alberta Oil and Gas Conservation Regulations, Alta. Reg. 151/71, § 1–020(10).

Maximum surcharge absorption capability (MSAC)

The total difference between the cost of gas to a facility and the ceiling on incremental pricing which is applicable to the facility, *i.e.*, the total amount of incremental cost the facility can absorb before its price of gas will rise above the applicable ceiling under the regulations implementing the incremental pricing provisions of the NATURAL GAS POLICY ACT OF 1978 (*q.v.*). 19 FPS 5–371.

See also INCREMENTAL PRICING.

Mcf

Thousand cubic feet. The standard unit for measuring the volume of natural gas.

MCOGA

The Mid-Continent Oil and Gas Association.

mds.

Abbreviation for millidarcies, a measure of permeability.

Mean of the range of values (MROV)

A factor employed by the Secretary of the Interior in evaluating competitive lease bids on submerged lands of the Outer Continental Shelf.

> "This is the Geological Survey's estimate of the value of the tract based on its analysis of geological data and a computer model simulation of production history and projections of dis-

counted cash flow. Bids above MROV are almost always accepted." Kerr-McGee Corp. v. Watt, 517 F. Supp. 1209 at 1210, 71 *O.&G.R.* 494 at 495 (D.D.C. 1981).

See also AVERAGE EVALUATION OF TRACT (AEOT); DISCOUNTED MROV (DMROV).

Measured reserves or resources

"Reserves or resources for which tonnage is computed from dimensions revealed in outcrops, trenches, workings and drill holes and for which the grade is computed from the results of detailed sampling. The sites for inspection, sampling, and measurement are spaced so closely and the geologic character is so well defined that size, shape, and mineral content are well established. The computed tonnage and grade are judged to be accurate within limits which are stated, and no such limit is judged to be different from the computed tonnage or grade by more than 20 percent." 2 *OCS Oil and Gas—An Environmental Assessment,* A Report to the President by the Council on Environmental Quality (April 1974) at p. 11.

"Identified reserves from which an energy commodity can be economically extracted with existing technology and whose location, quality, and quantity are known from geologic evidence supported by engineering evidence." Outer Continental Shelf Lands Acts Amendments and Coastal Zone Management Act Amendments, Joint Hearings before the Senate Committees on Interior and Insular Affairs and Commerce, 94th Cong., 1st Sess. [Serial No. 94–14 92–104] at p. 1283 (Report by the Comptroller General).

See also RESERVES.

Measurement base

A base employed in the measurement of gas volume. See 18 C.F.R. § 157.13 (d) (1980).

Measurement units

Barrel of oil: 42 U. S. Gallons at 60 degrees F.

Mcf. of Gas: 1,000 cubic feet at specified pressure base, often 14.65 pounds per square inch and 60 degrees F.

API Gravity: Standard (American Petroleum Institute) basis for measurement of gravity.

See also Btu; CONVERSION FACTORS.

Measurement-while-drilling (MWD)

Technology by which a driller can determine soil properties and measure whether his well is on course without pulling pipe and bit and lowering instruments into the hole. An MWD device stays in the hole and takes its bearings in a very brief time. *Forbes Magazine,* Jan. 3, 1983, p. 102; *The Wall Street Journal,* Dec. 20, 1983, p. 12, col. 1.

Measuring devices

Devices for measuring the volume, quality and characteristics of oil or gas produced.

Median line

The agreed boundary between individual countries facing the same area of continental shelf.

MEPC

The Marine Environment Protection Committee (*q.v.*).

MER

Maximum efficient rate (Mer) (*q.v.*)

MER allowable

An Allowable (*q.v.*) based on the MER of the particular well, pool or field. See Dutton, "Proration in Texas: Conservation or Confiscation?," 11 *Sw. L.J.* 186 at 188 (1957).

MER field

The term applied in Texas to a field (*e.g.,* the Hawkins Field) to which the Railroad Commission assigns an aggregate allowable called the maximum efficient rate of production or MER. This is a limit on the number of barrels which may be pumped daily from the field as a whole. The advantage of the MER designation is that whenever a lease operator cannot produce its allowable, the Commission distributes pro rata any unused allowable from one lease to every producing well in the field. United States v. Exxon Corp., *Federal Energy Guidelines* Par. 26539 (Temp. Emer. Ct. of App. 1985).

MER hearing

A public hearing by a regulatory commission preliminary to the fixing of the MER for a reservoir. See Dutton, "Proration in Texas: Conservation or Confiscation?," 11 *Sw. L.J.* 186 at 189 (1957).

Mercaptan

A compound containing sulphur in place of oxygen.

Merchantable oil

Oil of such quality as to be acceptable by a pipe line company or other purchaser. Frequently oil as produced contains BASIC SEDIMENT (*q.v.*) and water which must be removed before the oil can be turned into a pipeline. The royalty owner typically must bear a proportionate share of the expenses of removal of these impurities. Vedder Petroleum Corp., Ltd. v. Lambert Petroleum Lands Co., 50 Cal. App. 2d 102, 122 P.2d 600 (1942); *Id.*, 74 Cal. App. 2d 720, 169 P.2d 435 (1946).

Mercury number

A measure of the free sulfur in a sample of naphtha. Mercury is shaken with a sample of naphtha and the amount of discoloration in the sample is compared with a standard to determine the number. 55 *Oil and Gas Journal* 193 (No. 45, Nov. 11, 1957).

Merger, doctrine of

(1) The doctrine that, in the absence of fraud, mistake, etc., the stipulations of a contract for purchase and sale of real property are presumed to be merged in a subsequently delivered and accepted deed made in pursuance of such contract. For applications of this doctrine, see McSweyn v. Musselshell County, Mont., 632 P.2d 1095, 70 *O.&G.R.* 542 (Mont. 1981); El Sol Corp. v. Jones, 97 N.M. 645, 642 P.2d 1104, 72 *O.&G.R.* 509 (1982).

(2) The extinguishment of a lesser estate by merger into a greater estate when the greater and the lesser estate coincide and meet in one and the same person without any intermediate estate. Thus if the reversion following an estate for years descends to or is purchased by the tenant for years, the term of years is merged in the inheritance and shall no longer exist. The doctrine has been held inapplicable to horizontal divisions of realty. Humphreys-Mexia Co. v. Gammon, 113 Tex. 247, 254 S.W. 296 at 301-2 (1923); Gibson Drilling Co. v.

B & N Petroleum Inc., 703 S.W.2d 822, 90 *O.&G.R.* 321 (Tex. App., Tyler, 1986), error ref'd n.r.e.).

Metallurgical coal

Coal with strong or moderately strong coking properties that contain no more than 8.0 percent ash and 1.25 percent sulfur, as mined or after conventional cleaning.

Meter

A measuring device used to ascertain the quantity or volume of oil or gas produced or passing through the device. See FLOW METER; DIFFERENTIAL PRESSURE FLOW METER; ORIFICE METER.

A device measuring the gravitational pull of rocks. See GRAVITY METER.

Methane

A simple hydrocarbon associated with petroleum. It is gaseous at ordinary atmospheric pressure Of the many hydrocarbons that make up natural gas, methane is the lightest and most abundant. See Interstate Oil Compact Commission, *Oil and Gas Production* 26 (1951).

For discussions of ownership of gas in coal deposits see the following:

Dunn, Gremillion, and Pearson, "The Technological, Economic, and LEgal Aspects of Methane Production from Coal Seams," International Bar Ass'n Section on Energy and Natural Resources, *International Energy Law* (1984) (Topic 9);

Farnell, "Methane Gas Ownership: A Proposed Solution for Alabama," 33 *Ala. L. Rev.* 521 (1982);

McGinley, "Legal Problems Relating to Ownership of Gas Found in Coal Deposits," 80 *W. Va. L. Rev.* 369 (1978);

Craig and Myers, "Ownership of Methane Gas in Coalbeds," 24 *Rocky Mt. Min. L. Inst.* 767 (1978).

See also COALBED GAS; FIREDAMP.

Methane drainage license

A license to get natural gas in the course of operations for making and keeping safe coal mines whether or not disused. J. Salter, *U.K. Onshore Oil and Gas Law* 1-302 (1986).

See also COALBED GAS; FIREDAMP.

Methanol

A simple form of alcohol [METHYL ALCOHOL (*q.v.*)] usually known as wood alcohol.

Natural gas may be converted into this form for overseas transportation after which it may be burned directly or as a boiler fuel or be reconverted into substitute natural gas by the receiving gas pipeline company. Unlike LNG (liquefied natural gas), methanol requires neither compression nor refrigeration during transit; however it weighs twice as much and occupies nearly one and a half times the volume of an equivalent amount of LNG in energy content. As it can be transported in conventional crude oil tankers with minor modifications, the capital costs for methanol tankers are considerably less than for LNG vessels. A methanol plant is generally more capital intensive than an LNG liquefication facility of comparable size and, because of conversion losses, methanol requires more natural gas feedstock than an equivalent LNG plant. Commercial possibilities for methanol are substantial in producing countries with plentiful supply of surplus natural gas located suitably long distances from market. See The Chase Manhattan Bank, *The Petroleum Situation* (March 31, 1974).

"[T]he energy loss through methanol conversion and transport, even by normal oil tanker, may be in the order of 35 to 40 percent, compared with the 15 to 20 percent for LNG, and it is generally believed that if a decision is to be made purely on the economics of transport, methanol conversion will not match LNG as an economic means of transporting larger quantities of natural gas." Russell, *Geopolitics of Natural Gas* 52 (1983).

Methyl alcohol (CH_3OH)

A poisonous liquid, also known as methanol or wood alcohol, which is the lowest member of the alcohol series.

Metric ton

A unit of weight equal to 1,000 kilograms, which is equivalent to 2,204.62 pounds.

See also CONVERSION FACTORS; TON.

Micellar flooding

See SURFACTANT FLOODING.

Microemulsion flooding

See SURFACTANT FLOODING.

Mid-continent area

Generally the area lying between the Rocky Mountains and the Mississippi river, the Canadian border and the Gulf of Mexico, or more specifically, the greater part of Kansas and Oklahoma, all of Texas except the coastal belt, southeastern New Mexico, northern Louisiana, southern Arkansas and western Missouri.

Mid-continent gravity high

The term applied to a rift valley, five miles deep, filled with a billion-year accumulation of sediment, running from western Lake Superior southwest along Minnesota's boundary with Wisconsin, across Iowa and the southeast corner of Nebraska into Kansas. The valley, which evidenced abnormally high gravity in a series of deep seismic surveys, may mark where the continent began to split apart more than 1.1 billion years ago. Conjecture that the valley may constitute a giant oil reservoir led to drilling activities into the valley in 1984 by Texaco and to strenuous leasing activity by various oil companies. *The New York Times,* Oct. 16, 1984, p. 22, col. 4.

Mid-continent lease

A term descriptive generally of an UNLESS LEASE (*q.v.*) or PRODUCERS 88 LEASE (*q.v.*) but not descriptive of any particular lease form.

Middle distillates

Refinery products in the middle of the distillation range of crude oil, including kerosene, kerosene-base jet fuel, home heating fuel, range oil, stove oil and diesel fuel. These products have a fifty percent boiling point in the ASTM D86 standard distillation test falling between 371 degrees and 700 degrees F. 38 F.R. 34419. Above the middle distillate range are the lighter, quick-to-evaporate, highly flammable products such as gasoline and naptha; below the middle distillate range are such products as heavy residual fuels and asphalt.

Regulations concerning the allocation of middle distillates are contained in 10 C.F.R. § 211.121 *et seq.* (1980).

Mid-La

The name commonly used for Public Service Comm'n v. Mid-Louisiana Gas Co., 463 U.S. 319 (1983), which held that the maximum lawful prices fixed in the NATURAL GAS POLICY ACT (NGPA) (*q.v.*) applied to intracorporate transfers from the production department of a pipeline to the distribution department and fixed the amount which could be passed through by the pipeline to its customers as its cost of acquisition. See El Paso Natural Gas Co. v. American Petrofina Co. of Texas, 715 S.W.2d 177 at 181, ____ *O.&G.R.* ____ at ____ (Tex. App., Houston, 1986).

Mid-way price

The term used by one writer in describing transactions between major foreign oil companies when one had available more oil than it required and another had less oil than it required. The former sold its surplus oil to the latter at the mid-way price, *viz.*, the price equivalent to the cost of production plus half the difference between the cost and the posted price. Al-Chalabi, *OPEC and the International Oil Industry: A Changing Structure* 34 (1980).

See also OIL PURCHASE AND SALE CONTRACT; QUARTER-WAY PRICE.

Migration

The subsurface movement of oil and gas in response to difference in pressure in the reservoir. Migration may be local (to a well bore) or may be regional (see FIELD DRAINAGE). See Graham, "Fair Share or Fair Game?" 8 *Nat. Res. Law.* 61 at 79 (1975).

milcf

Million cubic feet.

Millidarcy

One one-thousandth (.001) of a DARCY (*q.v.*). A unit of measurement of PERMEABILITY OF ROCK (*q.v.*). If the rate of flow is one cubic centimeter per second for a liquid with a viscosity of one centipoise, the permeability of the rock is one darcy.

Mineral

Although scientifically this term refers to a chemical element or compound occurring naturally as a product of inorganic processes, it has been broadened colloquially in the oil, gas and coal extractive industries to include these products of organic processes. In most of the producing states it is a rule of property that the term "minerals" includes oil and gas unless the instrument creating the mineral interest by grant or reservation reveals that the parties intended the term to have a more restrictive meaning. Extrinsic evidence of intent in this regard is generally admissible only where the language of the instrument is ambiguous. See TREATISE §§ 219–219.7; Kirgis, "Mineral Reservations by Railroads and Local Government Bodies," 2 *Rocky Mt. Min. L. Inst.* 1 (1956).

For a persuasive argument that salt water should be classified as a mineral belonging to the mineral owner whereas domestic water should be considered a nonmineral appurtenant to the surface estate, see L. Hudson, "Salt Water is a Mineral: Ownership of a Natural Resource of Increasing Importance in Oil-Producing States," 50 *Texas L. Rev.* 448 (1972). In Robinson v. Robbins Petroleum Corp., 501 S.W.2d 865 at 867, 46 *O.&G.R.* 348 at 350–351 (Tex. 1973), the court commented as follows on this matter:

> "We are not attracted to a rule that would classify water according to a mineral contained in solution. Water is never absolutely pure unless it is treated in a laboratory. It is the water with which these parties are concerned and not the dissolved salt. If a mineral in solution or suspension were of such value or character as to justify production of the water for the extraction and use of the mineral content, we might have a different case. The substance extracted might well be the property of the mineral owner, and he might be entitled to use the water for purposes of production of the mineral. [Citation omitted]. In either case the water itself is an incident of surface ownership in the absence of specific conveyancing language to the contrary."

In Sun Oil Co. v. Whitaker, 483 S.W.2d 808, 42 *O.&G.R.* 256 (Tex. 1972), it was held that an oil and gas lessee had the implied right to free use of so much fresh water as was reasonably necessary to produce oil from its oil wells.

United States v. Union Oil Co. of Cal., 549 F.2d 1271, 55 *O.&G.R.* 425 (9th Cir. 1977), *cert. denied,* 434 U.S. 930 (1977), held that a reservation of "all coal and other minerals" in a patent under the Stock-Raising Homestead Act included geothermal steam and associated resources.

Geothermal Kinetics, Inc. v. Union Oil Co. of Cal., 75 Cal. App. 3d 56, 141 Cal. Rptr. 879, 58 *O.&G.R.* 22 (1977), held that a grant of minerals included geothermal resources, including steam therefrom.

Renewable Energy, Inc., 89 I.D. 496, 67 IBLA 304 (Sept. 30, 1982), held that a reservation of "all minerals" in a patent under section 8 of the Taylor Grazing Act embraced geothermal resources.

Andrus v. Charlestone Stone Products Co., 406 U.S. 604 (1978), held that water was not a locatable mineral under the mineral law of 1872.

An opinion of the Solicitor of the Department of the Interior has ruled that (1) geothermal steam as defined in the Geothermal Steam Act of 1970 is not a "mineral" as that term is used in the mineral leasing laws, and (2) only lands in wilderness areas designated subsequent to the passage of the Steam Act of 1970 were available for geothermal leasing. Geothermal Leasing in Designated Wilderness Areas, 88 I.D. 813 (1981).

Mineral acre

The full mineral interest in one acre of land. Dudley v. Fridge, 443 So. 2d 1207 at note 1, 80 *O.&G.R.* 1 (Alabama 1983).

Trades are often negotiated on the basis of a certain sum per mineral acre. Thus if *A* owns 100 acres of land and agrees to sell *B* one-half the minerals therein, *B* is purchasing 50 mineral acres. Certain differences will occur depending on whether the deed is worded as an undivided one-half interest or as 50 undivided mineral acres. If the land contains more than 100 acres, the former mode will give *B* one-half of the excess, whereas the latter mode limits *B* to 50 acres in the aggregate. But conversely, if the land contains less than 100 acres, the former mode will cut down *B's* interest whereas the latter insures that *B* gets at least 50 acres, if that much is owned by *A*. See Woods v. Sims, 154 Tex. 59, 273 S.W.2d 617, 4 *O.&G.R.* 193 (1954); Texas Osage Co-Operative Royalty Pool v. Garcia, 176 S.W.2d 798 (Tex. Civ. App. 1943); Daniel v. Allen, 129 S.W.2d 392 (Tex. Civ. App. 1939); TREATISE § 320.2.

The definition in this MANUAL was cited in Harris v. Griffith, 210 So. 2d 629 at 636, 28 *O.&G.R.* 398 at 407 (Miss. 1968).

Mineral deed

A conveyance of an interest in the minerals in, on or under a described tract of land. The grantee is given operating rights on the land; easements of access to the minerals are normally implied unless expressly negated.

To be distinguished are leases (which ordinarily contain express and implied obligations regarding drilling and development) and royalty deeds (which convey only a non-operating interest in minerals, if, as and when produced by the owner of the operating rights). The former distinction has been held to be significant in a number of legal contexts, including (1) the application of the doctrine of abandonment to the interest created by the instrument, (2) the implication of covenants by the grantee or lessee, (3) application of capital gains income tax provisions to the transaction, and (4) in Texas, the determination of whether the conveyance is permissible when Relinquishment Act lands are involved. The latter distinction (between mineral and royalty deeds) is particularly difficult, and the legal consequences of the distinction are considerable. In some states, *e.g.*, Texas, a grant of "royalties" is normally construed to be a royalty grant and not a mineral grant. On the other hand there is some authority, *e.g.*, in California, that a grant of "royalties" is a grant of minerals. In other states, *e.g.*, Oklahoma, a grant of "royalties" is frequently said by the courts to be ambiguous and hence extrinsic evidence is admitted to construe the instrument as either a royalty or a mineral grant. For a discussion of the problem of distinguishing mineral and royalty grants, see TREATISE §§ 302–307.4; Maxwell, "The Mineral-Royalty Distinction and the Expense of Production," 33 *Tex. L. Rev.* 463 (1955).

Mineral interest

The property interest created in oil and gas after a SEVERANCE (*q.v.*) by MINERAL DEED (*q.v.*) or oil and gas LEASE (*q.v.*). Its duration is like that of common law estates, namely, in fee simple, in fee simple determinable, for life or for a fixed term of years. The prime characteristic is the right to enter the land to explore, drill, produce and otherwise carry on mining activities. It is this attribute of operating rights that distinguishes a mineral interest from a ROYALTY INTEREST (*q.v.*). A hybrid interest has arisen, the NON-EXECUTIVE MINERAL INTEREST (*q.v.*), which has certain attributes of a mineral interest but is much more likely a royalty interest. See TREATISE §§ 301, 320–320.3.

In general it can be said that the owner of a mineral interest has all the rights, powers, privileges and immunities with regard to the minerals as his predecessor in title—the fee simple owner before severance—had before him, except as the severing instrument creates obligations expressly or impliedly.

The definition in this MANUAL was paraphrased and cited in Stratmann v. Stratmann, 204 Kan. 658 at 662, 465 P.2d 938 at 943, 36 *O.&G.R.* 585 at 591 (1970).

See also NON-OPERATING MINERAL INTEREST, FOR TAX PURPOSES; PER CENT INTEREST; SEVERED MINERAL INTEREST; TERM MINERAL OR ROYALTY INTEREST.

Mineral Land Tax Act

A British Columbia Act, 1973 (B.C.), c. 53, providing for a tax on mineral lands held in fee simple, which would bring revenue to the province similar to that brought in by the Mineral Royalties Act on minerals extracted from lands held by mineral claims and mineral leases. Under the regulations issued under the Act, the value of the mineral land was assessed on the previous year's revenue from the production of minerals. In Granduc Mines Limited (NPL) v. R. in Right of British Columbia, [1979] 1 W.W.R. 682 (B.C. Sup. Ct. 1978), the Act was sustained against the challenge that it was in reality an ultra vires commodity tax rather than a tax on land.

Mineral lease

"[A] contract by which the lessee is granted the right to explore for and produce minerals." Louisiana Mineral Code Article 114 [R.S. 31:114 (1975)].

Mineral leasing act

See FEDERAL LEASING ACT.

Mineral owner's fund

A fund maintained by the Oklahoma State Treasury under the provisions of 52 Okla. Stat. § 551–558, effective July 1, 1984, which is held in trust for property owners whose royalty and bonus interests are bound by pooling orders under the law relating to unknown or lost property owners.

Mineral rights

Article 16 of the Louisiana Mineral Code [R.S. 31:16 (1975)] uses the term "mineral rights" as a generic term to describe three basic interests, namely, the MINERAL SERVITUDE (*q.v.*), the MINERAL ROYALTY (*q.v.*) and the MINERAL LEASE (*q.v.*). "This enumeration does not exclude the creation of other mineral rights by a landowner." The comment to this Article notes that the term "mineral rights" has sometimes (erroneously) been used as if synonymous with mineral servitudes. See TREATISE §§ 216–216.8.

Mineral royalty

(1) A term sometimes used to describe a NONPARTICIPATING ROYALTY (*q.v.*). See Nabors, "The Louisiana Mineral Servitude and Royalty Doctrines," 25 *Tulane L. Rev.* 30 at 38 (1950).

(2) In Louisiana, "the right to participate in production of minerals from land owned by another or land subject to a mineral servitude owned by another. Unless expressly qualified by the parties, a royalty is a right to share in gross production free of mining or drilling and production costs." Louisiana Mineral Code Article 80 [R.S. 31:80 (1975)]. The Louisiana law of mineral royalties is codified in Articles 80–104 of the Mineral Code [R.S. 31;80 (1975)]. See TREATISE §§ 216–216.8.

See also PRESCRIPTION.

Mineral servitude

In Louisiana, "the right of enjoyment of land belonging to another for the purpose of exploring for and producing minerals and reducing them to possession and ownership." Louisiana Mineral Code Article 21 [R.S. 31:21 (1975)]. The Louisiana law of mineral servitudes is codified in Articles 21–79 of the Mineral Code [R.S. 31:21–79 (1975)]. See TREATISE §§ 216–216.8.

See also PRESCRIPTION.

Minerals Management Service (MMS)

By Secretarial Order No. 3071, Jan. 19, 1982, the Secretary of the Interior established this Service and transferred to it the minerals-related functions of the Conservation Division of the Geological Survey, including issuing permits, monitoring development operations, and collecting royalties. 47 Fed. Reg. 4751 (Feb. 2, 1982). References in 30 C.F.R. Part 251 and other departmental regulations to Survey were changed to MMS by final rule on June 30, 1982. 47 Fed. Reg. 28,386.

For "An Analysis of Problem Areas Related to the Management of the Federal Minerals Royalty Management Program by the Minerals Management Service of the Department of the Interior, with Recommended Solutions," see "Federal Minerals Royalty Management," A Report prepared by the Staff of the House Committee on Interior and Insular Affairs, 98th Cong., 2d Sess. (Committee Print No. 8).

See Muys, "Gas Royalty Valuation Standards and Procedures Applicable to Federal and Indian Leases," 37 *Sw. Legal Fdn. Oil & Gas Inst.* 2-1 (1986).

See also FEDERAL LEASE.

Mineral Workings (Offshore Installations) Act of 1971

The act providing for the safety, health and welfare of persons on installations concerned with the underwater exploitation and exploration of mineral resources in the waters in or surrounding the United Kingdom, and generally for the safety of such installations and the prevention of accidents on or near them. Stat. 1971, c. 61.

Minimum acceptable bid

A tract evaluation prepared by the staff of the United States Geological Survey as a basis for evaluating bids for leases on Outer Continental Shelf Lands. The decision of the Secretary of the Interior whether or not to lease a tract has been based in part on the comparison of the highest bid received and the USGS tract evaluation.

See also FEDERAL LEASE; RANGE OF VALUES METHOD; RISK-FREE VALUE.

Minimum allowable

The per well production below which an ALLOWABLE (*q.v.*) may not be fixed. See, *e.g.*, the discussion of the minimum allowable in Alberta in Crommelin, "Government Management of Oil and Gas in Alberta," 13 *Alberta L. Rev.* 146 at 180 (1975).

Minimum bill

(1) A tariff provision permitting Liquified Natural Gas companies to recover out-of-pocket expenses from a Buyer during a period when the Seller is unable to deliver gas. Southern Natural Gas Co. v. Federal Energy Regulatory Comm'n, 780 F.2d 1552 (11th Cir. 1986); 813 F.2d 364 (11th Cir. 1987).

(2) A MINIMUM COMMODITY BILL (*q.v.*).

Minimum commodity bill

A provision of a gas purchase and sale contract, tariff or certificate approved by the Federal Energy Regulatory Commission requiring a pipeline customer to pay for a minimum volume of gas (typically from sixty-six to ninety percent of the amount of gas the customer is entitled to demand under the contract) whether or not the customer purchases that amount of gas. See Wisconsin Gas Co. v. Federal Energy Regulatory Comm'n, 758 F.2d 669 (D.C. Cir. 1985), 770 F.2d 1144 (D.C. Cir. 1985), *cert denied,* ___ U.S. ___; 106 S.Ct. 1968, 1969 (1986); Mississippi River Transmission Corp. v. Federal Energy Regulatory Comm'n 759 F.2d 945 (D.C. Cir. 1985).

Minimum commodity bills enable pipelines to cover their own take-or-pay obligations to gas producers. See TAKE-OR-PAY CLAUSE.

Minimum contract quantity

The amount of gas or substituted payment required to be taken or paid under a TAKE-OR-PAY CONTRACT (*q.v.*). Freede v. Comm'r, 86 T.C. 340, 88 *O.&G.R.* 640 (1986).

Minimum rate

The minimum price which must be paid for jurisdictional gas sold for resale in interstate commerce. See JURISDICTIONAL SALES. Minimum rates have been an integral part of the producer rate schedule since Permian I [Area Rate Proceeding (Permian Basin Area), 34 F.P.C. 158 (1964), *aff'd,* Permian Basin Area Rate Cases, 390 U.S. 747 (1968)]. The minimum rate is designed to encourage exploration and development and to provide an incentive to maximize production from existing wells. See, *e.g.,* Tenneco Co. v. Federal Energy Regulatory Comm'n, 571 F.2d 837, 61 *O.&G.R.* 268 (5th Cir. 1978), *cert. denied under Rule 60,* 439 U.S. 801 (1978), sustaining the validity of Opinions No. 749 *et seq.* establishing a maximum national rate of 29.5 cents/mcf and a minimum national rate of 18 cents/mcf for gas from wells commenced before January 1, 1973.

See also PRICE CONTROL OF OIL, GAS AND PETROLEUM PRODUCTS.

Minimum royalty

(1) A payment to be made regardless of production, such payment frequently to be chargeable against future production, if any, accruing to the royalty interest.

For many years minimum royalty was an acceptable method of minimizing taxes to both lessor and lessee where it was substituted for a large bonus. For the lessor, it resulted in spreading the income over a period of years; for the lessee, upon proper election, it permitted the payments to be deducted rather than capitalized, as was required of bonus. Burke and Bowhay, *Income Taxation of Natural Resources* ¶ 4.09 (1981).

However, if the lease terminated without production, the lessor was required to restore the depletion allowance. The Supreme Court sustained the Commissioner's addition to income in the year of the lease's termination the amount of depletion allowance taken on minimum royalty in previous years, where there was no production. Douglas v. Comm'r, 322 U.S. 375 (1944).

Pittsburgh National Bank v. Allison Engineering Co., 279 Pa. Super. 442, 421 A.2d 281 (1980), concluded that it was so well-established as to be a rule of law that a minimum royalty provided for by a coal lease was not an advance royalty to be recouped from later tonnage royalties, but it was a liquidated rental for property whether or not the coal is mined, and the minimum royalty may not be applied to payment for the coal remaining in place unless expressly so provided.

Hutchison v. Sunbeam Coal Corp., ____ Pa. ____, 519 A.2d 385 (1986), concluded that "Implying a duty to mine in the face of a minimum advance royalty clause ignores the terms agreed to by the contracting parties."

Wiggins v. Warrior River Coal Co., 696 F.2d 1356, 77 *O.&G.R.* 8 (11th Cir. 1983), concluded that surrender of a coal lease under the provisions of its surrender clause did not extinguish the minimum royalty obligation of the lessee.

See also DEFERRED MINIMUM ANNUAL ROYALTY.

(2) The term minimum royalty may also be used to designate minimum payments required to be paid to the lessor by the lessee after production has been obtained. The income tax consequences of such payments depend on whether the payments are recoverable by the lessee from future production accruing to the lessor's royalty. See Burke and Bowhay, *op. cit. supra,* ¶ 15.08.

(3) The minimum fraction or percentage of production specified by applicable statutes which must be paid under leases of federal or state lands. The Mineral Leasing Act authorizes the Secretary of the Interior to reduce production royalties in mineral leases below the statutory minimum rates established for those minerals whenever, in his judgment, it is necessary to do so in order to promote development, or whenever in his judgment the leases cannot be successfully operated under the terms provided therein. Reduction of Production Royalties Below Statutory Minimum Rates, 87 I.D. 69 (Dec. 11, 1979).

58 Pa. Stat. §§ 33, 34 (enacted in 1979), provide that a lease or other agreement conveying the right to remove or recover oil, natu-

ral gas, or gas of any other designation from lessor to lessee shall not be valid if such lease does not guarantee the lessor at least one-eighth royalty. If royalty payable under an existing lease is less than one-eighth, the royalty is subject to escalation in the event of new drilling, deeper drilling, redrilling, artificial well stimulation, hydraulic fracturing, or any other procedure for increased production.

See also Bullard and Johnson, "Minimum Royalties," 34 *O.&G. Tax Q.* 726 (1986).

See also ADVANCE ROYALTY; ROYALTY.

Minimum royalty status

The status of a FEDERAL LEASE (*q.v.*) after the discovery of oil or gas in paying quantities when rental paying status terminates and the lessee is obliged to pay minimum royalty to keep the lease alive. See *Rocky Mt. Min. L. Fdn. The Law of Federal Oil and Gas Leases* § 12.07 (1985).

Minimum take provision

A provision of a contract, tariff or certificate approved by the Federal Energy Regulatory Commission which requires a pipeline customer to take physically a certain amount of gas and which does not offer a pipeline customer an option to pay for gas not taken. Wisconsin Gas Co. v. Federal Energy Regulatory comm'n, 758 F.2d 669 at 672 (D.C. Cir. 1985), 770 F.2d 1144 (D.C. Cir. 1985), *cert. denied*; ____ U.S. ____; 106 S.Ct. 1968, 1969 (1986).

Minimum tender

A requirement that a minimum amount of oil be offered for shipment before it will be accepted by a pipeline. See Wolbert, *American Pipelines* 22–46 (1952), 4 *Okla. L. Rev.* 20–44 (1951).

Minimum well-head price

The minimum price, fixed by a state regulatory agency under authority of state law, which may be paid at the well head for gas produced and which may be used in accounting to royalty owners for their interest in production. Minimum well-head price statutes were enacted in Oklahoma and Kansas and were held valid in Cities Service Gas Co. v. Peerless Oil & Gas Co., 340 U.S. 179 (1950), and Kansas-Nebraska Natural Gas Co. v. State Corporation Comm'n, 169 Kan. 722, 222 P.2d 704 (1950). However, after it was held that the Federal Power Commission had exclusive jurisdiction over the price of gas sold in interstate commerce for resale, Phillips Petroleum Co. v. Wisconsin, 347 U.S. 672 (1954), the Supreme Court has held that such minimum well head price statutes cannot be validly applied to such gas. Natural Gas Pipeline Co. v. Panoma Corp., 349 U.S. 44 (1955).

Mining partnership

A partnership arising from express agreement or by implication from conduct of concurrent owners of an operating interest in minerals. Both a joint interest in the property and joint operation are essential to the creation of a mining partnership by implication. An agreement between concurrent owners that one shall operate the property and both shall share in costs and profits does not give rise necessarily to a mining partnership unless there is also some showing of joint control over the operations. The authority of one mining partner to bind another is less extensive than the authority of a general partner to bind another as the mining partnership is a non-trading partnership and the authority of a partner to bind his mining partners is limited to that expressly granted or necessarily implied from the purposes and objectives of the partnership. See Jones, "Mining Partnership in Texas," 12 *Texas L. Rev.* 410 (1934), for a discussion of the characteristics of a mining partnership. See TREATISE §§ 435–435.2.

Mirror legislation

The term applied to the legislation enacted by the seven state governments of Australia and the Commonwealth under an agreement by which the governments undertook to legislate with respect to offshore petroleum operations in identical terms and to refrain from amending such legislation without prior unanimous agreement. Under this agreement, the Commonwealth enacted the PETROLEUM (SUBMERGED LANDS) ACT 1967 (*q.v.*), and the seven states enacted statutes of the same name later in 1967. Crommelin, "Petroleum (Submerged Lands) Act: The Nature and Security of Offshore Titles," 2 *Austl. Mining & Petroleum L.J.* 135 (1979).

Miscibility

A single phase state of oil and gas in the reservoir. Smith, "The Engineering Aspects of Pressure Maintenance and Secondary Recovery Operations," 6 *Rocky Mt. Min. L. Inst.* 211 at 228 (1961).

Miscible displacement method

A method of fluid injection. This method requires that three fluids exist in the reservoir: the mobile oil to be displaced, a displacing fluid moving as a bank behind the oil, and a fluid injected for the sole purpose of propelling the displacing fluid through the reservoir. The method is discussed in Lopez & Parsley, "Microbes, Simulators, and Satellites: The Prudent Operator Pursues Enhanced Recovery Under the Implied Covenants," 58 *N.D. L. Rev.* 501 at 528 (1982); Roark, "Engineering Aspects of Fluid Injection into Oil Reservoirs Which Require Legal Action," A.B.A., Section of Mineral and Natural Resources Law, *1957 Proceedings* 230 at 233 (1957).

See also FLUID INJECTION; SECONDARY RECOVERY.

Miscible-phase recovery project

A recovery program calling for injection successively of different fluids, first propane, then gas, then water. See 55 *Oil and Gas Journal* 156 (No. 46, Nov. 18, 1957).

See also FLUID INJECTION; SECONDARY RECOVERY.

Mist

Small particles of water contained in natural gas. See Continental Oil Co. v. Federal Power Comm'n, 247 F.2d 904, 7 *O.&G.R.* 1534 (5th Cir. 1957).

Mistake clause

A term which has been applied to a lease clause which excuses a lessee for errors in payment of delay rentals. D. Pierce, *Kansas Oil and Gas Handbook* §§ 9.39, 11.20. See TREATISE § 606.6.

Mixed base oil (or intermediate base oil)

Crude oil which is not predominately either paraffinic or naphthenic in characteristics. Oils produced in Michigan, northwestern Ohio, and Indiana are classed as intermediate or mixed base oil as are oils produced in the Rocky Mountain fields and in California.

See also ASPHALT BASE OIL; PARAFFIN BASE OIL.

Mixed condition

See POTESTATIVE CONDITION.

Mixed sharing arrangement

Syn. for DIVISIBLE SHARING ARRANGEMENT (*q.v.*).

MLP

MASTER LIMITED PARTNERSHIP (*q.v.*).

Mmcf.

One million (one thousand thousand) cubic feet.

MMS

MINERALS MANAGEMENT SERVICE (*q.v.*).

Mobile rig

A movable DRILLING RIG (*q.v.*) used to drill offshore exploratory or wildcat wells. A JACK-UP RIG (*q.v.*) may be floated to the location of a proposed well and jacked up on legs to provide a stationary platform above the water level for the purposes of drilling. A floating type mobile drilling rig floats to the location of the proposed well and continues to float while it is drilling the well. A floating rig is held on location solely by anchors and the drill pipe which extends from the drilling platform to the ocean floor. Gates Rubber Co. & Subsidiaries v. Commissioner, 74 T.C. 1456, 67 *O.&G.R.* 637 (1980) *aff'd,* 694 F.2d 648 (10th Cir. 1982), and Sun Oil Co. v. Commissioner, 74 T.C. 1481, 68 *O.&G.R.* 353 (1980), *aff'd,* 677 F.2d 294, 76 *O.&G.R.* 619 (3d Cir. 1982), *acq.* I.R.B. 1983-26 (1983), held that the deduction for INTANGIBLE DRILLING AND DEVELOPMENTS COSTS (*q.v.*) is available for a PRE-PLATFORM WELL (*q.v.*) drilled by a mobile rig.

MOC

The Myanma Oil Corporation of Burma.

Modified Btu method

A modification of the BTU METHOD (*q.v.*) of allocating costs between different operation or between different products. See Just and Reasonable National Rates for Sales of Natural Gas From Wells Commenced Prior to January 1, 1973, Federal Power Commission Opinion No. 749, Docket No. R–478 (Dec. 31, 1975).

For other methods of allocating costs see ACCOUNTING METHODS.

Modified NGAA contract

A form of contract proposed by the Natural Gasoline Association of America which provides for the determination of the price by the addition of a portion of the sales price for residue gas and a portion of the sales price or value of the liquids recovered. See Shamrock Oil & Gas Corp. v. Comm'r, 35 T.C. 979, 13 *O.&G.R.* 1090 at 1102 (1961).

Modified single marketable product method

A method of allocating joint production costs between gas and liquids. See Joseph, "Background and Analysis of Trial Examiner's Decision in Phillips Case," 11 *Sw. Legal Fdn. Oil & Gas Inst.* 1 at 24 (1960).

For other methods of allocating costs see COST ALLOCATION METHODS.

MOIP

The Mandatory Oil Import Program. See OIL IMPORT QUOTA.

Molecular theory

The theory of the Federal Power Commission that once natural gas from different sources is mixed in an interstate pipeline, the molecules of the gas are no longer identifiable in relation to their source, and therefore a part of commingled gas, which originally might have been nonjurisdictional, loses that status since at least part of its molecules will move across state lines in interstate commerce. See California v. Lo-Vaca Gathering Co., 379 U.S. 366 at 369 (1965); Chandler, "Government Regulation—Gas and Gas Companies," 43 *Tex. L. Rev.* 958 at 960 (1965).

See also COMMINGLING THEORY; JURISDICTIONAL SALES.

Money left on the table

A term used for the amount of difference between the first and second high bid in competitive lease sales. The substantial amount of this difference in bids has been said to evidence the competitive quality of the bidding. Energy Data Requirements of the Federal Government (Part III—Federal Offshore Oil and Gas Leasing Policies), Hearings before the Subcommittee on Activities of Regulatory Agencies of the Permanent Select Committee on Small Business, House of Representatives, 93rd Cong., 2d Sess. (1974) at 352, 381, 388.

See also LEASE BIDDING SYSTEMS.

Money management fund

"In the oil and gas business, a money management fund is an organization which raises money and places it with various operators for the purpose of conducting exploration. . . . [A] money management fund does not actively function as an operator." Brountas v. Commissioner, 73 T.C. 491 at 498 (1979), 74 T.C. 1062, 67 *O.&G.R.* 477 (1980), *vacated and remanded*, 692 F.2d 152, 75 *O.&G.R.* 193 (1st Cir. 1982), *cert. denied*, 462 U.S. 1106, 103 S.Ct. 2453 (1983).

Monkey board

The platform on which the "monkey" (derrick man) stands while he is working. *API Quarterly* 3 (Spring 1957).

Monocline

Tilted rock strata. It differs from an anticline, which is dome-shaped, and from a syncline, which is U-shaped, in that the strata dip in one direction only, absent faulting. See GEOLOGICAL STRUCTURE.

Monte Carlo simulation

A method of estimating the extent to which uncertainty about the input variables in a complex mathematical model produces uncertainty in the outputs of the model. The model is operated using values selected at random from estimated distributions of the likely values of each input variable. This process is repeated many times (several hundred or more), giving a large sample of output values based on a wide range of combinations of values of input variables. These calculated results are then combined to give an estimate of the mean value and range of uncertainty for each output variable.

MOPPS

The MARKET-ORIENTED PROGRAM PLANNING STUDY (*q.v.*).

More wells-more oil theory

The theory that the more wells drilled over a reservoir, the more oil that will be ultimately recovered from the reservoir. This theory was used in the early days of conservation to oppose well spacing regulations. Today, most experts are agreed that the theory is in error and that maximum recovery can be obtained by relatively wide spacing, 20–, 40–, or even 80–acre spacing, depending on the reservoir characteristics.

The Texas courts rejected the more wells-more oil theory as a valid basis for an attack on well spacing regulations. See Gulf Land Co. v. Atlantic Ref. Co., 134 Tex. 59, 131 S.W.2d 73 (1939); Railroad Comm'n v. Shell Oil Co., 139 Tex. 66, 161 S.W.2d 1022 (1942); Hawkins v. Texas Co., 146 Tex. 511, 209 S.W.2d 338 (1948).

Most favored lessor agreement

An agreement by a lessee to give the lessor the benefit of more favorable provisions of subsequent leases entered into by the lessee with other lessors in a specified area in the vicinity of the premises leased by the lessor. See Scott, "Unusual Provisions in Oil and Gas Leases," 33 *Sw. Legal Fdn. Oil & Gas Inst.* 139 at 148, 177 (1982).

Most favored nation clause

(1) A provision in a GAS PURCHASE CONTRACT (*q.v.*) increasing the price to be paid for natural gas by a purchaser to the seller-producer if any producer in the field receives a higher price for his gas than that stipulated in the contract. An example of such a clause is:

> "If at any time or times subsequent to the date of execution of this contract, Buyer shall enter into a contract providing for the purchase of gas in [names of counties in which the field is located] at a price per 1,000 cubic feet higher than the price per 1,000 cubic feet payable at the same time hereunder and for gas of a similar character taken under similar conditions of delivery, pressures, reservations, or life or term of contract, then Buyer will increase the price of gas thereafter received hereunder so that it will equal the price payable at the same time under such other contract."

A two-party favored nations clause (*syn.:* first-party favored nations clause) provides that if the buyer purchases gas in the same field or area at a higher price than is paid under the contract in question, it must thereafter pay to seller the same price it is paying to other sellers. A third-party favored nations clause provides that the buyer will pay seller a price equal to the highest price paid by any buyer to any seller in the same field or area. See TREATISE §§ 726–726.1.

See also CONTRACT PRICING AREA; ESCALATOR CLAUSE.

For the effect upon a favored nation clause of the Alberta Natural Gas Pricing Agreement Act of 1975, see Town of Castor v. Candel Oil Ltd., 107 D.L.R. 3d 247 (Alta Q.B. 1979).

Kerr-McGee Corp. v. Northern Utilities, Inc., 500 F. Supp. 624, 68 *O.&G.R.* 143 (D. Wyo. 1980, found a third party favored nations clause unenforceable on the grounds that, under the facts of the instant case, the clause was unconscionable, unjust, and contrary to public policy. Judgment in this case was reversed and the cause remanded, 673 F.2d 323, 75 *O.&G.R.* 413 (10th Cir. 1982), *cert. denied*, 459 U.S. 989, 103 S.Ct. 344 (1982). *Compare* Amoco Production Co. v. Kansas Power & Light Co., 505 F. Supp. 628, 68 *O.&G.R.* 1 (D. Kan. 1980), holding that an FCP CLAUSE (*q.v.*) was not unconscionable nor against public policy.

(2) Also, a provision in a CONCESSION (*q.v.*) or similar agreement between a host government and a foreign petroleum company obligating the latter to extend to the host government the benefit of any more favorable arrangements which the petroleum company might make with any other host government in connection with exploration and production. Lavenant, "Changing Concepts of the World's Mineral Development Laws With Especial Reference to West Africa," in International Bar Ass'n, *World Energy Laws* (Proceedings of the IBA Seminar on World Energy Law held in Stavanger, Norway) 117 at 121 (1975).

Mother Hubbard case

An antitrust case instituted on September 30, 1940 by the Department of Justice against the American Petroleum Institute, twenty-two major oil companies, and 379 of their subsidiaries, alleging unlawful anticompetitive behavior at every level of the petroleum industry. The case was formally dropped in January, 1951. See Adams and Brock, "Deregulation or Divestiture: The Case of Petroleum Pipelines," 19 *Wake Forest L. Rev.* 705 at 727 (1983).

See also PIPELINE.

Mother Hubbard clause

See COVER ALL CLAUSE.

Motor gasoline

Gasoline used to fuel a motor. Regulations concerning the mandatory allocation of motor gasoline are contained in 10 C.F.R. § 211.101 *et. seq.* (1980).

Mouse hole

Syn. for RAT HOLE (*q.v.*).

MPPR

Mandatory Petroleum Price Regulations. See State of Louisiana v. Department of Energy, 507 F. Supp. 1365 (W.D. La. 1981), 519 F. Supp. 351 (W.D. La. 1981), *aff'd in part, rev'd in part,* 690 F.2d 180 (Temp. Emer. Ct. App. 1982), *cert. denied,* 460 U.S. 1069, 103 S. Ct. 1522 (1983).

MPR

(1) Maximum permissive rate (*q.v.*) of production. See, *e.g.*, Provisions Governing the Limitation and Allocation of Production of Oil, Saskatchewan MRO 118/68 A 62, 5 Lewis and Thompson, *Canadian Oil and Gas* Division D, Part X[5] (1971).

See also Water-oil ratio penalty factor.

(2) Maximum production rate. See Department of the Interior Geological Survey Conservation Division, OCS Order No. 11 (May 1, 1974).

See also Maximum efficient rate (MER).

MRL

Maximum rate limitation (*q.v.*).

MROV

Mean of the range of value (*q.v.*)

MSAC

Maximum surcharge absorption capability (*q.v.*).

M³CF

Billion cubic feet.

MTA

The Maden Tetkik ve Aramu Enstitusu (Mining Research Institute). See Shwadran, *The Middle East, Oil and the Great Powers* 489 (3d ed. revised and enlarged 1973).

Mud

A heavy drilling fluid introduced into the drill stem under hydrostatic pressure. The mud proceeds down the drill stem, through openings in the drilling bit, up the sides of the hole, and out into the mud pits. As it proceeds back into the mud pits, it is cleansed of drill cuttings and prepared for reintroduction into the drill stem. This mud or drilling fluid, in addition to lubricating the bit and removing the cuttings from the hole, keeps the drill stem free from interference from the sides of the bore as well as from sub-surface pressures which in here in the formations through which the well is cut. In normal operation, the amount of mud introduced into the drill stem is the same as the amount of mud reclaimed from the well. In other words, a continuous, even circulation of drilling fluid is maintained. See Fidelity-Phoenix Fire Insurance Co. of New York v. Dyer, 220 F.2d 697, 4 *O.&G.R.* 973 (5th Cir. 1955).

The weight of mud varies from about 8 pounds per gallon to as much as 17 pounds per gallon according to the make-up of the mud. The weight of mud may be expressed in pounds per cubic foot, or pounds per square inch, or, in relation to hole depth, in terms of pounds per square inch per 1,000 feet of hole.

See also ADA MUD; AQUAGEL; BARITE; BAROID; BENTONITE; BLOWOUT; CIRCULATION OF MUD; DRILLING FLUIDS; KICK; LOSING RETURNS; PILL.

Mud analysis

Examination and testing of drilling MUD (*q.v.*) to determine its physical and chemical qualities.

Mud man

The operator of the valve at the end of the mud hose. See Covington v. Loffland Bros. Co., 152 So. 2d 108 (La. App. 1963).

Mud pit

See SLUSH PIT.

Multiple base-point system

A pricing system under which multiple geographical locations are accepted by buyers and sellers of oil as the assumed shipping point of the oil for the purpose of posted price and shipping costs. See Danielsen, *The Evolution of OPEC* 59 (1982).

See also BASE POINT PRICING; BASING POINT; EQUALIZATION POINT; GULF-PLUS PRICING STRUCTURE; PERSIAN GULF PRICING SYSTEM; PHANTOM FREIGHT; SINGLE BASE-POINT SYSTEM.

Multiple community lease

A term employed by one writer to describe the effect of the execution by the owners of separate parcels of land of counterparts of a lease which describes a larger area than that owned by the individual lessor and provides that the interests of all lessors in the described area shall be considered pooled and unitized. Hoffman, *Voluntary Pooling and Unitization* 83 (1954).

See also COMMUNITY LEASE.

Multiple completion

The completion of a single well into more than one producing horizon. Such a well may produce simultaneously from the different horizons, or alternately from each.

See also DUAL COMPLETION.

Multiple completion well

A well producing from two or more formations by means of separate tubing strings run inside the casing, each of which carries crude oil from a separate and distinct producing formation. The separate tubing strings distinguish this form of well from a COMMINGLED WELL (*q.v.*), which produces from two or more oil bearing formations through a single tubing string in the common well casing, and a RECOMPLETED WELL (*q.v.*), which produces from only one formation. See Energy Consumers and Producers Ass'n, Inc. v. Department of Energy, 632 F.2d 129 (Temp. Emer. Ct. of App. 1980), *cert. denied,* 449 U.S. 832, 101 S.Ct. 102 (1980) (sustaining the validity of a ruling that in calculating "average daily production" for purposes of the exemption from price controls of STRIPPER WELL OIL (*q.v.*), a multiple completion well was considered as two (or more) wells, but a commingled well was considered as a single well).

Multiple filing

Filing of multiple drawing entry cards or offers for non-competitive federal oil and gas leases, prohibited by 43 C.F.R. 3112.5–2. In June Oil and Gas, Inc. v. Andrus, 506 F. Supp. 1204, 72 *O.&G.R.* 411 (D. Colo. 1981), *aff'd sub nom.* June Oil & Gas, Inc. v. Watt, 717 F.2d 1323, 78 *O.&G.R.* 450 (10th Cir. 1983), *cert. denied,* 104 S. Ct. 2169 (1984), and Grynberg v. Watt, 717 F.2d 1316 (10th Cir. 1983), *cert. denied,* 104 S. Ct. 2169 (1984), the court found violation of the regulation where: (1) filings were made by children's trust and children's parents, one of whom was co-trustee of children's trust, and (2) offers were submitted by two closely related corporations. In Pullman v. Chorney, 509 F. Supp. 162, 69 *O.&G.R.* 247 (D. Colo. 1981), *aff'd*, 712 F.2d 447, 78 *O.&G.R.* 14 (10th Cir. 1983), an unsuccessful applicant, whose application was not amongst the first three drawn in a lease lottery, lacked standing to seek judicial invalidation of the lease alleging violation of the multiple filing regulations. Cranston v. Clark, 767 F.2d 1319 (9th Cir. 1985) rejected a claim of violation of the multiple filing regulations.

See also NON-COMPETITIVE LEASE.

Multiple Mineral Development Act (or Multiple Use Act)

The Act of August 13, 1954, 68 Stat. 708, permitting oil and gas leases and mining claims on the same land, with the oil and gas lessee obtaining his rights under his lease and the mining claimant being accorded his rights to go to patent, subject, however, to the oil and gas lessee's interest. Under this Act, an oil and gas lessee can force mineral claimants to reassert their claims to oil and gas or else be foreclosed from asserting such claims at any time in the future. See *Rocky Mt. Min. L. Fdn. The Law of Federal Oil and Gas Leases* ch. 23 (1985); 43 C.F.R. § 3740 (1978).

Multiple use

"[T]he management of the various surface and subsurface resources so that they are utilized in the combination that will best meet the present and future needs of the American people; the most judicious use of the land for some or all of these resources or related services over areas large enough to provide sufficient latitude for periodic adjustments in use to conform to changing needs and conditions; the use of some land for less than all of the resources; and harmonious and coordinated management of the various resources, each with the other, without impairment of the productivity of the land, with consideration being given to the relative values of the various resources, and not necessarily the combination of uses that will give the greatest dollar return or the greatest unit output." 43 C.F.R. § 2400.0–5 (o) (1978).

For a detailed discussion, see Lear, "Multiple Mineral Development Conflicts: An Armageddon in Simultaneous Mineral Operations?" 28 *Rocky Mt. Min. L. Inst.* 79 (1982).

Multipoint back pressure test

A test which measures the relationship of short-term gas flow to the back pressure of a pipeline but is not a measure of the well's long-term capacity or the gas reserves. Sunflower Electric Cooperative, Inc. v. Tomlinson Oil Co., 7 Kan. App. 2d 131, 638 P.2d 963 at 966, 75 *O.&G.R.* 60 at 65 (1981).

See also BACK PRESSURE; PRESSURE.

Multi-zone well

"[A] well for the segregated production or injection from or into more than one zone through the same well bore." Saskatchewan Oil and Gas Conservation Regulations, 1969, O.C. 2272/68, § 102(u).

Muscle-in clause

The name applied in Texas to a provision of the Texas Pooling statute that the Railroad Commission shall not require the force pooling of a mineral interest with production acreage equal to or greater than the standard proration unit unless requested by the owner of a mineral interest with production acreage smaller than the production pattern who has not been provided a reasonable opportunity to pool voluntarily. Broussard v. Texaco, Inc., 479 S.W.2d 270 at 274, 42 *O.&G.R.* 75 at 85 (Tex. 1972).

For a discussion of this clause, see Douglass & Whitworth, "Practice Before the Oil and Gas Division of the Railroad Commission of Texas," 13 *St. Mary's L.J.* 719 at 745 (1982).

MWD

MEASUREMENT-WHILE-DRILLING (MWD) (*q.v.*)

. . N . .

Naked owner

In Louisiana, "[t]he ownership of a thing burdened with a Usufruct (*q.v.*) is designated as naked ownership." La. Civ. Code Art. 478 (1980 Special Pamphlet). The owner of such thing is known as the naked owner. "A usufruct terminates by confusion when the usufruct and the naked ownership are united in the same person." La. Civ. Code Art. 622 (1980 Special Pamphlet).

The respective rights of the usufructuary and naked owner in minerals are codified in Articles 188–196 of the Louisiana Mineral Code [R.S. 31:188–196 (1975) (1980 Supp.).] See Treatise § 512.3.

Naphtha

A loosely defined petroleum fraction containing primarily aliphatic (linear) hydrocarbons with boiling points ranging from 125 to 240 degree C. It is thus intermediate between gasoline and kerosine, and contains components of both. Its principal uses are in solvents and paint thinners and as a raw material for the production of organic chemicals, but it is expected to be used increasingly as a raw material for the production of synthetic natural gas. See Hammond, Metz, and Maugh, *Energy and the Future* 163 (1973).

Regulations concerning the mandatory allocation of certain naphthas (defined as petroleum fractions whose boiling points fall within the temperature range of 85 degrees to 430 degrees F.) are contained in 10 C.F.R. § 211.181 *et seq.* (1980).

Naphthene base

See Asphalt base oil.

Nassau plan

A technique for the purchase and sale of oil property. Under this plan, seller transferred the leasehold to a broker for a cash consideration, on which seller received capital gains treatment. Broker borrowed, with personal liability, some portion of the purchase price from a financial institution, pledging the purchased property as security for repayment of the borrowed sum plus interest. It was said that more advantageous financing was secured than under the A-B-C Transaction (*q.v.*) since the financial institution had the entire property as security for the funds advanced, and hence a more favorable rate of interest could be obtained. The broker then assigned the property to purchaser for a cash payment, such assignment to become effective when there has been realized from the net proceeds of production a sum sufficient to satisfy the debt to the financial institution plus interest and an additional sum of money specified in the agreement. Broker then assigned the lease to operator for a cash consideration. Operator did not assume the indebtedness but took subject to it. His interest was terminable upon the satisfaction of the sums specified in the sale to purchaser; his profit was made from the additional sum specified in the assignment to purchaser. See "The 'Nassau' Plan of Acquisition of Oil Properties," 4 *O. & G. Tax O.* 214 (1955), and TREATISE § 423.11.

National Energy Board

A nine-member Canadian board established by the National Energy Board Act (R.S.C. 1970, c. N–6) and charged with a variety of responsibilities relating to energy, including certification of pipe lines, regulation of tolls or tariffs, and licensing importation and exportation of power, oil or gas.

National Energy Conservation Policy Act of 1978

Pub. L. No. 95–619 (Nov. 9, 1978). The major provisions of this Act related to:

(1) residential energy conservation;

(2) energy conservation for schools and hospitals and buildings owned by units of local government and public care institutions;

(3) energy efficiency standards for automobiles, other consumer products, and industrial equipment; and

(4) federal energy initiatives, including solar heating and cooling in federal buildings.

National Energy Program (NEP)

The name given the energy program published on October 28, 1980, by the government of Canada dealing with the pricing of oil on the Canadian market, foreign ownership of the oil industry, a new administrative regime for oil and gas prospective lands under federal jurisdiction, and proposals for increased governmental participation in the petroleum sector.

Reference Re Proposed Federal Tax on Exported Natural Gas, [1982] 1 S.C.R. 1004, [1982] 5 W.W.R. 577 (Sup. Ct. of Canada 1982), invalidated under the British North America Act, 1867 (now the Constitution Act, 1867) a tax proposed under the National Energy Program on the export of natural gas which, prior to its export, belonged to the Crown in right of Alberta.

For discussions of the program see the following:

Olmstead, Krauland and Orentlicher, "Expropriation in the Energy Industry: Canada's Crown Share Provision as a Violation of International Law," 29 *McGill L.J.* 439 (1984) (arguing that the back-in provision of the Crown under this Program constitutes an expropriation under international law and is therefore subject to the principle of customary international law requiring prompt, adequate and effective compensation);

Lucas, "The Canadian National Energy Program Legislation," 1 *J. of Energy & Natural Resources Law* 104 (1983);

Hendry, "Regulatory Reform and the National Energy Board," 7 *Dalhousie L.J.* 235 (1983);

Bell, "Petroleum Taxation in Canada," [1982] 2 *OGLTR* 82;

Watkins and McKee, "Recent Developments in Petroleum Taxation and the Canadian Ownership Rules Under the National Energy Program," 20 *Alta. L. Rev.* 46 (1982);

MacDonald, "Current Developments in Oil and Gas Law," *Energy Law 1981,* Seminar of the International Bar Association Committee on Energy and Natural Resources 136 (1981);

Carter, "Canadian Oil and Gas Operations," 2 *id.* at 171.

See also CANADA OIL AND GAS LAND ADMINISTRATION (COGLA); PETROLEUM COMPENSATION CHARGE; PETROLEUM COMPENSATION PAYMENT (NCP); PETROLEUM INCENTIVE PROGRAM ACT; PETROLEUM INCENTIVES PROGRAM (PIP).

National Environmental Policy Act of 1969 (NEPA)

83 Stat. 852, 42 U.S.C. § 4321 *et seq.*

National Iranian Oil Company (NIOC)

For a discussion of the history of this company, see Shwadran, *The Middle East, Oil and the Great Powers* 157 *et seq.* (3d ed. revised and enlarged, 1973).

Nationalization

A term loosely used to describe a change in the socio-economic structure of a state resulting in national ownership or control of an industry or of property of a specified kind. This is not generally viewed as a "term of art" and frequently is used as synonymous with the term expropriation although the latter term is sometimes used in reference to a change affecting only the rights or property of individuals. As customarily used, neither of these terms necessarily suggests that compensation is or is not payable to the owners of interests affected. See Vicuna, "Some International Law Problems Posed by the Nationalization of the Copper Industry by Chile," 67 *Am. J. Int. Law* 711 at 719–721 (1973).

For discussions of nationalization or expropriation of the oil industry see the following:

El Sheikh, *The Legal Regime of Foreign Private Investment in the Sudan and Saudi Arabia* 85 *et seq.*, 194 *et seq.* (1984);

Hossain and Chowdhury, *Permanent Sovereignty Over Natural Resources in International Law* (1984);

Chester, *United States Oil Policy and Diplomacy* (1983);

Schneider, *The Oil Price Revolution* (1983);

"The International Law of Expropriation," 75 *Am. J. of Int. L.* 437 (1981);

White, "Expropriation of the Libyan Oil Concessions—Two Conflicting International Arbitrations," 30 *Int. & Comp. L.Q.* 1 (1981);

Levenant, "Changing Concepts of the World's Mineral Development Laws With Especial Reference to West Africa," in International Bar Ass'n, *World Energy Laws* (Proceedings of the IBA Seminar on World Energy Law held in Stavanger, Norway) 117 (1975);

Comment, "American Oil Investors' Access to Domestic Courts in Foreign Nationalization Disputes," 123 *U. Pa. L. Rev.* 610 (1975);

Milen and Savino, "Nationalization or Regulation? Constitutional Aspects of the Control of the Saskatchewan Oil Industry," 39 *Sask. L. Rev.* 23 (1974–75);

Richardson and Quigley, "The Resource Industry, Foreign Ownership and Constitutional Methods of Control," *Id.* at 92;

Fisher, Golbert and Maghame, "British Petroleum v. Libya: A Preliminary Comparative Analysis of the International Oil Companies' Response to Nationalization," 7 *Southwestern U.L. Rev.* 68 (1975).

Distinctions occasionally made among the terms 'confiscation,' 'expropriation,' 'indigenization,' 'liquidation,' 'nationalization,' and 'requisition' are discussed in Akinsanya, *The Expropriation of Multinational Property in the Third World* 3 (1980).

See also CONFISCATION; DIVESTMENT; EXPROPRIATION.

National oil company

A state-owned company engaged in a variety of oil and gas activities. For detailed discussions of the history and operations of national oil companies in a number of countries, see the papers on such companies in *Energy Law 1981,* Seminar of the International Bar Association Committee on Energy and Natural Resources, Topic 3 (1981).

National Petroleum Association

An association of smaller petroleum firms organized to fight the Standard Oil trust. See Chester, *United States Oil Policy and Diplomacy* 25 (1983).

National Petroleum Council (NPC)

An advisory committee to the Department of Energy appointed by the Secretary of Energy.

National Petroleum Reserve

A term employed in the CRUDE OIL WINDFALL PROFIT TAX ACT OF 1980 (*q.v.*) to refer to the NATIONAL PETROLEUM RESERVE IN ALASKA (*q.v.*) and to the NAVAL PETROLEUM RESERVES (*q.v.*).

The Internal Revenue Service ruled that Congress has established only one National Petroleum Reserve, namely the reserve in Alaska formerly known as Naval Petroleum Reserve Number 4. Letter Ruling 8124063, IRS Ltr. Rul. Rep. (CCH) (1981).

National Petroleum Reserve in Alaska

The area in Alaska, formerly Naval Petroleum Reserve No. 4, administered by the Secretary of the Interior under the provisions of 42 U.S.C. § 6501 *et seq.* See NAVAL PETROLEUM RESERVES.

National rate

The rate authorized by 18 C.F.R. §§ 2.56(a) and 2.56(b) (1980) for sales of natural gas in interstate commerce for resale. The national rate was higher than that previously authorized under the AREA PRICING POLICY (*q.v.*). A two-tier system was created, with one price for gas from wells commenced on or after January 1, 1973, and new dedications of natural gas to interstate commerce on or after that date, and a lower price for natural gas from wells commenced prior to that date.

In Opinion No. 770 issued July 27, 1976 [10 FPS 5–293] the Federal Power Commission prescribed a uniform national base rate for post-January 1, 1975 gas of $1.42 per Mcf (subject to specified escalation and adjustments) and a uniform national base rate of $1.01 per Mcf (subject to specified adjustments) for 1973–1974 biennium gas. In Opinion No. 770–a [10 FPS 5–854] the order was modified with respect to the 1973–1974 biennium gas to establish a $0.93 per Mcf rate with one cent per annum escalator in each calendar year. The Commission's orders were sustained in The Second National Natural Gas Rate Cases (American Public Gas Ass'n v. Federal Power Comm'n), 567 F.2d 1016, 12 FPS 6–37 (D.C. Cir. 1977).

See also PRICE CONTROL OF OIL, GAS AND PETROLEUM PRODUCTS.

National rate case

Shell Oil Co. v. Federal Power Comm'n, 520 F.2d 1061, 53 *O.&G.R.* 392 (5th Cir. 1975), *reh. denied,* 525 F.2d 1261, 53 *O.&G.R.* 433 (5th Cir. 1976), *cert. denied,* 426 U.S. 941 (1976), which sustained the validity of orders of the Federal Power Commission (Opinion No. 699, 51 F.P.C. 2212, as amended) involving the establishment of a national rate for jurisdictional sales of natural gas.

See also The Second National Natural Gas Rate Cases (American Public Gas Ass'n v. Federal Power Comm'n), 567 F.2d 1016, 59 *O.&G.R.* 351 (D.C. Cir. 1977), *cert. denied,* 435 U.S. 907 (1978).

National Wilderness Preservation System (NWPS)

A system for preservation of WILDERNESS AREAS (*q.v.*). Lessees of Bureau of Land Management and Forest Service lands which are being considered for inclusion in this System must accept highly restrictive lease stipulations for the purpose of preserving the areas' suitability for wilderness consideration.

See FEDERAL LAND POLICY AND MANAGEMENT ACT OF 1976 (FLPMA); WILDERNESS ACT OF 1964.

Native gas

(1) Gas originally in place in a particular underground structure as opposed to injected gas. See Stamm, "Legal Problems in the Underground Storage of Natural Gas," 36 *Tex. L. Rev.* 161 (1957); Mississippi River Transmission Corp. v. Simonton, 442 So. 2d 764 (La. App. 1983), *writ denied,* 444 So.2d 1240 (La. 1984), *cert. denied,* ____ U.S. ____, 105 S. Ct. 586 (1984).

(2) Gas which has not been previously withdrawn from the earth. Kan. Stat. Ann. § 55–1201(c) (1976).

See also CUSHION GAS; GAS STORAGE, SUBSURFACE; WORKING GAS.

Native gas entitlement

The quantity of gas which an operator is permitted to produce under a special rule adopted by the Texas Railroad Commission for an underground reservoir into which gas is injected for storage purposes. An operator who was not a participant in the gas storage program was permitted to produce its entitlement, calculated on the basis of productive acre feet of reservoir and a recovery factor determined by the Commission. This scheme was adopted in response to the holding in Lone Star Gas Co. v. Murchison, 353 S.W.2d 870, 16 *O.&G.R.* 816, 94 A.L.R.2d 529 (Tex. Civ. App. 1962, error ref'd n.r.e.), that the owner of gas does not lose title thereto by storing the same in a well-defined underground reservoir. See Railroad Comm'n v. Lone Star Gas Co., 587 S.W.2d 110, 64 *O.&G.R.* 542 (Tex. 1979).

See also GAS STORAGE, SUBSURFACE.

Natural condensate crude oils

Hydrocarbons which are liquid when under atmospheric conditions and in a gaseous state when under the original conditions of the reservoir, which are not obtained by the processes of absorption, adsorption, compression, refrigeration or a combination of such processes, and having a gravity higher than 40.9 degree API at 15.56 degree C (60 degree F). Joint Resolution Nos. 1307 and 2342 of the Ministries of Finance and of Mines and Hydrocarbons, Republic of Venezuela [OPEC, *Selected Documents of the International Petroleum Industry 1971* 261 at 262].

Natural gamma ray logging

A process whereby gamma rays naturally emitted by formations traversed by a bore hole are measured. A tool containing a radiation detector is lowered into the bore hole, and as a result of the impingement thereon of gamma rays naturally emitted by the formations, output signals indicative of said gamma rays are produced and transmitted to the earth's surface. The signals are utilized to produce a record of gamma rays detected in correlation with the depth of the detector in the bore hole. The record thus obtained in the form of a curve indicating relative number per unit of time of natural gamma rays at different depths, is a conventional natural gamma ray log, sometimes simply called a gamma ray log. See Well Surveys, Inc. v. McCullough Tool Co., 199 F. Supp. 374 (N. D. Okla. 1961). The natural gamma ray log shows the presence of formations of a lithologic type which can contain oil.

See also WELL LOG.

Natural gas

Hydrocarbons which at atmospheric conditions of temperature and pressure are in a gaseous phase.

It has been urged by one writer that the term "natural gas" should be defined as a gas which occurs naturally; under this definition helium may be included in a lease of natural gas. McCombe, "Helium and Its Place in the Petroleum and Natural Gas Lease," 2 *Alberta L. Rev.* 9 (1962).

Pruitt, "Mineral Terms—Some Problems in Their Use and Definition," 11 *Rocky Mt. Min. L. Inst.* 1 at 16 (1966), has remarked that:

> "The ordinary rarefied or gaseous hydrocarbons found in the earth are referred to generally as 'natural gas.' Non-combustible natural gases occurring in the earth, such as carbon dioxide, hydrogen sulphide, helium and nitrogen, are generally referred to by their proper chemical names. Often, however, non-combustible gases are found in combination with combustible gases and the mixture is referred to generally as 'natural gas,' without any attempt to distinguish between the combustible and non-combustible gases."

See also GAS; MANUFACTURED GAS.

Public Serv. Comm'n of State of N.Y. v. Federal Power Comm'n, 543 F.2d 392, 56 *O.&G.R.* 438 (D.C. Cir. 1976), held that gas derived from liquid hydrocarbon feedstock is "artificial" or "manufactured" gas and not "natural gas" as defined by the Natural Gas Act.

Northern Natural Gas Co. v. Grounds, 441 F.2d 704, 39 *O.&G.R.* 574 (10th Cir. 1971), *cert. denied,* 404 U.S. 951 (1971), held that references in leases and gas purchase contracts to gas or natural gas applied to the entire gas stream absent express reservation of any constituent elements, and helium passed thereunder unless expressly reserved. *Grounds* is discussed in Stucky, "Current Developments and Views Concerning Rights and Status of Landowner-Lessors," 21 *Sw. Legal Fdn. Oil & Gas Inst.* 83 at 102 (1970).

Natural Gas Act (NGA)

An Act regulating the transportation and sale of natural gas in interstate commerce. 52 Stat. 821, as amended, 15 U.S.C.A. § 717–717(w).

For a political history of the regulation of natural gas, see Sanders, *The Regulation of Natural Gas* (1981). See also FEDERAL POWER COMMISSION.

Natural Gas Association of America (NGAA)

A trade association now known as the Natural Gas Processors Association (NGPA).

See also MODIFIED NGAA CONTRACT; NGAA CONTRACT; NGAA 1932 FORM.

Natural gas company

In the NATURAL GAS ACT (*q.v.*), "a person engaged in the transportation of natural gas in interstate commerce, or the sale in interstate commerce of such gas for resale." 15 U.S.C.A. § 717a(6).

Natural gas liquids (NGL)

Hydrocarbons found in natural gas which may be extracted or isolated as LIQUEFIED PETROLEUM GAS (*q.v.*) and NATURAL GASOLINE (*q.v.*).

The importance of distinguishing natural gas liquids from CONDENSATE (*q.v.*) is emphasized in Seddelmeyer, "Royalties on Processed Gas," 36 *Sw. Legal Fdn. Oil & Gas Inst.* 5-1 (1985).

Regulations concerning the mandatory allocation of natural gas liquids are contained in 10 C.F.R. § 211.81 *et seq.* (1980). See Henke, "Natural Gas Liquid Pricing Under DOE Regulations," 26 *Rocky Mt. Min. L. Inst.* 857 (1980); Smith, "The Regulation of Natural Gas Liquids: An Introduction of DOE Approaches and Problems," 21 *So. Tex. L.J.* 98 (1980).

Natural gas liquid products (NGLP)

The separate products derived from natural gas liquids, including ethane, butane, propane, propane-butane mixtures, and natural gasoline.

Natural gasoline

A liquid similar to motor fuel recovered as DRIP GASOLINE (*q.v.*) or produced in natural gasoline plants, but generally having a lower octane number and being more volatile than commercial motor fuel. A light, volatile, liquid hydrocarbon mixture recovered from natural gas. For the most part, the individual components of natural gasoline are the same as those contained in ordinary gasoline distilled from crude oil, namely, propane, butanes, pentanes, hexanes and heptanes, though as a rule natural gasoline contains more of the lighter fractions, straight-run gasoline more of the heavier ones. The only essential difference between natural gasoline and ordinary straight-run gasoline is in the relative proportion of their components, as a reuslt of which natural gasoline is more volatile. Natural gasoline may be blended with straight-run or cracked motor gasolines to give added volatility or used as a chemical raw material from which can be separated many individual hydrocarbons.

See also ALBINO OIL; CASINGHEAD GASOLINE; CASINGHEAD PETROLEUM SPIRIT; LOW TEMPERATURE EXTRACTION (LTX); WATER-WHITE OIL; WHITE OIL.

Natural gasoline plant

A plant for the processing of natural gas for the extraction of natural gasoline, motor fuel, liquified petroleum gases, and other natural gas liquids.

Natural Gas Pipeline Safety Act (NGPSA)

An Act enacted in 1968 (49 U.S.C. § 1671 *et seq.*) designed to provide for the prescription and enforcement of minimum federal safety standards for the transportation of natural and other gas by pipeline and for pipeline facilities. Natural Gas Pipeline Co. v. Railroad Comm'n, 679 F.2d 51 (5th Cir. 1982), held that the Act preempted, with respect to interstate pipeline facilities, Rule 36 of the Texas Railroad Commission relating to procedures and safeguards to warn and protect the general public against the accidental release of hydrogen sulphide from facilities for gathering, processing, and transportation of natural gas.

For purposes of regulation of a pipeline under this Act, classification of the line as a GATHERING LINE (*q.v.*), DISTRIBUTION LINE (*q.v.*), or TRANSMISSION LINE (*q.v.*) may be of significance. See Hamman v. Southwestern Gas Pipeline, Inc., 721 F.2d 140, 78 *O.&G.R.* 552 (5th Cir. 1983).

Natural Gas Policy Act of 1978 (NGPA)

Pub. L. No. 95–621 (Nov. 9, 1978). The major provisions of this Act related to:

(1) a single national market for gas sales, eliminating the jurisdictional sale-nonjurisdictional sale distinction;

(2) extension of price controls on gas until January 1, 1985 when (with certain exceptions) they were to expire for six months after which (until July 1, 1987), either the President or Congress could reimpose controls for eighteen months;

(3) a national price ceiling for gas escalated with inflation and annual increases until 1985, with special provisions for gas sold under existing intrastate contracts, sales under rollover contracts, high cost natural gas, and stripper well natural gas;

(4) incremental pricing of natural gas to industrial users in order to insulate residential consumers from price increases;

(5) presidential authority to allocate gas in emergencies.

For detailed discussions of this Act see Moody and Garten, "The Natural Gas Policy Act of 1978: Analysis and Overview," 25 *Rocky Mt. Min. L. Inst.* 2–1 (1979), and the symposium papers in 16 *Houston L. Rev.* 1025–1301 (1979).

A constitutional challenge to the validity of this Act was rejected in Oklahoma v. Federal Energy Regulatory Comm'n, 494 F.Supp. 636 (W.D. Okla. 1980), *aff'd,* 661 F.2d 832, 71 *O.&G.R.* 617 (10th Cir. 1981), *cert. denied,* 457 U.S. 1105 (1982), *reh. denied,* 458 U.S. 1132, 103 S.Ct. 16 (1982).

Tenneco, Inc. v. Sutton, 530 F. Supp. 411 (W.D. La. 1981), sustained the constitutionality of the NGPA and invalidated, under the supremacy clause of the Constitution of the United States, certain Louisiana constitutional and statutory provisions designed to give Louisiana users first priority at obtaining new natural gas that may be found in the state.

Consumer Energy Council of America v. Federal Energy Regulatory Commission, 673 F.2d 425 (D.C. Cir. 1982), *aff'd,* 463 U.S. 1216, 103 S.Ct. 3556, *reh. denied,* 463 U.S. 1250, 104 S.Ct. 40 (1983), held that the one-house legislative veto provision of this Act was unconstitutional.

For a discussion of the operation of the curtailment plan under this Act, see Process Gas Consumers Group v. United States Dept. of Agriculture, 694 F.2d 728 (D.C. Cir. 1981), *modified on rehearing en banc,* 694 F.2d 778 (D.C. Cir. 1982), *cert. denied,* 461 U.S. 905, 103 S. Ct. 1874 (1983).

Baber v. United States, 537 F. Supp. 1135 (E.D. La. 1982), *aff'd without opinion,* 699 F.2d 1161 (5th Cir. 1983), sustained the constitutionality of price controls imposed under the Act against a claim that the incentive-based approach to rate setting for gas production permitted substantially higher prices for "new" gas than was available for complainant's "old" gas.

Transcontinental Gas Pipeline Corp. v. State Oil & Gas Board of Mississippi, 457 So.2d 1298, 83 *O.&G.R.* 295 (Miss. 1984), concluded that the enactment of the NGPA ended the federal preemption of RATABLE TAKING (*q.v.*) orders issued by state regulatory commissions applicable to *deregulated* natural gas. The judgment in this case was reversed, 470 U.S. 1083, 106 S.Ct. 709; 87 *O.&G.R.* 550, *reh. denied,* ___ U.S. ___, 106 S.Ct. 1485 (1986), the court holding, by five to four, that a state ratable take order continued subject to federal preemption.

The case is discussed in S. Williams, "Federal Preemption of State Conservation Laws After the Natural Gas Policy Act: A Preliminary Look," 56 *U. of Colo. L. Rev.* 521 (1985).

Pennzoil Co. v. Public Service Comm'n, ___ W.Va. ___, 327 S.E.2d 444, ___ *O.&G.R.* ___ (1985), *cert. denied,* ___ U.S. ___, 106 S.Ct. 74 (1985), concluded that a state may establish a price for an intrastate producer's sale of gas in intrastate commerce at a level lower than the federal ceiling set by the Natural Gas Policy Act.

See also Ringleb, "Natural Gas Producer Price Regulation Under the NGPA: Regulatory Failure, Alternatives, and Reform," 20 *Houston L. Rev.* 709 (1983).

See also BEHIND THE PIPE EXCLUSION; FIRST SALE; INCENTIVE PRICE GAS; 102 GAS; PRICE CONTROL OF OIL, GAS AND PETROLEUM PRODUCTS; SOUTHLAND EXCLUSION.

Natural Gas Price Protection Act

An Oklahoma statute, 52 Okla. Stat. Ann. § 260.1 *et seq.* (1980 Supp.) designed to curtail the operation of certain types of indefinite escalator clauses contained in certain natural gas agreements involving Oklahoma intrastate deliveries. Similar statutes were enacted in other states, *e.g.*, Kansas [Kan. Stat. 1979, c. 171, 65 *O.&G.R.* 138] and New Mexico [N.M. Stat. 1978, c. 97, 65 *O.&G.R.* 149], the general purpose of the acts being retardation of escalation of gas prices in the state as the result of the enactment of the NATURAL GAS POLICY ACT OF 1978 (*q.v.*)

The constitutionality of the Kansas Natural Gas Price Protection Act was sustained in Energy Resources Group v. Kansas Power and Light Co., 230 Kan. 176, 630 P.2d 1142, 71 *O.&G.R.* 228 (1981), *aff'd*, 459 U.S. 400, 76 *O.&G.R.* 593 (1983).

Pickrell Drilling Co. v. State Corporation Comm'n, 232 Kan. 397, 654 P.2d 477, 79 *O.&G.R.* 460 (1982), held that the Kansas Natural Gas Price Protection Act authorized a monthly escalation in the price of natural gas under a natural gas purchase contract; whether the contract in question authorized such a price increase was held to be an issue reserved for the district court rather than the Corporation Commission.

For a study of another legislative approach to consumer protection from high prices for natural gas see Pridgen and Harris, "The Wyoming Natural Gas Consumers' Act of 1985: An Experiment in Controlling Natural Gas Prices and a Response to Indefinite Price Escalation Clauses," 21 *Land & Water L. Rev.* 141 (1986).

See also PRICE CONTROL OF OIL, GAS AND PETROLEUM PRODUCTS.

Natural gas price regulation

The regulation of the price of natural gas has taken a variety of forms. Regulation by the Federal Power Commission and its successor, the Federal Energy Regulatory Commission, under the Natural Gas Act was designed to protect the consumer of natural gas from excessive prices. See FEDERAL POWER COMMISSION. In Louisiana, efforts were made to prevent "the sale of intrastate natural gas at a price below the fair market value of such gas." See La. R.S. § 30:591 *et seq.* (1975), and to prevent the movement in interstate commerce of natural gas produced in Louisiana. La. R.S. §§ 30:607, 30:1002 (1975) (1980 Supp.). In some other states legislation was enacted to curtail the operation of certain types of escalator clauses in natural gas contracts involving intrastate deliveries. See NATURAL GAS PRICE PROTECTION ACT.

See also PRICE CONTROL OF OIL, GAS AND PETROLEUM PRODUCTS.

Natural Gas Pricing Agreement Act

An Alberta statute, 1975 (2nd Sess.) (Alta.), c. 38, providing for the regulation of prices paid for gas under gas sales contracts and resale contracts. See Town of Castor v. Candel Oil Ltd., 107 D.L.R. 3d 247 (Alta. Q.B. 1979).

Natural Gas Processors Association (NGPA)

A trade association, the successfor of the Natural Gas Association of America (NGAA).

See also MODIFIED NGAA CONTRACT; NGAA CONTRACT; NGAA 1932 FORM.

Natural gas producer

An operator who owns wells producing natural gas. Under the Natural Gas Act (15 U.S.C.A. §§ 717–717w), "production or gathering" of gas was exempted from regulation by the Federal Power Commission. In Phillips Petroleum Co. v. Wisconsin, 347 U.S. 672, 3 *O.&G.R.* 745 (1954), it was held that sale in interstate commerce of natural gas for resale was not within the exemption, and accordingly this activity by natural gas producers was subject to the Commission's jurisdiction. See Symposium on the Federal Regulation of Natural Gas Producers, 44 *Georgetown L.J.* 551 *et seq.* (1956).

Naval petroleum reserves

Proved, or probable, reserves of unproduced petroleum, held by the U.S. Navy for production in time of special need. Four such reserves on public lands of the United States were set aside from disposition by executive orders issued between 1912 and 1924 and committed by act of Congress to the jurisdiction of the Secretary of the Navy: Reserve No. 1 at Elk Hills, California, No. 2 at Buena Vista Hills, California, No. 3 at Teapot Dome, Wyoming, and No. 4 on the North Slope of Alaska. See Production of Oil and Gas on Public Lands, Hearings before the Subcommittee on Public Lands of the House Committee on Interior and Insular Affairs, 93rd Cong., 1st and 2d Sess. (Serial No. 93–40) at pp. 55, 437. In 1976 the bulk of Naval Petroleum Reserve No. 4 in Alaska was transferred to the Secretary of the Interior for administration and redesignated as the National Petroleum Reserve in Alaska. 42 U.S.C. § 6502. In 1977 Naval Petroleum Reserves 1, 2 and 3 along with Oil Shale Reserves 1, 2, and 3 were transferred to the Secretary of Energy for administration. 42 U.S.C. § 7156.

See also NATIONAL PETROLEUM RESERVE; NATIONAL PETROLEUM RESERVE IN ALASKA; RESERVES.

For a construction of the unit plan contract entered into by the United States and Standard Oil Co. of California relating to the development and operation of Naval Petroleum Reserve No. 1, Elk

Hills, California, see Standard Oil of Calif. v. United States, 685 F.2d 1322, 685 F.2d 1337 (Ct. Cl. 1982).

Necessary parties

Those persons whose interest in litigation is such that they ought to be made parties if at all possible. See TREATISE § 875 *et seq.*

See also INDISPENSABLE PARTIES; PROPER PARTIES.

Negative commerce clause

The term applied to the construction of the Commerce Clause of the Constitution of the United States which limits the authority of the states to enforce unreasonable burdens on interstate commerce. See Transcontinental Gas Pipeline Corp. v. State Oil and Gas Board of Mississippi, 457 So.2d 1289, 83 *O.&G.R.* 295 (Miss. 1984) (holding that this doctrine did not invalidate a Ratable take order of the State Oil & Gas Board). The judgment in this case was reversed, 470 U.S. 1083, 106 S.Ct. 709, 87 *O.&G.R.* 550, *reh. denied,* ___ U.S. ___, 106 S.Ct. 1485 (1986), the court holding, by five to four, that a state ratable take order continued subject to federal preemption. The majority opinion did not reach the commerce clause argument; the dissenters concluded that the state order was not invalidated by the commerce clause.

Negative election

An ELECTION TO PARTICIPATE (*q.v.*) effected by a failure to respond to a notice of proposed operations. A number of standard forms of operating agreements provide for a negative election. See Conine, "Rights and Liabilities of Carried Interest and Nonconsent Parties in Oil and Gas Operations," 37 *Sw. Legal Fdn. Oil & Gas Inst.* 3-1 at 3-27 (1986).

Negative nomination

The term applied to arguments submitted by state and federal officials that certain offshore tracts should not be open for leasing because of competing risks, sensitive ecological conditions, or hazards and risks which make drilling and production undesirable from a safety or environmental standpoint. Swan, *Ocean Oil and Gas Drilling & the Law* 49 (1979).

See also NOMINATION OF TRACT FOR LEASING.

Negative community doctrine

A term which has been used to describe the NON-OWNERSHIP THEORY (*q.v.*) of the nature of the landowner's interest in oil and gas. Colby, "The Law of Oil and Gas," 31 *Cal. L. Rev.* 357 at 380 (1943).

Negative pledge

An agreement by a borrowers not to encumber any of its assets or its interest under a production license without the prior written approval of the lender. Swan, *Ocean Oil and Gas Drilling & the Law* 135 (1979).

See also McCormick, "Legal Issues in Project Finance," 1 *J.E.R.L.* 21 at 27 (1983).

See also PROJECT FINANCING.

Negative rule of capture

A phrase employed in contrast to the phrase RULE OF CAPTURE (*q.v.*) to indicate that just as under the rule of capture a landowner may capture such oil and gas as will migrate from adjoining premises to a well bottomed on his own land, so also may he inject into a formation substances which may migrate through the structure to the land of others, even if this results in the displacement under such land of more valuable with less valuable substances (*e.g.*, the displacement of wet gas by dry gas). The law on this subject has not as yet been fully developed, but it seems reasonable to suggest the qualification that such activity will be permitted, free of any claim for damages, only if pursued as part of a reasonable program of development and without injury to producing or potentially producing formations. Liability for this conduct has been imposed by several courts under the theory of nuisance. See TREATISE § 204.5.

Negotiated contract price requirement

A requirement imposed by the Federal Energy Regulatory Commission in identifying TIGHT FORMATION GAS (*q.v.*) entitled to an incentive price ceiling that availability of the incentive price depends on the presence of specified pricing provisions in the private contracts governing the production and sale of such gas. The Commission was sustained in Pennzoil Co. v. Federal Energy Regulatory Comm'n, 671 F.2d 119 (5th Cir. 1982).

NEPA

The National Environmental Policy Act of 1969, 83 Stat. 852, 42 U.S.C. § 4321 *et seq.*

Netback

A long-term contract to sell crude oil on the basis of the price it fetches as a refined product. Netback deals usually allow for enough time to transport the oil and refine it before picking the price at which it is based. *The Wall Street Journal,* March 6, 1986, p. 6.

Net-back payment

A payment made under the provisions of a so-called NET-BACK SALE (*q.v.*).

Net-back pricing

A method of determining wellhead price of oil or gas by deducting from a price paid downstream for the product, the transportation and other costs incurred between the wellhead and the downstream place of sale. See McDill, "Natural Gas Pricing in Canada," 17 *Alberta L. Rev.* 120 at 123 (1979).

See also Marathon Oil Co. v. United States, 604 F.Supp. 1375, 87 *O.&G.R.* 455 (D. Alaska 1985), *aff'd,* 807 F.2d 759, 90 *O.&G.R.* 6 (9th Cir. 1986) (sustaining use of net back method for computing gas royalties).

See also PROCEEDS-LESS-EXPENSE-METHOD; WORK-BACK VALUATION METHOD.

Net-back sale

A transfer by lease or other agreement of an interest in gas or casinghead gas in consideration of a specified portion of the proceeds realized from the sale of liquid and/or other products recovered and sold after an extraction, treatment or other manufacturing process.

Net drainage

"[D]rainage not equalized by counter-drainage." Ariz. Rev. Stat. § 27–501 (12) (1976) (1979 Supp.).

See also DRAINAGE; UNCOMPENSATED DRAINAGE.

Net economic value

As this term was used in analyzing the validity of a five-year schedule of offshore oil and gas leasing activity by the Secretary of the Interior, the value "is defined as the difference between the market value of the expected hydrocarbon resources in a planning area less the direct costs of producing those resources and transporting them to market." State of California v. Watt, 712 F.2d 584 at 601 (D. C. Cir. 1983).

See also OUTER CONTINENTAL SHELF (OCS).

Net income for depletion allowance

Gross income from the property, less deductions for such expenses as overhead, taxes, intangible drilling and development costs, depreciation, *etc.* Section 613 of the Internal Revenue Code of 1954 provided that the depletion allowance shall be figured at 27½% of the gross income from the property, excluding rental and royalty payments, but that the allowance shall not exceed 50% of the taxpayer's taxable income from the property, computed without the depletion allowance. The term "taxable income" in the 1954 Code means the same thing as "net income," which was the term used in Section 114 of the 1939 Code. See Sen. Rep. No. 1622, 83rd Cong., 2nd Sess. 330 (1954). The Tax Reform Act of 1969 reduced the rate of percentage depletion for oil and gas from 27½% to 22%, and the Tax Reduction Act of 1974 further restricted the availability of percentage depletion. See I.R.C. § 613A.

See also DEPLETION, PERCENTAGE.

Net leasehold

A term sometimes used to indicate the quantum of production available to working interest owners. See, *e.g.*, Moore v. Tristar Oil and Gas Corp., 528 F. Supp. 296 at 300 (S.D.N.Y. 1981), in which a leasehold subject to a 20% royalty was described as an 80% net leasehold. A limited partnership offering provided for a 5% overriding royalty for the general partners until the limited partners recovered 100% of their initial capital contributions; thus, the share of the limited partners was described as a 75% net leasehold, and the share of the general partners was described by the court as a 5% net leasehold, with a step up after "payout" to a 10% overriding royalty and a 10% working interest in all the limited partnership's property.

See also REVENUE INTEREST.

Net liquid credit

A credit against the cost of gas for the liquids extracted by processing operations. See Permian Basin Area Rate Proceeding, 34 F.P.C. 159 at 195, 23 *O.&G.R.* 103 at 138 (Opinion No. 468, Aug. 5, 1965), *remanded,* Skelly Oil Co. v. Federal Power Comm'n, 375 F.2d 6, 26 *O.&G.R.* 237 (10th Cir. 1967), *aff'd in part and rev'd in part sub nom. In re* Permian Basin Area Rate Cases, 390 U.S. 747, 28 *O.&G.R.* 689 (1968).

Net pay proration formula

The term employed in Northern Michigan Exploration Co. v. Public Service Comm'n, 153 Mich. App. 635, 396 N.W.2d 487 at 489, ____ *O.&G.R.* ____ (1986), for a gas proration formula which gave 90 percent weight to acre-feet of net pay, that is, the estimated volume of recoverable natural gas, and 10 percent weight to the well's open flow capacity.

See also PRORATION FORMULA.

Net proceeds interest

Syn: NET PROFITS INTEREST (*q.v.*).

Net profit share lease (NPSL)

An Outer Continental Shelf lease that provides for payment to the United States of a percentage share of the net profits for production of oil and gas from the tract. Proposed 10 C.F.R. § 390.002.

Net profit share rate (NPSR)

The percentage share of the net profit share base payable to the United States under a NET PROFIT SHARE LEASE (*q.v.*). Proposed 10 C.F.R. § 390.002.

Net profits bidding

Competitive bidding for leases in which the lease is awarded to the person offering to pay the largest share of net profits to the lessor. See, *e.g.*, Cal. Pub. Res. Code § 6827 (1977).

See also LEASE BIDDING SYSTEMS.

Net profits interest

A share of gross production from a property, measured by net profits from operation of the property. It is carved out of the working interest. A net profits interest is an economic interest in oil and gas and is accordingly entitled to the depletion allowance. Kirby Petroleum Co. v. Comm'r, 326 U.S. 599 (1946); Burton-Sutton Oil Co. v. Comm'r, 328 U.S. 25 (1946). See TREATISE §§ 424–424.4; "Tax Consequences of Net Profits Interests in Oil and Gas Transactions," *P–H Oil and Gas Taxes* ¶ 1009 (1979).

Allied Chemical Corp. v. American Independent Oil Co., 623 S.W.2d 760, 71 *O.&G.R.* 590 (Tex. App., Houston, 1981, error ref'd n.r.e.), was concerned with the construction of a net profits interest in an Iranian oil consortium as to whether wind-up expenses incurred subsequent to the Iranian revolution could be charged against past quarterly payments of profits yet held by the payor.

The definition in this MANUAL was quoted in Louisiana Land & Exploration Co. v. Donnelly, 394 F.2d 273 at 277, 29 *O.&G.R.* 512 at 520 (5th Cir. 1968).

Christy v. Petrol Resources Corp., 102 N.M. 58, 691 P.2d 59, 82 *O.&G.R.* 555 (N.M. App. 1984), concluded that this term "has no independent meaning, and . . . the nature of plaintiff's interest must be determined from the provisions of the instrument which created plaintiff's interest." In the instant case the term was found to describe an interest in cash bonus and not a royalty interest nor an interest in the title to land.

Exxon Corp. v. City of Long Beach, 812 F.2d 1256, ____ *O.&G.R.* ____ (9th Cir. 1987), concluded that the tax imposed under the CRUDE OIL WINDFALL PROFIT TAX ACT OF 1980 (*q.v.*) was not an excise tax chargeable to a net profits interest.

See also CARRIED INTEREST.

Net profits revenue interest

This term has been construed by an Australian court to mean the difference between accumulated revenue from sales of product and accumulated costs including royalties, exploration expenses and normal operating costs and lifting costs. Australian Energy Ltd. v. Lennard Oil N/L, [1986] Qd.R. ____ (Sup. Ct. of Queensland, 14 March 1986).

Net profits royalty

A payment of a specified portion of the net profits from production, sometimes offered in Saskatchewan in lieu of a cash bonus payment for a Crown lease at public land sales. Matthews, "Operating Methods in the Oil and Gas Industry," in Harbeau (Ed.), *Oil and Gas Production and Taxes* 92 at 102 (1963).

For a discussion of the usage of this term in Australia, see Ryan, "Australia: Petroleum Royalties—Part I," [1985/86] 5 *OGLTR* 121; Part II, [1985/86] 6 *OGLTR* 160.

See also BONUS.

Net profits status

As used in a letter agreement providing for conversion of an overriding royalty to a net profits interest when the property reached a "net profits status," Aminoil USA, Inc. v. OKC Corp., 629 F.Supp. 647 at 648, 90 *O.&G.R.* 234 (E.D. La. 1986), *aff'd sub nom.* Phillips Oil Co. v. OKC Corp., 812 F.2d 265, ____ *O.&G.R.* ____ (5th Cir. 1987), defined this term as follows:

> "in general terms, when the income from this mineral property exceeded the costs and expenses of exploration and production."

Net realization accounting method

A method of accounting for the value of gas based on the value of component parts of the gas stream derived by processing gas through a gasoline extraction plant, with allowance made for the cost of manufacturing such component parts. Jicarilla Apache Tribe v. Supron Energy Corp., 782 F.2d 855, 88 *O.&G.R.* 519, *opinion modified,* 793 F.2d 1171, 88 *O.&G.R.* 531 (10th Cir. 1986), *cert. denied,* 107 S.Ct. 471, 472 (1986); Supron Energy Corp., 46 IBLA 181, IBLA 79–374, GFS (O&G) 1980–75 (March 21, 1980).

See also ACCOUNTING METHODS.

Net revenue interest

(1) A term which has been used to describe a share of the working interest not required to contribute to, nor liable for, any portion of the expense of drilling and completing the initial well on the premises.

(2) This term has also been employed in reference to the lessee's share of production after satisfaction of all royalty, overriding royalty, oil payments, or other nonoperating interests. Thus, if a lease is burdened by a 1/8th royalty and a 1/8th of 8/8ths overriding roy-

alty, the net revenue interest of the lessee is 6/8ths of production. See Scott, "How to Prepare an Oil and Gas Farmout Agreement," 33 *Baylor L. Rev.* 63 at 73 (1981).

(3) The share of unit production attributable to an interest bound by the unit agreement. See, *e.g.*, Gillring Oil Co. v. Hughes, 618 S.W.2d 874, 71 *O.&G.R.* 415 (Tex. Civ. App. 1981) (contributor of 25 net acres to 320-acre unit providing for 25 percent royalty has a net revenue interest of 25/320 of 25 percent, *viz.*, 1.9531 percent; owner of 6.23 percent of the working interest in the unit acreage has a net revenue interest of 6.23 percent of the 75 percent attributable to the working interest under the agreement, *viz.*, 4.6725 percent).

(4) An interest either decimal or percentage (usually decimal), in a revenue stream, net of all other interests burdening that stream. Where a lessor executes a lease with a one-eighth royalty, the lessor's net revenue interest is O.125, and the lessee's net revenue interest is O.875. If the lease is assigned reserving a one-sixteenth overriding royalty, the lessor's net revenue interest is O.125, the overriding royalty owner's net revenue interest is O.0625, and the WORKING INTEREST (*q.v.*) owner's net revenue interest is O.8125.

Net royalty

(1) A term sometimes used to describe a NET PROFITS INTEREST (*q.v.*).

(2) The right of participation, limited to the terms of an existing lease, in the proceeds from the sale of oil and/or gas produced from a specified tract or well after prior payment of "Landowner's Royalty" and "Over-riding Royalty" and after payment of all production equipment, acidization, operating cost, taxes, assessment and any other deductions authorized by a Trust Agreement under which such right of participation is created. Saskatchewan Amended Regulations, Securities Act, O.C. 1704/52, July 14, 1952; 1 *O.&G.R.* 1541 at 1548 (1952).

The definition in this MANUAL was quoted in Louisiana Land & Exploration Co. v. Donnelly, 394 F.2d 273 at 277, 29 *O.&G.R.* 512 at 520 (5th Cir. 1968).

For a discussion of the usage of this term in Australia, see Ryan, "Australia: Petroleum Royalties—Part I," [1985/86] 5 *OGLTR* 121; Part II, [1985/86] 6 *OGLTR* 160.

See also DEFERRED NET ROYALTY; PREFERRED NET ROYALTY; ROYALTY.

Net social value

As this term was used in analyzing the validity of a five-year schedule of offshore oil and gas leasing activity by the Secretary of the Interior, the value "is calculated by subtracting external costs from net economic value." State of California v. Watt, 712 F.2d 584 at 601 (D.C. Cir. 1983).

Net uncompensated drainage

See UNCOMPENSATED DRAINAGE

Neutron-fast neutron log

See NEUTRON LOGGING.

Neutron-gamma ray log

See NEUTRON LOGGING.

Neutron logging

A process whereby formations traversed by a bore hole are bombarded with neutrons and radiations emitted by said formations are measured.

Neutron logging is performed by lowering into the bore hole a tool containing a neutron emitting source and a detector which produces output signals indicative of the radiation impinging thereon as a result of neutron bombardment of the formations, transmitting said output signals to the surface of the earth, and utilizing said signals to produce a record of radiation detected in correlation with the depth of said detector in the bore hole. The record thus obtained by the parties in the form of a curve indicating relative number per unit of time of radiations emitted at different depths by the subsurface formations as a result of the neutron bombardment is a conventional neutron log. As a result of neutron-bombardment a formation may emit either neutrons or gamma rays or both. When the gamma rays are detected, the resulting neutron log is termed a neutron-gamma ray log. When the neutrons are detected, the resulting neutron log is termed a neutron-neutron log. When fast neutrons are detected, the resulting log is termed a neutron-fast neutron log. Well Surveys, Inc. v. McCullough Tool Co., 199 F.Supp. 374 (N.D. Okla. 1961).

The neutron log tells whether or not a particular formation which could contain oil contains any fluid, although it does not tell whether that fluid be water or oil.

See also WELL LOG.

Neutron-neutron log

See NEUTRON LOGGING.

New contract

This term is defined in § 2 of the NATURAL GAS POLICY ACT OF 1978 (*q.v.*) (Pub. L. No. 95–621) as any contract, entered into on or before the date of the enactment of this Act, for the first sale of natural gas which was not previously subject to an existing contract.

New-field wildcat well

This term is employed in Alberta to describe a well (1) located at a relatively considerable distance outside the limits of producing (or producible) pools as these limits are known at the time of licensing and (2) drilled on a geologic structure or in a geologic environment where hydrocarbons have not yet been discovered. The Province of Alberta Energy Resources Conservation Board, Informational Letter No. IL–OG 72–16 (Aug. 31, 1972).

See also WILDCAT WELL.

New gas

Gas being made available for the first time by a contract of purchase and sale. See Searls, "Decision of Federal Power Commission in Phillips Petroleum Company Case and Effect on Producers of Commission's Statement of General Policy No. 61–1, as amended," 12 *Sw. Legal Fdn. Oil & Gas Inst.* 1 at 5 (1961).

In the Permian Basin Area Rate Proceeding, new gas was defined as gas moving under contracts entered into on or after January 1, 1961. 34 F.P.C. 158 at 189, 23 *O.&G.R.* 103 at 130 (Opinion No. 468, Aug. 5, 1965), *remanded,* Skelly Oil Co. v. Federal Power Comm'n, 375 F.2d 6, 26 *O.&G.R.* 237 (10th Cir. 1967), *aff'd in part and rev'd in part sub nom. In re* Permian Basin Area Rate Cases, 390 U.S. 747, 28 *O.&G.R.* 689 (1968).

See also OLD GAS; NEW NATURAL GAS; ONE-PRICE SYSTEM; REPLACEMENT CONTRACT POLICY; TWO-PRICE SYSTEM; VINTAGE.

New gas well

For purposes of the Alberta Natural Gas Royalty Regulations (Alta. Reg. 16/74), a new gas well means a well licensed after January 1, 1974, that obtains natural gas from a pool initially discovered after that date.

New lease

This term is defined in § 2 of the NATURAL GAS POLICY ACT OF 1978 (*q.v.*) (Pub. L. No. 95–621) as meaning with respect to the Outer Continental Shelf a lease entered into on or after April 20, 1977 of submerged acreage.

Newly discovered crude oil

For purposes of the CRUDE OIL WINDFALL PROFIT TAX ACT OF 1980 (*q.v.*), this term is given the same meaning as in the June 1979 Department of Energy regulations § 212.79, *viz.,* domestic crude oil which is: (1) produced from a new lease on the Outer Continental Shelf; or (2) produced (other than from the Outer Continental Shelf) from a property from which no crude oil was produced in calendar year 1978. Internal Revenue Code § 4991.

Newly discovered reservoir

This term is defined by Section 402 of the National Energy Act (H.R. 8444), as passed by the House of Representatives on August 5, 1977, as any reservoir which, on or before August 20, 1977, was not discovered, by the drilling of a well, to contain natural gas.

New natural gas

This term is defined in Section 102 of the NATURAL GAS POLICY ACT OF 1978 (*q.v.*) (Pub. L. No. 95–621) as including each of the following categories of natural gas:

(A) New OCS leases.—Natural gas determined in accordance with section 503 to be produced from a new lease on the Outer Continental Shelf.

(B) New onshore wells.—Natural gas determined in accordance with section 503 to be produced (other than from the Outer Continental Shelf) from—

(i) any new well which is 2.5 miles or more (determined in accordance with paragraph (2)) from the nearest market well; or

(ii) any completion location, of any new well, which is located at a depth at least 1,000 feet below the deepest completion location of each marker well within 2.5 miles (determined in accordance with paragraph (2)) of such new well.

See also BEHIND THE PIPE EXCLUSION.

New oil

For purposes of price regulation under the EMERGENCY PETROLEUM ALLOCATION ACT OF 1973 (*q.v.*), new oil is production from a property in excess of production in 1972 and all of the subsequent production from a property not producing in 1972. *The New York Times,* Feb. 20, 1975, p. 56, col. 1.

See also ENTITLEMENT PROGRAM; OLD OIL; RELEASED OIL.

For purposes of the Alberta Petroleum Royalty Regulations (Alta. Reg. 93/74), new oil means crude oil produced from a new oil well, or with respect to crude oil obtained as a result of an enhanced recovery scheme under an order dated on or after January 1, 1974, that portion of the crude oil so obtained attributable to the increase in reserves recognized as resulting from the scheme authorized by such order. A new oil well means a well for which the license was issued on or after April 1, 1974, and produces oil from a newly discovered pool or, under specified circumstances, produces oil from a previously discovered pool.

New, onshore production well

For purposes of the NATURAL GAS POLICY ACT OF 1978 (*q.v.*), this term is defined as "any new well (other than a well located on the Outer Continental Shelf)—

"(1) The surface drilling of which began on or after February 19, 1977;

"(2) Which satisfies applicable Federal or State well-spacing requirements, if any; and

"(3) Which is not within a proration unit—

"(A) Which was in existence at the time the surface drilling of such well began:

"(B) Which was applicable to the reservoir from which such natural gas is produced; and

"(C) Which applies to a well [i] which produced natural gas in commercial quantities or [ii] the surface drilling of which was begun before February 19, 1977, and which was thereafter capable of producing natural gas in commercial quantities." See 18 C.F.R. § 274.204 (1980).

In L & B Oil Co. v. Federal Energy Regulatory Commission, 665 F.2d 758, 73 *O.&G.R.* 399 (5th Cir., Unit A, 1982), the court held that a well qualified as a new, onshore production well even though spudding in of the well had occurred prior to the critical date specified by the statute. In this case the new well was held to be commenced by drilling through the cement plug in a previously abandoned dry hole.

New well

This term is defined in § 2 of the NATURAL GAS POLICY ACT OF 1978 (*q.v.*) (Pub. L. No. 95–621) as any well the surface drilling of which began on or after February 19, 1977 or the depth of which was increased, by means of drilling on or after that date to a completion location which is located at least 1000 feet below the depth of the deepest completion location of such well attained before that date.

NGAA

Natural Gasoline Association of America (now Natural Gas Processors Association).

NGAA contract

A form of contract which was at one time proposed by the Natural Gasoline Association of America.

See also MODIFIED NGAA CONTRACT.

NGAA 1932 Form

A form for the purchase and sale of casinghead gas which was approved by the Natural Gasoline Association of America (now Natural Gas Processors Association of America) in 1932. The NGAA 1939 Form was another form of a casinghead gas contract, approved in 1939.

NGL

NATURAL GAS LIQUIDS (*q.v.*)

NGLP

NATURAL GAS LIQUID PRODUCTS (*q.v.*).

NGPA

(1) NATURAL GAS PROCESSORS ASSOCIATION (*q.v.*), the successor to the NATURAL GASOLINE ASSOCIATION OF AMERICA (*q.v.*).

(2) The NATURAL GAS POLICY ACT OF 1978 (*q.v.*).

NGPSA

The NATURAL GAS PIPELINE SAFETY ACT (*q.v.*)

NIGC

The National Iranian Gas Company.

Nigerian National Oil Corporation (NNOC)

For studies of the operation of this company see Olisa, "The Nigerian National Oil Company," International Bar Ass'n, 1 *Energy Law 1981* at p. 89; Sasegbon, "Current Developments in Oil and Gas Law: Nigeria," *Id.* at p. 361.

Nigerian National Petroleum Corporation (NNPC)

The successor to the Nigerian National Oil Corporation (NNOC). See Olisa, "The Nigerian National Petroleum Corporation," International Bar Ass'n, *Energy Law 1981* at p. 89.

NIOC

The NATIONAL IRANIAN OIL COMPANY (*q.v.*).

Nm^3

Abbreviation for NORMAL CUBIC METER (*q.v.*).

NNOC

The NIGERIAN NATIONAL OIL CORPORATION (*q.v.*).

NNPC

The NIGERIAN NATIONAL PETROLEUM CORPORATION (*q.v.*).

Nodding donkey

The term employed in the United Kingdom for DONKEY HEAD (*q.v.*). J. Salter, *U.K. Onshore Oil and Gas Law* 5-080 (1986).

No-fee exchange

An exchange of transportation services by pipelines under which neither company charges the other for transporting its gas. Tennessee Gas Pipeline Co. v. Federal Energy Regulatory Comm'n, 809 F.2d 1138 (5th Cir. 1987).

"No-go" area

In the United Kingdom this is an area defined in a Structure plan as inappropriate for exploratory drilling. J. Salter, *U.K. Onshore Oil and Gas Law* 1-508 (1986).

No-log, no-payment contract

A form of TURNKEY CONTRACT (*q.v.*) under which the drilling operator can simply walk away from the prospect and not get paid. It differs from a "no-out" turnkey contract which requires that the operator must continue drilling until casing point is reached, no matter what the cost. Brountas v. Commissioner, 73 T.C. 491 at 523 (1979), 74 T.C. 1062, 67 *O.&G.R.* 477 (1980), *vacated and remanded*, 692 F.2d 152, 75 *O.&G.R.* 193 (1st Cir. 1982), *cert. denied*, 462 U.S. 1106, 103 S. Ct. 2453 (1983).

Nomination of tract for leasing

A statement of interest in leasing a tract for mineral development. 43 C.F.R. § 3301.3 (1978). For a discussion of the employment of nominations in the leasing of Outer Continental Shelf Lands, see Crommelin, "Offshore Oil and Gas Rights: A Comparative Study," 14 *Nat. Res. J.* 457 (1974). In the leasing of Outer Continental Shelf Lands The Bureau of Land Management of the Department of the Interior first calls for nominations of tracts. This is followed by an Environmental Impact Statement, the publication of notice of the lease offer in the Federal Register, and, finally, the award of a lease to the highest responsible qualified bidder by means of competitive sealed bids. See Sierra Club v. Morton, 510 F.2d 813 (5th Cir. 1975).

The State of Alaska employs a system of nominations in determining what tracts should be offered for lease. See Moore v. State of Alaska, 553 P.2d 8, 56 *O.&G.R.* 1 (Alaska 1976).

See also NEGATIVE NOMINATION.

Nominations by producers

Declarations by producers showing the volume of oil or gas they need to produce through their wells in order to supply their markets. See Choctaw Gas Co. v. Corporation Comm'n, 295 P.2d 800, 5 *O.&G.R.* 1226 (Okla. 1956).

Nominations by purchasers

Statements by purchasers of oil or gas of the amount they expect to purchase in a given future month. Guided in part by such nominations but more by the estimates of demand supplied by the Bureau of Mines, state regulatory commissions estimated the market demand for petroleum products and fixed the ALLOWABLE (*q.v.*) for the state. For a Louisiana Gas Purchaser's Nomination Form see 5 *O.&G.R.* 479 (1956).

Nominations (in Concessions and Participations)

A statement by the government and the oil companies making up the operating company of a concession of each party's offtake requirements by grade and location for a planned year. See Note, "From Concession to Participation: Restructuring the Middle East Oil Industry," 48 *N.Y.U. L. Rev.* 774 at 808 (1973).

See also CONCESSION.

Non-abandoning party

A term applied in a Rocky Mountain unit operating agreement to a person who objects to the proposed abandonment of a well by the unit operator and who is entitled under the terms of the agreement to take over the well upon payment of the salvage value of the well to the parties electing to abandon the well. Rocky Mountain Unit Operating Agreement Form 1 (Undivided Interest) May, 1954, Section 25.2, TREATISE § 920.3.

Nonaccredited investor

For purposes of REGULATION D (*q.v.*)of the Securities and Exchange Commission providing for a PRIVATE OFFERING EXEMPTION (*q.v.*) under the Federal Securities Act limited to not more than 35 nonaccredited investors (but available for offers made to an unlimited number of accredited investors), a nonaccredited investor is one who does not fall within the definition of an ACCREDITED INVESTOR (*q.v.*)contained in Rule 501, 17 C.F.R. § 230.501(a) (1982). See TREATISE § 441.4.

Non-allocable costs

See PRODUCTION-RELATED COSTS.

Nonapportionment

Allocation of royalties to a royalty owner having an interest in the specific parcel on which a producing well is located rather than dividing royalties among the owners of interests in the land subject to the lease.

See also APPORTIONMENT.

Non-associated gas

Free gas not in contract with crude oil in the reservoir.

Non-associated gas reservoirs

Separate and unconnected gas reservoirs within an area designated by a regulatory agency as a field.

See also FIELD; RESERVOIR.

Non-branded independent marketer

A person who is engaged in the marketing or distributing of refined petroleum products, but who (1) is not a refiner, (2) is not a person who controls, is controlled by, is under common control with, or is affiliated with a refiner (other than by means of a supply contract), and (3) is not a branded independent marketer. 38 Fed. Reg. 34419 (Dec. 13, 1973).

Non-commercial well

(1) A well that produces insufficient oil or gas to repay the costs of drilling, equipping, and operating it.

(2) A well that produces insufficient oil or gas to repay the current operating expenses, whether or not original drilling and equipment costs have been recovered.

See also COMMERCIAL WELL.

Non-competitive lease

An oil and gas lease on federal lands, issued upon application without bidding. All federal leases are non-competitive leases except for those on lands on a known geologic structure in a producing oil and gas field. Non-competitive leases are for a term of 5 years and so long thereafter as oil or gas is produced in paying quantities.

For discussions of this method of leasing federal lands, see the following:

Allenbright, *$10 Wildcat* (1979);

Rocky Mt. Min. L. Fdn. Law of Federal Oil and Gas Leases chs. 5–6 (1985);

Hoffman, *Oil and Gas Leasing on Federal Lands* (1957);

Genegler, "Decisions and Developing Trends in BLM Regulations Affecting Oil and Gas Filings," 26 *Rocky Mt. Min. L. Inst.* 791 (1980);

Malone, "Oil and Gas Leases on U.S. Government Lands," 2 *Sw. Legal Fdn. Oil & Gas Inst.* 309 (1951).

McDonald, *The Leasing of Federal Lands for Fossil Fuels Production* 76 (1979), concludes that competitive lease sales would involve no more administrative cost than the present lottery system, probably would result in greater capture by the government of economic rent, and would improve the efficiency of resource allocation.

Haspel, "Drilling for Dollars: The Federal Oil-Lease Lottery Program," *Regulation* (July/Aug. 1985) p. 25, argues that the lottery system is "more socially efficient than a public competitive sale requiring costly and slow fair-market-value determinations across the board."

See also BUY-BACK AGREEMENT; COMPETITIVE LEASE; DEPARTMENTAL LEASE; DRAWING ENTRY CARD; FEDERAL LEASE; LEASING SERVICE COMPANY; MULTIPLE FILING; OPEN PARCEL LEASE; PUT OPTION; QUALIFIED APPLICANT; SIMULTANEOUS FILINGS; TEN PER CENT (RENTAL) RULE.

Non-compliance, Affidavit of

See AFFIDAVIT OF NON-COMPLIANCE.

Non-confidential pool

In Alberta, a DESIGNATED POOL (*q.v.*) which (1) has been designated by an order of the Board for a period of one year or longer, or (2) contains five or more wells that are cased for production from the pool or production spacing units containing in aggregate five or more drilling spacing units, or (3) is or was on gas production, or (4) does not contain a CONFIDENTIAL WELL (*q.v.*), or (5) containing more than one producing well when the designation was made and has been designated by the Board as non-confidential upon application by the licensee of wells in the pool. Alberta Oil and Gas Conservation Regulations (Alta. Reg. 151/71) § 12–150(1)(3).

Non-consent interest

The name which has been applied to a form of carried interest held by non-consent parties under a widely used form of operating agreement. In Railroad Commission v. Olin Corp., 690 S.W.2d 628, 88 *O.&G.R.* 579 (Tex. App., Austin, 1985), non-consent parties were held liable under Texas statutes for the cost of plugging a well in which they had declined to participate. In denying error, n.r.e., 701 S.W.2d 641, 88 *O.&G.R.* 586 (Tex. 1985), the Supreme Court approved only the result reached by the court of appeals requiring Olin Corp. and Tenexplo to pay for the plugging of the well. This case and carried interests generally are discussed in detail in Conine, "Rights and Liabilities of Carried Interest and Nonconsent Parties in Oil and Gas Operations," 37 *Sw. Legal Fdn. Oil & Gas Inst.* 3-1 (1986).

Non-consent party

A party to a joint venture, a joint operating agreement, or a pooling or unitization agreement who does not agree in advance to participate in drilling, reworking, deepening, or plugging back of a well. Under such circumstances, the interest of the non-consent party becomes subject to a NON-CONSENT PENALTY (*q.v.*). Railroad Comm'n v. Olin Corp., 690 S.W.2d 628, 88 *O.&G.R.* 586 (Tex. App., Austin, 1985), held that the interest of a non-consent party is a MANAHAN-TYPE CARRIED INTEREST (*q.v.*). Error was ref'd n.r.e. by the Supreme Court, 701 S.W.2d 641, 88 *O.&G.R.* 586 (Tex. 1985) (approving only the result reached by the court of appeals requiring Olin Corp. and Tenexplo to pay for the plugging of the well).

Non-consent penalty

A penalty against a party to a joint venture, a joint operating agreement, or a pooling or unitization agreement who did not agree in advance to participate in the costs of drilling, reworking, deepening, or plugging back of a particular well by the operator or another party to the agreement. The penalty may be in terms of acreage, production or cash. Industry practice in voluntary pooling agreements between lessees calls for non-consent penalties ranging from 200 to 300 percent for development wells, at least 300 percent for most exploratory (wildcat) wells, and in very expensive areas, particularly offshore operations, as much as 1,000 percent.

Hamilton v. Texas Oil & Gas Corp., 646 S.W.2d 316, 76 *O.&G.R.* 300 (Tex. App., El Paso, 1982, error ref'd n.r.e.), sustained the validity of a 400 percent non-consent penalty provision in a joint operating agreement.

Traverse Oil Co. v. Chairman, Natural Resources Comm'n, 153 Mich. App. 679, 396 N.W.2d 498, ____ *O.&G.R.* ____ (1986), held that imposition of a non-consent penalty was improper because the wells in question had been drilled before the petition for compulsory pooling had been heard. Contrary to the applicable statute, the non-consenting party "was not afforded the opportunity to participate in the drilling costs and avoid the penalty because the wells were completed before pooling was ordered. Thus, the circuit court did not err when it concluded that the Supervisor was not authorized to impose a penalty under these circumstances."

See also the following:

Giles, "Practical Applications During a Pool's Life," in *Rocky Mt. Min. L. Fdn. Basic Oil and Gas Technology for Lawyers and Landmen* (1979);

Ryan, "Current Problems in Federal Unitization With Particular Reference to Unit Operating Agreements," 2 *Rocky Mt. Min. L. Inst.* 157 (1956);

Nicholls, "Some Practical Problems of Joint Venture Agreements," 3 *Australian Mining and Petroleum L.J.* 41 (1981);

TREATISE §§ 905.2, 921.10.

See also BONUS PENALTY; RISK CHARGE STATUTE; SOLE RISK CLAUSE.

Non-consent principle

The view that a majority may control the drilling of a well on a unitized area and that a party in interest may refuse to participate in the drilling of a well on the unitized tract. If the well is non-productive, the non-consentor will not participate in the costs; if the well is productive he may participate in the proceeds of production only on the basis of a NON-CONSENT PENALTY (*q.v.*).

For a discussion of a variety of ways of handling non-consent problems see White, "Alternatives for Handling Nonconsent in Joint Mining Operations," *Rocky Mt. Min. L. Fdn. Mining Agreements Inst.* 6–1 (1979).

Non-consent well

A well drilled in a unitized area by the operator or one of the participating parties to which a particular party in interest has not consented. The non-consentor is not liable for any of the costs if the well is non-productive; if the well is productive, he will be entitled to share in the proceeds only on the basis of a NON-CONSENT PENALTY (*q.v.*).

Non-conventional oil recovery stipulation

A stipulation implementing the COMBINED HYDROCARBON LEASING ACT OF 1981 (CHLA) (*q.v.*) imposed by certain Bureau of Land Management leases. Havoco of America, Ltd., IBLA 82-390, GFS(O&G) 1982-118 (Interior Board of Land Appeals 1982), approved the inclusion of the following stipulation in a lease:

> "Under the provisions of Public Law 97-98, this lease includes all deposits of nongaseous hydrocarbon substances other than coal, oil shale, or gilsonite (including all vein-type solid hydrocarbons). Development by methods not conventionally used for oil and gas extraction such as fire flooding and including surface mining will require the lessee to submit a plan of operations and will be subject to regulations governing development by such methods when those rules are issued by the Bureau of Land Management (BLM), the U.S. Geological Survey, and the rules or procedures of the surface managing agency, if other than BLM. Development may proceed only if the plan of operations is approved."

Non-development, Affidavit of

See AFFIDAVIT OF NON-DEVELOPMENT.

Non-drilling lease

A lease which grants the lessee the usual rights relative to oil or gas under described premises but which provides that a well shall not be surfaced on the premises. Production from the premises under such circumstances will require that any well drilled be surfaced on other premises. See Milton, "Tax Consequences of a Non-Drilling Lease and Similar Agreements," *P–H, Oil and Gas Taxes* ¶ 2007 (1975).

A non-drilling lease may be executed to prevent the drilling of a well in the gas cap with consequent reduction of reservoir pressure and ultimate loss of recoverable oil. Under these circumstances, adjoining landowners may contribute to the payments made to the lessor under the terms of the lease in lieu of drilling and the payment of royalties. See Cartan v. Commissioner, 30 T.C. 308, 9 *O.&G.R.* 833 (1958).

A non-drilling lease may be issued on certain acquired lands for oil and gas where surface activities would not be compatible with the purpose for which the land was acquired, M.R. Diggs, Jr., 12 IBLA 187, GFS(O&G) 1973–71.

Non-drilling party

(1) As defined in a Rocky Mountain unit operating agreement, a party not obligated to contribute to the costs incurred in drilling, deepening, or plugging back a well in accordance with the agreement. See Rocky Mountain Unit Operating Agreement Form 1 (Undivided Interest) May, 1954, Section 1.11, TREATISE § 920.3.

(2) A party to a unit agreement who is not responsible for drilling but having an election to participate in the drilling of a proposed well. See Upchurch, "Formation of the Exploration and Development Unit," *1959 Sw. Legal Fdn. Nat'l Inst. for Petroleum Landmen* 1 at 22 (1960).

Non-excluded oil

Natural gas not excluded from the definition of oil for purposes of the Petroleum Revenue Tax. See Daintith and Willoughby, *A Manual of United Kingdom Oil and Gas Law* 109–110 (1977).

Nonexecutive interest

(1) The generic term inclusive of nonexecutive mineral interests and royalty interests.

(2) In Louisiana, a mineral right that does not include the executive right, such as the mineral royalty, a landowner's interest in minerals the executive right to which has been granted to another, or a mineral servitude the executive right to which has been granted to another. Louisiana Mineral Code Article 108 [R.S. 31:108 (1975)]. For a discussion of the nature and characteristics of the nonexecutive interest in Louisiana see TREATISE § 339.4.

Nonexecutive mineral interest

A term that has been used to describe an interest in oil and gas that lacks the right to join in the execution of oil and gas leases and (probably) the right to develop. For example, such an interest is created by this grant: *A*, owner in fee simple absolute of Blackacre, conveys to *B* one-half of all oil, gas or other minerals in or under the [described] land, reserving to *A* the exclusive right to execute oil and gas leases on the land forever. *B* has a nonexecutive mineral interest.

Other names for the same type of interest are: participating royalty and nonparticipating mineral interest.

It will be observed that the practical difference between a NONPARTICIPATING ROYALTY (*q.v.*) and a nonexecutive mineral interest is that the latter shares in bonus and delay rental as well as royalty under existing and future leases. The former shares in royalty only. This may make a substantial difference if the owner of the EEXECUTIVE RIGHT (*q.v.*) leases the land for 1/8 royalty plus a large oil payment. State National Bank of Corpus Christi v. Morgan, 135 Tex. 509, 143 S.W.2d 757 (1940), held on similar facts that the nonparticipating royalty did not share in the oil payment. *Cf.* Griffith v. Taylor, 156 Tex. 1, 291 S.W.2d 673, 5 *O.&G.R.* 1371 (1956).

HNG Fossil Fuels Co. v. Roach, 99 N.M. 216, 656 P.2d 879, 76 *O.&G.R.* 88 (1982), held that the trial court did not err in holding that the term "non-participating" as used in a mineral deed meant that the owner of such interest was not entitled to participate in executing leases and did not participate or share in bonuses or delay rentals.

A number of cases have dealt with the problems created by nonexecutive mineral interests:

Benge v. Scharbauer, 152 Tex. 447, 259 S.W.2d 166, 2 *O.&G.R.* 1350 (1953);

Odstreil v. McGlaun, 230 S.W.2d 353 (Tex. Civ. App. 1950);

McLain v. First National Bank, 263 S.W.2d 324, 3 *O.&G.R.* 477 (Tex. Civ. App. 1953);

De Busk v. Cosden Petroleum Corp., 262 S.W.2d 767, 3 *O.&G.R.* 665 (Tex. Civ. App. 1953);

Allison v. Smith, 278 S.W.2d 940, 4 *O.&G.R.* 1136 (Tex. Civ. App. 1955 error ref'd n.r.e.);

Superior Oil Co. v. Stanolind Oil & Gas Co., 230 S.W.2d 346 (Tex. Civ. App. 1950), *aff'd,* 150 Tex. 317, 240 S.W.2d 281 (1951).

See also Jones, "Exercise of Executive Rights in Connection with Non-Participating Royalty and Non-Executive Mienral Interests," 15 *Sw. Legal Fdn. Oil & Gas Inst.* 35 (1964); Jones, "Separation of the Exclusive Leasing Power from Mineral Ownership," 2 *Sw. Legal Fdn. Oil & Gas Inst.* 271 (1951); TREATISE §§ 324.4, 326, 328–330, 338–339.3.

See also PARTICIPATING ROYALTY.

Non-firm gas

Gas which is not required to be delivered or not required to be taken under the terms of a GAS PURCHASE CONTRACT (*q.v.*).

Non-freehold interest (or estate)

A personal property interest in land or chattel real. An interest in land with a duration less than a life or fee interest.

Non-invited application

An application in the United Kingdom for a PRODUCTION LICENSE (*q.v.*) in accordance with the provisions of Regulation 6 of The Petroleum (Production) Regulations 1976. See Henderson *et al., Oil and Gas Law: The North Sea Exploitation* 3.1015 (1979).

Non-joint drilling

Drilling of a well or wells other than for the joint account on lands subject to a Joint Operating Agreement.

The usual Joint Operating Agreement provides that certain wells will be drilled for the joint account. Usually any party desiring to drill a well (or deepen or rework a well which was drilled as a Joint account well) may give notice thereof to the other parties who may elect to participate in the well by giving notice of such election within a specified time. If the other parties do not elect to participate, the drilling may be prosecuted by the interested party. If such well is completed as a producer, the non-participating parties under the terms of the agreement usually are entitled to a share of the production but only after the drilling party or parties have received from production an amount in excess of the amount (commonly twice the amount) expended by the drilling party or parties on the well or wells. See Hazlett, "Drafting of Joint Operating Agreements," 3 *Rocky Mt. Min. L. Inst.* 277 at 292 (1957).

See also JOINT ACCOUNT WELL.

Non-jurisdictional sales

A term used to describe sales of natural gas which are not subject to the jurisdiction of the Federal Power Commission under the Natural Gas Act. The NATURAL GAS POLICY ACT OF 1978 (*q.v.*), Pub. L. No. 95–621, provided for a single national market for gas sales, eliminating the jurisdictional sale-nonjurisdictional sale distinction.

See also AREA PRICING POLICY; MOLECULAR THEORY; VOLUMETRIC METHOD OF ALLOCATION.

Non-leasing oil and gas interests

A term used generically to encompass both nonparticipating royalty interests and nonexecutive mineral interests. See Lustgarten and Olpin, "Safeguarding Non-Leasing Oil and Gas Interests Derived from the Landowner," 38 *Texas L. Rev.* 550 (1960).

Non-marginal unit

A proration unit that will produce at a rate equal to the top unit ALLOWABLE (*q.v.*) for the proration period for the pool. New Mexico Oil Conservation Comm'n, *Rules and Regulations* 4 (1958).

Nonoperating interest

An interest in production from a mineral property which does not share in operating rights, *e.g.*, a NONEXECUTIVE INTEREST, an OVERRIDING ROYALTY, or ROYALTY.

Nonoperating working interest

The working interest or a fraction thereof in a tract the owner of which is without operating rights by reason of an operating agreement.

Nonoperating mineral interest, for tax purposes

A term used in the Internal Revenue Code § 614 (e). It is defined as an interest other than an operating MINERAL INTEREST (*q.v.*), that is, one that does not bear a share of operating expenses. Familiar examples are: royalty, overriding royalty, and oil payment.

Under this section of the Code, such interests can be aggregated, under certain circumstances, to form a single property for tax purposes, upon a showing of undue hardship. See Bird, "The 'Property' for Purposes of Depletion," 33 *Texas L. Rev.* 785 (1955).

See also AGGREGATION OF PROPERTIES; DEPLETION, PERCENTAGE; OPERATING MINERAL INTEREST, FOR TAX PURPOSES; OPERATING UNIT, FOR TAX PURPOSES; PROPERTY UNIT, FOR TAX PURPOSES.

Non-ownership theory

The theory that no person owns oil and gas until it is produced, but that the right to produce is limited to those persons who own land upon which a well may be drilled. This theory developed at a time when it was generally believed that oil and gas were as migratory as the birds in the air, or at least as migratory as underground waters. A jurisdiction adopting this theory must necessarily hold, conceptually, that any interest in the minerals created by a landowner is necessarily non-possessory or incorporeal in character; this means that the owner of such an interest is limited to non-possessory as opposed to possessory remedies for the protection of his interest. See Lilly v. Conservation Comm'r of La., 29 F.Supp. 892 at 897 (E.D. La. 1939); TREATISE § 203.1.

See also CORRELATIVE RIGHTS THEORY; FERAE NATURE; OWNERSHIP IN PLACE THEORY; OWNERSHIP OF STRATA THEORY; QUALIFIED OWNERSHIP THEORY.

Nonparticipating area

That part of a unit area to which production is not allocated under the terms of the unit agreement. 30 C.F.R. § 226.2(i) (1980). The lease is held in effect by unit production both as to the PARTICIPATING AREA (*q.v.*) and the nonparticipating area. If the nonparticipating area is committed to another unit, the lease is segregated into two separate leases. 43 C.F.R. § 3107.4 (1978). On the rental obligations of the lessee as to the segregated lease, see Bass Enterprises Production Co., IBLA 80–6, 47 IBLA 53, GFS (O&G) 1980–95 (Apr. 14, 1980).

Nonparticipating mineral interest

See NONEXECUTIVE MINERAL INTEREST.

Nonparticipating royalty

An expense-free interest in oil or gas, as, if and when produced. The prefix "nonparticipating" indicates the interest does not share in bonus or rental, nor in the right to execute leases or to explore and develop.

The quantum of the royalty is determined by the instrument creating it; *e.g.*, a one-sixteenth nonparticipating royalty is one out of every sixteen barrels of oil produced on the land, cost free and at the surface. An instrument using the term "one-half of all present and future royalties on oil produced and saved from" the land would also give the royalty owner one out of every sixteen barrels of oil, cost free at the surface, if but only if the lease provided for a one-eighth royalty. Presumably, an owner under such language would get more or less as the lease royalty was greater or less than one-eighth.

The most often litigated problem regarding nonparticipating royalty is construction of the instrument as to the quantum of the interest. This issue is often resolved by determining whether the interest is a royalty or a mineral interest. See Maxwell, "The Mineral-Royalty Distinction and the Expense of Production," 33 *Tex. L. Rev.* 463 (1955); TREATISE §§ 302–307.4.

Another problem is the validity of the interest under the Rule against Perpetuities. The Kansas case of Lathrop v. Eyestone, 170 Kan. 419, 227 P.2d 136 (1951) held perpetual nonparticipating royalty to be void under the Rule. There is a California holding suggesting the same result. Dallapi v. Campbell, 45 Cal. App. 2d 541, 114 P.2d 646 (1941). However, a well reasoned Arkansas opinion held the interest good under the perpetuities rule. Hanson v. Ware, 224 Ark. 430, 274 S.W.2d 359, 4 *O.&G.R.* 325 (1955). The great majority of cases, and of oil and gas jurisdictions *assume* the validity of perpetual royalty without discussion. See TREATISE §§ 322–326.

A third problem is the relationship between the royalty owner and the EXECUTIVE (*q.v.*), the owner of the EXCLUSIVE LEASING POWER (*q.v.*). When must the executive exercise the leasing power? Can he agree to pooling? For what term may he lease? See the able discussion of these matters in Jones, "Non-Participating Royalty," 26 *Tex. L. Rev.* 569 (1948); Jones, "Separation of the Exclusive Leasing Power from Mineral Ownership," 2 *Sw. Legal Fdn. Oil & Gas Inst.* 271 (1951); Jones, "Exercise of Executive Rights in Connection with Non-Participating Royalty and Non-Executive Mineral Interests," 15 *Sw. Legal Fdn. Oil & Gas Inst.* 35 (1964); TREATISE §§ 301, 338–339.3.

The definition in this MANUAL was quoted in the following cases:

Whitehall Oil Co. v. Eckart, 197 So. 2d 664 at 667, 26 *O.&G.R.* 778 at 782 (La. App. 1966), *rev'd sub nom.* Gardner v. Boagni, 252 La. 30, 209 So. 2d 11, 29 *O.&G.R.* 229 (1968);

Harris v. Griffith, 210 So. 2d 629 at 635, 28 *O.&G.R.* 398 at 406 (Miss. 1968).

See also NONEXECUTIVE MINERAL INTEREST; PARTICIPATING ROYALTY; PERPETUAL NONPARTICIPATING ROYALTY.

Non-processed gas

Gas that is not processed in a gas plant for the removal of liquids.

Nonproratable allowable

An allowable granted as an exception to the SCHEDULE ALLOWABLE (*q.v.*).

In Texas, for example, exempted from schedule allowables are (1) the East Texas field, (2) fields producing on discovery well allowable, and (3) stripper fields. See Zimmermann, *Conservation in the Production of Petroleum* 218 (1957).

Nonrecourse financing

Financing of a project by a loan which, subject to exceptions, is repayable only to the extent that the project for which it is made generates sufficient funds for repayment as distinguished from recourse financing in which case the loan constitutes an unlimited obligation of the borrower and is dischargeable out of any assets which the borrower may from time to time own. The major advantage of nonrecourse financing is that accounting practice has permitted it to be excluded from the balance sheet of the borrower. Its major disadvantage is that it is usually significantly more expensive than recourse financing.

See the following:

Christian, "Introduction to Commercial Bank and Non-Bank Institutional Financing in the Minerals Industry," *Rocky Mt. Min. L. Inst. on Mineral Financing* 2-1 at 2-14 (1982);

Hurd, "A survey of U.S. Oil and Gas Development and Willoughby, "Limited Recourse Loans," in *Proceedings of the Petroleum Law Seminar* (Jan. 8–13, 1978), organized by the Committee on Energy and Natural Resources, Section on Business Law, International Bar Association.

See also LEVERAGED LEASE; LIMITED RESOURCE FINANCING, PROJECT FINANCING.

Nonrecourse note

A promissory note executed without personal liability but secured by an interest in an oil and gas lease. On the use of such notes in oil and gas financing see Backar v. Western States Producing Co., 547 F.2d 876, 57 *O.&G.R.* 273 (5th Cir. 1977), and Brountas v. Commissioner, 73 T.C. 491 at 538 *et seq.* (1979), 74 T.C. 1062, 67 *O.&G.R.* 477 (1980) (rejecting the contention that the nonrecourse note portion of a lease purchase and turnkey drilling agreement was a sham, and holding that the note was a liability treated as a contribution of money to a partnership and therefore part of the contributor's basis), *vacated and remanded,* 692 F.2d 152, 75 *O.&G.R.* 193 (1st Cir. 1982), *cert. denied,* 462 U.S. 1106, 103 S.Ct. 2453 (1983).

See also Gibson Products Co. v. United States, 637 F.2d 1041 (5th Cir. 1981) (holding that nonrecourse note given by partnership for purchase of oil and gas leases and for drilling obligations, with partnership's liability contingent upon production from wells drilled by payee, was not a production payment entitled to be treated as a loan and deductible as intangible drilling cost).

Non-recoverable gas

Natural gas contained in a gas reservoir which cannot be economically withdrawn. Arkla, Inc. v. United States, 592 F.Supp. 502, 83 *O.&G.R.* 209 (W.D. La. 1984), *rev'd and remanded,* 765 F.2d 487, 85 *O.&G.R.* 431 (5th Cir. 1985), *reh. denied,* 772 F.2d 904 (5th Cir. 1985), *cert. denied,* 106 S.Ct. 1374 (1986).

Non-recurrent fee

A fee paid for the use of a license area in the first six years under a Norwegian production license. See Krohn, Kaasen, *et al., Norwegian Petroleum Law* 2–23 (1978).

See also PRODUCTION LICENSE.

Non-standard unit

A pooling or spacing UNIT (*q.v.*) which deviates in acreage or conformation from the standard units established by a regulatory commission. See Rutter & Wilbanks Corp. v. Oil Conservation Comm'n 87 N.M. 286, 532 P.2d 582, 50 *O.&G.R.* 488 (1975).

"No-out" turnkey contract

See TURNKEY CONTRACT.

No-prejudice clause

A clause in a lease or other agreement to the effect that execution of the instrument shall in no way prejudice a particular claim made by one or more of the parties. Ward v. Gohlke, 279 S.W.2d 422, 4 *O.&G.R.* 1403 (Tex. Civ. App. 1955, error ref'd).

NOPV

NOTICE OF PROBABLE VIOLATION (*q.v.*).

No-risk service agreement

Syn. for PURE SERVICE AGREEMENT (*q.v.*).

Normal cubic meter (Nm^3)

A cubic meter of natural gas measured at atmospheric pressure and at a temperature of 15 degree C (60 degree F).

See also STANDARD CUBIC FOOT.

Normanna case

A term used to describe Atlantic Refining Co. v. Railroad Comm'n, 162 Tex. 274, 346 S.W.2d 801, 14 *O.&G.R.* 362 (1961).

Norm price

The administratively determined value for petroleum extracted from the Norwegian Continental Shelf employed for the assessment of the ordinary income tax and the special tax for petroleum activity. This value is intended to correspond to the price which in the relevant period could have been obtained in a sale between independent parties in a free market. Act of 13 June 1975 (No. 35) relating to the taxation of submarine petroleum resources, *etc.*, Section 4. See Krohn, Kaasen, *et al.*, *Norwegian Petroleum Law* 2–28 (1978); Henderson *et al.*, *Oil and Gas Law: The North Sea Exploration* 4.2020 *et seq.*, 4.2515 *et seq.* (1979).

Northern Tier Pipeline Co.

A pipeline company organized to build an oil pipeline originating in Port Angeles, Washington, and terminating in Clearbrook, Minnesota. For a case dealing with multiple challenges to the validity of the permit, see NO OILPORT! v. Carter, 520 F. Supp. 334 (W.D. Wash. 1981).

See also PIPELINE.

North Sea Continental Shelf Case

A decision of the International Court of Justice in 1969 affirming that there was a regime of customary international law on the continental shelf and that this regime was represented by arts. 1 to 3 of the CONVENTION ON THE CONTINENTAL SHELF (1958) (*q.v.*) [1969] ICJ Reports at p. 40.

Norwegian Special Tax

A special tax levied on "windfall" profits of petroleum companies created by the OPEC-led increase in the price of oil. See Hossain, *Law and Policy in Petroleum Development* 192 (1979).

Norwegian trench

A trench in the Continental shelf close to the coast of Norway which poses a major obstacle to the transportation of crude oil and gas to Norway from her North Sea fields inasmuch as the trench is too deep for a pipeline.

Notation rule

The rule that before certain lands formerly included in an oil and gas lease were available for leasing, a tract book notation in the land office records was required. Such notation was required when a lease was cancelled, relinquished or terminated for failure to pay rentals, but was not required when a lease expired at the end of its primary term. The purpose of the rule was to afford all members of the public an equal opportunity to file an offer for the lands. The importance of the notation question has been reduced by a 1959 amendment to departmental regulations providing that lands in cancelled or relinquished leases or in leases which terminate by nonpayment of rentals shall be subject to the filing of a new lease only after notation on the official records and posting of the lands as available for further leasing. See *Rocky Mt. Min. L. Fdn. Law of Federal Oil and Gas Leases* § 3.08 (1985).

For an application of the notation rule to cause rejection of an OVER-THE-COUNTER LEASE OFFER (*q.v.*), see Paiute Oil & Mining Corp., IBLA 82-798, GFS(O&G) 1982-228 (Sept. 3, 1982).

For a detailed discussion of this rule, see B.J. Toohey, C.D. Toohey & C.W. Toohey, 88 IBLA 66, 92 I.D. 317 (Interior Board of Land Appeals 1985).

See also FEDERAL LEASE.

No-term lease

A lease which may be kept alive indefinitely by the payment of delay rentals.

This was an early form of oil and gas lease no longer in general use, although an occasional contemporary no-term lease arises from mistake. Thus in Rosson v. Bennett, 294 S.W. 660 (Tex. Civ. App. 1927), the lease provided for a three year primary term but the unless type delay rental clause provided for the initial payment of rentals at the end of the three year primary term. The result was the creation of a no-term lease. It is unlikely that any modern lease is intended to be for "no-term." Most no-term leases found to have been created by conveyances in recent decades probably resulted from mistake or misunderstanding in the completion of the blanks in store-bought lease forms.

Lessors generally dislike the no-term lease because there is no assurance that exploratory or developmental operations will ever be undertaken, yet the lease may be kept alive indefinitely by the payment of rentals. Lessees came to dislike this lease form when some courts held it to create an estate at will, terminable at the will of either party, and when other courts declared that a lessor might be rejection of tendered rentals and the making of a demand for development of the premises obtain cancellation of the lease if there were no development within a reasonable time after such rejection of rentals and demand for development, and because of fear of invalidity of the lease under the Rule against Perpetuities. See TREATISE § 601.3.

Notice and demand clause

A frequent provision in oil and gas leases requiring the giving of notice of breach of an express or implied duty under the lease and the making of demand for performance as a prerequisite to any legal action for the breach. There is often also provided that the lessee shall have a short period of time (30, 60, or 90 days) after notice and demand, and prior to the bringing of legal action, for performance of the duty. The precise terms of these clauses vary considerably. See TREATISE §§ 682–682.5.

See also DEFAULT CLAUSE; GOOD FAITH CLAUSE; JUDICIAL ASCERTAINMENT CLAUSE.

Notice and reassignment clause

See REASSIGNMENT CLAUSE.

Notice of Probable Violation (NOPV)

The notice issued by the ECONOMIC REGULATORY ADMINISTRATION (ERA) (*q.v.*) to begin a proceeding where there is reason to believe that a violation of a Department of Energy regulation has occurred, is continuing or is about to occur. 10 C.F.R. § 205.191 (1980).

NPC

The NATIONAL PETROLEUM COUNCIL (*q.v.*).

NPSL

NET PROFIT SHARE LEASE (*q.v.*).

NPSR

Net profit share rate (*q.v.*).

NTPC

Northern Tier Pipeline Co. (*q.v.*)

NRECA

The National Rural Electric Cooperative Association.

NRI

Net revenue interest (*q.v.*).

..O..

O&GR

Abbreviation for *Oil & Gas Reporter,* published by the Southwestern Legal Foundation, containing reports of cases dealing with oil, gas, and other minerals.

OAPEC

ORGANIZATION OF ARAB PETROLEUM EXPORTING COUNTRIES (*q.v.*).

Obligation well

A well required to be drilled in return for an assignment of a property interest in the land being drilled.

A Canadian author, Brown, "Independent Operations, Obligatory Operations and Challenge of Operator Provisions in Joint Venture Agreements," 8 *Alberta L. Rev.* 216 at 219 (1970), has offered several definitions of an obligation (or obligatory) well:

> "a well which is required to be drilled pursuant to the terms of the leases or any order or regulation applicable to the joint lands, waiver of which requirement cannot be obtained by payment of compensatory royalty, negotiation, or other means";
>
> "a well that is required to be drilled pursuant to the documents of title or any laws (unless the obligation is not being enforced) even though the time for commencement may be extended";
>
> "a well that is required to be commenced and drilled on the said lands pursuant to the said leases or the regulations applicable thereto, and which if not drilled will result in the forfeiture of all or a portion of the said lands."

See also FREE WELL; OBLIGATION WELL DOCTRINE.

Obligation well doctrine

A doctrine in effect under the Treasury Regulations before 1942, under which a taxpayer who drilled a well in return for the assignment of an interest in the land was required to capitalize his intangible drilling and development costs as part of the cost of acquisition of the land. Under the present regulations, the costs of drilling such a well must be capitalized only to the extent of the excess over the proportional interest owned or to be owned by the driller-assignee.

Thus if *A* assigns an undivided one-half interest in a leasehold to *B* in return for a well, *B* capitalizes half the drilling costs and is entitled to the option to deduct intangibles as to the other one half. Treasury Decision 5276, 1943 Cum.Bull. 151; U.S. Treas. Reg. § 1.612–4 (a)(3) (1980). See Fielder, "Option to Deduct Intangible Costs," 33 *Texas L. Rev.* 825 at 835–838 (1955); Burke and Bowhay, *Income Taxation of Natural Resources* ¶ 14.03 (1981).

Obligation well farm-out

A form of FARM-OUT (*q.v.*) in which the owner of a lease agrees to convey a drillsite (and perhaps a partial interest in other acreage) upon the completion of a well on the drillsite by the grantee at his own expense. The grantor may retain an overriding royalty or other interest in the drillsite. For a discussion of the tax consequences see Gregg, "Oil and Gas Farmouts—Implications of Revenue Ruling 77–176," 29 *Sw. Legal Fdn. Oil & Gas Inst.* 601 (1978).

Obligatory work program

Syn. for MANDATORY WORK PROGRAM (*q.v.*).

Observation well

A well used for observation of reservoir pressure, fluid interface movements or other pool phenomena. In Alberta, the allowable of a well used for this purpose may be transferred to another well or wells upon approval of the Oil and Gas Conservation Board. See Alberta Oil and Gas Conservation Board, Transfer of Oil Allowable (Sept. 30, 1957).

See also ALLOWABLE; TRANSFERRED ALLOWABLE.

Obstacle

Facts which prevent the exercise of a MINERAL SERVITUDE (*q.v.*) in Louisiana. While the obstacle exists, PRESCRIPTION (*q.v.*) of non-usage does not run against the servitude.

The obstacle theory in Louisiana is closely akin to the concept of *force majeure.* See McCollam, "A Primer for the Practice of Mineral Law Under the New Louisiana Mineral Code," 50 *Tulane L. Rev.* 729 at 757 (1976).

The law concerning suspension of prescription by obstacle in Louisiana is codified in Articles 59–61, 97–100 of the Louisiana Mienral Code [R.S. 31:59–61, 97–100 (1975)]. See this TREATISE § 216.3(d).

Obstruction, doctrine of

The doctrine that a lessee may suspend operations under the terms of a lease contract pending determination of a communicated assertion that the lease is no longer valid and subsisting. French v. Tenneco Oil Co., 725 P.2d 275, 90 *O.&G.R.* 97 (Okla. 1986). See TREATISE § 604.7.

21st Century Investment Co. v. Pine, 724 P.2d 834, ____ *O.&G.R.* ____ (Okla. App. 1986, *cert. denied*), applied the doctrine of obstruction to interference by the surface owner as distinguished from interference by the lessor:

> "So to recapitulate, we hold that under these statutory provisions, a stipulation in the lease will be implied that vests in lessee the lessor's surface entry and use rights—rights which the law will protect and enforce. And if during the term of the lease the exercise of such rights is temporarily prevented by the lessor, the surface owner, or some force majeure, the law will imply that the lease provides for an extension of the primary term of the lease for such time as is reasonably required to restore to the lessee the ability to exercise his right of entry and use."

See also D. Pierce *Kansas Oil and Gas Handbook* § 8.14 (1986).

Occupational Safety and Health Act

29 U.S.C. § 651 *et seq.*

OCS

The OUTER CONTINENTAL SHELF (*q.v.*).

OCS royalty oil

The Government's royalty portion of oil produced under a SECTION 6 LEASE (*q.v.*) or a SECTION 8 LEASE (*q.v.*) when royalty on oil is paid in kind or taken in kind or is being considered for such payment or taking. 30 C.F.R. § 225a.2 (h) (1980).

Octane

An hydrocarbon of the paraffin series. It is liquid at ordinary atmospheric conditions, although small amounts may be present in the gas associated with petroleum. See Interstate Oil Compact Commission, *Oil and Gas Production* 26 (1951).

Octane number

A performance rating used to classify motor fuels. Special one-cylinder test engines are used to determine octane numbers. "The names octane, isooctane, and 2,2,4–trimethyl pentane are used to refer to the same pure chemical which is a good motor fuel having a high antiknock rating. This fuel which we will call isooctane was chosen as a standard fuel and assigned a value of 100. Heptane is a poor motor fuel and knocks badly. It was chosen as the zero reference fuel. The octane number of the fuel sample is the percent of isooctane that must be blended into heptane to match the knocking tendency of the sample when compared in the test engine. For example, an 80-octane-number gasoline will have the same knocking response in the test engine as a blend of 80 percent isoctane in heptane. Tetraethyl lead, a chemical which can be added to finished gasoline, has the property of increasing the octane number. The octane number of the leaded gasoline is determined also by comparison in the test engine with isooctane blended into heptane." 55 *Oil and Gas Journal* 193 (No. 45, Nov. 11, 1957). See Nelson, "How Octane Numbers Have Been Improved," *Id.* at 194.

Octane rating

A rating of gasoline in terms of anti-knock qualities. The higher the octane number or rating, the greater the anti-knock qualities of the gasoline.

OD

Abbreviation for Outside diameter.

OECD

The ORGANIZATION FOR ECONOMIC COOPERATION AND DEVELOPMENT (*q.v.*).

Office of Appeals and Hearings

A now defunct office of the Department of the Interior charged with hearing appeals from the several state offices of the Bureau of Land Management. The decisions of this office have no value or effect as precedent, as they were not included in a periodic index nor did they constitute final department action which exhausted the administrative remedy. Cheyenne Resources, Inc., 87 I.D. 110 (1980).

This office has now been replaced by the OFFICE OF HEARINGS AND APPEALS (*q.v.*). 43 C.F.R. § 4.1 (1981).

Office of Hearings and Appeals

(1) The office of the ECONOMIC REGULATORY ADMINISTRATION (ERA) (*q.v.*) authorized to issue a Remedial Order or Order of Disallowance after proceedings to determine whether a violation of a Department of Energy regulation has occurred, is continuing or is about to occur. 10 C.F.R. § 205.190 (1980).

(2) An authorized representative of the Secretary of the Interior for the purpose of hearing, considering, and determining, as fully and finally as might the Secretary, matters within the jurisdiction of the Department of the Interior involving hearings and appeals and other review functions of the Secretary. 43 C.F.R. § 4.1 (1981).

(3) The Office of the Department of Energy which was charged with the exceptions process by which a person, firm or entity subject to a valid statutory or administrative rule was relieved from the legal obligation to comply with that rule because of the special features of the situation. See Schuck, "When the Exception Becomes the Rule: Regulatory Equity and the Formulation of Energy Policy Through An Exceptions Process," 1984 *Duke L.J.* 163 (1984).

Office of Pipeline and Producer Regulation (OPPR)

The office in the FEDERAL ENERGY REGULATORY COMMISSION given responsibility for dealing with certain uncontested applications or uncontested amendments to applications. 18 C.F.R. § 375.307 (1980).

Office of Private Grievances and Redress

An office of the Department of Energy charged with receipt and consideration of petitions seeking special redress, relief or other extraordinary assistance apart from or in addition to other proceedings made available by regulations. 10 C.F.R. § 205.230 (1980).

See also ECONOMIC REGULATORY ADMINISTRATION (ERA).

Off-lease gas

Gas sold or used off the producing lease.

Off-pattern penalty

Syn. for ALLOWABLE PENALTY (*q.v.*).

Off-peak gas

Gas which is to be delivered and taken when demand is not at its peak.

Offset clause

An express provision in an oil and gas lease requiring the lessee to drill an OFFSET WELL (*q.v.*) under certain circumstances. Usually those circumstances are (1) the completion of and production from a well on adjoining premises, (2) within a specified distance of the lease property lines, (3) where drainage is taking place, and (4) where a reasonably prudent operator would drill under the same or similar circumstances. Absent such a clause, a covenant to protect the premises against drainage is normally implied in oil and gas leases. The implied covenant is usually, but not always, negated by an express clause on the matter. See Millette v. Phillips Petroleum Co., 209 Miss. 687, 48 So. 2d 344 (1950), 72 So. 2d 176, 3 *O.&G.R.* 803, 74 So. 2d 731, 4 *O.&G.R.* 38 (1954); TREATISE §§ 671.3, 826.3.

See also OFFSET WELL COVENANT.

Offset distance

A term used in certain lease forms with reference to the distance from the leasehold boundary of a well on other premises which must be offset by a well on the leased premises. *E.g.*,

> "If before the leased land has been fully drilled, a well producing oil in paying quantities (herein called an 'outside well') is drilled upon adjacent land not owned or controlled by Lessors within three hundred thirty (330) feet (herein called 'offset distance') from a boundary of the leased land, Lessee shall offset such outside well. . . ."

Offset royalty

A royalty payable under the provisions of an occasional lease in lieu of the drilling of an offset well.

When a lessee has separate leases on two adjacent tracts, *A* and *B*, if he drills a well on tract *A* which drains tract *B*, under the OFFSET WELL COVENANT (*q.v.*) he will normally be obligated to drill an offset well on tract *B* to protect it from drainage. The drilling of such additional well may be uneconomic in that existing wells suffice to recover the oil or gas in place. Under these circumstances, the lessee may elect to pay the owners of royalty interests in tract *B* an offset royalty, if the lease of tract *B* contains an offset royalty clause, instead of drilling the offset well otherwise required. The offset royalty may be a flat annual sum or may be measured in some other way, *e.g.*, by the royalty which would have been paid if the offset well had been drilled and placed in production. One type of offset royalty clause appears in Foster v. Atlantic Refining Co., 329 F.2d 485, 20 *O.&G.R.* 422 (5th Cir. 1964).

For a case concluding that an overriding royalty owner was entitled to recover offset royalty for drainage when the drilling of a well on the drained tract was precluded by the lessor who was also the lessor of the tract containing the draining well, see Cook v. El Paso Natural Gas Co., 560 F.2d 978, 58 *O.&G.R.* 206 (10th Cir. 1977).

See also COMPENSATORY ROYALTY; SUBSTITUTE ROYALTY.

Offset royalty clause

An express lease clause permitting the lessee to pay royalty in lieu of drilling an offset well. See OFFSET ROYALTY.

Offset well

(1) A well drilled on one tract of land to prevent the drainage of oil or gas to an adjoining tract of land, on which a well is being drilled or is already in production.

Prior to spacing regulations, wells along a surface property line were sometimes drilled in such profusion that they looked somewhat like fence posts. Under spacing regulations, wells are required to be drilled on tracts of a specified size. Where the spacing unit is forty acres, the well can be drilled in the center. This type of development of an oil field is called direct offsetting, since the wells will be directly north and south or east and west of each other. Where the spacing unit is 20 acres, the well on each unit must be diagonal with the well on the next unit. This pattern of development is called diagonal offsetting.

See also EQUIDISTANT OFFSET RULE.

(2) In Pennsylvania this term is also used to describe a well proposed to be drilled at a distance of less than 1,000 feet from the nearest existing well though an underlying coal seam. Einsig v. Pennsylvania Mines Corp., 69 Pa. C. 351, 452 A.2d 558, 75 *O.&G.R.* 554 (Commonwealth Ct. of Pa. 1982).

Offset well covenant

A contractual duty, either expressed or implied in an oil and gas lease, to use due diligence to protect the leasehold from drainage. Also called the protection covenant and the drainage covenant. Where the duty is an implied one, the lessee must drill an offset well on the lease if substantial drainage is taking place and if an ordinary prudent operator would do so under similar circumstances. The latter phrase usually means that the lessee must drill an offset well if such well would produce oil in paying quantities, that is, would probably pay for itself and show some profit. Gerson v. Anderson-Pritchard Prod. Co., 149 F.2d 444 (10th Cir. 1945); Coyle v. North American Oil Consol., 201 La. 99, 9 So. 2d 473 (1942); Ramsey Petroleum Corp. v. Davis, 184 Okla. 155, 85 P.2d 427 (1938); Texas Pacific Coal & Oil Co. v. Barker, 117 Tex. 418, 6 S.W.2d 1031 (1928). See generally TREATISE §§ 821–823.3.

Perhaps the most difficult substantive problem with the implied offset covenant is raised when the lessee owns the adjoining, draining well but refuses to drill an offset on plaintiff's land because the offset well would not produce oil in paying quantities. Some cases hold the lessee bound to drill anyway, making an exception to the paying quantities requirement because it is the lessee's act which causes the drainage. See, *e.g.*, Bush Oil Co. v. Beverly Lincoln Land Co., 69 Cal. App. 2d 246, 158 P.2d 754 (1945). Some hold the ordinary rule applicable without regard to the lessee's acts. See, *e.g.*, Blair v. Clear Creek Oil & Gas Co., 148 Ark. 301, 230 S.W. 286 (1921). For a veiw that the former rule is correct, see Seed, "The Implied Covenant to Refrain from Depletory Acts," 3 *U.C.L.A. L. Rev.* 508 (1956); for the contrary view, see TREATISE §§ 824–824.3.

Where the offset covenant is expressed in the lease, it governs the obligation of the lessee, unless (in some states) the lessee is causing the drainage. Such covenants usually require the lessee to drill only where an ordinary, prudent operator would drill under similar circumstances, *i.e.*, when it would be profitable to drill. However, the express clause will often provide that "if a well is brought in within [150 or 300 feet] of the leased premises," the lessee shall offset, and this has been interpreted to mean that if the draining well is at a greater distance, no duty subsists, unless drainage is caused by the lessee's own operations on other premises. Millette v. Phillips Petroleum Co., 209 Miss. 687, 48 So. 2d 344 (1950).

See also COMPENSATORY ROYALTY CLAUSE; DEPLETORY COVENANT; DRAINAGE; FRAUDULENT DRAINAGE; IMPLIED COVENANTS; OFFSET DISTANCE; PERMITTED DRAINAGE.

Offshore oil and gas development

For a discussion of certain problems arising from development of offshore mineral resources, see Spicer, "Some Admiralty Law Issues in Offshore Oil & Gas Development," 20 *Alta. L. Rev.* 153 (1982); Vass, "A Comparison of American and British Offshore Oil Development During the Reagan and Thatcher Administrations," 21 *Tulsa L.J.* 23, 225 (1985).

See also OUTER CONTINENTAL SHELF; OUTER CONTINENTAL SHELF LANDS ACT OF 1953.

Offshore Pollution Liability Agreement

An agreement entered into by a number of major oil companies in September 1974 by which operators bind themselves to accept liability for costs arising from pollution from their offshore facilities up to certain limits and in response to claims made in accordance with the agreement, and to contribute to the guarantee fund set up under the agreement. See Daintith and Willoughby, *A Manual of United Kingdom Oil and Gas Law* 64–66, 488–501 (1977); Swan, *Ocean Oil and Gas Drilling & The Law* 181–186 (1979).

Off-system customer

A customer outside a pipeline's traditional market area that purchases gas from the pipeline on a short-term, interruptible basis. Tennessee Gas Pipeline Co. v. Federal Energy Regulatory Comm'n, 809 F.2d 1138 (5th Cir. 1987).

Off-system gas

Gas produced by pipeline companies and sold to other pipeline companies. City of Chicago, Illinois v. Federal Power Comm'n, 458 F.2d 731 at 734 (D.C. Cir. 1971), *cert. denied,* 405 U.S. 1074 (1972).

Off-system sale

A sale of natural gas by an interstate pipeline of natural gas that is excess to the pipeline's current demand, that is of a short-term, interruptible nature, and that is made to a customer outside or away from the pipeline's traditional or historical market area. See Off-System Sales, FERC Statement of Policy (April 25, 1983), 24 FPS 5-257; Hollis, "Notable Recent Developments in Federal Natural Gas Regulation," 34 *Sw. Legal Fdn. Oil & Gas Inst.* 31 at 40 (1983); Allison,

"Natural Gas Pricing: The Eternal Debate," 37 *Baylor L. Rev.* 1 at 68 (1985).

See also GAS PURCHASE CONTRACT.

Off-system storage

Storage of natural gas by customers of interstate gas pipelines as distinguished from on-system storage, *viz.*, storage of gas by the interstate gas pipeline. See Transcontinental Gas Pipe Line Corp., F.P.C. Opinion No. 778, 10 FPS 5–1045 at 5–1059.

Syn.: Behind the meter storage.

Offtake

A term employed in numerous agreements between foreign oil companies and host nations to refer to the removal of oil from the place of production for marketing.

See also CONCESSION.

Offtake price

The price which a parent company pays a joint producing venture for a barrel of crude oil. Krueger, *The United States and International Oil* 33 (1975).

Off-target penalty

The amount by which the allowable of a well is reduced by reason of its location outside its TARGET AREA (*q.v.*). Alberta Oil and Gas Conservation Regulations, Alta. Reg. 151/71, § 4–070.

OGDC

The Oil and Gas Development Corporation of Bangladesh.

OGLTR

The *Oil & Gas Law and Taxation Review,* published by ESC Publishing Ltd., Oxford.

OIAB

The Oil Import Appeals Board. See OIL IMPORT QUOTA.

OII

OIL INVESTMENT INSTITUTE (*q.v.*).

OIL

OIL INSURANCE LIMITED (*q.v.*).

Oil

"[C]rude petroleum oil and other hydrocarbons regardless of gravity which are produced at the wellhead in liquid form and the liquid hydrocarbons known as distillate or condensate recovered or extracted from gas, other than gas produced in association with oil and commonly known as casinghead gas." N. D. Laws 1953, ch. 227, § 3 (4), N. D. Century Code § 38–08–02(8) (2d Repl. Vol. 1980).

Dispute occasionally arises as to the meaning of "barrel of oil" as such term is used in a lease or contract. Thus in Scoville v. De Bretteville, 50 Cal. App. 2d 622, 123 P.2d 616 (1942), an operating agreement provided for termination of the interest of certain parties if the first well be completed "for 200 barrels per day or less." The court declared that the phrase has a technical meaning given to it by those engaged in the oil business and admitted evidence to the effect that the phrase means daily production of 200 barrels of clean marketable oil fit for commercial use over a period of 30 days after the well was put on production, and that the phrase does not mean emulsified oil and water and does not include gas or casinghead gasoline produced from such gas. It concluded:

> "When used in an oil lease or a contract dealing with oil in the sense here appearing, the terms, when referring to oil, should be held to mean crude petroleum as produced from a well less free water therein, and less water and other foreign substances emulsified in it which render it commercially unfit for market as oil in the state in which it was produced. Certainly the term oil does not include gas or gasoline extracted from such gas unless such specific meaning be clearly given it in the contract in question. . . . Plaintiffs cannot add the number of barrels of casinghead gasoline to the number of barrels of oil mixed with water and other impurities in order to reach a production of more than 200 barrels."

See also Hardwick, *The Oilman's Barrel* (1958).

In some instances the term oil is defined so as to include natural gas. Thus for purposes of the Petroleum Revenue Tax established by the Oil Taxation Act 1975, oil was defined as including natural gas. But inasmuch as the British Gas Corporation is a monopoly buyer of gas, the Act provided that gas sold to that Corporation under a contract made before June 30, 1975 should be disregarded for purposes of the Petroleum Revenue Tax. Such gas was described as "excluded oil." When a field produces both excluded and non-excluded oil, costs must be apportioned. See Daintith and Willoughby, *A Manual of United Kingdom Oil and Gas Law* 109–110 (1977).

See also ABANDONED OIL; ABSORPTION OIL; ALBINO OIL; ARABIAN LIGHT OIL; ASPHALT BASE OIL; BACK-UP CRUDE; BARREL OF OIL; BASIC SEDIMENT; BENCHMARK CRUDE; BLACK OIL; BONNY LIGHT OIL; BRIDGING CRUDE; BUNKER "C" FUEL OIL; BUY-BACK OIL; BUY/SELL OIL; CALL ON OIL; CASE OIL; CLEAN OIL; COAL OIL; CONTRABAND OIL; CONTROLLED CRUDE OIL; COST OIL; COST RECOVERY OIL; CRUDE OIL; CRUDE OIL SELF SUFFICIENCY; CUT OF OIL; CUT OIL; DEAD OIL; DENSITY OF PETROLEUM; DILUENT; DIESEL OIL; DIRTY OIL; DISTILLATE FUEL OIL; DRY OIL; EQUITY OIL; EXCESS OIL; EXCLUDED OIL; EXEMPT CRUDE OIL; EXEMPT ALASKAN OIL; EXEMPT FRONT-END OIL; EXEMPT INDIAN OIL; EXEMPT OIL; EXEMPT ROYALTY OIL; EXEMPT STRIPPER WELL OIL; FIRST TIER OIL; FORWARD OIL PURCHASE; FRAC OIL; FRONT-END TERTIARY OIL; GAS OILS; GREEN OIL; HEATING OIL; HEAVY FUEL OIL; HEAVY OIL; HOT OIL; ILLEGAL OIL OR GAS; IMPUTED STRIPPER WELL CRUDE OIL EXEMPTION; IMPUTED STRIPPER WELL LEASE OIL PRICE; INCENTIVE OIL; INCREMENTAL TERTIARY OIL; INDEPENDENT PRODUCER OIL; KEROSINE; LEGAL OIL OR GAS; LIGHT PETROLEUM PRODUCTS (LPP); LIVE OIL; LOAD OIL; LOWER TIER CRUDE OIL; LUBRICATING OIL; MERCHANTABLE OIL; MIDDLE DISTILLATES; MIXED BASE OIL (OR INTERMEDIATE BASE OIL); NATURAL CONDENSATE CRUDE OILS; NEWLY DISCOVERED CRUDE OIL; NEW OIL; NON-EXCLUDED OIL; OCS ROYALTY OIL; OIL PAYMENT; OIL SHALE; OLD OIL; PARAFFIN BASE OIL; PENNSYLVANIA GRADE CRUDE OIL; PETROLEUM; PICK-UP OIL; PIPELINE OIL; PROFIT OIL; PROVEN OIL OR GAS PROPERTY TRANSFER; RECONSTITUTED CRUDE OIL; RECOVERABLE OIL IN PLACE; REFERENCE CRUDE; RELEASED OIL; RESIDUAL FUEL OILS; RESIDUE OIL; ROAD OIL; ROYALTY OIL AUCTION; ROYALTY OIL (OR GAS); SADERLOCHIT OIL; SALE OF OIL AT ARMS' LENGTH; SCRUBBER OIL; SECOND TIER OIL; SEDIMENT OIL; SHALE OIL; SKIM OIL; SOUR OIL; STABILIZED CRUDE OIL; STRIPPER WELL OIL; SWEET OIL; SYNCRUDE; SYNTHETIC CRUDE OIL; TIER 1 OIL; TIER 2 OIL; TIER 3 OIL; TOPPER CRUDE OIL; UNSTABILIZED CRUDE OIL; UPPER TIER CRUDE OIL; WAR RELIEF CRUDE; WASH OIL; WATER-WHITE OIL; WET OIL; WHITE OIL.

Oil age 86–C form

A lease form frequently employed in California. The form contains numerous blanks to be filled in by the parties upon execution and all forms bearing this nomenclature are not identical in terms. Hence a contract to execute an Oil Age 86–C form cannot support an action of specific performance unless a completed form is incorporated into the contract by reference or the contract spells out in detail the provisions of the lease. Whatever the variations in the forms bearing this nomenclature, an Oil Age 86–C Form lease is an OR LEASE (*q.v.*) rather than an UNLESS LEASE (*q.v.*) and is executed for a term of years and so long thereafter as oil or gas is produced. In other words, a certain structural pattern is usually indicated by the phrase "Oil Age 86–C form," but the phrase in no way indicates the details of the leasing arrangement. An example of this form of lease appears in Williams, Maxwell, Meyers, and Williams, *Cases on Oil and Gas* 979 (5th ed. 1987).

Oil and Gas Field Code Master List—1982

A standard code for all oil and/or gas fields throughout the United States prepared by the Energy Information Administration of the Office of Oil and Gas in the Department of Energy.

See also FIELD; GEOLOGICAL FIELD; WELL NAME REGISTER.

Oil and Gas Royalty Management Act of 1982

Pub. Law No. 97-451, 97th Cong., 2d Sess. (1983), establishing recordkeeping and reporting requirements on production from federal and Indian lands. See 30 C.R.F. Parts 210, 212, 217–219, 228–229, 241.

Problems of the federal government's royalty accounting system on federal and Indian lands are discussed in the following:

ABA Natural Resources Law Section Task Force Report on Federal Oil and Gas Royalty Matters, 15 *Nat. Res. Law.* 727 (1983):

"Oil and Gas Royalty Recovery Policy on Federal and Indian Lands," 23 *Nat. Res. J.* 391 (1983).

Oil bonus

A term occasionally used to describe an oil payment reserved by a lessor in addition to the cash bonus and royalty covenanted to be paid by the lessee. Sheppard v. Stanolind Oil & Gas Co., 125 S.W.2d 643 (Tex. Civ. App. 1939, error ref'd).

See also BONUS; OIL PAYMENT.

Oil charter

A CONTRACT OF AFFREIGHTMENT (*q.v.*) for the carriage of oil by sea. For a discussion of the details of oil charters see "The Tonnage Contract," [1982] 1 *OGLTR* 32. Under a Time charter, the shipowner undertakes to put at the disposition of the charterer a vessel within a specified area over a certain period of time. Under a Voyage charter the type of cargo and the port of destination are specified.

See also SHORT DELIVERY (0.5% ALLOWANCE) ISSUE.

Oil-country tubular goods

Well casing and tubing, drill pipe, standard pipe, line pipe, *etc.*

Oil equivalency clause

An ESCALATOR CLAUSE (*q.v.*) of a GAS PURCHASE CONTRACT (*q.v.*) designed to preserve a parity between the price paid for gas and the price paid for oil in terms of Btu content of the two products. See Pierce, "Developments in Natural Gas Regulation: High Cost Gas, Deregulation, and Contract Issues," 33 *Sw. Legal Fdn. Oil & Gas Inst.* 1 at 11 (1982); Pierce, "Natural Gas Regulation, Deregulation, and Contracts," 68 *Va. L. Rev.* 63 (1982).

See also COMMODITY VALUE OF NATURAL GAS.

Oil exchange agreement

See EXCHANGE AGREEMENT.

Oil Extraction Tax Development Fund

A special fund established by a North Dakota initiated measure funded by a special oil extraction tax upon the extraction of oil from the earth in the state. The validity of the initiated measure was sustained in Sunbehm Gas, Inc. v. Conrad, 310 N.W.2d 629, 70 *O.&G.R.* 629 (N.D. 1981).

See also SEVERANCE TAX.

Oil field

Any area which is underlain by one or more reservoirs containing oil. The name of an oil field is usually derived from its geographical location—the town, county, or general area in which it lies, such as, the Oklahoma City field and the East Texas field. See Wotton v. Bush, 251 P.2d 376, 2 *O.&G.R.* 6 (Cal. App. 1952), 41 Cal. 2d 460, 261 P.2d 256, 3 *O.&G.R.* 12 (1953).

See also FIELD; OIL POOL; RESERVOIR.

Oil field equipment

"[O]ilfield supplies, oilfield machinery, materials, heavy machinery, buildings, tubing, tanks, boilers, engines, casing, wire lines, sucker rods, oil pipe lines, gas pipe lines, and all other materials used in digging, drilling, torpedoing, oeprating, completing, maintaining, or repairing any such oil or gas wells or oil pipe lines or gas pipe lines, or in the construction or dismantling of refineries, casing-head gasoline plants, and carbon black plants." Neb. Laws 1951, ch. 185, § 1 (2), Neb. Rev. Stat., 1943 § 57–301 (1978 Reissue).

Oil futures market

See FUTURES MARKET.

Oil Import Compensation Regulations

Canadian regulations providing for compensation to be made in respect to petroleum imported into Canada. See Irving Oil Ltd. v. The Queen, 96 D.L.R.3d 534 (Federal Court, Trial Division, 1979).

Oil import quota

A system, initially voluntary and then mandatory, for restricting imports of oil into the United States. It was replaced, effective May 1, 1973, with a LICENSE FEE SYSTEM (*q.v.*).

For discussion of the history of the quota scheme, see the following:

Chester, *United States Oil Policy and Diplomacy* 30 (1983);

Fox, *Federal Regulation of Energy* ch. 8 (1983);

Barber, "The Eisenhower Energy Policy: Reluctant Intervention," in Goodwin (Ed.), *Energy Policy in Perspective* 205 at 229 (1981);

World Oil Development and U.S. Oil Import Policies, Committee Print, Committee on Finance, U.S. Senate, 93rd Cong., 1st Sess. (Dec. 12, 1973);

Dam, "Implementation of Import Quotas: The Case of Oil," 14 *J. Law & Econ.* 1 (1971);

Cicchetti and Gillen, "The Mandatory Oil Import Quota Program: A Consideration of Economic Efficiency and Equity," 13 *Nat. Res. J.* 399 (1973);

Note, "Debilitating Symbiosis: Taxation and Supply Regulation in the United States Oil Industry," 3 *Law and Policy in International Business* 388 (1971);

Frank and Well, "United States Oil Imports: Implications for the Balance of Payments," 13 *Nat. Res. J.* 431 (1973).

Oil import regulations are contained in 10 C.F.R. § 213 (1980).

See also BROWNSVILLE LOOP.

Oil Investment Institute (OII)

An organization of companies offering participations in oil and gas drilling programs.

Oil Insurance Limited (OIL)

A company organized in 1970 to provide oil pollution coverage. See Swan, *Ocean Oil and Gas Drilling and the Law* 186 (1979); Outer Continental Shelf Lands Act Amendments and Coastal Zone Management Act Amendments, Joint Hearings before the Committees on Interior and Insular Affairs and Commerce, U.S. Senate, 94th Cong., 1st Sess., Serial No. 94–14 (93–100) at p. 1161.

Oil leg

In the RELATIVE COST METHOD OF ALLOCATION (*q.v.*)., the oil leg is the unit cost of oil from leases producing oil only. See Permian Basin Area Rate Proceeding, 34 F.P.C. 159 at 215, 23 *O.&G.R.* 103 at 166 (Opinion No. 468, Aug. 5, 1965), *remanded,* Skelly Oil Co. v. Federal Power Comm'n, 375 F.2d 6, 26 *O.&G.R.* 237 (10th Cir. 1967), *aff'd in part and rev'd in part sub nom., In re* Permian Basin Area Rate Cases, 390 U.S. 747, 28 *O.&G.R.* 689 (1968).

Oil man's deal

This term has been used by one writer to describe a method of obtaining financing of drilling and lease acquisition costs.

"An 'oil man's deal' in its most basic form involves 'promoted interests.' A typical example is an independent oil operator having a lease which appears to be a good drilling prospect and finding at least three investors willing to pay one-third of the costs (including leasehold reimbursement costs) in order to obtain a 25 percent interest in the property. Thus, from an oil operator's standpoint, he obtains his lease acquisition costs back, gets one well drilled, essentially free to him, and participates in 25 percent of the income. Further activities involving developmental wells are usually drilled 'heads up,' i.e., each party, including the oil operator, bears his pro rata share of the costs." Bean, "Entity Selection—An Experience in Alchemy—A Comparison of Corporations, Partnerships, and Joint Ventures," 30 *Sw. Legal Fdn. Oil & Gas Inst.* 363 at 366 (1979).

See also PROJECT FINANCING.

Oil market

See FEDERAL CRUDE OIL MARKET; FUTURES MARKET; INTERNATIONAL PETROLEUM EXCHANGE.

Oil patch

The term applied to an area in which there is substantial oil and gas exploration and development operations. See, *e.g.*, Chieftain Development Co. Ltd. and Lachowich, 129 D.L.R.3d 285 at 291 (Alta. Q.B. 1981).

Oil payment

A share of the oil produced from a described tract of land, free of the costs of production at the surface, terminating when a specified sum from the sale of such oil has been realized. Oil payments may be reserved by a lessor, by an assignor of a lease, or carved out by the owner of a working interest or royalty interest. It is possible, though rare, for a fee simple landowner to assign an oil payment before or after leasing. The duty to deliver oil under an oil payment subsists if, as, and when the oil is produced; there is no personal liability to pay the sum specified in the instrument creating the oil payment. An oil payment is an interest in land. Tennant v. Dunn, 130 Tex. 285, 110 S.W.2d 53 (1937); State v. Quintana Petroleum Corp., 134 Tex. 179, 133 S.W.2d 112, 134 S.W.2d 1016 (1939).

The form of the oil payment appearing in the latter case was as follows: The lessor reserved "one-fourth (1⁄4) of the remainder of any oil, gas or minerals produced from said land . . . until the proceeds of the sale (such sale to be made at not less than the market price) by grantor of said one-fourth of the remainder shall aggregate Two Million Dollars ($2,000,000) whereupon this reservation of title to said 1⁄4 interest shall terminate and this interest shall vest in grantee and its assigns." Many other and different forms of creating oil payments are in use.

The uses of oil payments include the following:

(1) By a lessor, in lieu of a large bonus or an overriding royalty.

(2) By an assignor of a lease, in lieu of or in addition to an overriding royalty and cash.

(3) By the owner of a working interest for financing operations, by assignment of the oil payment to a supply company, a drilling contractor, or as collateral for a loan.

(4) As a federal income tax saving device. In this connection, there was at one time a difference between a reserved or retained oil pay-

ment—which was used in the A-B-C TRANSACTION (*q.v.*)—and a CARVED-OUT OIL PAYMENT (*q.v.*).

For discussions of oil payments, see TREATISE §§ 422–423.13; Walker, "Oil Payments," 20 *Tex. L. Rev.* 259 (1942).

See also ADVANCE PAYMENT FINANCING; CARVED-OUT OIL PAYMENT; DEFERRED-PAYMENT OPEN-END SALE; DEFERRED PRODUCTION PAYMENT; EQUIPMENT PRODUCTION PAYMENT; EQUITY PRODUCTION PAYMENT; FRONT END OF OIL PAYMENT; HORIZONTAL CUT OIL PAYMENT; LONG OIL PAYMENT; OIL BONUS; PRIMARY PRODUCTION PAYMENT; PROJECT FINANCING; RESERVED OIL PAYMENT; SHORT-LIVED IN-OIL PAYMENT; SHORT OIL PAYMENT; TWO-TO-ONE AGREEMENT; VERTICAL CUT OIL PAYMENT.

Oil pool

An underground reservoir or trap containing oil.

A distinction has been recognized between an oil field and an oil pool. The latter is an oil-saturated, single and separate reservoir, with a single pressure system, so that production anywhere in the pool affects the reservoir pressure throughout the pool. An oil field, on the other hand, may contain two or more oil pools as defined above. Wherever two or more reservoirs are found in close proximity, they may be classified as part of the same field. However, in common usage, a single separate oil pool may be referred to as an oil field.

See also FIELD; OIL FIELD; POOL; RESERVOIR.

Oil purchase and sale contract

See ADAPTATION CLAUSE; ARABIAN LIGHT OIL; BASE POINT PRICING; BENCHMARK CRUDE; BONNY LIGHT OIL; CIF PRICING; CONTRACT OF AFFREIGHTMENT; DIFFERENTIAL; FAS PRICING; FOB PRICING; GRAVITY DIFFERENTIAL; KICKOUT CLAUSE; MARKER PRICE; MID-WAY PRICE; QUARTER-WAY PRICE; SHORT DELIVERY (0.5% ALLOWANCE) ISSUE; SPOT MARKET; SULFUR DIFFERENTIAL; TRANSPORT COST DIFFERENTIAL.

Oil recovery efficiency

A term encompassing both rate of production and ultimate amount of oil recovery. See Nelson and McNiel, "Oil Recovery by Thermal Methods," 17 *Interstate Oil Compact Bull.* 56 (Dec. 1958).

Oil royalty

The ROYALTY (*q.v.*) paid by an operator to royalty owners on oil produced and saved.

For many years the typical oil royalty in the mid-continent area was 1/8th of the oil produced and saved, although the royalty could be some other fraction of production, *e.g.*, 1/6th or 1/4th. In some parts of the industry, anything larger than a 1/8th royalty may be called an OVERRIDING ROYALTY (*q.v.*) in practice, even though it goes to the landowner. Thus a 1/6th royalty may be called "an 1/8th royalty and a 1/24th override." In many leases, particularly in California, the royalty is expressed in terms of a percentage rather than a fraction of production.

A typical oil royalty clause provides as follows:

> "The royalties to be paid by Lessee are: (a) on oil, one-eighth of that produced and saved from said land, the same to be delivered at the wells or to the credit of Lessor into the pipe line to which the wells may be connected; Lessee may from time to time purchase any royalty oil in its possession, paying the market price therefor prevailing for the field where produced on the date of purchase."

The royalty clause quoted above provides that the royalty for oil shall be paid "in kind" whereas the royalty for gas is usually payable in money, that is, "the market value at the well of one-eighth of the gas sold or used off the premises or in the manufacture of gasoline or other product therefrom." Typically both oil and gas royalties are paid in the same manner, however; that is, after production is obtained, the lessor and lessee sign a DIVISION ORDER (*q.v.*), which is a contract of sale to the purchaser of the gas or oil, and payment is thereafter made directly by the purchaser to the lessor and the lessee respectively. Despite this practice the typical lease form provides for different treatment of the oil and gas royalties, as a result of which the lessor's interest in the oil royalty may be treated as realty and his interest in gas royalty treated as personalty. For some of the legal consequences of this different conceptual classification of the oil and gas royalty provisions, see TREATISE §§ 641–643.6. The oil royalty is free of the costs of production but (absent some express contrary provision in the instrument creating the royalty) is subject to production or gathering taxes and, usually, to other expenses incurred after the oil is brought to the surface, *e.g.*, expenses of transportation or treatment. Molter v. Lewis, 156 Kan. 544, 134 P.2d 404 (1943).

Oil royalty trust

See ROYALTY TRUST.

Oil run

The production of oil during a designated period of time.

Oil sands

Sands and other rock materials which contain crude bitumen and includes all other mineral substances in association therewith. The Alberta Oil Sands Technology and Research Authority Act (S. A. 1974, c. 49) § 1 (f).

Oil sands deposit

A natural reservoir containing or appearing to contain an accumulation of oil sands separated or appearing to be separated from any other such accumulation. In Alberta, the Energy Resources Conservation Board is authorized to designate an oil sand deposit by order describing the surface area vertically above the oil sands deposit and by naming the geological formation, member or zone in which the deposit occurs or by such other method of identification as the Board considers suitable. Alberta Oil and Gas Conservation Act, R.S.A. 1970, c. 267, § 33.

Oil scrubbing

"The removal of certain impurities from manufactured or natural gas by passing the gas through an oil spray or bubbling the gas through an oil bath." American Gas Ass'n, *Glossary for the Gas Industry* (3d ed. 1981).

Oil Service Company of Iran (OSCO)

An organization owned by members of the IRANIAN CONSORTIUM (*q.v.*). Under a 1973 agreement, the Consortium members became privileged buyers of Iranian crude, and the companies organized OSCO, which replaced the Consortium's previous operator, the Iranian Oil Exploration and Producing Company. See United States—OPEC Relations, Selected Materials prepared by the Congressional Research Service, Committee on Interior and Insular Affairs, United States Senate, 94th Cong., 2d Sess. (1976) at p. 113.

See also CONCESSION.

Oil shale

A formation containing hydrocarbons which cannot be recovered by an ordinary oil well but which, if outcropping or at a relatively shallow depth, may be mined by solid mineral mining methods and the hydrocarbons extracted from the mined ore by a treatment process. Considerable deposits of oil shale have been discovered but the cost of mining and treatment has generally been too great for the oil recovered from such shale to compete on price with oil from oil wells. See I.R.B. 1957–45, 17, 8 *O.&G.R.* 515 (1958).

"Oil shale is a fine-grained, laminated, sedimentary rock containing organic material (sometimes called 'kerogen') from which appreciable amounts of oil can be obtained by the application of heat. Oil shale does not contain any appreciable amounts of oil as such. When the rock is crushed and heated to certain temperatures the solid organic material derived from pre-existent aquatic plant and animal life undergoes a chemical transformation that produces a substance known as shale oil. Raw shale oil bears little resemblance to natural crude oil. It is a black, highly-viscous substance that contains appreciable quantities of nitrogen and sulfur. Once it cools below 90 degree Fahrenheit it is as difficult to pour 'as a barrel of frozen jello.' In order to upgrade shale oil to the crude oil level most of the nitrogen and sulfur must be removed and the wax-forming components, that are responsible for shale oil's annoying characteristic of hardening once it cools, must be eliminated or rearranged." United States Department of the Interior, Bureau of Land Management, Post Hearing Brief and Appendix for the Contestant, United States v. Frank W. Winegar, May 20, 1968, page 2. This Brief, copies of which are on file in various law libraries in the Rocky Mountain region and the west, includes a large collection of materials on oil shale and its development.

"It is estimated that America's western oil shale deposits contain at least 1,800,000,000,000 barrels of oil . . . Department of the Interior estimates of the extent of western deposits based on shales yielding 25 gallons of 'crude oil' per ton in layers of 10 feet or more thick are in the area of 600,000,000,000 barrels; if 15-gallon-per-ton shales are included, 11,200,000,000 more barrels are added." Annotation 61 A.L.R.3d 1109 at 1112 (1975).

Shell Oil Co. v. Andrus, 591 F.2d 597, 64 *O.&G.R.* 260 (10th Cir. 1979), *aff'd,* 446 U.S. 657, 67 *O.&G.R.* 185 (1980), validated six pre-1920 shale placer mining claims which had been held invalid by the Department of Interior on the ground that they did not constitute discoveries of a valuable mineral deposit.

Utah Resources International, Inc. v. Utah Board of State Lands, 26 Utah 2d 342, 489 P.2d 615, 41 *O.&G.R.* 416, 61 A.L.R.3d 1101 (1971) held that lessees under "oil, gas and hydrocarbon" lease specifically excluding "oil shale" were not entitled to enjoin lessor from issuing an oil shale lease on the same premises.

See also Tosco Corp. v. Hodel, 611 F.Supp. 1130 (D. Colo. 1985) (validating placer mining claims in western Colorado). This case was settled by an Aug. 4, 1986 agreement. See 2 *Nat. Res. & Environment* 74 (Fall 1986), 804 F.2d 590 (10th Cir. 1986).

See also the following:

Dobray, "Oil Shale, Tar Sands, and the Definition of a Mineral: An Old Problem in a New Context," 22 *Tulsa L.J.* 1 (1986);

Duncan, "Oil Shale Mining Claims: Alternatives for Resolution of an Ancient Problem," 17 *Land & Water L. Rev.* 1 (1982);

Robinson and Walta, "Water for Oil Shale: Framework for the Legal Issues," 58 *Denver L.J.* 703 (1981);

Dempsey, "Oil Shale and Water Quality," *Id.* at 715;

Laitos, "The Effect of Water Law on the Development of Oil Shale," *Id.* at 751;

Moffett, "Federal Oil Shale Policy: An Analysis of Development Alternatives," 13 *Houston L. Rev.* 701 (1976);

Legal Study of Oil Shale on Public Lands Prepared for the Public Land Law Review Commission by University of Denver College of Law (1970), in U.S. Public Land Law Review Commission, *Energy Fuel Mineral Resources of the Public Lands* (1970);

Oil Shale Leasing, Hearing before the Subcommittee on Minerals, Materials and Fuels of the Senate Committee on Interior and Insular Affairs, 94th Cong., 2d Sess. on S. 2413 (March 17, 1976);

Baker and Mulford, "Problems and Policies of Oil Shale Development," 19 *Stan. L. Rev.* 190 (1966);

Oil Shale Symposium, 43 Denver L.J. 1–89 (1966);

Walker, "A Look at Oil Shale—As Viewed by a Practicing Attorney," 18 *Sw. Legal Fdn. Oil & Gas Inst.* 289 (1967);

Dominick, "Oil Shale—The Need for a National Policy," 2 *Land & Water L. Rev.* 61 (1967).

Oil string

See CAPITAL STRING.

Oil-water contract line

The line of demarcation between the water zone and the oil zone in a petroleum reservoir.

See also GAS-OIL CONTACT LINE.

Oil-water ratio

The relation between the volume of oil and the volume of water produced from a well.

See also GAS-OIL RATIO.

Oil well

A well capable of producing crude petroleum oil. Some statutes define oil wells and gas wells in terms of the gas-oil ratio. See, *e.g.*, Tex. Nat. Res. Code § 86.002 (6) (1978): " 'Oil well' means any well that produces one barrel or more of oil to each 100,000 cubic feet of gas."

Colorado Interstate Gas Co. v. HUFO Oils, 626 F.Supp. 38, ___ *O.&G.R.* ___ (W.D. Tex. 1985), *aff'd*, 802 F.2d 133, ___ *O.&G.R.* ___ (5th Cir. 1986) *reh. en banc denied*, 806 F.2d 261 (5th Cir. 1986), and HUFO Oils v. Railroad Commission, 717 S.W.2d 405, ___ *O.&G.R.* ___ (Tex. App., Austin, 1986), held that WHITE OIL (*q.v.*) extracted from natural gas by LOW TEMPERATURE EXTRACTION (*q.v.*) could not be counted as "oil" for purposes of classification of a well as an oil well or a gas well.

For discussion of problems arising from classification of a well as a gas well or as an oil well when gas and oil are separately owned, see TREATISE § 219.7; Midkiff, "Phase Severance of Gas Rights from Oil Rights," 63 Tex. L. Rev. 133 (1984); "Big, Small Energy Firms Fight Over Texas Gas," *The Wall Street Journal*, Sept. 21, 1984, p. 33.

In Kilpatrick Oil & Gas Co., 81 I.D. 162, 15 IBLA 216, GFS(O&G) 1974–37, although a 640-acre spacing pattern had been established by the Oklahoma Corporation Commission on the ground that natural gas would be the hydrocarbon encountered as a result of drilling a well, it was concluded that the well in question was an oil well. The opinion noted that "There is no federal definition of what constitutes an oil well as opposed to a gas well. This lack of a ready-made formula does not, however, bar intelligent classification." The well in question had a gas-oil ratio between 6,000:1 and 7,000:1, and the oil had a corrected gravity of 36.9 degree to 37.1 degree API.

Bolton v. Coats, 514 S.W.2d 482, 50 *O.&G.R.* 79 (Tex. Civ. App. 1974), *rev'd and remanded on other grounds*, 533 S.W.2d 914, 53 *O.&G.R.* 379 (Tex. 1975), held that a Railroad Commission finding that a well is a gas well rather than an oil well is not subject to collateral attack.

A dry hole is generally not viewed as a "gas well" or as an "oil well" as those terms are customarily used in contracts unless required by express wording of the contract or necessary implication. See Nafco Oil & Gas, Inc. v. Tartan Resources Corp., 522 S.W.2d 703, 52 *O.&G.R.* 273 (Tex. Civ. App. 1975, error ref'd n.r.e.).

For a discussion of certain of the factors significant in distinguishing an "oil well" from a "gas well", see Clymore Production Co. v. Thompson, 13 F. Supp. 469 (W.D. Tex. 1936).

Oil well heating

A THERMAL METHOD OF OIL RECOVERY (*q.v.*). See Nelson and McNiel, "Oil Recovery by Thermal Methods," 17 *Interstate Oil Compact Bull.* 56 at 57 (Dec. 1958).

See also SECONDARY RECOVERY; TERTIARY RECOVERY.

Oil well servicing

See WELL SERVICING.

Oil zone

The layer or area of a TRAP (*q.v.*) occupied by oil.

See also GAS CAP; SECONDARY GAS CAP; WATER ZONE.

OIPA

Oklahoma Independent Petroleum Association.

Old gas

Gas already made available by an existing contract of purchase and sale.

In the Permian Basin Area Rate Proceeding, old gas was defined as gas moving under contracts entered into before January 1, 1961. 34 F.P.C. 159 at 189, 23 *O.&G.R.* 103 at 130 (Opinion No. 468, Aug. 5, 1965), *remanded,* Skelly Oil Co. v. Federal Power Comm'n, 375 F.2d 6, 26 *O.&G.R.* 237 (10th Cir. 1967), *aff'd in part and rev'd in part sub nom. In re* Permian Basin Area Rate Cases, 390 U. S. 747, 28 *O.&G.R.* 689 (1968).

See also NEW GAS; ONE-PRICE SYSTEM; REPLACEMENT CONTRACT POLICY; TWO-PRICE SYSTEM; VINTAGE.

Old lease

A lease other than a NEW LEASE (*q.v.*).

Old natural gas

Natural gas other than NEW NATURAL GAS (*q.v.*).

Old oil

For purposes of price regulation under the EMERGENCY PETROLEUM ALLOCATION ACT OF 1973 (*q.v.*), old oil is production from a property up to the 1972 level of production. *The New York Times,* Feb. 20, 1975, p. 56, col. 1.

See also ENTITLEMENT PROGRAM; NEW OIL; RELEASED OIL.

Old oil entitlement program

See ENTITLEMENT PROGRAM. The history of this entitlement program is summarized in Exxon Corp. v. Department of Energy, 601 F.Supp. 1395 (D. Dela. 1985), *aff'd in part and rev'd in part,* 802 F.2d 1400 (Temp. Emer. Ct. of App. 1986).

Old well

Any well other than a NEW WELL (*q.v.*).

Once a stripper, always a stripper

A "rule" of the Federal Energy Administration that a well, once entitled to STRIPPER WELL (*q.v.*)status for price control purposes, shall continue to be entitled to such status despite an increase in production. The rule was designed to remove any producer disincentive to increase production from his marginal wells. See Southland Royalty Co. v. Federal Energy Adm'n, 512 F.Supp. 436 at 440 (N.D. Tex. 1980).

One-eighth rule

A rule of the Bureau of Land Management for eliminating anomalously low bids in a competitive lease sale for purposes of calculating the AVERAGE EVALUATION OF TRACT (AEOT) (*q.v.*) on the ground that such bids unduly affect the average. Kerr-McGee Corp. v. Watt, 517 F. Supp. 1209 at 1213, 71 *O.&G.R.* 494 at 502 (D.D.C. 1981).

One hundred and eighty day emergency sales

Temporary short term sales by certain persons, distributing companies and intrastate pipelines who are exempt from the provisions of the Natural Gas Act to meet emergency needs of natural gas distribution companies and pipeline companies. Under Federal Power Commission Orders No. 402 (43 F.P.C. 707) and 402–A (43 F.P.C. 822), the Commission announced a policy permitting such sales without jeopardizing the exempt status of the seller. These sales were at unregulated prices for no more than sixty days. [See SIXTY-DAY EMERGENCY SALES.] This policy was reaffirmed and expanded by Order No. 418 (44 F.P.C. 1574) in December 1970. In 1973 the Commission expanded the scope of these emergency programs by extending the 60 day period to 180 days by Order 491 (50 F.P.C. 742). While appeal of the order was pending in the courts, the 180-day extension was terminated by Order 491–D (51 F.P.C. 1139). Subsequently, in Consumers Federation of America v. Federal Power Comm'n, 515 F.2d 347, 51 *O.&G.R.* 119 (D. C. Cir. 1975), *cert. denied,* 423 U.S. 906 (1975), the court declared that the Commission had "unduly stretched" its authority under the Natural Gas Act in authorizing 180–day emergency sales.

One hundred percent oil division order

A DIVISION ORDER (*q.v.*) stating that the operator of the well involved owns 100 percent of the crude oil produced from the well. Under this form of order, the purchaser pays the operator, acting as receiving agent for all the interest owners, and the operator then distributes the proceeds among the various royalty and working interest owners. Holliman, "Division Orders—A Primer," 34 *Sw. Legal Fdn. Oil & Gas Inst.* 313 at 349 (1983).

102 gas

Under a colloquial method of referring to classifications of gas under the NATURAL GAS POLICY ACT OF 1978 (NGPA) (*q.v.*), the term 102 gas refers to "new gas" and gas from newly discovered reservoirs on old OCS leases. The number is the NGPA section prescribing ceiling prices for these categories of gas. See Pierce, "An Overview of Regulation," in Pierce, *Natural Gas Regulation Handbook* 30 at 49 (1980).

102 statement

The ENVIRONMENTAL IMPACT STATEMENT (*q.v.*) required by section 102(2)(c) of the National Environmental Policy Act of 1969, Pub. L. No. 91–190, 83 Stat. 852, 42 U.S.C. § 4321 *et seq.*

103 gas

Gas from new onshore production wells. See 102 GAS.

104 gas

Gas previously dedicated to interstate commerce. See 102 GAS.

105 gas

Gas sold under existing intrastate contracts. See 102 GAS.

106 gas

Gas sold under rollover contracts. See 102 GAS.

107 gas

High cost gas. See 102 GAS.

108 gas

Stripper well gas. See 102 GAS.

109 gas

A catch-all category applying to several types of supplies not covered by other sections of the NGPA. See 102 GAS.

One-price system

A proposed system for regulation of gas sales contracts by the Federal Power Commission involving a single price for "old" and "new" gas. See Permian Basin Area Rate Proceeding, 34 F.P.C. 159 at 186, 23 *O.&G.R.* 103 at 126 (Opinion No. 468, Aug. 5, 1965), *remanded,* Skelly Oil Co. v. Federal Power Comm'n, 375 F.2d 6, 26 *O.&G.R.* 237 (10th Cir. 1967), *aff'd in part and rev'd in part sub nom. In re* Permian Basin Area Rate Cases, 390 U.S. 747, 28 *O.&G.R.* 689 (1968).

See also NEW GAS; OLD GAS; REPLACEMENT CONTRACT POLICY; TWO-PRICE SYSTEM; VINTAGE.

One-third for one-fourth deal

See THIRD FOR A QUARTER DEAL.

1/3–2/3 allowable formula

A formula for allocating allowable production of oil, whereby one-third of production is allocated on a per well basis and two-thirds on an acreage or acre-feet of sand basis. Where the application of this formula results in net, uncompensated drainage of larger tracts, the formula is void under the decision in Halbouty v. Railroad Comm'n, 163 Tex. 417, 357 S.W.2d 364, 16 *O.&G.R.* 788, *cert. denied,* 371 U.S. 888 (1962).

ONGC

The Oil and Natural Gas Commission of India.

On-lease gas

Gas produced and consumed on the same lease.

On-system gas

Gas which is produced by a pipeline company or its affiliate and transported by the pipeline company through its own pipelines to the purchaser. City of Chicago, Illinois v. Federal Power Comm'n, 458 F.2d 731 at 733 (D.C. Cir. 1971), *cert. denied,* 405 U.S. 1074 (1972).

On-system storage

See OFF-SYSTEM STORAGE.

On the pump

A phrase used in reference to a well that no longer flows from natural reservoir energy but is produced by means of a pump.

OPAB

Oljeprospektering—AB of Sweden.

OPEC

ORGANIZATION OF PETROLEUM EXPORTING COUNTRIES (*q.v.*).

Open bonus bid

Under leasing procedures applicable to the Outer Continental Shelf Lands, the Secretary of Interior may call for oil and gas lease bids on one of two bases: (1) a fixed royalty with an open bonus, or (2) a specified and fixed bonus, with an open royalty of not less than 12½%. When the bid is on an open bonus basis, the bidder who submits the highest bonus offer gets the lease. If the bid is on an open royalty basis, the bidder who submits the highest royalty offer will obtain the lease. See Stone, "Continental Shelf Natural Gas," 4 *Natural Resources Lawyer* 809 at 813 (1971).

See also LEASE BIDDING SYSTEMS.

Open-end gas royalty clause

A gas royalty clause under which the value of royalty per Mcf is to be determined at the wellhead. Lafitte Co. v. United Fuel Gas Co., 177 F. Supp. 52 at 59, 11 *O.&G.R.* 977 at 983 (E.D. Ky. 1959), *aff'd,* 284 F.2d 845, 13 *O.&G.R.* 744 (6th Cir. 1960).

See also ROYALTY.

Open-end lease

A lease providing for determination of the market value of gas for royalty purposes at the wellhead. Lafitte Co. v. United Fuel Gas Co., 177 F. Supp. 52 at 60, 11 *O.&G.R.* 977 at 984 (E.D. Ky. 1959), *aff'd,* 284 F.2d 845, 13 *O.&G.R.* 744 (6th Cir. 1960).

Open flow

The production of oil or gas by virtue of reservoir energy without artificial restriction on the rate of flow.

Open flow capacity

The maximum output of an oil or gas well as a result of natural reservoir energy in the absence of artificial restriction on the rate of flow.

Open flow pressure

The native RESERVOIR PRESSURE (*q.v.*) when oil or gas is produced in open flow.

Open flow test

A test to determine the open flow capacity and pressure. During the test artificial restrictions on the rate of flow are eliminated.

Open hole

Portion of well bore without casing.

Open lease area

A category of federal lands that possess average resource values which would not be in serious conflict with oil and gas exploration and development. These lands are leased by the Bureau of Land Mangagement subject to standard stipulations which provide for the protection of the resource values and environmental components commonly associated with the national resources lands and require the lessee to take certain measures to mitigate possible impacts that might be created by oil and gas exploration and development. These stipulations do not impose major restrictions as to the lessee activities but provide for operations under controlled conditions. Lundberg and Garver, "Federal Land Use Planning and Management—Its Effect on Oil and Gas Operations," Appendix III, in *Rocky Mt. Min. L. Fdn. Inst. on the Overthrust Belt—Oil and Gas Legal and Land Issues* (1980).

See also FEDERAL LEASE.

Open lease area subject to no surface occupancy

A category of federal lands that have special values where oil and gas operations would not be compatible or could not be allowed to conflict with the present surface resources or land uses. These areas could include camping and picnic areas, research areas, scenic areas, R&PP patents and leases, critical wildlife habitat, significant historical and archaeological areas, buffer zones along the boundaries of primitive and wild and scenic river corridors, etc. Exploratory drilling is permitted under Bureau of Land Management leases but is limited to whipstocking or slant drilling from off-site locations. The leases areas in this category are therefore limited to that feasible for drilling in this fashion. A maximum of one mile is considered feasible. Lundberg and Garver, "Federal Land Use Planning and Management—Its Effect on Oil and Gas Operations," Appendix III, in *Rocky Mt. Min. L. Fdn. Inst. on the Overthrust Belt—Oil and Gas Legal and Land Issues* (1980).

See also FEDERAL LEASE.

Open lease area subject to special stipulations

A category of federal lands that contain significant resource values where serious conflict from oil and gas exploration and development might occur; therefore, leasing by the Bureau of Land Management in this category is subject to additional special stipulations that could provide special protection to the watersheds, specific crucial wildlife habitat areas, unique archaelogical and historical sites, etc. The special stipulations may limit exploration to various times of the year, prescribe special construction techniques, limit the location of developments, or require other special resources protection. Lundberg and Garver, "Federal Land Use Planning and Management—Its Effect on Oil and Gas Operations," Appendix III, in *Rocky Mt. Min. L. Fdn. Inst. on the Overthrust Belt—Oil and Gas Legal and Land Issues* (1980).

See also FEDERAL LEASE.

Open mine doctrine

A doctrine which developed at common law and which permits a life tenant to continue to sever and appropriate minerals from a mine which was opened before the creation of the life estate. With this exception, a life tenant normally may not sever minerals without the concurrence of the owner of future interests in the land. The doctrine has been applied to life estates in oil and gas properties. The basis of the open mine doctrine appears to be that a life tenant given the beneficial enjoyment of land is entitled to enjoy the land in the same manner as it was enjoyed before the creation of the life estate.

The doctrine has been applied both to conventional and legal life estates. In the case of legal life estates, it appears to be applied as a matter of law. In the case of conventional life estates, the creator of the estate may, by an appropriate manifestation of intent, increase or decrease the rights of the life tenant, but in the absence of such manifestation of intent, the doctrine is generally applied.

Dispute sometimes arises concerning the application of the doctrine when there has been no drilling on the land prior to the creation of a life estate but the land has been leased for development. By the weight of authority, the mere execution of a lease, without any drilling operations on the land, will suffice to constitute the opening of a mine. See Woodward, "The Open Mine Doctrine in Oil and Gas Cases," 35 *Tex. L. Rev.* 538 (1957); TREATISE § 513.

Open parcel lease

A NON-COMPETITIVE LEASE (*q.v.*) of a parcel which has never been leased before or which was previously made available as a lottery lease but was not sought by any qualified applicant. An open parcel lease is available on a first-come, first-served basis to any qualified applicant who files an offer to lease accompanied by the required filing fee and first year rental with the Bureau of Land Management office. Nicolazzi v. Comm'r of Internal Revenue, 79 T.C. 109, 73 *O.&G.R.* 619 (1982).

Open royalty bid

See OPEN BONUS BID.

Open storage

Storage of oil after production, in open surface pits or earthen tanks.

Operating agreement

An agreement between or among interested parties for the testing and development of a tract of land. Typically one of the parties is designated as the operator and the agreement contains detailed provisions concerning the drilling of a test well, the drilling of any additional wells which may be required, the sharing of expenses, and accounting methods. The authority of the operator, and restrictions thereon, are spelled out in detail in the typical agreement. See TREATISE §§ 503–503.2, 920–921.19.

See Smith, "Duties and Obligations Owed by an Operator to Nonoperators, Investors, and Other Interest Owners," 32 *Rocky Mt. Min. L. Inst.* 12-1 (1986).

See also AAPL FORM 610-1977; AAPL FORM 610-1982; AREA OF INTEREST; AREA OF MUTUAL INTEREST AGREEMENT; INDIVIDUAL LOSS PROVISION; JOINT LOSS PROVISION; JOINT OPERATING AGREEMENT; MAINTENANCE OF UNIFORM INTEREST CLAUSE; WITHERING CLAUSE.

Operating committee

A committee composed of representatives of lessees who have joined in a UNITIZATION AGREEMENT (*q.v.*) which has the general overall management and control of the unit and the conduct of its business affairs and the operations carried on by it.

Operating expenses

Expenses incurred in the operation of a producing property.

An operating, pooling or unitization agreement usually specifies in detail the operating expenses which are to be apportioned among the several parties in interest and the accounting methods to be followed. The agreement will normally provide specifically the extent to which overhead, field and district expenses are to be included as operating expenses.

When a concurrently owned tract is developed by one concurrent owner or his lessee without the joinder of other concurrent owners, in most states the operator must account to the non-joining concurrent owner or owners for a proportionate share of the proceeds of development less a proportionate share of the expenses of drilling the well or wells and operating expenses. Dispute frequently arises in this situation over the items to be included in operating expenses. See TREATISE §§ 503.2, 920–921.19.

Under an oil and gas lease, operating expenses are the burden of the owner of the working interest in the property and a royalty interest is free of the burden of such expenses.

Operating interest

The mineral interest minus the royalty interest. An interest in oil and gas that is burdened with the cost of development and operationg of the property. The operating interest is normally created by an oil and gas lease.

For purposes of the regulations governing fractional interest leases of federal lands, which require a statement showing the extent of the offeror's ownership of operating rights to the fractional mineral interests not owned by the United States, it has been held that a statement of the effect that the offeror does not own an oil and gas lease on any part of the tract was sufficient to negate any "operating rights." Arthur E. Meinhart, 80 I.D. 395, 11 IBLA 139, GFS(O&G) 1973–60 (1973). The opinion, citing and quoting the definition in this MANUAL, declared that "In the field of oil and gas law, the terms 'operating right,' 'operating interest,' and 'working interest' are synonymous."

Syn.: WORKING INTEREST.

Operating mineral interest, for tax purposes

In federal income tax law, the term is defined by Internal Revenue Code § 614(d) as:

". . . an interest in respect of which the costs of production of the mineral are required to be taken into account by the taxpayer for purposes of computing the 50 percent limitation [on percentage depletion] provided for in Section 613, or would be so required if the mine, well, or other natural deposit were in the production stage."

Section 614 permits a taxpayer to aggregate two or more separate operating mineral interests which are part or all of an operating unit and to treat such as one property for tax purposes. A familiar example of an operating mineral interest is a working interest under a lease. See Bird, "The 'Property' for Purposes of Depletion," 33 *Texas L. Rev.* 785 (1959); Fiske, "Depletion Problems: The Unit of Property, Aggregating Property Interests," 10 *O.&G. Tax Q.* 66 (1966); Williams, "Aggregation of Natural Resources Properties," II *Id.* 198 (1962).

See also AGGREGATION OF PROPERTIES; DEPLETION, PERCENTAGE; NONOPERATING MINERAL INTEREST, FOR TAX PURPOSES; OPERATING UNIT, FOR TAX PURPOSES; PROPERTY UNIT, FOR TAX PURPOSES.

Operating unit, for tax purposes

"Operating unit" is a term used in the 1954 Internal Revenue Code § 614, which provides in part: "If a taxpayer owns two or more separate operating mineral interests which constitute part or all of an *Operating unit,* he may elect . . ." to aggregate these interests as one property or he may treat them separately. The Code does not define the term "operating unit." However the Senate Committee Report [83rd Cong., 2d Sess., S. Rep. No. 1622, p. 333 (1954)] states the following:

"The term 'operating unit' is susceptible to a reasonable interpretation. In general, the term contemplates an aggregation only of interests which may conveniently and economically be operated together as a single working unit. Thus, interests that are geographically widespread may not be considered parts of the same operating unit merely because one set of accounting records is maintained by the taxpayer, or merely because the products of such interest are processed at the same treatment plant."

See Treas. Reg. § 1.614–2 (c) (1980).

See also DEPLETION, PERCENTAGE; OPERATING MINERAL INTEREST, FOR TAX PURPOSES.

Operation

This term, frequently found in oil and gas leases, is not a term of art with a clearly understood definition. In most instances it appears to refer to activity leading to the production of oil and gas; thus it has been held not to include the payment of royalties. Bouterie v. Kleinpeter, 258 La. 605, 245 So. 2d 548, 39 *O.&G.R.* 256 (1971) (citing this MANUAL).

See also Adolph v. Sterns, 235 Kan. 622, 684 P.2d 372, 82 *O.&.G.R.* 64 (1984), construing the term "developed or operated" as employed in the habendum clause of a lease, citing this MANUAL.

Operational unit

A term employed by one writer to describe a UNIT (*q.v.*) "essentially designed to permit the application of conservation practices in a developed field." Roark, "Matters of Mutual Concern to the Lawyer and Engineer in the Unitization Agreement," 7 *Sw. Legal Fdn. Oil & Gas Inst.* 275 at 277 (1956).

Operations clause

The term sometimes used to apply to a DRILLING OPERATIONS CLAUSE (*q.v.*) or to a CONTINUOUS DRILLINGS OPERATIONS CLAUSE (*q.v.*). See D. Pierce, *Kansas Oil and Gas Handbook* § 11.14 (1986).

Operations for oil and gas

The exploring, testing, surveying or otherwise investigating the potential of the subject lands for oil and gas, the actual drilling or preparation for drilling of wells therefor, or any other actions directed towards the eventual production or attempted productin of oil and gas from such lands. Burns Ind. Stat. Ann. § 32–5–7–1 (e) (Code Ed. 1973).

In a number of contexts it may be necessary to determine whether there has been a cessation of operations for oil and gas. See, *e.g.*, Loriaux v. Corporation Comm'n, 514 P.2d 941, 46 *O.&G.R.* 193 (Okla. 1973) (holding that operator had ceased operations for at least 90 days so that he was obliged to plug the wells under rule of the Corporation Commission).

Operator

A person, natural or artificial (*e.g.*, corporate) engaged in the business of drilling wells for oil and gas.

For purposes of a pooling or unitization agreement, the term may be defined in manner as follows:

"'Operator' is hereby defined as any owner of the right, in whole or in part, to search for and produce unitized substances within the . . . Field, whether such right be derived from the ownership of the entire title free of lease, or by oil, gas and mineral leases or by any other species of agreement conferring such right and who has signed or ratified this agreement. Where a party to this agreement contributes land in fee that is unleased, he shall be considered an 'operator' as herein defined, as to 7/8ths thereof and a 'royalty owner' as herein defined, as to 1/8th thereof." Operators Agreement, Seeligson Field Unit. See Myers, *The Law of Pooling and Unitization* 103 (1957).

Operators agreement

The agreement among owners of the working interest in properties included within a pooling or unitization agreement spelling out the rights and duties of the unit operator and other parties. For examples of such agreements, see TREATISE §§ 920.2–920.6.

Operators committee

A committee of those owning working interests in a pooled or unitized area charged with decision on matters delegated to it by a unit agreement. For a typical clause setting forth the powers of such a committee see Myers, *The Law of Pooling and Unitization* 132 (1957).

OPIC

The OVERSEAS PRIVATE INVESTMENT CORPORATION (*q.v.*).

OPLA

An acronym sometimes used for the OFFSHORE POLLUTION LIABILITY AGREEMENT (*q.v.*).

OPOL

An acronym sometimes used for the OFFSHORE POLLUTION LIABILITY AGREEMENT (*q.v.*).

OPPR

OFFICE OF PIPELINE AND PRODUCER REGULATION (*q.v.*).

Optimum rate of flow (or production)

Production from a well at the rate of output which will realize maximum production. An oil well operated at full capacity will suffer a premature decline in its rate of output and an ultimate loss underground of a material proportion of the oil that otherwise would be recovered.

See also MAXIMUM EFFICIENT RATE (MER).

Optional certificating procedure

An optional procedure adopted by F.P.C. Orders Nos. 455, 455–A and 455–B for certificating new gas sales by natural gas producers which permitted the producer, in lieu of certification at the area or national rate, to seek authorization at higher rates as stated in its gas sales contract, provided the producer was willing to forego indefinite price escalations and certain other rate advantages associated with the F.P.C.'s area or national rate regulation. See 18 C.F.R. § 2.75 (1979). The order of the Commission was affirmed in Moss v. Federal Power Comm'n, 502 F.2d 461, 48 *O.&G.R.* (D.C. Cir. 1974), except to the extent it authorized certification with PREGRANTED ABANDONMENT (*q.v.*). On the latter point the Court of Appeals was reversed and the Commission was affirmed by the Supreme Court. 424 U.S. 494, 54 *O.&G.R.* 247 (1976).

In Public Serv. Comm'n of N.Y. v. Federal Energy Regulatory Comm'n [Optional Certificates II], 589 F.2d 542 (D. C. Cir. 1978), the court invalidated the standard employed by the Commission in this procedure and remanded the case to the Commission to formulate and justify its rate standards.

Option farm-out

An arrangement under which "the farmor grants an option that 'ties up' the acreage during the option period. In return the farmee furnishes geological information to the farmor from a well drilled at the farmee's sole risk and cost on acreage offsetting the farmor's acreage. The option farm-out is a form of support to the drilling party who is about to prove the farmor's acreage. The option assures the drilling party that if the well is productive, the farmor is committed to granting a farm-out. If the offset well is dry, the farmee is not obligated to drill additional wells unless it feels some geological justification exists for another exploratory well in the area." Himebaugh, "An Overview of Oil and Gas Contracts in the Williston Basin," 59 *No. Dak. L. Rev.* 7 at 30 (1983).

See also FARM-OUT.

Option to exchange

An option which permits a person to elect to exchange an interest in one property for an interest in another, *e.g.*, on the assignment of a drill site by *A* to *B, A* may retain an offset tract and an option to exchange a given fractional interest therein for a given fractional interest in the drill site after the completion of a well. See Cook, "The Disposition of Oil and Gas Interests," a paper delivered before the Section of Real Property, Probate and Trust Law, American Bar Assn., July 12, 1957, p. 7; TREATISE § 426.

See also CONVERTIBLE INTEREST.

Or clause

The lease clause in an OR LEASE (*q.v.*) form in which the lessee covenants in the alternative to drill or to do something else (pay rentals, forfeit, surrender).

See also DELAY RENTAL CLAUSE.

ORCO process

A secondary recovery process involving the treatment of a crude oil reservoir with controlled amounts and concentrations of carbon dioxide or solutions of carbon dioxide. The name comes from Oil Recovery Corporation, owner of patents on the process. See Hughes, "Legal Problems of Water Flooding, Recycling and Other Secondary Operations," 9 *Sw. Legal Fdn. Oil & Gas Inst.* 105 at 106 (1958); Christensen & Merliss, "The *ORCO* Process—A Contribution to Conservation," 3 *IOCC Comm. Bull.* 44 (June 1961).

See also SECONDARY RECOVERY; TERTIARY RECOVERY.

Organization for Economic Cooperation and Development (OECD)

A Paris-based group of 24 countries established in 1960 to promote economic growth and development. For discussions of this organization, see the following:

Krueger, *The United States and International Oil* 319 (1975);

OECD, *Energy Prospects to 1985* (A Report of the Secretary General) (1975);

"The Economics of Energy and Natural Resource Pricing," A Compilation of Reports and Hearings of the Ad Hoc Committee on the Domestic and International Monetary Effect of Energy and

Other Natural Resource Pricing, House Committee on Banking, Currency and Housing, 94th Cong., 1st Sess. (March 1975) at p. 463.

Organization of Arab Petroleum Exporting Countries (OAPEC)

A 1968 organization of the Arab countries in the ORGANIZATION OF PETROLEUM EXPORTING COUNTRIES (OPEC) (*q.v.*). The text of the agreement for the establishment of this organization is contained in OPEC, *Selected Documents of the International Petroleum Industry 1968* at p. 371. See Mikdashi, *The Community of Oil Exporting Countries* (1972).

For a discussion of the formation of this organization see Danielsen, *The Evolution of OPEC* 153 (1982).

For a paper asserting that Saudia Arabia has used OPEC to mask its manipulations of the oil market, see Epstein, "The Cartel That Never Was," 251 *The Atlantic* No. 3 (March 1983, p. 68). For another discussion of the influence of Saudi Arabia in the world energy market see Quandt, *Saudi Arabia's Oil Policy* (Brookings Institution 1982).

Organization of Petroleum Exporting Countries (OPEC)

An organization of many of the petroleum exporting countries. OPEC meets periodically to discuss matters of common interest, especially the price to be charged for petroleum exports. At year-end 1972, the nations in OPEC accounted for 77.5 percent of free-world petroleum reserves.

For discussions of the history and operation of OPEC and its relationship to the United States and other petroleum importing countries, see the following:

Ahrari, *OPEC: The Failing Giant* (1986);

Ghosh, *OPEC, The Petroleum Industry, and United States Energy Policy* (1983);

Schneider, *The Oil Price Revolution* (1983);

Danielsen, *The Evolution of OPEC* (1982);

Al-Chalabi, *OPEC and the International Oil Industry* (1980);

Weisberg, *The Politics of Crude Oil Pricing in the Middle East 1970–1975* (1977);

Rustow and Mugno, *OPEC: Success and Prospects* (1976);

Shwadran, *The Middle East, Oil and the Great Powers* 505 *et seq.* (3d ed. revised and enlarged 1973);

Mikdashi, *The Community of Oil Exporting Countries* (1972);

Rouhani, *A History of OPEC* (1971);

Mughraby, *Permanent Sovereignty Over Oil Resources* (1966);

United States-OPEC Relations, Selected Materials prepared by the Congressional Research Service, Committee on Interior and Insular Affairs, United States Senate, Pursuant to S. Res. 45, A National Fuels and Energy Policy Study, 94th Cong., 2d Sess. (1976);

Multinational Oil Corporations and U.S. Foreign Policy, Report to the Committee on Foreign Relations, United States Senate, by the Subcommittee on Multinational Corporations, 93d Cong., 2d Sess. (Jan. 2, 1975).

World Oil Development and U.S. Oil Import Policies, Committee Print, Senate Committee on Finance, 93d Cong., 1st Sess, p. 14 (Dec. 12, 1973);

Adelman, "Effects of Simultaneous Recession and Oversupply," International Bar Association Section on Energy and Natural Resources, *International Energy Law* (1984) (Topic 1).

Best, "Middle East Oil and the U.S. Energy Crisis; Prospects for New Ventures in a Changed Market," 5 *Law & Policy in International Business* 215 (1973);

Vafai, "Conflict Resolution in the International Petroleum Industry," 5 *J. World Trade Law* 427 (1971).

Orifice meter

A device that measures the volume of gas delivered through a pipe. Such meters are commonly used to determine the amount of gas delivered by a producer to a pipeline purchaser.

Original oil in place

"The estimated number of stock tank barrels of crude oil in known reservoirs prior to any production is defined as 'original oil-in-place.' Known reservoirs include (1) those that are currently productive; (2) those to which proved reserves have been credited but from which there has been no production; and (3) those that have been depleted." American Petroleum Institute Division of Statistics, *Organization and Definitions for the Estimation of Reserves and Productive Capacity of Crude Oil* 19 (Technical Report No. 2, June 1970).

See also RESERVES.

Or lease

One of the two principal forms of modern oil and gas leases. The other principal form is the UNLESS LEASE (*q.v.*).

Both the Or lease and the Unless lease are granted for a primary term (*e.g.*, five years) and "so long thereafter" as oil or gas is produced. The two forms differ in their provisions concerning drilling. The lessee in an Unless lease makes no promise to drill or to pay or tender rentals; however the effect of the delay rental clause of this lease is that his interest will terminate automatically on the ANNIVERSARY DATE (*q.v.*) of the lease during the primary term if there is then no production or if drilling operations are not then being prosecuted *unless* delay rentals are paid or tendered before the anniversary date. In an Or lease, on the other hand, the lessee promises to drill on or before the first anniversary date "or" to do something else, *e.g.*, pay rentals, forfeit the lease, *etc.*

The delay rental clause of an Or lease might provide as follows:

> "Lessee agrees to commence a well on said premises within one year from the date hereof or thereafter pay the Lessor as rental $. . . . . each year in advance to the end of this term, or until said well is commenced, or this grant is surrendered as herein stipulated."

The basic element of this clause is that the lessee covenants to drill "or" to do something else. The "something else" may be expressed in a variety of ways: "or pay rentals"; "or pay rentals or surrender the lease"; "or forfeit the lease"; "or pay rentals or forfeit the lease." Upon failure of the lessee to commence the drilling of a well, the lessor has a cause of action on the covenant of the lessee. See Cohn v. Clark, 48 Okla. 500, 150 Pac. 467 (1915).

Under neither the Unless nor the Or lease may a lessee keep the lease alive after the expiration of the primary term merely by the payment of rentals.

See TREATISE §§ 607–607.8.

See also DELAY RENTAL CLAUSE; DRILL OR FORFEIT LEASE; DRILL OR PAY LEASE; OIL AGE 86-C FORM.

Orphan well

A term applied to a well which has been abandoned without being properly plugged. Emens and Lowe, "Ohio Oil and Gas Conservation Law—The First Ten Years (1965–1975)," 37 *Ohio State L. J.* 31 at 48 (1976).

OSCO

The Oil Service Company of Iran (*q.v.*).

OSD

Oil sands deposit (*q.v.*).

OSHA

The Occupational Safety and Health Act, 29 U.S.C. § 651.

OSWA I

The name given the case styled *In re* Other Southwest Area Rate Case, 484 F.2d 469 (5th Cir. 1973), *cert. denied,* 417 U.S. 973 (1974).

Outage gauge

A measure of the quantity of oil in a tank calculated by measuring the distance between the top of the oil and the top of the tank and subtracting such measurement from the total height of the bank. See Irving and Draper, *Accounting Practices in the Petroleum Industry* 58 (1958).

See also Automatic gauge; Innage gauge.

Outcrop

A layer of rock which appears on the surface. Also used as a verb; *e.g.,* "The Austin Chalk, a sedimentary formation, outcrops at Austin, Texas."

Outer boundary line

"Where several contiguous parcels of land in one or different ownerships are operated as a single oil or gas lease or operating unit, the term 'outer boundary line' means the outer boundary line of the lands included in the lease or unit. In determining the contiguity of any such parcels of land, no street, road or alley lying within the lease or unit shall be deemed to interrupt such contiguity." Calif. Pub. Res. Code § 3601 (1972).

Outer conducter

A short string of Casing (*q.v.*) run in a borehole in offshore drilling operations to serve as an anchorage for the installation of equipment on the sea bed. *Syn.:* Anchor string; Foundation pile.

Outer continental shelf (OCS)

"[A]ll submerged lands lying seaward and outside of the area of lands beneath navigable waters as defined in section 2 of the Submerged Lands Act (43 U.S.C. 1301) and of which the subsoil and seabed appertain to the United States and are subject to its jurisdiction and control." 30 C.F.R. § 250.2 (hh) (1980).

The right of the United States, to the exclusion of the seaboard states, to exercise sovereign rights over the seabed and subsoil underlying the Atlantic ocean, lying more than three geographical miles seaward from the ordinary low-water mark and from the outer limits of the inland waters on the coast, extending seaward to the outer edge of the continental shelf was reaffirmed in United States v. Maine, 420 U.S. 515 (1975).

In the leasing of Outer Continental Shelf Lands, the Bureau of Land Management of the Department of the Interior first calls for the nomination of tracts for leasing. This is followed by an Environmental Impact Statement, the publication of notice of the lease offer in the Federal Register, and, finally, the award of a lease to the highest responsible qualified bidder by means of competitive sealed bids. See Sierra Club v. Morton, 510 F.2d 813 (5th Cir. 1975).

Reference re the Seabed and Subsoil of the Continental Shelf Offshore Newfoundland, [1984] 1 S.C.R. 86, 5 D.L.R.4th 385 (Supreme Court of Canada 1984), concluded that Canada has the right to explore and exploit in the continental shelf off Newfoundland. See de Maestral, "Reference re Ownership of the Bed of the Strait of Georgia and Related Areas and Reference re Newfoundland Continental Shelf," 30 *McGill L.J.* 293 (1985).

Re Attorney-General of Canada and Attorney-General of British Columbia, [1984] 1 S.C.R. 388, 8 D.L.R.4th 161 (Supreme Court of Canada 1984), concluded that the lands, including mineral and other natural resources of the seabed and subsoil covered by the waters between mainland British Columbia and Vancouver, were the property of British Columbia, and not of Canada.

Genina Marine Services, Inc. v. Mark Producing Co., 490 So.2d 1158, ___ *O.&G.R.* ___ (La. App. 1986), held that the Louisiana Oil Well Lien Act applied to property located on that portion of the Outer Continental Shelf adjacent to the boundaries of the State of Louisiana.

For discussions of leasing and development of outer continental shelf lands, see the following:

Fox, Federal Regulation of Energy ch. 4 (1983);

Mead, Moseidjord, Muraoka and Sorensen, *Offshore Lands: Oil and Gas Leasing and Conservation on the Outer Continental Shelf* (1985);

Martin, "Outer Continental Shelf Leases and Operating Regulations," *Rocky Mt. Min. L. Fdn. Law of Federal Oil and Gas Leases* ch. 25 (1984);

Valencia, "Tamimg Troubled Waters: Joint Development of Oil and Mineral Resources in Overlapping Claim Areas," 23 *San Diego L. Rev.* 661 (1986);

Jones, "The Legal Framework for Energy Development on the Outer Continental Shelf," 10 *UCLA-Alaska L. Rev.* 143 (1981);

Goldberg, "Offshore Oil Leases—Are Endangered Species Threatened?" 10 *UCLA-Alaska L. Rev.* 175 (1981);

Outer Continental Shelf Leasing Program, Hearings before a Subcommittee of the House Committee on Appropriations, 93d Cong., 2d Sess. (1974);

Outer Continental Shelf Oil and Gas Development, Hearings before the Subcommittee on Minerals, Materials and Fuels of the Senate Committee on Interior and Insular Affairs, 93d Cong., 2d Sess. (1974);

Gremillion, "Offshore Leases in the Gulf of Mexico—Joint Venture Agreements and Related Matters," 25 *Sw. Legal Fdn. Oil & Gas Inst.* 205 (1974).

State of California et al. v. Watt et al., 668 F.2d 1290 (D.C. Cir. 1981) (reviewing and finding certain errors in the leasing program prepared by the Secretary of the Interior pursuant to the Outer Continental Shelf Lands Act), *on subsequent appeal,* 712 F.2d 584 (D.C. Cir. 1983) (sustaining the validity of the revised five-year schedule of offshore oil and gas leasing activity prepared by the Secretary of the Interior).

See also AVERAGE EVALUATION OF TRACT (AEOT); DEEP SEABED MINERAL RESOURCES ACT; DISCOUNTED MROV (DMROV); FEDERAL LEASE; GEOMETRIC AVERAGE EVALUATION OF TRACT (GAEOT); GEORGES BANK; MEAN OF THE RANGE OF VALUES (MROV); MINERALS MANAGEMENT SERVICE (MMS); MINIMUM ACCEPTABLE BID; MIRROR LEGISLATION; NET ECONOMIC VALUE; NET PROFIT SHARE LEASE (NPSL); NET PROFIT SHARE RATE (NPSR); NET SOCIAL VALUE; NEW LEASE; OCS ROYALTY OIL; OFF SHORE OIL AND GAS DEVELOPMENT; ONE-EIGHTH RULE; POST SALE ANALYSIS CHART; PRIVATIZATION; PROBLEM BID; PRODUCER RESERVATION GAS; RANGE OF VALUES METHOD; RISK FREE VALUE; SECTION 6 LEASE; SECTION 8 LEASE; TRUMAN PROCLAMATION; WINNER'S CURSE.

Outer Continental Shelf Lands Act of 1953

A statute [67 Stat. 462, 43 U.S.C. § 1331 *et seq.*] setting out detailed provisions for the exercise of the exclusive jurisdiction of the United States in the subsoil and seabed of the Outer Continental Shelf and for the leasing and development of the resources of the seabed.

Major amendments to this Act were adopted by Congress in 1978 by Pub. L. No. 95–372, 92 Stat. 629.

Substantial litigation has accompanied efforts to lease lands under this Act. See, *e.g.*, Commonwealth of Massachusetts v. Andrus, 594 F.2d 872 (1st Cir. 1979), vacating a preliminary injunction against a lease sale in the Georges Bank region off the coast of New England, *on remand,* 481 F. Supp. 685 (D. Mass. 1979), motion for injunction pending appeal denied *sub nom.* Conservation Law Foundation of New England v. Andrus, 617 F.2d 296 (1st Cir. 1979).

On-Structure Deep Stratigraphic Test Wells, 87 I.D. 517 (Oct. 29, 1980), ruled that deep stratigraphic tests, on or off structure potentially holding oil or gas, are "Geological explorations" authorized by the Outer Continental Shelf Lands Act of 1953, and that the Secretary of the Interior could authorize permittees to conduct such tests on a structure before it was leased.

See Breeden, "Federalism and the Development of Outer Continental Shelf Mineral Resources," 28 *Stanford L. Rev.* 1107 (1976).

See also ADDITIONAL ROYALTY; WORST CASE ANALYSIS.

"Out of balance" production plan

A plan for delivery of gas produced from a unit or from a property in which two or more persons have an interest in production wherein the full stream of gas is delivered to the purchaser from one owner for a period of time but the percentage interest of other owners in the gas produced is viewed as "banked" or held in reserve for later compensatory delivery. Cox v. Federal Energy Regulatory Comm'n, 581 F.2d 449, 62 *O.&G.R.* 580 (5th Cir. 1978).

See also BALANCING; CANCELLED UNDERAGE; DEEMED PURCHASE FORMULA; DEFERRED PRODUCTION AGREEMENT; GAS BANK AGREEMENT; LIFTING; LIFTING TOLERANCE; OVERLIFT; SPLIT CONNECTION; UNDERAGE; UNDERLIFT; UNDERLIFT/OVERLIFT PROVISION.

Out of line price

A price for gas "out of line" with other prices for gas produced and sold for resale in interstate commerce.

See also IN LINE PRICE.

Outpost well

As used by the American Petroleum Institute and the American Association of Petroleum Geologists, a well drilled in the hope of making a long extension of a partly developed pool.

Syn.: Extension test.

Outside gas

Syn.: EXTRANEOUS GAS (*q.v.*).

Outside well

A term used in certain lease forms to describe a well on other premises which must be offset by a well on the leased premises.

Overage

The amount of production from a well in excess of the ALLOWABLE (*q.v.*) for the well. See Choctaw Gas Co. v. Corporation Comm'n, 295 P.2d 800, 5 *O.&G.R.* 1226 (Okla. 1956).

Overhead

See ADMINISTRATIVE OVERHEAD; DISTRICT EXPENSES.

Overholding

An area in Canada where the mineral rights are held by the landowner rather than vested in the Crown in the right of the Province. See No. 331 v. Minister of National Revenue, 56 D.T.C. 143, 14 Tax A.B.C. 406, 5 *O.&G.R.* 1284 (Income Tax Appeal Board of Canada 1956).

Overlift

(1) The term utilized in a JOINT OPERATING AGREEMENT (*q.v.*), PRODUCTION SHARING CONTRACT (*q.v.*), SERVICE CONTRACT (*q.v.*), or other contract between or among two or more parties having an interest in production indicating that a party has, during a given contract period, taken and removed more than its obligated share of production for the period in question.

(2) The amount of crude in excess of its equity in a CONCESSION (*q.v.*) taken by a party to a joint venture. Note, "From Concession

to Participation: Restructuring the Middle East Oil Industry," 48 *N.Y.U. L. Rev.* 774 at 780 (1973).

The controversy among members of the so-called IRANIAN CONSORTIUM (*q.v.*) about overlifting is discussed in Multinational Oil Corporations and U.S. Foreign Policy, Report to the Committee on Foreign Relations, United States Senate, by the Subcommittee on Multinational Corporations, 93d Cong., 2d Sess. (Jan. 2, 1975) at pp. 105–114.

See also BALANCING; CANCELLED UNDERAGE; DEEMED PURCHASE FORMULA; DEFERRED PRODUCTION AGREEMENT; GAS BANK AGREEMENT; LIFTING; LIFTING TOLERANCE; "OUT OF BALANCE" PRODUCTION PLAN; OVERLIFT; SPLIT CONNECTION; UNDERAGE; UNDERLIFT; UNDERLIFT/OVERLIFT PROVISION.

Overproduction

Production in excess of MARKET DEMAND (*q.v.*) or production in excess of ALLOWABLE (*q.v.*).

The excess in production when the monthly production of a gas well exceeds its monthly allowable. State proration orders frequently provide for the subtraction of the amount overproduced in one period from the allowable for a succeeding period. See, *e.g.*, Republic Natural Gas Co. v. State Corporation Comm'n, 173 Kan. 172, 244 P.2d 1196, 1 *O.&G.R.* 1152 (1952); State of Louisiana, Department of Conservation, State-wide Order No. 29–F, Nov. 8, 1955, 5 *O.&G.R.* 474 at 476 (1956); Administrative Ruling, Railroad Commission of Texas, 5 *O.&G.R.* 1100 at 1104 (1956); Choctaw Gas Co. v. Corporation Comm'n, 295 P.2d 800, 5 *O.&G.R.* 1226 (Okla. 1956).

Syn.: OVERAGE.

See also BALANCING PERIOD; UNDERPRODUCTION.

Over-ride

See OVERRIDING ROYALTY.

Overriding royalty

An interest in oil and gas produced at the surface, free of the expense of production, and in addition to the usual landowner's royalty reserved to the lessor in an oil and gas lease.

In Meeker v. Ambassador Oil Co., 308 F.2d 875 at 882, 18 *O.&G.R.* 642 at 650 (10th Cir. 1962), *rev'd,* 375 U.S. 160, 19

O.&G.R. 363 (1963), *rehearing denied,* 375 U.S. 989 (1964), the following definition is offered:

> "An overriding royalty is a fractional interest in the gross production of oil and gas under a lease, in addition to the usual royalties paid to the lessor, free of any expense for exploration, drilling, development, operating, marketing and other costs incident to the production and sale of oil and gas produced from the lease. It is an interest carved out of the lessee's share of the oil and gas, ordinarily called the working interest, as distinguished from the owner's reserved royalty interest. It is generally held that an overriding royalty is an interest in real property."

Meeker was concerned with the question of whether an overriding royalty survived the termination of the underlying lease, and its definition of an overriding royalty was dictum. The propriety of the inclusion of the word "marketing" and the words "and sale" in the quoted definition is questioned. The weight of authority in the United States is that a royalty or overriding royalty interest is subject to the burden of a proportionate share of post-production costs. The law in Kansas may be different. See TREATISE § 645.2 note 8. The general rule may also be inapplicable to certain public lands by reason of provisions of statutes or regulations relating to leasing and transfers of interests in such lands. Moreover by the terms of a particular lease or other instrument affecting royalty or overriding royalty, the royalty or overriding royalty interest may be freed from the burden of certain post-production costs.

The term "royalty" whether created by grant or reservation in a deed or reserved to the lessor by an oil and gas lease, was well recognized and understood in the United States in the nineteenth century. The term "overriding royalty" is of more recent origin. In the early years of this century the term was applied to a lease royalty in excess of the usual one-eighth lease royalty, and at a somewhat later time the term came to be applied primarily (almost exclusively) to an interest in production carved out of the lessee's working interest by grant or reservation. The history of this evolution of the term "overriding royalty" is as follows.

In the nineteenth century, in most states, the customary royalty reserved by a lessor in an oil and gas lease was one-eighth. Beginning in the first two decades of the twentieth century an occasional lessor—particularly one executing a lease on a parcel of land in the midst of producing wells—demanded a lease royalty in excess of one-eighth. There was, however, concern based on careless dicta in a few cases that there could be no lease royalty in excess of the usual one-eighth royalty. This led to a common practice of executing a lease containing a standard one-eighth royalty provision and appending to the lease a "rider" which provided for an additional payment, *e.g.*, one-sixteenth, which was variously described as a "bonus royalty," "royalty bonus," "excess royalty," "excess or overriding royalty," or simply "overriding royalty." The use of a "rider" to provide for an additional royalty was a common practice for many years.

In yet other situations a lease with a standard one-eighth royalty clause contained an additional clause providing for an additional payment.

By about 1960 the employment of an "overriding royalty" as an additional consideration to a lessor for a lease had substantially (but not entirely) disappeared. By this date it was customary for the royalty clause to specify the full royalty (*e.g.*, one-sixth, one-fourth) to be paid the lessor rather than to have the lease provide in a single clause, or in two clauses, or in a single clause and an annex for a "one-eighth royalty" and some additional "overriding royalty."

Another early usage of the term overriding royalty was in an application to a royalty interest conveyed to another for cash, goods or services apart from a lease, or reserved in a transfer of the premises to another—a so-called nonparticipating royalty. Use of the word "overriding" in connection with the royalty thus granted or reserved added nothing to the meaning of the term "royalty" in these contexts. This usage of the term "overriding royalty" had substantially disappeared by 1960.

Thus as of 1960 the primary usage of the term "overriding royalty" in the United States was in connection with interests created by an oil and gas lessee by grant or by reservation, and this continues to be true at the present time.

During the second decade of this century the custom developed in Oklahoma (and elsewhere in the mid-continent area of the United States) of assigning leases for a cash consideration and a retained "carried interest" or "net profits" interest.

Occasionally during the second decade of this century (and almost universally by the end of the third decade) lease assignments also provided for a reserved overriding royalty for the assignor (rather than a carried interest or net profits interest as provided for by lease assignments executed at an earlier time). The special advantage of the overriding royalty to the assignor, as distinguished from these other types of reserved interest, was that the overriding royalty was not subject to the recovery by the operator of the lease or well of production costs or of operating costs.

Evidence of this evolution of the lease assignment is found in the treatises on oil and gas law published during and shortly subsequent to these decades.

Doubtless the evolution in the form of the consideration for a lease assignment from a carried interest or a net profits interest to an overriding royalty had multiple explanations, including the following:

(a) "Lease hounds" who had acquired leases without expectation of drilling but for the purpose of sale to an operator who would drill preferred a form of payment (royalty) which would begin when production and sale of oil began rather than at a later time after the recovery of the operator's costs, *viz,* carried or net profits interests.

(b) After the introduction of an income tax in the United States including a provision for a deduction for depletion, it was important that the interest in production retained by the assignor of a lease be described in such a way as to entitle its owner to the very substantial benefit of the percentage depletion deduction. For a period of years there was doubt and controversy as to the varieties of interest subject to the deduction. The many controversies were not resolved until a number of years had elapsed. Undoubtedly the controversy contributed to the evolution of the language used in lease assignments to describe the grantor's reserved interest in production. Careful scriveners in the early 1920's came to use "royalty" terminology to describe the reserved interest and to provide that the source of the payment must be the minerals produced and sold rather than the cash received from the sale of the land itself. The earlier practice of describing the interest reserved by the grantor in the lease assignment as a carried interest or net profits interest came to be suspect as a basis for qualifying for the percentage depletion deduction, and it increasingly came to be the practice to describe the interest reserved as a "royalty"—for example as an "excess royalty" or as an "overriding royalty."

By about 1940, and increasingly so in subsequent years, the term "overriding royalty" in the United States of America has been employed primarily in connection with instruments executed by lessees (as distinguished from the initial lease from a lessor to a lessee) by which a royalty has been "carved out" of the interest of the lessee or "reserved" in a transfer of the lessee's interest. Such an instrument has no effect upon the "royalty" reserved to the lessor by the original lease, but a new or additional royalty is created by the instrument in which the lessee (or the lessee's successor) is the grantor.

A typical carved-out overriding royalty may be created in exchange for goods, services or money. A typical reserved overriding royalty may be created by a farm-out agreement or other instrument having the effect of transferring to the grantee all or some portion of the interest of the lessee (or the lessee's successor) in described premises for a valuable consideration of cash and/or a royalty (described customarily as an overriding royalty). For a variety of reasons (including important tax considerations) the parties might bargain for a larger royalty if the amount of cash involved was smaller. Thus the owner of a lease might offer to transfer the lease for a cash payment of $100 per acre; this offer might produce a counter offer of an overriding royalty of one-eighth; the bargaining might result in an agreement upon a cash payment more modest than $100 and a more modest overriding royalty, *e.g.*, a cash payment of $10 per acre and a one-sixteenth overriding royalty.

One of the most important aspects of an "overriding royalty" (whether reserved by the lessor in a lease, as in the earlier usage of the term, or created by a subsequent instrument executed by the lessee or the lessee's successor) is that it is a "royalty," *viz.*, in the absence of an express agreement to the contrary it is free of costs of which the lessor's royalty is free and it is subject to the costs to which the lessor's royalty is subject. See TREATISE § 418.1.

There is no uniformity on the size of the interest; in general, it is not commonly greater than one-eighth, and one-sixteenth, one-thirty-second, and one-sixty-fourth, or even smaller fractions are usual.

An outstanding characteristic of overriding royalty is that its duration is limited by the duration of the lease under which it is created. Thus, when *A*, the lessee of Blackacre, assigns the lease to *B*, reserving a 1/16 overriding royalty, the continued existence of this interest depends on the acts of *B* in keeping the lease alive, by paying delay rentals, producing oil before the expiration of the primary term, etc. Unless expressed, there is no duty by *B* to keep the lease and hence the overriding royalty alive. Collins v. Atlantic Oil Prod. Co., 74 F.2d 122 (5th Cir. 1934). Nor does *A* have any power, apart from express agreement, to keep the lease and override alive. La Laguna Ranch Co. v. Dodge, 18 Cal. 2d 132, 144 P.2d 351 (1941). There may, however, be a duty to use good faith in determining whether to let the lease expire. See Probst v. Hughes, 143 Okla. 11, 286 Pac. 875 (1930); Phillips Petroleum Co. v. McCormick, 211 F.2d 361, 3 *O.&G.R.* 1070 (10th Cir. 1954); Rees v. Briscoe, 315 P.2d 758, *O.&G.R.* 1452 (Okla. 1957); TREATISE §§ 420–420.2.

It is common now in assignment agreements which reserve an overriding royalty to provide for notice by the assignee to the assignor of intention to allow the lease to lapse and in such event to require the reassignment of the lease. See Atlantic Ref. Co. v. Moxley, 211 F.2d 916 3 *O.&G.R.* 9128 (5th Cir. 1954).

Cities Service Oil v. Pubco Petroleum Corp., 497 P.2d 1368 at 1372, 43 *O.&G.R.* 403 at 410 (Wyo. 1972), in holding that the driller of an oil well did not acquire a statutory lien on an overriding royalty reserved in a farm out agreement, defined an overriding royalty as follows:

> "The term 'overriding royalty' has been defined in numerous judicial opinions as an interest in oil and gas production at the surface, free of the expense of production, and in addition to the usual land owner's royalty reserved to the lessor in an oil and gas lease. As stated in 2 Williams and Meyers, Oil and Gas Law, § 418.1, p. 341: An overriding royalty is, first and foremost, a 'royalty interest.' "

In Skyeland Oils Ltd. v. Great N. Oil Ltd., 68 D.L.R. 3d 318 at 328, [1976] 5 W.W.R. 370 at 381 (Alberta Sup. Ct. 1976), the court concluded that "gross overriding royalty" was to be calculated at the stated per cent 'of the gross proceeds of production without any deduction other than for transportation of the petroleum substances to a refinery or a gas plant as the case may be," *viz.*, without deduction for landowner's or other royalty.

The definition in this MANUAL was cited in De Mik v. Cargill, 485 P.2d 229 at 232, 39 *O.&G.R.* 79 at 82 (Okla. 1971). The case discusses a number of aspects of overriding royalties in Oklahoma and holds that an overriding royalty is not partitionable at the suit of the working interest owner.

In Moore v. Tristar Oil and Gas Corp., 528 F. Supp. 296 at 311 (S.D.N.Y. 1981), the court concluded, on the basis of expert testimony, that the term "overriding royalty" includes not merely an interest in production but also an interest in sales proceeds, which can be considered advance payments for the oil and gas to be produced at some later time, when a partnership interest in an oil and gas property is sold. Hence, on the sale of the interest of general partners (owning an overriding royalty) and limited partners in a property, a portion of the sales proceeds was allocable to the overriding royalty interest of the general partners.

Edward v. Prince, ____ Mont. ____, 719 P.2d 422, ____ *O.&G.R.* ____ (1986), was concerned with a 1952 lease which reserved a royalty of one-eighth and further provided for an overriding royalty to the lessor of one percent. Subsequently, lessor assigned an overriding royalty of one-fourth of one percent. The court concluded that the assigned interest was not a perpetual royalty but was in fact an overriding royalty which was extinguished when the lease terminated.

DaMac Drilling, Inc. v. Shoemake, 11 Kan.App.2d 38, 713 P.2d 480, 88 *O.&G.R.* 281 (1986), concluded that an overriding royalty is essentially a royalty "more like the royalty held by a lessor than the working interest held by a lessee," and held that an overriding royalty was not subject to foreclosure by a lien claimant whose claim arose subsequent to recording of the assignment of a leasehold reserving the override.

Del-Ray Oil & Gas, Inc. v. Henderson Petroleum Corp., 797 F.2d 1313, ___ *O.&G.R.* ___ (5th Cir. 1986), declared that a reserved interest described by the transfer agreement as a "Carried Working Interest," "amounted to an overriding royalty" for purposes of the Louisiana rule under which reservation of an overriding royalty causes a transfer to be classified as a sublease rather than as an assignment.

Tidelands Royalty "B" Corp. v. Gulf Oil Corp., 611 F.Supp. 795, 86 *O.&G.R.* 162 (N.D. Tex. 1985), *rev'd and remanded,* 804 F.2d 1344, ___ *O.&G.R.* ___ (5th Cir. 1986), was concerned with the rights of an overriding royalty owner against a lessee for alleged fraudulent drainage. The trial court concluded that under Louisiana law, which governed the case, an overriding royalty interest is generally entitled to the same implied covenants that apply to protect royalty interests under leases. The court of appeals, however, concluded that the owner of an overriding royalty created by grant (as opposed to the owner of an overriding royalty created by reservation in a sublease) is not entitled to the benefit of implied lease covenants. The relationship between the lessee and the owner of the overriding royalty created by grant was said to be akin to that of executive and nonexecutive owners. Under Article 109 of the Louisiana Mineral Code [see TREATISE § 339.4] the executive is subject to a good faith duty to the nonexecutive under some circumstances, but this duty is different from the duty owed a lessor by a lessee. The case was remanded for a determination of whether there was a violation of the executive's good faith duty in the instant case.

See also the following:

Ryan, "Australia: Petroleum Royalties—Part I," [1985/86] 5 *OGLTR* 121, "Part II," [1985/86] 6 *OGLTR* 154;

Davidson, "The Overriding Royalty," 27 *L.S.U. Min. L. Inst.* 38 (1980).

Syn.: OVER-RIDE.

See also LIMITED OVERRIDING ROYALTY; QUALIFIED OVERRIDING ROYALTY INTEREST; ROYALTY.

Overrun penalty

A penalty for unauthorized overruns for gas taken by a customer in excess of its maximum contract demand. [Consolidated Gas Supply Corp. v. Federal Power Comm'n, 520 F.2d 1176 at 1190 (D.C. Cir. 1975)] or in excess of the amount authorized to be taken under a CURTAILMENT PLAN (*q.v.*) [F.P.C. Order No. 697–A (Dec. 19, 1974)].

Overseas Private Investment Corporation (OPIC)

A corporation created by the Foreign Assistance Act of 1969 (22 U.S.C. §§ 2191–2200a) and formally organized in 1971 to encourage private investment in developing countries. The programs of OPIC include preinvestment assistance, investment insurance and investment financing.

For discussions of OPIC see the following:

El Sheikh, *The Legal Regime of Foreign Private Investment in the Sudan and Saudi Arabia* 158 (1984);

Mikdashi, "Policy Issues in Primary Industries," 7 *Vanderbilt J. Transnat'l L.* 281 at 296 (1974);

Zakariya, "Insurance Against the Political Risks of Petroleum Investment," 4 *J. of Energy & Natural Resources Law* 217 (1986).

Over-the-counter lease

A lease of federal lands to the first qualified applicant by the Bureau of Land Management office responsible for the state in which the lands are located and covering lands not previously leased by the government for oil and gas activity. See *Rocky Mt. Min. L. Fdn. Law of Federal Oil & Gas Leases* Ch. 5 (1985); Hawley, "Federal Oil and Gas Leases—The Sole Party in Interest Debacle," 27 *Rocky Mt. Min. L. Inst.* 987 at 989 (1982).

Over-the-counter lease offer

A noncompetitive oil and gas lease offer filed pursuant to section 17 of the Mineral Leasing Act, as amended, 30 U.S.C. § 226(c) (1971), providing that if the lands to be leased are not within any known geological structure of a producing oil or gas field, the person first making application for the lease who is qualified to hold a lease under this chapter shall be entitled to a lease of such lands without competition. See Emery Energy, Inc., IBLA 82-77, GFA(O&G) 1982-146 (May 26, 1982), IBLA 82-662, GFS(O&G) 1982-155 (June 4, 1982).

See also NOTATION RULE.

Overthrust belt

The term applied to a complex geologic zone extending from Alaska to Mexico. Some 120 million years ago, at the start of the Cretaceous period, the ocean trough just west of the present-day Overthrust belt began to be deformed as two of the earth's continents converged on the basin as they drifted toward one another. As the two continents collided, horizontal compression forces pushed the sediments in the bottom of the ocean up and over one another. Folds and thrusts were formed as a result. The vertical movement along many of the large thrust faults is 15,000 feet or more, and the horizontal movement of the thrust is five or more miles.

The first major discovery in the overthrust belt was made in Turner Valley, Alberta, Canada, in 1924. More than 500 dry holes were drilled in the belt in the United States before a 1974 discovery of the Pineview Field in northeastern Utah, setting off an extensive search along the Belt from northern Montana to southern Arizona. See Work, "The Overthrust Belt," 18 *Sw. Legal Fdn. Exploration and Economics of the Petroleum Industry* 77 (1980); Mountain States Legal Foundation v. Andrus, 499 F. Supp. 393, 69 *O.&G.R.* 160 (D. Wyo. 1980).

For a collection of papers dealing with legal and land issues involved in development of the Overthrust belt see *Rocky Mt. Min. L. Fd. Inst. on the Overthrust Belt—Oil and Gas Legal and Land Issues* (1980).

See also EASTERN OVERTHRUST BELT (EOB).

Owner of an operating mineral interest

A term employed in the 1956 proposed Treasury Regulations, § 1.614–2 (b). See Stroud, "Major Points of Impact of New Natural Resources Regulations on Oil and Gas," 8 *Sw. Legal Fdn. Oil & Gas Inst.* 393 at 403 (1957).

Ownership certificate

A term sometimes employed to describe a certificate issued under a PER CENT INTEREST arrangement. See Thompson v. Commissioner, 28 F.2d 247 (3d Cir. 1928).

Ownership in place theory

The theory that a landowner owns the oil and gas which was originally in place beneath his surface acreage. Under this theory, the landowner may create by grant or reservation a corporeal or possessory interest in the minerals, separate from the estate in the surface. This theory has been accepted in Arkansas, Kansas, Michigan, Mississippi, Montana, New Mexico, Ohio, Pennsylvania, Tennessee, Texas and West Virginia. Despite the theory of ownership in place, title to the oil and gas in place may be lost by legitimate drainage under the RULE OF CAPTURE (*q.v.*). See Elliff v. Texon Drilling Co., 146 Tex. 575, 210 S.W.2d 558, 4 A.L.R.2d 191 (1948); TREATISE § 203.3.

Syn.: ABSOLUTE OWNERSHIP THEORY.

See also CORRELATIVE RIGHTS THEORY; NON-OWNERSHIP THEORY; OWNERSHIP OF STRATA THEORY; QUALIFIED OWNERSHIP THEORY.

Ownership of strata theory

The theory that, although a landowner does not own oil and gas in place in his land, he does own the strata or formations containing the oil and gas within the limits of the vertical planes representing the boundaries of his tract. This theory appears to be followed in Illinois and possibly in Kentucky. See TREATISE § 203.4.

See also CORRELATIVE RIGHTS THEORY; NON-OWNERSHIP THEORY; OWNERSHIP IN PLACE THEORY; QUALIFIED OWNERSHIP THEORY.

. . P . .

Pacific Lease Agreement

An agreement closely similar to a GAS LEASE AGREEMENT (*q.v*.). See El Paso Natural Gas Co. v. Sun Oil Co., 708 F.2d 1011 at 1016 (5th Cir. 1983).

Packer

A device used on casing or tubing to prevent fluid from passing; material employed to prevent water or other foreign substances from entering a sand.

See also PRODUCTION INJECTION PACKER.

Packing

See GRAVEL PACKING.

Pad

An area of some 75 × 150 feet around a well which serves as a foundation for the drilling rig. Robinson Rat Hole Service, Inc. v. Richardson Oils, Inc., 393 S.W.2d 629 at 630, 23 *O.&G.R.* 587 at 588 (Tex. Civ. App. 1965, error ref'd n.r.e.).

PAD

PETROLEUM ADMINISTRATION FOR DEFENSE (PAD) (*q.v.*).

PAD Districts

Five geographical areas into which the nation was divided by the PETROLEUM ADMINISTRATION FOR DEFENSE (PAD) (*q.v.*) in 1950 for purposes of administration.

Paid up lease

A lease effective during the primary term without further payment of delay rentals, the aggregate of rentals for the entire primary term having been paid in advance. The delay rental clause may be deleted from the lease if rentals are paid up, but it appears generally preferable to leave the delay rental clause in the lease since striking the clause may give rise to a covenant to drill an exploratory well [See

EXPLORATION COVENANT] during the primary term. If the clause is left in the lease and rentals paid up, the lease should recite the payment of the rentals in order to protect the lessee in the event the lessor's interest is assigned during the primary term to a person who does not know that the lease was paid up. See Malone, "Problems Created by Express Lease Clauses Affecting Implied Covenants," 2 *Rocky Mt. Min. L. Inst.* 133 (1956); TREATISE § 603.1.

Paleontologist

A scientist who deals with the life of past geological periods, basing his study on fossils.

Palmer v. Bender assignment

A term occasionally used to describe a transaction involving the assignment of a working interest for cash, in which assignment an overriding royalty is retained. See Appleman, "Sales and Assignments of Leases and Other Interests in Oil and Gas," 1 *Sw. Legal Fdn. Oil & Gas Inst.* 427 at 439 (1949).

See also ASSIGNMENT.

P & A

Plug and abandon, *viz.*, the placing of a plug in a dry hole, then abandoning the well.

Paper barrel

Oil traded on the futures market for delivery a few months ahead and mostly used by players for hedging their actual buys of oil or for speculating to make money. On futures markets traders rarely intend to take delivery of the oil or to deliver it. *The Wall Street Journal,* March 6, 1986, p. 6.

Syn. Video barrel

Paraffin base oil

Crude oil containing an appreciable amount of wax (paraffin). In general, the oil produced in Pennsylvania, New York, West Virginia, and southeastern Ohio are paraffin base oils, as well as some of the oil produced in Texas and California. Paraffin base oils are usually lighter in color and gravity than asphaltic oils and are excellent sources of high-grade lubricants.

See also ASPHALT BASE OIL; MIXED BASE OIL.

Paraffin wax

Wax removed from petroleum distillates and residues by chilling, dewaxing, and de-oiling. When separating from solution it is a colorless, more or less translucent, crystalline mass, slightly greasy to touch, and consisting of a mixture of solid hydrocarbons in which the paraffin series predominate. 38 Fed. Reg. 34,416 (Dec. 13, 1973).

Paramarginal reserves or resources

The portion of IDENTIFIED-SUBECONOMIC RESERVES OR RESOURCES (*q.v.*) that (a) borders on being economically producible or (b) is not commercially available solely because of legal or political circumstances. 2 *OCS Oil and Gas—An Environmental Assessment,* A Report to the President by the Council on Environmental Quality (April 1974) at p. 12.

See also RESERVES.

Pari passu undertaking

An agreement by a borrower that it will not grant security to other creditors, but that as far as possible it will not allow any other creditor to obtain priority over the credit given by those to whom the undertaking is given. McCormick, "Legal Issues in Project Finance," 1 *J.E.R.L.* 21 at 27 (1983).

See also PROJECT FINANCING.

Partial assignment

The transfer of less than the whole interest created in either lessor or lessee by execution of an oil and gas lease. This transfer may occur in one of two ways: (1) by conveyance of an undivided interest, or (2) by conveyance of part of the tract under lease in severalty. Some of the problems arising from either form of partial assignment are the same, but others differ depending on the form.

In the case of assignment by the lessor of an undivided interest in the royalty, the usual question is whether one co-owner can bring an action for breach of express or implied drilling covenants without the joinder of all other co-owners. See Sun Oil Co. v. Oswell, 258 Ala. 326, 62 So. 2d 783, 2 *O.&G.R.* 145 (1953); Theissen v. Weber, 128 Kan. 556, 278 Pac. 770 (1929); Compton v. Fisher-McCall, 298 Mich. 648, 299 N.W. 750 (1941); Royal Petroleum Corp. v. Dennis, 160 Tex. 392, 332 S.W.2d 313, 12 *O.&G.R.* 578 (1960).

In the case of assignment by the lessee of an undivided interest in the lease, it seems clear that acts by either cotenant are acts of the other, sufficient to keep the lease alive.

In the case of assignment by the lessor of the lease benefits in a segregated portion of the leasehold (*e.g.*, the SW 1/4 of Section 3), the usual problem is the apportionment of royalty between assignor and assignee. That is, the royalty may be divided according to the proportion that the land of each bears to the whole leasehold acreage, the APPORTIONMENT (*q.v.*) rule. Or the full royalty may be paid to the owner of the segregated tract on which the well is located, the NONAPPORTIONMENT (*q.v.*) rule. Absent express lease provisions, the second rule of nonapportionment is followed in a majority of producing states. See, *e.g.*, Central Pipe Line Co. v. Hutson, 401 Ill. 447, 82 N.E.2d 624 (1948); Japhet v. McRae, 276 S.W. 669 (Tex. Com. App. 1925); Carlock v. Krug, 151 Kan. 407, 99 P.2d 858 (1940); Gypsy Oil Co. v. Schonwald, 107 Okla. 253, 231 Pac. 864 (1924). There is some support for the apportionment theory: Standard Oil Co. v. John N. Mills, 3 Cal. 2d 128, 43 P.2d 797 (1935); Griffith v. Gulf Ref. Co., 215 Miss. 15, 60 So. 2d 518, 61 So. 2d 306, 1 *O.&G.R.* 1627 (1952); Stayton, "Apportionment and the Ghost of a Rejected View," 32 *Texas L. Rev.* 682 (1954).

Where an ENTIRETY CLAUSE (*q.v.*) is present in the lease, apportionment is sometimes applied in nonapportionment jurisdictions. Thomas Gilcrease Foundation v. Stanolind Oil & Gas Co., 153 Tex. 197, 266 S.W.2d 850, 3 *O.&G.R.* 673 (1954); Krone v. Lacy, 168 Neb. 792, 97 N.W.2d 528, 11 *O.&G.R.* 492 (1951). *Contra:* Iskian v. Consolidated Gas Utilities Co., 207 Okla. 615, 251 P.2d 1073, 2 *O.&G.R.* 240 (1952). See Hardwicke & Hardwicke, "Apportionment of Royalty to Separate Tracts." 32 *Texas L. Rev.* 660 (1954); TREATISE § 521.4.

In the case of assignment by the lessee of portions of the working interest in severalty, several problems may arise:

(1) The effect of non-payment of rentals by one assignee. This contingency is nearly always provided for in the lease, under which the lease lapses only as to the assignee's portion of the lease hold. See TREATISE § 407–407.2.

(2) The effect of the partial assignment upon the habendum clause of the lease. It is generally held that production anywhere on the leasehold will continue the lease in force as to all assignees, whether they have drilled or not. See Berry v. Tidewater Assoc. Oil Co., 188 F.2d 820 (5th Cir. 1951), and the many cases cited therein. In some instances, Louisiana is *contra.* See TREATISE § 406.

(3) The effect of the partial assignment upon the covenant obligations of the lease. See TREATISE §§ 409–409.4.

For a general discussion of the various problems arising out of partial assignments, see TREATISE §§ 404–410.

See also ASSIGNMENT; SUBLEASE.

Partial cancellation

Cancellation of the lease insofar as it covers undeveloped portions of the leased premises or insofar as it covers undeveloped formations. In a limited number of cases, the remedy of partial cancellation has been given for breach of implied covenants of an oil and gas lease, either by an absolute decree of partial cancellation or a conditional decree of partial cancellation. See TREATISE § 844.2.

See also ALTERNATIVE DECREE; CANCELLATION DECREE; CONDITIONAL DECREE OF CANCELLATION.

Partial looping

A method of expansion of the carrying capacity of a pipeline by constructing a second pipeline parallel to a portion of the existing pipeline. See Battle Creek Gas Co. v. Federal Power Comm'n, 281 F.2d 42 (D.C. Cir. 1960).

See also LOOPING.

Partial ownership clause

Syn.: PROPORTIONATE REDUCTION CLAUSE (*q.v.*).

Partial requirements customer

A customer who obtains gas from two or more natural gas suppliers. See Atlantic Seaboard Corp. v. Federal Power Comm'n, 404 F.2d 1268 (D.C. Cir. 1968).

Partial requirements rate schedule

A RATE SCHEDULE (*q.v.*) applicable to a PARTIAL REQUIREMENTS CUSTOMER (*q.v.*) requiring the customer to pay for a minimum volume of gas, both monthly and annually, regardless of whether the gas is used. See Atlantic Seaboard Corp. v. Federal Power Comm'n, 404 F.2d 1268 (D.C. Cir. 1968).

Participant

(1) A term used in some unitization agreements to describe an owner at the date of the agreement, and each successor, assignee or transferee of such owner, of the right to develop and operate lands within the unitized area and to produce unitized substances, whether as lessee or otherwise, including the owner of such lands not under lease as well as the lessee of such lands under lease. Belridge Oil Co. v. Commissioner, 27 T.C. 1044, 7 *O.&G.R.* 673 at 676 (1957), *aff'd,* 267 F.2d 291, 10 *O.&G.R.* 662 (9th Cir. 1959).

(2) A subscriber to a LEASE ACQUISITION FUND (*q.v.*)

Participating area

That part of a unit area to which production is allocated in the manner described in a unit agreement. 30 C.F.R. § 226.2 (i) (1980).

Participating financing arrangement

A financing arrangement in which the lender obtains an EQUITY KICKER (*q.v.*). See Wilson, "Tax Considerations in Selecting a Mineral Financing Vehicle," *Rocky Mt. Min. L. Inst. on Mineral Financing* 7-1 at 7-95 (1982).

Participating interest

(1) As defined in a Rocky Mountain unit operating agreement, the proportion (expressed as a percentage) that the acreage of a party's Committed Working Interest or Interests bears to the total acreage of all the Committed Working Interests of the parties. See Rocky Mountain Unit Operating Agreement Form 1 (Undivided Interest) May, 1954, Section 1.6, TREATISE § 920.3.

(2) The percentage of cost and benefits under a unit operating agreement borne and to be received by various parties. See *Rocky Mt. Min. L. Fdn. Landman's Legal Handbook* 155 (3d ed. 1977).

(3) A portion of the working interest, frequently evidenced by a certificate. See *Miller's Oil and Gas Federal Income Taxation* § 14–1 (1980 Edition).

(4) Fractional undivided interest or right of participation in the oil or gas or in the proceeds from the sale of oil or gas, produced from a specified tract or tracts, or well(s) which right is limited in duration to the terms of an existing lease and which is subject to any portion of the expense of development, operation, or maintenance. 17 C.F.R. § 230.300 (a)(5) (1980).

(5) This term is employed in certain operating agreements between host nations and foreign oil companies to designate the percentage in which each party is to participate in the costs and benefits of the agreement. See, *e.g.*, the Operating Agreement between Abu Dhabi and the Middle East Oil Co., Ltd., in OPEC, *Selected Documents of the International Petroleum Industry 1970* at p. 172.

Participating royalty

A royalty interest, independent of a subsisting lease, if any, which shares in some other lease benefits than gross production, such as bonus, rental, or the right to join in the execution of leases. The term is ambiguous since it does not indicate in each particular *which* other lease benefit is joined to the royalty interest.

This term has also been used to describe a so-called PER CENT INTEREST (*q.v.*). United States v. Adamant Co., 197 F.2d 1, 1 *O.&G.R.* 1072 (9th Cir. 1952), *cert. denied,* 344 U.S. 903 (1952).

See also NONEXECUTIVE MINERAL INTEREST; NONPARTICIPATING ROYALTY; ROYALTY.

Participation

(1) The term which has come to be applied to the arrangements between certain host nations and foreign oil companies for the exploitation of natural resources involving national ownership of an interest in the concessions for development of those resources. See Note, "From Concession to Participation: Restructuring the Middle East Oil Industry," 48 *N.Y.U. L. Rev.* 774 (1973).

For a discussion of participation agreements see Blinn, Duval, Le Leuch, and Pertuzio, *International Petroleum Exploration & Exploitation Agreements* ch. 7 (1986).

The difficulty of defining this term was emphasized in Hunt v. Mobil Oil Corp., 465 F. Supp. 195 at 239 (S.D. N.Y. 1978), *aff'd without opinion,* 610 F.2d 806 (2d Cir. 1979). The court observed:

> "[w]hatever conflicts there may be, one concept seems to emerge from the various definitions offered at trial: participation concerned a working relationship between the host government and a concessionaire whereby the government had an equity interest in the company's concession."

For specific aspects or provisions of Participations see the entries under CONCESSION.

(2) The term is also applied to the division of a loan among several financial institutions as a means of enabling an originating lender to

accommodate large customers which it could not otherwise handle. See LOAN PARTICIPATION.

Participation agreement

See PARTICIPATION.

Participation crude

That portion of the crude oil produced by an oil company which is deliverable as the host nation's share of production under the terms of a PARTICIPATION (*q.v.*) agreement.

See also BRIDGING CRUDE; BUYBACK OIL; CONCESSION; PHASE-IN CRUDE.

Participation formula

The formula employed in the allocation of costs and proceeds of production under an operating, pooling or unitization agreement. A variety of factors have been utilized in participation formulae, including the following (listed approximately in the order of frequency as revealed by one study): (1) number of wells, current and cumulative production; (2) productive sand volume; (3) productive acreage; (4) estimated reserves; (5) total acreage; (6) number of wells and current production; (7) acreage and number of wells; (8) allowable; (9) allowable and potential; (10) number of wells, bottom-hole pressures, acreage, and sand thickness; (11) cumulative production, number of wells, volume of oil and gas sands, and current production; and (12) number of wells, productive acre-feet, and productive acreage. The difficulty of obtaining agreement on a participation formula has been a considerable barrier to the adoption of plans for cooperative, pooled or unitized development. See TREATISE §§ 970–970.4.

Participation type contract

A contract for the sale of casinghead gas or wet gas providing for the seller to receive a varying portion of the products extracted from the gas or of the proceeds of sale of such products, depending on the richness of the gas in liquefiable hydrocarbon content.

See also PRODUCTS ROYALTY CLAUSE.

Participator

A person liable for the Petroleum Revenue Tax established by the Oil Taxation Act, 1975. See Daintith and Willoughby, *A Manual of United Kingdom Oil and Gas Law* 110 (1977).

Parties, joinder of

See INDISPENSABLE PARTIES; NECESSARY PARTIES; PROPER PARTIES.

Partition

The conversion of a concurrent estate—either a joint tenancy or a tenancy in common—into (1) a fund of money, by sale, which is divided pro rata by the tenants or (2) into estates owned in severalty. The former is partition by sale; the latter partition in kind. Either form of partition may be made by voluntary agreement or by judicial action. In general, courts favor partition in kind where feasible. On the availability of partition and the considerations governing the form of partition in oil and gas property, see Strait v. Fuller, 184 Kan. 120, 334 P.2d 385, 10 *O.&G.R.* 145 (1959); Henson v. Bryant, 330 P.2d 591, 9 *O.&G.R.* 923 (Okla. 1958); Sweeny v. Bay State Oil & Gas Co., 192 Okla. 28, 133 P.2d 538 (1943); TREATISE §§ 506–507.

See also EQUITABLE PARTITION; LICITATION.

Partnership

See COMPLETION PARTNERSHIP; DRILL OR DROP PROVISION; GAIN CHARGE BACK; LIMITED PARTNERSHIP; MINING PARTNERSHIP; QUALIFIED PARTNERSHIP; REPURCHASE PRICE; TAX PARTNERSHIP AGREEMENT.

Partnership-for-partnership roll-up

See EXCHANGE OFFER.

Party-in-interest statement

A statement required in an application for a federal lease or in a request for approval of an assignment or sublease thereof indicating whether or not the offeror for the lease or the assignee or sublessee is the sole party in interest in the offer, assignment or sublease. Nondisclosure of the interests of other parties may result in loss of priority of an offer or may affect the validity of the lease, sublease or assignment. See *Rocky Mt. Min. L. Fdn. Law of Federal Oil and Gas Leases* § 20.08[9] (1985).

See also FEDERAL LEASE.

PASO

Petroleum Accountants Society of Oklahoma.

PASO form

A form of accounting procedure devised by the Petroleum Accountants Society of Oklahoma for operating agreements. The form may be found in Irving and Draper, *Accounting Practices in the Petroleum Industry* 147 (1958).

Pass-on provision

Syn: PASS-THROUGH PROVISION (*q.v.*).

Pass-through prohibition

A provision of a law or regulation designed to prevent particular increased costs from being passed through to the consumer by price increases. Thus several states enacted gross receipts taxes or similar taxes applicable to oil companies and sought to prohibit the "pass-through" of the tax to the consumer by means of increases in price. In Mobil Oil Corp. v. Tully, 653 F.2d 497 (Temp. Emer. Ct. of App. 1981), *vacated and remanded for reconsideration in light of expiration of federal price control authority,* 455 U.S. 245 (1982), *remanded to Dist. Ct.,* 689 F.2d 186 (Temp. Emer. Ct. of App. 1982), this pass-through prohibition was held to be invalid by reason of preemption by federal regulation.

Eagerton v. Exchange Oil and Gas Corp., 404 So. 2d 1, 71 *O.&G.R.* 205 (Ala. 1981), sustained the validity of a severance tax statute pass-through prohibition designed to prevent passage of the burden of the tax, directly or indirectly, from the producer or severer of oil or gas to the consumer. *Eagerton* was affirmed in part, reversed in part, and remanded *sub nom.* Exxon Corp. v. Eagerton, 462 U.S. 176, 103 S.Ct 2296, 77 *O.&G.R.* 209 (1983) (holding the pass-though prohibition was pre-empted by federal law insofar as it applied to the sale of gas in interstate commerce but not insofar as it applied to producer sales of gas in intrastate commerce; sustaining the pass-through prohibition against challenges under the contracts and equal protection clauses of the Constitution; and remanding the case on the question of the severability of the pass-through prohibition from the balance of the Act, that being a question of state law). On remand, 440 So. 2d 1031, 79 *O.&G.R.* 424 (Ala. 1983), the court gave effect to the severability clause of the statute and sustained the act despite invalidity of the pass-through prohibition. Eagerton v. Terra Resources, Inc. 426 So. 2d 807, 76 *O.&G.R.* 187 (Ala. 1982), appeal dism'd for want of substantial federal question, 464 U.S. 801 (1983), rejected a construction of the statute that would exempt gas from the tax.

For a study of pass-through prohibitions in New York, see Brown, "New York State Oil Company Gross Receipts Taxation," 32 *O.&G. Tax Q.* 271 (1983).

Pass-through provision

A provision of a price control law or regulation permitting certain increased costs to be "passed through" to consumers by allowable price increases. McCulloch Gas Transmission Co. v. Public Service Comm'n, 627 P.2d 173 at 180 (Wyo. 1981).

See also ANTI-PASSTHROUGH PROVISION.

Pass-through royalty

A ROYALTY (*q.v.*) paid on production from a well drilled upon or through one tract and bottomed under another tract. Hearings of California Senate Fact Finding Committee on Natural Resources 33 (Jan. 6, 1964); Stucky, "Current Developments and Views Concerning Rights and Status of Landowner-Lessors," 21 *Sw. Legal Fdn. Oil & Gas Inst.* 83 at 88 (1970).

Patent

The original conveyance granting to the recipient legal title to public lands, and containing all the reservations for easements, rights-of-way, or other interests in land, provided by the applicable act or imposed on the land by applicable law.

PAW

(1) PETROLEUM ADMINISTRATION FOR WAR (*q.v.*).

(2) The acronym PAW is also used for the Petroleum Association of Wyoming.

Pay-as-you-go basis

Payment of expenses incurred in a drilling operation as the expenses are incurred, as distinguished from prepayment of the expenses. See also PREPAID IDC. See Keller v. Comm'r of Internal Revenue, 79 T.C. 7, 74 *O.&G.R.* 129 (1982), *aff'd,* 725 F.2d 1173, 80 *O.&G.R.* 639 (8th Cir. 1984).

Payback of gas

When extraordinary relief from a CURTAILMENT PLAN (*q.v.*) is granted, the order may be conditioned on the obligation that when curtailment is not in effect, the pipeline shall withhold volumes over and above the purchaser's minimum requirements as a payback for volumes delivered in excess of those daily volumes to which the purchaser would be entitled under the normal operation of the curtailment plan. The rationale of the requirement is that "it encourages expeditious conversion to alternate fuel, deters exploitation of extraordinary relief, prevents an undue advantage going to the recipient of relief, and partially restores volumes taken from other customers." Texas Eastern Transmission Corp., F.P.C. Opinion No. 716, 3 FPS 5–531 at 5–541 (Dec. 16, 1974).

Payback order

(1) An order of the Federal Power Commission or its successor, the Federal Energy Regulatory Commission, requiring a producer or pipeline company to "pay back" to a buyer entitled to the gas under a contract or Commission certificate an amount of gas equal to that which had been diverted to another buyer under a CURTAILMENT PLAN (*q.v.*).

(2) An order by the Federal Power Commission or its successor, the Federal Energy Regulatory Commission, requiring a gas producer to "pay back" to a buyer entitled to the gas under a Commission certificate an amount of gas equal to that which had been improperly delivered to another buyer in violation of the Natural Gas Act. See McCombs v. Federal Energy Regulatory Comm'n, 705 F.2d 1177, 78 *O.&G.R.* 601 (10th Cir. 1980) (holding that the Commission lacked authority to issue the order under the facts of the instant case), *vacated and remanded on other grounds, appeal dism'd per stipulation,* 710 F.2d 611 (10th Cir. 1983).

Tenneco Oil Co., 23 FPS 5-938 (FERC Opinion No. 10-B, Dec. 23, 1982), rejected a payback demand under the facts of the instant case.

Texas Gas Exploration Corp., F.E.R.C. Opinion No. 182, 24 FPS 5-564 (July 20, 1983), dealt with the price to be paid the supplier upon the delayed delivery of payback gas.

For a discussion of cases on payback orders see Horvath, "The Federal Energy Regulatory Commission's Authority to Order In Kind Refunds of Natural Gas," 33 *Case West. Res. L. Rev.*458 (1983).

Pay horizon

The geological deposit in which oil and gas is found in commercial quantities. See HORIZON.

Paying production

See PRODUCTION; PRODUCTION IN PAYING QUANTITIES.

Paying quantities

See PRODUCTION IN PAYING QUANTITIES.

Payment for surface acreage clause

A lease clause providing for a payment to be made to the lessor for surface acreage utilized by the lessee in its operations. See Scott, "Unusual Provisions in Oil and Gas Leases," 33 *Sw. Legal Fdn. Oil & Gas Inst.* 139 at 152 (1982).

Pay out

(1) In a CARRIED INTEREST ARRANGEMENT (*q.v.*), the recovery from production by the CARRYING PARTY (*q.v.*) of development and operating costs.

(2) In a PRODUCTION PAYMENT (*q.v.*) the recovery by the payee of the stipulated sum of money from production.

(3) Generally, the recovery from production of costs of drilling and equipping a well.

In Energy Oils, Inc. v. Montana Power Co., 626 F.2d 731 at 736. 68 *O.&G.R.* 255 at 263 (9th Cir. 1980), the court said that "In the parlance of the oil and gas industry, 'payout' refers to the recoupment of costs of production by a driller or developer pursuant to an agreement like the ones in issue here."

Humble Exploration Co. v. AMCAP Petroleum Associates—1977, 658 S.W.2d 860, 79 *O.&G.R.* 205 (Tex. App., Dallas, 1983, error ref'd n.r.e.), held that for purposes of the vesting of a reversionary BACK IN INTEREST (*q.v.*), the tax imposed under the CRUDE OIL WINDFALL PROFIT TAX ACT OF 1980 (*q.v.*) was a cost required to be recovered from production before payout was achieved.

Pay-out period

The period required for a well to produce sufficient oil or gas to reimburse the investment in the well. In the sale of producing wells, for many years the price of the well typically was in the neighborhood of one-half of the expected net proceeds of the well after deducting operating expenses; in other words, the purchaser expected to receive over the period of production of the well, $2 for each $1 of investment. See Fiske, "The Valuation of Oil and Gas Properties in Estates and Trusts," 2 *Rocky Mt. Min. L. Inst.* 371 (1956).

Pay string

See FLOW STRING.

Pay-up privilege

An option given the carried party in a CARRIED INTEREST ARRANGEMENT (*q.v.*) to pay the carrying party the balance due for carrying him, in which case the parties thereafter shall share in operating and management of the premises. See "The Carried Interest Pay-Up Privilege," 3 *O.&G. Tax Q.* 185 (1954).

PCP

PETROLEUM COMPENSATION PAYMENT (*q.v.*).

PCRC

The PETROLEUM CORPORATION OF THE PEOPLE'S REPUBLIC OF CHINA (*q.v.*).

PCWPC

The PERMANENT COUNCIL OF THE WORLD PETROLEUM CONGRESS (*q.v.*).

PDO

Petroleum Development Oman.

Peak shaving

The use of a supplemental supply of gas (*e.g.*, propane-air mixtures) for distribution by gas utilities to augment normal pipeline supplies during peak demand periods of relatively short duration. See Valley Gas Co. v. Federal Power Comm'n, 487 F.2d 1182, 47 *O.&G.R.* 409 (D.C. Cir. 1973); 38 Fed. Reg. 34422.

PEMEX

Petroleos Mexicanos (*q.v.*).

Penalty clause

A clause in a legal instrument providing for the assessment of a penalty under certain stated circumstances. Thus some unit agreements or joint operating agreements include a clause providing that if one party refuses to drill or participate in the expenses of drilling a well, the other (or others) may proceed with the drilling in which event he (or they) may receive all income from the property until recovery of 200% to 300% of actual expenses. See Stroud, "Major Points of Impact of New Natural Resources Regulations on Oil and Gas," 8 *Sw. Legal Fdn. Oil & Gas Inst.* 393 at 403 (1957).

See also CONTINENTAL OFFSHORE STRATIGRAPHIC TEST (COST).

Penalty gas

Quantities of gas provided in excess of the contracted amount for a given period of time. Penalty gas customarily commands a higher price than gas supplied in accordance with the provisions of the gas purchase contract.

Pencil abstract

A term apparently used to describe an abbreviated or BOB-TAIL ABSTRACT (*q.v.*). The term "is neither widely understood nor self-defining." Jean Oakason, 22 IBLA 311 at 312, GFS(O&G) 132 (Nov. 10, 1975).

Penn Square Bank N.A.

An Oklahoma City bank, heavily engaged in oil and gas investments, which was declared insolvent on July 5, 1982. Because of the Bank's extensive LOAN PARTICIPATION (*q.v.*) program involving other banks around the country, the collapse of Penn Square Bank resulted in difficult problems for a number of banking institutions. See

Fisher & Muratet, "The Aftermath of Penn Square Bank: Protecting Loan Participants From Setoffs," 18 *Tulsa L.J.* 261 (1982).

Pennsylvania grade crude oil

Oil with characteristics similar to the crude oil produced in Pennsylvania from which superior quality lubricating oils are made.

Pentane

An hydrocarbon of the paraffin series. It is liquid at ordinary atmospheric conditions, although small amounts may be present in the gas associated with petroleum. See Interstate Oil Compact Commission, *Oil and Gas Production* 26 (1951).

Percentage

Syn.: PER CENT INTEREST (*q.v.*). See Phillips v. Bruce, 41 Cal. App. 2d 404, 106 P.2d 922 (1941).

Percentage depletion

See DEPLETION, PERCENTAGE.

Percentage of proceeds contract

A contract for the purchase of gas providing that the payment to be made by the purchaser shall be a percentage of the proceeds realized by said purchaser on the resale of said gas. See Phillips Petroleum Co. v. Adams, 513 F.2d 355, 51 *O.&G.R.* 370 (5th Cir.), *rehearing en banc denied,* 515 F.2d 1183 (5th Cir.), *cert. denied,* 423 U.S. 930 (1975).

Percentage sale

A sale of gas by a producer to the operator of a processing plant at a price which is a percentage of the proceeds from the resale of the residue gas or products obtained from the gas. See 18 C.F.R. § 154.91(e) (1980).

Per cent interest

An undivided interest in the royalty, mineral or working interest, expressed in terms of a percentage of the whole, *e.g.*, a 50 per cent mineral interest or a 12½ per cent royalty interest. The term is not one of art but typically it refers to a fractional or percentage interest created by the owner of executive or operating rights in the premises by grant or reservation, but the so-called percent interest may or may not include executive or operating rights. See TREATISE §§ 425–425.2.

See also OWNERSHIP CERTIFICATE; PRODUCTION ASSIGNMENT; PRODUCTION CERTIFICATE.

Percussion drilling

Syn.: CHURN DRILLING (*q.v.*).

Perfect ownership

The term employed in Louisiana to describe an interest which is generally analogous to that described by the common law term "fee simple absolute." Louisiana Civil Code art. 490 (1870) provides that "Ownership is perfect, when it is perpetual, and when the thing is unencumbered with any real right toward any other person than the owner." See McCollam, "A Primer for the Practice of Mineral Law Under the New Louisiana Mineral Code," 50 *Tulane L. Rev.* 729 at 736 (1976).

Perforation

The making of holes in casing and cement (if present) to allow formation fluids to enter the well bore. One common method of perforating is by shooting pellets through the casing by means of a special gun lowered into the hole.

See also BULLET PERFORATOR; GUN PERFORATION; JET PERFORATION.

Performance guarantee

A provision of a PETROLEUM INTERNATIONAL AGREEMENT (PIA) (*q.v.*) or CONCESSION (*q.v.*) by which the parent company of an international oil company guarantees performance of the obligations of that company to the host country. See Blinn, Duval, Le Leuch, and Pertuzio, *International Petroleum Exploration & Exploitation Agreements* 128 (1986).

Performance-type leasing

A leasing program for public lands whereunder the basic criteria for acceptance of a bid is the development program guaranteed by the bidder rather than the amount of bonus or royalty bid. See Statement of John F. O'Leary, Natural Gas Policy Issues, Hearings before the Committee on Interior and Insular Affairs, United States Senate, Pursuant to S. Res. 45, 92nd Cong., 2d Sess., February 25, 29, and March 2, 1972, Serial No. 92–22, at page 655.

The performance-type licensing program adopted for the North Sea by the United Kingdom is described in Kenneth Dam, "Oil and Gas Licensing and the North Sea," 8 *J. L. & Economics* 51 (1965).

"[B]y a process which is none too clear to the outsider looking in after the fact, a 'going price' came to be known for each area. This going price was denominated in such things as holes drilled and exploration work undertaken. He who was unwilling to pay the going price could not expect to be awarded a license. This system could thus be characterized as a competitive bidding system in which the bid was the work programme of the applicant." *Id.* at 59.

For a thorough discussion of the use of various licensing (or leasing) systems to capture the economic rent for the lessor, see K. W. Dam, *Oil Resources* (1976).

See also LEASE BIDDING SYSTEMS.

Periodic flowing

A technique to clear MUD (*q.v.*) out of a well by allowing it to build up a head of pressure and then opening the flow valve into the pits. The head of gas is followed by a flow of oily mud. After the flow ceases, it is shut off to accumulate more pressure, after which the process is repeated.

Syn.: "Bleeding" a well, "rocking" a well. See Rogers v. Osborn, 152 Tex. 540, 261 S.W.2d 311, 2 *O.&G.R.* 304, 1439 (1953).

See also BLOWING A WELL; CLEANING A WELL.

Periodic increase clause

See ESCALATOR CLAUSE.

Permanent carried interest

A CARRIED INTEREST (*q.v.*) which is to be carried for the life of the lease, as opposed to a LIMITED CARRIED INTEREST (*q.v.*) which is to be carried for the initial development phase only of the operation. A permanent carried interest is treated as the equivalent of a NET PROFITS INTEREST (*q.v.*), and hence, when a lease is conveyed, the grantor retaining a permanent carried interest, the transaction is treated as a lease rather than as a sale for tax purposes. See Burke and Bowhay,

Taxation of Natural Resources § 4.01 (1980); "Carried Interests Revisited by Tax Court," 8 *O.&G. Tax Q.* 159 at 161 (1959).

Syn: Unlimited carried interest.

Permanent cessation of production

A prolonged interruption in production from an oil or gas well. Permanent cessation of production terminates a lease or term interest in the secondary term. See TREATISE §§ 334.8, 604.4.

See also CESSATION OF PRODUCTION; TEMPORARY CESSATION OF PRODUCTION.

Permanent Council of the World Petroleum Congress (PCWPC)

A council, composed of members from a number of nations, which meets in Congress every four years to consider papers on topics related to petroleum.

Permeability of rock

A measure of the resistance offered by rock to the movement of fluids through it. It is measured in darcies or millidarcies.

See also DARCY; MILLIDARCY; WETTING.

Permit

See DRILLING PERMIT; EXPLORATORY PERMIT; GEOPHYSICAL EXPLORATION PERMIT; WELL PERMIT.

Permit (Canada)

A right to explore for oil and gas in a specified area. See, *e.g.*, 4 *O.&G.R.* 546 (1955), for the terms of permits applicable to Indian Reserves. See also Saskatchewan Petroleum and Natural Gas Regulations, 1969, O.C. 8/69, Part II.

Permit rent

The annual advance rent payable during the term of a permit to explore for oil and gas. See the Saskatchewan Petroleum and Natural Gas Regulations, 1969, O.C. 8/69, § 10.

See PERMIT (CANADA).

Permitted charging clause

A clause in a joint venture agreement providing that, notwithstanding the restrictions imposed by the agreement on transfers of the interest of a party, a party may grant a floating charge over its interest to secure borrowings to meet its commitments to the joint venture. Merralls, "Mining and Petroleum Joint Ventures in Australia: Some Basic Legal Concepts," 3 *Australian Mining & Petroleum L.J.* 1 at 19 (1981).

See also JOINT ADVENTURE.

"Permitted" drainage

A term used by Professor Merrill [Merrill, "Permitted Drainage—The Sellers Case and Local Law," 4 *Okla. L. Rev.* 58 (1951)] to describe a rule of law that required a lessee to pay damages for failure to protect against drainage without proof that the protection well would probably be profitable. In contrast to such rule was the rule that required proof of profit if a lessor sought cancellation for failure to protect from drainage. The distinction, if ever valid, is not recognized in Oklahoma now. Whether a lessor seeks damages or cancellation for breach of the offset well covenant, he must prove that the offset well would be profitable, in the ordinary case. See Sunray Mid-Continent Oil Co. v. McDaniel, 361 P.2d 683, 14 *O.&G.R.* 348 (Okla. 1961); TREATISE § 822.2, note 16–28.

See also DRAINAGE.

Permitted production

The allowable for a particular well or lease.

Perpetual carried interest

Syn.: PERMANENT CARRIED INTEREST (*q.v.*).

Perpetual lease

Syn. NO-TERM LEASE (*q.v.*). The validity of a perpetual lease for the quarrying of limestone was sustained in Davis v. Kokomis Quarry, Inc., 77 Ill. App.3d 1011, 33 Ill. Dec. 883, 397 N.E.2d 216 (1979).

Perpetual nonparticipating royalty

NONPARTICIPATING ROYALTY (*q.v.*) of perpetual duration. Classified by duration, there are two other types of nonparticipating royalty:

(1) defeasible term royalty (see TERM MINERAL OR ROYALTY INTEREST), which endures for a fixed term and so long thereafter as production exists, and

(2) FIXED TERM ROYALTY (*q.v.*), which endures for a period certain, such as twenty years.

Perpetuities, Rule Against

A rule invalidating future interests limited to become possessory at a remote future time. See TREATISE § 322 *et seq.* for a discussion of numerous oil and gas transactions that have been subjected to attack for alleged violation of this Rule.

Persian-Gulf pricing system

A SINGLE BASE-POINT SYSTEM (*q.v.*) with the Persian Gulf as the base point. See Danielsen, *The Evolution of OPEC* 166 (1982).

Pertamina

P.N. Pertamina [Perusahaan Negara Pertambangan Minjak dan Gas Bumi National], Indonesia's Oil and Natural Gas Enterprise, with responsibility for all activities pertaining to handling and production of oil minerals and natural gas.

See the following discussions:

Chandler, "Current Developments in Oil and Gas Law: The ASEAN Countries," International Bar Ass'n, 1 *Energy Law 1981* at p. 217;

Clapham, "Legal Aspects of Foreign Investments in Oil & Mining," *Int'l Bus. Law* 113 (March 1979 Special Issue);

Fabrikant, "Production Sharing Contracts in the Indonesian Petroleum Industry," 16 *Harv. Int. L.J.* 303 (1975);

OPEC, *Selected Documents of the International Petroleum Industry* 1968 at p. 7.

Per-well charge

In a joint operation or drilling program, this is a monthly charge per well based upon the depth of a well. The charge compensates the operator for supervising the drilling operations and it is separate from other charges which reimburse the operator for its direct and indirect costs of administrative overhead and program management. See Keller v. Comm'r of Internal Revenue, 79 T.C. 7, 74 *O.&G.R.* 129 at 145 (1982), *aff'd,* 725 F.2d 1173, 80 *O.&G.R.* 639 (8th Cir. 1984).

See also DRILLING FUND; JOINT OPERATING AGREEMENT.

Petitory action

An action in Louisiana "brought by a person who claims the ownership, but who is not in possession, of immovable property or of real right, against another who is in possession or who claims the ownership thereof adversely, to obtain judgment recognizing the plaintiff's ownership." La. Code of Civil Procedure Art. 3651 (1961). The action may be brought by a person who claims ownership, but who is not in possession, against: (1) an adverse claimant of ownership who is in possession; (2) a person in possession who may not be asserting any adverse claim of ownership; or (3) an adverse claimant of ownership who is out of possession. The defendant's possession, or lack of it, determines the burden of proof imposed on the plaintiff. See La. Code of Civil Procedure Art. 3653 (1961).

Petrangol

The Companhia de Petroleos de Angola.

Petro-Bonds

A proposed form of bonds to be issued by a corporation with oil reserves, the bonds to be issued at par bearing a lower than market rate of interest but payable at maturity, at the election of the holder, in either the number of dollars stated or in the number of dollars produced by an index based on the price of oil. See Mann, "Financing Oil and Gas Operations—Recent Developments," 33 *Sw. Legal Fdn. Oil & Gas Inst.* 407 at 424 (1982):

> "The object, obviously, would be to provide the bond holder with the potential of an economic benefit above a nominal rate of interest if oil prices increase before maturity. At the same time, protection against an oil price decline would be provided by the option to receive the face value."

See also PROJECT FINANCING.

Petrobras

PETROLEO BRASILEIRO SA (*q.v.*), the Brazilian Petroleum Corporation.

Petro-Canada

Canada's National Oil Company incorporated by Act of the Parliament of Canada in 1975. See Harrison, "State Involvement in the Canadian Petroleum Industry: The Petro-Canada Experience," in International Bar Ass'n, *Proceedings of the Energy Law Seminar* (organized by the Committee on Energy and Natural Resources, Section on Business Law) Topic R, Paper 4 (1979); "The Need for National Oil Companies and Their Relationship to Government and Industry," International Bar Ass'n, *Energy Law 1981* 31.

See also SPECIAL RENEWAL PERMIT.

Petrochemicals

Chemicals derived from oil and natural gas.

For a detailed analysis of the petrochemical industry, see Hearings before the Committee on Interior and Insular Affairs, United States Senate, Pursuant to S. Res. 45, A National Fuels and Energy Policy Study, 93d Cong., 1st Sess., May 1, 1973, at page 617, reporting that total petrochemical sales in 1970 were almost $19 billion.

PETROCORP

The PETROLEUM CORPORATION OF NEW ZEALAND Ltd. (PETROCORP) (*q.v.*).

Petrodollars

The term applied to the surplus oil revenues of Arab and other oil-exporting countries after the dramatic increase in the price of oil as a result of the embargo established by the Arab nations at the time of the Arab-Israeli war in 1973. Many such petrodollars were "recycled" by loans, bank deposits, or investments in oil consuming countries.

See "Balance-of-Payment Adjustment to Higher Oil Prices: Managing the Petrodollar Problem," in "The Economics of Energy and Natural Resource Pricing," Committee Print, A Compilation of Reports and Hearings of the Ad Hoc Committee on the Domestic and International Monetary Effect of Energy and Other Natural Resource Pricing, House Committee on Banking, Currency and Housing, 94th Cong., 1st Sess., March, 1975; Campbell and Mytelka, "Petrodollar Flows, Foreign Aid and International Stratification," 9 *J. World Trade L.* 557 (1975); Salacuse, "Arab Capital and Middle Eastern Development Finance," 14 *J. World Trade L.* 283 (1980).

Petrofracturing

A process in which a mixture of oil, sand and chemical is pumped under pressure into an oil-bearing sand at the bottom of a well for the purpose of increasing the flow of oil. There are two methods of conveying the mixture from the top of the well into the sand at the bottom: (1) the tubing and packer method, by which the emulsion is injected through steel tubing inserted inside the well casing, and a packer is fitted against the walls of the casing at the bottom to prevent the emulsion from rising; and (2) the casing method, by which the fluid is injected directly into the well casing itself. See Dowell, Inc. v. Lyons, 238 F.2d 633, 7 *O.&G.R.* 248 (6th Cir. 1956).

See also HYDRAULIC FRACTURING; SANDFRACING.

Petrolbangla

The national oil company of Bangladesh.

Petroleo Brasileiro SA (PETROBRAS)

The Brazilian Petroleum Corporation created in 1953. See Chester, *United States Oil Policy and Diplomacy* 199 (1983); Keener, "Current Legal Developments in Brazilian Energy Laws and Performance of Services Thereunder," International Bar Ass'n Section on Energy and Natural Resources, *International Energy Law* (1984) (Topic 2); Weiland, "Survey of Oil and Gas Development Policy in Brazil," *Ibid.*

Petróleos de Venezuela S.A. (Petrovén)

A Venezuelan holding company with separate subsidiaries for oil operations, petrochemicals, purchasing, and research and development.

Petroleos Mexicanos (PEMEX)

The national oil company of Mexico. For a discussion of the history of PEMEX and its subjection to suit in the United States, see Matter of the Complaint of Sedco, Inc., 543 F. Supp. 561 (S.D. Tex. 1982).

See also Chester, *United States Oil Policy and Diplomacy* (1983); Barrera, "The International Sale of Natural Gas: The PEMEX-Border Gas, Inc. Contract," 17 *Tex. Inter. L. J.* 15 (1982).

Petroleos Peruanos (Petroperu)

The national oil company of Peru. See Harten, "Oil and Gas Law and Policies in Peru," International Bar Ass'n Section on Energy and Natural Resources, *International Energy Law* (1984) (Topic 2).

Petroleum

A complex liquid mixture of hydrocarbon compounds, oily and inflammable in character.

In Louisiana, petroleum is defined by statute as "crude petroleum, crude petroleum products, distillate, condensate, liquified petroleum gas, any hydrocarbon in a liquid state, any product in a liquid state which is derived in whole or in part from any hydrocarbons, and any mixture or mixtures thereof." La. Rev. Stat., L.S.A.—R.S. § 45–251 (1951) (1980 Supp.)

Petroleum is defined by The Petroleum (Production) Act 1934, 24 & 25 Geo. 5, c. 36, § 1 as including "any mineral oil or relative hydro-carbon and natural gas existing in its natural condition in strata, but does not include coal or bituminous shales or other stratified deposits from which oil can be extracted by destructive distillation."

See also CRUDE OIL; OIL.

Petroleum Accountants Society of Oklahoma

The organization that devised the PASO FORM (*q.v.*).

Petroleum Administration Act

The Canadian Statute, 23–24 Eliz. II, c. 47 (1975), as amended by Stat. 26–27 Eliz. II, c. 24 (1978), imposing a charge on the export of crude oil and petroleum products, providing compensation for certain petroleum costs, and regulating the price of Canadian crude oil and natural gas in interprovincial and export trade. The Act was designed to achieve a uniform price, exclusive of transportation costs and service costs, for crude oil and gas used in Canada outside its province of production, to achieve a balance in Canada between the interests of consumers and producers in Canada, to protect consumers in Canada from instability of prices for petroleum and gas in the international markets, and to encourage the discovery, development, and production of a supply of crude oil and gas adequate to the self-sufficiency of Canada. Eligible importers of petroleum are entitled to import compensation under the Act and suppliers of petroleum to areas in short supply are entitled to transfer payments for making supplies available. See Irving Oil Ltd. v. The Queen, 96 D.L.R.3d 534 (Federal Court, Trial Division, 1979).

See also PETROLEUM IMPORT COST COMPENSATION REGULATIONS.

Petroleum Administration for Defense (PAD)

An agency established on October 3, 1950, by Order No. 25991, 15 Fed. Reg. 6767, to administer the defense responsibilities of the Secretary of the Interior with respect to petroleum and gas. The Secretary was designated Petroleum Administrator and the activities were to be directed by a Deputy Administrator. The organization was patterned after that of the PETROLEUM ADMINISTRATION FOR WAR (PAW) which operated during World War II.

Petroleum Administration for War (PAW)

The federal agency regulating drilling practices (by its control of oil field supplies such as casing) and the distribution of petroleum products during World War II. PAW was established by Exec. Order No. 9276, 7 F.R. 10091 (1942). The history of the agency is sketched in Frey and Ide, *A History of the Petroleum Administration for War* (1946), and in Ely, "The Government in the Exercise of the War Power," in Murphy, Ed., *Conservation of Oil and Gas, A Legal History, 1948* (1949) at p. 664.

Petroleum and Gas Revenue Tax (PGRT)

A levy imposed by the Government of Canada on the wellhead revenue from the production of oil and gas. See Brussa, "Canada's Petroleum and Gas Revenue Tax," [1983/84] 11 *OGLTR* 254.

This tax was eliminated effective 1 October 1986. See [1986/87] 3 *OGLTR* D-29.

Petroleum and Submarine Pipe-Lines Act 1975

The Act establishing the British National Oil Corporation (BNOC) and making provisions for licenses to search for and get petroleum. Stat. 1975, c. 74.

Petroleum Authority of Thailand (PTT)

This organization is discussed in Chandler, "Current Developments in Oil and Gas Law: The ASEAN Countries," International Bar Ass'n 1 *Energy Law* 1981 at p. 217.

Petroleum Board

See FEDERAL PETROLEUM BOARD.

Petroleum coke

A solid residue which is the final product of the condensation process in cracking, and consisting mainly of highly polycyclic aromatic hydrocarbons very poor in hydrogen. 38 Fed. Reg. 34,416 (Dec. 13, 1973).

Petroleum compensation charge

A levy on all Canadian and imported oil to permit compensation of eastern Canadian refiners relying on higher-cost imported oil. See Lucas, "The Canadian National Energy Program Legislation," 1 *J. of Energy & Natural Resources Law* 104 at 105 (1983).

See also NATIONAL ENERGY PROGRAM (NEP).

Petroleum compensation payment (PCP)

A payment made to refineries in eastern Canada importing foreign crude oil after 1974, the amount of the payment approximating the difference between the average cost of the imported oil (purchased at the world or international price) and the controlled domestic price of conventionally produced crude oil. The PCP payment was made from the PETROLEUM COMPENSATION CHARGE (*q.v.*). See Norcen International Ltd. v. Suncor Inc., 36 Alta.L.R.2d 218; [1985] 4 W.W.R. 35 (Alta. Q.B. 1985) (dealing with PCP payments made under an extension of the program to producers of synthetic oil and whether such payments were part of the "price received" for purposes of royalty payment), appeal *allowed in part,* [1986] 4 W.W.R. 57 (Alta. Ct. App. 1986).

Petroleum Corporation of New Zealand, Ltd. (PETROCORP)

A corporation, the shares of which are owned by the government, organized under the provisions of the Companies Act 1955 as a commercial enterprise. For discussion of the company and of petroleum development in New Zealand see the following:

Fisher, "Law and Policy for Accelerating Petroleum Exploration and Development in New Zealand," 16 *Victoria University of Wellington L. Rev.* 11 (1986);

Fisher, "State Participation in Petroleum Development in New Zealand," [1986/87] 7 *OGLTR* 190;

Haughey and Gundersen, "Energy Law in New Zealand," 2 *J. of Energy & Nat. Resources L.* 117 (1984);

Symposium, Petroleum Development and New Zealand Law, 14 *Victoria University of Wellington L. Rev.* 1 et seq. (1984);

Hogg, "The New Zealand Experience—Public Sector Participation in the New Zealand Oil Industry," International Bar Ass'n Committee on Energy and Natural Resources, *Energy Law in Asia and the Pacific* 373 (1982).

Petroleum Corporation of the People's Republic of China (PCRC)

For a discussion of this company's activities, see Barrows, "China—Chinese Oil Regulations and Proposed Petroleum Contracts," International Bar Ass'n, *Energy Law 1981* at p. 173; Bevan, "Exploration in China: What Next?" *Id.* at 195.

Petroleum gas equipment

Equipment used for the production of gas from petroleum derivatives, such as propane, butane, or gasoline. 18 C.F.R. § 201.311 (1980).

Petroleum Import Adjustment Program

A program proclaimed by the President of the United States [45 Fed. Reg. 22,864, 25,371 and 27,905 (1980)] designed to reduce imports of oil by raising the domestic retail price of gasoline by ten cents per gallon. The program was invalidated in Independent Gasoline Marketers Council v. Duncan, 492 F. Supp. 614 (D. .C. 1980).

Petroleum Import Cost Compensation Regulations

Regulations SOR/75–384 (P.C. 1975–1487, June 30, 1975) made pursuant to the PETROLEUM ADMINISTRATION ACT (*q.v.*). See Irving

Oil Ltd. v. The Queen, 96 D.L.R.3d 534 (Federal Court, Trial Division, 1979).

Petroleum Incentives Program Act

A Canadian Act establishing categories of incentives, eligibility rules, administrative provisions, and enforcement powers and duties designed to provide incentive payments to applicants who are Canadian controlled and have a Canadian Ownership rate of at least 50 percent. See Lucas, "The Canadian National Energy Program Legislation," 1 *J. of Energy & Natural Resources Law* 104 at 108 (1983).

See also NATIONAL ENERGY PROGRAM (NEP).

Petroleum incentives program (PIP)

A program of public grants to those engaged in exploration and, in some cases, development, depending upon the rate of Canadian ownership and control of enterprises. See MacDonald, "Current Developments in Oil and Gas Law," *Energy Law 1981,* Seminar of the International Bar Association Committee on Energy and Natural Resources Law 136 at 143 (1981).

For a discussion of certain of the problems encountered in the administration of this program, see "Canada Beset by Huge Costs in Oil Program," *The Wall Street Journal,* Oct. 31, 1983, p. 27.

Petroleum international agreement (PIA)

The term employed by one treatise to describe any major type of petroleum exploration/exploitation agreement. Blinn, Duval, Le Leuch, and Pertuzio, *International Petroleum Exploration & Exploitation Agreements* 12 (1986).

Petroleum license

The right, granted by the Board of Trade on behalf of the Crown to search and bore for and get petroleum. The Petroleum (Production) Act 1934, 24 & 25 Geo 5, c. 36, § 2. The powers of the Board of Trade in respect to mines and minerals under this act were subsequently transferred to the Ministry of Fuel and Power. The title of the Minister of Fuel and Power was changed to the Minister of Power in 1957, and the Ministry of Power was dissolved and the functions of the Minister of Power were transferred to the Minister of Technology in 1969.

See also CONCESSION; EXPLORATION LICENSE; PRODUCTION LICENSE.

Petroleum (Production) Act 1934

Statutes of England, 24 & 25 Geo. 5, c. 36, vesting in the Crown the property in petroleum and natural gas within Great Britain and making provision with respect to the searching and boring for and getting of petroleum and natural gas.

Petroleum province

A region with common geological characteristics which embraces a number of oil and gas reservoirs. See PROVINCE.

Petroleum Revenue Tax (PRT)

A tax established by the United Kingdom Oil Taxation Act 1975. The details of the tax and its operation are discussed in the following:

Henderson *et al., Oil and Gas Law: The North Sea Exploitation* 4.1010 *et seq.* (1979);

Daintith and Willoughby, *A Manual of United Kingdom Oil & Gas Law* 107–143 (1977);

Skinner, "Oil and Gas Policy—The Part Played by Tax Considerations," *Int'l Bus. Law.* 169 (March 1979 Special Issue).

See also ADVANCE PETROLEUM REVENUE TAX (APRT) SYSTEM; SUPPLEMENTARY PETROLEUM TAX.

Petroleum (Submerged Lands) Act 1967 (PSLA)

Act No. 118 of 1967, the principal Austrailian statute dealing with off-shore petroleum exploration and development. For discussions of the Act, see Lang and Crommelin, *Australian Mining and Petroleum Laws* (1979); Reid, "Commonwealth-State Relations Offshore Mining and Petroleum Legislation; Recent Developments; an Historic Milestone or Millstone?" 2 *Austl. Mining & Petroleum L.J.* 58 (1980).

See also MIRROR LEGISLATION.

Petroleum tar sands

Native asphalt, solid and semisolid bitumen, and bituminous rock (including oil-impregnated rock or sands from which oil is recoverable only by special treatment after the deposit is mined or quarried). Under the Mineral Leasing Act Revision of 1960, 30 U.S.C. § 184, the maximum acreage which may be held under lease by a person in any one State is limited to 7,680 acres. See 43 C.F.R. § 3501.1–4(b)(6) (1978).

See also HEAVY OIL; REVERSE COMBUSTION.

The U.S. Department of Energy's Assistant Secretary for Resource Applications defined Tar Sand for the purpose of DOE's Alternate Fuels Incentives Programs as follows:

> "Tar sand is any consolidated or unconsolidated rock (other than coal, oil shale, or gilsonite) that (1) contains a hydrocarbonaceous material with a gas-free viscosity, measured at reservoir temperature, greater than 10,000 centipoise, or (2) contains a hydrocarbonaceous material that is extracted from the mined or quarried rock." 39 *Oil & Gas Compact Bull.* 10 (1980).

The Tar Sands Subcommittee of the Enhanced Recovery Committee of the Interstate Oil Compact Commission adopted the following definition at its 1981 meeting:

> "Tar sand is any consolidated or unconsolidated rock containing a crude oil which is too viscous at natural reservoir temperature to be commercially producible by conventional primary recovery techniques." 30 *Oil & Gas Compact Bull.* 4 (June 1981).

It was reported that several agencies have adopted a similar definition with the following quantitative cut-offs:

	Tar sand	Heavy oil
Viscosity, centipoises	10,000	100 to 10,000
Gravity, °API	10	10 to 20

See also Dobray, "Oil Shale, Tar Sands, and the Definition of a Mineral: An Old Problem in a New Context," 22 *Tulsa L.J.* 1 (1986).

See also ALSANDS PROJECT; SPECIAL TAR SANDS AREA.

Petrolian Nasional Berhad (Petronas)

The Malasyian national oil company. See Moorthy, *PETRONAS—Its Corporate and Legal Status;* Chandler, "Current Developments in Oil and Gas Law: The ASEAN Countries," International Bar Ass'n, 1 *Energy Law,* 1981 at p. 217; "The Malaysian National Oil Corporation—Is It a Government Instrumentality?," 30 *Int. & Comp. L.Q.* 638 (1981); Moorthy, "Legal Aspects of Foreign Investment in Resources Projects in Malaysia," *Int'l Bus. Law* 81 at 86 (March, 1979, Special Issue).

Petromin

The General Petroleum and Minerals Organization, a Public Organization under the laws of the Kingdom of Saudi Arabia "entrusted by the laws of Saudi Arabia with the promotion and achievement of development projects related to petroleum operations and other mining endeavors in order to increase the industrial wealth and the national welfare in Saudi Arabia." See OPEC, *Selected Documents of the International Petroleum Industry 1967* at pp. 190 and 209.

Petronas

The Malaysian national oil company, PETROLIAN NASIONAL BERHAD (*q.v.*).

Petroperu

The PETROLEOS PERUANOS of Peru (*q.v.*).

Petrovén

Petróleos de Venezuela S.A., a holding company with separate subsidiaries for oil operations, petrochemicals, purchasing, and research and development.

PFA

PARTICIPATING FINANCING ARRANGEMENTS (*q.v.*).

PGA clause

PURCHASED GAS ADJUSTMENT CLAUSE (*q.v.*).

PGRT

The PETROLEUM AND GAS REVENUE TAX (*q.v.*).

Phantom freight

The additional freight obtainable from sales of oil from a source closer to the point of delivery than the base point employed for purposes of calculating freight under BASE-POINT PRICING (*q.v.*). See Danielsen, *The Evolution of OPEC* 59 (1982).

Phase-in crude

The share of PARTICIPATION CRUDE (*q.v.*) which the host nation *may* sell and which the operating oil company *must* accept. "This provision, in effect, offers the governments an assured dump market while they develop their own crude outlets." See "The Economics of Energy and Natural Resource Pricing," Committee Print, A Compilation of Reports and Hearings of the Ad Hoc Committee on the Domestic and International Monetary Effect of Energy and Other Natural Resource Pricing, House Committee on Banking, Currency and Housing, 94th Cong., 1st Sess. March 1975, at p. 100.

See also BRIDGING CRUDE; BUYBACK OIL; CONCESSION.

Phase severance

A term applied to the severance of the ownership of gas and gas rights from oil and oil rights. See Midkiff, "Phase Severance of Gas Rights from Oil Rights," 63 *Tex. L. Rev.* 133 (1984).

See also HORIZONTAL SEVERANCE; SEVERANCE; VERTICAL SEVERANCE.

Philippines National Oil Company (PNOC)

A state owned oil company. See Chandler, "Current Developents in Oil and Gas Law: The ASEAN Countries," International Bar Ass'n, 1 *Energy Law 1981* at p. 217.

Physical depletion

See DEPLETION.

Physical waste

Operational losses in the production of oil and gas. There are two main divisions of loss of oil and gas, namely, surface loss and underground loss. Surface loss of oil is due principally to evaporation and surface loss of gas is due principally to burning at field flares or blowing into the atmosphere. Underground loss is due to failure to recover the maximum quantity which theoretically could be produced, as by dissipation of reservoir pressure.

"[T]he loss or destruction of oil or gas after recovery thereof such as to prevent proper utilization and beneficial use thereof, and the loss of oil or gas prior to recovery thereof by isolation or entrapment, by migration; by premature release of natural gas from solution in oil, or in any other manner such as to render impracticable the recovery of such oil or gas." 30 C.F.R. § 221.2(n)(1) (1980).

See also WASTE.

PIA

PETROLEUM INTERNATIONAL AGREEMENT (*q.v.*).

PIAP

The PETROLEUM IMPORT ADJUSTMENT PROGRAM (*q.v.*)

Pick-up oil

Oil which has escaped from a well or storage tank by overflow or seepage recovered by a PICK-UP STATION (*q.v.*).

Pick-up station

A surface pit or other type of trap utilized to gather oil which has escaped from a well or storage tank by overflow or seepage.

Pig

A scraping device for cleaning and testing petroleum and natural gas pipelines.

Piled steel platform

A conventional drilling and production platform for offshore drilling and production operations. A steel jacket enclosing conductor pipes is pinned to the sea bed by long steel piles and is surmounted by a steel deck on which is located housing, a drilling rig, and other installations.

Pill

The term applied to drilling mud containing lubricant additives which is circulated down the drill pipe and back up the annulus to where a drill pipe is stuck. The pill dislodges the stuck pipe. When the drill pipe is freed the pill is circulated to the surface, removed and set aside for disposal. American Petroleum Institute v. Environmental Protection Agency, 787 F.2d 965, 89 *O.&G.R.* 8 (5th Cir. 1986).

Pincher Creek Decision

The decision of the Public Utilities Board of Alberta, pursuant to an application under Section 9 of The Gas Utilities Act, relating to charges and deductions to be allowed for processing costs in determining the value of gas for royalty purposes. See Rae, "Royalty Clauses in Oil and Gas Leases," 4 *Alberta L. Rev.* 323 at 346 (1965); Muir, "Utilization of Alberta Gas," 13 *Alberta L. Rev.* 64 (1975).

Pinch out

A trap formed by the disappearance or wedging out of a porous, permeable rock between two layers of impervious rock.

PIP

PETROLEUM INCENTIVES PROGRAM (*q.v.*).

Pipeline

A tube or system of tubes used for the transportation of oil or gas. Types of oil pipelines include: lead lines, from pumping well to a storage tank; flow lines, from flowing well to a storage tank; lease lines, extending from the wells to lease tanks; gathering lines, extending from lease tanks to a central accumulation point; feeder lines, extending from leases to trunk lines; and trunk lines, extending from a producing area to refineries or terminals.

In the case of gas, the GATHERING SYSTEM (*q.v.*) delivers the gas to the main pipeline which takes the gas directly to the distributor at the place of consumption.

Static capacity of a pipeline is calculated by multiplying the square of the pipe diameter (in inches) by .0009714 to give barrels of oil per lineal foot or by multiplying the square of pipe diameter (in inches) by .005454 to give cubic feet of gas per lineal foot. The quantity passing through the line in a given period will depend on initial pressure, flow characteristics, ground elevation, density, delivery pressure, and the booster stations employed.

For a detailed analysis of the pipeline industry see Wolbert, *U. S. Oil Pipe Lines* (1979). "Today there are over 227,000 miles of operating crude and products lines (including gathering lines) in the United States, exceeding by nearly 40 percent the total miles of mainline railroad right-of-way." *Id.* at 26.

For a detailed examination of the history of pipeline regulation and an order prescribing new criteria for the derivation of maximum permissible rates of return, see Williams Pipe Line Co., 23 F.P.S. 5-685 (F.E.R.C. Opinion No. 154, Nov. 30, 1982).

Farmers Union Central Exchange, Inc. v. Federal Energy Regulatory Comm'n, 734 F.2d 1486 (D.C. Cir. 1984), *cert. denied,* 105 S.Ct. 507 (1984), discusses at length the responsibilities of, and factors to be considered by, the Federal Energy Regulatory Commission in determining "just and reasonable" oil pipeline rates.

For a collection of papers delivered at a 1983 Symposium on Contracts for the Construction of Oil and Gas Pipelines, see *International Business Lawyer* (July/August 1984).

See also the following:

Mogel, "Impact of FERC Order No. 436 on the Natural Gas Industry: Will It Affect Contracting Practices?" 32 *Rocky Mt. Min. L. Inst.* 15-1 (1986);

Pierce, "Reconsidering the Roles of Regulation and Competition in the Natural Gas Industry," 97 Harv. L. Rev. 345 (1983) (arguing that the natural gas market would function more efficiently if Congress deregulated gas pipeline companies and required them to compete against one another);

Malet, "Oil Pipelines as Common Carriers: Issues of Form and Substance," 20 *Houston L. Rev.* 801 (1983);

Rappoport, "The Structure of Gas Tariffing Agreements," [1985/86] 7 *OGLTR* 175;

Fisher, "Access to Submarine Pipelines and Tariffs: The Legal Framework," [1982] 1 *OGLTR* 9;

Adams and Brock, "Deregulation or Divestiture: The Case of Petroleum Pipelines," 19 *Wake Forest L. Rev.* 705 (1983) (a detailed argument for requiring divestiture of pipeline ownership by integrated oil companies);

Mitchell (ed.), *Oil Pipelines and Public Policy* (American Enterprise Institute, 1979), discussing proposals for industry reform and reorganization.

See also AGREEMENT ON PRINCIPLES; ALASKA NATURAL GAS PIPELINE FINANCING ACT; ANGTA; ANGTS; BACK-HAUL ARRANGEMENT; BIG INCH PIPELINE; DISTRIBUTION LINE; FLOW LINE; GATHERING LINE; HEPBURN ACT; HIGH-VOLUME SYSTEM; HINSHAW PIPELINE; INDEPENDENT PIPELINE; INTERMEDIATE-VOLUME SYSTEM; LINE LOSS; LINE PACK GAS; LITTLE BIG INCH PIPELINE; LOOP; LOOPING; LOOP LINES; LOW-VOLUME SYSTEM; MANDATORY CONTRACT CARRIAGE; MOTHER HUBBARD CASE; MINIMUM TENDER; NATURAL GAS PIPELINE SAFETY ACT (NGPSA); NO-FEE EXCHANGE; NORTHERN TIER PIPELINE CO.; OFF-SYSTEM CUSTOMER; PARTIAL LOOPING; PIPELINE CONSENT DECREE OF 1941; PRUDENT PIPELINE STANDARD; QUALITY

BANK; SERVICE LINE; TAPLINE; TAPS AGREEMENT; THROUGHPUT AND DEFICIENCY AGREEMENT; TRANS-ALASKA PIPELINE AUTHORIZATION ACT; TRANSIT PIPELINE TREATY; TRANSMISSION LINE; TRANSMISSION SYSTEM; TRUNK LINE; TURNED INTO THE LINE; UNCONNECTED WELL; UNDIVIDED INTEREST PIPELINE; YAMBURG-URENGOI PIPELINE.

Pipeline consent decree of 1941

The agreement entered into by the Department of Justice, 20 major oil companies, and 59 pipeline companies stipulating that dividends paid by the pipeline companies to their shipper-owners would not be unlawful rebates if they did not exceed 7 percent of the Interstate Commerce Commission's valuation of the pipelines' properties. Since the dividend limit was based on valuation rather than on equity in the pipelines, debt capital has been resorted to for much of the cost of constructing pipelines, thus leading to a high rate of return on equity capital. See Report to the Congress by the Comptroller General, *Petroleum Pipeline Rates and Competition* 14 (July 13, 1979). Debt financing of construction costs has been facilitated by THROUGHPUT AND DEFICIENCY AGREEMENTS (*q.v.*). The result has been debt-equity of 90:10 or higher.

For a discussion of this decree see Adams and Brock, "Deregulation or Divestiture: The Case of Petroleum Pipelines," 19 *Wake Forest L. Rev.* 705 at 729 (1983).

Pipeline gas

A term used to describe gas which has sufficient pressure to enter the high pressure lines of the purchaser for distribution to its customers without further compression and which is sufficiently dry so that the liquid hydrocarbons therefrom will not drop out in the transmission lines. Greenshields v. Warren Petroleum Corp., 248 F.2d 61, 8 *O.&G.R.* 937 (10th Cir. 1957), *cert. denied,* 355 U.S. 907 (1957).

Pipeline gauger

A person who gauges the run of oil or gas for the pipeline purchaser. See Cox v. De Soto Crude Oil Purchasing Corp., 55 F. Supp. 467 (W. D. La. 1944).

Pipeline interest

A term occasionally used to describe a royalty or overriding royalty interest. See State v. Walters, 244 Iowa 1253, 58 N.W.2d 4, 2 *O.&G.R.* 649 (1953), *cert. denied,* 346 U.S. 940 (1954).

Pipeline oil

Oil of such quality as to be acceptable for pipeline shipment.

Pipeline prorationing

See PURCHASER PRORATIONING.

Pipeline quality gas

Gas of the quality which may be taken by a pipeline purchaser.

This term is defined by Section 416 of the National Energy Act (H.R. 8444), as passed by the House of Representatives on August 5, 1977, as meaning a mixture of hydrocarbons in a gaseous state (i) the principal ingredient of which is methane and (ii) which is interchangeable and compatible with natural gas as determined by a rule of the Commission.

Pipeline rider

An employee of an oil or gas pipeline company whose job is to check the condition of the pipeline and the right of way from time to time.

Pipeline title opinion

Syn.: Division order title opinion. See TITLE OPINION.

Pipe stringing

See STRINGING PIPE.

PIR

PROGRESSIVE INCREMENTAL ROYALTY (*q.v.*).

PLA

PACIFIC LEASE AGREEMENT (*q.v.*).

Plant fuel

Fuel employed by a lessee in operating a plant (*e.g.*, a DEHYDRATION PLANT or TREATING PLANT (*q.v.*)) or a plant to remove sulfur from oil or gas produced by the lessee. Piney Woods County Life School v. Shell Oil Co., 726 F.2d 225, 79 *O.&G.R.* 244 (5th Cir. 1984), *reh. denied,* 750 F.2d 69 (5th Cir. 1984), *cert. denied,* ___ U.S. ___, 105 S. Ct. 1868 (1985) held that plant fuel is "gas used off the lease" for purposes of the royalty clause of leases there construed.

Plant operating agreement

The agreement incident to a pooling or unitization agreement concerning the operation of a plant for the handling, processing and compression of certain of the unitized substances and for the furtherance of such pressure maintenance and other fluid injection programs as are carried on under the agreement. See Myers, *The Law of Pooling and Unitization* § 5.21 (2d ed. 1967).

Plant operator

The person designated by a PLANT OPERATING AGREEMENT (*q.v.*) to operate, maintain, alter, enlarge and extend the plant authorized by such agreement.

Plant protection gas

Minimum volumes of gas required to prevent physical harm to plant facilities or danger to plant personnel when such protection cannot be afforded through the use of an alternate fuel. Statement of Chairman John N. Nassikas, Federal Power Commission, "Federal Power Commission Oversight—Natural Gas Curtailment Priorities," Hearing before the Senate Committee on Commerce, 93d Cong., 2d Sess., June 20, 1974, at p. 82; F.P.C. Order No. 493 (Sept. 21, 1973).

For a discussion of the operation of curtailment plans on plant protection gas, see Process Gas Consumers Group v. United States Dept. of Agriculture, 694 F.2d 728 (D.C. Cir. 1981), *modified on rehearing en banc,* 694 F.2d 778 (D.C. Cir. 1982), *cert. denied,* 461 U.S. 905, 103 S.Ct. 1874 (1983).

Plat book

A book containing plats arranged according to township and range numbers preserved in District Land Offices of the BUREAU OF

LAND MANAGEMENT (*q.v.*). See *Rocky Mt. Min. L. Fdn. Landman's Legal Handbook* 114 (3d ed. 1977). The plats show information concerning the lands appearing thereon as to whether patented or not, whether subject to lease, etc.

Platform

See GRAVITY STRUCTURE; HYBRID PLATFORM; JACK-UP RIG; MOBILE RIG; MAT SUPPORTED JACK-UP; PILED STEEL PLATFORM; TEMPLET-TYPE PLATFORM; TENSION LEG PLATFORM.

Platform privileges

Privileges to be on or about a drilling well at all times and to have access to all reports, records, logs, samples and cores. Augusta Oil Co. v. Watson, 204 Kan. 495 at 499, 464 P.2d 227 at 231, 35 *O.&G.R.* 147 at 153 (1970).

PLATO

(1) The acronym for the DRILLING FUND (*q.v.*) involving Pennzoil Louisiana and Texas Offshore, Inc. See Collins, "Recent Developments Affecting Investors in Oil and Gas," 22 *Tulane Tax Inst.* 55 at 81 (1973).

(2) A proposed voluntary agreement among tanker owners, not unlike TOVALOP (*q.v.*) providing higher levels of compensation for pollution damages, cost of taking preventive measures and cost of threat removal measures. See "PLATO: Pollution Agreement Among Tanker Owner," [1985/86] 9 *OGLTR* 237.

See also CRISTAL.

Platt's Oil Price Handbook and Oilmanac

A standard reporting service on petroleum and product prices at major centers.

PLCA

Pipe Line Contractors Association.

Pledged production payment

See EQUIPMENT PRODUCTION PAYMENT.

Plug

(1) (Verb) To stop the flow of water, gas or oil from one stratum to another in connection with the abandoning of a well.

(2) (Noun) The object placed in the well bore to stop the flow of water, gas or oil from one stratum to another in connection with the abandoning of a well.

Plug back

"To cement off lower section of casing; to block fluids below from rising in casing to a higher section being tested." Bureau of Mines, *A Dictionary of Mining, Mineral, and Related Terms* (1968); William Perlman, 93 I.D. 159 (April 2, 1986).

Plugging of well

The sealing off of the fluids in the strata penetrated by a well, so that the fluid from one stratum will not escape into another or to the surface. This is usually accomplished by introducing cement and MUD (*q.v.*) into the hole. Conservation regulations of many states require the plugging of abandoned wells.

This term was defined in a jury instruction as "closing" a well-bore "in such a way or manner as to prevent the migration of oil, gas, salt water, or other substance, from one stratum into another." Salmon Corp. v. Forest Oil Corp., 536 P.2d 909 at 911, 52 *O.&G.R.* 413 at 417 (Okla. 1974). The court concluded that failure of a lessee to comply with the Osage Indian Agency's requirements as to plugging of well would subject such lessee to liability to a subsequent lessee required to replug the wells in the course of a secondary recovery operation on proof that compliance with those requirements would have sealed off the wells in such a way as to have withstood the increased pressure of waterflooding.

See Douglass, "The Obligations of Lessees and Others to Plug and Abandon Oil and Gas Wells," 25 *Sw. Legal Fdn. Oil & Gas Inst.* 123 (1974).

State v. Wallace, 40 Ohio Misc. 29, 69 Ohio App. 2d 228, 318 N.E.2d 883, 49 *O.&G.R.* 507 (Municipal Court of Hancock County, 1974), *appeal dism'd on procedural ground,* 43 Ohio St. 2d 1, 330 N.E.2d 697 (1975), held unconstitutional as an illegal delegation of legislative authroity a statute imposing criminal sanctions for failure to comply with an administrative order requiring the plugging of a well "which is or becomes incapable of producing oil and gas in commercial quantities."

Houser v. Brown, 28 Oh.App.3d 358, 505 N.E.2d 1021, ___ *O.&G.R.* ___ (1986), held that a lease assignee became subject to a statutory duty to plug a well incapable of paying production by accepting an assignment of the lease on which the nonpaying well was located, and he could not relieve himself of that statutory duty by surrendering the lease to the lessor.

PNOC

The Philippines National Oil Company (*q.v.*).

POGG power

The "Peace, Order and Good Government" or residual power of the Canadian Parliament. See Richardson and Quigley, "The Resources Industry, Foreign Ownership and Constitutional Methods of Control," 39 *Sask. L. Rev.* 92 (1974–75).

POGO plan

A plan for financing oil and gas exploration developed primarily for use in financing offshore exploration. The basic form is corporate and the investor receives shares of capital stock and subordinated convertible debentures of a new subsidiary corporation.

"A 'POGO' type fund became somewhat popular a few years ago and typically involves a major or quasi-major oil company with participations in offshore oil and gas leases contributing these leases to a new corporation. The new corporation then raises funds for drilling by a public offering. The concept was that if the oil and gas operations were successful, the separate drilling fund corporation would at some point merge into a large public oil company, usually the affiliate of the drilling fund corporation. This concept was a result of some investment banker's imagination in seeking different ways to raise capital primarily to finance expensive offshore oil and gas activities." Bean, "Entity Selection—An Experience in Alchemy—A Comparison of Corporations, Partnerships, and Joint Ventures," 30 *Sw. Legal Fdn. Oil & Gas Inst.* 363 at 365 (1979).

For other discussions of the POGO plan see the following:

Record, "Recent Developments in Exploration Financing," 24 *Sw. Legal Fdn. Oil & Gas Inst.* 111 at 123 (1973);

Collins, "Recent Developments Affecting Investors in Oil and Gas," 22 *Tulane Tax Inst.* 55 at 77 (1973).

See also Drilling fund; PLATO.

Point

One percentage point of interest in production. For example, a royalty of 12½% is sometimes referred to as 12½ points. Albrecht v. Imperial Oil Ltd., 21 W.W.R. 560, 7 *O.&G.R.* 739 (Alberta Supreme Court, 1957).

Political risk loan

A form of PROJECT FINANCING (*q.v.*) in which the field's sponsors guarantee all commercial risks but the banks take the political risks of expropriation, changes in tax and royalty, and depletion controls. See Adamson, "North Sea Financing—A Commercial Banker's View," in International Bar Ass'n, *Proceedings of the Energy Law Seminar* (organized by the Committee on Energy and Natural Resources, Section on Business Law) Topic N, Paper 1 (1979).

For a discussion of national programs of investment insurance against political risks, see the following:

El Sheikh, *The Legal Regime of Foreign Private Investment in the Sudan and Saudi Arabia* 158 *et seq.* (1984);

Zakariya, "Insurance Against the Political Risks of Petroleum Investment," 4 *J. of Energy & Natural Resources Law* 217 (1986).

Polymerization

A process whereby light hydrocarbon molecules are combined to form a high octane gasoline blending stock. The reaction is produced by the use of high pressures and temperatures in the presence of a catalyst.

Pool

(1) (Noun). An underground reservoir containing or appearing to contain a common accumulation of oil and natural gas. A zone of a structure which is completely separated from any other zone in the same structure is a pool. Ore. Laws 1953, c. 667, § 1 (7), O. R. S. § 520.005; Wash. Laws 1951, ch. 146, § 3 (4), RCW 78.52.010. An underground accumulation of petroleum in a single and separate natural reservoir characterized by a single pressure system so that production of petroleum from one part of the pool affects the reservoir pressure throughout its extent. A pool is so bounded by geologic barriers that it is effectively separated from other pools that may be present. Buckley, *Petroleum Conservation* 80 (Am. Inst. of Mining & Metallurgical Engineers, 1951).

State of Texas v. Secretary of the Interior, 580 F. Supp. 1197, 80 *O.&G.R.* 573 (E.D. Tex. 1984), concluded that "*pool* may be construed to include a stratigraphic interval containing one or more reservoirs." Thus, under this construction, the term "pool" is more encompassing than is the term "reservoir." For purposes of Section 8 lands [see SECTION 8 LEASE], the term "pool" was "construed as referring to hydrocarbon-prone area which may or may not be subject to cross migration."

See also ALLOCATED POOL; COMMON SOURCE OF SUPPLY; CONFIDENTIAL POOL; DESIGNATED POOL; FIELD; NON-CONFIDENTIAL POOL; OIL POOL; RESERVOIR.

(2) (Verb) To combine two or more tracts of land into one unit for drilling purposes. This may be accomplished voluntarily, or through compulsion.

See also COMPULSORY POOLING; POOLING; WELL SPACING.

Pooled unit

A unit formed by the bringing together of separately owned interests under the provisions of pooling clauses of leases or of some special agreement. See Whelan v. Manziel, 314 S.W.2d 126, 9 *O.&G.R.* 390 (Tex. Civ. App. 1958, error ref'd n.r.e.), where a pooled unit is distinguished from a proration unit.

Pooling

A term frequently used interchangeably with UNITIZATION (*q.v.*) but more properly used to denominate the bringing together of small tracts sufficient for the granting of a well permit under applicable spacing rules, as distinguished from unitization, which term is used to describe the joint operation of all or some portion of a producing reservoir. Pooling is important in the prevention of drilling of unnecessary and uneconomic wells, which will result in physical and economic waste. See Hoffman, *Voluntary Pooling and Unitization* (1954).

The term pooling is also used occasionally to describe cross-conveyances of mineral or royalty interests by separate owners or conveyances of such interests to a trustee for the purpose of sharing the income from production of wells drilled anywhere on the consolidated tract. See Carlson v. Tioga Holding Co., 72 N.W.2d 236, 4 *O.&G.R.* 1755 (N.D. 1955).

The former usage of the term relates to the working interest alone or to the working and non-operating interests; the latter usage typically relates to the non-operating interests only. On pooling generally, see TREATISE Ch. 9.

The definition in this MANUAL was cited in Whelan v. Manziel, 314 S.W.2d 126, 9 *O.&G.R.* 390 at 396 (Tex. Civ. App. 1958, error ref'd n.r.e.).

See also COMPULSORY POOLING; CONSENT PARTY; CONTRACT THEORY OF POOLING; CROSS-ASSIGNMENT; CROSS-TRANSFER OF ROYALTIES; EQUITABLE POOLING; LANDOWNERS' ROYALTY POOL; UNITIZATION.

Pooling agreement

An agreement bringing together separately owned interests for the purpose of obtaining a well permit under applicable spacing rules.

Pooling by a drilling and spacing unit

Pooling of an entire drilling and spacing unit for all formations, as distinguished from POOLING BY THE BOREHOLE (*q.v.*) which is limited and designed to cover only one borehole and the production from those formations tested or established to be productive of hydrocarbons within the unit.

Pooling by the bore hole

Pooling limited and designed to cover only one bore hole and the production from those formations tested or established to be productive of hydrocarbons within the unit, as distinguished from pooling of an entire drilling and spacing unit for all formations. Amoco Production Co. v. Corporation Comm'n, ____ P.2d ____, ____ *O.&G.R.* ____, 57 *Okla. B.J.* 1961 (Okla. App. 1986), invalidated a Corporation Commission order which declared that a prior forced pooling order was limited to only one bore hole, and hence non-consenting owners were entitled to a second election to participate in the drilling of a second well on the spacing unit.

See also Dunmire, "Oklahoma Forced Pooling," *Institute on Oil and Gas Conservation Law and Practice* (Rocky Mt. Min. L. Fdn. 1985).

Pooling clause

A lease clause authorizing a lessee to "pool" or join the particular leased premises with other leases for the purpose of aggregating a tract sufficient for a well permit under applicable spacing regulations. Also, a lease clause authorizing the lessee to unitize the leased premises with other parcels.

A typical pooling clause provides as follows:

"Lessee is granted the right, power and option at any time or times to pool and combine the land covered by this lease or any portion thereof with any other land, lease or leases in the vicinity thereof when in the Lessee's judgment it is necessary or advisable to do so. Such pooling may include all oil, gas and other minerals or may be limited to one or more such substances and may extend to all such production or may be limited to any one or more zones or formations."

The clause will typically provide further for (1) a maximum size of the unit to be formed, (2) notification to the lessor of the formation of the unit, (3) provision for apportionment of royalties, and (4) the effect of production or other operations within the unit upon the lease, both as to the portion of the leased premises included within the unit and as to the portion of the leased premises excluded from the unit. Considerable care needs to be exercised in the drafting of the latter provision or the lessor may find that inclusion of a small portion of a leasehold in a unit will suffice to excuse payment of delay rentals on the substantial portion of the leasehold excluded from the unit and that production on the unit, from which the lessor receives only a nominal payment, will suffice to keep the entire leasehold alive after the expiration of the primary term.

On the contents of pooling clauses, see TREATISE §§ 668–670.8.

See also ALL OR NOTHING CLAUSE; PUGH CLAUSE.

Pooling, compulsory

See COMPULSORY POOLING.

Pooling, equitable

See EQUITABLE POOLING.

Pool of capital doctrine

The name given the rule that a person who contributes services or property to the exploration or development of a mineral property in exchange for an interest in the mineral property does not have taxable income on the receipt of the mineral interest. The taxpayer is deemed to have made a nontaxable investment in the venture rather than a taxable sale of goods or services. See Glancy, "Compensating Key Employees in the Oil and Gas Business," 33 *Sw. Legal Fdn. Oil & Gas Inst.* 369 at 371 (1982).

See also the following:

Morgan, "Revenue Ruling 83-46: Taxing the Service Contributor to Oil Well Development—The IRS Abandons the Pool of Capital Doctrine," 22 *Houston L. Rev.* 813 (1985);

Dumas, "The Pool of Capital Doctrine in Oil and Gas Taxation: Its Status Under Revenue Ruling 83-46," 52 *Tenn. L. Rev.* 291 (1985);

Crichton, "Planning Multi-Party Operations: A Primer on Pool of Capital Doctrine," 30 *L.S.U. Min. L. Inst.* 360 (1984);

Parker, "Contribution of Services to the Pool of Capital," 35 *Sw. Legal Fdn. Oil & Gas Inst.* 313 (1984).

See also DRILLING FUND.

Popping

The blowing of natural gas into the air. In the 1930's this was a common practice with respect to sour gas and casinghead gas, after the liquid constituents had been removed, because there was no market for the gas. See Cheek, "Legal History of Conservation of Gas in Texas," in Am. Bar Assn., *Legal History of Conservation of Oil and Gas* 269 at 278 (1938).

See also FLARING OF GAS.

Pore space

See SATURATED HYDROCARBON PORE SPACE.

Porosity of rock

The relative volume of the pore spaces between mineral grains as compared to the total rock volume. This porosity measures the capacity of the rock to hold oil, gas, and water. The usual range of porosities is from 15 to 20 per cent, but they may be as high as 43 per cent or higher in highly fractured and cavernous limestones.

Port Acres case

A term used to describe Halbouty v. Railroad Comm'n, 163 Tex. 417, 357 S.W.2d 364, 16 *O.&G.R.* 788 (1962), *cert. denied sub nom.* Dillon v. Halbouty, 371 U.S. 888, 17 *O.&G.R.* 173 (1962).

Possibility of reverter

The property interest left in a grantor or lessor after a grant of land or minerals subject to a special limitation. Upon the occurrence of the event specified in the special limitation, the granted estate reverts to the grantor or lessor without the necessity of affirmative re-entry.

In a limited number of cases, however, it has been held that the interest of the lessee has not terminated despite occurrence of the event specified in the clause of special limitation. See Williams, "Primary Term and Delay Rental Provisions," 2 *Sw. Legal Fdn. Oil & Gas Inst.* 93 at 115 *et seq.* (1951); TREATISE § 604.7.

The DELAY RENTAL CLAUSE (*q.v.*) of the UNLESS LEASE (*q.v.*) contains such a special limitation in that the estate granted is to revest in the lessor at any anniversary date of the lease during the primary term if there is then no production or if drilling operations have not then been commenced unless delay rentals are paid.

To be compared is the delay rental clause of an OR LEASE (*q.v.*), which has the effect of creating a POWER OF TERMINATION (*q.v.*) in the lessor rather than a possibility of reverter. Upon the happening of the event stated by the clause of limitation, the estate is vested in the owner of the possibility of reverter automatically; hence equitable considerations are said to be irrelevant. Baldwin v. Blue Stem Oil Co., 106 Kan. 848, 189 Pac. 920 (1920).

In the law of many jurisdictions, the habendum clause of a lease creates two possibilities of reverter: (1) upon the expiration of the primary term without production [absent a SAVINGS CLAUSE (*q.v.*)], and (2) upon the cessation of production after the primary term.

Posted field price

The announced price at which a crude oil purchaser will buy the oil (of specified quality) from a field. At one time, the price was actually announced by a statement posted in the field. Now, the announcement is usually made in the newspapers.

It is not always clear that posted field price is a proper measure of the "value" of oil produced. See, *e.g.*, Bass Development Corp. v. Mississippi State Tax Commission, 271 So. 2d 432, 43 *O.&G.R.* 167 (Miss. 1973), dealing with a contract whereby the ultimate purchasers of oil agreed to pay lessors an additional twenty-five cents per barrel of royalty oil in consideration of waiver of lessors' right to take royalty in kind, the agreement providing that if the posted price should exceed $2.00 per barrel the contract would terminate unless the former party elected to continue it in effect. The court concluded that severance tax was payable on the payment of twenty-five cents per barrel while declaring that the value of the working interest oil remained the posted field price. In other words, working interest oil was viewed as having a value of $2. per barrel and royalty oil as having a value of $2.25 per barrel for severance tax purposes. One may speculate why a purchaser of oil would be willing to pay lessors a premium of twenty-five cents per barrel of royalty oil for waiving the right to take royalty in kind; was it because the royalty owner would have been able to sell the oil at a higher price than the posted field price, thus evidencing its artificial character?

See also POSTED PRICE.

Posted price

The term "Posted price" is defined in 10 C.F.R. § 212.31 (1980) as "a written statement of crude petroleum prices circulated publicly among sellers and buyers of crude petroleum in a particular field in accordance with historic practices, and generally known by sellers and buyers within the field."

Syn.: POSTED FIELD PRICE (*q.v.*)

Also, in the case of foreign production, a price fixed by government order on the basis of which royalties and taxes are assessed.

"A 'posted price' in the foreign oil industry traditionally has been a *public offering price by the seller, f.o.b. port of origin,* based on his assessment of the value of petroleum to him, in terms of replacement and opportunity costs, and its value to buyers around the world. While the posted price is by its very nature the most visible to the public, the competitively significant price is the *actual transaction price of oil delivered to refineries* in the consuming countries. It is an individually negotiated price. An unaffiliated refining company in, say, West Germany, is interested only in the net delivered price per barrel because this is the price which determines his competitive ability to sell refined products in his market area. Typically, various oil-producing firms will offer him a variety of deals designed to satisfy his requirements. Each proposal will involve a somewhat different package of attributes including for instance: a specified *type* of crude oil, an *f.o.b. price* per barrel at the port of origin, a *transportation charge* per barrel from that port or origin to a refinery, a *schedule of deliveries,* and specified *terms of payment.* In addition, a seller may suggest a variety of other features to make his proposal more attractive. These may include agreements to provide technical assistance, to make loans or extend special credits, to buy back surplus products from the refiner, or to provide a variety of quid pro quo's. Indeed, the number of different factors that may be involved in sellers' negotiations with the buyer is limited only by the ingenuity of the human mind." Jacoby, *Multinational Oil* 218 (1974).

Temp. Treas. Reg. § 150.4989-1(c)(8)(B) described posted price as:

"a written statement of crude oil prices constituting an offer to purchase oil at that price circulated publicly among sellers and buyers of crude oil in a particular field in accordance with historic practices. Although the formality of a printed price bulletin such as is published by major purchasers is not necessary for a price to be a valid posted price, the formality of a publicly circulated written notice is necessary. The requirement that the offer be in writing and publicly circulated eliminates oral offers and offers made only to specified producers. Accordingly, other than the published price bulletins of the type traditionally issued by major oil companies, written offers to purchase constitute a 'posted price' only if they are bona fide public offers of general applicability to crude oil producers in the field. For example, a letter from a purchaser to all crude oil producers in a field or in an area would constitute a posted price if the letter was a bona fide offer to purchase from all producers in that field or area. A written contract, of course, would not qualify as a posted price because it represents an agreement between a buyer and a specific producer, not a bona fide offer to purchase from all producers."

Osborn v. Department of Energy, CCH *Federal Energy Guidelines* ¶ 26,475 (Temp. Emer. Ct. App. 1984), concluded that an offer by a potential buyer circulated to some, but not all, of the producers in the area of his operations was not a posted price within the meaning of Department of Energy regulations.

See also ADJUSTED POSTED PRICE; BUYBACK OIL; EXPECTED THIRD PARTY PRICE; FLAT SALE OF CRUDE OIL; GUARANTEED SALES PRICE; INTERNATIONAL MARKET PRICE; PRICE; REALIZED PRICE; REFERENCE PRICE; TAX REFERENCE PRICE.

Posting

As used in regulations of the Federal Power Commission, and of its successor, the Federal Energy Regulatory Commission, the term means "(a) making a copy of a natural-gas company's tariff and contracts available during regular business hours for public inspection in a convenient form and place at the natural-gas company's offices where business is conducted with affected customers and (b) mailing to each customer affected a copy of such tariff or part thereof at the time it is sent to the Commission for filing." 18 C.F.R. § 154.16 (1980).

Post sale analysis chart

A chart prepared by the Bureau of Land Management (BLM) following an Outer Continental Shelf (OCS) lease sale to evaluate the high bid to determine whether it satisfies the statutory objective of return of fair market value. See Kerr-McGee Corp. v. Watt, 517 F. Supp. 1209, 71 *O.&G.R.* 494 (D.D.C. 1981).

Syn.: Post sale matrix.

Post sale matrix

Syn.: POST SALE ANALYSIS CHART (*q.v.*).

Potential

The actual or properly computed daily ability of a well to produce oil or gas as determined by a test made in conformity with rules prescribed by the regulatory commission. IOCC, *A Suggested Form of General Rules and Regulations for the Conservation of Oil and Gas* (1960), Rule III. In the case of oil wells, potential may also be expressed in barrels per hour. See WELL POTENTIAL.

Potential value

Syn.: SPECULATIVE VALUE (*q.v.*). See Daggett, *Mineral Rights in Louisiana* 388 (rev. ed. 1949).

Potestative condition

A condition "which makes the execution of the agreement depend on an event which it is in the power of the one or the other of the contracting parties to bring about or to hinder." La. Civ. Code Art. 2024 (1977).

Other conditions are described as casual or mixed. A casual condition "depends on chance, and is in no way in the power either of the creditor or of the debtor." *Id.,* Art. 2023. A mixed condition "is one that depends at the same time on the will of one of the parties and on the will of a third person, or on the will of one of the parties and also on a casual event." *Id.,* Art. 2025.

An obligation is null that has been contracted on a potestative condition on the part of him who binds himself (Art. 2034), but this provision is limited to potestative conditions which make the obligation depend solely on the exercise of the obligor's will; "if the condition be, that the obligor shall do or not do a certain act, although the doing or not doing of the act depends on the will of the obligor, yet the obligation depending on such condition, is not void." Art. 2035.

Power gas

A low-energy gaseous fuel, generally produced from coal, whose principal combustible components (carbon monoxide and hydrogen) are generally diluted by air. Also called producer gas, it differs from COAL GAS (*q.v.*) in that the energy content is only about 150 to 250 Btu per standard cubic foot. Because of its low energy content, power gas cannot be transported economically and is generally burned at the production site for the generation of electricity. See Hammond, Metz, and Maugh, *Energy and the Future* 164 (1973).

Power of re-entry

See POWER OF TERMINATION.

Power of resumption

In some of the states of Australia, the power of the Crown to resume privately owned land containing minerals, on payment of compensation. See Lang and Crommelin, *Australian Mining and Petroleum Laws* 159 (1979).

Power of termination

The power or right of a grantor or lessor to re-enter the estate granted or leased upon the occurrence of a stated event or breach of a condition and terminate the granted or leased estate. Affirmative re-entry or its equivalent (an action at law) is required before the estate is terminated, whereas when an estate is granted subject to a special limitation [the grantor or lessor retaining a POSSIBILITY OF REVERTER (*q.v.*)] the estate granted is automatically terminated upon the occurrence of the stated event.

The delay rental clause of the OR LEASE (*q.v.*) provides for a power of termination rather than a possibility of reverter [which is found in the delay rental clause of an UNLESS LEASE (*q.v.*)]. The power of termination is considered a forfeiture clause and equity may grant relief against the forfeiture under some circumstances; in the case of a special limitation, the equities are usually considered irrelevant and relief against the automatic reversion of the estate is rarely if ever available. See Walker, "The Nature of the Property Interests Created by an Oil and Gas Lease in Texas," 8 *Texas L. Rev.* 483 at 536–540 (1930).

Syn.: Right of re-entry, power of re-entry, re-entry clause, grant on condition subsequent.

See also FORFEITURE CLAUSE; TERMINATION OF LEASE.

Powerplant and Industrial Fuel Use Act of 1978

Pub. L. No. 95–620 (Nov. 9, 1978). The major provisions of this Act related to:

(1) restrictions on the use of oil and natural gas for new and existing power plants and major fuel-burning installations;

(2) an investigation and study of the alternative national uses of coal to meet the nation's energy requirements consistent with national policies for the protection and enhancement of the quality of the environment and for economic recovery and full employment.

For a symposium on this Act, see 29 *U. Kan. L. Rev.* 297 *et seq.* (1981).

PPA

NATURAL GAS PRICE PROTECTION ACT (*q.v.*).

Practically impenetrable substance

See IMPENETRABLE SUBSTANCE.

Preference eligible refiner

A small, independent refiner made eligible for purchase of government royalty oil produced in a given area under the provisions of 30 U.S.C. § 192, as amended. See Laketon Asphalt & Refining, Inc. v. United States Dep't of Interior, 476 F. Supp. 668 (N.D. Ind. 1979), *aff'd,* 624 F.2d 784 (7th Cir. 1980).

Preference right

A first or prior right to acquire a lease or other interest, *e.g.*, the preference right of an agricultural entryman to an oil and gas lease under the federal Mineral Leasing Act of 1920. See Brown, "The Preferential Right of an Entryman Under the Federal Leasing Act," 3 *Rocky Mt. Min. L. Inst.* 671 (1957).

See also Richard W. Rowe, 20 IBLA 59, 82 I.D. 174 (1975) (distinguishing between a preference right to a new lease and a "statutory priority right" as the first qualified applicant in the event the Department decides to issue a lease).

Preference right lease

This term is used by the Department of the Interior regulations to describe a lease given to a prospecting permittee who makes a commercial discovery. Natural Resource Defense Council v. Berklund, 609 F.2d 553 (D.C. Cir. 1979), rejected the contention that the term "preference right" signifies no more than a right of first refusal should the Secretary decide to award a lease to anyone, holding that the term meant an automatic entitlement of a prospecting permittee who establishes the presence of commercial quantities of coal in the area covered by its permit.

A lease of public lands issued to a person having a preference right. See 43 C.F.R. § 3520 (1978).

Preferential right of purchase

(1) A right reserved to parties to a pooling or unitization agreement to buy any part of a committed working interest which a party proposes to sell; before the sale by the latter may be made, he must offer to sell the same interest to the other parties on the same terms at which the proposed sale is to be made. See TREATISE § 921.13.

(2) A right reserved by a party to a farm-out or other agreement to buy the interest of the other party provided it was willing to pay for such interest at a price which was offered therefor in good faith. See, *e.g.*, Luling Oil & Gas Co. v. Humble Oil & Refining Co., 144 Tex. 475, 191 S.W.2d 716 (1945).

Syn.: First refusal clause.

Palmer v. Liles, 677 S.W.2d 661, 82 *O.&G.R.* 376 (Tex. App., Houston, 1984, error ref'd n.r.e.), held that a contractual prohibition of assignment of an interest in property did not amount to a preferential right of purchase or right of first refusal.

Barela v. Locer, 103 N.M. 407, 708 P.2d 307 (1985), concluded that a right of first refusal to acquire mineral rights contained in a realty purchase agreement was not merged in a subsequent warranty deed which, though reserving minerals, made no reference to the purchaser's right of first refusal to acquire mineral rights.

See also Rainbow Oil Co. v. Christmann, 656 P.2d 538, 77 *O.&G.R.* 401 (Wyo. 1982) (holding that farmor's preferential right to purchase had not been triggered by transfers by farmee, such transfers not having been "sales").

In some jurisdictions the Rule against Perpetuities has been held to be applicable to a preferential right of purchase. See, *e.g.*, Producers Oil Co. v. Gore, 437 F. Supp. 737, 60 *O.&G.R.* 78 (E.D. Okla. 1977). On appeal, the United States Tenth Circuit Court of Appeals certified to the Oklahoma Supreme Court the question of whether the preemptive opinion provisions in question violated the Oklahoma Rule against Perpetuities, and the question was answered in the negative. Producers Oil Co. v. Gore, 610 P.2d 772 (Okla. 1980). Thereafter, the Court of Appeals vacated the judgment of the federal district court in this case and remanded it for proceedings consistent with the opinion of the Oklahoma court. 634 F.2d 487 (10th Cir. 1980). See TREATISE § 322 at note 17.

See also the following:

Kutzschbach, "Operating Agreement Considerations in Acquisitions of Producing Properties," 36 *Sw. Legal Fdn. Oil & Gas Inst.* 7-1 at 7-3 *et seq.* (1985);

Scott, "Restrictions on Alienation Applied to Oil and Gas Transactions," 31 *Rocky Mt. Min. L. Inst.* 15-1 (1985);

Allen and Cottee, "The Effect of the Rule Against Perpetuities on Pre-Emptive Rights in Joint Ventures," 4 *Australian Mining & Petroleum L.J.* 190 (1982);

Abright, "Preferential Right Provisions and their Applicability to Oil and Gas Instruments," 32 *Sw. L.J.* 803 (1978).

In Post v. Prati, 90 Cal. App. 3d 626, 153 Cal Rptr. 511, 62 *O.&G.R.* 153 (1979), the court sustained the validity of a statute giving a "bidding preference in favor of a surface owner" whose land contains geothermal resources owned by the state when such resources are offered for lease.

Preferred net royalty

A prior right of participation, limited to the terms of an existing lease, in the entire net proceeds from the sale of oil and/or gas produced from a specified tract or well until a certain fixed preferred amount in dollars has been paid to the holders thereof as set forth in "Trust Agreement," but such right of participation is subject to prior payment of (a) "Landowner's Royalty" and "Over-riding Royalty"; (b) all production equipment, acidization, operating cost, taxes, assessment and any other deductions authorized by the "Trust Agreement" under which such right of participation is created. After payment of said fixed preferred amount, "Preferred Net Royalties" rank *pari passu* with "Net Royalties" and "Deferred Net Royalties" in the net proceeds from the sale of oil and/or gas. Saskatchewan Amended Regulations, Securities Act, O.C. 1704/52, July 14, 1952, 1 *O.&G.R.* 1541 (1952).

See also DEFERRED NET ROYALTY; NET ROYALTY; ROYALTY.

Preferred use

Syn.: SUPERIOR USE (*q.v.*). See Discussion Notes, 7 *O.&G.R.* 1047 (1957).

Pregranted abandonment

A provision of a certificate of public convenience and necessity issued by the Federal Power Commission or its successor, the Federal Energy Regulatory Commission, for the sale of natural gas for resale in interstate commerce which authorizes abandonment on a future date certain. See 18 C.F.R. §§ 2.70, 2.75 (1980). The power of the commission to issue a certificate with such a provision was sustained in Moss v. Federal Power Comm'n, 424 U.S. 494, 54 *O.&G.R.* 247 (1976).

See also ABANDONMENT OF FACILITIES OR SERVICE; LIMITED TERM CERTIFICATE.

Pre-I.D. payment

PRE-INITIAL DELIVERY PAYMENT (*q.v.*).

Pre-initial delivery payment

Prepayment for gas agreed to be made to the producer of gas by the pipeline purchaser in the event the pipeline is not hooked up by a specified time. The promise for payment is made in exchange for the producer's promise to commit gas owned by it to the pipeline purchaser upon completion of the pipeline. Forest Oil Corp. v. Tenneco, Inc., 626 F.Supp. 917, 89 *O.&G.R.* 291 (S.D. Miss. 1986).

Prepaid IDC

Advance payment by a limited partner to the general partner of the costs of drilling oil and gas wells. For rulings on the taxable year in which the limited partner may claim an income tax deduction for intangible drilling and development costs see Rev. Rul. 80-70, 1980-11 I.R.B. 7, 64 *O.&G.R.* 245 (March 17, 1980), Rev. Rul. 71-252, 1971-1 C.B. 146.

On the deductibiltiy of prepaid IDC, see Keller v. Comm'r, 79 T.C. 7, 74 *O.&G.R.* 129 (1982), *aff'd,* 725 F.2d 1173, 80 *O.&G.R.* 639 (8th Cir. 1984); Behnke and Gentzler, "Deductibility of Prepaid Intangible and Development Costs in the Year of Payment—A Current Review," 17 Tulsa L.J. 428 (1982).

See also INTANGIBLE DRILLING AND DEVELOPMENT COSTS (IDC); PAY-AS-YOU-GO BASIS.

Prepayment provision

A provision in (or supplementary to) a GAS PURCHASE CONTRACT (*q.v.*) relating to an interest-free loan or advance payment for gas to be delivered at some future time. A typical provision of this kind provides for a payment based on the producer's recoverable gas reserves, the payment to be recovered out of subsequent deliveries of gas. See Holland, "Comparative Analysis of Gas Purchase Contracts," 9 *Alberta L. Rev.* 479 (1972).

Pre-platform well

A well drilled in deep water from a mobile rig to determine whether there is a reservoir containing hydrocarbons. If production is found, additional wells are drilled to determine the extent of the reservoir and the optimum location for a platform. These wells are drilled in a conventional manner but are in many instances plugged and abandoned because it is uneconomic to complete them under present technology. See Bullion, "Special Tax Considerations in Relation to Offshore Operations and Financing," *Rocky Mt. Min. L. Fdn. Offshore Exploration, Drilling and Development Institute* 14–3 (1975).

Gates Rubber Co. & Subsidiaries v. Commissioner, 74 T.C. 1456, 67 *O.&G.R.* 647 (1980), *aff'd,* 694 F.2d 648 (10th Cir. 1982), and Sun Oil Co. v. Commissioner, 74 T.C. 1481, 68 *O.&G.R.* 353, *aff'd,* 677 F.2d 294, 76 *O.&G.R.* 619 (3d Cir. 1982) *acq.*, I.R.B. 1983-26 (1983), held that the deduction for INTANGIBLE DRILLING AND DEVELOPMENT COSTS (*q.v.*) is available for a pre-platform well.

Syn.: BORE HOLE, ESCROW WELL, EXPENDABLE WELL (*q.v.*).

See also LINE TEST WELL.

Prescription

(1) At common law, a means of creating or extinguishing an incorporeal interest in land, such as an easement. See 3 Powell, *Real Property* ¶ 413, 423, 424 (1952).

(2) In Louisiana, a means of creating or extinguishing some right. In particular, mineral servitudes and mineral royalties (except for certain servitudes or royalties reserved in transfers to governmental agencies) are subject to extinguishment of operation of the civil law concept of prescription *liberandi causa* on ten years nonuse. And ti-

tle to land may be acquired by prescription *acquirendi causa* (acquisitive prescription). It is immaterial to the application of the doctrine of prescription *liberandi causa* whether the mineral servitude or mineral royalty was created by grant or by reservation, or whether the owner of the interest has the right to enter upon the premises and drill. The grant of an interest for a term in excess of ten years does not prevent extinguishment of the interest upon the expiration of a ten year period of nonuse. Under earlier law the running of the prescriptive period might be suspended in certain cases by the minority of the owner or co-owner of the interest, but this restriction on the prescription doctrine has been eliminated by statute. The running of the prescriptive period against a mineral servitude may be interrupted by the commencement of drilling operations in good faith, whether or not successful in obtaining production, or by an acknowledgment of the servitude which is made for the purpose of interrupting the running of the prescriptive period. In the case of mineral royalties, however, actual production as opposed to drilling operations, is necessary to interrupt the prescriptive period. Once prescription *liberandi causa* has been interrupted, the ten year period starts anew. Prescription *liberandi causa* is discussed in this TREATISE at § 216 *et seq.*, and prescription *acquirendi causa* is discussed in this TREATISE at § 224.6. The law concerning prescription *liberandi causa* is codified in Articles 27–61, 85–100, 107, and 126 [R.S. 31:27–61, 85–100, 107, 126 (1975)], and the law concerning prescription *acquirendi causa* is codified in Articles 153–163 [R.S. 31:153 to 31:163 (1975)] of the Louisiana Mineral Code.

See also ACKNOWLEDGEMENT; ACQUISITIVE PRESCRIPTION; ADOPTION; EXTENSION; OBSTACLE; REVERSIONARY INTEREST; SUSPENSION OF PRESCRIPTION.

Pressure

See BACK PRESSURE; BACK PRESSURE METHOD; BASE PRESSURE; BLEED LINE; BLOW-OUT; BLOW-OUT PREVENTER; BOTTOM HOLE ABANDONMENT PRESSURE; BOTTOM HOLE PRESSURE; CASING PRESSURE; CLOSED PRESSURE; CROSS-FLOW; DELIVERABILITY STANDARD PRESSURE; DELIVERY PRESSURE; DIFFERENTIAL PRESSURE; DIFFERENTIAL PRESSURE FLOW METER; FIELD PRESSURE; FLOWING TUBING PRESSURE (FTP); FLOW TEST METER; GAS PRESSURE; HEAD; HIGH PRESSURE AREA; HIGH PRESSURE GAS INJECTION; HYDROSTATIC PRESSURE; KICK; MULTIPOINT BACK PRESSURE TEST; OPEN FLOW PRESSURE; PERIODIC FLOWING; PSIG; RESERVOIR ENERGY; RESERVOIR LIMIT TEST; RESERVOIR PRESSURE; ROCK PRESSURE; SATURATION PRESSURE; SHUT-IN PRES-

SURE; STANDARD PRESSURE BASE; SWABBING THE HOLE; TUBING PRESSURE.

Pressure clause

The clause in a GAS PURCHASE CONTRACT (*q.v.*) providing that the agreement shall terminate should gas pressure from the properties drop below the point where delivery would not be possible against the working pressure of the purchaser's gas line. Skelly Oil Co. v. Federal Power Comm'n, 532 F.2d 177, 54 *O.&G.R.* 553, 9 FPS 6–12 (10th Cir. 1976).

Pressure-decline-curve method

A method of estimating non-associated gas reserves in reservoirs which do not have a water drive. The method is discussed in Leeston, Crichton and Jacobs, *The Dynamic Natural Gas Industry* 47–8 (1963).

Pressure flooding

A method of water flooding involving the application of additional hydraulic pressure to that of the hydrostatic head. See Lytle, "History, Present Status, and Future Possibilities of Secondary Recovery Operations in Pennsylvania," 1 *IOCC Comm. Bull.* 29 at 33 (Dec. 1959).

See also SECONDARY RECOVERY; WATER FLOODING.

Pressure maintenance

The injection of gas, water or other fluids into oil or gas reservoirs to maintain pressure or retard pressure decline in the reservoir for the purpose of increasing the recovery of oil or other hydrocarbons therefrom. IOCC, *A Suggested Form of General Rules and Regulations for the Conservation of Oil and Gas* (1960), Rule III.

See also BUBBLE POINT OF OIL; CYCLING; RECYCLING; SECONDARY RECOVERY.

Pressure, shut in

See SHUT IN PRESSURE.

Price

See ADAPTATION CLAUSE; ADJUSTED BASE PRICE; ADJUSTED POSTED PRICE; AREA PRICING POLICY; BENCHMARK CRUDE; BUYBACK OIL; CUR-

RENT BTU RELATED PRICE; DIFFERENTIAL; ENTITLEMENT PROGRAM; ESCALATOR CLAUSE; EXPECTED THIRD PARTY PRICE; FAIR FIELD PRICE METHOD; FIELD PRICE; FLAT SALE OF CRUDE OIL; FPC CLAUSE; FPC PRICE PROTECTION CLAUSE; GNP IMPLICIT PRICE DEFLATOR; GRANDFATHER PRICE; GUARANTEED SALES PRICE; GULF-PLUS PRICING STRUCTURE; IMPUTED ALBERTA BORDER PRICE; INCREMENTAL PRICING; IN-LINE PRICE; INTERNATIONAL MARKET PRICE; MARKET PRICE; MID-WAY PRICE; MINIMUM WELLHEAD PRICE; NATURAL GAS PRICE PROTECTION ACT; NEGOTIATED CONTRACT PRICE REQUIREMENT; NET-BACK PRICING; NORM PRICE; OFFTAKE PRICE; ONE-PRICE SYSTEM; POSTED FIELD PRICE; POSTED PRICE; PROCEEDS-LESS-EXPENSE METHOD; QUARTER-WAY PRICE; REALIZED PRICE; REDUCED PGA METHOD; REFERENCE PRICE; REMOVAL PRICE; REPURCHASE PRICE; RESERVATION PRICE; ROLLED IN PRICE; SUSPECT PRICE; TAX REFERENCE PRICE; THRESHOLD PRICE; TRANSFER PRICE; TWO-PRICE SYSTEM; TWO-TIER PRICING SYSTEM; WEIGHTED AVERAGE ARM'S LENGTH PRICE; WELL-HEAD PRICE; WORK-BACK VALUATION METHOD.

Price control of oil, gas and petroleum products

Under the decision in Phillips Petroleum Co. v. State of Wisconsin, 347 U.S. 672, 3 *O.&G.R.* 745 (1954), the Federal Power Commission was charged with responsibility for regulating the rates charged by a natural gas producer and gatherer in the sale in interstate commerce of gas for resale. The subsequent history of price control of natural gas is traced in Freeport Oil Co. v. Federal Energy Regulatory Comm'n, 638 F.2d 702 (5th Cir. 1980), and in Williams, Maxwell and Meyers, *Cases on Oil and Gas* 42 *et seq.* (4th ed. 1979). The NATURAL GAS POLICY ACT OF 1978 (*q.v.*) includes provision for the expiration (with certain exceptions) of price controls on natural gas in 1985.

For a discussion of the regulation of the well-head price of natural gas, see Gilliam, "Wellhead Regulation Under the Natural Gas Act and the Natural Gas Policy Act," American Gas Ass'n, *Regulation of the Gas Industry* ch. 20 (1981).

Price control of oil and petroleum products was imposed by President Nixon on August 15, 1971, acting under the ECONOMIC STABILIZATION ACT OF 1970 (ESA) (*q.v.*). Controls were soon lifted on the economy as a whole but were continued on the petroleum industry. See the mandatory price regulations in 10 C.F.R. § 212 (1980). On January 30, 1981, by executive order, President Reagan decontrolled prices of crude oil and refined petroleum products. 45 Fed. Reg. 9901.

Several states sought to control intrastate natural gas sales prices. In Louisiana, the Energy Act of 1973 was designated to avoid "the sale of intrastate natural gas at a price below the fair market value of such gas, especially as compared to the price of other fuels." La. R.S. § 30.592 (1975). In some other states, legislation was enacted to curtail the operation of certain types of indefinite escalator clauses in natural gas contracts involving intrastate deliveries. See NATURAL GAS PRICE PROTECTION ACT.

For discussions of the legislative and administrative history of federal price controls and regulation of the petroleum industry, see the following:

Fox, *Federal Regulation of Energy* Chs. 6, 15–21 (1983);

Goodwin (Ed.), *Energy Policy in Perspective* (1981);

Kalt, *The Economics and Politics of Oil Price Regulation* (1981);

Lane, *The Mandatory Petroleum Price and Allocation Regulations: A History and Analysis* (1981);

Allison, "Natural Gas Pricing: The Eternal Debate," 37 *Baylor L. Rev.* 1 (1985);

Pierce, "Natural Gas Regulation, Deregulation, and Contracts," 68 *Va. L. Rev.* 63 (1982);

Aman, "Institutionalizing the Energy Crisis: Some Structural and Procedural Lessons," 65 *Cornell L. Rev.* 491 (1980).

See also ADVANCE PAYMENT ORDER; ALTERNATIVE FUEL COST; ANNUAL INFLATION ADJUSTMENT FACTOR; AREA PRICING POLICY; AREA RATE CLAUSE; BASE PERIOD CONTROL LEVEL (BPCL); BUY-SELL LIST; BUY-SELL OIL; CATCO CASE; CEILING PRICE; COMMODITY CHARGE THEORY; COMPLETION LOCATION; COMPOSITE PRICE CEILING; CONDENSATE; CONTRACT DATE VINTAGING; CONTRACT PRICE; CONTROLLED CRUDE OIL; COST BANK; COST OF LIVING COUNCIL; CRUDE OIL WINDFALL PROFIT TAX ACT OF 1980; CURRENT BTU RELATED PRICE; DEEPER DRILLING EXCEPTION; ECONOMIC REGULATORY ADMINISTRATION; ECONOMIC STABILIZATION ACT OF 1970 (ESA); EFFECTIVE TARIFF; EMERGENCY PETROLEUM ALLOCATION ACT OF 1973; END USE RATE SCHEDULE; ENTITLEMENT PROGRAM; ESCALATOR CLAUSE; EVERGREEN CLAUSE; EXEMPT CRUDE OIL; EXISTING CONTRACT; FAIR FIELD PRICE METHOD; FEDERAL ENERGY ADMINISTRATION; FEDERAL ENERGY REGULATORY COMMISSION; FEDERAL POWER COMMISSION; FIRST TIER OIL; FPC PRICE PROTECTION CLAUSE; FRONT-END TERTIARY OIL; GLOBAL SETTLEMENT; GNP IMPLICIT PRICE DEFLATOR; GRANDFATHER CLAUSE; GRANDFATHER PRICE; HIGH COST NATURAL GAS; HIGH PRIORITY USER; IMPUTED STRIPPER WELL CRUDE OIL EXEMPTION; IMPUTED STRIPPER WELL LEASE OIL PRICE; INCENTIVE PRICE GAS; INCENTIVE RATE OF RETURN (IROR); INCREMENTAL PRICE METHOD; INCREMEN-

TAL PRICING; INJECTION WELL; IN LINE PRICE; JURISDICTIONAL SALES; LOWER TIER CRUDE OIL; MAXIMUM SURCHARGE ABSORPTION CAPABILITY (MSAC); MINIMUM RATE; MINIMUM WELL HEAD PRICE; MOLECULAR THEORY; NATIONAL RATE; NATIONAL RATE CASE; NATURAL GAS ACT; NATURAL GAS POLICY ACT OF 1978; NATURAL GAS PRICE PROTECTION ACT; NEW CONTRACT; NEW LEASE; NEWLY DISCOVERED RESERVOIR; NEW NATURAL GAS; NEW OIL; NEW WELL; OLD OIL; ONE HUNDRED AND EIGHTY DAY EMERGENCY SALES; ONE-PRICE SYSTEM; PASS-THROUGH PROHIBITION; PASS-THROUGH PROVISION; PETROLEUM ADMINISTRATION ACT; PETROLEUM ADMINISTRATION FOR DEFENSE (PAD); PETROLEUM ADMINISTRATION FOR WAR (PAW); PRODUCED AND SOLD; PRODUCTION ENHANCEMENT PROCEDURES; PROPERTY; QUALIFIED PRODUCTION ENHANCEMENT GAS; RATE BASE APPROACH; RATE SCHEDULE; RATE TILTING; REPLACEMENT CONTRACT POLICY; ROLLED-IN ALLOCATION METHOD; ROLLOVER CONTRACT; ROLLOVER GAS; SADLEROCHIT OIL; SECOND TIER OIL; SIXTY DAY EMERGENCY SALES; STRIPPER WELL NATURAL GAS; STRIPPER WELL OIL; SUCCESSOR TO AN EXISTING CONTRACT; TERTIARY INCREMENTAL PROGRAM; THRESHOLD PRICE; TIGHT FORMATION; TIGHT FORMATION GAS; TRANSFER PRICE; TWO-PRICE SYSTEM; TWO-TIER PRICING SYSTEM; UPPER TIER CRUDE OIL; WELL COMMENCEMENT DATE VINTAGING; WELL DETERMINATION.

Price escalation clause

See ESCALATOR CLAUSE.

Price protection act

NATURAL GAS PRICE PROTECTION ACT (*q.v.*).

Price redetermination clause

An ESCALATOR CLAUSE (*q.v.*) in a GAS PURCHASE CONTRACT (*q.v.*). By virtue of this clause a readjustment of the contract price may be made periodically or at the end of some stated period.

See Wyatt, "Effect of Deregulation Upon Existing and New Gas Contracts," 32 *L.S.U. Min. L. Inst.* 1 at 10 (1986).

Price spike

The specter of substantial price increases for natural gas when decontrolled in 1985. Morgan & Patterson, "The Natural Gas Policy Act of 1978," 71 *Ky. L.J.* 105 at 106 (1982–83). For a study of the actual trend of natural gas pricing subsequent to the adoption of the NATURAL GAS POLICY ACT OF 1978 (NGPA) (*q.v.*), see "Natural

Gas Pricing," Committee Print 98-Q, a Staff Report prepared for the Subcommittee on Oversight and Investigations of the Committee on Energy and Commerce, U.S. House of Representatives, 98th Cong., 1st Sess., Nov. 1983.

Syn: Gas fly-up.

Pricing area

See CONTRACT PRICING AREA.

Primary production

Production from a reservoir by primary sources of energy, that is, from natural energy in the reservoir when it is in an early stage of production, with little loss of pressure and with most wells still flowing.

This definition was quoted and adopted in Sivert v. Continental Oil Co., 497 S.W.2d 482 at 487, 46 *O.&G.R.* 355 at 363 (Tex. Civ. App. 1973, error ref'd n.r.e.).

See also SECONDARY RECOVERY; TERTIARY RECOVERY.

Primary production payment

A production payment which must be satisfied out of production before payment begins on a deferred production payment. See Discussion Notes, 7 *O.&G.R.* 321 (1957).

Syn.: Front end of production payment.

See also OIL PAYMENT.

Primary recovery

As defined by a subcommittee of the American Petroleum Institute, "the oil, gas, or oil and gas recovered by any method (natural flow or artificial lift) that may be employed to produce them through a single well bore; the fluid enters the well bore by the action of native reservoir energy or gravity." American Petroleum Institute, *Secondary Recovery of Oil in the United States* 255 (1942).

Primary term

The period of time, typically five or ten years, during which a lease may be kept alive by a lessee even though there is no production in paying quantities by virtue of drilling operations on the leased land or the payment of rentals. After the expiration of the primary term, the lease usually can be kept alive only by PRODUCTION IN PAYING

QUANTITIES (*q.v.*), absent some savings clause in the lease, such as a SHUT-IN GAS WELL CLAUSE, DRILLING OPERATIONS CLAUSE OR CONTINUOUS DRILLING OPERATIONS CLAUSE (*q.v.*).

The habendum clause of a typical contemporary lease grants the land for a primary term "and so long thereafter" as oil or gas is produced, in manner as follows:

> "It is agreed that this lease shall remain force for a term of ten years from date and as long thereafter as oil, or gas of whatsoever nature or kind, or either of them is produced from said land or drilling operations are continued as hereinafter provided."

The subsequent drilling or delay rental clause of the lease typically provides for possible extinguishment of the lessee's interest on any anniversary date of the lease before the expiration of the primary term. In the UNLESS LEASE (*q.v.*), the delay rental clause provides for termination of the lessee's interest on the anniversary date during the primary term if no well has been commenced or completed *unless* rentals are paid. In the OR LEASE (*q.v.*), the drilling clause contains a covenant to drill or to do something else (*e.g.*, pay rentals, forfeit, surrender) before a stated anniversary date, and if there is a breach of the covenant, the lessor has a cause of action for the breach and in some instances may terminate the lessee's interest prior to the expiration of the primary term. See TREATISE §§ 601–635.

For purposes of the Mineral Leasing Act of 1920, the phrase "primary term" has been said to include the entire period in the life of the lease prior to the period of extension because of production. See Olpin, "Processing of Lease Applications and Terms of Leases," *Rocky Mt. Min. L. Fdn. Law of Federal Oil & Gas Leases* 195 at 206 (1967); 67 I.D. 357 (Sept. 23, 1960).

Ashland Oil, Inc., 79 I.D. 532, 7 IBLA 58, GFS(O&G) 41 (Aug. 9, 1972), held that a lease which had been extended because of production not on it, but on a unit, is not within its primary term. Actual drilling operations on a lease so extended created no right to an extension under the Mineral Leasing Act.

Modern Exploration, Inc. v. Maddison, 708 S.W.2d 872 at 879, ___ *O.&G.R.* ___ at ___ (Tex. App., Corpus Christi, 1986), apparently took the position that the primary term of a lease does not end so long as production continues; such a view is contrary to the clear weight of authority.

Inexco Oil Co., 20 IBLA 134, GFS(O&G) 1975–52 rejected the contention that the primary term includes anything more than the initial term of years specified in the lease.

See also SECONDARY PRIMARY TERM; SECONDARY TERM.

The definition in this MANUAL of primary term was quoted and discussed in Fox v. Thoreson, 398 S.W.2d 88, 23 *O.&G.R.* 808 (Tex. 1966).

Primary term clause

The lease clause specifying the PRIMARY TERM (*q.v.*) of the interest granted the lessee.

Principal meridian

"A line which runs in a north-south direction from an initial point and from which are initiated other lines for the cadastral survey of the public lands within a specified area. Each principal meridian has a correlated base line that runs through the same initial point. Every principal meridian has a distinctive name, *e.g.*, Huntsville Meridian and Fourth Principal Meridian." United States Department of the Interior Bureau of Land Management, *Glossary of Public-Land Terms* 37 (1949).

Private offering exemption

An exemption under the Federal Securities Act and under the BLUE SKY LAW (*q.v.*) of some states for certain private offerings as defined in the statute or regulations. See TREATISE § 441.4.

See also REGULATION B; REGULATION D; RULE 146.

Private placement drilling fund

"A private placement drilling fund is substantially the same as a public drilling fund except for the fact that the transaction relies upon the 'private placement' exception to public registration with the Securities and Exchange Commission, and the units of participation are usually larger and spread among fewer 'sophisticated investors.' In recent years, these transactions also have usually taken the form of limited partnerships. In fact, there are substantial private placement 'offerings' that involve a limited partnership with just one investor." Bean, "Entity Selection—An Experience in Alchemy—A Comparison of Corporations, Partnerships, and Joint Ventures," 30 *Sw. Legal Fdn. Oil & Gas Inst.* 363 at 365 (1979).

See also DRILLING FUND.

Privatization

A term which has been applied to the sale of mineral rights by the federal government without a primary lease, thus shifting the management of resources from the public sector to the private sector. Mead, Moseidjord, Miraoka and Sorensen, *Offshore Lands: Oil and Gas Leasing and Conservation on the Outer Continental Shelf* 112 (1985).

Probable reserves

An estimate of RESERVES (*q.v.*) taking into consideration known geology, previous experience with similar types of reservoirs, and seismic data if available.

Problem bid

A bid for an Outer Continental Shelf lease that falls below the MEAN OF THE RANGE OF VALUE (MROV) (*q.v.*) and the DISCOUNTED MROV (DMROV) (*q.v.*) but equals or exceeds the AVERAGE EVALUATION OF TRACT (AEOT) (*q.v.*). See Superior Oil Co. v. Watt, 548 F. Supp. 70, 74 *O.&G.R.* 423 (D. Del. 1982) (sustaining the rejection of a problem bid by the Secretary of the Interior).

Proceeds

The money obtained by an actual sale. Waechter v. Amoco Production Co., 217 Kan. 489 at 512, 537 P.2d 228 (1975), *on rehearing,* 219 Kan. 41, 546 P.2d 1320, 53 *O.&G.R.* 350 (1976). In this case the court concluded that the gas royalty clauses in question required the lessee to account to the lessor for proceeds rather than market value of the gas produced:

> "Nor can we say the parties used the terms 'proceeds' and 'market value' as equivalents in the royalty clauses. They were not used interchangeably. . . . Proceeds ordinarily refer to the money obtained by an actual sale. The connotation is not without significance in the gas business. Where the sale is at the wellhead the lessor does not consent to the uncertainties of what the market or fair value or price of the gas may be—he is willing to take what the lessee sells it for, relying on the lessee's self-interest in obtaining the best price possible."

See also Lightcap v. Mobil Oil Corp., 221 Kan. 448, 562 P.2d 1, 57 *O.&G.R.* 487 (1977), *cert. denied,* 434 U.S. 876 (1977), *reh. denied,* 440 U.S. 931 (1979), and Exxon Corp. v. Middleton, 613 S.W.2d 240, 67 *O.&G.R.* 431 (Tex. 1981) (distinguishing a "proceeds lease," *viz.*, one providing for royalty of a portion of the proceeds of sale of oil or gas, from a "market value" lease, *viz.*, one providing for royalty of a portion of the market value of oil or gas produced and sold), *on remand, dism'd in part, rev'd and remanded in part on joint motion of parties,* 619 S.W.2d 115, 69 *O.&G.R.* 115 (Tex. Civ. App. 1981).

Holmes v. Kewanee Oil Co., 233 Kan. 544, 664 P.2d 1335, 77 *O.&G.R.* 447 (1983), *cert. denied,* ___ U.S. ___, 106 S. Ct. 322 (1985), concluded that the royalty payable under a lease providing for royalty of one-eighth "of the gross proceeds at the prevailing market rate" is based on "market value."

See also PERCENTAGE OF PROCEEDS CONTRACT.

Proceeds interest

A term which has been used to describe a PER CENT INTEREST (*q.v.*). Kuechler, "Oil and Gas; 'Overriding Royalties'; 'Proceeds Interests'," 26 *Calif. L. Rev.* 480 (1938).

Proceeds lease

A lease providing for a royalty of a portion of the proceeds of the sale of oil or gas as distinguished from a MARKET VALUE LEASE (*q.v.*) under which the royalty is based on the market value of the product rather than the proceeds of the sale of the product.

Proceeds-less-expense method

A method to determine the value of oil or gas at the wellhead in the absence of comparable sales. The method is discussed in Northern Natural Gas Co. v. Grounds, 393 F. Supp. 949 at 970, 51 *O.&G.R.* 453 at 486 (D. Kan. 1974).

See also NET BACK PRICING; WORK-BACK VALUATION METHOD.

Processed gas

Gas that is processed in a gasoline plant for the removal of liquids.

Process gas

(1) Natural gas utilized by industrial users as a raw material in creating an end product rather than as (a) an agent for heating, cooling, dehydrating or otherwise affecting industrial process materials,

or (b) for other industrial purposes. State of Louisiana v. Federal Power Comm'n, 503 F.2d 844 at 872 (5th Cir. 1974).

(2) Gas use for which alternate fuels are not technically feasible such as in applications requiring precise temperature controls and precise flame characteristics. Statement by Chairman John N. Nassikas of the Federal Power Commission, "Federal Power Commission Oversight—Natural Gas Curtailment Priorities," Hearing before the Senate Committee on Commerce, 93rd Cong., 2d Sess., June 20, 1974, at p. 83; F.P.C. Order No. 493 (Sept. 21, 1973); 18 C.F.R. § 2.78(c)(8) (1979).

Process Gas Consumers Group v. Federal Energy Regulatory Comm'n, 712 F.2d 483 (D.C. Cir. 1983) sustained the validity of a final rule issued by the Commission defining the extent to which certain agricultural users of natural gas would have priority access to gas at time of shortage despite clear reservations by the court as to the merits of the rule.

The term "process fuel" as used in the NATURAL GAS POLICY ACT (*q.v.*) was said to have the same meaning as process gas, thus excluding boiler fuel from the definition. Process Gas Consumers v. U.S. Department of Agriculture, 657 F.2d 459 (D.C. Cir. 1981).

Processing agreement

An instrument executed by lessors authorizing the extraction of gasoline or other liquid products from the gas produced under a unit. Whelan v. Placid Oil Co., 274 S.W.2d 125, 4 *O.&G.R.* 442 (Tex. Civ. App. 1954, error ref'd n.r.e.).

Processing plant

A plant to remove liquefiable hydrocarbons from wet gas or casing-head gas. The process employed is described in Freeland v. Sun Oil Co., 184 F. Supp. 754 at 756, 13 *O.&G.R.* 758 at 761 (W.D. La. 1959), *aff'd,* 277 F.2d 154, 13 *O.&G.R.* 764 (5th Cir. 1960), *cert. denied,* 364 U.S. 826 (1960), as follows:

> "The gas, which is carried full stream to the plant, is first sent through an inlet separator which removes the condensate from this full stream gas. After the condensate is removed by the inlet separator, the separator gas is sent to absorption towers where additional liquids are absorbed from such gas. The residue gas remaining after the absorption tower process is then sent through a dehydrator and is delivered to the pipe line company or is returned to the cycling unit by the producers. All liquids recovered, both from the inlet separator and from the absorption tower pro-

cess, are then further processed to obtain propanes, butanes, motor fuel and other products."

See also Shamrock Oil & Gas Corp. v. Commissioner, 35 T.C. 979, 13 *O.&G.R.* 1090 at 1128–30 (1961).

Produced

This term may refer to production in measurable quantities or to production in commercial quantities. Seneca Oil Co. v. Department of Energy, *CCH, Energy Management* ¶ 26,372 (W.D. Okla. 1982), held that the Department of Energy Ruling 1980–3 was invalid insofar as it adopted the former definition of this term. This judgment was reversed with directions, 712 F.2d 1384 (Temp. Emer. Ct. App. 1983), the court concluding that Ruling 1980-3 was a reasonable and legally correct interpretation of the applicable legislative regulation as it existed until the effective date of amendments of November 25, 1980.

Produced and sold

This term, as used in regulations creating a two-tier pricing system for crude oil, was the subject of dispute in Tenneco Oil Co. v. Federal Energy Administration, 613 F.2d 298, 65 *O.&G.R.* 452 (Temp. Emergency Ct. App. 1979). To calculate the amount of new oil produced in a given month, producers were to determine the amount "produced and sold" from a property and subtract the BCPL (*q.v.*), which was defined as the amount of crude petroleum "produced and sold" from that property during the same month in 1972. Tenneco, the owner of an oil producing property, delivered oil from the property in accordance with a processing agreement under which the processor "topped" the lightest hydrocarbons (about 20%) and returned the balance (about 80%) to Tenneco for use to fuel steam generators providing steam for injection into oil reservoirs to aid in the recovery of crude oil. The FEA contended that the fuel consumed by Tenneco was "produced and sold" within the meaning of the price regulations; the court rejected the contention, holding that the processing or use of oil was not a sale.

Producer

(1) An operator who owns wells that produce oil or gas. See also INDEPENDENT PRODUCER; NATURAL GAS PRODUCER.

(2) *Syn.:* PRODUCING WELL (*q.v.*).

Producer gas

Syn.: POWER GAS (*q.v.*).

Producer gas equipment

Equipment used for the production of producer gas. 18 C.F.R. § 201.309 (1979).

Producer nomination

See NOMINATIONS BY PRODUCERS.

Producer reservation gas

Outer continental shelf gas that under a contract between the producer and a pipeline is reserved for the producer's own purposes. Since OCS gas crosses a state border when it is delivered onshore, the Federal Energy Regulatory Commission must authorize the transportation of the producer's gas. Tenneco Oil Co., 23 FPS 5-938 (Opinion No. 10-B, Dec. 23, 1982); Hollis, "Notable Recent Developments in Federal Natural Gas Regulation," 34 *Sw. Legal Fdn. Oil & Gas Inst.* 31 at 56 (1983).

See also CHANDELEUR INCENTIVE DOCTRINE.

Producers 88 Lease

See 88 LEASE.

"Produce to earn" farm-out

A FARM-OUT AGREEMENT (*q.v.*) under which the farmee earns no rights unless production is obtained. See Schaefer, "The Ins and Outs of Farmouts: A Practical Guide for the Landman and the Lawyer," 32 *Rocky Mt. Min. L. Inst.* 18-1 at 18-21 (1986).

See also "DRILL TO EARN" FARM-OUT.

Producible well

A term sometimes used as meaning the same as a "well capable of producing in paying quantities." Kerr-McGee Oil Industries, Inc., 73 I.D. 110, GFS SO–1966–30 (April 14, 1966).

See also WELL.

Producing interval

That portion of an oil well through which oil is taken into the well, thereupon to be raised to the mouth of the well at the surface. Victory Oil Co. v. Hancock Oil Co., 125 Cal. App. 2d 222, 270 P.2d 604, 3 *O.&G.R.* 1233 (1954).

Producing days

See SCHEDULED ALLOWABLE DAYS.

Producing sand

A rock stratum that contains recoverable oil or gas. Strictly, the term would apply only to a sandstone, but in loose usage it also applies to other sedimentary rocks.

Producing state preference statute

A statute designed to give persons in a producing state a preference right to scarce natural resources produced in the state. See, *e.g.*, Tex. Nat. Res. Code § 52.291 *et seq.*, enacted in 1975 (Texas consumers given a preferential right to natural gas produced from state owned lands); La. R.S. § 30:144, enacted in 1979 (Louisiana refiner given preferential right to in-kind royalty oil); La. R.S. 30:607, enacted in 1979 (Louisiana consumers given preferential right to state-owned natural gas). For a discussion of such statutes, see Anson and Schenkkan, "Federalism, the Dormant Commerce Clause, and State-Owned Resources," 59 *Tex. L. Rev.* 71 (1980).

See also RULE 69.

Producing well

A well that produces oil or gas. It is not a term of art, for it may mean a well that produces in paying quantities (that is, a well for which proceeds from production exceed operating expenses) or it may mean a well that produces in any quantity whatsoever. The term does not include a well that has discovered oil or gas but does not produce either. Rogers v. Osborn, 152 Tex. 540, 261 S.W.2d 311, 2 *O.&G.R.* 1439 (1953); Holchak v. Clark, 284 S.W.2d 399, 5 *O.&G.R.* 595 (Tex. Civ. App. 1955, error ref'd). When the meaning of the term arises in connection with the termination of an interest created for a term of years and so long thereafter as oil or gas is produced, it is usually held that producing well means a well producing in paying quantities. See Alsip's Adm'r v. Onstott, 283 S.W.2d 711, 5 *O.&G.R.* 334 (Ky. 1955).

See also PRODUCTION IN PAYING QUANTITIES; WELL.

In Aeroplane Oil & Refining Co. v. Disch, 203 Ky. 561, 262 S.W. 939 (1924), the court declared that it was shown by proof that oil men do not consider a well a producing well unless it produces at least five barrels a day, but in construing an instrument that contained this term, it applied the meaning of the term in ordinary speech, that is, a well that is producing some oil.

Product

Any commodity made from oil or gas, including refined crude oil, crude tops, topped crude, processed crude petroleum, residue from crude petroleum, crackingstock, uncracked fuel oil, fuel oil, treated crude oil, residuum, gas, oil, casinghead gasoline, natural gas gasoline, naphtha, distillate, gasoline, kerosene, benzine, wash oil, waste oil, blended gasoline, lubricating oil, blends or mixtures of oil with one or more liquid products or by-products derived from oil or gas, and blends or mixtures of two or more liquid products or by-products derived from oil or gas. Code of Ala. 1975 § 9–17–1(9).

Production

(1) The act or process of producing; that which is produced. The typical contemporary lease requires that there be production in order to keep a lease alive after the expiration of the primary term. Occasionally leases attempt to define the character of production sufficient to keep a lease alive after the expiration of the primary term. Among the variant forms are the following: "so long thereafter as there is production in paying quantities"; ". . . production in any quantity"; ". . . production whether or not in paying quantities"; ". . . as oil, gas or other minerals is or can be produced." Absent a definition of the term in the lease, "production" sufficient to keep a lease alive after the expiration of the primary term under the "so long thereafter" clause is normally construed to mean production in paying quantities, that is, production in quantities sufficient to yield a return in excess of operating costs, even though drilling and equipment costs may never be repaid and the undertaking considered as a whole may ultimately result in a loss. See Garcia v. King, 139 Tex. 578, 164 S.W.2d 509 (1942). If there is a permanent cessation of production, at or after the expiration of the primary term, the lessee's interest in the premises will terminate. If, however, the cessation of production is temporary in character, the lease will not be extin-

guished if the production is resumed within a reasonable time. Some courts have been more than generous in finding that prolonged cessation of production was merely temporary. See TREATISE § 604.4.

(2) As used in common speech, producing oil or gas wells, *e.g.*, in the sentence, "Smith has production in Harris County." This would normally be understood to mean oil production unless the word "gas" is added.

For purposes of the Natural Gas Act it becomes necessary to determine when production is completed. See Continental Oil Co. v. Federal Power Comm'n, 266 F.2d 208, 10 *O.&G.R.* 601 (5th Cir. 1959), *cert. denied,* 361 U.S. 827, 11 *O.&G.R.* 305 (1959), for a detailed discussion of this matter.

In allocating costs between operating and nonoperating owners it may be necessary to determine when "production is completed," *viz.*, what is the "place of production" or "point of production." See *e.g.*, Merritt v. Southwestern Electric Power Co., 499 So.2d 210 at 213 (La. App. 1986) (concluding that "the point of production" was the wellhead). See TREATISE §§ 645–645.3.

This definition was quoted in Glass v. Commissioner, 76 T.C. 949, 69 *O.&G.R.* 418 (1981).

See also CESSATION OF PRODUCTION; CONSTRUCTIVE PRODUCTION; PERMANENT CESSATION OF PRODUCTION; PRODUCTION IN PAYING QUANTITIES; QUALIFIED PRODUCTION; QUALIFIED ROYALTY PRODUCTION; TEMPORARY CESSATION OF PRODUCTION.

Production, affidavit of

See AFFIDAVIT OF PRODUCTION.

Production and marketing covenant

The implied covenant in an oil and gas lease requiring the lessee to produce and market the product. See IMPLIED COVENANTS.

Production area shipment point

The decisive place for the determination of the quantity of production under a Norwegian production license. This is "the place where the pipeline to the land terminal is connected to the main terminal of the production site in the North Sea. If the transport is by means of tanker, the point of shipment is considered to be that point where the petroleum produced passes the ship's side." Krohn, Kaasen, *et al., Norwegian Petroleum Law* 2–27 (1978).

Production assignment

A term occasionally used to describe a participating interest in the production from a leasehold, sometimes evidenced by a certificate. See Rawco, Inc., Ltd. v. Commissioner, 37 B.T.A. 128 (1938).

Syn.: PER CENT INTEREST (*q.v.*)

See also ASSIGNMENT.

Production bonus

An additional BONUS (*q.v.*) payable by an operating oil company to a host nation upon the attainment of a specified oil production. See, *e.g.,* Paragraph 6.1 of an Abu Dhabi Petroleum Concession Agreement in OPEC, *Selected Documents of the International Petroleum Industry* 1967 at p. 165.

See also the discussion of the requirement of a production bonus under certain Norwegian licenses in K. W. Dam, *Oil Resources* 61 (1976).

Production casing

See CASING.

Production certificate

A certificate evidencing a PER CENT INTEREST (*q.v.*). Such certificates may be in the form of Preferred and Common, the holders of the former being entitled to payment of an amount equal to their contribution before anything is paid on the common interests. Monrovia Oil Co. v. Commissioner, 83 F.2d 417 (9th Cir. 1936). The certificate may evidence participation in a specifically named well only. Rogan v. Blue Ridge Oil Co., Ltd., 83 F.2d 420 (9th Cir. 1936), *cert. denied,* 299 U. S. 574 (1936).

Production, commercial

See PRODUCTION; PRODUCTION IN PAYING QUANTITIES.

Production company

A company engaged primarily in exploration for and production of oil, and not in transportation, refining or marketing of petroleum.

Production costs

See PRODUCTION-RELATED COSTS.

Production enhancement gas

See QUALIFIED PRODUCTION ENHANCEMENT GAS.

Production enhancement procedures

Procedures, undertaken in order to increase production, which entitles a producer to a higher maximum lawful price for gas produced. See Federal Energy Regulatory Commission Order No. 107, High-Cost Natural Gas: Production Enhancement Procedures, 21 FPS 5–585 (Nov. 13, 1980). Among such procedures are the following: re-entry into a well that has been plugged and abandoned; re-entry into a well to drill deeper, or to sidetrack, to a different location; re-completion by reperforation of a zone from which natural gas has been produced or by perforation of a different zone; repair or replacement of faulty or damaged casing, tubing or related downhole equipment; fracturing, acidizing, or installing compression equipment; installation of equipment necessary for removal of excessive water, brine, or condensate from the well bore in order to establish, continue, or increase production from the well; workover operations designed to reduce production of excessive water or brine in order to establish, continue, or increase production of gas from the well; operations for disposing of water or brine, the presence of which prohibits or severely limits gas production from the well; workover operations to control sand production in the well bore, or to remove sand from the well bore and downhole equipment in order to continue to produce gas from the well; and "inert" gas injection. See 18 C.F.R. § 271.803 (1980).

See also SECONDARY RECOVERY; TERTIARY RECOVERY.

Production entity

For purposes of the Alberta Natural Gas Royalty Regulations (Alta. Reg. 16/74), production entity means the area of (a) a block, project or production spacing unit as defined in The Oil and Gas Conservation Act, or (b) a unit operation as defined in The Mines and Minerals Act, or (c) the drilling spacing unit of a well that is not within the area of a block, project or production spacing unit referred to in clause (a) or of a unit operation referred to in clause (b).

Production facilities

Facilities used in the production of oil after completion of a well. For federal income tax purposes, the Revenue Service regards a well as completed when a CHRISTMAS TREE (*q.v.*) is installed. Pumping equipment, salt water disposal equipment, flow lines, separators, storage tanks, treating equipment, etc. are production facilities, and the Revenue Service requires capitalization of production facilities as equipment costs. See Burke and Bowhay, *Income Taxation of Natural Resources* ¶ 1.13 (1981).

Production fund

An investment fund formed to acquire and operate producing oil and gas properties or nonoperating interests in such properties.

See also DRILLING FUND; INCOME PROGRAM; LEASE ACQUISITION FUND; LIMITED PARTNERSHIP; ROYALTY TRUST.

Production in commercial quantities

This term was defined for purposes of the BEHIND THE PIPE EXCLUSION (*q.v.*) of the NATURAL GAS POLICY ACT OF 1978 (NGPA) (*q.v.*) in True Oil Co. v. Federal Energy Regulatory Commission, 663 F.2d 75, 71 *O.&G.R.* 445 (10th Cir. 1981). In the economic and practical sense, the term was said to require "a capability to market," and a well may be capable of producing natural gas in commercial quantities before the completion of marketing facilities.

> "But, the act in question here speaks not in terms of capability but of the fact of production. 'Production in commercial quantities' requires means of transportation of the product from the producer to the consumer. Otherwise the quantities are not commercial in the plain sense of the word."

For purposes of an UNDEVELOPED ACREAGE CLAUSE (*q.v.*) of a GAS LEASE-SALES AGREEMENT (GLA) (*q.v.*), El Paso Natural Gas Co. v. American Petrofina Co. of Texas, 715 S.W.2d 177, ___ *O.&G.R.* ___ (Tex. App., Houston, 1986), concluded that both the basic lease royalty and the cost of overriding royalties burdening the property were to be considered as costs in determining whether undeveloped acreage was capable of producing in commercial quantities.

Production injection packer

A device inserted into an oil and gas well to seal off one zone from another, generally to stop water from entering the well bore and interfering with production. Transamerica Oil Corp. v. Lynes, Inc., 723 F.2d 758 (10th Cir. 1983).

Production in paying quantities

Production in such quantity as to enable the operator to realize a profit.

The term has different meanings for purposes of the habendum clause of the lease and for purposes of the covenants, express or implied, in the lease. For purposes of the habendum clause, that is, for the purpose of keeping the lease in force after the expiration of the primary term, paying quantities means production in quantities sufficient to yield a return in excess of operating costs, even though drilling and equipment costs may never be repaid and the undertaking considered as a whole may ultimately result in a loss. For purposes of measuring the duties of the lessee under the covenants of the lease, express or implied, the term means production in quantities sufficient to yield a return in excess of drilling, development and operating costs. Thus, if drainage occurs, under the Offset well covenant (*q.v.*) a lessee is normally required to drill an offset well to protect the leased premises from drainage, but he is not required to do so (subject to certain exceptions) unless the well, if drilled, would produce in paying quantities in the latter sense, that is, unless the well would repay all costs of drilling and operation. See Transport Oil Co. v. Exeter Oil Co., Ltd., 84 Cal. App. 2d 616, 191 P.2d 129 (1948). See Treatise §§ 604.6–604.6(h).

El Paso Natural Gas Co. v. American Petrofina Co. of Texas, 715 S.W.2d 177, ____ *O.&G.R.* ____ (Tex. App., Houston, 1986), concluded that under the Unprofitability clause (*q.v.*) of a Gas Lease-Sales Agreement (GLA) (*q.v.*) both the basic lease royalty and any overriding royalty burdening a property were to be considered in determining profitability, although for lease habendum clause purposes only the basic lease royalty would be so considered.

See also Yates Petroleum Corp., 89 I.D. 480, 67 IBLA 246 (Sept. 24, 1982), emphasizing that this term takes its meaning from the context, and finding that as used in a unit agreement, the term incorporated a requirement that the costs of drilling must be recouped. However it was held that for purposes of the extension provisions of 30 U.S.C. § 226(j) (1976), production in paying quantities "requires that the well drilled be able to produce sufficient hydrocarbons to recover the costs of operating and marketing but need not recoup the costs of drilling."

American Resources Management Corp., IBLA 79–10, GFS(O&G) 1979–58, concluded that the term "a well capable of producing oil or gas in paying quantities" refers to a well which is actually in physical condition to produce a sufficient quantity of oil or gas to yield a reasonable profit over and above the costs of operating the well and marketing the product. A satisfactory test of a well to establish its capability is necessary.

Article 124 of the Louisiana Mineral Code [R.S. 31:124 (1975) (1980 Supp.)] provides that production "is considered to be in paying quantities when the production allocable to the total original right of the lessee to share in production under the lease is sufficient to induce a reasonably prudent operator to continue production in an effort to secure a return on his investment or to minimize any loss." The Comment to this Article discusses in considerable detail the Louisiana cases and the concept of SERIOUS CONSIDERATION (*q.v.*)

Cases on the meaning of "paying quantities" are collected in Annotation, "Meaning of 'Paying Quantities' in Oil and Gas Lease," 43 A.L.R.3d 8.

See also the following:

Schnell v. Hudson, 141 Ill. App. 3d 617, 96 Ill.D. 16, 490 N.E.2d 1052, ____ *O.&G.R.* ____ (1986) (citing this MANUAL);

Solicitor's Opinion, "Section 2(a)(2)(A) of the Mineral Leasing Act of 1920," 92 I.D. 537 (Feb. 12, 1985).

A number of the factors going into the determination of whether production is in paying quantities are discussed in Discussion Notes, 12 *O.&G.R.* 695 (1960). See also TREATISE§§ 604.6–604.6 (h).

See also ADMINISTRATIVE OVERHEAD; CAPABLE WELL; COMMERCIAL QUANTITY; COMMERCIAL WELL; PRODUCTION.

Production license

In the United Kingdom, the authorization by the Secretary of State for Energy to engage in exploration for and exploitation of petroleum, whether oil or natural gas. At one time the license had an initial term of six years at the end of which the license could be continued for a further 40 years as to not more than one-half of the original area. Later licenses have an "initial term" of four years which may be continued for a "second term" of three years, subject to due performance and observance of prescribed terms and conditions. The license may elect to continue the license for a "third term" of thirty years as to a part of the original area (called the "continuing part"); the license is "determined" (terminated) as to the residue of the area, called the "surrendered part". The surrendered part (including any portions previously surrendered) must amount to not less than two-thirds of the number of sections contained in the area originally comprised in the license. Details of the licensing procedure are set forth in The Petroleum (Production) Regulations 1976. See Henderson *et al., Oil and Gas Law: The North Sea Exploitation* 3.1014 *et seq.* (1979); J. Salter, *U.K. Onshore Oil and Gas Law* (1986).

In Norway, a license granting exclusive right of exploration for and exploitation of petroleum in specific areas. See Krohn, Kaasen, *et al., Norwegian Petroleum Law* Part 2 (1978), for a detailed study of the production license.

See also AREA FEE; BLOCK; ENTITLEMENT; EXPLORATION LICENSE; EXPLORATION RETENTION LICENSE; EXPLORATORY LICENSE (CANADA); EXPLORATORY TITLE; INVITED APPLICATION; NON-INVITED APPLICATION; NON-RECURRENT FEE; PETROLEUM LICENSE; RECONNAISSANCE LICENSE.

Production loan

A loan on a producing property, usually taken to finance further development of a producing reservoir. See PROJECT FINANCING.

Production of gas

The act of bringing forth gas from the earth. Saturn Oil & Gas Co. v. Federal Power Comm'n, 250 F.2d 61, 8 *O.&G.R.* 365 (10th Cir. 1957), *cert. denied,* 355 U.S. 956, 8 *O.&G.R.* 843 (1958).

See also PRODUCTION.

Production or decline curve (S curve)

The annual production of an oil or gas reservoir through time is a dome-shaped profile with its peak usually to the left of center. The progress of the production from its peak toward depletion is called the decline curve. If this is plotted as cumulative production it follows a gradual S-shape as it approaches the total, or ultimate, production of the reservoir. 58 *Resources for the Future* 2 (March 1978).

Production or gathering exclusion

The Natural Gas Act of June 21, 1938, 52 Stat. 821, 15 U.S.C.A. § 717 provides for regulation of "the business of transporting and selling natural gas for ultimate distribution to the public" but Section 1(b) of the Act exempted from regulation the "production or gathering" of natural gas. Over the years there has been a steady erosion of the scope of the production or gathering exclusion, as noted in Shell Oil Co. v. Federal Energy Regulatory Comm'n, 566 F.2d

536, 60 *O.&G.R.* 310 (5th Cir. 1978), *aff'd by equally divided court,* 440 U.S. 192 (1979). In that case, however, the court concluded that the production or gathering exclusion rendered invalid FPC Order No. 539–A providing for a certificate condition that the seller of natural gas "shall observe the standard of a prudent operator to develop and maintain deliverability from reserves dedicated hereunder."

> "To hold that the power to issue Order No. 539–B is within the jurisdiction of the FERC would all but eliminate the 'production or gathering' exclusion and would allow the FERC to encroach on areas reserved to the states."

See also Northwest Central Pipeline Corp. v. State Corporation Comm'n, 240 Kan. 638, 732 P.2d 775, ___ *O.&G.R.* ___ (1987) (holding that proration order cancelling certain underages in production of gas allowable fell within the production or gathering exclusion).

Production payment

Another name for OIL PAYMENT (*q.v.*). Production payment is a broader term, since it would include interests in oil, gas, sulphur, or other minerals. However, oil payment is the more common term even where minerals other than oil are included.

Freede v. Comm'r, 86 T.C. 340, 88 *O.&G.R.* 640 (1986), held that a TAKE-OR-PAY CONTRACT (*q.v.*) gave a gas purchaser a production payment in the gas in place not taken but paid for by the purchaser in a given year.

Blinn, Duval, Le Leuch, and Pertuzio, *International Petroleum Exploration & Exploitation Agreements* 273 (1986), observe that production payments, like most other forms of project lending, originated in the United States; however, they have proved more difficult to transpose to other parts of the world where oil in the ground is the property of the host country and the grantor acquires a property right only after the oil has been extracted.

See also ADVANCE PAYMENT FINANCING; EQUITY PRODUCTION PAYMENT; FORWARD OIL PURCHASE; PROJECT FINANCING.

Production payment reservation agreement

An agreement, incident to a pooling or unitization agreement, concerning production payments reserved in such agreement. See Myers, *The Law of Pooling and Unitization* § 15.35 (2d ed. 1967).

Production payment trust

A trust in the form of a Royalty Trust (*q.v.*) that has as its corpus production payments rather than royalty interests. See Crichton, "Royalty Trusts and Other Exotic Distributions to Shareholders," 40 *N.Y.U. Inst. on Federal Taxation* 12–1 at 12–45 (1982).

Production-related costs

Under Order No. 94 of the Federal Energy Regulatory Commission, 45 F.R. 53099 (1980), designed to implement its authority to allow a production-related cost allowance under Section 110 of the Natural Gas Policy Act of 1978 (NGPA) (*q.v.*), the Commission adopted the following definitions:

" 'Production costs' means all costs incurred for exploration, development, production and abandonment operations, enhanced recovery techniques (including costs of compression incurred in the production of stripper well natural gas to which the pricing provisions of Subpart H of Part 271 apply), gaslift pumping or other liquid lifting equipment located on or in the vicinity of the wellhead or the point of commingling gas on the offshore platform from which the gas is produced, and costs that attend compression necessary for lifting liquids, cycling gas in a gas-condensate reservoir or pressurizing an oil reservoir.

" 'Non-allocable costs' means all costs incurred for the construction or operation of facilities to recover, separate, extract, process, treat, dehydrate, store, or transport crude oil or natural gas liquids or both.

" 'Production-related costs' means costs (excluding production costs and non-allocable costs) of compressing, gathering, processing, treating, liquefaction, conditioning, or transporting natural gas, or other similar costs."

Production shack

Syn. for Doghouse (*q.v.*). See Champlin Petroleum Co. v. Heinz, 665 S.W.2d 544 (Tex. App., Corpus Christi, 1983, error ref'd n.r.e.) (holding that maintenance of such a shack on a leasehold was not a sufficient basis for establishing venue under a statute referring to "a fixed and established place of business").

Production sharing contract

A contract for the development of mineral resources under which the contractor's costs are recoverable each year out of the production but there is a maximum amount of production which can be applied to this cost recovery in any year. In many such contracts, the maximum is 40%. This share of oil produced is referred to as "cost oil." The balance of the oil (initially 60%) is regarded as "profit oil" and is divided in the net profit royalty ratio—for instance, 55% to the government. After the contractor has recovered its investment, the amount of "cost oil" will drop to cover operating expenses only and the profit oil increases by a corresponding amount.

For discussions of the details of production sharing contracts, see the following:

Blinn, Duval, Le Leuch, and Pertuzio, *International Petroleum Exploration & Exploitation Agreements* ch. 5 (1986);

Mikesell, *Petroleum Company Operations & Agreements in the Developing Countries* (1984);

Taverne, "Methods of Participation of Host Countries in Crude Oil Exploration and Production Ventures in the Middle East and Northern Africa," in International Bar Ass'n, *World Energy Laws* (Proceedings of the IBA Seminar on World Energy Law held in Stavanger, Norway) 133 (1975);

Hossain, *Law and Policy in Petroleum Development* 138 (1979);

"Outer Continental Shelf Oil and Gas Development," Hearings before the Subcommittee on Minerals, Materials and Fuels of the Senate Committee on Interior and Insular Affairs, 93rd Cong., 2d Sess. (1974) at p. 1192 (Statement submitted by the Natomas Company);

Fabrikant, "Production Sharing Contracts in the Indonesian Petroleum Industry," 16 *Harv. Int. L.J.* 303 (1975).

For a typical Indonesian Production Sharing Contract, see OPEC, *Selected Documents of the International Petroleum Industry 1968* at p. 81.

For specific aspects or provisions of contracts of this kind see the entries under CONCESSION.

Production spacing unit

The drilling SPACING UNIT (*q.v.*) for a well, which may be referred to as a single production spacing unit, or one established by Board order consisting of one or more drilling spacing units, which may be referred to as a multiple production spacing unit. Alberta Oil and Gas Conservation Regulations (Alta. Reg. 151/71) § 5–010.

Production string

A string of casing set above the pay zone or through the pay zone and cemented in place to prevent water encroachment into the pay zone or the loss of oil and/or gas from the pay zone into nonproductive zones. The last, longest and smallest string of casing placed in a well. See Ball, Ball, and Turner, *This Fascinating Oil Business,* 97 (2d ed. 1965).

Syn.: Capital string; Oil string.

Production tax

(1) In one usage, a SEVERANCE TAX (*q.v.*); that is, a tax levied on each unit of production—barrell of oil or thousand cubic feet of gas. Severances taxes are usually levied as occupation taxes.

(2) In another and inconsistent usage, an ad valorem property tax, measured by the value of the product removed annually, or by such value less certain expenses.

Thus the same term may describe two different sorts of taxes, measured by different means. The local type of statute, whether an occupational severance tax or a real property ad valorem tax, seems to govern the meaning of the term in each state. See Hill, "State Taxation of Oil and Gas," 33 *Tex. L. Rev.* 854 (1955); Tippit, "Property Taxation of Oil and Gas Interests," 24 *Rocky Mt. L. Rev.* 170 (1952).

Production term

Syn.: SECONDARY TERM (*q.v.*).

Production unit

A somewhat artless term which was found to be ambiguous in Holly Energy, Inc. v. Patrick, 239 Kan. 528, 722 P.2d 1073, 90 *O.&G.R.* 34 (1986) (affirming the trial court's determination from extrinsic evidence of the meaning of the term as employed in the instrument construed).

Productive capacity of crude oil

The maximum daily rates of production which can be attained under specified conditions.

"The ninety-day crude oil productive capacity is the maximum daily crude production rate, at the point of custody transfer, that could be achieved in ninety days (following December 31 of any given year) with existing wells and equipment, and surface facilities—plus work and changes that can be reasonably accomplished within the time period using present service capabilities and personnel and with productivity declining as it would under capacity operation." American Petroleum Institutes Division of Statistics, *Organization and Definitions for the Estimation of Reserves and Productive Capacity of Crude Oil* 21 (Technical Report No. 2, June 1970).

Productivity factor

A factor employed by the Federal Power Commission in determining just and reasonable rates. In Opinion No. 770–A, 10 FPS 5–854 at 5–884 (Nov. 5, 1976), the Commission employed a productivity factor of 300 Mcf per successful foot drilled to compute the denomination for each incremental cost calculation in the discounted cash flow analysis employed.

Products royalty clause

A clause, occasionally appearing in oil and gas leases, providing that where gas or casinghead gas is used in the manufacture of gasoline or other products, the lessor will receive a stipulated fraction of the net proceeds from the sale of such gasoline or other products. In another form, the clause will provide that lessor is to receive a fraction of the proceeds from the sale of gasoline or other products manufactured from gas or casinghead gas produced on the lease, less a proportionate share of the manufacturing expense. See Hardwicke, "Problems Arising out of Royalty Clauses," 29 *Tex. L. Rev.* 790 at 696 (1951); TREATISE § 643.5.

The difficulties of determining the royalty due on gas under the usual lease provision make the products royalty clause desirable from the lessor's viewpoint. Regarding these difficulties, see Sneed, "Value of Lessor's Share of Production Where Gas Only Is Produced," 25 *Tex. L. Rev.* 641 (1947).

Profitability

In various contexts the question of whether production is "profitable" may be raised, *e.g.*, for habendum clause purposes and for measuring the duties of the lessee under the covenants of a lease. See PRODUCTION IN PAYING QUANTITIES. El Paso Natural Gas Co. v. American Petrofina Co. of Texas, 715 S.W.2d 177, ___ *O.&G.R.* ___ (Tex. App., Houston, 1986), concluded that under the UNPROF-

ITABILITY CLAUSE (*q.v.*) of a GAS LEASE-SALES AGREEMENT (GLA) (*q.v.*), both the basic lease royalty and any overriding royalty burdening a property were to be considered in determining profitability, although for lease habendum clause purposes only the basic lease royalty would be so considered.

Profit á prendre

An incorporeal interest in land authorizing entry upon a tract of land and the severance and removal of a part of the corpus of the land. In some of the oil and gas producing states, *e.g.*, California, the working interest of an oil and gas lessee is treated as a *profit á prendre;* in some other states, *e.g.*, Texas, the working interest is treated as a separate corporeal estate in land.

For a discussion of certain of the difficulties which may arise from rigidity in classification of petroleum titles as *profits á prendre* in Australia, see Crommelin, "Petroleum (Submerged Lands) Act: The Nature and Security of Offshore Titles," 2 *Austl. Mining & Petroleum L.J.* 134 at 142 *et seq.* (1979).

Profit oil

Under a so-called PRODUCTION SHARING CONTRACT (*q.v.*) between a contractor and the host government, some portion of the oil produced is applied to the recovery of costs incurred by the operator ("cost oil") and the balance of the oil, described as "profit oil" is divided between the contractor and the host government on an agreed basis, for instance, 55% to the government.

See Blinn, Duval, Le Leuch, and Pertuzio, *International Petroleum Exploration & Exploitation Agreements* 75 (1986).

Profit sharing bidding

A form of lease bidding in which the variable is the percentage of the total profits to be paid to the lessor by the successful lessee. See the following:

Mead, Moseidjord, Muraoka and Sorensen, *Offshore Lands: Oil and Gas Leasing and Conservation on the Outer Continental Shelf* 96 (1985);

Gaffney, *Oil and Gas Leasing Policy: Alternatives for Alaska in 1977* (1977) (Appendix L by R. F. Rooney).

See also LEASE BIDDING SYSTEMS.

Program management fee

In a joint operation or drilling program this is a fee paid the operator for its managing the activities of the operation or program. See Keller v. Comm'r of Internal Revenue, 79 T.C. 7 at 21, 74 *O.&G.R.* 129 at 146 (1982), *aff'd,* 725 F.2d 1173, 80 *O.&G.R.* 639 (8th Cir. 1984).

See also DRILLING FUND; JOINT OPERATING AGREEMENT.

Progressive incremental royalty

A proposed (but unimplemented) royalty provision for leases of Crown lands in Canada under which fields were to be subject to an increased royalty after achieving a 25 percent floor rate of return based on revenues received after deducting operating costs, basic royalty, and allowances for investment and income tax. See Hossain, *Law and Policy in Petroleum Development* 178 note 35, 220 (1979).

Project costs

The costs incurred in making geological and geophysical studies and surveys of a project area. A project area is a large territory designated for survey, from which smaller areas of potentially productive land are selected or more intensive study, and ultimately for leasing and exploratory drilling.

Under I.T. 4006, 1950–1 Cum. Bull. 48, project costs must be capitalized. The ultimate allocation of such costs among properties depends on the acreage acquired and other future actions. See Burke and Bowhay, *Income Taxation of Natural Resources* ¶ 13.03 (1979).

Project financing

A term applied to a program to raise debt or debt-type capital to finance major development well programs, the construction of associated production facilities, and the transportation of minerals to market.

For discussions of project financing, see the following:

Blinn, Duval, Le Leuch, and Pertuzio, *International Petroleum Exploration & Exploitation Agreements* ch. 15 (1986);

Rocky Mt. Min. L. Inst. on Mineral Financing (1982);

Burke and Meyer, "Federal Income Tax Classification of Natural Resource Ventures: Co-Ownership, Partnership or Association?," 37 *Sw. L.J.* 859 (1984);

Swan, *Ocean Oil and Gas Drilling & The Law* 130 *et seq.* (1979);

McCormick, "Legal Issues in Project Finance," 1 *J.E.R.L.* 21 (1983);

Barnett and Coffin, "New Financing Techniques in the Oil and Gas Industry," 34 *Sw. Legal Fdn. Oil & Gas Inst.* 431 (1983);

Mitchell, "Project Financing—The Bankers Approach to Project Risk," International Bar Ass'n, *Energy Law in Asia and the Pacific* 711 (1982);

Cheyne, "Project Finance—Structure," *Id.* at 732 (1982);

Ladbury, Fox, and Nettle, "Current Legal Problems in Project Financing," 3 *Australian Mining and Petroleum L.J.* 139 (1981);

Hunt and Camp, "Project Financing—Oil and Gas Ventures," 27 *Sw. Legal Fdn. Oil & Gas Inst.* 215 (1976).

For a detailed discussion of project financing of pipelines, see Ozark Gas Transmission System, Opinion No. 125, 16 FERC ¶ 61,099; Opinion No. 125–A, 17 FERC ¶ 61,024 (1981).

See also ADVANCE PAYMENT FINANCING; COMFORT LETTER; CONSENT CLAUSE; COST COMPANY; CROSS-CHARGE; CROSS-DEFAULT CLAUSE; DRILLING FUND; DRILL OR DROP PROVISION; FORWARD OIL PURCHASE; FORWARD SALE; GAIN CHARGE BACK PROVISION; JOINT ADVENTURE; LOAN PARTICIPATION; LIMITED RESOURCE FINANCING; MATURITY CLAUSE; NEGATIVE PLEDGE; NON-RECOURSE FINANCING; OIL MAN'S DEAL; PARI PASSU UNDERTAKING; PETRO-BONDS; PETROLEUM INCENTIVES PROGRAM (PIP); POLITICAL RISK LOAN; PRODUCTION LOAN; PROJECT WATCHDOG; 66.3 COMPANY; TAKE-OR-PAY CONTRACT; TAKE-OR-PAY FINANCING; THROUGHPUT AND DEFICIENCY AGREEMENT; TWO-TO-ONE AGREEMENT; WRAP-AROUND CARVED-OUT PRODUCTION PAYMENT.

Project Independence

A program initiated in March 1974 designed to improve the energy position of the United States and perhaps to gain independence from reliance on foreign energy sources by 1985. See Federal Energy Administration, *Project Independence Report* (Nov. 1975); "Project Independence," Hearings before the Senate Committee on Interior and Insular Affairs," 93rd Cong., 2d Sess. (Nov. 21, 1974), Serial No. 93–54 (92–89); De Marchi, "Energy Policy Under Nixon: Mainly Putting Out Fires," in Goodwin (Ed.), *Energy Policy in Perspective* 295 at 458 (1981).

Project watchdog

An engineer employed to report to the financing institutions on the progress of a project and the continuing credit worthiness of the project. See "The Emerging Role of the Reporting Engineer: Project Watchdog," International Bar Ass'n Section on Energy and Natural Resources, *International Energy Law* (1984 (Topic 10)).

See also PROJECT FINANCING.

Prone drilling unit (Prone spacing)

See STANDUP DRILLING UNIT (STANDUP SPACING).

PROOF

The Petroleum Royalty Owners of Florida.

Propane

A hydrocarbon associated with petroleum. It is gaseous at ordinary atmospheric conditions but is readily converted to the liquid state. When compressed to a liquid, it is usually handled in metal containers under high pressure. It is highly volatile, and when released into the atmosphere, vaporizes instantly, and in certain quantities, forms a highly explosive mixture, heavier than air. It is odorless and colorless, and its presence cannot be detected unless there has been added to the liquid propane an adequate odorizing agent which will give a distinctive stench noticeable to persons with an ordinary sense of smell. See Interstate Oil Compact Commission, *Oil and Gas Production* 26 (1951); Parkinson v. California Co., 255 F.2d 265 (10th Cir. 1958).

See also LIQUEFIED PETROLEUM GAS.

Proper parties

Those persons whose interest in litigation is such that they appropriately may be joined in the litigation but whose absence will cause no concern. See TREATISE § 875 *et seq.*

See also INDISPENSABLE PARTIES; NECESSARY PARTIES.

Property

The term used in a variety of tax statutes and regulations and in producer price statutes and regulations to identify the source of production. The definition of the term "has been heavily shrouded in both ambiguity and controversy since its inception." Overstreet and Wilcox, "The Department of Energy Crude Oil 'Property' Definition—A Controversial Concept With Critical Continuing Importance Under the Windfall Profit Tax Act," 26 *Rocky Mt. Min. L.*

Inst. 645 at 746 (1980) (discussing in detail the definition of this term under successive crude oil producer price regulations, current judicial and administrative litigation, and use of the DOE definition under the Crude Oil Windfall Profit Tax Act of 1980).

For a discussion of the definition of this term as used in implementing the STRIPPER WELL EXEMPTION (*q.v.*), See Sauder v. Department of Energy, 648 F.2d 1341 (Temp. Emer. Ct. of App. 1981).

See also Pennzoil Co. v. United States Department of Energy, 680 F.2d 156 (Temp. Emer. Ct. App. 1982), *cert. dism'd pursuant to Rule 53,* 459 U.S. 1190, 103 S. Ct. 841 (1983) (concluding that the property definition in the case of unitized property focused upon the right to produce, not the fee or leasehold nature of ownership interest; for purposes of price control, DOE regulations required that 1972 base production control levels of leases later designated a unit must be aggregated for comparison with total production from the unit during the critical periods in determining the quantity to be priced as new oil, if any).

State of Louisiana v. Department of Energy, 507 F. Supp. 1365 (W.D. La. 1981), 519 F. Supp. 351 (W.D. La. 1981), held that reservoir-wide production units established by the Louisiana Office of Conservation constituted separate "properties" for the purpose of federal oil and gas pricing regulations. The case was reversed on this point, 690 F.2d 180 (Temp. Emer. Ct. App. 1982), *cert. denied,* 460 U.S. 1069, 103 S. Ct. 1522 (1983).

Property unit, for tax purposes

The accounting unit for determining the depletion allowance in federal taxation. The term was defined for the first time by the 1954 Internal Revenue Code § 614: "The term 'property' means each separate interest owned by the taxpayer in each mineral deposit in each separate tract or parcel of land."

There is authority to support the proposition that four conditions must occur to create a single property unit for tax purposes:

(1) one parcel of land, including contiguous tracts

(2) the several interests must be acquired at the same time

(3) from the same person

(4) and must be of the same nature, *i.e.,* working interests or royalties, etc.

See Berkshire Oil Co., 9 T.C. 903 (1947); Herndon Drilling Co., 6 T.C. 628 (1946); Bird, "The 'Property' for Purposes of Depletion," 33 *Tex. L. Rev.* 785 (1955); Burke and Bowhay, *Income Taxation of Natural Resources* ¶ 16.01 *et seq.* (1980).

See also AGGREGATION OF PROPERTIES; DEPLETION, PERCENTAGE; NONOPERATING MINERAL INTEREST, FOR TAX PURPOSES; OPERATING MINERAL INTEREST, FOR TAX PURPOSES; OPERATING UNIT, FOR TAX PURPOSES.

Proportional Btu adjustment provision

A provision of a GAS PURCHASE CONTRACT (*q.v.*) providing for the price of gas to vary proportionately with variation of the Btu content of the gas from 1,000 Btus per Mcf. Kaiser-Francis Special Account C v. Federal Energy Regulatory Comm'n, 675 F.2d 249, 73 *O.&G.R.* 614 (10th Cir. 1982).

Proportionate increase clause

A lease clause providing for the increase of rentals and royalties in proportion to any estate or interest or acreage in addition to that specifically described which passes under the lease or to any after-acquired interest or reversion after a term or other interest which passes under the lease. See TREATISE §§ 686–686.1.

Proportionate profits method

A method used to determine a taxpayer's constructive gross income from mining for purposes of the depletion deduction taken under Section 611 of the Internal Revenue Code when the taxpayer engages in an integrated mining-manufacturing process. See Commissioner of Internal Revenue v. Portland Cement Co. of Utah, 450 U.S. 156 (1981).

Proportionate reduction clause

A clause commonly included in contemporary leases providing for the reduction of the payments to a lessor if his interest is less than that which he purported to lease, as follows:

> "If said lessor owns a less estate in the above described land than the entire and undivided fee simple estate therein, then the royalties and rentals herein provided shall be paid the lessor only in proportion which his interest bears to the whole and undivided fee."

Variations in the form of the clause are legion. If the parties have agreed on the payment of a substantial bonus or on a production payment, the clause may provide for a proportionate reduction of "bonus and production payments" in addition to "royalties and rentals."

A lease executed by a concurrent owner normally purports to cover all of the minerals in the described tract. The lessee will usually seek to have the lease executed in this fashion so that he may be entitled to the benefit of the doctrine of estoppel by deed in the event the leasing cotenant thereafter should acquire some or all of the outstanding undivided interest in the minerals. A number of problems for the parties may arise from this practice; hence before executing the lease they should carefully consider the consequences and the interrelation of the several clauses of the lease form adopted for use. Specifically, in drafting the lease, the parties should carefully analyze the interrelation of the granting, delay rental, royalty, proportionate reduction clause may give rise to considerable difficulty in any lease executed by a concurrent owner, even one which purports to lease only the lessor's undivided interest. See TREATISE §§ 686.2–686.11.

Syn.: Pro rata clause, Lesser estate clause, Lesser interest clause.

Proposed remedial order

An order issued by the ECONOMIC REGULATORY ADMINISTRATION (ERA) (*q.v.*), after a finding that a violation of a Department of Energy regulation has occurred, is continuing, or is about to occur, which sets forth the relevant facts and law. 10 C.F.R. § 205.192 (1980).

Proratable allowables

A term used to describe non-exempt allowables or allowables subject to the market demand factor. Thus in Texas some allowables were not subject to being reduced by the market demand factor (*viz.*, EXEMPT ALLOWABLES for discovery, marginal and special situation wells, and for county-regular, salt-dome, and certain waterflood fields). Allocation of the Texas monthly market demand for crude oil involved the subtraction from the market demand of the exempt allowables after which the remainder (proratable allowables) was allocated. See Governors' Special Study Committee of the Interstate Oil Compact Commission, *A Study of Conservation of Oil and Gas in the United States* 105–107 (1964).

See also ALLOWABLE.

Pro rata clause

See PROPORTIONATE REDUCTION CLAUSE.

Pro rata plan

The name given a form of gas curtailment plan under which all customers would receive the same proportion of the natural gas they contracted for. See Consolidated Edison Co. of New York v. Federal Energy Regulatory Comm'n, 676 F.2d 763 (D.C. Cir. 1982).

See also CURTAILMENT PLAN; END USE PLAN.

Proration clause

A term sometimes used in referring to an ENTIRETY CLAUSE (*q.v.*). See Central Pipe Line Co. v. Hutson, 401 Ill. 447, 82 N.E.2d 624 (1948).

Proration formula

The basis on which the field ALLOWABLE (*q.v.*) is allocated to the wells in the field. These formulae vary considerably in the factors given weight: some allocate production on a per well basis only; some on a combination of per well allocation plus an acreage factor (see 50–50 ALLOWABLE FORMULA); some include acre feet of formation, bottom hole pressure, potential, well depth, and expense of drilling.

The definition in this MANUAL was quoted in Northern Michigan Exploration Co. v. Public Service Comm'n, 153 Mich. App. 635, 396 N.W.2d 487 at 492, ____ *O.&G.R.* ____ (1986).

See also NET PAY PRORATION FORMULA.

Prorationing

(1) Restriction of production by a state regulatory commission, usually on the basis of market demand. The commission determines what amount shall be produced in a state during a given period of time and then allocates this total amount among the producing fields in the state (field allowables) and then allocates the field allowable to the various leaseholds and wells within the field (lease and well allowables).

In times of high demand the problem of prorationing is relatively simple. State regulatory agencies with power to restrict production to prevent waste and protect correlative property rights are then concerned only with limiting production from particular pools and wells to the maximum efficient rate (MER). When, however, available productive capacity is such that production at the MER for all wells will glut the market and result in waste by reason of excess surface storage, the problem of limiting production becomes more complex. In all major producing states except California there is some mechanism available whereby a regulatory agency of the state exercises power to prorate production. [To a limited extent, prorationing has been accomplished by voluntary agreement in California through the California Conservation Committee of producers.]

The mechanics of the process are relatively simple. The initial step is to make a determination of what the whole state should produce. A formula developed by the Federal Oil Conservation Board during the Hoover administration is followed. This involves a technique of forecasting consumption during short periods of time followed by an analysis of the amount of crude oil needed to satisfy this demand. This is broken down among the producing states by the Bureau of Mines by tracing the past history of crude oil from producing states to refineries and finally to consumers. The state prorationing authorities, guided by the estimates furnished by the Bureau of Mines, fix the allowables—the amount which may be produced per day from the various fields, pools, and wells in the state—in order that the production from the state shall not exceed a reasonable estimate of market demand. See Williams, Maxwell, Meyers, and Williams, *Cases on Oil and Gas* 201 (5th ed. 1987).

For a discussion of the origin and impact of market demand prorationing, see Danielsen, *The Evolution of OPEC* 87 (1982).

For an argument that prorationing on the basis of market demand results in waste, see Vafai, "Market Demand Prorationing and Waste—A Statutory Confusion," 2 *Ecology L. Q.* 118 (1972).

For a discussion or proposed reforms to remedy inadequacies in the existing statutory scheme for gas production and ratable taking, see Falk, "Natural Gas Regulation and Vested Property Interests: Ratable Taking, Proration Standards, and Fieldwide Civil Liability," 62 *Texas L. Rev.* 691 (1983).

See also the following:

Symposium: Workshop on Natural Gas Prorationing and Ratable Take Regulation, 57 *U. of Colo. L. Rev.* 149-393 (1986);

Libecap and Wiggins, "Contractual Responses to the Common Pool: Prorationing of Crude Oil Production," 74 *American Economic Review* 87 (1984);

Hollingsworth and Snider, "Some Aspects of 1985 Deregulation of Petroleum," 25 *Alta. L. Rev.* 36 at 42 (1986) (discussing prorationing in Alberta);

Erickson, "Crude Oil Prices, Drilling Incentives and the Supply of New Discoveries," 10 *Nat. Res. J.* 27 (1970);

Kahn, "The Combined Effects of Prorationing, and Depletion Allowance and Import Quotas on the Cost of Producing Crude Oil in the United States," 10 *Nat. Res. J.* 53 (1970);

Lovejoy, "Oil Conservation, Producing Capacity, and National Security," 10 *Nat. Res. J.* 64 (1970);

Dutton, "Proration in Texas: Conservation or Confiscation?" 11 *Sw. L.J.* 186 (1957).

See also ALLOWABLE; ASSOCIATED GAS PRORATION; HENZE TYPE PRORATION ORDER.

(2) This term is also applied to the allocation of capacity of an undersized pipeline among shippers. See Flexner, "Oil Pipelines: The Case for Divestiture," in Mitchell, ed., *Oil Pipelines and Public Policy* 3 at 11 (1979).

(3) Another use of the term is in connection with purchases by a pipeline when the allowable production for a given period is in excess of the amount of oil which the purchasing company wishes to take. See PURCHASER PRORATIONING (OR PIPELINE PRORATIONING).

Proration unit

(1) The area in a pool that can be efficiently and economically drained by one well, as determined by the commission. N.M. Stat., 1973, § 70–2–17 (B).

(2) The acreage assigned to an individual well for the purpose of allocating allowable production thereto. See Whelan v. Manziel, 314 S.W.2d 126, 9 *O.&G.R.* 390 (Tex. Civ. App. 1958, error ref'd n.r.e.), where a proration unit is distinguished from a pooled unit.

See also GAS PRORATION UNIT; HIGH GAS-OIL RATIO PRORATION UNIT.

It is emphasized in Rutter & Wilbanks Corp. v. Oil Conservation Comm'n, 87 N.M. 286, 532 P.2d 582, 50 *O.&G.R.* 488 (1975), that the terms proration unit and SPACING UNIT (*q.v.*) are not synonymous as employed in the New Mexico statutes.

An unusual lease clause construed in Fisher v. Walker, 683 S.W.2d 885, 84 *O.&G.R.* 378 (Tex. App., El Paso, 1985, error ref'd n.r.e.), was held to cause termination of a lease at the expiration of its primary term as to each proration unit upon which there was neither a producing well nor a shut-in gas well for which shut-in gas royalty payment had been made currently.

Prospect

A term frequently employed in various types of oil and gas agreements and that may be defined very broadly or narrowly according to the context. Thus, in Wurzlow v. Placid Oil Co., 279 So. 2d 749 at 754 (La. App. 1973), *writ ref'd,* 282 So. 2d 140 (La. 1973), the court observed:

"The term is of course a term of art, and its meaning must be determined from the context in which it is used. Philologically, it is formed from two Latin words 'pro,' meaning forward or ahead and 'spicere' meaning to see or look. There are, of course, many shades of meaning attributed to the term, depending on the frame of reference in which it is applied; but from all of the evidence bearing on its meaning in the oil and gas industry, the literal translation of forward looking or looking to the future seems a quite proper basis on which to build a more technical and more accurate definition."

The court then turned to parol evidence to assist it in defining the term as used in the instrument construed:

". . . [We] have reached the conclusion that in the oil and gas industry, a prospect commences with the determination of the existence of a certain geological structure, conducive to the production of oil and gas underlying a certain area of land. The actual existence of such minerals must then be determined and confirmed by actual drilling and production of such minerals. The continued exploration and drilling of additional wells then determine the extent of the area underlain by the geological structure which originally formed the basis for the drilling of the first well or wells. When by drilling it is ascertained that the limits of the producing geological structure have been reached, then the whole area underlain by that structure becomes a 'field.' From that, we conclude that a 'prospect' contemplates, in its optimum aspect, the creation of a 'field.'"

Blackmore v. Davis Oil Co., 671 P.2d 334, 80 *O.&G.R.* 431 (Wyo. 1983), defined this term as:

"[A] promoter's assessment of a drilling or mining site which is based on information obtained from observations, tests and other sources."

Prospecting license

Syn.: EXPLORATION LICENSE (*q.v.*).

Protection covenant

Another name for the OFFSET WELL COVENANT (*q.v.*).

Protectionist natural resource legislation

See Producing State Preference Statute.

Protection lease

A quit claim lease, mainly in the form of an ordinary oil and gas lease, taken from a person who may have an interest in the land, but providing that the obligations of the lessee shall not take effect until the interest of the lessor has been determined by a court. The purpose of the protection lease is to protect the lessee in case title of the original lessor should fail. It is used where a quit claim of possible outstanding interests cannot be obtained.

Several cases have held that the taking of protection leases does not give any cause of action to the original lessor. Nabors Oil & Gas Co. v. Louisiana Oil Ref. Co., 151 La. 361, 91 So. 765 (1922); Shell Oil Co. v. Howth, 138 Tex. 357, 159 S.W.2d 483 (1942). See also Treatise § 697.4.

See also Cover Lease; Top Lease.

Protection well

Another name for an Offset well (*q.v.*).

Protective leasing

"Where jurisdiction over disposition of mineral deposits in land set apart for other Government agencies has been transferred to the Department of the Interior because of drainage of its oil or gas content, such land must be offered for lease by competitive bidding. Protective leases may cover public domain lands which have been withdrawn from oil or gas leasing or acquired lands not subject to leasing under the Acquired Lands Leasing Act." 43 C.F.R. § 3100.3–3 (1978).

Protective string

See Casing.

Protest clause

A clause in a Gas purchase contract (*q.v.*) authorizing the buyer to protest any new rate schedule and any rate changes before the Federal Power Commission. See Pacific Natural Gas Co. v. Federal Power Comm'n, 276 F.2d 350 (9th Cir. 1960).

Provable reserves

A term coined by Chief Judge Bazelon's majority opinion for the court in Transcontinental Gas Pipe Line Corp. v. Federal Power Comm'n, 562 F.2d 664 at 668 (D.C. Cir. 1976), *cert. denied,* 436 U.S. 930 (1978), to describe reservoirs of gas which might be moved from the "possible" or "probable" categories into the category of "proved reserves" by "physically and economically achievable acts lying entirely within the control of a pipeline or producer." The dissenting opinion of Circuit Judge MacKinnon concluded that the majority "have coined an *ad hoc* definition and gratuitously endowed it with their own non-scientific trappings." 562 F.2d at 670, n.1.

See also RESERVES.

Proved acreage

"Proved acreage is the area which has been credited with proved reserves. Acreage is credited with proved reserves if the presence of a productive formation has been verified by drilling and testing. Undrilled acreage adjacent to drilled acreage and certain other undrilled acreage are also credited with proved reserves if geological and engineering information demonstrate with reasonable certainty that the underlying formations are continuous and productive." American Petroleum Institute Division of Statistics, *Organization and Definitions for the Estimation of Reserves and Productive Capacity of Crude Oil* 18 (Technical Report No. 2, June 1970).

See also RESERVES.

Proved developed reserves

"[P]roved reserves estimated to be recoverable through existing wells. Reserves in proved reservoirs penetrated by wells but currently not being produced are classified as 'developed' if it is anticipated that such reserves will be recovered through existing wells requiring no more than workover operations." American Petroleum Institute Division of Statistics, *Organization and Definitions for the Estimation of Reserves and Productive Capacity of Crude Oil* 13 (Technical Report No. 2, June 1970).

See also RESERVES.

Proved undeveloped reserves

"[E]conomically recoverable reserves estimated to exist in proved reservoirs which will be recovered from wells to be drilled in the future. Reserves in undrilled areas are included in proved reserves estimates if they are considered proved by geologic analysis of the current well information." American Petroleum Institute Division of Statistics, *Organization and Definitions for the Estimation of Reserves and Productive Capacity of Crude Oil* 14 (Technical Report No. 2, June 1970).

See also RESERVES.

Proven oil or gas property transfer

For purposes of the CRUDE OIL WINDFALL PROFIT TAX ACT OF 1980 (*q.v.*), this term means any transfer (including the subleasing of a lease or the creation of a production payment which gives the transferee an economic interest in the property) of an interest (including an interest in a partnership or trust) in any proven oil or gas property (within the meaning of section 613A(c)(9)(A)). Internal Revenue Code § 4988.

Proven or semi-proven acreage ("Drainage") method of evaluation

A method of evaluation of bids received for leases on Outer Continental Shelf Lands, defined as follows:

> "Leasing tract occupies part of a drilled structure. Geologic and engineering data adequate to prepare structure and net pay maps, to make standard reserve calculations, and to perform profitability analyses utilizing appropriate rate of return and discount factors. Any production found on unleased acreage would be considered a field extension." Exxon Company, U.S.A., 15 IBLA 345 at 355 note 7, GFS(OCS) 55 (May 14, 1974).

See also RANGE OF VALUES METHOD; RISK-FREE VALUE; WILDCAT ACREAGE METHOD OF EVALUATION.

Proven reserves

Oil that is still in the ground but that has been located and determined to be recoverable.

United States Department of the Interior, *An Appraisal of the Petroleum Industry* 13–14 (1965), declares that the term proven (or proved) reserves is frequently used:

> "to denote the amount of oil in known deposits which is estimated to be recoverable under current economic and operating conditions. Reserves, so defined, are probably on the conservative side. For example, oil which can be recovered by secondary recovery methods is only included after installation of secondary recov-

ery equipment. Because of the manner in which the development of a field and recovery technology proceeds in increments after the discovery well, 80 to 90% of the additions to proved reserves have been through revisions and extensions of previous estimates of the proved reserves of older fields, rather than as additions from new exploratory discoveries, although they all trace their lineage back to the original wildcat well. For most of the past thirty years, the ratio of proved reserves to annual production of crude oil has kept in a narrow range of between 12 and 14 to 1, although it has declined in recent years to slightly over 11 to 1 because additions to reserves have not kept pace with production."

The following is the definition of proved reserves adopted by the AGA in its annual publication, *Reserves of Crude Oil, Natural Gas Liquids, and Natural Gas in the United States and Canada and United States Productive Capacity,* Volume 28, June 1974. The first two paragraphs of the following definition appear on page 103 of this publication, the third paragraph is derived from page 99 and the last paragraph is derived from pages 96 and 97:

"Proved Reserves are the estimated quantity of natural gas which analysis of geologic and engineering data demonstrate with reasonable certainty to be recoverable in the future from known oil and gas reservoirs under existing economic and operating conditions. Reservoirs are considered proved that have demonstrated the ability to produce by *either actual production or conclusive formation test.*

"The area of a reservoir considered proved is *that portion delineated by drilling* and defined by gas-oil, gas-water contacts or limited by the structural deformation or lenticularity of the reservoir. In the absence of fluid contacts, the lowest known structural occurrency of hydrocarbons controls the proved limits of the reservoir. The proved area of a reservoir may also include the *adjoining portions* not delineated by drilling but which can be evaluated as economically productive on the basis of geological and engineering data available at the time the estimate is made. Therefore, the reserves reported should include total proved reserves which may be in either the drilled or the undrilled portions of the field or reservoir.

"Natural gas reserves take into account the shrinkage of the reservoir gas volume resulting from the removal of the liquefiable portions of the hydrocarbon gases and the reduction of volume due to the exclusion of non-hydrocarbon gases where they occur in sufficient quantity to render the gas unmarketable.

"The proved reserves estimated are to include all gas reserves regardless of size, availability of market, ultimate disposition or use." Federal Trade Comm'n v. Texaco, Inc., 517 F.2d 137 at note 2 (D.C. Cir. 1975).

Adelman, Bradley, and Norman, *Alaskan Oil: Costs and Supply* 16 (1971), define the term as follows:

"Proved reserves, as estimated by the American Petroleum Institute—American Gas Association (API-AGA), are those quantities recoverable 'with reasonable certainty . . . under existing economic and operating conditions.' This covers little beyond facilities already in place: the drilled portion of a reservoir and the adjoining area judged productive on the basis of 'available geological and engineering data.' Reserves coming from application of improved recovery techniques are included as proved reserves only if the facilities have already been installed or at the very least there has been 'successful testing by a pilot project.' Proved reserves are that small part of oil-in-place which has been developed for production by the drilling and connecting of wells and associated facilities; the total of planned production from all facilities already installed and paid for."

See also RESERVES.

Proven territory

Territory so situated with reference to known producing wells as to establish the general opinion that because of its relation to them, petroleum is contained in it. Burns' Ind. Stat. Ann. § 14–4–3–1(3) (Code Ed. 1973).

See also SEMI-PROVEN TERRITORY.

Province

A geological term employed to describe an area throughout which geological history has been substantially the same or which is characterized by particular structural or physiographical features.

See also FAVORABLE PETROLEUM GEOLOGICAL PROVINCE (FPGP); GEOLOGIC PROVINCE; PETROLEUM PROVINCE.

PR rate

Partial requirements rate schedule (*q.v.*).

PRT

The PETROLEUM REVENUE TAX (*q.v.*) established by the Oil Taxation Act 1975. See Daintith and Willoughby, *A Manual of United Kingdom Oil and Gas Law* 107–143 (1977).

Prudent man standard

A test applied in assessing the valuableness of mineral claims to determine whether a patent may be issued:

"As first stated in Castle v. Womble, 19 L.D. 455, 457 (1894), '[W]here minerals have been found and the evidence is of such a character that a person of ordinary prudence would be justified in the further expenditures of his labor and means, with a reasonable prospect of success, in developing a valuable mine, the requirements of the statute are met.' This 'prudent-man' standard is supplemented by the so-called 'marketability' test. The claimant must show that a man of ordinary prudence could extract and market the claimed minerals at a profit. This requires that there exists, at the time of discovery rather than at some speculative future date, a market for the discovered minerals that is sufficient to attract the efforts of a person of ordinary prudence." Roberts v. Morton, 389 F. Supp. 87 at 91 (D. Colo. 1975), *aff'd,* 549 F.2d 158 (10th Cir. 1976), *cert. denied,* 434 U.S. 834 (1977).

Prudent operator standard

The generally applicable test for determining whether the lessee has breached his IMPLIED COVENANTS (*q.v.*). The lessee is held to that performance of the covenants that would be made by an ordinary, prudent operator under the same or similar circumstances.

The test does not mean the same thing for all implied covenants. In the case of the OFFSET WELL COVENANT (*q.v.*), it usually means that breach of covenant has occurred if an offset well would probably produce oil in paying quantities. The same is true of the REASONABLE DEVELOPMENT COVENANT (*q.v.*). But in the case of the FURTHER EXPLORATION COVENANT (*q.v.*), some courts have held the duty to be breached without proof of probable profitable production. See Meyers, "The Implied Covenant of Further Exploration," 34 *Tex. L. Rev.* 553 (1956).

Generally, see TREATISE §§ 806–806.3.

Prudent pipeline standard

A standard utilized by the Federal Energy Regulatory Commission in reviewing purchase gas adjustment filings which pipelines must make in order to pass through increased purchase costs. A five-pronged standard was defined by the Commission in Transcontinental Gas Pipeline Corp., Order on Rehearing (Nov. 12, 1975) (No. RP76–2) as including the following elements: (1) the pipeline's need for gas; (2) the availability of other gas supplies; (3) the amount of gas dedicated to the purchase; (4) comparison of the price with appropriate market prices in the same or nearby areas; and (5) the relationship between the purchaser and the seller. See Morgan and Garrison, "Enforcement Policies and Procedures of the Federal Energy Regulatory Commission, 15 *Tulsa L.J.* 501 at 517 (1980).

PSC

PRODUCTION SHARING CONTRACT (*q.v.*).

psi

Pounds per square inch.

psia

Pounds of pressure per square inch absolute.

PSIG

Pounds per square inch gauge. "If pressure is measured relative to absolute zero, it is called absolute pressure; when measured relative to atmospheric pressure as a base, it is called gauge pressure. This is because practically all pressure gauges register zero when open to the atmosphere and hence measure the difference between the pressure of the fluid to which they are connected and that of the surrounding air." Daughtery and Franzini, *Fluid Mechanics With Engineering Applications* 28 (7th ed. 1977); Gilmore v. Oil and Gas Conservation Comm'n, 642 P.2d 773 at note 5, 75 *O.&G.R.* 172 at note 5 (Wyo. 1982).

See also PRESSURE.

PSLA

The PETROLEUM (SUBMERGED LANDS) ACT 1967 (*q.v.*).

PSU

PRODUCTION SPACING UNIT (*q.v.*).

PTT

The PETROLEUM AUTHORITY OF THAILAND (*q.v.*).

Public drilling fund

This term has been used by Bean, "Entity Selection—An Experience in Alchemy—A Comparison of Corporations, Partnerships, and Joint Ventures," 30 *Sw. Legal Fdn. Oil & Gas Inst.* 363 at 364 (1979), to describe those investments registered with the Securities and Exchange Commission initiated by an oil company or independent oil operator who has either undeveloped properties or "expertise" and desires to raise investor money from the public to provide the capital for the venture and to spread the risk.

"The offerings in recent years have ranged from $1 million to $20 million, and the 'unit' size for participation has decreased, *e.g.*, an investor now with $5,000 or $10,000 may be eligible to buy a unit of participation in a drilling fund. The drilling fund usually contemplates the formation of a limited partnership with the fund promoter being the general partner and the investors being limited partners. The general partner ordinarily contributes oil and gas leases, and the limited partners contribute funds for drilling and completion. The manner in which they share the revenues varies, but customarily the limited partners receive in excess of 50 percent of the net revenues after they recoup the drilling costs. The limited partners, in addition, are allocated all or substantially all of the deductions attributable to intangible drilling and development costs. There is also a 'blind pool' drilling fund in which the promoter puts up some of the funds and raises the rest of the money from public investors with no predetermined drilling locations but general 'areas of interest.' The idea is to generate a 'pool of funds' in order to acquire leases, explore, drill, and, hopefully, produce from such leases."

See also DRILLING FUND.

Public lands

Land owned by the state or federal government.

In the case of federally owned public land, there are two classifications: the public domain and acquired lands. In addition to public lands, the federal government also supervises Indian lands. The public domain is land acquired by the federal governemnt by treaty. Acquired land is land purchased or condemned by or donated to the federal government. In general, the Leasing Act of 1920, as amended, 30 U.S.C.A. § 226 governs the leasing of both types of federal public land. See also 30 U.S.C.A. § 351. See Hoffman, *Oil and Gas Leasing on Federal Lands* (1957); Malone, "Oil and Gas Leases on U.S. Government Lands," 2 *Sw. Legal Fdn. Oil & Gas Inst.* 309 (1951); *Rocky Mt. Min. L. Fdn. Law of Federal Oil and Gas Leases* Ch. 3 (1985); Comptroller General's Report to the Congress, *Actions Needed to Increase Onshore Oil and Gas Exploration and Development* (1981).

The distinction between acquired lands and public domain lands is discussed in Bobby Lee Moore, A–30433 (Mimeo Dec., Dep't of the Interior, Nov. 1, 1965), holding that public land which has been patented and has passed into private ownership does not regain the status of public land upon being acquired subsequently by the United States through purchase or condemnation.

See also ACQUIRED FEDERAL LANDS; ACQUIRED LANDS LEASING ACT OF 1947; ALASKA NATIONAL INTEREST LANDS CONSERVATION ACT (ANILCA); ALASKA NATIVE CLAIMS SETTLEMENT ACT OF DEC. 18, 1971 (ANCSA); ALLOTMENT; APPROPRIATED PUBLIC LANDS; BID FILES; BOARD OF LAND APPEALS; BUREAU OF LAND MANAGEMENT; CHERRYSTEMMING PRACTICE; CLASSIFICATION AND MULTIPLE USE ACT OF SEPT. 19, 1964; FEDERAL LAND EXCHANGE; FEDERAL LEASE; FLMPA; INDIAN ALLOTMENT; INDIAN LANDS; ISOLATED TRACT; MINERALS MANAGEMENT SERVICE (MMS); MULTIPLE MINERAL DEVELOPMENT ACT (OR MULTIPLE USE ACT OF SEPT. 19, 1964; OUTER CONTINENTAL SHELF (OCS); OUTER CONTINENTAL SHELF LANDS ACT OF 1953; RARE; RIGHT OF WAY LEASING ACT OF 1930; SUBMERGED LANDS ACT OF 1953; WITHDRAWAL.

Many states also own land. Most notable are Texas, which retained title to its public lands when entering the Union, and Alaska. Leasing of state-owned public land is governed by local statutes which vary considerably from state to state.

For a detailed discussion of the leasing of Texas public lands see Whitworth, "Leasing and Operating State-Owned Lands for Oil and Gas Development," 16 *Texas Tech L. Rev.* 673 (1985).

See also EXCESS LANDS; RELINQUISHMENT ACT LANDS; VACANCY.

Public limited partnership (PLP)

"[A]n organizational structure classified as a limited partnership, the ownership interests in which are either freely tradable on an established securities market or are represented by freely tradable depositary receipts registered on an established securities market. In either case, the freely tradable entity usually is a limited partner in another limited partnership through which all operations of the PLP are conducted. Because of the free tradability of the ownership interests and depositary receipts, investors possess a liquid asset that may be easily converted to cash." Manford and Kalteyer, "Restructuring Oil and Gas Operations into Public Limited Partnerships," 35 *Sw. Legal Fdn. Oil & Gas Inst.* 361 at 363 (1984).

See also LIMITED PARTNERSHIP.

Publicly traded limited partnership

See MASTER LIMITED PARTNERSHIP.

Public Utilities Regulatory Policies Act of 1978 (PURPA)

Pub. L. No. 95–617 (Nov. 9, 1978). Major provisions of this Act related to:

(1) a requirement that state public utility commissions consider rate reforms (time-of-day, seasonal, or lifeline rates) when reviewing utility prices beginning in 1981;

(2) authorization for the Department of Energy to intervene in state proceedings to advocate rate reforms and to appeal commission decisions in state courts;

(3) authorization for any rate payer to participate in the regulatory proceedings and to be compensated for his costs by the utility involved or through a state program; and

(4) a requirement that public utilities provide information to state commissions and the Department of Energy on the cost of providing electric service at different times of day and to different types of customers.

The constitutionality of this Act was sustained in Federal Energy Regulatory Comm'n v. Mississippi, 456 U.S. 752 (1982), *reh. denied,* 458 U.S. 1131 (1982).

Pugh clause

The name given to a type of pooling clause which provides that drilling operations on or production from a pooled unit or units shall maintain the lease in force only as to lands included within such unit or units. This clause was said to have been originated in 1947 by Lawrence C. Pugh of Crowley, Louisiana, and to take its name from him. Similar clauses were in use in other states prior to 1947. See, *e.g.*, the 1943 lease construed in Rist. v. Westhoma Oil Co., 385 P.2d 791, 19 *O.&G.R.* 692 (1963). See TREATISE §§ 669.14, 670.4.

See also ALL OR NOTHING CLAUSE; EXTENDED PRIMARY TERM; FREESTONE CLAUSE; SECONDARY PRIMARY TERM; STATUTORY PUGH CLAUSE.

Bibler Brother Timber Corp. v. Tojac Minerals, Inc., 281 Ark. 431, 664 S.W.2d 472, 81 *O.&G.R.* 24 (1984), was concerned with the provision of a lease pooling clause that in the event only a part of the leasehold was included in a voluntary unit, "then the remaining portion of the lands embraced by this lease shall be subject to delay rental payments as provided in Paragraph 4 [the delay rental clause of the lease]." The court concluded that the quoted language did not amount to a Pugh clause permitting the leasehold to be canceled as to excluded acreage in the secondary term.

Pugh clause rental

Rentals paid under the terms of a PUGH CLAUSE (*q.v.*) on the acreage in a lease excluded from a unit which includes other acreage from the same lease. Payment of such rental is required to preserve the lease as to the acreage excluded from the unit when there is no drilling on such excluded acreage or on a unit which includes such acreage. See Canik v. Texas International Petroleum Corp., 308 So. 2d 453, 52 *O.&G.R.* 363 (La. App. 1975), *writ denied,* 310 So. 2d 850 (La. 1975).

Pulling a well

A term applied to the act of removing pipe and other underground equipment from the well. Corpus, Jr. v. K-J Co., 720 S.W.2d 672, ____ *O.&G.R.* ____ (Tex. App., Austin, 1986, error ref'd n.r.e.).

See also PULLING CASING.

Pulling casing

The removal of casing from a hole, upon the abandonment of a well, to salvage its value. Most oil and gas leases expressly provide that the lessee may remove casing after the lease has expired. See TREATISE §§ 674–674.4.

Pumping schedule

A program of pumping a well for a period of hours each day and then allowing time for additional fluid to enter the well base to be pumped out. See Long v. Magnolia Petroleum Co., 166 Neb. 410, 89 N.W.2d 245, 9 *O.&G.R.* 41 at 54 (1958).

Pumping station

One of the pumping plants located at intervals along a main pipeline (a trunk line) to maintain the flow to the terminal point. Both oil and gas pipelines have pumping stations. The interval between the stations depends on the terrain, the nature of the product being transported, and the diameter of the pipe, among other factors. Smaller sized pumping stations on a natural gas pipeline are called booster stations.

Pumping well

A well which is not a FLOWING WELL (*q.v.*) and from which oil is produced by the use of artificial lifting methods, such as pumping. See Ferguson v. Housh, 227 S.W.2d 590 (Tex. Civ. App. 1950).

Pump, on the

See ON THE PUMP.

Purchase agreement

An agreement for the purchase and sale of oil and/or gas produced from designated leases, setting forth the terms and conditions of purchase and sale, and requirements as to quality and condition of the product and measurement of quantities.

Purchase contract

A contract for the sale and purchase of oil or gas entered into by the purchaser and the owners of interests in the oil or gas. See TREATISE §§ 724–738.

See also GAS PURCHASE CONTRACT; KICKOUT CLAUSE.

Purchase-contract carriage arrangement

A phrase used to describe an arrangement whereby a large consumer of gas purchases gas from producers and then makes a contract with a pipeline company for the transmission of such gas from seller to buyer. In the Matters of Transcontinental Gas Pipe Line Corp., 21 F.P.C. 138, 9 *O.&G.R.* 1199 (Jan. 30, 1959).

Purchased gas adjustment clause

A clause in a RATE SCHEDULE (*q.v.*) providing for automatic changes in rates for every change, *e.g.*, of 1 cent per Mcf or more, in the rate at which the company purchased gas. Report of the Committee on Natural Gas, A.B.A., Mineral Law Section, *1956 Proceedings* 126 at 151 (1956).

The validity of a purchased gas adjustment clause was sustained in San Antonio Independent School District v. City of San Antonio, 550 S.W.2d 262 (Tex. 1976), against the claim that it amounted to an unlawful delegation of legislative authority over ratemaking.

The operation of this clause is discussed in Adair and Helman, "Distributor Rates," American Gas Ass'n, *Regulation of the Gas Industry* 40-1 at 40-66 (1981).

An argument against employment of automatic fuel adjustment clauses in fixing utility rates is made in Leaffer, "Automatic Fuel Adjustment Clauses: Time for a Hearing," 30 *Case West. Res. L. Rev.* 228 (1980).

For an argument in favor of use of this form of clause in natural gas utility tariffs, see Fowler, "Purchased Gas Adjustment Clauses: An Adjuster's Viewpoint," 6 *St. Mary's L.J.* 567 (1974).

See also PRUDENT PIPELINE STANDARD.

Purchase letter

An agreement, usually contained in a letter, whereby the owner of a lease agrees to drill a test well at a specified location, upon the completion of which the lease owner agrees to convey certain acreage under the lease or under adjoining leases to the assignee, who agrees to pay a stipulated sum of money for the assignment. Purchase letters take the form of a DRY HOLE AGREEMENT (*q.v.*) or a BOTTOM HOLE LETTER (*q.v.*) depending upon whether the agreement calls for completion of the test well as a dry hole or to a specified depth. Purchase letters may be used by the assignor to finance the drilling of the well. See Bank v. Republic Supply Co., 166 S.W.2d 373 (Tex. Civ. App. 1942). For forms, see Williams, Maxwell, Meyers, and Williams, *Cases on Oil and Gas* 992–994 (5th ed. 1987). See TREATISE §§ 431–431.2.

For other forms of letter agreements, see LETTER.

Purchase rights

The rights created by a covenant entitling a contracting party to share in future acquisitions. See Courseview, Inc. v. Phillips Petroleum Co., 298 S.W.2d 890, 7 *O.&G.R.* 1068 (Tex. Civ. App. 1957), *modified,* 158 Tex. 397, 312 S.W.2d 197, 9 *O.&G.R.* 249 (1957).

See also AREA OF MUTUAL INTEREST AGREEMENT.

Purchaser nomination

See NOMINATIONS BY PURCHASERS.

Purchaser prorationing (or pipeline prorationing)

Informal prorationing by pipeline when the allowable production for a given period is in excess of the amount of oil which the purchasing company wishes to take because of market conditions or lack of storage facilities.

For discussions of this form of prorationing see the following:

Wolbert, *U.S. Oil Pipe Lines* 356 (1979);

American Petroleum Institute, *Witnesses for Oil, The Case Against Dismemberment* 155 (1976) (describing the policy employed by Colonial Pipeline Co. when its line becomes full and space must be prorated among shippers);

Rogers, "Common Purchaser, Market Demand, Pipeline Proration," 9 *Sw. Legal Fdn. Oil & Gas Inst.* 45 (1958);

TREATISE § 724.4.

See also PRORATIONING.

Purchaser representative

For purposes of REGULATION D (*q.v.*) of the Securities and Exchange Commission providing for a PRIVATE OFFERING EXEMPTION (*q.v.*) under the Federal Securities Act, it is required that the issuer reasonably believe that any NONACCREDITED INVESTOR (*q.v.*), either alone or acting with a "purchaser representative," understood the merits and risks of the offering. For this purpose, a purchaser representative must meet certain criteria specified in Rule 501(h), 17 C.F.R. § 230.501(h) (1982) (relating to knowledge and experience, acknowledgement of status by the purchaser in writing after disclosure in writing of material relationship of the representative and the issuer). See TREATISE § 441.4.

Pure service agreement

A form of service agreement—as distinguished from a RISK SERVICE CONTRACT (*q.v.*)—between a host country and an international oil company under which the international oil company is paid a flat fee for its services. Under this form of agreement the oil company does not carry any element of exploration risk. See Blinn, Duval, Le Leuch, and Pertuzio, *International Petroleum Exploration & Exploitation Agreements* 97 (1986).

Syn.: No-risk service agreement.

Purging a tank

A process employed to eliminate moisture and other matters which adversely affect liquefied petroleum gas placed in the tank. Parkinson v. California Co., 255 F.2d 265 (10th Cir. 1958).

Purification equipment

Apparatus used for the removal of impurities from gas and apparatus for conditioning gas, including pumps, wells, and other accessory apparatus. 18 C.F.R. § 201.317 (1980).

PURPA

The Public Utilities Regulatory Policies Act of 1978 (*q.v.*).

Put option

The term used to describe an agreement between a leasing service and its client for whom the service files a Drawing entry card (*q.v.*) in a simultaneous noncompetitive oil and gas lease offer. Under this agreement the service agrees in advance to purchase, at the client's sole election, a specified percentage of any lease which the client might be awarded at a pre-determined price. The leasing service has no right to compel the client to convey any interest to it, so that when the lease issues to the client, the service has no enforceable interest therein. Nicolazzi v. Commissioner, 79 T.C. 109, 73 *O.&G.R.* 619 (1982); D. E. Pack, 40 IBLA 45 at 46, GFS(O&G) 1979–38 (1979). See also Harry S. Hills, IBLA 80–135, 48 IBLA 356, GFS(O&G) 1980–132 (July 11, 1980), remanding case for determination of whether nondisclosure of put option violated regulations requiring disclosure of other parties in interest and prohibiting multiple filings in simultaneous oil and gas lease filings.

Put-together

See Exchange offer.

. . Q . .

Qatar Petroleum Company

For a discussion of this national petroleum company, see Shwadran, *The Middle East, Oil and the Great Powers* 434–436 (3d ed. revised and enlarged, 1973).

Qmax

In Alberta, the maximum daily rate at which a gas well can produce without causing reservoir damage. Oil and Gas Conservation Regulations (Alta. Reg. 151/71) § 1–020 (19).

QNPC

The Qatar National Petroleum Corporation.

QPC

The QATAR PETROLEUM COMPANY (*q.v.*).

Quad

A quadrillion of Btu's. This unit of measurement is used in connection with energy consumption. A barrel of crude oil, containing 42 gallons, contains 5.8 million Btu's. Natural gas contains about one million Btu's per thousand feet (Mcf). One million barrels of oil per day equals two quads per year, and one trillion cubic feet of natural gas equals about one quad. Report of the House Committee on Ways and Means on Title II of H.R. 6831, the Energy Tax Act of 1977, 95th Cong., 1st Sess., July 13, 1977, p. 7.

Qualified applicant

A person who is qualified to hold federal oil and gas leases and who has filed a valid application for a non-competitive lease. All public domain lands not within the known geologic structure of a producing oil or gas field which are otherwise available for lease are subject to lease to the first qualified offeror or applicant. See *Rocky Mt. Min. L. Fdn. Law of Federal Oil and Gas Leases* Ch. 4 (1985). For an illustrative case dealing with defining this term, see Ashley v. Andrus, 486 F. Supp. 1319 (E.D. Wis. 1980), *aff'd,* 655 F.2d 105, 70 *O.&G.R.* 365 (7th Cir. 1981).

See also FEDERAL LEASE; NON-COMPETITIVE LEASE.

Qualified charitable interest

For purposes of the CRUDE OIL WINDFALL PROFIT TAX ACT OF 1980 (*q.v.*), this term means an economic interest in crude oil if:

(A) such interest is—

(i) held by an organization described in clause (ii), (iii), or (iv) of section 170(b)(1)(A) which is also described in section 170(c)(2), or

(ii) held—

(I) by an organization described in clause (i) of section 170(b)(1)(A) which is also described in section 170(c)(2), and

(II) for the benefit of an organization described in clause (i) of this subparagraph, and

(B) such interest held by the organization described in clause (i) or subclause (I) of clause (ii) of subparagraph A of January 21, 1980, and at all times thereafter before the last day of the taxable period. Internal Revenue Code § 4994.

The definition of this term in the CRUDE OIL WINDFALL PROFIT TAX ACT OF 1980 was modified by the Economic Recovery Tax Act of 1981 to include an interest "held by an organization described in section 170(c)(2) which is organized and operated primarily for the residential placement, care, or treatment of delinquent, dependent, orphaned, neglected, or handicapped children."

Qualified governmental interest

For purposes of the CRUDE OIL WINDFALL PROFIT TAX ACT OF 1980 (*q.v.*), this term means an economic interest in crude oil if: (A) such interest is held by a state or political subdivision thereof or by an agency or instrumentality of a state or political subdivision thereof, and (B) under the applicable state or local law, all of the net income received pursuant to such interest is dedicated to a public purpose. Internal Revenue Code § 4994.

Section 35 of the Mineral Leasing Act of 1920, as amended, 30 U.S.C. § 191, provides a formula for distributing a share of royalty revenues to the states in which the federal government realizes such revenues. A Solicitor's opinion has ruled that the states do not have an "economic interest" in federal royalty revenues for purposes of the exemption provided by the windfall profit tax. Effect of the Crude Oil Windfall Profit Tax Act of 1980 on the States' Share of Federal Oil Royalties, M–36929, 87 I.D. 661 (Dec. 30, 1980).

Qualified overriding royalty interest

For purposes of the CRUDE OIL WINDFALL PROFIT TAX ACT OF 1980 (*q.v.*), this term means an overriding royalty interest in existence as such an interest on January 1, 1980, but only if on February 20, 1980, there was in existence a binding contract under which such interest was to be converted into an operating mineral interest (within the meaning of section 614(d)). Internal Revenue Code § 4992.

Qualified ownership theory

The theory that landowners whose tracts overlay a producing formation have correlative rights in the formation. The interest created in a mineral grantee in a state following this theory is usually classified as a *profit a prendre.* This theory appears to be followed in California, Indiana, Louisiana and Oklahoma. See TREATISE § 203.2.

See also CORRELATIVE RIGHTS THEORY; NON-OWNERSHIP THEORY; OWNERSHIP IN PLACE THEORY; OWNERSHIP OF STRATA THEORY.

Qualified partnership

A term which has been used to describe an operating agreement entered into by owners of undivided leasehold interests for the management of the leasehold by an appointed operator. See Fillman, "Effect on the Investor's Group of New Subchapter K," 7 *Sw. Legal Fdn. Oil & Gas Inst.* 721 at 725 (1956).

Qualified production

For purposes of the category of independent producer oil under the CRUDE OIL WINDFALL PROFIT TAX ACT OF 1980 (*q.v.*), qualified production for any quarter means the number of barrels of taxable crude oil: (A) of which such person is the producer, (B) which is removed during such quarter, (C) which is tier 1 oil or tier 2 oil, and (D) which is attributable to the independent producer's working interest in a property. Internal Revenue Code § 4992.

Qualified production enhancement gas

Gas produced by PRODUCTION ENHANCEMENT PROCEDURES (*q.v.*) entitled to a higher maximum lawful price under the Natural Gas Policy Act of 1978. See Federal Energy Regulatory Commission Order No. 107, 21 FPS 5–585 (Nov. 13, 1980), 18 C.F.R. § 271.803 (1980).

Qualified royalty production

For the purposes of Section 6429 of the CRUDE OIL WINDFALL PROFIT TAX ACT OF 1980 (*q.v.*) as amended by the ECONOMIC RECOVERY TAX ACT OF 1981 (*q.v.*), this term is defined as meaning "with respect to any qualified royalty owner, taxable crude oil which is attributable to an economic interest of such royalty owner other than an operating mineral interest (within the meaning of section 614(d)). Such term does not include taxable crude oil attributable to any overriding royalty interest, production payment, net profits interest, or similar interest of the qualified royalty owner" that is created after June 9, 1981, out of a specified type of operating mineral interest and is not created pursuant to a binding contract entered into prior to such date.

Effective January 1, 1981, the credit or refund for royalty owners was increased from $1,000 to $2,500. For 1982 and later years the dollar credit or exemption was replaced by an exemption of two barrels average daily production of taxable crude oil (for 1982 through 1984) and an exemption of three barrels average daily production of taxable crude oil for 1985 and thereafter. The Technical Corrections Act of 1982, Pub. L. No. 97-448, added Code Section 6430 under which each individual or estate income beneficiary of a trust is entitled to a credit or refund of windfall profit tax paid by the trust on his or her allocable share of the qualified royalty production of the trust, effective for taxable years beginning after December 31, 1981. See Maultsby and Jelks, "Windfall Profit Tax Relief for Qualified Trust Beneficiaries," 32 *O.&G. Tax Q.* 261 (1983). See also, Fambrough, "The Impact of the Windfall Profit Tax on Royalty Owners," 32 *O.&G. Tax Q.* 328 (1983).

Qualified subscriber

A term used in the West Edmond Hunton Lime Unit agreement for a party who does not elect to pay his proportionate share of the UNIT EXPENSE (*q.v.*) but elects to have it payable together with a specified rate of interest from his proportionate share of the unit production. See Meyers, *The Law of Pooling and Unitization* 625 (1957).

See also UNQUALIFIED SUBSCRIBER.

Qualified tertiary injectant expenses

For purposes of the CRUDE OIL WINDFALL PROFIT TAX ACT OF 1980 (*q.v.*), this term means any expense allowable as a deduction under section 193. Internal Revenue Code § 4988.

Qualified tertiary recovery project

For purposes of the CRUDE OIL WINDFALL PROFIT TAX ACT OF 1980 (*q.v.*), this term means: (A) a qualified tertiary enhanced recovery project with respect to which a certification as such has been approved and is in effect under the June 1979 energy regulations, or (B) any project for enhancing recovery of crude oil which meets specified requirements. Internal Revenue Code § 4993.

See also TERTIARY INCREMENTAL PROGRAM.

Qualified tract

A tract bound to a pooling or unitization agreement by the owners of a stated percentage of interests therein. See, *e.g.*, the definition in the Seeligson agreement quoted in Myers, *The Law of Pooling and Unitization* 117 (1957).

Qualified trust beneficiaries

See QUALIFIED ROYALTY PRODUCTION.

Quality bank

The term applied to a provision of a tariff for pipeline transportation of petroleum to adjust for quality differentials. Under this provision the pipeline carrier establishes a "quality bank" to compute adjustments among all shippers for differences in the weighted average gravity of crude petroleum each shipper introduces into the system. The higher the weighted averaged gravity of crude petroleum, the greater is its value. Operation of the "quality bank" provides that a shipper who introduces high average gravity petroleum into the system, but as a result of commingling, receives lower gravity petroleum at delivery will be reimbursed for the difference, and that a shipper introducing low gravity petroleum, but receiving higher gravity crude, will be billed for the difference. ARCO Pipe Line Co., Docket Nos. IS79–7 and OR78–1, 17 FPS 5–266 (Oil Pipeline Board, March 12, 1979); Mobil Alaska Pipeline Co., Docket No. IS79–8, 17 FPS 5–385 (Oil Pipeline Board, March 22, 1979).

Quality standards

Standards for pipeline quality gas relating to the carbon dioxide, hydrogen sulphide, total sulphur and other impurities found in gas, the pressure and the Btu adjustment. See Permian Basin Area Rate Proceeding, 34 F.P.C. 159 at 239, 23 *O.&G.R.* 103 at 200 (Opinion

No. 468, Aug. 5, 1965), *remanded,* Skelly Oil Co. v. Federal Power Comm'n, 375 F.2d 6, 26 *O.&G.R.* 237 (10th Cir. 1967), *aff'd in part and rev'd in part sub nom. In re* Permian Basin Area Rate Cases, 390 U.S. 747, 28 *O.&G.R.* 689 (1968).

Quarter-way price

The TAX-PAID COST (*q.v.*) of crude plus one fourth of the difference between that cost and the POSTED PRICE (*q.v.*). Under the terms of some participation agreements between foreign oil companies and host nations, the price paid by the companies on BRIDGING CRUDE (*q.v.*) was the quarter-way price. Al-Chalabi, *OPEC and the International Oil Industry: A Changing Structure* 44 (1980).

See also MID-WAY PRICE; OIL PURCHASE AND SALE CONTRACT.

Quitclaim

An instrument releasing all interest (or the described interest) in land owned by the grantor at the time the instrument takes effect. The operative words of a quitclaim are: ". . . release, remise and forever quitclaim all right, title and interest in the following described land. . . ." A quitclaim purports to act only on the interest the grantor now owns; it does not pass an after-acquired title as a warranty deed does. Quitclaims are extensively used in title curative work.

Quota

See OIL IMPORT QUOTA.

. . R . .

Rabbit

Syn.: Pig (*q.v.*).

Radial drainage

"The concept that a well will drain the reservoir in a circular pattern consisting of an equal radius around the well hole. Radial drainage is assumed unless there is proof that due to the location of the well on the structure, it drains from one direction more than another." Amoco Production Co. v. North Dakota Industrial Comm'n, 307 N.W.2d 839 at 847, n.8, 70 *O.&G.R.* 283 at 294, n.8 (N.D. 1981), *noted,* 58 *N.D. L. Rev.* 675 (1982).

See also Drainage.

Radiation well logging

Syn.: Radioactivity well logging (*q.v.*).

Radioactivity well logging

A term originally applied to methods of detecting and measuring natural radiation from strata penetrated by a well but which has come to be a generic term used to designate any well logging in which radiations coming from the formations, whether they be natural or artificially produced, are detected and measured. The commonly used kinds of radioactivity well logging are Natural gamma ray logging, Neutron logging, and Gamma ray-gamma ray logging (*q.v.*). Radioactivity well logging is sometimes called radioactivity well surveying or radiation well logging. Well Surveys, Inc. v. McCullough Tool Co., 199 F. Supp. 374 at 376 (N.D. Okla. 1961).

See also Well log.

Radioactivity well surveying

Syn.: Radioactivity well logging (*q.v.*).

Railroad Commission

See Texas Railroad Commission

Ram blow-out preventer

A wellhead device that uses horizontal sliding gates or rams, forced toward each other by hydraulic pressure or mechanical screws, to close the well bore or around pipe in the well bore. "Blind" rams are used to close the hole when no tools or pipe are in the hole. "Pipe" rams have a semi-circular notch in the closing surface which fits around the body of the pipe when the rams are closed. "Blind-shear" rams are blind rams capable of cutting through most pipe in the well bore and tubing effecting full closure of the well.

See also BLOW-OUT PREVENTER.

Random deviation

The intentional DEVIATION (*q.v.*) of a well from the vertical without regard to compass direction for one of the following reasons: (a) to straighten a hole which has become crooked in the normal course of drilling; (b) to sidetrack a portion of a hole because of mechanical difficulty in drilling. Texas Railroad Commission, Special Order No. 54, 17 *O.&G.R.* 109 at 111 (1963); 16 Tex. Admin. Code § 3.11.

See also DIRECTIONAL DEVIATION.

Range of values method

A method developed by the United States Geologic Service to determine a value to be given a tract of OCS lands offered for lease. See Outer Continental Shelf Leasing Program, Hearings Before a Subcommittee of the Committee on Appropriations, House of Representatives, 93d Cong., 2d Sess. (1974) at p. 14.

See also PROVEN OR SEMI-PROVEN ("DRAINAGE") METHOD OF EVALUATION; RISK-FREE VALUE; WILDCAT ACREAGE METHOD OF EVALUATION.

RAP

Regie Autonome de Petrole.

RARE

ROADLESS AREA REVIEW AND EVALUATION (*q.v.*).

RAR method

The reserves added realization method of allocating exploratory costs. See Joseph, "Background and Analysis of Trial Examiner's

Decision in Phillips Case," 11 *Sw. Legal Fdn. Oil & Gas Inst.* 1 at 19 (1960).

For other methods of allocating costs, see ACCOUNTING METHODS.

Ratable taking

(1) Production of oil and/or gas in such quantities that each landowner whose tract overlies a producing formation will be able to recover a fair share of the oil and/or gas originally in place beneath his land. See FAIR SHARE OF OIL OR GAS IN PLACE.

(2) Production in accordance with allowables fixed by state regulatory agencies. See ALLOWABLE.

(3) In a number of states, statutes declare transporters of oil to be common carriers and purchasers of gas common purchasers and prohibit discrimination in favor of one producer against another, or in favor of any one source of supply as against another. Expressly or by implication such statutes may require ratable taking by purchasers from each producer. See COMMON PURCHASER ACT. See also Kelly, "Gas Proration and Ratable Taking in Texas," 19 *Texas B. J.* 763 (1956).

(4) Under a GAS PURCHASE CONTRACT (*q.v.*), a clause obligating buyer to purchase gas from seller ratably with other purchases from other sellers. For a discussion of the meaning of the term in such contracts see Howell, "Gas Purchase Contracts," 4 *Sw. Legal Fdn. Oil & Gas Inst.* 151 at 169 (1953), and TREATISE § 724.4.

Transcontinental Gas Pipeline Corp v. State Oil & Gas Board of Mississippi, 457 So.2d 1298, 83 *O.&G.R.* 295 (Miss. 1984), sustained the validity of Rule 48 of the State Oil and Gas Board requiring ratable taking by purchasers of oil or gas from producers in the same common source of supply, commenting in part as follows:

> "A caveat need be added: we do not hold that a pipeline purchaser may offer any terms, take-it-or-leave-it, and meet its Rule 48 obligations. Offering a working interest owner a choice between a substantially below market price or otherwise wholly unreasonable terms, on the one hand, and drainage, on the other, is simply not a ratable taking and is a violation of Rule 48. To comply with its Rule 48 obligations the pipeline must offer in good faith reasonable terms, including a reasonable price, determined by reference to prevailing market conditions and other appropriate economic considerations." 457 So.2d at 1331, 83 *O.&G.R.* at 352-3.

The judgment in this case was reversed, 470 U.S. 1083, 106 S.Ct. 709; 87 *O.&G.R.* 550; *reh.denied*; ____ U.S. ____; 106 S.Ct. 1485

(1986), the court holding, by five to four, that a state ratable take order continued subject to federal preemption.

See also the following:

Symposium: Workshop on Natural Gas Prorationing and Ratable Take Regulation, 57 *U. of Colo. L. Rev.* 149-393 (1986);

Taylor, "The Excess Gas Market—Recent Legal Problems Precipitated by Excess Gas Deliverability, and Applicable Regulatory Provision," 35 *Sw. Legal Fdn. Oil & Gas Inst.* 87 (1984);

Chamberlain, "A New Dimension in the Ratable Taking of Natural Gas in Oklahoma: Enrolled House Bill 1221," 20 *Tulsa L.J.* 77 (1984).

Rate base approach

A method of valuing gas for rate purposes:

"Under this method the natural gas in place and the properties and equipment used in producing it are included in the rate base along with the Company's other utility properties at the original cost of the properties less the accrued depreciation and depletion reserves. In addition to a return on such production properties, there are included in the costs of service, all operating expenses chargeable to production. All expenses associated with the production of liquid hydrocarbons, such as natural gasoline, are included in expenses and corresponding credits are made to expenses for the sale of the products extracted. Only such Federal and State income taxes as are actually paid by the Company are included in allowable expenses. Savings in Federal and State income taxes arising from the statutory allowance of percentage depletion and intangible well drilling costs are distributed to functions, thus reducing the allowable expense of such function." In the Matter of the Arkansas Louisiana Gas Co. (Arkansas Public Service Comm'n, Nov. 3, 1955), 5 *O.&G.R.* 127, *rev'd,* Acme Brick Co. v. Arkansas Public Service Comm'n, 227 Ark. 436, 299 S.W.2d 208, 6 *O.&G.R.* 1395 (1957).

See also ACCOUNTING METHODS COST OF PRODUCTION METHOD; FAIR FIELD PRICE METHOD.

Rate of take provision

The provision of a GAS PURCHASE CONTRACT (*q.v.*) specifying the rate at which gas shall be taken. In earlier years it was common to provide that the take shall be at the rate of 1/8.0 or 1/7.3. The latter rate, or the daily take of one Mcf for each 7,300 Mcf of proved reserves, equated to taking the reserves over a twenty-year period.

More recently some contracts have provided that take be at the rate of 1/3.65 for a period of time and then at the rate of 1/6.50. See Cassin, "Gas Purchase Contractors—Enticing a Shy Genie from an Invisible Lamp," 25 *Sw. Legal Fdn. Oil & Gas Inst.* 27 at 45 (1974).

Rate schedule

Defined by 18 C.F.R. § 154.93 (1980) as "the basic contract and all supplements or agreements amendatory thereof, effective and applicable on and after June 7, 1954, showing the service to be provided and the rates and charges, terms, conditions, classifications, practices, rules and regulations affecting or relating to such rates or charges, applicable to the transportation of natural gas in interstate commerce or the sale of natural gas in interstate commerce for resale subject to the jurisdiction of the Commission."

In 18 C.F.R. § 154.11 (1980), the term is described as "a statement of a rate or charge for a particular classification of transportation or sale of natural gas subject to the jurisdiction of the [Federal Energy Regulatory] Commission, and all terms, conditions, classifications, practices, rules and regulations affecting such rate or charge. This term also includes any contract for which special permission has been obtained in accordance with § 154.52."

See also PARTIAL REQUIREMENTS RATE SCHEDULE; PURCHASED GAS ADJUSTMENT CLAUSE; QUALITY STANDARDS; TARIFF (OR FPC GAS TARIFF); TARIFF-AND-SERVICE AGREEMENT.

Rate tilting

Varying the method employed to allocate costs to demand rates or commodity rates.

Thus, some portion of a pipeline's fixed costs (investment in lines, etc.) is allocated to demand rates and the remaining portion to commodity rates. Variable costs (operating costs that change with volume of gas handled) may be allocated entirely to the commodity rates. By rate tilting is meant varying the allocation of fixed costs to demand rates or commodity rates so as to decrease (or increase) the cost and price of the commodity component. See Hearings Before Senate Committee on Interstate and Foreign Commerce on Amendments to the Natural Gas Act, 84th Cong., 1st Sess. at 924 (1955).

See also COMMODITY CHARGE; DEMAND RATE.

Rat hole

A shallow hole drilled adjacent to the well hole for the placement of certain tools or parts of the drilling rig equipment during its operation. Robinson Rat Hole Service, Inc. v. Richardson Oils, Inc., 393 S.W.2d 629 at 630, 23 *O.&G.R.* 587 at 588 (Tex. Civ. App. 1965, error ref'd n.r.e.).

Rat-hole ahead, to

To drill a hole of reduced size in the bottom of the regular well bore to facilitate the taking of a drill stem test.

Ratification of lease

(1) An agreement ratifying and confirming a lease executed by a concurrent owner other than the original lessor, or conduct by such person which by implication ratifies and confirms the lease. A concurrent owner may ratify a lease to which he was not a party by accepting benefits under the lease or by signing a division order. See Humble Oil & Refining Co. v. Clark, 126 Tex. 262, 87 S.W.2d 471 (1935); TREATISE §§ 505.2, 658.1, 708.

(2) Conduct which operates to revive a lease which has been terminated, *e.g.*, execution of a mineral deed or other instrument in which reference is made to the lease as being a valid, existing lease.

Raw gas

Gas as produced from a well before the extraction therefrom of liquefiable hydrocarbons. See Natural Gas Pipe Line Co. v. Corporation Comm'n, 272 P.2d 425, 3 *O.&G.R.* 1076 (Okla. 1954), *rev'd,* 349 U.S. 44, 4 *O.&G.R.* 905 (1955).

This term is defined by the Alberta Mineral Rights Assessment Regulations (Alta. Reg. 357/73) as meaning: (i) a mixture containing methane, other paraffinic hydrocarbons, nitrogen, carbon dioxide, hydrogen sulphide, helium and minor impurities, or some of them, which is recovered or is recoverable at a well from an underground reservoir and which is gaseous at the conditions under which its volume is measured or estimated, and (ii) a mixture mainly of pentanes and heavier hydrocarbons that may be contaminated with sulphur compounds, that is recovered or is recoverable at a well from an underground reservoir and that may be gaseous in its virgin reservoir state but is liquid at the conditions under which its volume is measured or estimated.

Rayne Field case

United Gas Improvement Co. v. Continental Oil Co., 381 U.S. 392, 22 *O.&G.R.* 243 (1965), holding that sales of leases covering proven and substantially developed gas reserves to an interstate pipeline company were subject to Federal Power Commission jurisdiction.

Before the court of appeals decision in CATCO (*q.v.*), Texas Eastern Transmission Co. had sought certification to expand facilities to service eleven existing customers in the Rayne Field in Acadia Parish, Louisiana. The gas sales contracts provided for a price of 22.6 cents per Mcf plus 1.3 cents tax reimbursement. After the decision of the Court of Appeals for the Third Circuit in CATCO (and prior to the Supreme Court decision), the gas purchaser (Texas Eastern) and the producers renegotiated their contract and on December 4, 1958, they agreed upon another arrangement. Instead of a conventional wellhead sale of the gas at the price of 23.9 cents per Mcf, the new plan provided for the sale to Texas Eastern of the leasehold interests in the gas reserves in place for approximately $134 million (about $12.5 million down and the balance in sixteen annual installments)—a price which equated during the early years to about 23.5 cents per Mcf for the gas. The producers then terminated their original contract with Texas Eastern and withdrew their applications for certification of the gas sales contract.

Thereafter in Opinion No. 322 (21 F.P.C. 860) in 1959, the Commission granted Texas Eastern an unconditional certificate to build and operate the facilities needed to effectuate the lease-sale. Declaring that it lacked jurisdiction over the sale of the leases, the Commission did not, as a precondition to certification of pipeline construction, determine whether the $134 million price was compatible with the public interest. As a result, gas began to flow and the out-of-line price paid to producers was, as a cost-of-service item, reflected in the rates charged Texas Eastern customers.

The Court of Appeals for the District of Columbia reversed Opinion No. 322 granting the certificate, holding that the price paid by Texas Eastern to the producers was a factor requiring consideration by the Commission. 287 F.2d 143 (1960). On remand, the Commission concluded that it *did* have jurisdiction over lease sales (Opinion No. 378, 29 F.P.C. 249), and on this issue it was sustained by the Supreme Court in United Gas Improvement Co. v. Continental Oil Co., 381 U.S. 392, 22 *O.&G.R.* 243 (1965).

In response to Opinion No. 378, the producers filed applications in March 1966, for certificates of public convenience and necessity covering the lease sale. In Opinion No. 565 (42 F.P.C. 376) the Commission found that the lease-sale did not comport with public convenience and necessity and it ordered Texas Eastern to limit further payments to producers to amounts not exceeding a just and reasonable rate of 18.5 cents per Mcf and to cease payments when the producers received the full $134 million contract price. The producers were ordered to refund to Texas Eastern the excess, after specified adjustments, of payments above the 20-cent-in-line price prior to October 1, 1968, and thereafter above the 18.5-cent "just and reasonable rate"—a total of $31.5 million through 1967. About two-thirds of this sum was to be refunded by Texas Eastern to its customers, and rates charged by Texas Eastern were ordered trimmed to reflect a cost of 18.5 cents. On rehearing, the sharply divided Commission postponed all issues with regard to the refund liability of the producers or of Texas Eastern (Opinion No. 565–A). Denial of rehearing of Opinion No. 565–A produced additional confusion when commissioners shifted their positions. In Public Serv. Comm'n of the State of N.Y. v. Federal Power Comm'n, 543 F.2d 757 (D.C. Cir. 1974) [a case argued on November 8, 1971, decided 40 1/2 months later on March 25, 1974, with rehearing denied 17 months later on August 27, 1975], the court affirmed the Commission Orders in part, reversed in part, and remanded in part with directions. The court sustained the Commission in its CONVENTIONALIZATION OF LEASE-SALE (*q.v.*) to more nearly conform it to a normal gas-sale contract, but it held that the Commission was in error in Opinion No. 565–A when it ignored the previously established area rate of 18.5 cents and when it deferred rate reductions and refunds by producers to Texas Eastern and flow-through of the reductions and refunds by Texas Eastern.

See also GAS LEASE AGREEMENT; GAS LEASE-SALES AGREEMENT (GLA).

Realized price

In certain contracts between host nations and foreign oil companies the payments due the host nation may be based on realized price, *viz.*, the price really obtained on the world market for the sales concluded. See, *e.g.*, Articles 20 and 28 of the INOC-ERAP contract in OPEC, *Selected Documents of the International Petroleum Industry 1968* at p. 107.

The term is defined in Paragraph 10.4 of the Operating Agreement between Abu Dhabi and the Middle East Oil Co., Ltd. as:

"the total consideration received by such Second Parties for crude oil sold from the Concession Area to Non-Affiliates, less the necessary costs incurred for losses in shipment not recovered under insurance claims; bad debts; customers' rebates; credit costs (beyond thirty) 30 days, sales commission costs [limited to two percent (2%) of the f.o.b. value of such crude oil] and all direct costs incurred in performance of sales contracts. Sales to an Affiliate of Second Parties shall not be considered in determining realized price. In determining amounts due to the Ruler for crude oil sold by Second Parties to an affiliate the volume of crude oil shall be multiplied by the realized price." *Id. 1970* p. 172.

See also POSTED PRICE.

Real obligation

In Louisiana, a duty attached to immovable property, which passes with it into whatever hands it may come, without making the third possessor personally responsible. La. Civ. Code Art. 1997 (1977).

Real right

In Louisiana, the right correlative to the REAL OBLIGATION (*q.v.*) arising from a contract relative to immovable property. The right passes with the property. La. Civ. Code Art. 2011 (1977).

The Louisiana Code of Civil Procedure Art. 3664 (1961) (1980 Supp.), as amended in 1974, provides that "[t]he owner of a mineral right may assert, protect, and defend his right in the same manner as the ownership or possession of other immovable property, and without the concurrence, joinder, or consent of the owner of the land or mineral right."

Reamer

A tool used to enlarge or straighten a well bore or to split a casing.

Reasonable development

The orderly, diligent drilling up of well locations in a newly discovered oil or gas field in the manner of an ordinary, prudent operator. See REASONABLE DEVELOPMENT COVENANT.

Reasonable development covenant

The duty implied in an oil and gas lease obligating the lessee to use due diligence in drilling wells on the leasehold after discovery of oil or gas in the area. While most cases involve reasonable development after discovery of minerals on the leasehold, it seems clear that the duty obtains if the leasehold is proved by wells on adjoining tracts, at least where the lease is not being kept in force by payment of delay rentals. Myers v. Shell Petroleum Corp., 153 Kan. 287, 110 P.2d 810 (1941); Amerada Petroleum Co. v. Sledge, 151 Okla. 160, 3 P.2d 167 (1931).

To establish breach, the lessor must show that an ordinary, prudent operator would drill one or more additional wells. This usually involves expert testimony, showing among other things that an additional well would produce oil in paying quantities. Daughetee v. Ohio Oil Co., 263 Ill. 518, 105 N.E. 308 (1914); Myers v. Shell Petroleum Corp., *supra;* George v. Franklin, 219 Ky. 377, 292 S.W. 1093 (1927); Texas Pacific Coal & Oil Co. v. Barker, 117 Tex. 418, 6 S.W.2d 1031 (1928).

Remedies that have been recognized for breach of the covenant include:

(1) Absolute cancellation of the lease. Watson Land Co. v. Rio Grande Oil Co., 61 Cal. App. 2d 269, 142 P.2d 950 (1943).

(2) Conditional cancellation of the lease. Amerada Petroleum Co. v. Doering, 93 F.2d 540 (5th Cir. 1937).

(3) Damages. Daughetee v. Ohio Oil Co., *supra.* The usual measure of damages is the value of the royalty oil that would have been produced if the wells had been drilled. Texas Pacific Coal and Oil Co. v. Barker, *supra;* Midland Gas Corp. v. Reffitt, 286 Ky. 11, 149 S.W.2d 537 (1941). One case has held that such measure of damages overcompensates the lessee, since he is getting the value of oil in the ground that may be produced in the future. This case allowed as damages the amount of interest on the sum that would have been due the lessor if the wells had been drilled. Grass v. Big Creek Development Co., 75 W. Va. 719, 84 S.E. 750 (1915). *But see* Cotiga Development Co. v. United Fuel Gas Co., 147 W. Va. 484, 128 S.E.2d 626, 16 *O.&G.R.* 583 (1962).

See generally TREATISE §§ 831–835.3.

See also IMPLIED COVENANTS.

Reasonable market demand

The amount of oil reasonably needed for current consumption, together with a reasonable amount of oil for storage and working stocks.

In a number of producing states, the regulatory commission is authorized and/or directed to prorate production on the basis of reasonable market demand. By a technique developed by the Federal Oil Conservation Board during the Hoover administration, consumption during short periods of time is forecast by the Bureau of Mines. This is broken down among the producing states by tracing the past history of crude oil from producing states to refineries and finally to consumers. The state prorationing authority, guided by the estimates furnished by the Bureau of Mines, fixes the allowables—the amount which may be produced per day from the various fields, pools and wells in the state—in order that the production from the state shall not exceed a reasonable estimate of market demand.

The authority to fix allowables on the basis of a reasonable estimate of market demand is common in the several state regulatory agencies with the exceptions of: California, which lacks statutory prorationing procedures; Mississippi, where market demand may not be a basis of prorationing; Illinois, where production may not be limited to prevent or control economic waste or on the basis of market demand; and Colorado and Wyoming, where the Commissions are prohibited from restricting production of any pool or well to an amount less than can be produced without waste in accordance with sound engineering practices. See Hardwicke, "Market Demand as a Factor in the Conservation of Oil," 1 *Sw. Legal Fdn. Oil & Gas Inst.* 149 (1949).

See also ALLOWABLE; MARKET DEMAND; PRORATIONING.

Reassignment clause

A provision in the assignment of an oil and gas lease, commonly used when an overriding royalty is retained, requiring the assignee to give notice in advance to the assignor of an intent to let the lease lapse, and requiring reassignment of the lease before such termination. See Atlantic Ref. Co. v. Moxley, 211 F.2d 916, 3 *O.&G.R.* 1298 (5th Cir. 1954); Gladys Belle Oil Co. v. Turner, 12 S.W.2d 847 (Tex. Civ. App. 1929); TREATISE § 428.2.

Rebus sic stantibus

The principle of international law that if the relations between the parties, or circumstances relevant to a treaty, change substantially, one party may declare the treaty at an end.

Recapture of IDC

See INTANGIBLE DRILLING AND DEVELOPMENT COSTS (IDC).

Reclamation plant

A plant operated in the process of reclaiming, treating or washing waste petroleum, wash oil, pit oil, fugitive oil, basic sediment, or tank bottoms. 30 C.F.R. § 222.2(e) (1980).

Recompleted well

This term is applied to a well completed by the technique of drilling a separate well-bore from an existing casing in order to reach the same reservoir, or redrilling the same well bore to reach a new reservoir after production from the original reservoir has been abandoned. This type of well is distinguished from a MULTIPLE COMPLETION WELL (*q.v.*), which produces simultaneously through separate tubing strings from two or more producing horizons or alternately from each, and from a COMMINGLED WELL (*q.v.*), which produces from two or more oil-bearing formations through a common well casing and a single tubing string. See Energy Consumers and Producers Ass'n, Inc. v. Department of Energy, 632 F.2d 129 (Temp. Emer. Ct. App. 1980), *cert. denied,* 449 U.S. 832 (1980).

Recompletion

Redrilling the same well bore to reach a new reservoir after production from the original reservoir has been abandoned. See the dissenting opinion of Administrative Judge Irwin in William Perlman, 93 I.D. 159 (April 2, 1986).

Reconnaissance license

In Norway, this term is employed for a permit to explore for petroleum in the sea-bed or in its substrata. The license is employed basically for the conduct of geophysical surveys and is valid for a period of three years on the payment of a license fee annually in advance. It does not convey a right or priority in the obtaining of a PRODUCTION LICENSE (*q.v.*) and does not confer the right to drill for

petroleum. See Krohn, Kaasen, *et al., Norwegian Petroleum Law* 2–1 (1978); Horigan, "The North Sea," *Rocky Mt. Min. L. Fdn. International Minerals Acquisition and Operations Institute* 9–20 (1974).
Syn.: EXPLORATION LICENSE (*q.v.*).

Reconstituted crude oil

Hydrocarbons resulting from blending natural crude oil with one or more products. Joint Resolution Nos. 1307 and 2342 of the Ministries of Finance and of Mines and Hydrocarbons, Republic of Venezuela [OPEC, *Selected Documents of the International Petroleum Industry 1971* 261 at 263].

Reconstruction approach

Syn. for WORK-BACK VALUATION METHOD (*q.v.*). See Merritt v. Southwestern Electric Power Co., 499 So.2d 210 (La. App. 1986).

Reconvention

Article 374 of the 1870 Louisiana Code of Practice defined this term as "[t]he demand which the defendant institutes in consequence of that which the plaintiff has brought against him, . . ."

Under Article 1061 of the La. Code of Civil Procedure (1961), "[t]he defendant in the principal action may assert in a reconventional demand any action which he may have against the plaintiff in the principal action, even if these two parties are domiciled in the same parish and regardless of connexity between the principal and reconventional demands." The reconventional demand permits the defendant to assert whatever action he may have against the plaintiff, even though the demand may require the presence of third persons indispensable to the action, if jurisdiction over the latter can be obtained. *Id.,* Art. 1064.

Reconventional demand

See RECONVENTION.

Recourse financing

See NONRECOURSE FINANCING.

Recoverable oil-in-place

The net quantity of the gross original oil-in-place which can be expected to be recovered. This net quantity is dependent upon recovery efficiency and the economics of operation. American Petroleum Institute Division of Statistics, *Organization and Definitions for the Estimation of Reserves and Productive Capacity of Crude Oil* 19 (Technical Report No. 2, June 1970).

See also RESERVES.

Recovery factor

That portion of the total oil or gas in a reservoir which it is believed can be produced; the recovery factor is expressed frequently as a percentage. See Cockburn v. Mercantile Petroleum Inc., 296 S.W.2d 316, 7 *O.&G.R.* 306 (Tex. Civ. App. 1956, error ref'd n.r.e.).

Rectangular system of public land surveys

The system employed by the GENERAL LAND OFFICE SURVEY (*q.v.*) of the United States under which land is surveyed, and may be described by legal subdivision, section, township, and range.

Recycling

(1) A continuous reinjection of gas produced from a CONDENSATE GAS RESERVOIR (*q.v.*), after the liquid constituents have been removed. In recycling, the reinjected dry gas mixes with the wet gas so that over the period of the operation progressively less liquids are recovered until finally only dry gas remains in the reservoir. See CYCLING.

(2) This term is also applied to the lending, deposit or investment of the surplus oil revenues of Arab and other oil-exporting countries in oil consuming countries. See PETRODOLLARS.

Redetermination clause

See ESCALATOR CLAUSE.

Red-line agreement

An arrangement entered into in 1928 by Standard Oil Co. (New Jersey), Royal Dutch-Shell, and the Anglo-Iranian Oil to share the oil production of almost the entire Middle East. Under this agreement the parties were prevented from competing with themselves and with the Iraq Petroleum Co. for concessions in an area which included most of the old Ottoman Empire. See U.S. Congress, Senate Committee on Interior and Insular Affairs. Trends in Oil and Gas Exploration, Hearings 1972, p. 1154; Shwadran, *The Middle East,*

Oil and the Great Powers 237 *et seq.* (3d ed. revised and enlarged 1973); Danielsen, *The Evolution of OPEC* 118 (1982).

See also CONCESSION.

Redrilling

Operations designed to restore to production a well which has ceased to produce oil or gas. A producing well may so sand up that oil may not be produced in commercial quantities even though the formation into which the well is completed is capable of such production. In this situation, it may be necessary to shut down the well, pull the tubing, wash out the casing with mud and use explosives at the bottom of the well to dislodge the accumulated silt and sand.

"These costs are operating in nature and should be expensed. The cost of deepening a well is a cost of preparing for production, and is treated as intangible cost." Burke and Bowhay, *Income Taxation of Natural Resources* ¶ 14.15 (1981).

See also CLEANING A WELL; REWORKING OPERATIONS; WORKOVERS.

Reduced PGA method

The method adopted by FERC Order No. 49, 19 FPS 5–191 (Sept. 28, 1979), for INCREMENTAL PRICING (*q.v.*) by interstate pipelines and local distribution companies for natural gas acquisition costs. See Regulations Implementing the Incremental Pricing Provisions of the Natural Gas Policy Act of 1978, 19 FPS 5–370 at 371.

Reduction clause

Syn.: PROPORTIONATE REDUCTION CLAUSE (*q.v.*).

Reduction of rentals and royalties clause

Syn.: PROPORTIONATE REDUCTION CLAUSE (*q.v.*).

Reduction of royalties

The Mineral Leasing Act authorizes the Secretary of the Interior to reduce production royalties in mineral leases below the statutory minimum rates established for those minerals whenever in his judgment it is necessary to do so in order to promote development, or whenever in his judgment the leases cannot be successfully operated under the terms provided therein. Reduction of Production Royalties Below Statutory Minimum Rates, 87 I.D. 69 (Dec. 11, 1979).

Reduction works

(1) A plant for the removal of HELIUM (*q.v.*) from natural gas produced. Under the provisions of Federal lease forms, the government reserves ownership of helium and the right to erect reduction works on the premises for the extraction of such helium from natural gas.

(2) Any plant for removal of certain constituents of natural gas.

Reef

A type of reservoir TRAP (*q.v.*) composed of masses of rock, usually limestone, formed from the bodies of marine animals. Reef reservoirs are often characterized by high initial production which diminishes rapidly, requiring PRESSURE MAINTENANCE (*q.v.*) operations to sustain production.

Reel barge

A pipelaying barge which lays pipe by winding it off a reel or spool rather than by welding sections as is the usual practice. Kash, *et al., Energy Under the Oceans* 367 (1973).

Re-entry clause

See POWER OF TERMINATION

Reference crude

(1) *Syn.* for BENCHMARK CRUDE (*q.v.*) or MARKER CRUDE (*q.v.*).

(2) A crude oil subject to substantial trading activity or used as a pricing standard by host governments and refiners. 10 C.F.R. § 212.84(f)(1) (1980). In its regulation of the TRANSFER PRICE (*q.v.*) for imported crude oil, the Federal Energy Administration published monthly maximum prices for a list of crude oils, designated "reference crudes." See Stecker and Winslow, "Federal Energy Administration," 8 *Law & Policy in International Business* 499 at 505 (1976).

Reference price

A price specified by certain oil agreements to be utilized in determining the value of production for purposes of computation of royalty and taxable income. Thus in the agreement of 19 October 1968 between SONATRACH, Algeria's national oil Company, and Getty Oil Co. [OPEC, *Selected Documents of the International Petroleum Industry 1968* at p. 253] it is provided that if Getty's annual average sales price is less than the agreed reference price, the average sales price shall be increased to the level of the reference price in the computation of royalty and assessment of tax.

See also POSTED PRICE.

Referential incorporation

A mechanism employed by producing provinces in Canada requiring a lessee to comply with all legislative and regulatory changes enacted from time to time. Thus the Alberta Crown Petroleum and Natural Gas pro forma lease contains a "compliance with laws clause" obligating the lessee to comply with all provincial statutes and regulations in force from time to time. Alberta also employs a "variable royalty clause" which obligates the lessee to pay whatever royalty rates is periodically imposed by the regulations. See Black, "Comparative Licensing Aspects of Canadian and United Kingdom Petroleum Law," 21 *Texas Int. L. J.* 471 at 481 (1986).

Refined petroleum products

Gasoline, kerosine, distillates (including Number 2 fuel oil), LPG, refined lubricating oils, or diesel fuel. 38 F.R. 34420.

Refined product entitlement

An aspect of the ENTITLEMENT PROGRAM (*q.v.*) subsidizing the import of certain refined petroleum products. See Kalt, *The Economics and Politics of Oil Price Regulation* 59 (1981).

Refiner

A person who has any part in the control or management of any operation by which the physical or chemical characteristics of petroleum or petroleum products are changed, exclusive of the operations of passing petroleum through separators to remove gas, placing petroleum in settling tanks to remove basic sediment and water, dehydrating petroleum and generally cleaning and purifying petroleum. Within the term is included every person who blends petroleum with any product of petroleum. 30 C.F.R. § 222.2(d) (1980).

For a detailed discussion of the refining industry in the United States, see Copp, *Regulating Competition in Oil* (1976).

See also ACCOMMODATION SALES; BUY/SELL OIL; CATALYTIC CRACKING; COST BANK; CRACKING; HYDROCRACKING; INDEPENDENT REFINER; MANDATORY REFINERY YIELD CONTROL PROGRAM; PREFERENCE ELIGIBLE REFINER; RESELLER; SMALL REFINER BIAS; TOPPING PROCESS.

Refinery exchange

An adjustment made by refineries under the Australian CRUDE OIL ALLOCATION SCHEME (COAS) (*q.v.*), involving the exchange of allocations of indigenous crude oil by a remote refiner to another closer to the source of the crude in exchange for an allocation of other oil from a source closer to the former refiner. See Eves, "The Indigenous Crude Oil Allocation Scheme and Its Relationship With Indigenous Crude Oil Pricing Policies," 4 *Australian Mining & Petroleum L.J.* 159 at 175 (1982).

Refinery gas

A form of gas normally produced in the refining of crude oil which is predominately used for refinery fuel. 38 F.R. 34417 (Dec. 13, 1973).

See also STILL GAS.

Refinery tail gas

Gas (essentially methane, ethane, some propane in the first stages of refining, and hydrogen and carbon monoxide in later stages) separated from crude oil in the course of refining which cannot conveniently be used in the refinery either as a feedstock or a fuel. Daintith and Willoughby, *A Manual of United Kingdom Oil and Gas Law* 375 (1977).

See also TAIL GAS.

Refining agreement

See TAKE OR PAY CONTRACT.

Refundable money

See SUSPENSE MONEY.

Refunds Interest Rate (RIR) Procedures

Procedures for determining the interest rate required to be paid on amounts held subject to refund under the Natural Gas Act. FERC Order No. 47, 19 FPS 5–28 (Sept. 10, 1979).

See also ACCOUNTING METHODS.

Regional migration

See FIELD DRAINAGE.

Regular subdivision

Generally speaking, a subdivision of a section which is an aliquot part of 640 acres, such as a half-section of 320 acres, quarter-section of 160 acres, and quarter-quarter-section of 40 acres. BLM, *Glossary of Public Land Terms* (1949 ed.).

See also LEGAL SUBDIVISION; SURVEY.

Regulation B

A regulation of the Securities and Exchange Commission providing a conditional exemption under the Federal Securities Act to certain offerings of fractional, undivided interests not exceeding $250,000 if certain requirements are met. 17 C.F.R. § 230.300–346 (1982). See TREATISE § 441.4.

Regulation D

A regulation of the Securities and Exchange Commission, adopted in 1982 and embodied in a series of six rules (17 C.F.R. §§ 230.501–230.506 (1982)), which exempts from the registration requirements of the Securities Act of 1933 any issuer which offers and sells restricted securities, *viz.*, offerings and sales which:

(1) Take place without general advertising or general solicitation;

(2) Are made to an unlimited number of persons who either are "accredited investors" or who the issuer reasonably believes are "accredited investors";

(3) Are not made to more than thirty-five nonaccredited investors; and the issuer reasonably believed, immediately prior to making the sale, that the nonaccredited persons either alone or acting with their "purchaser representative" understood the merits and risks of the offering; and such nonaccredited investors understood that the information specified in Regulation D was furnished to nonaccredited investors and that a notice of sale was filed with the Commission.

For discussions of Regulation D, see the following:

Wertheimer, "Regulation D (Review and Update)," in Practicing Law Institute, *Oil and Gas Financings: Current Practice and Anticipated Developments* (1983);

Davenport, "Application of Federal Securities Laws to Mineral Financing," *Rocky Mt. Min. L. Inst. on Mineral Financing* 9-1 at 9-16 (1982);

Bjerke, "Regulation D Revised the Federal Private Offering Exemption—Will the States Follow?" 3 *Eastern Min. L. Inst.* 3-1 (1982);

Parnall, Kohl & Huff, "Private and Limited Offerings After a Decade of Experimentation: The Evolution of Regulation D," 12 *N. Mex. L. Rev.* 633 (1982);

TREATISE § 441.4.

See also ACCREDITED INVESTOR.

Regulatory pass-through cap

See CONTRACTUAL CAP.

Reinjection

Return of water or nonmarketed gas to a producing formation.

Reinstatement of lease

The revival of a lease which has terminated automatically for failure to pay or tender the proper amount of rentals. 30 U.S.C.A. § 188(c), as amended in 1970, permits, under specified circumstances, the reinstatement of federal leases which have terminated for failure of proper rental payment. See TREATISE § 606.3.

Related group

For purposes of the CRUDE OIL WINDFALL PROFIT TAX ACT OF 1980 (*q.v.*), this term means persons described in any of the following clauses: (A) a family, (B) a controlled group of corporations, (C) a group of entities under common control; or (D) if 50 percent or more of the beneficial interest in one or more corporations, trusts, or estates is owned by the same family, all such entities and such family. Internal Revenue Code § 4992.

Relational contract

A contract between or among parties who are incapable of reducing important terms of the arrangement to well-defined obligations. Such definitive obligations may be impractical because of inability to identify certain future conditions or because of inability to characterize complex adaptations adequately even when the contingencies can be identified in advance. Goetz and Scott, "Principles of Relational Contracts," 67 *Va. L. Rev.* 1089 at 1091 (1981). Meyers and Crafton, "The Covenant of Further Exploration—Thirty Years Later," 32

Rocky Mt. Min. L. Inst. 1-24 (1986), observe that the oil and gas lease is archetypically a relational contract and conclude that "in oil and gas leases, as in other relational contracts, the performing party is subject to two standards of conduct: he cannot act in bad faith and he must use his best efforts."

Relative cost method of allocation

A method of allocating joint production costs between gas and liquids in proportion to the known costs of producing each product separately. See Joseph, "Background and Analysis of Trial Examiner's Decision in Phillips Case," 11 *Sw. Legal Fdn. Oil & Gas Inst.* 1 (1960).

This method is explained in Hill v. Federal Power Comm'n, 335 F.2d 355 at 361, 21 *O.&G.R.* 214 at 221 (5th Cir. 1964), as follows:

> "The procedure is to determine the unit cost of producing gas from 'gas-only' leases. This is done by dividing the total costs of production from such leases by the number of Mcf of gas produced from them. The unit cost of producing gas from gas-only leases (the so-called gas leg) is multiplied by the number of units of gas produced from joint-product leases, and the unit cost of oil from oil-only leases is multiplied by the number of units of oil produced from those leases. The two figures derived state, in effect, what the gas and oil from the joint-product leases would have cost had they been produced from single-product leases. These two dollar amounts make it possible to compute the ratio of the total costs that would have been incurred in producing gas if all the gas had come from gas-only leases and all the oil had come from oil-only leases. Using ratios determined in this manner, the gas portion of the total actual production costs of the joint leases is then assigned to gas. The theory of this method of allocation is that the portion of the cost related to producing one of several products from joint-leases is the same as the ratio of production costs of those products produced by themselves."

This method of allocation is discussed in the Permian Basin Area Rate Proceeding, 34 F.P.C. 159 at 214 and 298, 23 *O.&G.R.* 103 at 165 and 277 (Opinion No. 468, Aug. 5, 1965), *remanded,* Skelly Oil Co. v. Federal Power Comm'n, 375 F.2d 6, 26 *O.&G.R.* 237 (10th Cir. 1967), *aff'd in part and rev'd in part sub nom. In re* Permian Basin Area Rate Cases, 390 U.S. 747, 28 *O.&G.R.* 689 (1968).

See also GAS LEG; OIL LEG.

For other methods of allocating costs, see ACCOUNTING METHODS.

Relative market value method

A method used by the Federal Power Commission in allocating gathering expenses between transportation operations and processing operations. See Federal Power Comm'n v. Colorado Interstate Gas Co., 348 U.S. 492, 4 *O.&G.R.* 897 (1955).

For other methods of allocating costs see ACCOUNTING METHODS.

Release

A statement filed by the lessee indicating that a lease has terminated or expired or has been surrendered or forfeited. The filing of such a release may be required by the terms of the lease or by state statute. See, *e.g.*, Kans. Stat. Ann. § 55–201 (1976). See TREATISE §§ 679–679.1.

Released oil

For purposes of price regulation under the Emergency Petroleum Allocation Act of 1973, released oil is "old" oil production equal to any volume of new oil produced. This released oil, unlike old oil, could be sold at market prices. *The New York Times,* Feb. 20, 1975, p. 56, col. 1.

See also NEW OIL; OLD OIL.

Release of record clause

A lease clause designed to facilitate the quieting of the lessor's title after the expiration, forfeiture or termination of a lease by requiring that the lessee execute and record an instrument evidencing the discharge of the lease. A common lease clause provides as follows:

> "The owner(s) and holder(s) of this lease at the time it expires or is terminated shall discharge this lease of record."

Even absent such a clause, in a number of the producing states there is a statutory requirement, on demand of the lessor, that the lessee release of record a lease that has expired, terminated or been forfeited. See TREATISE §§ 679–679.1.

Relief well

A well drilled to intersect another well at some point below the surface, used to regain control of a well that is out of control.

Relinquishment Act lands

Lands in which the minerals were reserved by the State of Texas on grant to private owners and in which a share of the proceeds of leasing were released to the private owners by the Relinquishment Act. See Walker, "The Texas Relinquishment Act," 1 *Sw. Legal Fdn. Oil & Gas Inst.* 245 (1949); Note, "Texas Relinquishment Act—Power of the Landowner to Convey the Mineral Interest," 32 *Texas L. Rev.* 637 (1952); Shields, "Leasing Lands Subject to the Texas Relinquishment Act," 13 *St. Mary's L.J.* 868 (1982).

Relinquishment clause

A clause in certain CONCESSION (*q.v.*) agreements providing for the relinquishment of a portion of the concession area at some future time.

See the following:

Blinn, Duval, Le Leuch, and Pertuzio, *International Petroleum Exploration & Exploitation Agreements* 131 (1986);

Mughraby, *Permanent Sovereignty Over Oil Resources* 49, 93 (1966);

Ely, "Changing Concepts of the World's Mineral Development Laws," in International Bar Ass'n, *World Energy Laws* (Proceedings of the IBA Seminar on World Energy Laws held in Stavanger, Norway) 4 at 30 (1975).

See also CHECKERBOARD RELINQUISHMENT.

Relinquishment of lease

The termination of a federal lease on the filing of a written relinquishment by the record title holder as provided by The Mineral Leasing Act of 1920, 30 U.S.C. §§ 187 and 187b. The filing of a written relinquishment by the record title holder is sufficient to surrender the lease as of the date on which it is filed. 43 C.F.R. § 3108.1 (1981). J. M. Dunbar, IBLA 81-921, GFS(O&G) 1982-76 (March 4, 1982), concluded that a relinquishment by the lessee was effective notwithstanding objection by prospective assignees of an interest in the lease.

Remainder oil

See COST RECOVERY OIL.

Remedial order

An order issued by the Office of Hearings and Appeals of the Economic Regulatory Administration (ERA) (*q.v.*) containing findings and conclusions following a proceeding to determine whether a violation of a Department of Energy regulation has occurred, is continuing, or is about to occur. 10 C.F.R. § 205.199B (1980).

Removal of fixtures clause

A typical clause in oil and gas leases providing that:

"Lessee shall have the right at any time during or after the expiration of this lease to remove all property and fixtures placed by Lessee on said land, including the right to draw and remove all casing."

The clause is designed to permit the lessee to remove fixtures after the lease has terminated or when it can no longer be operated at a profit. Usually there is no right to draw and remove the casing while the well is capable of producing in paying quantities. The phrase "at any time" in this clause is generally construed to mean "within a reasonable time." See Treatise §§ 674–674.6.

Removal price

For purposes of the Crude Oil Windfall Profit Tax Act of 1980 (*q.v.*), this term means the amount for which the barrel of crude oil being taxed is sold. Internal Revenue Code § 4988. Special provision is made for sales between related parties, oil removed from the premises before sale, and refining begun on premises.

Renegotiation clause

A clause of a Petroleum international agreement (PIA) (*q.v.*) or Concession (*q.v.*) providing for renegotiation of the agreement between the host country and the international oil company under specified circumstances, *e.g.*, changes in the price structure of crude oil or in taxation regulations. See Blinn, Duval, Le Leuch, and Pertuzio, *International Petroleum Exploration & Exploitation Agreements* 39 (1986); Hossain, *Law and Policy in Petroleum Development* 105 (1979).

See also Concession; Escalator clause.

Renewal contract

See Rollover gas.

Renewal-Extension clause

See EXTENSION AND RENEWAL CLAUSE

Renewal gas

Syn. for ROLLOVER GAS (*q.v.*).

Renewal lease

See EXCHANGE AND RENEWAL LEASE

Rental

See AD VALOREM CHARGE; DEAD RENT; DELAY RENTAL; ECONOMIC RENT; PERMIT RENT; PUGH CLAUSE RENTAL; RESOURCE RENT; SHUT-IN RENTAL; THROUGHPUT RENTAL.

Rental covenant

A term which has been employed to describe a royalty clause providing for a flat sum periodic payment (rather than a fraction or percentage of production, value or proceeds) for gas or casinghead gas. See the dissenting opinion dated June 26, 1963 of Hamilton, J., in *Southland Royalty Co. v. Pan American Petroleum Corp.* Thereafter three members of the court changed their vote, the former minority became a majority, and a new opinion was issued not using this terminology. 378 S.W.2d 50, 20 *O.&G.R.* 602 (Tex. 1964).

Rental date

The date during the primary term on or before which rentals are due and payable if the lease is to be kept alive by payment of such rentals.

Syn.: ANNIVERSARY DATE (*q.v.*); Rental paying date.

Rental period

The period of time for which rentals are paid in lieu of drilling operations.

Rental reduction agreement

An agreement modifying and reducing the delay rental payments called for by a previously executed lease.

Rental term

The period of time a lease may be kept alive by payment of rentals in lieu of drilling operations or production. The rental term usually has the same duration as the primary term under the habendum clause of the lease but some leases provide for a primary term longer than the rental term. See TREATISE § 605.3.

Rent royalty

A term utilized in Cities Serv. Oil Co. v. Hilburn, 351 So. 2d 860, 59 *O.&G.R.* 36 (La. App. 1977), to describe a MINERAL ROYALTY (*q.v.*) as distinguished from interests in production (overriding royalty or production payment) related to the lessee's working interest.

Replacement contract policy

The policy adopted by the Federal Power Commission in Opinion No. 639 (48 F.P.C. 1299), Opinion No. 699 (51 F.P.C. 2212), and Opinion No. 699–H of Dec. 4, 1974, under which a price increase can be obtained when a gas sales contract terminates:

> "If a gas contract dated prior to October 8, 1969, terminates, and the purchaser and seller enter into a new contract, gas sales under the new contract will be governed by the applicable pricing provisions relating to 'gas sold pursuant to a contract dated after October 7, 1969.' . . . In time this will result in the elimination of a two-price system, a result we believe intended by the original authors of vintaging and a result we wholeheartedly endorse." 48 F.P.C. at 1310.

In Skelly Oil Co. v. Federal Power Comm'n, 532 F.2d 177, 54 *O.&G.R.* 553, 9 FPS 6–12 (10th Cir. 1976), the court held that a producer was entitled to a rate increase based on the replacement contract policy.

In Zachary v. Federal Energy Regulatory Comm'n, 621 F.2d 155, 67 *O.&G.R.* 315 (5th Cir. 1980), *cert. denied,* 449 U.S. 1066, 101 S. Ct. 795 (1980), the court concluded that the replacement contract policy was inapplicable when the seller terminated delivery under a contract which was to continue "as long as gas is delivered hereunder in quantities commercial to Seller and Buyer," there being no question that gas was still deliverable under the contract in quantities commercial to both the seller and buyer.

In Public Serv. Comm'n v. Federal Power Comm'n, 543 F.2d 874, 58 *O.&G.R.* 101 (D.C. Cir. 1976), *cert. denied,* 429 U.S. 868 (1976), the court sustained the validity of application of the replacement contract policy to gas sold under a new contract replacing an expired contract.

See also Austral Oil Co. v. Federal Power Comm'n, 560 F.2d 1262, 60 *O.&G.R.* 283 (5th Cir. 1977); Superior Oil Co. v. Federal Energy Regulatory Comm'n 569 F.2d 971, 60 *O.&G.R.* 485 (5th Cir. 1978), *cert. denied,* 439 U.S. 834 (1978).

See also New gas; Old gas; One-price system; Two-price system; Vintage.

Repose, rule of

In Alabama, a lapse of twenty years of non-user will extinguish a claim to minerals under what is known as the rule of repose or prescription. See Shelton v. Wright, 439 So. 2d 55, 79 *O.&G.R.* 439 (Ala. 1983); Boshell v. Keith, 418 So. 2d 89 (Ala. 1982).

See Livingston, "Resolving Title Disputes in Severed Mineral Interests in Alabama," 36 *Ala. L. Rev.* 583 (1985).

See also Dormant minerals act.

Repressure gas

Gas purchased for injection into a reservoir for purpose of pressure maintenance. For tax treatment see *Miller's Oil and Gas Federal Income Taxation* § 9–7 (1980 Edition).

Repressuring operation

Fluid injection into a reservoir, the pressure of which has been substantially depleted, when the field is in the general pumping or stripper stage. The purpose of the injection is to increase pressure and recover more oil or gas. Repressuring is a form of Secondary recovery (*q.v.*).

Repudiation, doctrine of

The rule that a lessor who wrongfully repudiates its lease cannot complain if the lessee suspends operations. NRG Exploration, Inc. v. Rauch, 671 S.W.2d 649, 81 *O.&G.R.* 400 (Tex. App., Austin, 1984, error ref'd n.r.e.). See Treatise § 604.7.

Repurchase price

The price at which a managing partner or sponsor may purchase the interests of other partners in an oil and gas venture, computed in a manner specified by the partnership agreement. The price is usually based upon a valuation computed for the partnership's oil and gas reserves, net of any liabilities to which the reserves are subject, plus net values assigned to other assets. Reserve calculations can be expected to be based upon a computation of future net revenues, using assumed price and cost increases, with a present value determined using a discount tied to the prevailing prime lending rate at the time the repurchase price is computed. In many instances there will be deducted from the present value of the reserves an additional discount to reflect the uncertainties and risks associated with ultimately obtaining the estimated future net reserves.

Required well

As defined in a Rocky Mountain unit operating agreement, a well the drilling of which is required by the final order of an authorized representative of the Department of Interior. Rocky Mountain Unit Operating Agreement Form 1 (Undivided Interest) May, 1954, Section 17.1, TREATISE § 920.3.

Resale customer

A gas customer who purchases gas for resale. See Fort Pierce Utility Authority v. Federal Power Comm'n, 526 F.2d 993 at 995 (5th Cir. 1976).

See also DIRECT SALE CUSTOMER, GAS PURCHASE CONTRACT.

Resale gas

Gas purchased by a pipeline company for resale as opposed to TRANSPORTATION GAS (*q.v.*) which is transported by the pipeline for a fee. See Florida Economic Advisory Council v. Federal Power Comm'n, 251 F.2d 643 (D.C. Cir. 1957), *cert. denied,* 356 U.S. 959 (1958).

Resale restrictions

See DESTINATION AND RESALE RESTRICTIONS.

Reseller

For purposes of 1974 Federal Energy Office regulations designed to stabilize the domestic petroleum distribution system and protect small and independent refiners by freezing all petroleum supplier-purchaser obligations, a reseller was a middleman between a crude oil producer and a refiner. No substitution was permitted when a producer sold directly to a refiner, but a crude oil producer was permitted to substitute resellers provided the new reseller offered refiners supplied by the old reseller a right of first refusal to continue to purchase the producers crude oil. 10 C.F.R. § 211.63(d)(1)(iv) (1980). Although this term was used throughout the petroleum allocation regulations, it was left undefined. See Basin, Inc. v. Mobil Oil Corp., 616 F.2d 1199 (Temp. Emer. Ct. of App. 1980), holding that under the circumstances of the particular case, Mobil was a refiner rather than a reseller.

Reservation

(1) That which is newly created and reserved from a grant, *e.g.*, an easement reserved in the grant of land. See EXCEPTION.

(2) In Canada, the term "reservation" is used to describe a permit from the government for geological and geophysical surveys. The holder of a reservation who complies with applicable regulations may convert a part of the holdings under the reservation to leases. See CROWN RESERVE; CROWN RESERVE DRILLING RESERVATION; DRILLING RESERVATION.

Reservation Price

A minimum price set by the U.S. Geological Survey for a competitive lease of Outer Continental Shelf Lands. See Logue, Sweeney and Willett, "Optimal Leasing Policy for the Development of Outer Continental Shelf Hydrocarbon Resources," 51 *Land Economics* 191 at 204 (1975).

Reserve

That portion of the identified resource from which a usable mineral and energy commodity can be economically and legally extracted at the time of determination. The term *ore* is used for reserves of some minerals. 2 *OCS Oil and Gas—An Environmental Assessment,* A Report to the President by the Council on Environmental Quality (April 1974) at p. 10.

See also CROWN RESERVE; RESERVES.

Reserve added realization method (RAR method)

A method of allocating exploratory costs between different products. See Joseph, "Background and Analysis of Trial Examiner's Decision in Phillips Case," 11 *Sw. Legal Fdn. Oil & Gas Inst.* 1 at 19 (1960).

For other methods of allocating costs, see ACCOUNTING METHODS.

Reserved oil payment

An OIL PAYMENT (*q.v.*) which is reserved in the transfer of an interest in oil and gas. For example, a reserved oil payment may be created when executing a lease or when assigning the working interest in a lease.

Prior to the Tax Reform Act of 1969, a reserved oil payment was entitled to the percentage depletion allowance. Comm'r v. Fleming, 82 F.2d 324 (5th Cir. 1936). The use of reserved oil payments was essential in the A-B-C TRANSACTION (*q.v.*). Since 1969 the sale of a mineral interest subject to a reserved oil payment is treated as a sale subject to a mortgage.

See also CARVED OUT OIL PAYMENT.

Reserve index formula

A proration formula for natural gas. See Cities Service Gas Co. v. State Corporation Comm'n, 205 Kan. 655 at 660, 472 P.2d 257 at 261, 38 *O.&G.R.* 379 at 385 (1970), 207 Kan. 43, 483 P.2d 1123, 38 *O.&G.R.* 402 (1971).

Reserve life index

A measure of the estimated life of reserves calculated by dividing the proven reserves at the end of a year by the production during that year. Northern Natural Gas Co. v. O'Malley, 174 F.Supp. 176, 10 *O.&G.R.* 423 (D. Neb. 1959), *rev'd,* 277 F.2d 128, 12 *O.&G.R.* 335 (8th Cir. 1960).

For the relationship between the reserve life index and authorized depreciation of a pipeline see Memphis Light, Gas & Water Division v. Federal Power Comm'n, 504 F.2d 225 (D. C. Cir. 1974)

Reserve pit

A pit at the drilling site of a well to store the drilling fluid and strain the mud and other organic materials produced by the drilling. Amoco Production Co. v. Carter Farms Co., 103 N.M. 117, 703 P.2d 894, 86 *O.&G.R.* 84 (1985).

See also BURN PIT; SPILLOVER PIT.

Reserves

The unproduced but recoverable oil and/or gas in place in a formation which has been proven by production.

For a study of the problem of estimating American oil and gas resources, see Wildavsky and Tenenbaum, *The Politics of Mistrust* (1981).

Frazier and Berton, "Slippery Figures: Oil Firms' Reserves, Treated as Vital Data, May be Just a Guess," *The Wall Street Journal*, Aug. 28, 1986, discuss the wild variations in reserve estimates (differing by as much as 300 percent%) by oil companies drilling in the same field:

> "The wild variations can result from slightly different assumptions about rock characteristics, the thickness of the deposit, the amount of area a discovery well will drain and other such factors.
>
> . . .
>
> "Reserve estimates also can vary because of the temperament or biases of engineers—or because of outright manipulation. Industry critics say energy companies or lenders can shop for the result they want by selecting outside petroleum engineers by their reputations. For their part, outside engineers complain of pressure from their employers to produce attractive estimates.
>
> . . .
>
> "From company to company, there is little consistency."

For a study of production and reserves in the Soviet Union and other member countries (Poland, Romania, Hungary, the German Democratic Republic, Czechoslovakia, and Bulgaria) of COMECON (the Council for Mutual Economic Assistance), see Park, *Oil and Gas in Comecon Countries* (1979).

See also Assignment of reserves; Contracted reserves; Crown reserve; Dedication of reserves; Demonstrated reserves or resources; Discoveries; Established reserves; Extension; Gas behind the pipe; Hypothetical reserves or resources; Identified resources; Identified-subeconomic reserves or resources; Indicated additional reserves; Indicated reserves or resources; Inferred reserves or resources; Life index; Measured reserves or resources; Original oil in place; Paramarginal reserves or resources; Probable reserves; Productive capacity of crude oil; Provable reserves; Proved acreage; Proved developed reserves; Proved undeveloped reserves; Proven reserves; Proven territory; Recoverable oil-in-place; Recovery factor; Reserve; Reserve life index; Resource; Revisions; R/P ratio; Semi-proven territory; Speculative reserves or resources; Submarginal re-

SERVES OR RESOURCES; ULTIMATE RECOVERY; UNDISCOVERED RESOURCES; UNPROVEN AREA; VOLUMETRIC METHOD OF ESTIMATING RESERVES.

Reserves/production ratio

The ratio of proven reserves to annual production, expressed in years' supply.

Reserves recognition accounting

An accounting method prescribed by the Securities and Exchange Commission under which changes in proved reserve quantities, changes in selling prices and future production and development costs, and actual expenditures for property acquisition and exploration activities are recognized in the results of oil and gas producing activities in the year in which they occur. This accounting method has been criticized as containing a number of simplifying assumptions which, by their nature, call into question the economic significance of the resulting data. The results reached under this method include the valuation of additions and revisions to proved reserves during the year, without consideration given to oil and gas produced and sold, and hence the results differ significantly from funds provided or required by current exploration, development, and production operations and from net income of the exploration and production segment presented under generally accepted accounting principles. *Standard Oil Company (Indiana) Annual Report 1980* at p. 52.

See also ACCOUNTING METHODS.

Reservoir

(1) A porous, permeable sedimentary rock containing commercial quantities of oil or gas. Three types of reservoirs are encountered: (a) STRUCTURAL TRAP (*q.v.*); (b) STRATIGRAPHIC TRAP (*q.v.*), and (c) COMBINATION TRAP (*q.v.*). The reservoir is formed when escape of the oil or gas is prevented by surrounding layers of impervious rock. See TREATISE § 102.

State of Texas v. Secretary of the Interior, 580 F. Supp. 1197, 80 *O.&G.R.* 573 (E.D. Tex. 1984), adopted the following definition of reservoir, agreed upon by the parties, for purposes of the instant case:

"[T]he term 'reservoir' applies to an underground accumulation of oil or gas or both characterized by a single pressure system and is segregated from other such accumulations."

(2) By statute in Colorado, any subsurface sand, stratum or formation suitable for the injection and storage of natural gas therein, and the withdrawal of natural gas therefrom. Colo. Laws 1953, ch. 169, § 1 (1), Colo. Rev. Stat. 1973 § 34–64–102.

Syn.: Pool

See also COMMON RESERVOIR; CONDENSATE GAS RESERVOIR; DEPLETION TYPE RESERVOIR; FIELD; FRIGG FIELD RESERVOIR AGREEMENT; GAS CAP FIELD; GEOLOGICAL FIELD; GEOLOGICAL STRUCTURE; GEOMETRY OF A RESERVOIR; LENTICULAR RESERVOIR; NEWLY DISCOVERED RESERVOIR; NON-ASSOCIATED GAS RESERVOIRS; OIL FIELD; OIL POOL; TRAP.

Reservoir "behind the pipe"

A reservoir which will be produced in the future by (a) normal plug back and recompletion techniques. (b) mechanically opening up previously perforated zones, and (c) anticipated drilling of additional wells to accelerate production of additional volumes prior to depletion of other producing zones in the well bore. Order Instituting Investigation of Status of Non-producing Dedicated Reserves and to Show Cause, Docket No. R175–112, 4 FPS 5–263 at note 8 (Feb. 20, 1975).

See also GAS BEHIND THE PIPE.

Reservoir energy

The forces in a reservoir which propel the oil or gas to the well bore. Four sources of natural energy may be present in a reservoir: (1) gas expansion, of either gas in solution in the oil or of a natural gas cap; (2) water encroachment; (3) expansion of reservoir oil; and (4) gravity. The first three result from the reduction of pressure by opening a well to the surface. Of the four energy sources, by far the most important are the first two, for they account for most of the volume of oil produced.

See also COMBINATION DRIVE; DEPLETION DRIVE; DISSOLVED GAS DRIVE; GAS CAP DRIVE; GAS EXPANSION RESERVOIR; GRAVITATIONAL FORCE; SOLUTION GAS FIELD; WASTE OF RESERVOIR ENERGY; WATER DRIVE.

Reservoir limit test

"[A] drawdown test to determine the pore volume connected to a well. . . . The test requires that a well that has been shut in to stabilize the reservoir pressure be produced at a constant rate for a period long enough for the onset of a pseudosteady-state flow regime in the reservoir. At pseudosteady state, the pressure decline throughout the reservoir becomes a linear function of time with a proportionality constant that is directly related to the reservoir volume." Alberta Energy Resources Conservation Board, Informational Letter IL 83-1 (Jan. 13, 1983).

Reservoir pressure

The pressure at the face of the productive formation when the well is shut in. It is equal to the SHUT-IN PRESSURE (*q.v.*) plus the weight, in pounds per square inch, of the column of oil and gas in the well. Ball, Ball, and Turner, *This Fascinating Oil Business* 153 (2d ed. 1965).

Syn.: FORMATION PRESSURE; ROCK PRESSURE.

See also BOTTOM HOLE PRESSURE; OPEN FLOW PRESSURE.

Reservoir water

See BOTTOM WATER; CONNATE WATER; EDGE WATER.

Residential child care agency exemption

An exemption authorized by the ECONOMIC RECOVERY TAX ACT OF 1981 (*q.v.*) from the CRUDE OIL WINDFALL PROFIT TAX ACT OF 1980 (*q.v.*) for oil produced from certain oil interests held by a child care agency on January 21, 1980, and at all times thereafter.

Residual fuel oils

Those fuel oils commonly known as Nos. 4, 5, and 6 fuel oils, Bunker C and all other fuel oils which have a fifty percent boiling point over 700 degree F. in the AFTM D86 standard distillation test. 38 F. R. 34420.

"Fuel oils have been classified by use, by derivation, and by physical measurements, such as viscosity, specific gravity, and boiling range. The product coverage is substantially different by each classification. Under the original MOIP, 'fuel oil' was described by use, and 'residual fuel oil' was described by viscosity. Fuel oil was not redefined until 1973, when Proclamation 4210 introduced the classification for 'distillate fuel oils,' which was described by boiling range rather than use. On the other hand, residual fuel oil was redefined several times." World Oil Developments and U.S. Oil Import Policies, Committee Print, Committee on Finance, U.S. Senate, 93rd Cong., 1st Sess., at pp. 77–78 (Dec. 12, 1973).

Residual fuel oil, often called bunker oils, are heavier, high-viscosity oils, primarily used in industry, in large commercial buildings, and for the generation of electricity. Usually they must be heated before they can be pumped and handled conveniently.

Regulations concerning the mandatory allocation of residual fuel oils are contained in 10 C.F.R. § 211.161 *et seq.* (1980).

See also DISTILLATE FUEL OILS

Residual interest

A term employed in some Canadian cases concerned with compensation of a surface owner for damages caused by oil and gas explorations or related operations on his premises. See TREATISE § 219 at note 6. The term is used to distinguish a reversionary interest possessed by the owner when the easement is at an end from the interest which the owner possesses not only then but also during the currency of the easement:

> "To illustrate: were an oil company to seek right of entry onto lands (of identical value) of two adjoining owners, with the intention of sinking a well on one owner's property and of running a pipeline across the other owner's land, what would be the measure of compensation? If each owner retained the right to use the land taken after operations were completed, their residual interest might be the same and of comparable value but if the well-site property suffered permanent damage from deposits of drilling mud, oil spill and the like, that owner would have little or no reversionary interest, whereas the area in which the pipeline lay would have suffered little affection of the reversionary interest. An award of fee simple value to each owner would obviously be inequitable.
>
> "It is clear . . . that the residual interest of the owner should be valued and, where the value is ascertained, should be taken into account in awarding compensation for the land taken." Re Chieftain Development Co. Ltd. and Lachowich, 129 D.L.R.3d 285 at 297 (Alta. Q.B. 1981).

See also Dome Petroleum Ltd. v. Grekul, [1984] 1 W.W.R. 457 (Alta. Q.B. 1983); Dome Petroleum Ltd. v. Liivam Farms Ltd., [1982] 6 W.W.R. 206 (Alta. Q.B. 1982).

Residual refining equipment

Apparatus used in extracting, refining and handling of residuals from natural gas. 18 C.F.R. § 201.318 (1980).

Residual reserve clause

A clause in an Equity production payment (*q.v.*) agreement providing that the right will terminate at any time that the unproduced proven reserves underlying the property decline to a percentage (*e.g.*, 20 percent) of the unproduced proved reserves that existed on the date the right was created. Sometimes (*e.g.*, where none of the burdened properties contains proved reserves at the time the right is created) the clause provides that at any time after proved reserves are discovered, the right shall terminate when a percentage (*e.g.*, 80 percent) of the cumulative reserves have at any time been produced. Griffith, "Current Developments in Oil and Gas Taxation Other Than Legislative and Regulatory," 36 *Sw. Legal Fdn. Oil & Gas Inst.* 8-1 at 8-15 (1985).

Residue gas

Gas remaining after processing in a separator or other plant which removes liquid hydrocarbons contained in the gas when produced.

A Texas court has concluded that the term "residue gas" as used in the royalty provisions of a particular oil and gas lease refers to gas remaining after certain elements and compounds were removed by fractionation in a processing plant and does not refer to gas remaining after casinghead gas has been run through a lease separator. Read v. Britain, 414 S.W.2d 483, 27 *O.&G.R.* 70 (Tex. Civ. App. 1967), *aff'd*, 422 S.W.2d 902, 27 *O.&G.R.* 662 (Tex. 1967).

Residue oil

Oil which remains after simple distillation of crude oil. In the distillation process, the first productis to boil off are gasolines and naphthas. After this come the kerosenes. The next part of the crude comes under the general classification of distillates, which include home heating oil, certain industrial furnace oils, and diesel oil. The oil which remains is called residual or heavy fuel oil and is used as fuel for ships and steam locomotives and for industrial heating and power.

Resistivity

The electrical resistance of a cube of material one meter on each side as measured by well logs. The harder it is for current to flow in a material, the higher the resistivity. See Hilchie, "Well Logging," *Rocky Mt. Min. L. Fdn. Basic Oil and Gas Technology for Lawyers and Landmen* (1979).

Resolutory condition

"Conditional obligations are such as are made to depend on an uncertain event. If the obligation is not to take effect until the event happen, it is a suspensive condition; if the obligation take effect immediately, but is liable to be defeated when the event happens, it is then a resolutory condition." La. Civ. Code Art. 2021 (1977).

Article 133 of the Louisiana Mineral Code [R.S. 31:133 (1975)] provides that a mineral lease terminates at the expiration of the agreed term or upon the occurrence of an express resolutory condition. Thus the nonpayment of delay rental under an UNLESS LEASE (*q.v.*) or the failure to meet a drilling obligation within the time stated is the occurrence of an express resolutory condition causing termination of the lease without the necessity of putting the lessee in default as a prerequisite to judicial action. The Comments to Articles 123 and 133 of the Louisiana Mineral Code discuss a number of cases involving termination of a lease for failure to pay rentals. Although the courts have displayed a rather strict attitude in administering these resolutory conditions, several cases have permitted the lease to be preserved where there has been a good faith though erroneous effort to pay or a mutual error as to the amount due, or where nondelivery by a reliable and accepted mode of communication was beyond the control of the lessee.

Resource

A concentration of naturally occurring solid, liquid, or gaseous materials in or on the earth's crust in such form that economic extraction of a commodity is currently or potentially feasible. 2 *OCS Oil and Gas—An Environmental Assessment,* A Report to the President by the Council on Environmental Quality (April 1974) at p. 10.

See also RESERVES.

Resource allowance

In Canada, a deduction effective for the 1976 and subsequent taxation years designed to reduce the double taxation effect of federal and provincial legislation in the early 1970's. See Katchen and Bowhay, *Federal Oil and Gas Taxation* 63 (3d ed. 1979).

Resource inventory

Operations on the surface by a mineral owner designed to provide a would-be surface mine operator with the data required to be included in its surface mine permit applications. Such operations may include (1) soil surveys, (2) vegetation surveys, (3) wildlife surveys, (4) hydrological surveys, (5) archeological surveys, (6) topographical mapping surveys, (7) air quality monitoring, and (8) coal and overburden analysis. Western Energy Co. v. Genie Land Co., 195 Mont. 202, 635 P.2d 1297 (1981).

Resource rent

The "profits of an investment that remain after deducting that income which corresponds to the minimum return necessary to attract investment to the project in the first place. Such rent is a function of the quality of the resource, its location and the numerous other variables that affect the rate of return necessary to attract investment." Carden, "Taxation—Resources Tax, Royalties and Other Taxes Peculiar to the Mineral Industry," 1 *Australian Mining & Petroleum L.J.* 491 (1978).

Resource rent tax

A tax designated to capture RESOURCE RENT (*q.v.*). For a discussion of the Australian efforts to maximize the "government take" of resource rent, see Carden, "Taxation—Resources Tax, Royalties and Other Taxes Peculiar to the Mineral Industry," 1 *Australian Mining and Petroleum L.J.* 491 (1978), and the commentaries on this paper by Dowell (*id.* at 500) and Garnaut (*id.* at 504).

For a discussion of this form of tax see Kinna, "Investing in Developing Countries: Minimization of Political Risks," 1 *J. of Energy & Nat. Resources Law* 89 at 98 (1983):

> "The tax is payable in addition to normal income tax, but is concerned essentially with the company's cash flow rather than its profits in the normal accounting sense. The tax applies if and only if in any year the taxpayer's accumulated receipts exceed the accumulated value of expenditure multiplied by an interest rate ('accumulation rate') which is established at a level which reflects the cost of money plus risk attaching to the industry. In any year in which such a calculation produces a positive result the surplus is

taxed at a specified rate. A positive value in the current year of income means in broad terms that the taxpayer to that point has recouped not only his qualifying cash investment in the project but also an interest factor in excess of the accumulation rate, and a proportion of the positive excess (not all) accrues to the government. The tax has a number of advantages for both governments and companies. From the government's point of view it avoids the dilemma of having fully to commit itself to a level of financial benefits based upon the marginal mine negotiated under circumstances where the real profitability of a future development is unknown. From the company's point of view, if it never achieves the rate of return specified, the tax does not apply and so is not paid in relation to marginal projects. In the case of very profitable projects the tax adjusts itself automatically to obtain for government a higher share of the benefits. If in any year after tax becomes payable the company incurs further expenditures on exploration or development the results will almost certainly be that its accumulated cash position will become negative and the tax automatically will not apply while it remains so. Thus the burden of the tax does not apply during the investment recovery period and thereafter its incidence coincides with the company's own investment decisions. An agreement which provides a profit sharing arrangement based on the actual profitability of the project in this way will in most cases avoid later political pressure for change and consequently will minimize the political risks attaching to the investments."

Responsible person

The body corporate or partnership resident in the United Kingdom nominated by participators in an oil field to act for the participators in returning information to the Inland Revenue for purposes of the PETROLEUM REVENUE TAX (*q.v.*). See Daintith and Willoughby, *A Manual of United Kingdom Oil and Gas Law* 137 (1977).

Restitution gas

The term applied to gas supplied to a purchaser to make up for gas of which the purchaser was previously deprived under a CURTAILMENT PLAN (*q.v.*). Arizona Elec. Power Coop., Inc. v. Federal Energy Regulatory Comm'n, 631 F.2d 802, (D.C. Cir. 1980).

Restoration of depletion

See DEPLETION, RESTORATION OF.

Resulting area

A term employed in a unit operating agreement to refer to a participating area resulting from establishment, revision by contraction or enlargement, or combination. See Rocky Mountain Unit Operating Agreement Form 2 (Divided Interest) January, 1955, Section 13.1, TREATISE § 920.4.

Resumption of operations clause

A term employed by one writer to describe the lease provisions which are referred to herein as a DRY HOLE CLAUSE (*q.v.*) and a CESSATION OF PRODUCTION CLAUSE (*q.v.*). See 2 Kuntz, *Oil and Gas* § 26.13 (1964).

Resumption, power of

See POWER OF RESUMPTION.

Retained acreage clause

A lease clause authorizing the lessee to retain acreage around a producing well or acreage in a producing unit in the event of forfeiture of a lease. See TREATISE § 681.3.

Dawes v. Hale, 421 So. 2d 1208, 75 *O.&G.R.* 233 (La. App. 1982), held that a retained acreage clause authorizing the retention of forty acres around a producing well in the event of cancellation or termination of a lease did not have the effect of limiting the reasonable development covenant so as to require but one well for forty acres.

Tomlin v. Petroleum Corp. of Texas, 694 S.W.2d 441, 86 *O.&G.R.* 627 (Tex. App., Eastland, 1985), held that a retained acreage clause permitting the lessee to retain after the expiration of the primary term 40 acres for each producing *oil well* drilled had no application to a *gas well*, and therefore a gas well drilled during the primary term sufficed to hold the lease in effect as to all 326.5 acres covered by the lease.

SMK Energy Corp. v. Westchester Gas Co., 705 S.W. 2d 174, ____ *O.&G.R.* ____ (Tex. App., Texarkana, 1985, error ref'd n.r.e.), rejected the contention that an artlessly drafted lease rider was simply a Pugh clause and held that it resulted in termination of the lease at the end of its primary term as to undrilled spacing units.

Under a lease clause providing for termination at the end of the primary term except for acreage around a producing well, or acreage allocated to a well for production purposes, it has been held that the acreage allocated by the lessee to a well may not be acreage which is non-contiguous to the well site. Mayfield v. de Benavides, 693 S.W.2d 500, 85 *O.&G.R.* 162 (Tex. App., San Antonio, 1985; error ref'd n.r.e.).

See also ACREAGE RETENTION CLAUSE; UNDEVELOPED ACREAGE CLAUSE.

Retained interest

An interest, *e.g.*, oil payment or overriding royalty, reserved by the grantor upon the assignment of a working interest or other property interest in oil and gas.

See also CARVED OUT INTEREST.

Retained oil payment

See RESERVED OIL PAYMENT

Retention lease

A form of lease proposed in Australia designed to provide for tenure over currently non-commercial discoveries, *e.g.*, large offshore deposits of natural gas which are not currently able to be developed for a variety of reasons (such as lack of deep-water technology or unavailability of market) can be held if it can be demonstrated that they are not currently able to be developed commercially, but may become so within fifteen years. This form of lease is designed to provide an additional measure of encouragement for companies exploring in deep-water or gas-prone areas. See Reid, "1985 Amendments to Australian Offshore Petroleum Legislation," [1985/86] 2 *OGLTR* 54; [1986/87] 9 *OGLTR* D-99.

See also CONCESSION; EXPLORATION RETENTION LEASE.

Retention of oil on board

Syn: LOAD-ON-TOP (*q.v.*).

Retention pit

A surface pit utilized for the disposal of oilfield brine by evaporation or seepage.

Retroactive adjusting allowable

An ALLOWABLE (*q.v.*) designed to make retroactive adjustment for a period of time when a well or lease did not produce its fair and ratable share of oil or gas from a common source of supply.

In British American Oil Producing Co. v. Corporation Comm'n, 180 Okla. 468, 69 P.2d 669 (1937), the court required the Commission to grant such an allowable to a well which did not produce for a period of almost three months due to mechanical difficulties attributable to the administration of the poration law. And in Corporation Comm'n v. Phillips Petroleum Co., 536 P.2d 1284, 52 *O.&G.R.* 239 (Okla. 1975), the court sustained the validity of such an allowable granted in order to protect correlative rights.

Retrograde condensation

In reservoir mechanics, the formation of a liquid from a gas as pressure is reduced.

The normal result of a reduction in pressure is the transformation of a liquid to a gas. In a condensate reservoir, retrograde condensation causes the loss of petroleum, which adheres to the rock particles when it goes to liquid in the reservoir. PRESSURE MAINTENANCE (*q.v.*) is one method of combatting this loss.

See also CONDENSATE GAS RESERVOIR.

Revenue interest

The working interest less any royalty, overriding royalty, and carried interest.

See also NET LEASEHOLD.

Reverse combustion

A method designed for oil recovery from tar sands. Air is injected into the reservoir and ignition is initiated at the producing well. Continued air injection results in the combustion zone moving toward the injection well, opposite tothe direction of injected air movement. See Morse, "Trends in Oil Recovery Methods," 1 *IOCC Committee Bull.* 1 at 9 (Dec. 1959).

Reverse seven-spot pattern

A pattern of wells for air and gas drive in which each producing well is affected by three inputs. See Lytle, "History, Present Status, and Future Possibilities of Secondary Recovery Operations in Pennsylvania," 1 *IOCC Committee Bull.* 29 at 34 (Dec. 1959).

See also SECONDARY RECOVERY.

Reversionary interest

(1) In Louisiana, a landowner's interest in minerals after the creation of a MINERAL SERVITUDE (*q.v.*) arising from the possibility that the mineral servitude will be prescribed by ten years nonuser and the right to minerals revested in the landowner. See Hicks v. Clark, 225 La. 133, 72 So. 2d 322, 3 *O.&G.R.* 1059 (1954).

(2) In common law jurisdictions, "A reversionary interest is any future interest left in a transferor or his successor in interest." Restatement of Property § 154 (1936); 2 Powell on Real Property ¶ 271 (1950).

(3) *Syn.* for RESIDUAL INTEREST (*q.v.*).

Reverter

See POSSIBILITY OF REVERTER

Revision of estimated gas reserves

The adjustment of previous estimates of known gas fields. Northern Natural Gas Co. v. O'Malley, 174 F.Supp. 176, 10 *O.&G.R.* 423 (D. Neb. 1959), *rev'd,* 277 F.2d 128, 12 *O.&G.R.* 335 (8th Cir. 1960).

Revisions

Changes in earlier estimates of proved reserves, either upward or downward, resulting from new information (except for an increase in proved acreage). "Revisions for a given year also include (1) increases in proved reserves associated with the successful installation of improved recovery technique and (2) an amount which corrects the effect on proved reserves of the difference between estimated production for the previous year and actual production for that year." American Petroleum Institute Division of Statistics, *Organization and Definitions for the Estimation of Reserves and Productive Capacity of Crude Oil* 17 (Technical Report No. 2, June 1970).

See also RESERVES.

Reworking clause

A lease clause providing that the lease may be kept alive without production during the continuance of designated reworking operations. See THIRTY DAY-SIXTY DAY CLAUSE.

Reworking operations

Work performed on a well after its completion, in an effort to secure production where there has been none, restore production that has ceased or increase production. Cleaning out a hole that has silted up is a typical reworking operation. In Rogers v. Osborn, 152 Tex. 540, 261 S.W.2d 311, 2 *O.&G.R.* 304, 1439 (1953), the trial court defined reworking operations as follows:

> " 're-working operations' . . . means actual work as operations which have theretofore been done, being done over, and being done in good faith endeavor to cause a well to produce oil and gas or oil or gas in paying quantities as an ordinarily competent operator would do in the same or similar circumstances."

The appellate court neither approved nor disapproved of this definition. In the same case, the court held that PERIODIC FLOWING (*q.v.*) or bleeding a well could amount to reworking operations, where the jury so found.

See also Johnson v. Houston Oil Co., 86 So. 2d 97, 5 *O.&G.R.* 1169 (La. 1956); Ariz. R.S. § 27–551.

The legal definition of the term is important because many leases contain clauses such as or similar to the following:

> "If prior to discovery of oil or gas on the land lessee should drill a dry hole thereon, or if after discovery of oil or gas the production thereof should cease, this lease shall not terminate if lessee commences additional drilling or *reworking* operations within sixty days thereafter. . . . If at the expiration of the primary term, oil, gas or other mineral is not being produced on the land but lessee is then engaged in drilling or *reworking* operations thereon, this lease shall remain in force so long as such operations are prosecuted with no cessation of more than thirty days. . . ."

The term "reworking" is defined in one agreement form as "all operations designed to secure, restore or improve production through some use of a hole previously drilled, including, but not limited to, mechanical or chemical treatment of any horizon, deepening to test deeper strata, plugging back to test higher strata, etc." Myers, *The Law of Pooling and Unitization* § 15.06 at p. 601 (2d ed. 1967).

Sheffield v. Exxon Corp., 424 So. 2d 1297, 76 *O.&G.R.* 419 (Ala. 1983), in analyzing the meaning of this term, declared:

"The crucial test which must be met for an activity to constitute reworking is whether the operation is associated or connected with the physical site of the well or the unit. Additionally, the operation must be intimately connected with the resolution of whatever physical difficulty caused the well to cease production."

In Harry Bourg Corp. v. Union Producing Co., 197 So. 2d 172, 27 *O.&G.R.* 20 (La. App. 1967), *writ. ref'd,* 250 La. 903, 199 So. 2d 917, 27 *O.&G.R.* 28 (1967), the court concluded that "the word 'rework' has a definite, even though multiple, meaning in the oil and gas industry" and it rejected the contention that "reworking" required that activities "be of a drilling nature (either sidetracking or deepening)." The "reworking" in the instant case involved operations causing a well to produce gas from 14,550 feet after the original production from sand at 14,800 feet ceased.

In Lone Star Producing Co. v. Walker, 257 So. 2d 496 at 500, 41 *O.&G.R.* 350 at 358 (Miss. 1971), the court declared that it was not absolutely necessary that a work over rig be on the well site as a necessary incident to a reworking operation, and then observed that:

"It would be difficult, if not impossible, to formulate a rule that would with exactness define reworking operations such as those contemplated by the terms of the leases in question because the problems of capturing and producing oil and gas located thousands of feet below the surface of the earth are many and varied. Reworking operations may encompass testing, evaluation and other acts performed necessary to reworking a given well, and each case will have to be considered in the light of facts peculiar to that operation. One of the prime requirements is that the acts of the operator constitute a bona fide effort to rework a given well."

Serhienko v. Kiker, 392 N.W.2d 808, ____ *O.&G.R.* ____ (N.D. 1986), concluded that operations on other premises, on the success of which operation on the leasehold was contingent, did not constitute reworking operations on the leasehold.

Pshigoda v. Texaco, Inc., 703 S.W.2d 416, 90 *O.&G.R.* 135 (Tex. App., Amarillo, 1986; error ref'd n.r.e.), concluded that expenses incurred in reworking an oil well were properly considered as capital expenses rather than operating and marketing expenses and hence were not to be considered in determining whether production was in paying quantities for purposes of the habendum clause of a lease.

See also Jardell v. Hillin Oil Co., 476 So.2d 1118, 89 *O.&G.R.* 84 (La. App. 1985), *rev'd and rendered,* 485 So.2d 919, 89 *O.&G.R.* 99 (La. 1986), for a detailed discussion of what constitutes reworking operations.

Del-Ray Oil & Gas, Inc. v. Henderson Petroleum Corp., 797 F.2d 1313, ____ *O.&G.R.* ____ (5th Cir. 1986), declared that under *Jardell* reworking need not involve additional drilling and that *Jardell* does not suggest that reworking must take place below the ground.

The definition in this MANUAL was quoted in House v. Tidewater Oil Co., 219 So. 2d 616 at 622–623, 33 *O.&G.R.* 268 at 279 (La. App. 1969), *writ refused,* 253 La. 1081, 221 So. 2d 516 (1969).

See also CLEANING A WELL; DRILLING OPERATIONS; REDRILLING; WORK OVERS.

Rhabdomancy

The science of divination by rods or wands. See DOODLE BUG.

Rich gas

Gas containing substantial quantities of liquefiable hydrocarbons. *Syn.:* WET GAS.

Riding the well down

A colloquialism which has been applied to conduct or various parties during the drilling of a well.

(1) As applied to a lessor, the term is applied to conduct which may cause the court to find a lease preserved by estoppel and laches despite the expiration of the primary term. See LYING BEHIND THE LOG.

(2) The term has also been applied to conduct of an applicant for a compulsory pooling order. See PCX Corp. v. Oklahoma Corporation Comm'n, 699 P.2d 1103, 84 *O.&G.R.* 547 (Okla. App. 1984, *cert. denied*). In this case after an application for pooling by PCX was granted by the Corporation Commission, the applicant failed to prepare the order although it was the custom for the prevailing party to prepare the order and report in an uncontested case. After drilling was discontinued by PCX (apparently due to financial problems and drilling difficulties), PCX filed a motion to dismiss its pooling application. The court sustained the Commission's order granting pooling and denying PCX's motion to dismiss, reasoning that it would be improper to permit the applicant to "ride the well down" and then withdraw the request for a pooling order under which other parties affected would be entitled to a bonus and royalty.

(3) The term has also been applied to continued silence by a party to a joint venture during the drilling of a well, waiting until it was determined that the well was commercially productive before claim-

ing the right to acquire an interest in the well by payment of a share of costs. Heritage Resources, Inc. v. Anschutz Corp., 689 S.W.2d 952, 86 *O.&G.R.* 613 (Tex. App., El Paso, 1985, error ref'd n.r.e.).

(4) The term has been applied to owners in a unit who elect not to lease or to participate. They obtain a "free ride" with no exposure to the risk of payment of costs in the event of a dry hole or a well which produced but which never paid out. Napper, "Recent Developments in Legislation," 32 *L.S.U. Min. L. Inst.* 315 at 320 (1986).

Syn.: LYING BEHIND THE LOG (*q.v.*).

Rig

See DRILLING RIG.

Right of re-entry

See POWER OF TERMINATION

Right of Way Leasing Act of 1930

An Act authorizing the issuance of an oil and gas lease covering deposits underlying a right of way acquired under any law of the United States. 46 Stat. 373, 30 U.S.C. §§ 301–306. Regulations pertaining to this Act are found in 43 C.F.R. § 3100 *et seq.* (1978). See *Rocky Mt. Min. L. Fdn. Law of Federal Oil & Gas Leases* Ch. 8 (1985); Hoffman, *Oil and Gas Leasing on Federal Lands* 213 (1957).

Right to cure clause

Syn.: NOTICE AND DEMAND CLAUSE (*q.v.*). See Meyers, "The Oil and Gas Lessee's Obligation to Protect Its Lessor," 2 *Eastern Min. L. Inst.* 13–24 (1981).

Rig set-off

Moving a rig from over the well so that the well may be completed. Skids or rollers are placed under an assembled drilling rig and the rig is moved by means of trucks, bulldozers, or a combination of both. I.R.B. 1957–35, 21, 7 *O.&G.R.* 1345 (1957).

Rig-time work

Syn.: DAY WORK (*q.v.*).

Ring fence

The term applied to special corporation tax provisions introduced by the Oil Taxation Act 1975 designed "to place a fence around United Kingdom oil profits ensuring that corporation tax is paid on the full amount of them without any reduction for tax reliefs in respect of any other activity and that oil crossing the fence is valued at full market price." See Daintith and Willoughby, *A Manual of United Kingdom Oil and Gas Law* 101–104 (1977); Henderson *et al.*, *Oil and Gas Law: The North Sea Exploitation* 4.1039 *et seq.* (1979); Sherry, "Ring Fence Rules," [1985/86] 7 *OGLTR* 171.

Rio Blanco proposal

A proposed government-industry experiment for commercial gas stimulation by an underground nuclear explosion designed to create a chimney and a fracture system that surrounds and is connected to the chimney, thus stimulating the flow of gas through "tight" reservoirs characterized by low-permeability. See Rubin, Schwartz, and Montan, *An Analysis of Gas Stimulation Using Nuclear Explosives* (May 15, 1972).

Riparian lease clause

A portion of the description in an oil and gas lease relating to riparian lands, *e.g.*, as follows: "If this land is riparian to, bounds, or embraces within its boundaries a stream, lake or other body of water, then all of the lessor's river bed rights and lands under water, and all area now or hereafter added by accretion, are included and covered by this lease." McQueen, "Development of Lease Provisions: Mid-Continent Area," 6 *Sw. Legal Fdn. Nat'l Inst. for Petroleum Landmen* 83 at 93 (1965).

RIR procedures

REFUNDS INTEREST RATE (RIR) PROCEDURES (*q.v.*).

Risk-bearing service contract

See RISK SERVICE CONTRACT.

Risk bonus

Syn. for NON-CONSENT PENALTY (*q.v.*). See *In re* Application of Kohlman (Kohlman v. Depco, Inc.), 263 N.W.2d 674, 60 *O.&G.R.* 402 (S.D. 1978).

Risk charge statute

The term applied to a statute providing for a NON-CONSENT PENALTY (*q.v.*) to be borne by the owner of an operating interest in a compulsory unit who does not enter into a contractual agreement with the operator of the unit well providing for the payment of a proportionate share of unit development and operational costs. See Napper, "Recent Developments in Legislation," 32 *L.S.U. Min. L. Inst.* 315 at 318 (1986) (discussing the 1984 revision of La. R.S. 30:10(A)).

Risk compensation

Syn. for NON-CONSENT PENALTY (*q.v.*). See *In re* Application of Kohlman (Kohlman v. Depco, Inc.), 263 N.W.2d 674, 60 *O.&G.R.* 402 (S.D. 1978).

Risk fee

See RISK SERVICE CONTRACT.

Risk-free value

This term is defined in Kerr-McGee Corp., 6 IBLA 108, GFS (OCS) 1972–51 (June 5, 1972) as:

"the total possible recoverable resources, based on estimates by the government's experts. The 'risk value' is obtained from the risk-free value by applying a factor based on the reliability of all the data used in determining the risk free value and the discounted rate of the cash flow over the expected period of exploitation of the lease."

On the basis of calculations of risk value and risk free value, the government rejected the high bid for an oil and gas lease on Outer Continental Shelf lands as inadequate. In Kerr-McGee Corp. v. Morton, 527 F.2d 838, 540 *O.&G.R.* 149 (D. C. Cir. 1975), the court sustained the rejection of the bid by the Secretary of the Interior on the ground that the Secretary did not abuse his discretion in rejecting the bid.

For other cases dealing with the rejection of lease bids on OCS lands, see the following:

Chevron Oil Co. v. Andrus, 588 F.2d 1383 (5th Cir. 1979), *reh. en banc denied,* 591 F.2d 1343 (5th Cir. 1979), *cert. denied,* 444 U.S. 879 (1979); Superior Oil Co. v. Watt, 548 F. Supp. 78, 74 *O.&G.R.* 423 (D. Del. 1982).

Procedures employed in the evaluation of bids by the Secretary of the Interior are discussed in Kerr-McGee Corp. v. Watt, 517 F.Supp. 1209, 71 *O.&G.R.* 494 (D.D.C. 1981). Exxon Company, U.S.A., 15 IBLA 345, GFS(OCS) 1974–55 (May 14, 1974). Three evaluation categories are employed in this process: (1) PROVEN OR SEMI-PROVEN ACREAGE ("DRAINAGE") METHOD OF EVALUATION (*q.v.*); (2) WILDCAT ACREAGE METHOD (*q.v.*); and (3) Rank wildcat acreage method.

See also AVERAGE EVALUATION OF TRACT (AEOT); DISCOUNTED MROV (DMROV); MEAN OF THE RANGE OF VALUES (MROV); 1/8 RULE; POST SALE ANALYSIS CHART; RANGE OF VALUES METHOD.

Risk of the hole

The risk of some damage or mishap affecting the hole drilled for an oil or gas well. In Par-Co Drilling, Inc. v. Franks Petroleum Inc., 360 So. 2d 642, 62 *O.&G.R.* 36 (La App. 1978), the court concluded that under the usual TURNKEY CONTRACT (*q.v.*), the risk of the hole shifts to the operator-owner once the last core provided for by the contract is furnished. Control of the hole was said to shift at the same time.

Risk penalty

Syn. for NON-CONSENT PENALTY (*q.v.*). See *In re* Application of Kohlman (Kohlman v. Depco, Inc.), 263 N.W.2d 674, 60 *O.&G.R.* 402 (S.D. 1978).

Risk service contract

A SERVICE CONTRACT (*q.v.*) which places the burden of making original investments and taking risks on the company or "contractor." For successful efforts, the contractor is entitled to recover capital expended and interest plus a payment called the "risk fee."

See the following:

Blinn, Duval, Le Leuch, and Pertuzio, *InternationaL Petroleum Exploration & Exploitation Agreements* ch. 6 (1986);

Neto, "Risk-Bearing Service Contracts in Brazil," 3 *J. of Energy & Nat. Res. L.* 114 (1985);

Danielsen, *The Evolution of OPEC* 260 (1982).

See also CONCESSION.

Risk value

See RISK-FREE VALUE.

RMOGA

The ROCKY MOUNTAIN OIL & GAS ASSOCIATION (*q.v.*).

Roadless Area Review and Evaluation (RARE)

A program of the Forest Service to consider for inclusion in the NATIONAL WILDERNESS PESERVATION SYSTEM (NWPS) certain lands outside the previously designated "primitive" areas. See Short, "Wilderness Policies and Mineral Potential on the Public Lands," 26 *Rocky Mt. Min. L. Inst.* 39 at 44 (1980).

Road oil

Any heavy petroleum oil, including residual asphaltic oils, used as a dust palliative and surface treatment of roads and highways. It is generally produced in six grades from 0, the most liquid, to 6, the most viscous. 38 F. R. 34417 (Dec. 13, 1973).

Robber well

A term sometimes used to describe a well on other premises which is draining particular premises. See Sychuk, "Damages for Breach of an Express Drilling Covenant," 8 *Alberta L. Rev.* 250 at 254 (1970).

Rock, basement

See BASEMENT ROCK.

Rock bit

See BIT, ROCK.

Rock oil

A synonym for petroleum.

"Rocking" a well

See PERIODIC FLOWING

Rock pressure

Properly, the RESERVOIR PRESSURE (*q.v.*) or BOTTOM HOLE PRESSURE (*q.v.*). But the term is sometimes used, especially formerly, to designate the wellhead or SHUT-IN PRESSURE (*q.v.*). Some define rock pressure as the pressure taken on a well after it is closed in for 24 hours. See Steven v. Potlatch Oil & Refining Co., 80 Mont. 239, 260 Pac. 119 (1927).

Rock sediment

The combined cuttings and residue from drilling sedimentary rocks and formations, commonly known as sand pumpings. Page's Ohio Rev. Code Ann., § 4151.01 (LL) (1973).

Rocky Mountain Mineral Law Foundation

A nonprofit corporation located in Boulder, Colorado, composed of law schools, bar associations, mining associations, and oil and gas associations. The Foundation offers a series of institutes relating to oil, gas, water, and other minerals and publishes a variety of treatises on such subjects.

Rocky Mountain Oil & Gas Association (RMOGA)

A nonprofit corporation serving as a trade association of a number of member companies engaged in the exploration for and development of oil and gas.

Roddage fee

A fee payable to the grantor of an easement or his successor in interest for the enjoyment of an easement of a right-of-way for a pipe line, the amount of the fee being measured by the roddage of the pipe line. Northern Natural Gas Co. v. O'Malley, 174 F.Supp. 176, 10 *O.&G.R.* 423 (D. Neb. 1959), *rev'd,* 277 F.2d 128, 12 *O.&G.R.* 335 (8th Cir. 1960).

Rolled-in allocation method

A method of rate-making wherein the cost of new facilities and new gas supplies are collected or "rolled in" with the cost of older facilities and gas supplies for the purpose of determining the cost of the entire system which is then pro-rated among all of the customers. This method is generally disadvantageous to old customers of an existing pipeline since the cost of new facilities and new gas supplies historically has risen steadily and the rolled-in rate method requires old customers to pay a higher price and bear part of the cost of an expansion from which they receive little increase in service. See Battle Creek Gas Co. v. Federal Power Comm'n, 281 F.2d 42 (D.C. Cir. 1960).

United Gas Pipe Line Co. v. Federal Energy Regulatory Comm'n, 649 F.2d 1110 (5th Cir. 1981), *rehearing denied*, 664 F.2d 289 (5th Cir. 1981), affirmed a commission order refusing to apply the rolled-in allocation method to recover the cost of emergency gas purchases. See also Laclede Gas Co. v. Federal Energy Regulatory Comm'n, 722 F.2d 272 (5th Cir. 1984).

See also INCREMENTAL COST METHOD; MARGINAL COST PRICING.

Rolled-in price

A combination of lower and higher prices resulting in an average price. Shamrock Oil & Gas Corp. v. Comm'r, 35 T.C. 979, 13 *O.&G.R.* 1090 at 1102 (1961).

With growing disparity between the cost of "old gas" and the cost of "new gas," controversy developed over the question whether the Federal Power Commission and its successor, the Federal Energy Regulatory Commission, should continue its traditional practice of rolling in or averaging gas acquisition costs for purposes of calculating the unit rates to be paid by pipeline customers and ultimate consumers. Details of this controversy are traced in Pierce, "Natural Gas Policy Act of 1978," 47 *J. Kans.* B.A. 259 at 270 (1978). The Act discussed in this paper provided for new gas to be incrementally priced to industrial users, thus insulating residential consumers from price increases. See also Silverman, "Encouraging Conservation of Natural Gas Through the Price Mechanism," 57 *Denver L.J.* 545 (1980); Cormie, "Incremental Pricing Under the Natural Gas Policy Act of 1978," 57 *Denver L.J.* 1 (1979).

See also INCREMENTAL PRICING; MARGINAL COST PRICING ; NATURAL GAS POLICY ACT OF 1978 (NGPA).

Roller bit

See BIT, ROLLER.

Roll in, to

To include the cost of new facilities, service or supply as a part of the costs of operating an integrated company for the benefit of all customers served by a pipe line system. The Federal Power Commission generally required that cost of new facilities be rolled-in with over-all system costs for purpose of rate making but under special circumstances it required that a particular buyer bear the cost of some facilities. In the Matters of Texas Gas Transmission Corp., 22 F.P.C. 378 (Opinion No. 327, Aug. 10, 1959).

Rollover contract

This term is defined in § 2 of the NATURAL GAS POLICY ACT OF 1978 (*q.v.*) (Pub. L. No. 95–621) as any contract, entered into on or after the date of the enactment of this Act, for the first sale of natural gas that was previously subject to an existin gcontract which expired at the end of a fixed term (not including any extension thereof taking effect on or after such date of enactment) specified by the provisions of such existing contract, as such contract was in effect on the date of the enactment of this Act, whether or not there is an identity of parties or terms with those of such existing contract.

The Federal Energy Regulatory Commission has defined a "rollover" for purposes of this Act to require that the fixed term of the "existing intrastate contract" must expire and a new contract or amendment must be entered into. A rollover may not "occur" until both prerequisites have been met. Final Regulations Under Sections 105 and 105(b) of the Natural Gas Policy Act of 1978, FERC Order No. 68 (Jan. 18, 1980), 20 F.P.S. 5–12.

In Superior Oil Co. v. Pioneer Corp., 532 F.Supp. 731, 73 *O.&G.R.* 412 (N.D. Tex. 1982), the court found that a purchaser's option to extend the term of a gas purchase contract was not an EVERGREEN CLAUSE (*q.v.*) and that the new contract arising from exercise of the option was, therefore, a rollover contract rather than a SUCCESSOR TO AN EXISTING CONTRACT (*q.v.*). The judgment was vacated and dismissed for want of jurisdiction. 706 F.2d 603 (5th Cir. 1983), *cert. denied,* 461 U.S. 1041, 104 S. Ct. 706 (1984).

See also NEW CONTRACT.

Rollover gas

Gas sold pursuant to a renewal contract replacing a prior contract for the sale of the gas. The availability of the national rate for rollover gas when the renewal contract replaced one that had expired by its own terms was sustained in Shell Oil Co. v. Federal Power Comm'n, 520 F.2d 1061, 53 *O.&G.R.* 392 (5th Cir. 1975), *reh. denied,* 525 F.2d 1261 (5th Cir. 1976), *cert. denied.* 426 U.S. 941 (1976). See also The Second National Natural Gas Rate Cases (American Public Gas Ass'n v. Federal Power Comm'n), 567 F.2d 1016, 59 *O.&G.R.* 351 (D.C. Cir. 1977), *cert. denied,* 435 U.S. 907 (1978); Ashland Exploration, Inc. v. Federal Energy Regulatory

Comm'n, 631 F.2d 1018, 67 *O.&G.R.* 637, 21 F.P.S. 6–88 (D.C. Cir. 1980), *cert. denied,* 450 U.S. 915 (1981).

Roll up

The incorporation of a number of unincorporated oil and gas interests, usually in limited partnerships. Frequently such a transaction involves limited partnerships operated by a common general partner and occurs in order to simplify operations, capture a significant source of exploration capital (the money that had been distributed to the limited partners), and to provide liquidity to the investors in the form of publicly traded stock. See Maultsby, "Overview of Mineral Financing," *Rocky Mt. Min. L. Inst. on Mineral Financing* I-1 at I-12 (1982);

Wilson, "Tax Considerations in Selecting a Mineral Financing Vehicle," *Id.* 7-1 at 7-88 (1982).

See also EXCHANGE OFFER.

Roll-up provision

A provision in certain DRILLING FUND (*q.v.*) programs under which the investor may be able to trade his program interest for stock in the program manager's company or some other publicly traded company. The value of the stock the investor may receive is usually determined by the program manager and will presumably be less than the next present value of the expected production income. See Barnett and Coffin, "New Financing Techniques In the Oil and Gas Industry," 34 *Sw. Legal Fdn. Oil and Gas Inst.* 431 at 533 (1983), and the authorities cited at page 533 note 273.

See also CORPORATE ROLLUP.

Root of title

Under the Uniform Simplification of Land Transfers Act (USLTA) § 3-301(4) (approved in 1976), this term means:

> "a conveyance or other title transaction, whether or not it is a nullity, in the record chain of title of a person, purporting to create or containing language sufficient to transfer the interest claimed by him, upon which he relies as a basis for the marketability of his title, and which was the most recent to be recorded as of a date 30 years before time marketability is to be determined. The effective date of the 'root of title' is the date on which it is recorded."

Ross Martin form

The name sometimes given to the 1956 Model Form Operating Agreement of the American Association of Petroleum Landmen (AAPL Form 610). See Stewart, "Important Features of Joint Operating Agreements," 13 *Sw. Legal Fdn. Nat'l Inst. for Petroleum Landmen* 139 at 156 (1972); Young, "Oil and Gas Operating Agreements," 20 *Rocky Mt. Min. L. Inst.* 197 at 199 (1975).

Rotary bit

See BIT, ROTARY.

Rotary drilling

The now prevalent method of drilling oil wells, replacing CABLE TOOL DRILLING (*q.v.*). In essence, the principle of rotary drilling is the rotation of drill pipe, fastened to the bottom of which is a bit (or cutting tool), usually of the roller bit design. [See BIT, ROLLER]. The conical-shaped cutting tools in the bit grind a hole in the rock as the drill pipe turns. During drilling, drilling MUD (*q.v.*) is in constant circulation into the bottom of the hole and out again. This mud lubricates the bit, prevents blowouts and removes the cuttings from the hole.

The process of rotary drilling is described in Falcon Seaboard Drilling Co. v. Comm'r, 30 T.C. 1081, 9 *O.&G.R.* 578 (1958), as follows:

> "In drilling an oil well with a rotary type drill . . . the drill bit is fastened rigidly to a section of drill pipe, usually about 4½ inches in diameter and 30 feet long, which is held in an upright position by the drilling derrick and rotated mechanically from the surface level, forcing the revolving bit into the earth. The rotation is at the rate of from 50 to 150 revolutions per minute, depending on the formation. The bit is 3 or 4 inches larger in diameter than the drill pipe, leaving a space of 2 inches or so between the pipe and the earth wall. As the drill rotates a soft mud is pushed down under pressure inside the drill pipe and returns to the surface through the space between the pipe and the earth wall, bringing out the cuttings from the bottom of a hole. As the hole is deepened more sections of pipe are added. To change the drill bit, which in some formations has to be done often, the entire string of pipe must be pulled from the hole. As it is taken out the pipe is disjointed in 2 or 3 sections (lengths), depending on the heighth of the derrick, and stacked inside the framework of the derrick. Then

the bit is fastened on the bottom section of the pipe and all of the pipe put back in the hole. In deep well drilling this may become a time-consuming and expensive operation. As the mud returns to the surface it flows onto a 'shale shaker' which screens out the cuttings. These cuttings are examined from time to time for the geological information. They show when oil-bearing sands have been reached."

See also CABLE TOOL DRILLING; CANADIAN POLE SYSTEM; DRILLING RIG; TURBODRILLING.

Rotary table

Machinery in the derrick floor which rotates the drill string.

Rotterdam

See SPOT MARKET.

Roughneck

A driller's helper and general worker on a drilling rig.

Round trip

The process of removing drill pipe, replacing the bit, and returning the drill column to the hole. See Buster Gardner Drilling Co. v. Associated Oil & Gas Exploration, Inc., 214 So. 2d 267 at 271, 32 *O.&G.R.* 169 at 176 (La. App. 1968), *writ refused,* 253 La. 59, 216 So. 2d 306 (1968).

Roustabout

A common laborer around a drilling or producing well.

ROV

See RANGE OF VALUES METHOD.

Royalty

(1) The landowner's share of production, free of expenses of production.

(2) A share of production, free of expenses of production, *e.g.*, an OVERRIDING ROYALTY (*q.v.*) of 1/8 of the 7/8 working interest.

The landowner's royalty is frequently 1/8th production, but it may be any other fractional share of production (or, as is typical in California, the royalty may be expressed as a percentage of production rather than a fractional share of production). In some parts of the industry, anything larger than a 1/8th royalty may be called an OVERRIDING ROYALTY (*q.v.*) in practice, even though it goes to the landowner. Thus a 1/6th royalty may be called "an 1/8th royalty and a 1/24th override."

Royalty may be payable in kind (that is, the royalty owner is entitled to a share of the oil or gas as produced), or it may be payable in money (that is, the royalty owner is to be paid in money for the value or market price of his share of the product). The former type of royalty gives its owner in some states, *e.g.*, Texas, a corporeal interest, whereas the latter type of royalty may give rise only to a debtor-creditor relationship after production between the operator and the royalty owner. For other differences in the legal consequences of the two types of royalty clause, see TREATISE § 659.1. Cancellation of the lease is normally not an available remedy for non-payment of royalty. See TREATISE § 656.3.

Although the royalty is not subject to costs of production, usually it is subject to costs incurred after production, *e.g.*, production or gathering taxes, costs of treatment of the product to render it marketable, costs of transportation to market. Occasionally a lease provides that the royalty payable to the lessor shall be a larger or smaller fractional interest depending on the volume of production. A royalty is freely assignable.

The term royalty may be used in a more general or loose sense in some instances as covering all returns from a claimed interest in oil and gas. See Denio v. City of Huntington Beach, 22 Cal. 2d 580, 140 P.2d 392, 149 A.L.R. 320 (1943).

In United States v. 525 Co., 342 F.2d 759, 22 *O.&G.R.* 483 (5th Cir. 1965), the court said that the term "royalty" as used with respect to oil and gas matters, refers to the landowner's royalty, and not to oil payments.

Royalty, as used in connection with mineral leases, is defined by Article 213 of the Louisiana Mineral Code (R.S. 31:213) as:

> "any interest in production, or its value, from or attributable to land subject to a mineral lease, that is deliverable or payable to the lessor or others entitled to share therein. Such interests in production or its value are 'royalty,' whether created by the lease or by separate instrument, if they comprise a part of the negotiated agreement resulting in execution of the lease. 'Royalty' also includes sums payable to the lessor that are classified by the lease as constructive production."

As the Comment to this article indicates, the statutory definitions of bonus and royalty are intended to be complementary. Thus if a production payment is created at the time of the execution of a lease, it will be characterized as royalty (and hence payable to those persons entitled to share in royalty) if the production payment is payable from the property being leased, whereas it will be characterized as bonus (and hence payable to those persons entitled to share in bonus) if the production payment is granted by the lessee out of another producing lease.

"Generally, then, under subparagraphs (1) and (2) of Article 213, any interest in production or its value from or attributable to a lease granted by the holder of an executive right would be royalty and not bonus, even though it might be termed in the documentation as an overriding royalty or a production payment taken out of the working interest. Coupled with the provisions concerning executive rights, this means that one holding an executive interest cannot, by the device of calling an interest in production an overriding royalty rather than a lessor's royalty, deprive the holder of a mineral royalty or other nonexecutive interest of the right to share in production."

See TREATISE § 339.4.

Bonus is distinguished from "royalties" as that term is used in the Small Business Corporation Act in Swank & Son, Inc. v. United States, 362 F.Supp. 897, 46 *O.&G.R.* 291 (D. Mont. 1973).

The term "royalty" as used in a contract under which royalty was promised for services was held to include "advance royalty" received by the promisor which was recoverable from subsequent production, if any. Rouse v. McDonough, 622 P.2d 106, 68 *O.&G.R.* 587 (Colo. App. 1980).

Mobil Oil Corp. v. State of Michigan Department of Treasury, 121 Mich. App. 293, 328 N.W.2d 367, 75 *O.&G.R.* 434 (Mich. App. 1982), *aff'd,* 422 Mich. 473, 373 N.W.2d 730, 87 *O.&G.R.* 425 (1985), held that for purposes of the Michigan Single Business Tax Act, payments made to nonoperating landowners in connection with the production of oil and gas from property owned by the landowners were "royalties."

Comptroller of Treasury v. Shell Oil Co., 65 Md. App. 252, 500 A.2d 315, 87 *O.&G.R.* 223 (Md. Ct. of Special Appeals 1985), held that for purposes of calculating taxpayer's corporate income taxes, royalties paid by the taxpayer under certain oil and gas leases consituted "gross rent" as defined in one of the Comptroller's regulations.

For a discussion of the question whether a royalty is viewed as a proprietary interest or a contract interest under Australian law, see Ryan, "Australia: Petroleum Royalties—Part I," [1985/86] 5 *OGLTR* 121, "Part II," [1985/86] 6 *OGLTR* 154.

The definition in this MANUAL was cited in Whitehall Oil Co. v. Eckart, 197 So. 2d 664, 26 *O.&G.R.* 778 (La. App. 1966), *rev'd sub nom.* Gardner v. Boagni, 252 La. 30, 209 So. 2d 11, 29 *O.&G.R.* 229 (1968).

See also ACCRUED ROYALTY; ACREAGE BASED ROYALTY; ADDITIONAL ROYALTY; ADVANCE ROYALTY; APPORTIONMENT; BASE ROYALTY; BONUS ROYALTY; CASH SUBSTITUTE ROYALTY; CASINGHEAD GAS ROYALTY; COMPENSATORY ROYALTY; CREDITED ROYALTY SYSTEM; DEFERRED MINIMUM ANNUAL ROYALTY; DEFERRED NET ROYALTY; DISCOVERY ROYALTY; DIVISION ORDER; DRILL SITE ROYALTY; EXCESS ROYALTY; EXEMPT ROYALTY OIL; EXPENSED ROYALTY SYSTEM; FARMERS' OIL; FEDERAL-FLOOR PROVISION; FEE ROYALTY; FIXED PRICE ROYALTY CLAUSE; FIXED TERM ROYALTY; FREE GAS CLAUSE; GAS ROYALTY; GROSS ROYALTY; GUARANTEED ROYALTY PAYMENT; LANDOWNER ROYALTY; LESSOR-APPROVAL PROVISION; LESSOR'S ROYALTY; LIEU ROYALTY; MARKET-VALUE/AMOUNT REALIZED PROVISION; MINERAL ROYALTY; MINIMUM ROYALTY; NET PROFITS ROYALTY; NET ROYALTY; NON-PARTICIPATING ROYALTY; OFFSET ROYALTY; OIL ROYALTY; OPEN-END GAS ROYALTY CLAUSE; OVERRIDING ROYALTY; PARTICIPATING ROYALTY; PASS-THROUGH ROYALTY; PERPETUAL NON-PARTICIPATING ROYALTY; PREFERRED NET ROYALTY; PRODUCTS ROYALTY CLAUSE; PROGRESSIVE INCREMENTAL ROYALTY; QUALIFIED ROYALTY PRODUCTION; REDUCTION OF ROYALTIES; RENT ROYALTY; ROYALTY BONUS; ROYALTY IN KIND; ROYALTY OIL OR GAS; ROYALTY REDUCTION; ROYALTY SURCHARGE; SLIDING SCALE ROYALTY; STEP SCALE ROYALTY; SUBSTITUTE ROYALTY; SUSPENDED ROYALTY; TAKE-OR-PAY CLAUSE; TAPERED ROYALTY; TERM MINERAL OR ROYALTY INTEREST; UNACCRUED ROYALTY; VARIABLE ROYALTY.

Royalty acre

A full lease royalty on one acre of land; *e.g.*, in a one hundred acre tract leased for a 1/8 royalty, ownership of 1/2 of the royalty interest or of a 1/16 royalty is the equivalent of owning fifty royalty acres. See TREATISE § 320.3; Dickens v. Tisdale, 204 Ark. 838, 164 S.W.2d 990 (1942); Inslee v. Palmer, 153 Kan. 147, 109 P.2d 208 (1941).

Dudley v. Fridge, 443 So. 2d 1207 at 1208, 80 *O.&G.R.* 1 at 2 (Alabama 1983), defined a royalty acre "as a 1/8 royalty on the full mineral interest in one acre of land."

For a discussion of the question whether an interest described in terms of royalty acres is to be viewed as a fraction *of* lease royalty or as a fraction of a fixed 1/8 royalty, see TREATISE § 320.3.

For further discussion and citations, see MINERAL ACRE.

Royalty apportionment clause

A lease clause providing for the apportionment of royalties among the owners of interests in separate parcels included within a lease. In this TREATISE, this clause is described as an ENTIRETY CLAUSE (*q.v.*). Huie, Woodward, and Smith, *Cases on Oil and Gas* 811, n. 52 (2d ed. 1972), suggests that "Perhaps the kind of clause generally referred to as an *entirety clause* would be better described as a *royalty apportionment clause.*"

Royalty based on acreage

See ACREAGE BASED ROYALTY

Royalty bidding

Competitive bidding for leases in which the lease is offered to the person offering to pay the largest share of the proceeds of production, free of expenses of production.

See also LEASE BIDDING SYSTEMS.

Royalty bonus

A term occasionally used to describe an overriding royalty or oil payment reserved by a lessor. One practice is to describe any consideration received by or promised to a lessor on the execution of a lease in excess of the usual one-eighth royalty as bonus or royalty bonus. See Griffith v. Taylor, 156 Tex. 1, 291 S.W.2d 673, 5 *O.&G.R.* 1371 (1956); State national Bank of Corpus Christi v. Morgan, 135 Tex. 509, 143 S.W.2d 757 (1940); Sheppard v. Stanolind Oil & Gas Co., 125 S.W.2d 643 (Tex. Civ. App. 1939, error ref'd); Walker, "Oil Payments," 20 *Tex. L. Rev.* 259 at 272 (1942); TREATISE § 301 at notes 6–10.

See also BONUS; ROYALTY.

Royalty clause

The lease clause specifying the royalty to be paid by the lessee. See TREATISE §§ 641–663.

Royalty deed

An instrument in writing conveying a ROYALTY INTEREST (*q.v.*). The instrument must name the grantor and the grantee, describe the land, give the size of the interest, and contain the signature of the grantor.

Royalty deeds are not uniform as to duration of the interest. They may endure forever, or for a term of years and so long thereafter as oil or gas is produced, or for a fixed term of years, or for the duration of an existing oil and gas lease.

Nor is there any uniformity in the manner of designating the size of the interest. In Texas, Oklahoma and other states, use of fractions is common (*e.g.*, a 1/16 royalty). In California, the same interest is more likely to be called a 6-1/4% royalty.

It should be observed also that a difference exists between a 1/8 royalty and 1/8 *of* royalty. The former gives the right to one out of every eight barrels of oil produced. The latter usually gives the right to 1/8 of the usual 1/8 royalty, or one out of every 64 barrels of oil produced.

The portion of the definition in this TREATISE distinguishing between a 1/8 royalty and 1/8 *of* royalty was quoted in Knox v. Krueger, 145 N.W.2d 904 at 908, 26 *O.&G.R.* 181 at 186 (N. D. 1966).

See also MINERAL DEED.

Royalty expensing

Treating royalty as an expense in calculating income for tax purposes as distinguished from crediting royalty against income tax. See, *e.g.*, the Kuwait royalty expensing agreement in OPEC, *Selected Documents of the International Petroleum Industry 1967* at p. 256.

The history of the royalty expensing controversy between OPEC and foreign oil companies is traced in Mughraby, *Permanent Sovereignty Over Oil Resources* 138 *et seq.* (1966), and in Vafai, "Conflict Resolution in the International Petroleum Industry," 5 *J. of World Trade* 427 at 435 (1971).

Royalty-free clause

The lease clause providing that the lessee shall not be liable for royalty on certain lease products, *e.g.*, on products lost, consumed, or wasted by the lessee. See TREATISE § 644.5.

See also SUBSTITUTE FUEL CLAUSE.

Royalty gauger

A person who gauges the run of oil or gas for the royalty owner. See Cox v. De Soto Crude Oil Purchasing Corp., 55 F.Supp. 467 (W. D. La. 1944).

Royalty holiday programme

An incentive programme intended to reward a successful explorer under which an eligible well is entitled to a royalty-free period or to a royalty exemption for a volume of crude oil or gas calculated from a depth-related schedule. See Case Digest and National News, [1985/86] 1 *OGLTR* D-3.

Royalty in kind

The right to receive what is due under a royalty interest in specie, that is, in oil or gas itself.

Many leases provide that the lessor may take his share of the oil in kind, although it is the usual practice of the lessor to sell his oil to the pipeline purchaser by an instrument known as a DIVISION ORDER (*q.v.*). The form of the royalty, that is, whether in kind or in money, has been held to be of significance in the resolution of a variety of legal controversies. See TREATISE § 659.1.

For many years only rarely did leases provide for the taking of royalty in kind on gas; such provisions later became more frequent as a result of the desire of lessors to make NON-JURISDICTIONAL SALES (*q.v.*) of gas.

Royalty interest

The property interest created in oil and gas after a SEVERANCE (*q.v.*) by ROYALTY DEED (*q.v.*). Its duration is like that of common law estates, namely, in fee simple, in fee simple determinable, for life or for a fixed term of years. It is distinguished from a MINERAL INTEREST (*q.v.*) by the absence of operating rights. The owner of a royalty interest is entitled to a share of production, if, as and when there is production, free of the costs of production. See TREATISE §§ 301; 327–330.

See also NONPARTICIPATING ROYALTY; PARTICIPATING ROYALTY; PER CENT INTEREST; ROYALTY; SEVERED ROYALTY INTEREST; TERM MINERAL OR ROYALTY INTEREST.

Royalty oil auction

A December 1980 auction of contracts to buy Alaskan royalty share of Prudhoe Bay production. The oil was offered in lots, each lot representing a one-year contract for 4,963 barrels per day, beginning July 1, 1981. Approximately 95 valid bids were received, with an average premium of $1.11. The highest bid for a lot offered a premium of $3.29. The average premium offered by the seventeen high bidders who won contracts was about $2.57. The sale realized about $77 million for the state. *The Wall St. Journal,* Dec. 22, 1980, p. 14.

See also SIGNATURE BONUS.

Royalty oil (or gas)

Oil or gas payable "in kind" to the lessor under the terms of an oil and gas lease. Plateau, Inc. v. Department of the Interior, 603 F.2d 161 (10th Cir. 1979), invalidated a regulation limiting distribution of federal royalty oil to small business enterprises on the ground that the regulation adopted by the Department of the Interior was unauthorized by the governing statute.

See also EXEMPT ROYALTY OIL.

Royalty owner

A person who owns a royalty interest in production.

A pooling or unitization agreement, or one of the agreements incident to pooling or unitization, may define the term in manner as follows:

> "Royalty owner is defined as one who signs or ratifies the royalty owners agreement and who, subject to an operator's right to search for and produce oil, gas or other hydrocarbons, owns lands, mineral rights, royalties, overriding royalties, gas payments, oil payments, or other rights in the unitized substances that may be produced from the . . . field. The interest so owned by a royalty owner is herein referred to as 'royalty' or 'royalty interest.' " See Myers, *The Law of Pooling and Unitization* § 4.07 (2d ed. 1967).

In some instances this term is defined in such a way as to exclude the owner of an overriding royalty or other payment carved out of the working interest. See North Dakota Statutes 1981, c. 612, H.B. No. 1651, § 4, 69 *O.&G.R.* 612, adopting definitions for the Oil Extraction Tax law.

Royalty owners agreement

The agreement among owners of royalty production in properties included within a pooling or unitization agreement which evidences assent to the agreement and makes provision for the payment of royalties.

On the negotiation and contents of such an agreement, see Myers, *The Law of Pooling and Unitization* §§ 4.05–4.08 (2d ed. 1967).

Royalty owners credit

The credit allowed royalty owners under the CRUDE OIL WINDFALL PROFIT TAX ACT OF 1980 (*q.v.*) as amended in 1980 and 1981. The ECONOMIC RECOVERY TAX ACT OF 1981 (*q.v.*) increased this credit to $2,500 for the taxable year 1981. After 1981 the credit was to be changed to an exemption of certain amounts of production. For 1982 through 1984 the exemption for qualifed royalty owners (see QUALIFIED ROYALTY PRODUCTION) is two barrels per day. The exemption is to be increased to three barrels per day for 1985 and thereafter.

Royalty pool

A pooled or unitized area in which the owners of royalties in segregated portions of the area share in the royalty on production from the well or wells located thereon without regard to well locations. See LANDOWNERS' ROYALTY POOL.

Royalty proration clause

A term sometimes employed in referring to an ENTIRETY CLAUSE (*q.v.*). See Central Pipe Line Co. v. Hutson, 401 Ill. 447, 82 N.E.2d 624 (1948).

Royalty reduction

The Mineral Leasing Act authorizes the Secretary of the Interior to reduce production royalties in mineral leases below the statutory minimum rates established for those minerals whenever in his judgment it is necessary to do so in order to promote development, or whenever in his judgment the leases cannot be successfully operated under the terms provided therein. Reduction of Production Royalties Below Statutory Minimum Rates, 87 I.D. 69 (Dec. 11, 1979).

Royalty right

An interest in oil, gas or minerals paid, received, or realized as "royalty" under a lease but not including bonuses or rentals. Schlittler v. Smith, 128 Tex. 628, 101 S.W.2d 543 (1937).

Royalty surcharge

An additional royalty imposed in Saskatchewan on production from crown lands which (as supplemented by a mineral income tax on production from freehold lands) had the effect of moving into provincial revenues from and after a certain date the entire proceeds of any increase in value at the wellhead of crude oil produced in the province. The Saskatchewan royalty surcharge and mineral income tax were invalidated in Canadian Indus. Gas & Oil Ltd. v. Government of Saskatchewan, [1978] 2 S.C.R. 545, 80 D.L.R.3d 449, [1977] 6 W.W.R. 607 (Can. S. Ct. 1977), *application to vary dism'd,* [1979] 1 S.C.R. 37, 91 D.L.R.3d 555 (1978). The court concluded that the tax was, in reality, an export tax imposed upon the purchaser and was *ultra vires,* as a province has no legislative authority to fix prices in respect of the sale of goods in the export market. See Milen and Savino, "Nationalization or Regulation? Constitutional Aspects of the Control of the Saskatchewan Oil Industry," 39 *Sask. L. Rev.* 23 (1974–75); Lowery, "The Oil and Gas Conservation, Stabilization and Development Act, 1973," 13 *Alberta L. Rev.* 100 (1975).

Royalty tax credit

"In order to alleviate to some extent the disallowance of Crown royalties for federal tax purposes, Alberta allows a royalty tax credit. This credit is calculated as 25% of the taxpayer's 'attributed Alberta royalty income' for the year with a maximum credit of $1,000,000 for an individual or a corporation." Katchen and Bowhay, *Federal Oil and Gas Taxation* 75 (3d ed. 1979).

Royalty tax rebate

"Following the sharp increase in the price of oil in 1973, the provinces increased their royalties. The federal government reacted by disallowing all provincial levies as a deduction from income . . . . In order to alleviate the effect of the federal disallowance, Alberta enacted ameliorating legislation . . . .

"Alberta income tax is based on income earned in Alberta as calculated under the federal *Income Tax Act.* The royalty tax rebate is designed to eliminate Alberta tax on the disallowed payments to the crown. The rebate is based on 'attributed Canadian royalty income,' . . . ." Katchen and Bowhay, *Federal Oil and Gas Taxation* 75 (3d ed. 1979).

A similar system exists in Saskatchewan. *Id.* at 76.

Royalty transfer clause

A term used by at least one court to describe that part of a deed of land or minerals, subject to an existing lease, which conveys to the grantee an interest in the royalty under the existing lease. See McElvain v. Texas Co., 273 S.W.2d 676, 4 *O.&G.R.* 293 (Tex. Civ. App. 1954).

See also SUBJECT-TO CLAUSE.

Royalty trust

A term used to describe an arrangement wherein owners of fractional oil and gas royalty or overriding royalty interests deposit royalty deeds with a trustee, conveying legal title to him, in return for participation certificates. The trustee, as owner, files transfer or division orders and receives payment for royalty oil and in turn the trustee makes periodic distribution to the owners of participation certificates. See Royalty Participation Trust v. Comm'r, 20 T.C. 466, 2 *O.&G.R.* 1519 (1953), which held such a trust taxable as a corporation. See also TREATISE § 907.1.

Beginning around 1980, a number of new royalty trusts were established by oil companies for the purpose of avoiding corporate taxation of receipts from royalty interests, overriding royalty interests, and other nonoperating interests held by the companies. The royalty or other nonoperating interests were transferred to a trust which thereafter received the proceeds attributable to the interests and distributed them to holders of units in the trust. Certificates of beneficial interest in each trust were issued to the shareholders of the oil company creating the trust. Distribution of the certificates was a taxable transaction resulting in a taxable dividend to individual stockholders. A portion of the fair market value of the distribution was viewed as a return of capital, applied to reduction of the recipient's tax basis in the shares held, with any excess taxable as capital gain. The creation of the trusts depended upon a favorable ruling by the

Internal Revenue Service or a favorable court decision that, for income tax purposes, the trust would not be treated as an association taxable as a corporation and, further, that the trust would be taxed as a grantor trust. A favorable ruling by the Internal Revenue Service for the Houston Oil Royalty Trust was reported by *The Wall Street Journal,* Jan. 7, 1981, p. 14.

Early enthusiasm over investments in royalty trusts was dampened in the spring of 1984 by the failure of the Houston Oil Royalty Trust to achieve anticipated pay-out. Estimates of reserves were drastically reduced (due in part, perhaps, to the decline in the price of oil), sales of gas did not measure up to expectations (due in part, perhaps, to repudiation or renegotiation of the TAKE-OR-PAY CLAUSE (*q.v.*) of gas purchase contracts), some wells were lost while others did not produce anticipated quantities, and expenses of operation greatly exceeded earlier estimates. *The Wall Street Journal,* April 6, 1984, page 1, col. 6.

See also the following:

"Tax Consequences of Shareholder Royalty Trusts Are Determined," 32 *O. & G. Tax Q.* 444 (1983);

Wilson, "Tax Considerations in Selecting a Mineral Financing Vehicle," *Rocky Mt. Min. L. Inst. on Mineral Financing* 7-1 at 7-90 (1982);

Ahrenholz, "New Forms of Equity Financing," *Rocky Mt. Min. L. Inst. on Mineral Financing* 8-1 *et seq.* (1982);

Mann, "Financing Oil and Gas Operations—Recent Developments," 33 *Sw. Legal Fdn. Oil & Gas Inst.* 407 at 408 (1982) (summarizing the purposes and tax consequences of a royalty trust);

Gelinas, "Mineral Royalty Trust Transactions: The Use of the Grantor Trust to Avoid Corporate Income Tax," 37 *Tax L. Rev.* 225 (1982);

Pickens, "Optimum Reserve Base for Petroleum Companies," 20 *Sw. Legal Fdn. Exploration and Economics of the Petroleum Industry* 267 (1982);

"Mesa Petroleum Plans Second Royalty Trust for Its Shareholders," *The Wall Street Journal,* Oct. 7, 1982, p. 10, col. 2;

Crichton, "Royalty Trusts and Other Exotic Distributions to Shareholders," 40 *N.Y.U. Inst. on Fed. Taxation* 12–1 (1982) (distinguishing among various types of royalty trusts: (a) royalty trusts created on liquidation, (b) spin-off trusts, (c) financing trusts, and (d) acquisition trusts);

Record, "Current Developments in Oil and Gas Law," *Energy Law 1981,* Seminar of the International Bar Association Committee on Energy and Natural Resources 153 at 165 (1981);

"Certificate Holders Treated as Grantors of Trust With Oil and Gas Interests," 30 *O.&G. Tax Q.* 169 (1981);

"Transfer of Overriding Royalties in Oil and Gas Will Not Result in Recapture," 30 *O.&G. Tax Q.* 170 (1981);

Klayman, "Maximizing Tax Benefits on Transfers of Producing Oil and Gas Properties," 32 *Sw. Legal Fdn. Oil & Gas Inst.* 357 at 378 (1981);

Thurow, "Royalty Trusts Seen as Possible Defense for Oil Firms Worried About Takeovers," *Wall Street Journal,* Nov. 24, 1981, p. 4, col. 2;

Dollinger, "Royalty Trusts," 30 *O.&G. Tax Q.* 262 (1981).

See also Acquisition royalty trust; Drilling fund; Financing royalty trust; Gross royalty trust agreement; Income fund; Landowners' royalty pool; Lease acquisition fund; Production fund; Production payment trust; Spin-off royalty trust.

Royalty unitization agreement

An agreement for unitization signed by royalty owners which has the effect of giving the consent of royalty owners to the unitization plan and of providing for apportionment of royalties from production under the unit plan.

R/P ratio

The ratio of proven reserves to annual production. See Permian Basin Area Rate Proceeding, 34 F.P.C. 159 at 183, 23 *O.&G.R.* 103 at 122 (Opinion No. 468, Aug. 5, 1965), *remanded,* Skelly Oil Co. v. Federal Power Comm'n, 375 F.2d 6, 26 *O.&G.R.* 237 (10th Cir. 1967), *aff'd in part and rev'd in part sub nom. In re* Permian Basin Area Rate Cases, 390 U.S. 747, 28 *O.&G.R.* 689 (1968); Southern Louisiana Area Rate Cases v. Federal Power Comm'n, 428 F.2d 407 at 438, 37 *O.&G.R.* 311 at 352 (5th Cir. 1970), *cert. denied,* 400 U.S. 950 (1970).

RRT

Resource rent tax (*q.v.*).

Rule Against Perpetuities

A rule invalidating future interests limited to become possessory at a remote future time. See Treatise § 322 *et seq.* for a discussion of numerous oil and gas transactions that have been subjected to attack for alleged violation of this Rule.

Rule of approximation

A rule dating back to the nineteenth century when it was first used in connection with Homestead Entries, which were initially permitted by the Homestead Act of 1862. Litigation developed regarding attempted entries onto irregular tracts consisting of slightly more than 160 acres and the General Land Office, applying equitable principles, adopted a rule, which came to be known as the Rule of Approximation, to permit the homesteader to retain excessive acreage under certain circumstances. An 1883 statement of the rule was as follows:

"It is an established rule of this office [General Land Office] that where the excess above 160 acres is less than the deficiency would be should a subdivision be excluded from the entry, the excess may be included, and the contrary when the excess is greater than the deficiency."

As applied to federal oil and gas leases,

"the Rule provides that if an offer is filed for more than 2560 acres, and if the elimination of the smallest legal subdivision covered thereby reduces the total acreage to less than 2560 acres, then if the difference between the resulting acreage and 2560 acres (comprising the deficiency) is *more* than the difference between 2560 acres and the total acreage applied for (comprising the excess), a lease will issue on such total acreage even though it exceeds 2560 acres." Vernon, "The Maximum Acreage Requirement of Noncompetitive Federal Oil and Gas Lease Offers on the Public Domain," 3 *Nat. Res. J.* 291 at 295 (1963).

See also *Rocky Mt. Min. L. Fdn. Law of Federal Oil and Gas Leases* § 5.05 (1985) (noting that the Rule was deleted from the Regulations in 1980 with the increase in the maximum lease acreage).

Rule of capture

The legal rule of non-liability for (1) causing oil or gas to migrate across property lines and (2) producing oil or gas that was originally in place under the land of another, so long as the producing well does not trespass. This rule has been phrased as follows:

"The owner of a tract of land acquires title to the oil and gas which he produces from wells drilled thereon, though it may be proved that part of such oil or gas migrated from adjoining lands." Hardwicke, "The Rule of Capture and Its Implications as Applied to Oil and Gas," 13 *Tex. L. Rev.* 391 at 393 (1935).

This rule appears equally applicable in all jurisdictions, whatever the theory adopted as to the nature of the landowner's interest. Under this rule, absent some state regulation of drilling practices, a landowner, however small his tract, or wherever located on the producing structure, may drill as many wells on his land as he pleases and at such locations as meet his fancy, and he is not liable to the adjacent landowners whose lands are drained as a result of such operations. Likewise he may by means of a compression or vacuum pump, increase the production for his well through the result may be to drain his neighbor's property. The remedy of the injured landowner under such circumstances has generally been said to be that of self-help—"go and do likewise." This is true even in the states adopting the ownership in place theory; the courts reason that the "ultimate injury from the net results of drainage, where proper diligence is used, is altogether too conjectural to form the basis for the denial of a right of property in that which is not only plainly as much realty as any other part of the earth's contents, but realty of the highest value to mankind and often worth far more than anything else on or beneath the surface within the proprietor's boundaries." Stephens County v. Mid-Kansas Oil & Gas Co., 113 Tex. 160, at 167, 254 S.W. 290, at 292 (1923).

Where, however, by reason of negligence of one landowner, oil, gas or distillate is wasted by burning or by dissipation into the air or on the surface, an injured neighboring landowner may be entitled under some circumstances to recover damages for the taking of his property. Elliff v. Texon Drilling Co., 146 Tex. 575, 210 S.W.2d 558, 4 A.L.R.2d 191 (1948).

The rule of capture made it economically imperative that each mineral owner drill his land and produce at as rapid a pace as possible, for otherwise his land would be drained of oil and gas by wells on adjacent properties. Furthermore, the implied covenant in oil and gas leases that the lessee would protect the leased premises from drainage required the drilling of offset wells by lessees when wells off the leased premises began to drain the oil or gas. The result was profligate drilling and tremendous physical waste of oil which in many instances was produced even though there was no market available and stored on the surface where it was subject to loss by evaporation, fire and seepage. Frequently this was accompanied by dissipation of natural reservoir energy, production with excessive gas-oil ratios, and flaring of casinghead gas.

Reasoning from the rule of capture, courts in a number of states adopted the NONAPPORTIONMENT (*q.v.*) rule. Carlock v. Krug, 151 Kan. 407, 99 P.2d 858 (1940). The rule of capture has been criticized as "the harsh law of the tooth and claw" and lauded as necessary to the development of oil and gas. To the extent that production practices are regulated by a state administrative agency for the prevention of waste and the protection of correlative rights, the rule of capture is modified and limited. See Shank, "Present Status of the Law of Capture," 6 *Sw. Legal Fdn. Oil & Gas Inst.* 297 (1955); TREATISE §§ 204.4–204.5.

Big Piney Oil & Gas Co. v. Wyoming Oil and Gas Conservation Comm'n, 715 P.2d 557, ____ *O.&G.R.* ____ (Wyo. 1986), concluded that the Commission had power to restrict gas cap production from a lease when such production caused migration of oil from adjoining premises, which oil became nonrecoverable after migration, and when the gas cap producer had produced more gas from the common pool than was estimated to have been under its lease originally.

Able commentators on the United Kingdom law suggest that there is some room for doubt as to whether the rule of capture would be applied by British courts but note that provision for Unit development in clause 26 or the Petroleum (Production) Regulations 1976, Sched. 5, seems to have been framed on the assumption that it would. Daintith and Willoughby, *A Manual of United Kingdom Oil and Gas Law* 460–461 (1977).

Lagoni, "Oil and Gas Deposits Across National Frontiers," 73 *Am. J. Int'l L.* 215 (1979), discusses application of the rule of capture and other legal doctrines to problems created by national (as distinguished from private) boundary lines running across oil and gas deposits.

See also CONTRACT SYSTEM; CORRELATIVE RIGHTS; DRAINAGE; FAIR SHARE OF OIL OR GAS IN PLACE; NEGATIVE RULE OF CAPTURE.

Rule of indivisibility

The term applied by an opinion of the Solicitor of the Department of the Interior to the rule that a lease is not divided by inclusion of less than all of the leased premises in a unit formed for pooling or unitization. "New OCS Unitization Rules—Authority of the Secretary to Segregate Partially Unitized Offshore Leases," 87 I.D. 615 (Dec. 16, 1980). In some instances a lease may be viewed as divisible when less than all of the premises are included in a unit established by a voluntary or compulsory unit. See PUGH CLAUSE. See also TREATISE §§ 669.14, 670.4, 953.

Rule of May 29th

See VOLUNTARY SUBDIVISION.

Rule 10

A statewide rule of the Texas Railroad Commission regulating downhole commingling of oil or gas from separate strata penetrated by a single well. See Douglass & Whitworth, "Practice Before the Oil and Gas Division of the Railroad Commission of Texas," 13 *St. Mary's L.J.* 719 at 733 (1982); 16 Tex. Adm. Code § 3.10.

Rule 14

A rule of the Texas Railroad Commission requiring that a well that has become inactive be plugged or brought into compliance in some other way within a specified period of time. 16 Tex. Admin. Code § 3.14.

Rule 37

The state-wide well spacing rule of the Texas Railroad Commission, generally applicable throughout the state. 16 Tex. Adm. Code § 3.37.

The first spacing rule of general application in Texas was adopted in 1919, and provided for two-acre spacing. The distances have been changed from time to time, the most recent change having occurred in 1962, when the rule was amended to provide for 1200 feet between wells and 467 feet from property lines, which distances will result in 40 acre, direct offsetting, spacing patterns. The text of the present rule may be found in 16 *O.&G.R.* 1307 (1962). The history of the rule is given in Hardwicke, "Oil Well Spacing Regulations and Protection of Property Rights in Texas," 31 *Tex. L. Rev.* 99 (1952).

Rule 37 itself provides for two exceptions: (1) to prevent the confiscation of property, and (2) to prevent waste.

Moreover, the Commission has power to modify the spacing rule to meet special field conditions, and in such case will promulgate a special rule for the field.

Under Rule 37 no well can be legally drilled without a well permit, which cannot be granted unless the well site meets the minimum distance requirements, *unless* the smaller tract is entitled to an exception.

The exception to prevent confiscation of property may be granted to any tract, of whatever size, that had an independent existence before the discovery of oil in the vicinity. Such a tract is entitled to one well as a matter of right. However, tracts which have been subdivided in contemplation of oil production are not within the exception and are not each entitled to a well of right.

Texaco, Inc. v. Railroad Comm'n of Texas, 716 S.W.2d 138, ___ *O.&G.R.* ___ (Tex. App., Austin, 1986, error ref'd n.r.e.), concluded that a mineral lessee (as well as a landowner) has a property interest entitled to protection against confiscation, the voluntary subdivision rule has no application to a standard sized tract, and hence the Commission properly granted an exception permit to protect a lessee of a standard sized tract against confiscation.

See also CENTURY CASE, RULE OF; EIGHT-TIMES AREA RULE; SPACING UNIT; STRAIGHT HOLE CLAUSE; VOLUNTARY SUBDIVISION; WELL SPACING.

The second exception, to prevent waste, is narrowly construed. To obtain a well under it, the applicant must show that, without a well, oil will be lost and that this is a condition peculiar to applicant's land and not prevalent throughout the field.

A great many cases have been reported on Rule 37 and the literature is voluminous. The leading cases are: Gulf Land Co. v. Atlantic Ref. Co., 134 Tex. 59, 131 S.W.2d 73 (1939); Brown v. Humble Oil & Ref. Co., 126 Tex. 296, 83 S.W.2d 935 (1935); Brown v. Hitchcock, 235 S.W.2d 478 (Tex. Civ. App. 1951 error ref'd). See also Hardwicke, *op. cit. supra;* Sullivan (ed.), *Conservation of Oil and Gas, A Legal History,* 1948–1958, 236 (1960); Murphy (ed.), *Conservation of Oil & Gas, A Legal History,* 1938–1948, 490 (1949); Hyder, "Exceptions to the Spacing Rule in Texas," 27 *Tex. L. Rev.* 481 (1949); Meyers " 'Common Ownership and Control' in Spacing Cases," 31 *Tex. L. Rev.* 19 (1952). A brief summary of the operation of Rule 37, citing many of the cases, is given in Williams, Maxwell and Meyers, *Cases on Oil and Gas* 725–730 (4th ed. 1979).

In Railroad Comm'n v. Humble Oil & Refining Co., 424 S.W.2d 474, 28 *O.&G.R.* 52 (Tex. Civ. App. 1968, error ref'd n.r.e.), after tracing the history of Rule 37 and of its construction, the court held that the Railroad Commission erroneously granted a well permit as an exception to a tract voluntarily subdivided in 1931 subsequent to the execution of a lease on the parent tract which had caused Rule 37 to become operative.

For discussions of the history and politics of Rule 37, see the following:

Prindle, *Petroleum Politics and the Texas Railroad Commission* 47 *et seq.* (1981);

Douglass & Whitworth, "Practice Before the Oil and Gas Division of the Railroad Commission of Texas," 13 *St. Mary's L. J.* 719 (1982).

Rule 54

A rule adopted by the Texas Railroad Commission in 1954 requiring that the Commission be notified of any intentional deviation of a well and requiring a directional survey to be filed for any purposefully deviated well. See Prindle, *Petroleum Politics and the Texas Railroad Commission* 86 (1981); 16 Tex. Admin. Code § 3.11.

Rule 69

A statewide rule of the Texas Railroad Commission designed to restrict the sale of gas from state lands in the interstate market. The Rule and problems of its constitutionality are discussed in Douglass & Whitworth, "Practice Before the Oil and Gas Division of the Railroad Commission of Texas," 13 *St. Mary's L.J.* 719 at 752 *et seq.* (1982); Anson & Schenkkan, "Federalism, the Dormant Commerce Clause, and State-Owned Resources," 59 *Texas L. Rev.* 71 at 93 (1980).

See also PRODUCING STATE PREFERENCE STATUTE

Rule 146

A rule adopted by the Securities and Exchange Commission in 1975 (17 C.F.R. § 230.146 (1975)) providing some specific guidelines for the PRIVATE OFFERING EXEMPTION (*q.v.*). This Rulc was rescinded in 1982 and replaced by REGULATION D (*q.v.*). See TREATISE § 441.4.

Rulison project

An experiment for commercial gas stimulation by an underground nuclear explosion designed to create a chimney and a fracture system that surrounds and is connected to the chimney, thus stimulating the flow of gas through "tight" reservoirs characterized by low permeability. See Rubin, Schwartz, and Montan, *An Analysis of Gas Stimulation Using Nuclear Explosives* (May 15, 1972).

Run

(1) A transfer of crude oil from the stock tanks, where it is stored on the leased premises after production, to a pipe line. Long v. Magnolia Petroleum Co., 166 Neb. 410, 89 N.W.2d 245, 9 *O.&G.R.* 41 (1958).

(2) Oil or gas, measured at standard conditions, moved off the lease or unit for sale. IOCC, *A Suggested Form of General Rules and Regulations for the Conservation of Oil and Gas* (1960), Rule III.

Run sheet

A list of all instruments examined in the preparation of a TITLE OPINION (*q.v.*). See Herd, "Title Opinions for Oil and Gas Purposes—Structure and Information Needed by a Client," 33 *Sw. Legal Fdn. Oil & Gas Inst.* 285 at 290 (1982).

Run statement

An instrument supplied by the purchaser of oil or gas indicating to each interest owner the amount of oil or gas taken by the purchaser at any particular time, together with the division of payment among the various owners of interests, less severance or production taxes.

Run ticket

An instrument evidencing the amount of oil run from lease tanks into gathering lines on the basis of which payment for the oil is made. The run ticket is prepared by the gauger and records the amount of oil run from a tank, its gravity, temperature, impurities (BS & W), *etc.*

. . S . .

Sabbatino amendment

An amendment to the 1961 Foreign Assistance Act in 1964, 22 U.S.C. § 2370(e) (2), which opens access to the courts of the United States despite the ACT OF STATE DOCTRINE (*q.v.*) in two factual contexts involving a foreign sovereign's taking where (a) property appropriated without just compensation is sold by the expropriating nation to a third party who attempts to market the identifiable property in the United States and the original owner discovers the property and brings suit to replevy it, or (b) identifiable, traceable proceeds from the sale of allegedly expropriated property are located in the United States. See Comment, "American Oil Investors' Access to Domestic Courts in Foreign Nationalization Disputes," 123 *U. Pa. L. Rev.* 610 at 617 (1975).

Sadlerochit oil

Oil produced from the Sadlerochit reservoir at Prudhoe Bay, Alaska. The CRUDE OIL WINDFALL PROFIT TAX ACT OF 1980 (*q.v.*) exempts from tax all oil produced from wells in Alaska north of the Arctic Circle, other than oil from the Sadlerochit reservoir.

SAE number

A classification of lubricating oils, based on viscosity. Light oils have a low number and thick, viscous oils have a high number.

Safety net

(1) An agreement among oil companies to supply each other in the event of cut-backs, shut-ins or nationalization by the Libyan Government. See LIBYAN PRODUCERS AGREEMENT.

(2) A proposal made by Secretary of State Kissinger to establish a floor price for oil as a means of protecting and encouraging investments in alternative energy sources. See King, "Cartel Pricing in the International Energy Market: OPEC in Perspective," 54 *Or. L. Rev.* 643 at p. 658 (1975).

(3) An international oil lending program to be operated by the ORGANIZATION FOR ECONOMIC COOPERATION AND DEVELOPMENT OECD (*q.v.*), money for which would come from the industrialized nations and used to alleviate balance of payment problems and provide the

credits needed to purchase additional imports. Campbell and Mytelka, "Petrodollar Flows, Foreign Aid and International Stratification," 9 *J. of World Trade Law* 597 at 617 (1975).

Sagebrush rebellion

The name given the movement to divest federal ownership over much of the public lands, or at least to increase substantially state control over public lands. See Wilkinson, "The Field of Public Land Law: Some Connecting Threads and Future Directions," 1 *Pub. Land L. Rev.* 1 at 7 (1980).

Sale

See FIRST SALE; OFF-SYSTEM SALE.

Sale for cash with retained back-in

A sale of a partly developed property in which the seller retains a fractional working interest that will back-in after complete payout of the purchaser's investment in the property, including a return thereon. See Mann, "Financing Oil and Gas Operations—Recent Developments," 33 *Sw. Legal Fdn. Oil & Gas Inst.* 407 at 426 (1982).

See also BACK-IN RIGHT.

Sale of natural gas in place

See GAS LEASE AGREEMENT; GAS LEASE-SALES AGREEMENT (GLA); RAYNE FIELD CASE.

Sale of oil at arm's length

A term given a very restricted definition for purposes of the United Kingdom PETROLEUM REVENUE TAX (*q.v.*) as meaning a sale where:

(i) the contract price is the sole consideration for the sale, and

(ii) the terms of the sale are not affected by any commercial relationship (other than that created by the contract itself) between the buyer and the seller or persons connected with the buyer or the seller, and

(iii) neither the seller nor a connected person has any interest, direct or indirect, in the subsequent resale or disposal of the oil or any product derived therefrom.

See Daintith and Willoughby, *A Manual of United Kingdom Oil and Gas Law* 113 (1977).

Sale or lease

In federal income tax law, the concept which determines taxability of the transfer under the capital gains provisions of the Internal Revenue Code. If the transaction is a sale, the capital gains provisions will ordinarily apply; if it is a lease, income realized therefor will be ordinary income subject to depletion. See Burke and Bowhay, *Income Taxation of Natural Resources,* Chapters 3, 4 and 5 (1981); Hoffman, "Determination of Whether an Instrument Is a Lease or an Absolute Conveyance of Oil and Gas," 25 *Texas L. Rev.* 157 (1946); TREATISE §§ 205–205.6.

Sales realization method

A method of allocating joint exploration and production costs between gas and liquids in proportion to the amounts realized from the sales thereof. See Joseph, "Background and Analysis of Trial Examiner's Decision in Phillips Case," 11 *Sw. Legal Fdn. Oil & Gas Inst.* 1 at 24 (1960).

For other methods of allocating costs, see ACCOUNTING METHODS.

Salt dome

A mound or plug of salt buried in the subsurface. Salt domes are of two types: piercement type and non-piercement type. The former is a cylindrical plug which intrudes into formations above it, causing faulting. The latter is produced by local thickening of salt beds and gently raises the higher formations to form an anticline, without intrusion or faulting. Considerable amounts of oil are found around salt domes, especially in Louisiana where they are prevalent. Oil may be produced from the caprock usually found on top of a piercement type dome, from fault traps along the sides of the dome, and from various horizons in the anticline lying over the dome.

See also GEOLOGICAL STRUCTURE.

Salt water disposal

The disposition of salt water produced with the oil from a reservoir. The salt water disposal problem can be very serious. For example, in 1942 the East Texas Oil Field was producing about 400,000 barrels of oil per day and a little over the same quantity of salt water. The salt water cannot be disposed of on the surface because of pollution. It is therefore pumped back into the subsurface. In the case of the East Texas Field, the water was returned to the reservoir, below the oil-water contact line, thus maintaining reservoir pressure and increasing the ultimate recovery from the field. See Hardwicke, "Texas," in Murphy (ed.) *Conservation of Oil and Gas 1938–1948* 474–478 (1949); Gulf Refining Co. v. Board of Supervisors of Jasper County, 220 Miss. 225, 70 So.2d 517, 3 *O.&G.R.* 525 (1954).

Salt water disposal company

A company organized for the purpose of disposing of salt water produced with oil.

Salt water disposal district

The area included within a cooperative agreement among producers for the disposition of salt water produced with oil, *e.g.*, by reinjection.

Salt water disposal well

A well that returns salt water produced with the oil to the formation below the oil-water contact line or to some other formation, so as to prevent surface pollution. See SALT WATER DISPOSAL.

Leger v. Petroleum Engineers, Inc., 499 So.2d 953, ____ *O.&G.R.* ____ (La. App. 1986), held that a 1941 lease impliedly granted to the lessee the right to convert a dry hole into a salt water disposal well where the method did not damage the surface or sub-surface of the lessors' property. The conclusion was based on the "reasonable necessity" for the method of salt water disposal employed by the defendant.

Thompson v. Thompson, 391 N.W.2d 608, ____ *O.&G.R.* ____ (N.D. 1986), held that an instrument reserving oil and gas was ambiguous as to whether an existing salt water disposal well was included in the reservation; construing the instrument against the drafting party who caused the uncertainty to exist, the court held that the disposal well was included in the reservation.

Salt water shut-in allowable

A special allowable granted to operators who shut in wells producing excessive amounts of salt water. See "Transferred Allowables and Substitute Royalties," 5 *O.&G. Tax Q.* 59 at 61 (1956).

See also ALLOWABLE; TRANSFERRED ALLOWABLE.

Same-party top lease

See TOP LEASE.

Sample log

A record kept in connection with drilling a well, especially in CABLE TOOL DRILLING (*q.v.*). Samples of cuttings from the hole are saved and the depth of each recorded. From these data, a sample log is prepared showing the characteristics of the rock strata penetrated by the bit.

Samples, core

Cylindrical sections of rock penetrated by the bit and removed from the well for study. The more common word is CORE (*q.v.*). See CORING.

Sanctity of contract legislation

Proposed legislation designed to immunize new gas producer contracts, once approved by a final order of the Federal Power Commission, from subsequent change by the Commission. The Commission, in passing on the contracts, would be prohibited from using the cost of service rate base method and instead would look to supply and demand factors. For details of the legislation see Foster Associates, Inc., *An Analysis of the Regulatory Aspects of Natural Gas Supply* at page V–25 et seq. (Environmental Protection Agency, Publication No. APTD–1459) (1973). The Federal Power Commission supported such legislation "in the firm belief that Congressional action in this field will establish a reasonable level of prices consistent with adequate service to the consumer by encouraging development of required supplies and by avoiding uncertainty factors in producer pricing, thereby attracting capital at risk at a lower return than would otherwise prevail." F.P.C. Order No. 455, 48 F.P.C. 218 at 223 (Aug. 3, 1972).

Sand

The shorthand name for sandstone, one of the more prolific producers of oil and gas among the sedimentary rocks. In loose usage some sedimentary rocks other than sandstones are also referred to as "sands."

Sandfracing

An operation designed to loosen or break up tight formations which contain oil or gas, thus causing such formations to have more permeability and greater production.

"This operation involved the injection of a mixture or blend of crude oil and sand into the producing formation under high pressure by means of pressure pumps, followed by injections of rubberized nylon balls to seal off the fractured formation. The oil-sand mixture entered the well through a frack head which is secured to the top of the blow-out preventer at the well head. The frack head comprises a cylinder with two-inch nipples screwed into its sides and valves attached to the outside of the nipples. After the oil and sand are mixed in a blender, it passes through flow lines to pressure pumps from which it is conveyed under high pressure through other flow lines attached to the valves on the nipples. The mixture first passes through the valves, then through the nipples into the cylinders, thence into the well casing and to the bottom of the well hole where it is pressurized through perforations in the casing into the producing formation." Tyler v. Dowell, Inc., 274 F.2d 890, 12 *O.&G.R.* 1034 (10th Cir. 1960), *cert. denied,* 363 U.S. 812 (1960).

The question whether sandfracing may give rise to liability to another landowner is discussed in Keeton & Jones, "Tort Liability and the Oil and Gas Industry II", 39 *Tex. L. Rev.* 253 at 267 (1961), and Note, 39 *Tex. L. Rev.* 356 (1961). See also Gregg v. Delhi-Taylor Oil Corp., 162 Tex. 26, 344 S.W.2d 411, 14 *O.&G.R.* 106 (1961).

See also ACID FRACTURING; FLOW BACK PROCEDURES; FRACTURING; HYDRAULIC FRACTURING; PETROFRACTURING.

Sand thickness

In ordinary usage the distance between the top and bottom of the oil and gas producing zone of a rock stratum. Thus one speaks of having fifty feet of sand, meaning a paying horizon fifty feet thick. The term is often used although the stratum is not technically sandstone.

Saturated hydrocarbon pore space

The ratio between the volume of hydrocarbons and the volume of pore space in a reservoir. If hydrocarbons occupy 50% of the available pore space, the saturated hydrocarbon pore space is 50%.

Saturation

(1) The extent to which the pore space present in a formation is occupied by hydrocarbons or by connate water.

(2) The extent to which gas is dissolved in oil found in an underground formation.

Saturation factor

The decimal fraction of the pore space of reservoir rock occupied by oil.

Saturation pressure

The synonym for bubble point pressure where gas begins to be released from solution in oil.

Savings clause

A lease clause designed to enable a lessee to keep a lease alive under certain circumstances without the production otherwise required. Common savings clauses are the CONTINUOUS DRILLING OPERATIONS CLAUSE (*q.v.*); DRILLING OPERATIONS CLAUSE (*q.v.*); FORCE MAJEURE CLAUSE (*q.v.*); and SHUT-IN GAS WELL CLAUSE (*q.v.*).

Scattered gamma ray log

See GAMMA RAY-GAMMA RAY LOGGING

scf

Standard cubic feet of gas as determined by the pressure and temperature bases adopted in a particular state. In several states, *e.g.*, Arkansas, Oklahoma and Texas, scf of gas is determined on a pressure base of 14.65 psia and a temperature of 60 degree F. In some others, *e.g.*, Colorado, Louisiana and Mississippi, the pressure base is 15.025 psia and the temperature base is 60 degree F. See Weaver and Anderson, "Oil Recovery From Gas-Cap Reservoirs," *Bureau of Mines Monograph* 13 (1966) at page 3.

Schedule allowable

The allowable assigned a well or pool by a regulatory agency on its proration schedule. See Zimmermann, *Conservation in the Production of Petroleum* 218 (1957).

See also ACTUAL CALENDAR DAY ALLOWABLE; ALLOWABLE.

Scheduled allowable days

The number of days of production necessary to obtain the desired state-wide production for a month; the number of days in a month during which production is permitted by an order of a regulatory commission. See Dutton, "Proration in Texas: Conservation or Confiscation?," 11 *Sw. L. J.* 186, 190 (1957).

Syn.: SCHEDULED PRODUCING DAYS.

Scheduled producing days

Syn.: SCHEDULED ALLOWABLE DAYS (*q.v.*).

Schlumberger

The trade name of a pioneer electrical well surveying company. In many areas, it is common to speak of an electrical well log as a Schlumberger, even though the log was made by another company. The pronunciation is Slum-bur-jay, or Slum-bur-zhay.

See also WELL LOG.

Scintillation counter

A device used in RADIOACTIVITY WELL LOGGING (*q.v.*).

Scout

A person employed by an operator to gather information about the activities of competing operators. He seeks knowledge of leasing, geophysical and geological surveys, drilling, well reports, etc. In some cases, such information is freely exchanged among operators. In others, secrecy is sought, and the scout must learn what he can without any aid from the rival operator.

The legends concerning oil scouts are many. One concerns a scout who lay for forty-eight hours in cold mud under the floorboards of a competitor's well-drilling rig. What he saw and overheard netted him $50,000 when he was cut in on a land deal. "And even today, when an enemy scout is discovered, he is 'accidentally' pushed into a mud hole, or driving along a lonely two-rut forest road, finds that a large tree has mysteriously fallen, blocking his way back to the main highway." *The New York Times,* May 9, 1959, p. 25.

Scouting

(1) (Noun) The activities of a SCOUT (*q.v.*).

(2) (Verb) The seeking of information about the activities of competing operators. The word may be used generally, as: "He is scouting for the Humble." Or it may be used particularly, as: "He is scouting Gulf's Number 1 Jones."

Scout ticket

A written summary of the events occurring during well drilling operations, usually including data such as the type of rock formations penetrated and their oil or gas producing potential. Rev. Rul. 82-9.

Scrubber oil

Oil accumulated in the operation of casinghead natural gasoline plants. Sale of such oil is regulated in Texas under Rule 56 of the Statewide Rules of the Texas Railroad Commission.

Scrubbing plant

A plant for the purifying, scrubbing or otherwise treating of gas for the extraction or removal therefrom of hydrogen sulphide or other deleterious substance.

S-curve

See PRODUCTION OR DECLINE CURVE.

SDR

SPECIAL DRAWING RIGHTS (*q.v.*).

Seaboard interests

A term used to describe representatives of East Coast consumers and distributors appearing in Federal Power Commission proceedings. See Federal Power Comm'n v. Sunray DX Oil Co., 391 U.S. 9 at 19, 29 *O.&G.R.* 305 at 310 (1968).

Seaboard method

A method of classifying costs for purposes of cost allocation and rate design. The name comes from Atlantic Seaboard Corp., 11 F.P.C. 43 (1952), wherein the Commission determined that 50 percent of a pipeline's fixed transmission costs were to be recovered through the demand component of the pipeline's two-part "demand-commodity" rate, and the remaining 50 percent of the fixed costs and all of the variable costs were to be recovered through the commodity charge. See Columbia Gas Transmission Corp. v. Federal Energy Regulatory Comm'n, 628 F.2d 578 (D.C. Cir. 1979), vacating a Commission order employing the UNITED METHOD (*q.v.*) rather than the Seaboard method in allocating costs and designing pipeline rates. See Pierce, "An Overview of Regulation," in Pierce, *Natural Gas Regulation Handbook* 30 at 86 (1980).

See also COMMODITY CHARGE; DEMAND CHARGE.

Seal off

Introduction of cement or other sealing compound in the annular space between the well casing and the well bore to prevent the introduction of liquids (*e.g.*, salt water) from one formation penetrated by the well into another formation (*e.g.*, a formation containing potable water or a formation containing recoverable hydrocarbons).

Seals

Safety devices placed on tanks to protect a pipeline company from losses by preventing oil that was being pumped from one tank from "backing into" the line of another tank. Each time a gauger delivers oil from a tank into the pipeline, he must break the old seal on the tank, and when the delivery is over, he seals the tank with a new seal. See Bankers Life Insurance Co. of Nebraska v. Scurlock Oil Co., 447 F.2d 997 at 1001, 40 *O.&G.R.* 513 at 520 (5th Cir. 1971).

Seasonal gas

Gas which is to be delivered under the terms of a GAS PURCHASE CONTRACT (*q.v.*) at specified seasons of the year.

SEC

The Securities and Exchange Commission.

See TREATISE § 441.

Secondary casinghead gas

See CASINGHEAD GAS.

Secondary gas cap

A GAS CAP (*q.v.*) not present at the time of discovery of an oil producing zone but which is caused by the migration of gas freed from solution in the oil to the vacated space at the top of the structure to form a gas cap. See Interstate Oil Compact Commission, *Oil for Today and for Tomorrow* 21 (1953).

Secondary primary term

(1) A term used to describe the period subsequent to the expiration of the primary term during which a lease may be preserved without production by reason of the provisions of a drilling operations clause or a continuous drilling operations clause. Gulf Oil Corp. v. Reid, 161 Tex. 51, 337 S.W.2d 267, 12 *O.&G.R.* 1159 at 1183 (1960) (dissenting opinion). Presumably the term may also be used to describe the period subsequent to the expiration of the primary term during which the lease may be preserved without production by reason of the provisions of a dry hole clause.

(2) This term is also used to describe the period of extension of a lease beyond its primary term under the provisions of a PUGH CLAUSE (*q.v.*) as to lease acreage excluded from a drilling or producing unit which includes a portion only of the leased acreage. See Shown v. Getty Oil Co., 645 S.W.2d 555, 76 *O.&G.R.* 563 (Tex. App., San Antonio, 1982, error ref'd n.r.e.). See also the Pugh clause form quoted in the TREATISE at § 669.14 note 15.1.

See also PRIMARY TERM; SECONDARY TERM.

Secondary production payment

Syn.: DEFERRED PRODUCTION PAYMENT (*q.v.*).

Secondary recovery

Broadly defined, this term includes all methods of oil extraction in which energy sources extrinsic to the reservoir are utilized in the extraction. One of the early methods was the application of vacuum to the well, thus "sucking" more oil from the reservoir. The term is usually defined somewhat more narrowly as a method of recovery of hydrocarbons in which part of the energy employed to move the hydrocarbons through the reservoir is applied from extraneous sources by the injection of liquids or gases into th ereservoir.

Typically a differentiation is made between secondary recovery and pressure maintenance; the former involves an application of fluid injection when a reservoir is approaching or has reached the exhaustion of natural energy, while the latter involves an application of fluid injection early in the productive life of a reservoir when there has been little or no loss of natural reservoir energy. The fluid (water, gas or air) is injected into the formation through an input well and oil is removed from surrounding wells.

Air and gas injections may follow either one of two procedures. In one, the air or gas is used to drive or flush the oil toward the output wells. In the other method the reservoir is repressured and during the pressure build-up period the flow from the output wells must be restricted. Natural gas is used very frequently for repressuring because it is very soluble in oil, thus increasing its volume, decreasing its viscosity, reducing its surface tension, and lightening its specific gravity—all desirable effects resulting in the expenditure of less energy in producing oil. Air, on the other hand, being only slightly soluble in crude oil, has little or no effect in reducing viscosity and surface tension of the oil and may actually oxidize some of the crude petroleum and aggravate corrosive action on equipment.

In the typical water-flood project, there is an initial water-injection period of several months known as the fill-up before additional oil is forced into the producing wells. The end of this period is marked by a pick-up in oil production which is followed by a rapid increase in oil recovery. Combined oil and water production continues thereafter with the oil gradually decreasing and the water increasing until the economical limit of operations is reached.

Osborn v. Texas Oil & Gas Corp., 661 P.2d 71, 76 *O.&G.R.* 101 (Okla. App. 1982), held that "the corporation commission—once it found that a gas well offsetting a water driven secondary recovery unit maintained by gas pressure was 'causing waste and [would] continue to . . . so long as it is produced'—had authority to either shut the well in or permanently limit its production to a nonwasteful level."

Briggs v. Gaddis, 133 Ill.App.3d 704, 88 Ill.D. 737, 479 N.E.2d 350, 87 *O.&G.R.* 10 (1985), concluded that use of an injection well to dispose of salt water was not, under the circumstances of this case, a secondary recovery program.

See Anderson, "Oil Production Methods," Hearings Before a Special Committee Investigating Petroleum Resources Pursuant to S. Res. 36, 79th Cong., 1st Sess. 308 (June, 1945); Williams, "Problems in the Conservation of Gas," 2 *Rocky Mt. Min. L. Inst.* 295 (1956), Armstrong and Peters, "Enhanced Recovery of Oil," 5 *Eastern Min. L. Inst.* 13-1 (1984).

The term "secondary recovery" has been defined by a subcommittee of the American Petroleum Institute as "the oil, gas, or oil and gas recovered by any method (artificial flowing or pumping) that may be employed to produce them through the joint use of two or more well bores. Secondary recovery is generally recognized as being that recovery which may be obtained by the injection of liquids or gases into the reservoir for the purpose of augmenting reservoir energy; usually, but not necessarily, this is done after the primary-recovery phase has passed." American Petroleum Institute, *Secondary Recovery of Oil in the United States* 255 (1942).

On the question of the existence of a duty to engage in secondary or tertiary recovery operations, see Fant, "Legal Issues in Implementing Secondary and Tertiary Operations on Federal Oil and Gas Leases," 19 *Land & Water L. Rev.* 1 (1984).

Much of this definition was quoted and adopted in Sivert v. Continental Oil Co., 497 S.W.2d 482 at 487, 46 *O.&G.R.* 355 at 363 (Tex. Civ. App. 1973, error ref'd n.r.e.).

See also AIR INJECTION; ALCOHOL SLUG PROCESS; AMPHIPATHIC SLUG INJECTION; CIRCLE FLOOD; CONTROLLED GRAVITY DRAINAGE; ENHANCED RECOVERY; ENRICHED GAS INJECTION; FLUID INJECTION; GAS INJECTION; HIGH-ENERGY GAS FRACTURING; HIGH PRESSURE GAS INJECTION; HOT FLUID INJECTION; HYDRAULIC FRACTURING; HYDROCARBON SOLVENT SLUG INJECTION; IMPROVED RECOVERY TECHNIQUES; JETTING; LPG-GAS DRIVE; MISCIBLE DISPLACEMENT METHOD; MISCIBLE-PHASE RECOVERY PROJECT; NON-CONVENTIONAL OIL RECOVERY STIPULATION; OIL WELL HEATING; ORCO PROCESS; PRESSURE FLOODING; PRESSURE MAINTENANCE; PRODUCTION ENHANCEMENT PROCEDURES; REPRESSURING OPERATION; REVERSE SEVEN-SPOT PATTERN; STEAM STIMULATION; STIMULATE; SURFACTANT FLOODING; SWEEP; TERTIARY RECOVERY; THERMAL METHOD OF OIL RECOVERY; WATER FLOODING.

Secondary term

The period subsequent to the expiration of the primary term during which the lease or deed is continued in force by operation of the THEREAFTER CLAUSE (*q.v.*) of the lease or deed.

This phrase, secondary term, is also used by certain lease forms to describe a period of years subsequent to the expiration of the primary term during which a lease may be kept alive without production by means of an increased rental payment. See Section 15 of the lease form prescribed by N.M. Stat., 1953, § 7–11–3, 7 *O.&G.R.* 724 at 730.

This phrase, secondary term, has also been used to describe the period of time that the primary term of a lease has been extended by agreement of the lessor and lessee. Turner v. Reynolds Metal Co., ___ Ark. ___, 721 S.W.2d 626, ___ *O.&G.R.* ___ (1986).

See also PRIMARY TERM; SECONDARY PRIMARY TERM; EXTENDED-TERM ESTATE.

Second term

See PRODUCTION LICENSE.

Second tier oil

The term applied to NEW OIL (*q.v.*), RELEASED OIL (*q.v.*), and STRIPPER WELL OIL (*q.v.*) which by virtue of regulations issued under the Energy Policy and Conservation Act of 1976 (EPCA) could be sold at market price. FIRST TIER OIL (*q.v.*), on the other hand, was subject to a price ceiling. Subsequently, by virtue of the provisions of the Energy Conservation and Production Act of 1976 (ECPA), a ceiling price was imposed on second tier oil and a new category of EXEMPT CRUDE OIL (*q.v.*) was created.

Syn.: UPPER TIER OIL.

Section

An area of one square mile (640 acres). There are 36 sections in a township.

See also GENERAL LAND OFFICE SURVEY; LEGAL SUBDIVISION; LONG SECTION; LOT; REGULAR SUBDIVISION; SHORT SECTION; SPANISH SECTION; SURVEY.

Section 6 lease

An oil and gas lease originally issued by any State and currently maintained in effect pursuant to section 6 of the Outer Continental Shelf Lands Act (43 U.S.C. § 1335). See 43 C.F.R. § 3307 (1978).

Section 8 lease

An oil and gas lease issued by the United States pursuant to section 8 of the Outer Continental Shelf Lands Act (43 U.S.C. § 1337).

For a case dealing with the division between the state and the federal government of the proceeds of a Section 8 lease, see State of Texas v. Secretary of the Interior, 580 F. Supp. 1197, 80 *O.&G.R.* 573 (E.D. Tex. 1984). The court concluded that drainage was not the sole criterion relevant to disposition of revenue.

Securities regulation

Regulation by the federal government or by a state governing the sale or issuance of a security. See TREATISE §§ 441–441.5.

See also BLUE SKY LAW; INDUSTRY DEAL; LIMITED OFFER EXEMPTION; PRIVATE OFFERING EXEMPTION; REGULATION B; REGULATION D; UNIFORM LIMITED OFFERING EXEMPTION.

Security lease

A term employed in Willcutt v. Union Oil Co. of California, 432 So. 2d 1217 (Ala. 1983), 78 *O.&G.R.* 431, to describe a lease obtained from a person without a mineral interest in the affected premises in order to secure a release from any future claims by the lessor for noise or bother of the drilling or interference or spoliation of water and the like.

Sedimentary rock

One of the three basic forms of rock, the other two being igneous and metamorphic. Nearly all oil is produced from some form of sedimentary rock, especially from sandstones, limestones, conglomerates and (occasionally) fractured shales. Sedimentary rock is formed from matter deposited by streams, lakes, seas or other bodies of water.

See also DISCONFORMITY; FORMATION; LENS; UNCONFORMITY.

Sediment oil

Tank bottoms and any other accumulation of liquid hydrocarbons on an oil and gas lease, which hydrocarbons are not merchantable through normal channels. New Mexico Oil Conservation Comm'n, Case No. 1522, Order No. R–1299, Jan. 1, 1959.

SEG

The SOCIETY OF EXPLORATION GEOPHYSICISTS (*q.v.*).

Segregated lands

A term used in Rocky Mountain unit operating and joint operating agreements to refer to lands which by assignment or surrender have ceased to be subject to the unit operating agreement but remain subject to the unit agreement. See Rocky Mountain Unit Operating Agreement Form 1 (Undivided Interest) May, 1954, Article 27, TREATISE § 920.3; Rocky Mountain Joint Operating Agreement Form 3, November, 1959, Article 15, TREATISE § 920.5.

Seismic farm-out

An agreement under which "the farmee is to shoot a designated number of miles of seismic lines and provide copies of the geophysical data to the farmor. A seismic deal is usually made in rank wildcat areas. The farmor may require geophysical exploration in conjunction with the drilling of an exploratory well to earn an assignment or as consideration for granting an option to take a farm-out if the seismic data is encouraging. The advantage to the farmor is 'free' geophysical information; the advantage to the farmee or optionee is the opportunity to increase its acreage position if the area appears promising." Himebaugh, "An Overview of Oil and Gas Contracts in the Williston Basin," 59 *No. Dak. L. Rev.* 7 at 31 (1983).

See also FARM-OUT.

Seismic shot hole

A "hole drilled for a seismic shot. Usually is a *slim* hole, although has also been termed *core* hole." Report of the Committee on Regulatory Practices for Stratigraphic Test Holes, 17 *Interstate Oil Compact Bull.* 43 (Dec. 1958).

See also SLIM HOLE; STRATIGRAPHIC TEST HOLE; STRUCTURE TEST HOLE.

Seismic survey

See GEOPHYSICAL SURVEY.

Seismogram

The records produced by a seismographic survey.

See also MID-CONTINENT GRAVITY HIGH.

Seismograph

A device which records the vibrations of the earth. As used in the oil industry, it records the shock waves set off by a series of explosions. By obtaining the time interval between the explosion and the reflected and refracted shock wave, geophysicists can approximate the underground structure, since the deeper the strata the longer the time interval. From these data the geophysicists prepare a contour map indicating the presence of structural traps (if any) in the subsurface. See GEOPHYSICAL EXPLORATION.

Seismographic survey

A survey of an area (large or small) by means of a SEISMOGRAPH (*q.v.*).

The process is fully described in Phillips Petroleum Co. v. Cowden, 241 F.2d 586, 7 *O.&G.R.* 1291, 67 A.L.R.2d 433 (5th Cir. 1957).

See also GEOPHYSICAL SURVEY; SHOOTING BY SEISMOGRAPH.

Seismograph permit payments

Amounts received by a landowner for the privilege of conducting exploration on his land by seismograph. See *Miller's Oil and Gas Federal Income Taxation* § 19–19 (1980 Edition).

Seismometer

A device for receiving and recording impulses set up by an explosion and reflected by the earth in the course of a seismographic survey. Also called a geophone.

Selection bonus

The payment required by the terms of an ACREAGE SELECTION CLAUSE (*q.v.*) to keep a lease alive. Also a payment on an acreage basis agreed to be paid under the terms of an option to acquire a lease for such portion of the leasehold which the assignee shallelect to acquire. See Molero v. California Co., 145 So.2d 602, 17 *O.&G.R.* 720 (La. App. 1962).

See also BONUS.

Selection contract

An agreement authorizing a purchaser to select acreage as to which a lease is to be executed or assigned by the seller. See Stekoll Petroleum Co. v. Hamilton, 152 Tex. 182, 255 S.W.2d 187, 2 *O.&G.R.* 102 (1953). See also TREATISE §§ 696–696.1.

Selection date

The date by which a SELECTION BONUS (*q.v.*) must be paid by terms of an ACREAGE SELECTION CLAUSE (*q.v.*) in order to keep a lease in effect.

Selection lease

A lease containing an ACREAGE SELECTION CLAUSE (*q.v.*).

Self-help arrangement

An arrangement by a natural gas consumer to insure the continuing availability of natural gas supplies despite curtailment programs, or to insure a supply at moderate prices. This involvement occurs either through purchase at the well-head by the end user from a producer, or production of natural gas by the end user itself from wells it owns and develops. Difficult problems of determining the value of gas for royalty purposes may arise from such arrangements. See Keller, "Drafting the Modern Oil and Gas Lease," 2 *Eastern Min. L. Inst.* 15–6 (1981).

Seller's option gas

Gas which is to be delivered at seller's option.

Semi-proven territory

An area in which producing wells have been completed (usually at scattered points) but in which the confines of the reservoir have not been determined. Highly faulted and salt dome areas are frequently so classified because one well cannot prove a substantial area.

See also PROVEN TERRITORY.

Semi-submersible rig

A rig with a platform deck supported by columns which are connected to large underwater displacement hulls or large vertical caissons or some combination of the two. The columns, displacement hulls, or caissons are flooded on site. Kash, *et al.*, *Energy Under the Oceans* 39 (1973).

Matter of the Complaint of Sedco, Inc., 543 F. Supp. 561 (S.D. Tex. 1982), concluded that a semi-submersible rig which was constructed to be and was, in fact, utilized as an oceangoing watercraft was a "vessel" for purposes of invoking the Limitation of Liability Act, 46 U.S.C. §§ 183–189.

Separate estate doctrine

A term used to describe the TWO-GRANT THEORY (*q.v.*). See Pan American Petroleum Corp. v. Texas Pacific Coal & Oil Co., 340 S.W.2d 548, 14 *O.&G.R.* 277 (Tex. Civ. App. 1960, error ref'd n.r.e.).

Separate tract or parcel

An area of land separated geographically from another area or other areas in which the taxpayer may have an interest. For federal income tax purposes, separate interests exist in each of two or more areas of land which are separated geographically even if of the same type and acquired simultaneously. Likewise, the tracts or parcels are "separate" if acquired at different times or from different grantors even if not separated geographically. Burke and Bowhay, *Income Taxation of Natural Resources* ¶ 16.04 (1980).

See also PROPERTY UNIT, FOR TAX PURPOSES.

Separation

A process whereby liquid hydrocarbons are separated from gas. The term is sometimes used to describe a relatively simple process distinguished from FRACTIONATION (*q.v.*). See Vernon v. Union Oil Co., 270 F.2d 441, 11 *O.&G.R.* 688 (5th Cir. 1959), *rehearing denied,* 273 F.2d 178, 11 *O.&G.R.* 697 (5th Cir. 1960).

Separator

A tall, cylindrical tank in which gas in solution is separated from the oil. The oil is directed from the CHRISTMAS TREE (*q.v.*) into flow lines leading to the separator. There, the pressure is reduced and most of the gas frees itself from the oil. The gas is then often piped to a gasoline plant [either a COMPRESSION PLANT (*q.v.*) or an ABSORPTION PLANT (*q.v.*)] where the liquid hydrocarbons are removed to form CASINGHEAD GASOLINE (*q.v.*). The gas then may be flared or, as is now more common, sold to a gas pipeline company for domestic and industrial use.

See also COMBINATION PLANT; PROCESSING PLANT.

Serial register

A book maintained by the District Land Offices of the Bureau of Land Management which has a separate page for each mineral application, land exchange, special use permit, etc., for federal land arranged in the order they were filed. Comptroller General's Report to the Congress, *Actions Needed to Increase Federal Onshore Oil and Gas Exploration and Development* 70 (1981); *Rocky Mt. Min. L. Fdn. Landman's Legal Handbook* 114 (3d ed. 1977).

See also FEDERAL LEASE.

Serious consideration

In Louisiana it was established that not only was paying production required to hold a lease but it was also necessary that there be enough production to yield royalties sufficient to constitute "serious consideration" to the lessor for maintenance of the lease. Determinations of what constituted serious consideration were made by comparison of the amounts being received in royalties with the amount of the bonus, delay rentals, or shut-in royalties. Article 125 of the Louisiana Mineral Code (R.S. 31:125) eliminated the requirement that royalties paid the lessor be serious consideration for the continuation of the lease. However the amount of royalties being paid continues as a factor for determining whether the lessee is acting as a reasonable, prudent operator in continuing to produce the property or is acting out of improper motives. See the discussion of the matter in the Comments to Articles 124 and 125 of the Mineral Code [R.S. 31:124, 125 (1975) (1980 Supp.)].

Service agreement

(1) The regulations of the FEDERAL POWER COMMISSION (*q.v.*) and of its successor, the Federal Energy Regulatory Commission, defined the term as "an unexecuted form of agreement for service under a natural-gas company's tariff." 18 C.F.R. § 154.13 (1980).

(2) An agreement between an international oil company and a host country under which the oil company is paid a flat fee for its services. See Blinn, Duval, Le Leuch, and Pertuzio, *International Petroleum Exploration & Exploitation Agreements* 97 (1986).

See also PURE SERVICE AGREEMENT; SERVICE CONTRACT.

Service contract

(1) A "contract between an owner and an individual or company covering routine type of work on a lease, such as building roads, clearing locations, coring, acidization, perforating, drill-stem testing, and essentially all other operations on the lease except the actual drilling of the wells." Peurifoy, "Rights of Parties to Service Contracts," 12 *Rocky Mt. Min. L. Inst.* 403 (1967).

(2) The term applied to an arrangement between a host country and a foreign mineral company under which "the foreign firm assumes the managerial and technical responsibility and the financial and operational risks of exploring, developing and processing natural resources on its own, over a prearranged period. In return, the venturing firm is rewarded, short of a share of ownership, with a 'fee.' This can be a payment in kind or in money, and can be graduated according to size of discoveries, profits, foreign exchange savings, ventured resources or other variables. Service contracts are extremely flexible devices that meet the needs of host countries for filling gaps in managerial know-how, technology and other inputs. They can be adapted to widely diverse circumstances, and may satisfy a host country's objective of greater control over its natural resources consistent with maximum national economic gain." Mikdashi, "Policy

Issues in Primary Industries," 7 *Vanderbilt J. of Transnational Law* 281 at 305 (1974).

The origin of this form of contract is uncertain. One writer reports that one of the first service contracts was granted in Argentina in 1958, and it has been followed by other countries in South America. Brown, "Considerations Attending Investments in Oil and Gas Operations in Latin America," *Rocky Mt. Min. L. Fdn. International Minerals Acquisition and Operations Inst.* 13–14 (1974). Another writer declares that this form of contract originated in Iran in 1966 when the French Company ERAP became a contractor to the government NIOC and undertook to perform technical financial and other services for the account of NIOC.

Tocher, "Patterns and Trends in Agreements With Foreign Countries," *Rocky Mt. Min. L. Fdn. International Minerals Acquisition and Operations Inst.* 3-1 at 3-21 (1974), observed as follows:

> "These services involved commitments to exploration and development, the financing of operations and the marketing of production. Apart from the increased cost to the oil company, the major difference between a joint venture and a service contract is that under the service contract the national oil company retains title to the oil discovered and produced. The contractor is guaranteed a portion of the production at an agreed price which is fixed in the agreement at something less than the going market price. As service contracts have developed, the payment to the contracting foreign company can take the form of a per barrel fee as is done in Argentina, or a percentage of profits. The fee can be graduated according to size of discoveries, amount of risk capital invested or other factors."

See also the following:

Mikesell, *Petroleum Company Operations & Agreements in the Developing Countries* 92 *et seq.* (1984); Hossain, *Law and Policy in Petroleum Development* 158 (1979).

For specific aspects or provisions of agreements of this kind, see the entries under CONCESSION.

See also RISK SERVICE CONTRACT.

Service hole

A well drilled for injection, salt water disposal, or similar purpose. 38 *Oil & Gas Compact Bull.* 50 (June 1979).

Service line

A pipe or conduit of pipes, other than a flow line, used for the transportation, gathering or conduct of a mineral or water or other fluid in connection with the producing operations of an operator. Saskatchewan Surface Rights Acquisition and Compensation Act, 1968 (Stat. Sask. 1968, c. 73) § 2(1).

Servient estate

An estate burdened with a servitude or easement, or the parcel of land burdened by an easement for the benefit of another parcel [the DOMINANT ESTATE (*q.v.*)].

See also ACCOMMODATION DOCTRINE.

Servitude

(1) An easement or other incorporeal interest in land.

(2) In Louisiana, a severed mineral interest, whether reserved or granted. See MINERAL SERVITUDE; PRESCRIPTION.

Set casing

The cementing of CASING (*q.v.*) in the hole. The cement is introduced between the casing and the wall of the hole and then allowed to harden, thus sealing off intermediate formations and preventing fluids from them from entering the hole. It is customary to set casing in the completion of a producing well.

See Harper Oil Co. v. United States, 425 F.2d 1335 at 1342, 36 *O.&G.R.* 190 at 203 (10th Cir. 1970), quoting from the definition in this MANUAL.

Settled production

Production at a regular rate of flow over a substantial period of time. When a well first becomes productive, it may initially produce in substantial quantities (the FLUSH PRODUCTION [*q.v.*] stage); gradually the rate of flow from the well will generally level off at a plateau (the settled production stage) and the rate of production will remain relatively uniform for a considerable time. During the period of settled production the production graph appears as a slowly declining almost straight line. The final stage is that of STRIPPER PRODUCTION (*q.v.*).

Seven sisters

A term applied to the seven large international oil corporations [five from the United States: Exxon, Gulf, Texaco, Standard of California, and Mobil; two foreign corporations: British Petroleum and Royal Dutch Shell] which together control a major portion of production and refinery runs in the so-called Free World. Office of Emergency Preparedness, *Report on Crude Oil and Gasoline Price Increases of November 1970* p. 15 (April 1971). This term was apparently popularized by Enrico Mattei, the post-War head of the Italian government company, ENI. See Jensen, "International Oil—Shortage, Cartel or Emerging Resource Monopoly?" 7 *Vanderbilt J. of Transnational Law* 335 at 340 (1974). See also Sampson, *The Seven Sisters* (1975) (a journalistic exposé of "The Great Oil Companies and the World They Shaped"); Sherrill, *The Oil Follies of 1970–1980: How the Petroleum Industry Stole the Show (and Much More Besides)* (1980).

See also CONCESSION.

Seven-spot pattern

A pattern of WATER FLOODING (*q.v.*) in which the producing well is located in the center of a hexagon formed by six equally spaced injection wells. *Syn:* HEXAGONAL PATTERN. See WATER FLOODING.

Severance

Separation of a mineral or royalty interest from other interests in the land by grant or reservation. A mineral or royalty deed or a grant of the land reserving a mineral or royalty interest, by the landowner before leasing, accomplishes a severance as does his execution of an oil and gas lease.

See also HORIZONTAL SEVERANCE; PHASE SEVERANCE; VERTICAL SEVERANCE.

Severance beneficiary

A term employed in the Severance Beneficiary Tax Law of 1959 in Texas, 56th Leg., 3rd C.S., p. 187, ch. 1. By this Act, a severance beneficiary was defined as "any person for whose use and benefit gas is withdrawn from the land or waters of this State." The Act was held unconstitutional in Calvert, Comptroller v. Transcontinental Gas Pipeline Corp., 341 S.W.2d 679, 13 *O.&G.R.* 1197 (Tex. Civ. App. 1960, error ref'd).

Severance producer

A term employed in the Texas Dedicated Reserve Tax Act for "any person owning, controlling, managing or leasing any gas well and/or any person who produces in any manner any gas by taking it from the earth or waters of this State, and shall include any person owning any royalty or other interest in gas or its value, whether produced by him, or by some other person in his behalf, either by lease or contract or otherwise, when such person producing gas is in contractual relation with the dedicated reserve producer (either directly, or, if a royalty or other holder of an interest in gas in place and thereby entitled to a fractional share of the value of such gas in place, indirectly through the producer)." The Act was held to be unconstitutional in Calvert v. Panhandle Eastern Pipe Line Co., 371 S.W.2d 601, 19 *O.&G.R.* 742 (Tex. Civ. App. 1963, error ref'd n.r.e.).

Severance tax

A tax on the removal of minerals from the ground, usually levied as so many cents per barrel of oil or per Mcf of gas. The tax is sometimes levied as a percentage of the gross value of the minerals removed. See PRODUCTION TAX.

Under the CRUDE OIL WINDFALL PROFIT TAX ACT OF 1980 (*q.v.*) the calculation of "windfall profit" requires the deduction from the removal price of the amount of the severance tax imposed on the oil. This provision makes it necessary to determine whether particular state taxes on the removal of oil constitute a severance tax. See Rev. Rul. 80-218, 1980-32 I.R.B. 11, 65 *O.&G.R.* 465 (Aug. 11, 1980), holding that a specified form of privilege tax imposed by a state does not meet the requirements for the severance tax adjustment. For a detailed study of the severance and production taxes of the several producing states see Dickenson, "Severance Tax Adjustment Under the Windfall Profits Tax," 29 *O.&G. Tax Q.* 257 (1980).

For the allowability of a severance tax adjustment under the CRUDE OIL WINDFALL PROFIT TAX ACT OF 1980 (*q.v.*) for taxes imposed by various states see Rev. Rul. 82-86 (Idaho, Louisiana, Mississippi, Texas), Rev. Rul. 82-87 (Alabama, Indiana, Kentucky, Michigan, Nebraska, North Dakota, Oklahoma, South Dakota, Tennessee, Utah, Wyoming), Rev. Rul. 82-88 (California, Nevada, Ohio), Rev. Rul. 82-89 (Alaska), Rev. Rul. 82-90 (Arkansas), Rev. Rul. 82-91 (West Virginia); Rev. Rul. 82-92 (Colorado), Rev. Rul. 82-167 (Alaska), Rev. Rul. 83-92 (Montana).

The constitutionality of a Montana coal severance tax which could equal 30 percent of the contract sale price was sustained in Commonwealth Edison Co. v. Montana, 453 U.S. 609, 70 *O.&G.R.* 182 (1981), *reh. denied,* 453 U.S. 927 (1981). For a detailed discussion of *Commonwealth Edison Co. v. Montana,* see S. Williams, "Severance Taxes and Federalism: The Role of the Supreme Court in Preserving a National Common Market for Energy Supplies," 53 *U. Colo. L. Rev.* 281 (1982). See also Browde and DuMars, "State Taxation of Natural Resource Extraction and the Commerce Clause: Federalism's Modern Frontier," 60 *Oregon L. Rev.* 7 (1981).

Merrion v. Jicarilla Apache Tribe, 455 U.S. 130, 72 *O.&G.R.* 617 (1982), noted, 37 *Okla. L. Rev.* 369 (1984), sustained the validity of a severance tax imposed by the tribe with the consent of the Secretary of the Interior on oil and gas production from tribal lands. See also INDIAN LANDS.

Rev. Rul. 82-167, 1982-40 I.R.B. 10, 73 *O.&G.R.* 439 (Oct. 4, 1982), declared that the Alaska "cents-per-barrel" tax provided for by Alaska Stat. § 43.57.010 did not qualify as a severance tax for purposes of the federal CRUDE OIL WINDFALL PROFIT TAX ACT OF 1980 (*q.v.*) severance tax adjustment allowed by I.R.C. § 4988(a).

Eagerton v. Exchange Oil and Gas Corp., 404 So. 2d 1, 71 *O.&G.R.* 205 (Ala. 1981), sustained the validity of a statute increasing the severance tax against claims of unconstitutionality by reason of (1) applicability only to the Smackover Formation, found in only twelve counties of the state, (2) exemption of royalty owners from the burden of the tax, and (3) a PASS-THROUGH PROHIBITION (*q.v.*) designed to protect the consumer from the burden of the tax.

Eagerton was affirmed in part, reversed in part and remanded *sub nom.* Exxon Corp. v. Eagerton, 462 U.S. 176, 103 S. Ct. 2296, 77 *O.&G.R.* 209 (1983) (holding the pass-through prohibition was preempted by federal law insofar as it applied to sale of gas in interstate commerce but not insofar as it applied to sale of gas in intrastate commerce; sustaining the pass-through prohibition against challenges under the contracts and equal protection clauses of the Constitution; and remanding the case on the question of the severability of the pass-through prohibition from the balance of the Act, that being a question of state law). On remand, the court gave effect to the severability clause of the statute and sustained the act despite invalidity of the pass-through prohibition. 440 So. 2d 1031, 79 *O.&G.R.* 424 (Ala. 1983).

On subsequent appeal of *Eagerton sub nom.* Eagerton v. Terra Resources, Inc., 426 So. 2d 807, 76 *O.&G.R.* 187 (Ala. 1982), *appeal dism'd for want of a substantial federal question,* 464 U.S. 801 (1983), the court rejected a contention that gas was exempted from the tax.

See also the following:

W. Hellerstein, *State and Local Taxation of Natural Resources in the Federal System* (1986);

Hellerstein, "Political Perspectives on State and Local Taxation of Natural Resources," 19 *Georgia L. Rev.* 31 (1984);

Crumbley and Williams, "Texas Severance Tax on Oil and Gas Production," 32 *O.&G. Tax Q.* 352 (1983);

Shurtz, "State Taxation of Energy Resources: Are Consuming States Getting Burned?" 39 *Vand. L. Rev.* 55 (1983).

See also ADDITIONAL ROYALTY; OIL EXTRACTION TAX DEVELOPMENT FUND; YIELD TAX.

Severance tax credit

A tax credit against the severance tax as a bonus, incentive, or reward for the discovery of a new oil field in Arkansas. See P. & O. Falco Inc. v. Riley, 271 Ark. 562, 610 S.W.2d 255, 68 *O.&G.R.* 721 (1980) (holding that the tax credit was available only to operators and was not available to royalty owners).

Severed mineral interest

An expense-bearing interest in the minerals in, on and under a given tract of land owned by a person other than the surface owner.

The owner of a severed mineral interest normally has easement rights in the surface permitting him to enter upon the surface and use so much thereof as is reasonably necessary for purposes of exploration, development and production of minerals, and he may himself enter and drill or execute an oil and gas lease. The severed mineral interest may be the entire mineral interest or an undivided interest in the minerals. Occasionally when the mineral interest is held concurrently, the executive rights may be owned by one of the concurrent owners, in which event the other or others own a NONEXECUTIVE MINERAL INTEREST (*q.v.*).

The severed mineral interest may be granted or reserved for years, for life, in fee simple defeasible (*e.g.*, where the grant or reservation is for years "and so long thereafter" as oil or gas is produced), or in perpetuity. [For the prescriptibility of such interests in Louisiana, see PRESCRIPTION.] The owner of a severed mineral interest is usually entitled to share in the leasing rights and in bonuses, rentals and royalties paid under an oil and gas lease.

See also MINERAL DEED; MINERAL INTEREST; SEVERED ROYALTY INTEREST; TERM MINERAL OR ROYALTY INTEREST.

Severed royalty interest

A non-expense-bearing interest in the minerals produced and saved from a given tract of land owned by a person other than the surface owner of the premises.

The owner of such an interest is entitled to a share of production from wells located on the premises in which he has the interest, free of the costs of production. The interest may be created by a landowner prior or subsequent to the leasing of the land. The interest may be granted or reserved for years, for life, in fee simple defeasible (*e.g.*, when the grant or reservation is for years "and so long thereafter" as oil or gas is produced), or in perpetuity. [For the prescriptibility of such interests in Louisiana, see PRESCRIPTION.] The owner of a severed royalty interest is usually not entitled to share in bonuses or rentals paid under an oil and gas lease.

See also NONPARTICIPATING ROYALTY; ROYALTY DEED; ROYALTY INTEREST; SEVERED MINERAL INTEREST; TERM MINERAL OR ROYALTY INTEREST.

Shackle rod

Connecting rod between a power house and well by which the well is pumped.

Shale

A form of sedimentary rock composed of finely divided particles of older rocks deposited in the still waters of lakes and seas. Most shales are highly compacted muds and accordingly do not contain oil or gas in commercial quantities. See SEDIMENTARY ROCK.

Shale oil

Oil obtained by the treatment of kerogen obtained from OIL SHALE (*q.v.*). See 8 *O.&G.R.* 515 (1958).

The differences in chemical composition, chemical reaction, insolubility, and synthesis characteristics of shale oil and ordinary oil or petroleum were noted in Utah Resources International, Inc. v. Utah Board of State Lands, 26 Utah 2d 342, 489 P.2d 615 (1971) (holding that lessees under "oil, gas and hydrocarbon" lease specifically excluding "oil shale" were not entitled to enjoin lessor from issuing an oil shale lease on the same premises).

Shale shaker

A device into which drilling MUD (*q.v.*) is flowed on its return to the surface during drilling operations which screens out the cuttings which are then examined from time to time for geological information. Falcon Seaboard Drilling Co. v. Commissioner, 30 T.C. 1081, 9 *O.&G.R.* 578 (1958).

Shallow well

This term is defined by W. Va. Code § 22–4–1 (Cum. Supp. 1980) and § 22–4B–2 (Cum. Supp. 1980) as "any gas well drilled and completed in a formation above the top of the upper most member of the 'Onondaga Group' or at a depth less than six thousand feet, whichever is shallower." The West Virginia Code contains elaborate provisions dealing with problems arising from coal owners' objections to permits for well locations. See Snyder and Christian, "Oil and Gas Operations Through Coal Seams in West Virginia," 1 *Eastern Min. L. Inst.* 5–1 at 5–83 (1980).

See also DEEP WELL; WELL.

Shape of tract basis

A method of determining the ALLOWABLE (*q.v.*) for a well located on a tract of irregular shape. Thus in Lilly v. Conservation Comm'r of La., 29 F. Supp. 892 (E. D. La. 1939), the tract in question was 200 feet wide and 5000 feet long with an area of 23 acres. In calculating the allowable the Commissioner limited the length to 1320 feet for computing the acreage to be used for determining the allowable. Multiplying this length by the width of less than 200 feet produced an area of approximately six acres, on the basis of which calculated acreage the allowable for the well was determined.

Sharing agreement

The term applied to an agreement among oil companies to supply each other in the event of cut-backs, shut-ins or nationalization by the Libyan Government.

See also LIBYAN PRODUCERS AGREEMENT.

Sharing arrangement

In federal income tax law, a transaction wherein one party contributes to the acquisition, exploration, or development of an oil or gas property and receives as consideration an interest in the property to which the contribution is made. See G.C.M. 22730, 1941–1 Cum. Bull. 214. See also Burke and Bowhay, *Income Taxation of Natural Resources* ¶ 7.01 et seq. (1980).

A CARRIED INTEREST (*q.v.*) is a form of sharing arrangement. See TREATISE §§ 433–433.1.

See also DIVISIBLE SHARING ARRANGEMENT; EXCESS CASH; FUNCTIONAL ALLOCATION SHARING ARRANGEMENT.

Shipping papers

"[B]ills of lading covering oil or products transported by railway; manifest covering oil or products transported by truck or motor vehicle, and any written documents covering oil or products transported by pipe line, boat or barge." Tex. Rev. Civ. Stat. Ann. Art. 6066a, § 1(j) (1962).

Shoestring sands

A type of lenticular formation (see LENTICULAR RESERVOIR) in which a porous, permeable sandstone lens or streak is surrounded by impervious rock, frequently shale. Such a STRATIGRAPHIC TRAP (*q.v.*) is difficult to locate because of the absence of significant structural relief.

Shooting a well

Exploding nitroglycerine or other high explosive in a hole, to shatter the rock and increase the flow of oil or gas.

Shooting by seismograph

The making of a SEISMOGRAPHIC SURVEY (*q.v.*). The term "shooting" derives from the setting off of explosions in the ground. The shock waves from these explosions are recorded by a SEISMOGRAPH (*q.v.*), and from these records a contour map can be made.

The definition in this MANUAL was quoted in United Geophysical Corp. v. Culver, 394 P.2d 393 (Alaska 1964).

Shooting lease

An instrument granting permission to conduct a geophysical survey; it may or may not give the right to take an oil and gas lease on all or part of the lands. See Fiske, *Federal Taxation of Oil and Gas Transactions* §§ 1.04, 2.11 (1983 Revision).

Shooting option

A contract for exploration rights which contains an ACREAGE SELECTION CLAUSE (*q.v.*). SHOOTING RIGHTS (*q.v.*) do not include the latter clause.

For tax purposes, the consideration paid the landowner for the shooting option is treated as ordinary income if the selection option is not exercised and as lease bonus if the selection option is exercised; the grantee treats the consideration as geological and geophysical costs in the former case and as a capital investment in the lease or leases in the latter case. See Burke and Bowhay, *Income Taxation of Natural Resources* ¶ 15.04 (1981).

In Bayou Verret Land Co., Inc. v. Commissioner, 450 F.2d 850 at 856, 40 *O.&G.R.* 421 at 429 (5th Cir. 1971), the court concluded that the "Tax Court's holding that the advance lump sums received on the execution of the shooting and selection leases should be treated as lease bonus was not clearly erroneous."

Shooting rights

The right to enter upon land and make a geophysical survey. These rights are now uniformly granted by the oil and gas lease, but they can and frequently do exist apart from a lease. An operator may purchase shooting rights on a large area, and take leases on only the most favorable portion of such area.

The name probably derives from seismographic surveys, the making of which is called "shooting," from the setting off of explosive charges as a part of the survey process.

Shortage

The amount of oil or the amount of natural gas during a proration period by which a given PRORATION UNIT (*q.v.*) failed to produce an amount equal to that authorized on the proration schedule. New Mexico Oil Conservation Comm'n, *Rules and Regulations* 5 (1958).

See also PRORATIONING.

Short delivery (0.5% allowance) issue

The issue involved in a number of arbitration and judicial decisions whether a carrier is subject to liability for any shortage of delivery of oil by tanker not exceeding O.5%. See Pfeiffer, "International Oil Trading—The Practice and the Problems," International Bar Ass'n Section on Energy and Natural Resources, *International Energy Law* (1984) (Topic 8).

Short-lived in-oil payment

A term used by the Internal Revenue Service to describe an *assigned* OIL PAYMENT (*q.v.*) of shorter duration than the interest out of which it was carved.

The Revenue Service took the position that a short-lived oil payment was an assignment of income and that the consideration received for it was taxable to the assignee as ordinary, depletable income, not as capital gain. See G.C.M. 24849, 1946–1 Cum. Bull. 66. This ruling contemplated the possibility of different treatment for long-lived in-oil payments. See LONG OIL PAYMENT. However, in I.T. 4003, 1950–1 Cum. Bull. 10, the Service abandoned this distinction and took the position that all carved out oil payments of lesser duration than the underlying property interest are assignments of income, not sales. The United States Supreme Court has sustained this position. Commissioner v. P. G. Lake, Inc., 356 U.S. 260, 8 *O.&G.R.* 1153 (1958).

Short oil payment

An OIL PAYMENT (*q.v.*) with a short pay-out. See Discussion Notes, 4 *O.&G.R.* 1074 (1955).

Short section

A section of land according to the United States Governmental Survey which contains less than 640 acres. See Stevens v. State Corporation Comm'n, 185 Kan. 190, 341 P.2d 1021, 11 *O.&G.R.* 804 (1959).

See also GENERAL LAND OFFICE SURVEY; LONG SECTION; LOT.

Short ton

See TON.

Shot gun tank

A settling tank. Oil containing BASIC SEDIMENT (*q.v.*) and water may be run into this tank and after the oil accumulates on top of the foreign matter with which it is intermingled, the oil may be run into stock or storage tanks. See Switzer v. Driscoll, 183 So. 57 (La. App. 1938).

Shot hole

See SHOT POINT.

Shot point

The place where a hole is dug and an explosion set off in the making of a SEISMOGRAPHIC SURVEY (*q.v.*).

Shut-down days

Those days in a given month in excess of the days of production allowed under a proration order. See Rogers, "Common Purchaser, Market Demand, Pipeline Proration," 9 *Sw. Legal Fdn. Oil & Gas Inst.* 45 at 73 (1958).

See also ALLOWABLE; PRORATIONING.

Shut-down order

An order of a regulatory commission requiring that production from a well be terminated, temporarily or permanently.

Shut-down time

One of the rate provisions common in a DRILLING CONTRACT (*q.v.*), specifying the compensation to the independent drilling contractor when drilling operations have been suspended at the request of the operator.

See also DAY WORK; FOOTAGE CONTRACT; STAND-BY RIG TIME; TURNKEY CONTRACT.

Shut-in allowable

See SALT WATER SHUT-IN ALLOWABLE.

Shut-in gas well clause

A lease clause which authorizes a lessee to pay a shut-in gas well royalty and thereby keep a lease alive without actual production when and if a well has been drilled which is capable of producing gas in paying quantities but which is shut-in, usually by reason of lack of a market. A typical clause of this type provides as follows:

> "the royalties to be paid by lessee are: . . . a royalty of $50 per well on each gas well from which gas only is produced while gas therefrom is not sold or used off the premises, and while such royalty is so paid, said well shall be held to be a producing well. . . ."

Variants in the language of the clause are numerous. In some cases the clause has been so written as to apply to wells from which "gas and/or distillate only" is produced. The word "only" has been omitted by some draftsmen, and many leases expressly define a gas well to include wells capable of producing natural gas, condensate, distillate or any other gaseous substance, and wells classified as gas wells by any government authority.

In early leases, the sum required to be paid under the shut-in gas well clause to keep a lease alive was frequently nominal in amount. Such clauses today typically provide that the shut-in well royalty shall be equal at least to the delay rentals previously payable to keep the lease alive or, in the alternative, provide that the payment of a royalty under this clause shall suffice to keep the lease alive only as to a given number of acres.

In most (but not all) states timely payment of the shut-in royalty is requisite to keep the lease alive after the expiration of the primary term for unless payment is timely there cannot be said to be production required by the "thereafter" clause of the lease. Similarly, if under the provisions of the delay rental clause, "production" or payment of rentals is required on or before an anniversary date, there must be timely payment of either the shut-in royalty or of the delay rental to prevent termination of the lease. Payment or tender of the shut-in royalty will not keep a lease alive unless the well which was shut-in was capable of production in commercial quantities. The clause does not modify the implied covenant to use reasonable diligence in marketing the gas.

There has been some dispute as to whether payments under this clause are "royalties" to be paid to royalty owners or are "rentals" to be paid the persons entitled to such payments. In Morriss v. First National Bank of Mission, 249 S.W.2d 269, 1 *O.&G.R.* 1371 (Tex. Civ. App. 1952, error ref'd n.r.e.), it was held that such payments were "royalties." For purposes of the federal income tax law, however, such payments are usually treated as rentals. See Burke and Bowhay, *Income Taxation of Natural Resources* ¶ 15.09 (1981).

On the operation of the clause, see Walker, "Clauses in Oil and Gas Leases Providing for the Payment of an Annual Sum as Royalty on a Nonproducing Gas Well." 24 *Tex. L. Rev.* 478 (1946); Hardwicke, "Problems Arising Out of Royalty Clauses in Oil and Gas Leases in Texas," 29 *Tex. L. Rev.* 790 (1951); Treatise §§ 631–635.

The definition in this Manual was quoted in Canadian Superior Oil Ltd. v. Murdoch, 65 W.W.R. 473 at 479–480 (Alberta Sup. Ct. 1968), *appeal dismissed,* 68 W.W.R. 390, 4 D.L.R. 3d 629 (Atla. Sup. Ct. App. Div. 1969), *appeal dismissed,* [1969] S.C.R. vi, 6 D. L. R. 3d 464, 70 W.W.R. 768 (1969).

Shut-in pressure

The pressure at the casinghead or well-head when all valves are closed and no oil or gas has been allowed to escape for a period of time, usually more than 24 and less than 72 hours. These pressures may be recorded by a gauge on the CHRISTMAS TREE (*q.v.*).

Shut-in rental

A term sometimes used to described SHUT-IN ROYALTY. See, *e.g.*, the Comment to Article 213 of the Louisiana Mineral Code [R.S. 31:213 (1975)].

Shut-in royalty

A payment made when a gas well, capable of producing in paying quantities, is shut-in for lack of a market for the gas, under a SHUT-IN GAS WELL CLAUSE (*q.v.*). See TREATISE §§ 631 et seq.

Shut-in royalty title opinion

A TITLE OPINION (*q.v.*) designating the parties entitled to shut-in royalty and their respective shares. D. Pierce, *Kansas Oil and Gas Handbook* § 11.17 (1986).

Shut in, to

To close down a producing well temporarily, for repair, cleaning out, building up reservoir pressure, lack of a market, etc.

Shut-in well

A producing well that has been closed down temporarily for repairs, cleaning out, building up pressure, lack of a market, etc.

A change in the definition of "shut-in wells" in 1972 led to a major increase in the number of such wells reported in the Outer Continental Shelf area of the Gulf of Mexico. Until that year "the statistics on shut-in well completions did not include those that are left standing due to drilling on platforms, planning for secondary or other injection projects, delays in facilities, well-plugging by sand, or other mechanical problems, pressure depletion, or having an excessive gas-oil ratio. These well completions were considered 'active' because they were neither literally plugged with cement and finally abandoned, nor were they under current application for approval of workover or repair projects. Starting in 1972, the [Geological] Survey's Conservation Division, which supervises and reports on operations on Federal offshore areas, made the decision to expand the definition of shut-in well to include a large number of wells that were not actually producing that year, but which were not permanently plugged with cement and abandoned." Department of the Interior News Release, Dec. 12, 1974, reported in "Natural Gas Production and Conservation Act of 1974," Hearings before the Senate Committee on Commerce, 93rd Cong., 2d Sess., Dec. 4 and 5, 1974 at p. 57, Serial No. 93–129.

The definition in this MANUAL was quoted and adopted in Robert D. Snyder, 13 IBLA 327, GFS(O&G) 1973–111 (1973).

Shut-off test

A test to determine whether water from a well is penetrating into oil-bearing or gas-bearing strata or detrimental substances are infiltrating into underground or surface water suitable for irrigation or domestic purposes. See Cal.Pub. Res. Code §§ 3221–3223 (1972).

Side-line well

A term occasionally used to describe an offset well, *viz.*, a well drilled to prevent drainage to other premises. See Alphonzo E. Bell Corp. v. Bell View Oil Syndicate, 24 Cal.App.2d 587, 76 P.2d 167 (1938).

Side tracking

(1) An operation involving the use of a portion of an existing well to drill a second hole, resulting in a well that is partly old and partly new.

> "Rather than starting at the surface with a new hole and setting new casing strings all the way, it may be less expensive to utilize a portion of the casing in the original cased hole. To do this, a milling tool is used to grind out a 'window' through the side of the casing at some selected depth. After this is done, a whipstock is utilized to direct a drilling bit out of the window at some desired angle into previously undrilled earth strata. From this directional start a new hole is drilled to the desired formation depth and casing is set in the new hole and tied back to the older casing." Shell Oil Co. v. Federal Energy Regulatory Comm'n, 707 F.2d 230 at 233, 79 *O.&G.R.* 186 at 190 (5th Cir. 1983) (dealing with the vintaging of gas produced as a result of side-tracking).

See also Ebberts v. Carpenter Production Co., 256 S.W.2d 601, 2 *O.&G.R.* 726 (Tex. Civ. App. 1953, error ref'd n.r.e.).

Holt Oil & Gas Corp. v. Harvey, 801 F.2d 773, ____ *O.&G.R.* ____ (5th Cir. 1986), sustained a jury finding that a side tracking operation was a continuation of the original well as distinct from a subsequent or other operation as defined in an operating agreement.

(2) Drilling past obstructions in a well.

Side track, to

See SIDE TRACKING.

Side-wall core

A sample taken from the wall of the well bore. For a description of a method of taking a side wall core, see Calvert v. A-L Bit and Tool Co., 256 S.W.2d 224, 2 *O.&G.R.* 831 (Tex. Civ. App. 1953, error ref'd n.r.e.).

See CORING.

Signature bonus

A sum paid by the buyer on signing a contract for the purchase of crude oil for delivery in the future. Thus, Iran, in negotiating with Japanese oil and trading companies was said to seek a signature bonus of $1.80 to $2 a barrel. *The Wall Street Journal,* Feb. 11, 1981, p. 27.

See also ROYALTY OIL AUCTION.

Simultaneous filings

(1) Lease offers filed within a specified period and which are treated as filed simultaneously. Priority is determined in this instance by a public drawing. Lands in canceled or relinquished leases or in leases which terminate by operation of law for non-payment of rental, which are not withdrawn from leasing nor on a known geological structure of a producing oil and gas field, and lands covered by leases which expire by operation of law at the end of their primary or extended term are subject to the simultaneous filing provisions of 43 C.F.R. § 3112 (1978). A property which receives no applications may subsequently be leased to the first qualified applicant.

(2) Applications for entry filed within the time specified in 43 C.F.R. § 1821.2–3 (1978).

See *Rocky Mt. Min. L. Fdn. Law of Federal Oil and Gas Leases* Ch. 6 (1985); 44 Fed. Reg. 56176 (Sept. 28, 1979) (proposed rule making, 43 C.F.R., Part 3100, Subpart 3112).

See also Buy-back agreement; Drawing entry card; Federal lease; Leasing service company; Non-competitive lease; Put option; Sole party in interest.

Single base-point system

A pricing system under which one geographical location is accepted by buyers and sellers of oil as the point assumed to be the shipping point of the oil for purposes of the posted price and shipping costs. See Danielsen, *The Evolution of OPEC* 58 (1982).

See also Base-point pricing; Basing point pricing; Equalization point; Gulf-plus pricing structure; Multiple base-point system; Persian Gulf pricing system; Phantom freight.

Single phase reservoir

See Condensate gas reservoir.

Single window approach

The name applied to the governmental regulation of major mineral developments which involves a central coordinating body or process within government to channel negotiations with industry; "the term connotes both a coordinated *process* for negotiation between government and industry, and an *agreement* which is supplementary to normal legislative requirements." Saunders, "New Directions in Resource Management: The Single Window," in *Resources, The Newsletter of the Canadian Institute of Resources Law* (No. 5, June 1983 at p. 2).

> "The use of the single window in resource development has been quite common in other jurisdictions, most notably in the Australian states of Queensland and Western Australia, where it is not unusual to find detailed company-state agreements enacted as special public statutes. . . .
>
> "The potential advantages of a single window approach are readily apparent. Ideally, it permits a high degree of coordination in both the negotiation and implementation of resource developments, leading to faster and, one would hope, more informed decisions on the part of government. For major resource developments, involving large numbers of regulatory approvals and perhaps significant infrastructure items, there are obvious advantages to having a central coordinating point. That point may be a person, an agency, or even a set process (for example the coal approval process in Alberta). Of at least equal importance to greater

coordination is the potential for flexibility which the single window offers both government and industry. Within a range, it is possible to tailor an agreement to meet the particular requirements of both industry and government for each specific project." *Ibid.*

SIRIP

Société Irano-Italienne des Pétroles, a joint stock company owned by AGIP and NIOC. See Mughraby, *Permanent Sovereignty Over Oil Resources* 85 (1966).

Sistrunk formula

The name given to the rule in Mississippi requiring the Conservation Board to grant a location exception to nonproductive acreage outside of a unit and a full allowable thereto so long as proof is adduced that as much as five acres are underlain by oil. See Brunini, "Important Elements in the Development of Oil and Gas Conservation in Mississippi," 6 *IOCC Comm. Bull.* 1 at 11 (Dec. 1964).

See also RULE 37; WELL SPACING.

Sit-down search

See TITLE OPINION.

Sit-out

A term used to describe the position of a carried party under a CARRIED INTEREST ARRANGEMENT (*q.v.*); the carried party is said to "sit-out" while the carrying party drills a well at his own expense. See 3 *O.&G. Tax Q.* 73 (1954).

640-acre rule

The rule that the acreage in a lease offer for federal lands may not be less than 640 acres unless (1) the land is surrounded by land not available for leasing, or (2) the offer is accompanied by a showing that the lands are in an approved unit or cooperative plan of operation or a plan which has been approved as to form by the Director of the Geological Survey. See *Rocky Mt. Min. L. Fdn. Law of Federal Oil and Gas Leases* § 5.05 (1985).

Six-mile-square rule

The rule that the lands in a lease offer for federal lands must be entirely within an area of six miles square or within an area not exceeding six surveyed sections in length or width. See *Rocky Mt. Min. L. Fdn. Law of Federal Oil and Gas Leases* § 5.05 (1985).

Sixty-day clause

A term sometimes used to describe a DRILLING OPERATIONS CLAUSE (*q.v.*) or a CONTINUOUS DRILLING OPERATIONS CLAUSE (*q.v.*). The name comes from the fact that many such clauses permit a lease to be preserved by specified operations so long as such operations are prosecuted with no cessation of more than sixty consecutive days. See Geier-Jackson, Inc. v. James, 160 F. Supp. 524 9 *O.&G.R.* 264 (E. D. Tex. 1958).

The term may also be used to describe a DRY HOLE CLAUSE (*q.v.*) under some circumstances if such clause permits the resumption of drilling operations or rental payments within sixty days of the completion of a dry hole.

See also THIRTY DAY—SIXTY DAY CLAUSE.

Sixty-day emergency sales

Temporary short term sales by certain persons, distribution companies and intrastate pipelines which are exempt from the provisions of the Natural Gas Act to meet emergency needs of natural gas distribution companies and pipeline companies. Under the provisions of 18 C.F.R. §§ 2.68, 2.70 and 157.29 (1980), such sales may be made for periods up to and including 60 consecutive days without any express authorization by the Federal Power Commission or by its successor, the Federal Energy Regulatory Commission.

See also ONE HUNDRED AND EIGHTY DAY EMERGENCY SALES.

66.3 company

The term applied to a Canadian method of raising capital for oil and gas drilling ventures. Section 66.3 of the Income Tax Act provides that when shares are received by an investor who incurs Canadian exploration expense (CEE) or Canadian development expense (CDE) pursuant to a written agreement with the corporation solely in consideration of the issue to him of treasury shares, the shares are deemed to be inventory in the hands of the investor, rather than capital property as shares ordinarily would be, and are deemed to be acquired at a cost of nil. The CEE and the CDE expenses are deductible by the taxpayer as if incurred solely by him. "Thus the concept is one of incurring drilling for shares and the scheme may be codeworded as '66.3' shares or a '66.3 company.' " Libin, "Securities

Aspects of Specialized Financing," 19 *Alberta L. Rev.* 43 at 54 (1980).

See also DRILLING FUND.

Skeletonized abstract

Syn.: BOB-TAIL ABSTRACT (*q.v.*).

Skidding the rig

Moving the rig to a new location preparatory to drilling. *API Quarterly* 5 (Spring 1957); Administrative Ruling, Internal Revenue Service, Revenue Ruling 57-393, I.R.B. 1957-35, 21, 7 *O.&G.R.* 1345 (1957).

Amarex, Inc. v. Baker, 655 P.2d 1040, 75 *O.&G.R.* 329 (Okla. 1982), held that when an operator skidded his rig six feet, after losing his initial hole at a depth of 416.25 feet, and then proceeded to drill to a depth in excess of 12,000 feet, the latter drilling did not constitute a new well for purposes of development costs under a compulsory pooling order. The case is discussed in LeMay, "Amarex, Inc. v. Baker: Skidding the Rig and Continuous Operation," 55 *Okla. B.J.* 1085 (1984).

Skimming

Bailing oil which rises to the surface in the well casing. Cox v. Lasley, 639 P.2d 1219, 72 *O.&G.R.* 328 (Okla. 1982).

Skim oil

Oil recovered from a salt water gathering system prior to injection or other disposal of the water. In Texas a Monthly Skim Oil Report (Form P–18) is required to be filed by Salt Water Gathering Systems with the Railroad Commission, reporting the quantity and disposition of oil skimmed from water during the month.

Slander of title

A legal action, somewhat like libel and slander, in which the elements of the cause of action are: (1) ownership by plaintiff of the property in question; (2) publication to a third person; (3) of a false and injurious statement regarding the title to the property; (4) which causes the plaintiff specific pecuniary loss; (5) and which was animated by malice or an intent to disparge. See TREATISE § 232.

See also JACTITORY ACTION.

Slant drilling

See DIRECTIONAL DRILLING.

Slant well

Syn.: DIRECTIONAL WELL (*q.v.*).

Sliding scale nonoperating interest

A share of production (a royalty interest, overriding royalty interest, or oil payment) which varies in amount depending upon some contingency, *e.g.*, volume of production or manner of production. Thus an instrument creating an override may provide that it shall be 1/16th of 7/8ths of production if production is less than 100 barrels per day (or if production is by artificial means) and that it shall be 1/8th of 7/8th of production if production is more than 100 barrels per day (or if production is by flowing).

See also SLIDING SCALE ROYALTY; STEP SCALE ROYALTY.

Sliding scale royalty

A royalty varying in amount depending on the amount of production, *e.g.*, a 1/8th royalty if the production is 100 barrels per day or less, and a 3/16th royalty if the production is greater than 100 barrels per day. Difficult problems of interpretation of the sliding scale royalty clause arise when governmental regulations or a unitization agreement limit production or the amount of oil allocated to a particular tract. See TREATISE §§ 649–649.4.

See also STEP SCALE ROYALTY.

Rev.Rul. 76–34, 1976–4 I.R.B. 11 (Jan. 26, 1976), ruled that no part of a sliding scale royalty was to be viewed as a production payment within the meaning of Section 636(c) of the Internal Revenue Code providing for treatment of a production payment reserved by a lessor in a leasing transaction as if it were a bonus payable in installments.

Slim hole

A "hole drilled with less than normal diameter tools (less than 7⅞" rotary bit, thus 6¼" bit or less). Used primarily for seismic shot holes and structure tests, more rarely for strat tests." Report of the Committee on Regulatory Practices for Stratigraphic Test Holes, 17 *Interstate Oil Compact Bull.* 43 (Dec. 1958).

See also SEISMIC SHOT HOLE; STRATIGRAPHIC TEST HOLE; STRUCTURE TEST HOLE.

"Slim-hole" drilling and casing

Use of the smallest feasible drill hole and casing size.

Slope test

A test to determine whether (and to what extent) the course of a well deviates from vertical.

Sludge

Mud from a drill hole in boring; foreign matter in crude petroleum.

Slug injection

See ALCOHOL SLUG PROCESS; AMPHIPATHIC SLUG INJECTION; HYDROCARBON SOLVENT SLUG INJECTION; SECONDARY RECOVERY.

Slumping

The expression used to describe the erosion that takes place when the surface layer in the Arctic is disturbed and heat begins to melt the permafrost. The process leaves ugly scars on the landscape and may cause the ground to melt away beneath pipelines, leaving them without support. See Maxwell, *Energy From the Arctic: Facts and Issues* 36 (1973).

SLUP

The acronym for Special Land Use Permit. See Wilderness Society v. Morton, 479 F.2d 842 at 850 (D. C. Cir. 1973), *cert. denied,* 411 U.S. 917 (1973).

Slurry

A mixture of cement and water pumped into a borehole to seal off zones issuing fluids.

Slush pit

The excavation on a well site that holds the drilling MUD (*q.v.*) used in rotary drilling. Also called mud pit, slush pond, sump hole.

See Barbour, "Oil and Gas Well Operator's Liability to Lessor-Surface Owner for Slush Pit Overflow or Seepage," 44 *Miss. L.J.* 980 (1973).

Small diameter core

See CORING.

Smallest legal subdivision

For general purposes under the Public Land Laws, the smallest legal subdivision is defined as a quarter-quarter section. Gary E. Strong, IBLA 81-834, GFS(O&G) 1981-168 (Aug. 31, 1981).

See also GENERAL LAND OFFICE SURVEY; LEGAL SUBDIVISION.

Small explorer's credit

Syn.: ALBERTA ROYALTY TAX CREDIT (*q.v.*).

Small producer

In the Permian Basin Area Rate Proceeding a small producer was defined as a natural gas company selling jurisdictionally less than 10,000,000 Mcf annually on a nationwide basis. 34 F.P.C. 159 at 235, 23 *O.&G.R.* 103 at 194 (Opinion No. 468, Aug. 5, 1965), *remanded,* Skelly Oil Co. v. Federal Power Comm'n, 375 F.2d 6, 26 *O.&G.R.* 237 (10th Cir. 1967), *aff'd in part and rev'd in part sub nom. In re* Permian Basin Area Rate Cases, 390 U.S. 747, 28 *O.&G.R.* 689 (1968).

By Order No. 428, 45 F.P.C. 454, 37 *O.&G.R.* 605 (March 19, 1971), the Federal Power Commission sought to establish a blanket certificate procedure for small producers of natural gas, relieving them of almost all filing requirements, and subjecting them to indirect rather than direct regulation of rates. On review it was held that the Commission was free to engage in indirect regulation of small gas producers provided it insured that the rates paid by the pipelines, and ultimately borne by the consumer, are just and reasonable. The order of the Commission was set aside, however, and the case was ordered to be remanded to the Commission for further proceedings. Federal Power Comm'n v. Texaco, Inc., 417 U.S. 380, 49 *O.&G.R.* 97 (1974). The procedure for certification of small producer sales is contained in 18 C.F.R. § 157.40 (1980).

Small producer sales

Natural gas sales by a SMALL PRODUCER (*q.v.*).

Small refiner bias

Under the ENTITLEMENT PROGRAM (*q.v.*), small refiners were given additional entitlements as a subsidy to help them compete against the majors. This small refiner bias meant that small refiners having higher than normal supplies of old oil had to pay proportionately less than majors for new oil, or they had extra entitlements which they could sell. See Task Force on Reform of Federal Energy Administration, *Federal Energy Administration Regulation* 12, 28, 62–73, 78–81 (MacAvoy ed. 1977); Kalt, *The Economics and Politics of Oil Price Regulation* 59 (1981); 10 C.F.R. § 211.67(e) (1980).

SMP

SPECIAL MARKETING PROGRAM (*q.v.*).

SNG

(1) Synthetic natural gas (*q.v.*).

(2) Supplemental natural gas.

(3) Substitute natural gas, *viz.*, a gas manufactured from carbonaceous material which gas is composed primarily of methane.

Société Nationale Elf Aquitaine

A French state oil company.

Société Nationale pour la Recherche, la Production, le Transport, la Transformation et la Commercialization des Hydrocarbures (SONATRACH)

The Algerian national oil company. See Terki, "An Outline of the Legal System for the Exploration and Exploitation of Liquid Hydrocarbons in Algeria," [1983] 1 *OGLTR* 13.

Society of Exploration Geophysicists (SEG)

A professional organization of geophysicists primarily engaged in exploration for oil and gas and other minerals.

Society of Petroleum Engineers (SPE)

A professional organization of petroleum engineers.

Society of Professional Well Log Analysts (SPWLA)

A scientific society concerned with formation evaluation through well logging techniques. See WELL LOG.

SOEKOR

Suidelike Olie-Eksplorasiek-Orporasie (The Southern Oil Exploration Corporation of South Africa).

Soft rope

Rope of hemp or jute or sisal or nylon, as distinguished from wire rope. See Ball, Ball, and Turner, *This Fascinating Oil Business* 114 (2d ed. 1965).

SOG system

The simultaneous oil and gas leasing system. See NON-COMPETITIVE LEASE; SIMULTANEOUS FILINGS.

SoLa I and II

The name given to the first and second Southern Louisiana Area Rate cases. See Placid Oil Co. v. Federal Power Comm'n, 483 F.2d 880 (5th Cir. 1973), *affirmed sub nom.* Mobil Oil Corp. v. Federal Power Comm'n, 417 U.S. 283, 49 *O.&G.R.* 543 (1974).

SOLAS

The International Convention for the Safety of Life at Sea.

Sold at the well

The royalty clause of many leases provides for royalty based on value or proceeds of gas "at the well" or of gas "sold at the well." In Butler v. Exxon Corp., 559 S.W.2d 410 at 416, 59 *O.&G.R.* 529 at 539 (Tex. Civ. App. 1977), error ref'd n.r.e.), *on later appeal,* 585 S.W.2d 881, 68 *O.&G.R.* 692 (Tex. Civ. App. 1979), the court concluded that "a sale may occur 'at the well' even though delivery is made several hundred feet from the christmas tree." After error was granted in *Butler v. Exxon Corp.,* on joint motion of the parties to dismiss, the cause was dismissed as moot and the judgment of the court below was set aside. 619 S.W.2d 399, 68 *O.&G.R.* 701 (Tex. 1981).

In Exxon Corp. v. Middleton, 613 S.W.2d 240, 67 *O.&G.R.* 431 (Tex. 1981), however, the court concluded that " 'sold at the wells' means sold at the wells within the lease, and not sold at the wells within the fields." It further declared that "[t]o the extent the Court of Civil Appeals' interpretation of the royalty clause in *Butler, supra,* conflicts with our interpretation of this clause, it is disapproved." On remand of *Exxon Corp. v. Middleton,* the case was dismissed in part, reversed and remanded in part on joint motion of the parties. 619 S.W.2d 477, 69 *O.&G.R.* 115 (Tex. Civ. App. 1981).

Sole party in interest

Under the system of SIMULTANEOUS FILINGS (*q.v.*) for federal leases, an applicant must comply with the "sole party in interest" regulations of the Department of the Interior. The term is defined in 43 C.F.R. § 3100.0–5 (1980) as "a party who is and will be vested with all legal and equitable rights under the lease. No one is, or shall be deemed to be, a sole party in interest with respect to an application, offer or lease in which any other party has any of the interests described in this section." These regulations are designed in part to curtail the activities performed by a LEASING SERVICE COMPANY (*q.v.*). See Hawley, "Federal Oil and Gas Leases—The Sole Party in Interest Debacle," 27 *Rocky Mt. Min. L. Inst.* 987 (1982).

Sole risk clause

The name given a clause in some joint venture agreements permitting one party (the proposing party) to proceed with exploration or development operations at its sole risk when another party or parties elect not to participate. The proposing party is thereby entitled to receive all of the petroleum extracted in the sole-risk operation until it has recovered its expenses plus some additional sum. See Mughraby, *Permanent Sovereignty Over Oil Resources* 89 (1966).

The special problems involved in drafting sole risk clauses for exploratory wells are discussed in Black, "Brief Review of General and Special Provisions in Offshore Operating Agreements," *Rocky Mt. Min. L. Fdn. Offshore Exploration, Drilling and Development Institute* 6–7 (1975). In some instances the discovery well is not capable of being completed, and hence recoupment to the risking party from the discovery well will not work. In other cases, if the well is completed production may not suffice to recoup the risker's investment and a high penalty factor, *e.g.*, 1000 percent. Hence it may be necessary to provide for recoupment from development wells drilled into the discovered reservoir, to require the party electing not to participate to withdraw from the venture or reservoir area to be tested, or to reduce the interest of such party in the affected area or venture.

For a discussion of sole risk operations under Norwegian law, see Krohn, Kaasen, *et al., Norwegian Petroleum Law* 3–17 (1978).

See also Hossain, *Law and Policy in Petroleum Development* 124 (1979); Nicholls, "Some Practical Problems of Joint Venture Agreements," 3 *Australian Mining and Petroleum L.J.* 41 (1981).

See also NON-CONSENT PENALTY.

Solution gas

Gas which is dissolved in oil in the reservoir under pressure.

Solution gas expansion

See DISSOLVED GAS DRIVE.

Solution gas field

An oil reservoir deriving some or all of its natural energy for production from the expansion of natural gas in solution in the oil.

See also RESERVOIR ENERGY.

Solvent refined coal (SRC)

A promising synthetic fuel for the replacement of residual fuel oil or gas used in intermediate- and peak-load plants in the electric utility industry. Because of its low sulfur content and high heat values, SRC burns fairly cleanly and is not expected to require the expensive stack gas-scrubbing equipment usually needed to burn coal. Congressional Budget Office, *The Decontrol of Domestic Oil Prices: An Overview* 48 (1979).

SONATRACH

The Algerian national oil company, La Société Nationale pour la Recherche, la Production, le Transport, la Transformation et la Commercialisation des Hydrocarbures.

See Terki, "An Outline of the Legal System for the Exploration and Exploitation of Liquid Hydrocarbons in Algeria," [1983] 1 *OGLTR* 13.

Sour gas

Natural gas contaminated with chemical inpurities, notably hydrogen sulphide or other sulphur compounds, which impart to the gas a foul odor. Such compounds must be removed before the gas can be used for commercial and domestic purposes.

At one time sour gas was frequently used in the manufacture of CARBON BLACK (*q.v.*).

In Permian Basin Area Rate Proceeding, sour gas was considered to be gas containing 10 or more grains of hydrogen sulphide or 200 or more grains of total sulphur per Mcf. 34 F.P.C. 159 at 173, note 4, 23 *O.&G.R.* 103 at 108, note 4 (Opinion No. 468, Aug. 5, 1965), *remanded,* Skelly Oil Co. v. Federal Power Comm'n, 375 F.2d 6, 26 *O.&G.R.* 237 (10th Cir. 1967), *aff'd in part and rev'd in part sub nom. In re* Permian Basin Area Rate Cases, 390 U.S. 747, 28 *O.&G.R.* 689 (1968).

See also SULFINOL SOLUTION; SWEET GAS.

Sour oil

Crude oil containing significant quantities of hydrogen sulphide gas.

Southland exclusion

The provision of the NATURAL GAS POLICY ACT OF 1978 (*q.v.*) [§ 2(18)] designed to modify in part the ruling in California v. Southland Royalty Co., 436 U.S. 519 (1978), extending the dedication obligation of a lessee to a lessor who reacquires his mineral right by a reversion of the leasehold (and to the subsequent lessees of the lessor). See Miles, "The Meaning of the *Southland* Exclusion—Complexity and Ambiguity in the Natural Gas Policy Act," 58 *Tex. L. Rev.* 435 (1980); Falcon Petroleum v. Federal Energy Regulatory Comm'n, 642 F.2d 780, 69 *O.&G.R.* 205 (5th Cir., Unit A, 1981); Columbia Gas Transmission Corp. v. Allied Chemical Corp., 470 F. Supp. 532, 65 *O.&G.R.* 89 (E.D. La. 1979), 470 F. Supp. 552, 65 *O.&G.R.* 129 (E.D. La. 1979), *aff'd in part, rev'd in part, vacated in part and remanded* 652 F.2d 503, 73 *O.&G.R.* 147 (5th Cir. 1981).

Mineral Resources, Inc. v. Federal Energy Regulatory Comm'n, 808 F.2d 107 (D.C. Cir. 1986), held that the Southland exclusion was inapplicable to gas which was actually being sold in interstate commerce on May 31, 1978, although the lease had expired in 1972, since the lessors had continued to allow the lessee to sell the gas in interstate commerce and to accept royalties resulting from those sales.

Southwestern Legal Foundation

A nonprofit corporation located in Dallas, Texas, which conducts a variety of institutes on varied subjects (including an annual *Institute on Oil and Gas Law and Taxation*) and publishes a variety of books including the *Oil & Gas Reporter.*

S.P.

Spontaneous potential. See ELECTRICAL WELL LOG.

Space heating customer

A purchaser for gas for space heating purposes. The demand of such customers varies widely on a seasonal basis.

See also FIRM CUSTOMER; INTERRUPTIBLE CUSTOMER.

Space heating saturation

The percentage of existing residential and commercial consumers of a system who use gas for space heating purposes. Michigan Consolidated Gas Co. v. Federal Power Comm'n, 283 F.2d 204 (D.C. Cir. 1960).

Spacing

See WELL SPACING.

Spacing unit

The area allocated to a well under a WELL SPACING ORDER(*q.v.*). The distinction between a spacing or drilling unit and a PRORATION UNIT(*q.v.*) is noted in Rutter & Wilbanks Corp. v. Oil Conservation Comm'n, 87 N.M. 286, 532 P.2d 582, 50 *O.&G.R.* 488 (1975).

See also DRILLING SPACING UNIT; DRILLING UNIT; POOLING BY A DRILLING AND SPACING UNIT; RULE 37; STANDUP DRILLING UNIT (STANDUP SPACING); TARGET AREA; WELL SPACING.

Spanish section

The term commonly given in Texas to certain sections of land smaller than 640 acres, *e.g.*, sections containing 320 acres, more or less. Brown v. Getty Reserve Oil, Inc., 626 S.W.2d 810, 72 *O.&G.R.* 588 (Tex. App., Amarillo, 1981, error dism'd w.o.j.).

SPCC

SPILL PREVENTION CONTROL AND COUNTERMEASURE (*q.v.*).

SPE

The Society of Petroleum Engineers.

Special area

In the United Kingdom this is a small and sensitive area in which circumstances justify a presumption against exploration for oil and gas. J. Salter, *U.K. Onshore Oil and Gas Law* 1-508 (1986).

Special drawing rights

An accounting unit of the International Monetary Fund based on a weighted system involving a number of currencies. These rights may be used only by member governments in settling balance of payment deficits among themselves. See "Balance-of-Payment Adjustment to Higher Oil Prices: Managing the Petrodollar Problem," in "The Economics of Energy and Natural Resource Pricing," Committee Print, A Compilation of Reports and Hearings of the Ad Hoc Committee on the Domestic and International Monetary Effect of Energy and Other Natural Resource Pricing, House Committee on Banking, Currency and Housing, 94th Cong., 1st Sess., March, 1975.

Special limitation clause

See LIMITATION CLAUSE.

Special marketing program

A program designed to alleviate the problems arising from a TAKE-OR PAY CLAUSE (*q.v.*) in certain gas purchase contracts under which a purchasing pipeline would release its contract right to certain categories of gas and would transport the released gas to a direct purchaser from the seller of the gas, the seller crediting the pipeline's take-or-pay liability with the volume of release gas sold. See Maryland People's Counsel v. Federal Energy Regulatory Comm'n, 761 F.2d 768, 87 *O.&G.R.* 616, 761 F.2d 780, 87 *O.&G.R.* 638 (D.C. Cir. 1985) (invalidating orders implementing the program), *remanded to Comm'n,* 768 F.2d 450, 87 *O.&G.R.* 658 (D.C. Cir. 1985).

See also the following:

Griggs, "Restructuring the Natural Gas Industry: Order No. 436 and Other Regulatory Initiatives," 7 *Energy L.J.* 71 (1986);

S. Williams, *The Natural Gas Revolution of 1985* (American Enterprise Inst. 1985);

Allison, "Natural Gas Pricing: The Eternal Debate," 37 *Baylor L. Rev.* 1 at 67 (1985);

Weller, "Competition in the Natural Gas Industry," 1 *Nat. Res. & Environment* 21 (Vol.1, No 2, Spring 1985);

Moody, "The Natural Gas Industry After Partial Deregulation," 36 *Sw. Legal Fdn. Oil & Gas Inst.* 6-1 at 6-40 (1985).

Special project costs

Costs of acquiring and constructing tangible properties for other than customary oil and gas drilling and production operations, *e.g.*, compressor stations, secondary recovery facilities, salt water disposal facilities, living quarters, etc.

Special relief applications

Applications to the Federal Power Commission or to its successor, the Federal Energy Regulatory Commission, seeking special relief from area rate ceilings for natural gas prices by reason of such matters as reduced pressures, need for reconditioning, deeper drilling, or other factors making further production uneconomical at existing prices [18 C.F.R. § 2.76 (1980)] or to encourage the recovery of natural gas which would otherwise be flared or vented [18 C.F.R. § 2.77 (1980)]. Provisions for special relief permitting sellers to charge a rate in excess of the national rate is provided in 18 C.F.R. §§ 2.56a and 2.56b (1980).

Special Renewal Permit (SPR)

Under section 121 of the Canada Oil & Gas Land Regulations (1978), a permittee may apply for a Special Renewal Permit (SPR), thus delaying the need to go to lease, with attendant acreage surrenders. The SPR requirement, however, gives Petro-Canada the option of acquiring up to 25% of the acreage under the SPR (depending upon the Canadian ownership rate of the permittee). See Hunt, "Private Sector Legal Problems Arising from Canadianization of Petroleum Activities," *Resources, The Newsletter of the Canadian Institute of Resources Law* (No. 5, June 1983).

Special tar sand area

Under the provisions of the COMBINED HYDROCARBON LEASING ACT OF 1981 (CHLA) (*q.v.*), this term means an area designated by specified orders of the Secretary of the Interior as containing substantial deposits of tar sand.

See also PETROLEUM TAR SANDS.

Specialty contract

A contract for specialized services in the drilling of a well, such as electrical well logging. These are services that an independent drilling contractor does not normally render.

See also DRILLING CONTRACT.

Special warranty

A covenant of title in a deed, lease or assignment, the effect of which is to guarantee title against all defects arising out of claims of the grantor, lessor or assignor and of persons claiming by, through or from the grantor, lessor or assignor. Mineral and royalty deeds and oil and gas leases customarily have general warranty clauses; assignments of leases ordinarily contain only a special warranty, if any covenant of title is used at all.

See also GENERAL WARRANTY; WARRANTY.

Specific gravity

In the case of liquids, the ratio between the weight of equal volumes of water and another substance measured at standard temperature, where the weight of the water is assigned a value of 1. However, the specific gravity of oil is normally expressed in the industry in degrees of API GRAVITY (*q.v.*). In the case of gas, the ratio is between air and gas, where the weight of air is assigned a value of 1.

Spec shoot

Geophysical exploration on a speculative basis by a geophysical contractor made with the intention that the cost be recovered by sale of the information to one or more oil companies. Energy Data Requirements of the Federal Government (Part III—Federal Offshore Oil and Gas Leasing Policies), Hearings before the Subcommittee on Activities of Regulatory Agencies of the Permanent Select Committee on Small Business, House of Representatives, 93rd Cong., 2d Sess. (1974) at p. 363.

See also GEOPHYSICAL EXPLORATION; GROUP SHOOT.

Spectral logging

Discerning the energies of wave lengths of gamma rays given off by various elements within the formations surrounding the well bore and presenting this information at the surface of the earth in the form of gamma ray spectra, thus permitting discrimination between the various elements. Spectral logging is the process of detecting and measuring the energy of the gamma radiation in addition to the intensity thereof, thereby permitting a distinction to be made in the gamma ray emissions of radioactive substances of different characteristics and in the nature of the neutron capture gamma rays emitted by the nuclei of different materials; it is thus distinguished from conventional gamma ray, neutron-gamma ray and gamma ray-gamma ray logging which involve merely the measurement of the total intensity of all of the gamma rays impinging upon the detector with energies above some threshold level. See Well Surveys, Inc. v. McCullough Tool Co., 199 F. Supp. 374 (N.D. Okla. 1961).

See also WELL LOG.

Speculative reserves or resources

Undiscovered resources that may occur either in known types of deposits in a favorable geologic setting where no discoveries have been made, or in as yet unknown types of deposits that remain to be recognized. Exploration that confirms their existence and reveals quantity and quality will permit their reclassification as RESERVES (*q.v.*) or IDENTIFIED-SUB-ECONOMIC RESOURCES (*q.v.*). 2 *OCS Oil and Gas—An Environmental Assessment,* A Report to the President by the Council on Environmental Quality (April 1974) at p. 12.

Speculative value

The value that a landowner may get, in unproven territory, from the sale of an interest in oil and gas in the land. The wrongful destruction of speculative values may result in liability. For example, in Humble Oil and Ref. Co. v. Kishi, 276 S.W. 190, 291 S.W. 538 (Tex. Com. App. 1925, 1927), a trespasser who entered and drilled a dry hole on the land of another was held liable in damages for the difference in the lease price of the land before and after the entry and drilling. *Contra:* Martel v. Hall Oil Co., 36 Wyo. 166, 253 Pac. 862 (1927). See Green, "Protection from Trespass Destroying Speculative Value," 4 *Tex. L. Rev.* 215 (1926); 5 *Tex. L. Rev.* 323 (1927). For related cases, see Eagle Lake Improvement Co. v. United States, 141 F.2d 562 (5th Cir. 1944) (condemnation); American Surety Co. v. Marsh, 146 Okla. 261, 293 Pac. 1041 (1930). See TREATISE § 229.

Spillover pit

A pit drilled at the drilling site of a well to catch the drilling fluid that may spill over from the RESERVE PIT (*q.v.*) during the drilling operation. Amoco Production Co. v. Carter Farms Co., 103 N.M. 117, 703 P.2d 894, 86 *O.&G.R.* 84 (1985).

See also BURN PIT.

Spill prevention control and countermeasure (SPCC)

The Environmental Protection Agency requires that owners or operators of onshore and offshore facilities "that have discharged or . . . could reasonably be expected to discharge oil in harmful quantities . . . into or upon the navigable waters of the United States or adjoining shorelines, . . . prepare a Spill Prevention Control and Countermeasure plan." 40 C.F.R. § 112.3(a) (1980). See Cowles, "Environmental Regulation of Offshore Exploration, Production, and Development," 27 *Sw. Legal Fdn. Oil & Gas Inst.* 53 at 73 (1976).

Spin-off royalty trust

A ROYALTY TRUST (*q.v.*) arising as a result of the desire of a corporation with natural resources properties to distribute nonoperating mineral interests to its shareholders.

Spiral escalation clause

See ESCALATOR CLAUSE

Split connection

The term applied to the situation where two or more gas purchasers (rather than a single gas purchaser) are connected to a producing well. See Beren v. Harper Oil Co., 546 P.2d 1356, 53 *O.&G.R.* 531 (Okla. App. 1975, *as corrected on limited grant of certiorari*). See also TREATISE § 951.

Where tracts involve split connections and sales of gas produced to purchasers under different gas purchase contracts, royalty owners in a tract may be entitled to share with other royalty owners in the tract in the proportion that a royalty owner's acreage in such tract bears to the entire unit acreage.

"The end result of this sharing of the royalties from all gas produced from a tract which has been communitized is that each royalty owner receives a weighted average price for his royalty payment which may vary slightly from the contract price received by a royalty owner's lessee. This is due to the varying prices received under gas purchase agreements by the different working interests owners in a communitized tract." Barby v. Cabot Corp., 550 F. Supp. 188 at 189, 74 *O.&G.R.* 313 at 315 (W.D. Okla. 1981).

See also BALANCING; CANCELLED UNDERAGE; DEEMED PURCHASE FORMULA; DEFERRED PRODUCTION AGREEMENT; GAS BANK AGREEMENT; LIFTING; LIFTING TOLERANCE; "OUT OF BALANCE" PRODUCTION PLAN; OVERLIFT; SPLIT CONNECTION; UNDERAGE; UNDERLIFT; UNDERLIFT/OVERLIFT PROVISION.

Split firing

A system permitting the burning of a combination of oil and gas for boiler fuel. State of Louisiana v. Federal Power Comm'n, 503 F. 2d 844 at 860 (5th Cir. 1974).

Split formula

An allocation formula for unit production in which the participation factor is calculated separately for the period during which the estimated ultimately recoverable oil under primary operations is recovered and the period during which the remaining reserves are recovered as a result of the unitized program of operations. Roark, "Matters of Mutual Concern to the Lawyer and Engineer in the Unitization Agreement," 7 *Sw. Legal Fdn. Oil & Gas Inst.* 275 at 298 (1956).

For cases dealing with a split formula see Jones Oil Co. v. Corporation Comm'n, 382 P.2d 751, 18 *O.&G.R.* 1041 (Okla. 1963), *cert. denied,* 375 U.S. 931, 19 *O.&G.R.* 362 (1963); Producers Development Co. v. Magna Oil Corp., 371 P.2d 702, 17 *O.&G.R.* 769 (Okla. 1962). See TREATISE § 970.1.

Split lease

A lease issued by a state prior to June 5, 1950 covering land partly within the state and partly on the Outer Continental Shelf. By Section 6 of the OUTER CONTINENTAL SHELF LANDS ACT(*q.v.*), the lease was validated as to the land on the Outer Continental Shelf, and the result was to create two separate and distinct leases, one with the federal and the other with the state government. "Former State Leases Bisected by the Present State Line Dividing the Submerged Lands from the Outer Continental Shelf," GFS OCS–1955–8A (Solicitor's Opinion, Department of the Interior, Feb. 18, 1955).

Split sales

A term used to describe the separate sales of gas by persons having interests in a common gas reservoir. See Muir, "Split Sales of Gas," 9 *Alta. L. Rev.* 496 (1971); Upchurch, "Split Stream Gas Sales and the Gas Storage and Balancing Agreement," 24 *Rocky Mt. Min. L. Inst.* 665 (1978).

Split stream gas well

A well from which several persons receive their share of production "in kind." For a discussion of problems arising in connection with such wells, see Niebrugge, "Oil and Gas: Production Imbalance in Split Stream Gas Wells—Getting Your Fair Share," 30 *Okla. L. Rev.* 955 (1977). See TREATISE § 951.

Split stream test

A test to determine the distillate content of gas. This type of test is more economical than a full stream test for the same purpose. See Texas Gas Corp. v. Hankamer, 326 S.W.2d 944, 11 *O.&G.R.* 669 (Tex. Civ. App. 1959, error ref'd n.r.e.).

Spontaneous potential

See ELECTRICAL WELL LOG

Spot market

(1) The term applied to sales of domestic crude by majors to independents from the majors' overproduction or surplus. Note, "National Energy Goals and FEA's Mandatory Crude Oil Allocation Program," 61 *Va. L. Rev.* 903 (1975).

(2) A market for purchase and sale of crude oil or oil products on a short-term basis or for a single voyage or "spot" tanker charter. The rates in this market are not necessarily the same as those for long-term or medium-term charter tanker shipping agreements entered into at the same point in time. The European spot market in petroleum and its products is known by the short name Rotterdam,

named for the city which is a major center of this marketing activity. *The Wall Street Journal,* April 7, 1981, p. 38, col. 1; Dijkhof, "West European Oil Markets with Special Reference to Rotterdam—Some Legal and Contractual Aspects," 8 *Int'l Bus. Law.* 277 (1980). Other important spot markets are Singapore, the Caribbean, and the East Coast of the United States. OPEC, *Basic Oil Industry Information* 41 (1983).

See also DAISY CHAIN; FUTURES MARKET; NETBACK; PAPER BARREL.

Spot purchases (or sales) of gas

Contracts for the purchase and sale of gas on a short term basis. These contracts have traditionally been for lower prices than long-term pipeline contracts, this being the concession to the pipeline by the producer for the right to discontinue his spot sales when long-term arrangements are completed. Payne, "The Exemption of Producers from Regulation Under the Act as Viewed by the Interstate Pipeline Companies and Distributors," A.B.A., Section of Mineral Law, *1956 Proceedings* 40 at 50 (1956). See TREATISE § 720.

See also GAS PURCHASE CONTRACT.

SPQ

Synthetic pipeline quality gas, synonymous with SYNTHETIC NATURAL GAS (SNG) (*q.v.*).

SPR

(1) STRATEGIC PETROLEUM RESERVE (*q.v.*).
(2) SPECIAL RENEWAL PERMIT (SPR) (*q.v.*).

SPR Drawdown plan

STRATEGIC PETROLEUM RESERVE DRAWDOWN PLAN (*q.v.*).

See also STRATEGIC PETROLEUM RESERVE.

Spraberry type contract

A common type of contract providing for the purchase of casinghead gas by a pipeline which processes the gas, and pays the producer a fixed percentage of the proceeds from the sale of the extracted liquids, plus a fixed price for the residue gas delivered to the pipeline. See Permian Basin Area Rate Proceeding, 34 F.P.C. 159 at 208, 23 *O.&G.R.* 103 at 157 (Opinion No. 468, Aug. 5, 1965), *remanded,* Skelly Oil Co. v. Federal Power Comm'n, 375 F.2d 6, 26

O.&G.R. 237 (10th Cir. 1967), *aff'd in part and rev'd in part sub nom. In re* Permian Basin Area Rate Cases, 390 U.S. 747, 28 *O.&G.R.* 689 (1968).

See also Gas purchase contract.

SPS

Subsea production system, *viz.*, the complex of piping, valves and related equipment used to produce oil and gas from individual or connected subsea completions. Kash, et al., *Energy Under the Oceans* 52, 368 (1973).

Spudder

A colloquialism for a small drilling rig. See Hamco Oil & Drilling Co. v. Ervin, 354 P.2d 442, 12 *O.&G.R.* 1081 (Okla. 1960).

Spudding

See Spudding in.

Spudding bit

See Bit, spudding.

Spudding in

The first boring of the hole in the drilling of an oil well.

Because of the nature of the earth at the surface, regular drilling tools are not necessarily used to drill the first hundred or so feet of hole. Often, a special "spudding bit" will be used, and then regular drilling tools are substituted as the well gets down to rock formations. Under an Unless lease (*q.v.*) providing "If operations for drilling are not commenced on said land" or containing similar wording, it is usually held that spudding in amounts to commencement of operations for drilling. In fact, preliminary activities prior to spudding in will satisfy the clause. See Treatise § 606.1.

The definition in this Manual was cited by the court in Hilliard v. Franzheim, 180 So.2d 746 at 747 (La. App. 1965).

This definition was quoted and followed in L & B Oil Co. v. Federal Energy Regulatory Commission, 665 F.2d 758, 73 *O.&G.R.* 399 (5th Cir., Unit A, 1982).

Spud in

See Spudding in.

SPWLA

The Society of Professional Well Log Analysts, a scientific society concerned with formation evaluation through well logging techniques. See WELL LOG.

Squeeze

In an A-B-C TRANSACTION (*q.v.*), this term has been employed in reference to the difference between the interest paid by *C*, the purchaser of the production payment, and the increment accrual, *viz.*, the excess of the production payment over the purchase price thereof. The squeeze is *C*'s net profit. The amount of the squeeze varies with the transaction, being as high as one percent and, in larger transactions, as low as one-sixteenth of one per cent. See Sack, "ABC's of the ABC Oil Transaction," 59 *Northwestern L. Rev.* 591 at 595 (1964).

Squeeze a well

A technique designed to seal off a part of a well hole where a leak exists to permit introduction of a sealing agent. By the use of a packer, part of the hole is sealed off and then cement slurry under high pressures is forced into the fracture for hardening as a permanent closure. The process is discussed in Rorem v. Halliburton Oil Well Cementing Co., 246 F.2d 427, 7 *O.&G.R.* 1489 (5th Cir. 1957).

Squeeze cementing

Syn. for SQUEEZE JOB. See Pshigoda v. Texaco, Inc. 703 S.W.2d 416, 90 *O.&G.R.* 135 (Tex. Civ. App., Amarillo, 1986, error ref'd n.r.e.).

Squeeze job

An operation designed to force cement up on the outside of the casing to shut off leaks therein. After a squeeze job it is necessary that the cement be then drilled from the hole, preferably by a light drilling machine known as a spudder. See Wilson v. Holm, 164 Kan. 229, 188 P.2d 899 (1948); Trichel Contracting Co. v. Roland, 127 So.2d 214, 14 *O.&G.R.* 978 (La. App. 1961); Rorem v. Halliburton Oil Well Cementing Co., 246 F.2d 427, 7 *O.&G.R.* 1489 (5th Cir. 1957).

This term is defined in Dowell, Inc. v. Cichowski, 540 S.W.2d 342 at 344, 55 *O.&G.R.* 199 at 201 (Tex. Civ. App. 1976), as follows:

"A squeeze job is an operation, usually performed by an oil field service company, wherein cement is pumped down into the well and forced outside the casing through perforations deliberately made in the casing; such cement is forced into the strata and formations surrounding the well so as to create a seal or dam between the water and oil-bearing sand."

See also Waterbury v. Byron Jackson, Inc., 576 F.2d 1095, 61 *O.&G.R.* 167 (5th Cir. 1978).

SRC

SOLVENT REFINED COAL (*q.v.*).

Stabber

A person who assists in running casing into oil and gas wells. The stabber works on a board high in the derrick known as a stabbing board and guides the casing into its proper place. St. Julien v. Diamond M Drilling, 403 F.Supp. 1256 (E.D. La. 1975).

Stabilization clause

See LAW STABILIZING CLAUSE.

Stabilized crude oil

Crude oil which has been treated to separate out dissolved gas.

Stabilized liquid hydrocarbon

The product of a production operation in which the entrained gaseous hydrocarbons have been removed to the degree that said liquid may be stored at atmospheric conditions. 16 Tex. Admin. Code § 3.36(b)(2).

Stabilizer

A device in the drilling assembly to control the location of the contact point between the hole and the drill collars.

Standard casinghead gas contract

A form adopted by the National Gasoline Association of America. See CASINGHEAD GAS CONTRACT.

Standard cubic foot

The volume of gas contained in one cubic foot of space at a standard pressure base and at a standard temperature base. Whenever the conditions of pressure and temperature differ from the standard, conversion of the volume from these conditions to the standard conditions is made in accordance with the Ideal Gas Laws, corrected for deviation.

In several states, *e.g.*, Arkansas, Oklahoma and Texas, a standard cubic foot of gas is determined on a pressure base of 14.65 psia and a temperature of 60 degree F. In some other states, *e.g.*, Colorado, Louisiana and Mississippi, the pressure base is 15.025 psia and the temperature base is 60 degree F. In yet other states the pressure base and temperature employed differ from the above. See STANDARD GAS MEASUREMENT LAW.

See also NORMAL CUBIC METER.

Standard gas measurement law

A law providing a standard method of measuring gas.

See Tex. Nat. Res. Code § 91.052 (1978):

"(a) The term 'cubic foot of gas' or 'standard cubic foot of gas' means the volume of gas contained in one cubic foot of space at a standard pressure base and at a standard temperature base.

"(b) The standard pressure base shall be 14.65 pounds per square inch absolute, and the standard temperature base shall be 60 degrees Fahrenheit. If the conditions of pressure and temperature differ from this standard, conversion of the volume from these conditions to the standard conditions shall be made in accordance with the ideal gas laws, corrected for deviation."

"Eleven states have adopted a pressure base for measuring gas of 15.025 psia at 60 degree F., ten have adopted 14.65 at 60 degree F., five have adopted 14.73 at 60 degree F., and five have no requirement in this regard. (Ohio and Idaho are not included in the report of definitions, however, they have adopted pressure bases of 14.73 psia at 70 degree F., and 15.025 psia at 60 degree F., respectively.)" 26 *Oil & Gas Compact Bull.* 55 (June 1967). See also Weaver and Anderson, "Oil Recovery from Gas-Cap Reservoirs." *Bureau of Mines Monograph* 13 (1966) at page 3.

Standard pressure base

One of the factors used in determining the volume of gas produced. See STANDARD GAS MEASUREMENT LAW (*q.v.*).

Standard turnkey contract

See TURNKEY CONTRACT.

Standby Mandatory International Oil Allocation

Regulations designed to implement the INTERNATIONAL ENERGY PROGRAM (*q.v.*). 10 C.F.R. § 218 (1980).

See also ECONOMIC REGULATORY ADMINISTRATION (ERA).

Stand-by requirement

A provision of a GAS PURCHASE CONTRACT (*q.v.*) whereby seller is required to deliver, on demand, large quantities of gas above the minimum. Such provision makes it necessary for the seller to maintain stand-by capacity to meet such requirements. See Sartor v. United Gas Public Service Co., 186 La. 55, 1973 So. 103 (1937).

Stand-by rig time

Payment made under the provisions of a DRILLING CONTRACT (*q.v.*) during the period of time when drilling is temporarily held in abeyance pending agreement among interested parties on such a matter as whether to continue drilling, etc. *Syn.:* SHUT-DOWN TIME.

Standup drilling unit (Standup spacing)

When a DRILLING UNIT (*q.v.*) or SPACING UNIT (*q.v.*) is established on a geographical basis utilizing lines bounding sections or regular subdivisions thereof, the drilling unit or spacing unit will be in the form of a square (40, 160, 640 acre units or spacing) or in the form of a rectangle (20 or 80 acre units or spacing). A rectangular drilling unit or spacing unit in which the long axis of the rectangle runs north and south is sometimes described as a standup unit (or standup spacing). If the long axis of the rectangle runs east and west, the unit (or spacing) may be described as laydown, lie-down, or prone. See Calvert Drilling Co. v. Corporation Comm'n, 589 P.2d 1064 (Okla. 1979).

For a discussion of certain of the considerations relevant to the decision to create a standup drilling unit or a prone drilling unit, see Stacy v. Tomlinson Interests, Inc., 405 So.2d 93, 71 *O.&G.R.* 519 (Miss. 1981).

Murphy v. Amoco Production Co., 590 F.Supp. 455, 83 *O.&G.R.* 108 (D. N.D. 1984), concluded that a lessee did not breach the duty of good faith or of fair dealing owed his lessor in exercising the pooling clause of the lease by seeking to have the regulatory commission adopt a standup spacing order rather than a prone spacing order.

Amoco Production Co. v. North Dakota Industrial Comm'n, 307 N.W.2d 839, 70 *O.&G.R.* 283 (N.D. 1981), sustained the validity of a standup spacing order to protect correlative rights.

See also DRILLING SPACING UNIT; TARGET AREA; WELL SPACING.

Stand-up search

See TITLE OPINION.

State contract

The term frequently employed for an ECONOMIC DEVELOPMENT AGREEMENT (*q.v.*) or CONCESSION (*q.v.*). See Flint, "Foreign Investment and the New International Economic Order," in Hossain and Chowdhury, *Permanent Sovereignty Over Natural Resources in International Law* 144 at 145 (1984).

Statement of objections

A statement required to be filed by an aggrieved party to a PROPOSED REMEDIAL ORDER (*q.v.*), issued by the ECONOMIC REGULATORY ADMINISTRATION (ERA) (*q.v.*) in order to exhaust administrative remedies. 10 C.F.R. § 205.193 (1980).

Statewide hearing

See FIELD HEARING.

STATOIL

The Norwegian state oil company, Det norske stats oljeselskap a.s., established in 1972. The company is wholly owned by the state, and the Ministry of Petroleum and Energy is the General Meeting of the company. For discussions of the role of STATOIL in petroleum exploration and development, see the following:

Middelthon, "Statoil, The Norwegian National Oil Corporation," International Bar Ass'n, *Energy Law 1981* at p. 75;

Gisvold, "Norwegian Petroleum Law and Administration," [1982] 6 *OGLTR* 195;

Rud and Wattne, "Ten Years of State Involvement in the Petroleum Industry: Norway," in International Bar Ass'n, *Proceedings of the Energy Law Seminar* (organized by the Committee on Energy and Natural Resources, Section of Business Law) Topic R, Paper 2, (1979);

Middelthon, "STATOIL—Objectives and Perspectives," *International Business Lawyer* 71 (March 1979 Special Issue).

Statutory Pugh clause

The name which has been applied to statutes limiting the time during which lease acreage excluded from a producing spacing unit or pooled unit may be held in effect by production from the spacing unit or pooled unit, *e.g.*, as follows:

> "In case of a spacing unit of 160 acres or more, no oil and/or gas leasehold interest outside the spacing unit involved may be held by production from the spacing unit more than 90 days beyond expiration of the primary term of the lease." 52 Okla, Stat. § 87.1(b) (Supp.), discussed by Lowe, "Mineral Law Section Annual Survey of Significant Developments," 54 *Okla. B.J.* 859 at 862 (1983).

For other variants see the following: 53 Ark. Stat. Ann. 1971 §§ 321–323 (Supp.) (applicable to oil and gas leases entered into after the effective date of the Act, July 4, 1983);

Code Va. § 45.1-326(5) (providing that no oil or gas leasehold interest in land not contained in a statutory drilling unit may be held solely by production from the unit and payment of royalties due thereon for more than one year beyond the expiration of the primary term of the lease, subject to certain exceptions).

See also PUGH CLAUSE.

Statutory unitization

Syn.: COMPULSORY UNITIZATION (*q.v.*).

stb

Stock tank barrel of oil, or 42 U.S. Gallons at 60 degree F.

Steaming plant

A plant designed to remove excess water from oil as produced to render the oil merchantable. See TREATING PLANT.

Steam stimulation

A thermal recovery method involving the injection of steam into a producing well for a predetermined length of time after which the well is returned to productive status. See Keeling, "The Application of Advanced Recovery Techniques in the Mid-Continent Area," 8 IOCC Comm. Bull 11 (June 1966).

See also DOWNHOLE STEAM GENERATION; PRODUCED AND SOLD; SECONDARY RECOVERY; TERTIARY RECOVERY; THERMAL METHOD OF OIL RECOVERY.

Step-back of oil payment

The deferral of an oil payment. See DEFERRED OIL PAYMENT.

Step-out well

A well drilled adjacent to a proven well but located in an unproven area; a well drilled as a "step-out" from proven territory in an effort to ascertain the extent and boundaries of a producing formation.

Step-price increase clause

See ESCALATOR CLAUSE.

Step scale royalty

A royalty rate which increases by steps as the average production increases, *e.g.,* 12½% for the first 20 barrels per well per day, 16⅔% on the next 30 barrels, *etc.* A SLIDING SCALE ROYALTY (*q.v.*), on the other hand, is based on average production and is applicable to all production. See Schwabrow, "Supervision of Operations Under Federal and Indian Oil and Gas Leases by the United States Geological Survey," 8 *Rocky Mt. Min. L. Inst.* 241 at 258 (1963).

Step up clause

A periodic or step-price increase clause. See ESCALATOR CLAUSE.

Still gas

Any form or mixture of gas produced in refineries by cracking, reforming, and other processes, the principal constituents of which are methane and ethane.

See also REFINERY GAS.

Stimulate

This term is defined by W. Va. Code § 22–4–1(u) (Cum. Supp. 1980) as "any action taken by well operator to increase the inherent productivity of an oil or gas well including, but not limited to, fracturing, shooting or acidizing, but excluding cleaning out, bailing or workover operations."

See also SECONDARY RECOVERY.

Stipulation of interest

(1) An instrument amounting to certification of legal title and authorization for payment on royalty interests in accordance with the terms of an oil or gas purchase contract. Greenshields v. Warren Petroleum Corp., 248 F.2d 61, 8 *O.&G.R.* 937 (10th Cir. 1957), *cert. denied,* 355 U.S. 907 (1957); Hafeman v. Gem Oil Co., 163 Neb. 438, 80 N.W.2d 139, 7 *O.&G.R.* 41 (1956).

(2) A DIVISION ORDER (*q.v.*). Bounds, "Division Orders," 5 *Sw. Legal Fdn. Oil & Gas Inst.* 91 at 92 (1954).

Stipulation *pour autri*

In Louisiana, an advantage to a third person created as a condition or consideration of a contract. LSA-CC art. 1978 (1985). For cases dealing with the question whether a surface user clause of an oil and gas lease is a stipulation *pour autri* for a surface owner not a party to the lease see TREATISE § 673.6, note 29.

See also THIRD PARTY BENEFICIARY.

Stocking-out agreement

A colloquialism for a subscription agreement wherein investors agree to subscribe certain funds for drilling and equiping a well in exchange for a fractional interest therein and wherein the duties and obligations of the promoter are set forth. See Bush No. 1 c/o Stonestreet Lands Co. v. Comm'r, 48 T.C. 218 at 220, 27 *O.&G.R.* 87 at 89 (1967).

See also PROJECT FINANCING.

Stock tank

A large tank for temporary storage of WET OIL (*q.v.*) before it is admitted to treatment tanks (where it is heated or subjected to chemical treatment to remove water).

Stopcocking

Periodically shutting in wells to permit buildup of gas pressure in the sands about them and then opening the wells at intervals for production.

Stopcock, to

To control gas pressure in an oil well by closing the well at intervals to permit a build up of pressure.

Storage gas

Gas transferred from its original location in the ground to another underground formation near the market. See GAS STORAGE, SUBSURFACE.

Storage sprinkling

The term applied to the provision of a CURTAILMENT PLAN (*q.v.*) which categorizes summer storage injections on the basis of proportionate end-use of winter withdrawals. Federal Power Commission Orders No. 787, 11 FPS 5–397 (Jan. 26, 1977), 787–A, 12 FPS 5–230 (June 1, 1977), and 787–B, 13 FPS 5–668 (Nov. 29, 1977), *aff'd,* Elizabethtown Gas Co. v. Federal Energy Regulatory Comm'n, 636 F.2d 1328 (D. C. Cir. 1980).

For a discussion of storage sprinkling under a CURTAILMENT PLAN (*q.v.*), see Process Gas Consumers Group v. United States Dept. of Agriculture, 694 F.2d 728 (D.C. Cir. 1981), *modified on rehearing en banc,* 694 F.2d 778 (D.C. Cir. 1982), *cert. denied,* 461 U.S. 905, 103 S. Ct. 1874 (1983).

Storage tank

Tank for the accumulation of oil pending transferal to a pipeline company or other purchaser.

Storage well

Syn.: BOTTLE WELL (*q.v.*).

Storage withdrawal interruption policy

A policy for interrupting delivery of gas to an INTERRUPTIBLE CUSTOMER (*q.v.*), under which delivery of gas is automatically discontinued whenever the seller is withdrawing gas from its storage reservoirs. Great Western Sugar Co. v. Northern Natural Gas Co., 661 P.2d 684, 77 *O.&G.R.* 19 (Colo. App. 1982), *affirmed sub nom.* KN Energy, Inc. v. Great Western Sugar Co., ____ Colo ____, 698 P.2d 769, 85 *O.&G.R.* 17 (1985), *cert. denied,* 472 U.S. 1022, 105 S.Ct. 3489 (1985).

Stored gas

Gas produced from one formation and injected into another depleted formation near the market for purposes of temporary storage. The tax treatment of this gas is discussed in *Miller's Oil and Gas Federal Income Taxation* § 9–6 (1980 Edition).

West Bay Exploration Co. v. Amoco Production Co., 148 Mich. App. 197, 384 N.W.2d 407, ____ *O.&G.R.* ____ (1986), cited definitions in this MANUAL and concluded that leaving gas in place did not constitute "storage" as that word was used by the oil and gas industry and in the instrument construed. The judgment was vacated and the case remanded, 425 Mich. 878, 384 N.W.2d 407 (1986), but on remand, 155 Mich. App. 429, 399 N.W.2d 549 (1986), the court adhered to its prior decision.

Store lease

A printed lease form with certain blanks to be filled in by the parties. Romero v. Brewer, 58 Cal.App.2d 759, 137 P.2d 872 (1943).

Storer

A person who places petroleum or any petroleum product in any receptacle and keeps the same in any such receptacle for any period of time longer than is usually required in the ordinary conduct of business to move the same currently into the channels of trade and commerce, but excluding the ordinary working stocks of refiners and transporters by pipe line. 30 C.F.R. § 222.2(i) (1980).

Straddle plant

A plant for the removal of ethane, propane, butane and pentane from natural gas. The word "straddle" refers to the location of the plant on a pipeline system downstream from the fields where the gas is produced to distinguish a field plant located in the field where the gas is produced. See Alberta Energy Conservation Board Decision 76–2, Application 8856 (April 23, 1976).

Straight gas well

A well producing gas but not oil. Deep South Oil Co. v. Federal Power Comm'n, 247 F.2d 882, 7 *O.&G.R.* 1539 (5th Cir. 1957), *cert. denied in companion case,* 355 U.S. 930 (1958).

Straight hole clause

A clause frequently inserted in RULE 37 (*q.v.*) permits in Texas which conditions the permit to drill on an inclination survey being run periodically as the well is drilled.

The clause requires that the well be drilled within three degrees of the vertical, does not authorize a well to cross a lease boundary, and requires certain tests to check on compliance and sworn statements of compliance before an allowable is set. If a well is drilled out of tolerance, a hearing is required to determine if the well may be produced. Healey, "Oil and Gas—Orders of Railroad Commission—Power to Punish—Continued Existence of Rights Granted by a Drilling Permit are Not Conditioned on Drilling a Straight Hole," 42 *Tex. L. Rev.* 922 at 923 n2 (1964).

In 1946 the Texas Railroad Commission adopted a policy of inserting straight hole clauses in specific Rule 37 permits where the offset operators requested it. By 1948, the Commission had settled on a standard straight hole clause. State v. Harrington, 407 S.W.2d 467 at 475 n7, 25 *O.&G.R.* 582 at 591 n7 (Tex. 1966), *cert. denied,* 386 U.S. 944 (1967). See also R. W. Byram & Co., *Texas Oil and Gas Handbook* 18 (1958); Stewart v. Humble Oil & Refining Co., 377 S.W.2d 830.20 *O.&G.R.* 436 (Tex., 1964).

Strappage deduction

A deduction (*e.g.,* 1% or 2%) made in measuring oil produced. The oil is run into tanks which have been strapped (measured) and for which tank tables have been compiled. From the quantity indicated by the tank tables a strappage deduction may be taken before an accounting is made for the oil produced. See Luling Oil & Gas Co. v. Humble Oil & Refining Co., 144 Tex. 475, 191 S.W.2d 716 (1946).

Strapping

Measuring a tank for purposes of preparing a tank table.

Strategic petroleum reserve

A stockpile of oil stored for use in the event of an embargo by petroleum exporting countries. See Holcombe, "Strategic Petroleum Reserve," 26 *Oil & Gas Tax Q.* 457 (1978).

United States v. 43.42 Acres of Land, 520 F.Supp. 1042 71 *O.&G.R.* 31 (W.D. La. 1981), dealt with the problem of compensation for use of an underground cavity for the storage of crude oil under the strategic petroleum reserve program. The cavity had been created by the extraction of salt by the owner of a mineral servitude. The court concluded that the landowner rather than the servitude owner was the person entitled to compensation for the taking of the cavity for storage purposes. The mineral servitude owners were entitled only to compensation for the value of the right to explore for and reduce to possession the minerals (salt) on the land in question.

Statutory and administrative materials on the strategic petroleum reserve are collected in Fox, *Federal Regulation of Energy* ch. 9 (1983). Regulations of allocation of drawdowns from the reserve are contained in 10 C.F.R. Part 220. See TREATISE § 222.

See also ENERGY EMERGENCY PREPAREDNESS ACT OF 1982 (EEPA); FORWARD SALES OF STRATEGIC PETROLEUM RESERVE OIL.

Strategic petroleum reserve drawdown plan

A plan prepared in accordance with the provisions of the ENERGY EMERGENCY PREPAREDNESS ACT OF 1982 (EEPA) (*q.v.*) for the drawdown, sale, and distribution of strategic petroleum reserve oil in the event of a severe energy supply disruption, or to fulfill the obligations of the United States under the INTERNATIONAL ENERGY PROGRAM (IEP) (*q.v.*). See *CCH, Energy Management* ¶ 30,501 (Jan. 28, 1983).

See also FORWARD SALES OF STRATEGIC PETROLEUM RESERVE OIL.

Stratigraphic equivalent

In cases of horizontal severances of a leasehold, the assignment may seek to account for the nonuniform lay of subsurface structures by assigning down to the stratigraphic equivalent of a stated numerical depth beneath the surface in order to ensure that a productive reservoir is not split by the assignment. Thus the assignment may provide that it extends to the grantor's interest from the surface down to the stratigraphic equivalent of 4,000 feet beneath the surface, as measured in the bore of a designated well. D. Pierce, *Kansas Oil and Gas Handbook* § 7.06 (1986).

Stratigraphic interval

The body of strata between two stratigraphic markers. American Geological Institute, *Glossary of Geology* (R. Bates and J. Jackson, eds., 2d ed. 1980); Energy Reserves Group, Inc., 92 IBLA 219, GFS(O&G) 1986-67.

See also INTERVAL.

Stratigraphic test hole

A "hole drilled for stratigraphic information, including lithology (facies), porosity and permeability. It is drilled to penetrate a potentially productive zone, and thus may result in production. This may be a slim hole (not likely), a core hole (today most are drilled with a rock bit and then electric-logged rather than cored), and those structure tests that do not stop short of the expected producing zone or zones." Report of the Committee on Regulatory Practices for Stratigraphic Test Holes, 17 *Interstate Oil Compact Bull.* 43 (Dec. 1958). See TREATISE § 1.02.

On-Structure Deep Stratigraphic Test Wells, 87 I.D. 517 (Oct. 29, 1980), ruled that deep stratigraphic tests, on or off structures potentially holding oil or gas, are "geological explorations" authorized by the OUTER CONTINENTAL SHELF LANDS ACT OF of 1953 (*q.v.*), and that the Secretary of the Interior could authorize permittees to conduct such tests on a structure before it was leased. The opinion reported widespread agreement on four points:

> "First, a stratigraphic test is an accepted form of geological exploration. Second, its purpose is to gather geological information on the stratigraphy of an area believed capable of holding commercially valuable accumulations of oil or gas. Third, a stratigraphic test is most effective when it is drilled into this area. Fourth, oil or gas (called a ('hydrocarbon show') is the most reliable form of geological information on the presence of oil or gas."

See also SEISMIC SHOT HOLE; SLIM HOLE; STRUCTURE TEST HOLE.

Stratigraphic trap

A reservoir, capable of holding oil or gas, formed from a change in the character of reservoir rock from a break in its continuity. For example, the loss of porosity and permeability in a tight sandstone updip forms a stratigraphic trap. Such a trap is much harder to locate than a STRUCTURAL TRAP (*q.v.*), because it is not readily revealed by geological or geographical surveys. See TREATISE § 102.

See also COMBINATION TRAP; FAULT TRAP.

Strat tests

See STRUCTURE TEST HOLE.

Stream

The quantity in standard cubic feet per day of gas available from a specific source.

Stringer

A seam of rock between seams of coal or Devonian shale. The stringer may be potentially gas-producing. Under interim rules of the FERC relating to natural gas produced from Devonian shales, gas produced from stringers within Devonian shale lithologies did not qualify and was not deregulated. 44 F.R. 61950 (1979), as corrected, 44 F.R. 66786 (1979). As modified after protest, FERC revised the Devonian shale definition in the final rule to provide that gas will be deemed to be produced from Devonian shale if at least 95% of the gross Devonian age interval penetrated by the well bore has a gamma ray index of O.7 or more. 18 C.F.R. § 272.113(e) (1981). See Battaglia, "Selected Developments Under the NGPA," 2 *Eastern Min. L. Inst.* 14–14 (1981).

Stringing pipe

Removing pipe from a truck and placing it in an end to end position alongside the pipe-line ditch preparatory to welding. I.R.B. 1956–47, 28, 6 *O.&G.R.* 1141 (1956).

Stripper production

The final stage of production in the life of an oil well or oil field. This stage is characterized by low rates of production, sometimes no more than a barrel of oil per day. Under early, uncontrolled recovery practices, the FLUSH PRODUCTION (*q.v.*) stage was relatively brief, followed by a long stripper stage. Today, it is generally true that recovery practices extend the flush stage or the SETTLED PRODUCTION (*q.v.*) stage, recovering a greater percentage of the oil in place at this time, accordingly cut down the duration of the stripper stage.

Stripper well

A well which produces such small volume of oil that the gross income therefrom provides only a small margin of profit or in many cases, does not even cover actual cost of production.

The National Stripper Well Survey (Jan. 1, 1973), published by the Interstate Oil Compact Commission, defines a stripper well as one capable of producing only ten barrels of oil per day or less during the year under consideration. The survey reported 359,471 stripper wells produced 411,829,859 barrels of oil in 1972, the average daily production per well being 3.13 barrels.

Rapid escalation of crude oil prices in the 1970's made it economic to produce wells of very modest capacity. By 1976 the number of stripper wells had increased to 365,733 and the average daily production per well had fallen to 2.93 barrels. Abandonments during 1972 amounted to 13,483 and in 1976 they amounted to 9,916. Interstate Oil Compact Commission, *Compact Comments* (Nov. 1977).

Stripper wells comprise about 70 percent of the total number of wells in the United States and account for about 16 percent of oil production.

See also COUNTY REGULAR FIELDS; DOWNTIME; ONCE A STRIPPER, ALWAYS A STRIPPER.

Stripper well exemption

(1) The exemption from price control of stripper well leases under a series of statutes, beginning with the Trans-Alaska Pipeline Authorization Act. See Sauder v. Department of Energy, 648 F.2d 1341 (Temp. Emer. Ct. of App. 1981).

(2) The exemption from the CRUDE OIL WINDFALL PROFIT TAX ACT OF 1980 (*q.v.*) provided for by the ECONOMIC RECOVERY TAX ACT OF 1981 (*q.v.*) for stripper well oil. See EXEMPT STRIPPER WELL OIL.

See also IMPUTED STRIPPER WELL CRUDE OIL EXEMPTION.

Stripper well field

As defined by the National Stripper Well Survey (Interstate Oil Compact Commission, Jan. 1, 1973), a stripper well field is one in which the daily average per well production is ten barrels or less during the year under consideration.

Under price control regulations, STRIPPER WELL OIL (*q.v.*) was entitled to a higher price than was OLD OIL (*q.v.*). This gave rise to controversy whether an INJECTION WELL (*q.v.*) was to be counted as a well for the purpose of determining whether the per well production from the field did or did not exceed ten barrels a day. See Department of Energy Stripper Well Exemption Litigation, 690 F.2d 1375 (Temp. Emer. Ct. App. 1982), *cert. denied,* 459 U.S. 1127, 103 S. Ct. 763 (1983), on remand, 578 F. Supp. 586 (D. Kan. 1983), *on certi-*

fied questions, 744 F.2d 98 (Temp. Emer. Ct. App. 1984), *cert. denied,* ____ U.S. ____, 105 S. Ct. 576 (1984); Wiggins Brothers, Inc. v. Department of Energy, 667 F.2d 77 (Temp. Emer. Ct. App. 1981) (holding that injection wells are not counted for this purpose), *cert. denied,* 456 U.S. 905 (1982), *on remand,* 548 F. Supp. 547 (N.D. Tex. 1982) (injection well not to be counted for determining whether a property is within the MARGINAL PROPERTY RULE (*q.v.*)); Prosper Energy Corp. v. Department of Energy, 549 F. Supp. 300 (N.D. Tex. 1982).

See also FIELD.

Stripper well lease

For purposes of Federal Energy Administration and Department of Energy price control regulations, this term was defined as a property whose average daily production of crude petroleum and petroleum condensates per well did not exceed 10 barrels per day. 10 C.F.R. § 210.32(b). See Sauder v. Department of Energy, 648 F.2d 1341 (Temp. Emer. Ct. of App. 1981).

Stripper well natural gas

This term is defined in Section 108 of the Natural Gas Policy Act of 1978 (Pub. L. No. 95–621) as natural gas determined to be nonassociated natural gas produced during any month from a well if—

(A) during the preceding 90-day production period, such well produced nonassociated natural gas at a rate which did not exceed an average of 60 Mcf per production day during such period; and

(B) during such period such well produced at its maximum efficient rate of flow, determined in accordance with recognized conservation practices designed to maximize the ultimate recovery of natural gas.

In certain circumstances production in excess of 60 Mcf per production day may qualify if the excess was the result of recognized enhanced recovery techniques.

Stripper well oil

Oil produced from a well capable of producing not more than ten barrels a day. Under the provisions of the Emergency Petroleum Allocation Act of 1973 (EPAA), stripper well oil was initially exempt from price controls. Following the enactment of the Energy Policy and Conservation Act of 1975 (EPCA), a price ceiling was imposed on stripper well oil. After the enactment of the Energy Conservation and Production Act of 1976 (ECPA), stripper well oil was once again exempted from price controls. To qualify for the exemption it was not sufficient that a particular well produced not exceeding 10 barrels a day; it was also necessary that the average of all producing wells on the property not exceed 10 barrels per day. The exemption did not apply to gas well condensate. Southern Union Prod. Co. v. FEA, 569 F.2d 1147 (Temp. Emer. Ct. App. 1978). For purposes of the stripper well exemption, a MULTIPLE COMPLETION WELL (*q.v.*) was considered as two (or more) wells in calculating "average daily production," but a COMMINGLED WELL (*q.v.*) was treated as a single well for this purpose. Energy Consumers and Producers Ass'n, Inc. v. Department of Energy, 632 F.2d 129 (Temp. Emer. Ct. App. 1980), *cert. denied,* 449 U.S. 832 (1980).

See also EXEMPT CRUDE OIL; EXEMPT STRIPPER WELL OIL; IMPUTED STRIPPER WELL CRUDE OIL EXEMPTION; IMPUTED STRIPPER WELL LEASE OIL PRICE; PRICE CONTROL OF OIL, GAS AND PETROLEUM PRODUCTS; SECOND TIER OIL.

Stripper well property

For purposes of the North Dakota oil extraction tax law, this term is defined as a property "whose average daily production of oil, excluding condensate recovered in nonassociated production, per well did not exceed ten barrels per day during any preceding consecutive twelve-month period beginning after December 31, 1972. Wells which did not actually yield or produce oil during the qualifying twelve-month period, including disposal wells, dry wells, spent wells, and shut-in wells, are not production wells for the purpose of determining whether the stripper well property exemption applies." North Dakota Stat. 1981, c. 612, H.B. No. 1651, § 4, 69 *O.&G.R.* 612.

Stripper wheel

A circular appliance having a hub in the center which is attached to the string of the sucker rods for the purpose of unscrewing the string. The turning of this wheel creates the torque required for this purpose. See Corban v. Skelly Oil Co., 256 F.2d 775, 9 *O.&G.R.* 663 (5th Cir. 1958).

Syn.: BACK-OFF WHEEL.

Stripping job

The operation of dismantling the sucker rod in the course of bringing a pump to the surface for repair. Corban v. Skelly Oil Co., 256 F.2d 775, 9 *O.&G.R.* 663 (5th Cir. 1958).

Stripping law

The popular name for a Texas Act of 1933 under which it was legal to process gas to extract the liquefiable hydrocarbons and to waste the residue gas by simply venting it into the air. See Shamrock Oil & Gas Corp. v. Comm'r, 35 T.C. 979, 13 *O.&G.R.* 1090 at 1124 (1961).

Stripping plant

A manufacturing plant to strip or remove liquid hydrocarbons from wet gas, casinghead gas or condensate after production.

STR operations

Secondary and tertiary recovery operations.

See SECONDARY RECOVERY; TERTIARY RECOVERY.

Structural advantage

The ability of wells on one tract to drain oil from other tracts by reason of regional or field-wide migration [see FIELD DRAINAGE] to the tract overlying that part of the structure (*e.g.*, down structure in the case of a gas drive and up-structure in the case of a water drive) most advantageously situated for the recovery of oil. When production is limited by the fixing of allowables, tracts without a structural advantage may not be able to produce the recoverable oil in place because of migration to tracts having a structural advantage; the latter tracts will be able to produce more than the recoverable oil in place. The eastern part of the East Texas field has a structural advantage over the western part of the field. Structural advantage of one tract over another may be a factor in the granting of allowables. The tract less advantageously situated may be granted a somewhat larger allowable in order to minimize the structural advantage of the other tract. See Buckley, *Petroleum Conservation* 257 (1951).

Structural trap

A reservoir, capable of holding oil or gas, formed from crustal movements in the earth that fold or fracture rock strata in such manner that oil or gas accumulating in the strata are sealed off and cannot escape. The most common structural traps are (1) FAULT TRAPS (*q.v.*) (of numerous varieties), (2) ANTICLINES (*q.v.*), and (3) SALT DOMES (*q.v.*). See TREATISE § 102.

See also COMBINATION TRAP; TRAP.

Structure

A displacement of subsurface rock layers, caused by folding or fracturing of the earth's crust. In some instances, the term may be synonymous with STRUCTURAL TRAP (*q.v.*) as: "The well is right on the structure and is producing 500 barrels a day." In other instances, the term may be used to indicate a displacement of rock strata lacking a trap, or where a trap is present, lacking deposits of oil or gas in commercial quantities.

See also BASIN; DOWN-STRUCTURE; GEOLOGIC STRUCTURE; UP-STRUCTURE.

Structure test hole

A "hole drilled for geologic structure alone, although other types of information may be acquired during the drilling. This type of hole is drilled to a structural datum which is normally short of the known or expected producing zone or zones. This type of hole includes *slim* holes and many of those that have been termed *strat tests* as a misnomer. It need not be a shallow hole, although most fall in this category." Report of the Committee on Regulatory Practices for Stratigraphic Test Holes, 17 *Interstate Oil Compact Bull.* 43 (Dec. 1958).

See also SEISMIC SHOT HOLE; SLIM HOLE; STRATIGRAPHIC TEST HOLE.

Sub

Short, threaded drill pipe used to adapt parts of the drilling string which cannot otherwise be screwed together because of differences in thread size or design.

Subdivision

See LEGAL SUBDIVISION; REGULAR SUBDIVISION; SMALLEST LEGAL SUBDIVISION; SURVEY.

Subject-to clause

A clause commonly included in mineral and royalty conveyances made subsequent to a lease, providing that the conveyance is "subject-to" the mineral lease, as follows:

"Said lands or portions thereof, being now under oil and gas lease executed in favor of . . . .; it is understood and agreed that this sale is made subject to the terms of said lease, but covers and includes the same interest as first hereinabove named, of all the oil royalty and gas royalty and casinghead gas and gasoline royalty, and royalty from other minerals or products, due and to be paid under the terms of said lease, only insofar as it or they cover the above described land."

It would appear that one purpose for including such a clause in the deed is to avoid possible liability of the grantor on his warranty, but nevertheless some courts have apparently been led to give a subject-to clause the effect of a second conveyance, which may result in APPORTIONMENT (*q.v.*) of royalties and in the transfer of a greater or lesser interest than that conveyed by the granting clause. [See TWO GRANT THEORY.] The inclusion of this clause in the deed may also have the effect of ratifying or reviving a lease which has expired or been terminated unless it is provided that the deed is subject to "any *valid and subsisting* oil and gas lease of record." On the treatment of subject-to clauses, see TREATISE §§ 340–340.4.

See also FUTURE LEASE CLAUSE.

Sublease

In landlord and tenant law, a transfer of an interest in an estate for years of lesser size than the underlying estate. The most familiar is the transfer of an estate of lesser duration than the transferor has; *e.g.*, the owner of an estate for 10 years transfers to *A* for the next 5 years, reserving the last 5 years to himself. It has been held that reservation of interests other than the balance of the term, *e.g.*, a right of reentry, may result in a sublease.

The same problem arises in the conveyance of an oil and gas lease, with the reservation of a right to a reassignment and of overriding royalty. Do the common-law sublease-assignment doctrines apply here? There has been some indication that they do and that the original lessor cannot sue a sublessee for breach of covenant because there is no privity of estate between the two. See Hartman Ranch Co. v. Associated Oil Co., 10 Cal.2d 232, 73 P.2d 1163 (1937) (but liability imposed because of assumption clause in instrument transfering the lease); Berman v. Brown, 224 La. 619, 70 So.2d 433, 3 *O.&G.R.* 608 (1953).

Outside of Louisiana, it is far from clear whether, or when, the courts will apply the sublease-assignment doctrines to oil and gas transactions. See TREATISE §§ 412–414.

See also ASSIGNMENT; PARTIAL ASSIGNMENT.

Submarginal reserves or resources

The portion of IDENTIFIED-SUBECONOMIC RESOURCES (*q.v.*) which would require a substantially higher price (more than 1.5 times the price at the time of determination) or a major cost-reducing advance in technology. 2 *OCS Oil and Gas—A Environmental Assessment,* A Report to the President by the Council on Environmental Quality (April 1974) at p. 12.

See also RESERVES.

Submerged Lands Act of 1953

A statute [67 Stat. 29, 43 U.S.C. § 1301 *et seq.*] transferring to the States the rights to the seabed underlying the marginal sea within the limits defined in the Act and releasing the States from any liability to account for any prior income received from state leases that had been granted with respect to the marginal sea. The Act was held constitutional in Alabama v. Texas, 347 U.S. 272 (1954).

For a study of the several submerged lands cases in the Supreme Court of the United States, see Charney, "Judicial Deference in the Submerged Lands Cases," 7 *Vanderbilt J. of Transnational Law* 383 (1974).

See also PUBLIC LANDS; TIDE LANDS.

Subordination agreement

An agreement subordinating a prior lien to an oil and gas lease. Premises which have been mortgaged or which are subject to a deed of trust usually may not be developed by the owner nor by his lessee (unless the lease is senior to the security interest) without the consent of the secured creditor. Absent such consent, development of the land for minerals will generally be said to constitute voluntary waste which is enjoinable by the secured creditor or for which he may recover damages, and typically such "waste" will occasion an acceleration of the mortgage debt under the terms of such security agreements. Before land can be developed by the lessee of the mortgagor, it is usually necessary, therefore, to obtain a subordination agreement from the mortgagee. Such an agreement will normally provide specifically for the allocation of the proceeds of the lease between the mortgagor and the satisfaction of the debt for which the mortgage or deed of trust is security. See TREATISE § 697.3.

Subrogation clause

A lease clause subrogating the lessee to any lien upon the leased premises which the lessee elects to discharge in whole or in part. The clause is usually coupled with the warranty clause of the lease as follows:

> "Lessor hereby warrants and agrees to defend the title to said land and agrees that Lessee at its option may discharge any tax, mortgage or other lien upon said land, either in whole or in part, and in event Lessee does so, it shall be subrogated to such lien with the right to enforce same and apply rentals and royalties accruing here under toward satisfying same."
> See TREATISE § 685.3.

Subscriber

See QUALIFIED SUBSCRIBER; UNQUALIFIED SUBSCRIBER.

Subsea completion

A production well in which the CHRISTMAS TREE (*q.v.*) is located at or near the ocean bottom. Kash, *et al.*, *Energy Under the Oceans* 368 (1973).

Subsidence

Sinking or settling of land as the result of the removal of underground fluids.

For a detailed discussion of liability for subsidence of neighboring lands caused by the removal of underground fluids, see Friendswood Dev. Co. v. Smith-Southwest Indus. Inc., 576 S.W.2d 21, 62 *O.&G.R.* 218 (Tex. 1978).

Subsidence unit

A compulsory unit authorized by Cal. Pub. Resources Code §§ 3315–3347 (1972) (1980 Supp.) for the purpose of repressuring or maintaining pressure in subsurface oil and gas formations. This legislation is limited in application "to lands . . . overlying or immediately adjacent to a producing pool or pools, when such lands are subsiding, portions of which lands are subject to threat of inundation from the sea and which subsidence is endangering the life, health and safety of persons or which is damaging or is threatening to cause damage to, any surface or underground improvements located on such lands overlying or immediately adjacent to such pool or pools." See TREATISE § 912.3.

Substantial hardship clause

A provision of a contract for the purchase and sale of gas permitting the adjustment of the price of gas in the event of a change in the economic circumstances creating substantial hardship. See Superior Overseas Development Corp & Phillips Petroleum (UK) Ltd. v. British Gas Corp., (1982) 1 Lloyd's Rep. 262, discussed in [1982] 2 *OGLTR* 51.

Substitute fuel clause

(1) A provision in a GAS PURCHASE CONTRACT (*q.v.*) between a seller of gas (*e.g.*, a pipeline company) and a buyer of gas whereby the seller agrees to reimburse the buyer for any premium which the buyer must pay to obtain another fuel during periods of interruption of the gas supply. See International Paper Co. v. Federal Power Comm'n, 476 F.2d 121 (5th Cir. 1973); State of Louisiana v. Federal Power Comm'n, 503 F.2d 844 at 851 (5th Cir. 1974).

(2) A lease clause authorizing the lessee to take oil or gas from the premises, royalty-free, in satisfaction of the cost of other fuel or power expended by the lessee in lease operations. See TREATISE § 644.5. In certain cases, the lessee may find it more convenient to use in its operations electrical or other fuel power in lieu of oil and/or gas produced from the leasehold for fuel, or, during periods of price controls, the oil or gas produced from the leasehold may have a higher value than available substitute fuels, *e.g.*, for generation of steam employed in secondary recovery operations of heavy crude oil. The substitute fuel clause causes the lessor to share in the cost of the fuel employed just as the lessor would have shared in the cost had oil and/or gas produced from the leasehold been employed by the lessee in its operations under a lease clause authorizing royalty-free use of lease products in connection with lease operations. Rev. Rul. 82-160, 1982-37 I.R.B. 7, 73 *O.&G.R.* 437 (Sept. 13, 1982), declared that crude oil removed from the premises and exchanged for residual fuel oil used to power production process was subject to the CRUDE OIL WINDFALL PROFIT TAX ACT OF 1980 (*q.v.*).

See also ALTERNATIVE FUEL CLAUSE.

Substitute royalty

Payments by a lessee to a lessor in accordance with the terms of an agreement between the parties for the privilege of keeping a lease alive without producing from a well or wells drilled thereon, the allowable for such well or wells being transferred by the lessee to another lease or lessee. See "Transferred Allowables and Substitute Royalties," 5 *O.&G. Tax Q.* 59 at 80 (1956).

Sometimes used synonymously with OFFSET ROYALTY (*q.v.*).

See also COMPENSATORY ROYALTY; TRANSFERRED ALLOWABLE.

Substitute well clause

A clause in a FARM-OUT AGREEMENT (*q.v.*) permitting the farmee to abandon a well in which a mechanical or other operation difficulty or impentrable formation has been encountered above the specified contract depth and requiring him after doing so to commence the drilling of a substitute well to contract depth within a limited period of time. Holt, "Problems Relating to Arctic Farmout and Joint Operating Agreements," 10 *Alberta L. Rev.* 450 at 458 (1972).

Subsurface estate

Aleut Corp. v. Arctic Slope Regional Corp. 421 F.Supp. 862, 56 *O.&G.R.* 469 (D. Alaska 1976), held that the term "subsurface estate" as used in Section 7(i) of the Alaska Native Claims Settlement Act (ANCSA), 43 U.S.C. § 1606(i) [dealing with revenue sharing among Regional Corporations] included sand and gravel but the same term as used in Section 14(f) [dealing with the patenting of the surface estate in certain lands to a Village Corporation and the patenting of the subsurface estates in those lands to a Regional Corporation] did not include sand and gravel. The court reasoned that to include sand and gravel in the subsurface estate under the latter provision would enable the subsurface owner to destroy the surface by open pit mining, a result "[i]t appears implausible that Congress would have intended." The court recognized that its reasoning would not apply to coal even though mined by open pit methods for as to coal the legislative history was quite clear.

Subsurface storage

See GAS STORAGE, SUBSURFACE.

Subsurface trespass

The bottoming of a well on the land of another without his consent. Subsurface trespass results from the drilling of a "slant" or DIRECTIONAL WELL (*q.v.*), which may be intentional or inadvertent. Since subsurface trespass is as wrongful as surface trespass, the same liability attaches, *viz.*, damages in the amount of the value of the oil produced. Whether the trespasser is entitled to a credit for the cost of producing the oil depends on whether his trespass was made in good or bad faith, as it does in the case of surface trespass. See Alphonzo E. Bell Corp. v. Bell View Oil Syndicate, 24 Cal.App.2d 587, 76 P.2d 167 (1938); Williams v. Continental Oil Co., 215 F.2d 4, 3 *O.&G.R.* 2080 (1954) (availability of directional survey as discovery procedure); Hastings Oil Co. v. Texas Co., 149 Tex. 416, 234 S.W.2d 385 (1950). See also TREATISE § 227; "Suing a Slant-Driller for Subsurface Trespass or Drainage," 15 *Stan. L. Rev.* 665 (1963).

Nunez v. Wainoco Oil & Gas Co., 488 So.2d 955, ___ *O.&G.R.* ___ (La. 1986), *cert. den.;* ___ U.S. ___, 107 S.Ct. 391 (1986), declared that this definition was in accord with its prior decision.

Successful efforts accounting

A method of accounting for the costs of hydrocarbon exploration and discovery which involves an attempt to expense as many of the costs as possible in the periods in which these costs are incurred. Costs of property acquisition, successful exploratory wells, all development costs, and support equipment and facilities are capitalized. Unsuccessful exploratory wells are expensed when determined to be nonproductive. Production costs, overhead, and all exploration costs other than exploratory drilling are charged against income as incurred. See Baker, "Discussion of Drawbacks to Full-Cost in Petroleum Industry Accounting," 25 *O.&G. Tax Q.* 306 (1977); Durand, "Financial Reporting Effects of Changed Percentage Depletion Allowance in Oil and Gas Industry, 24 *O.&G. Tax Q.* 65 (1975).

See also ACCOUNTING METHODS; FULL COST ACCOUNTING.

Successor contract

See SUCCESSOR TO AN EXISTING CONTRACT.

Successor earned depletion

In Canada, a carryover of EARNED DEPLETION (*q.v.*) from a predecessor corporation to a successor corporation or a second successor corporation where there is a purchase of the assets of the predecessor or an amalgamation. See Katchen and Bowhay, *Federal Oil and Gas Taxation* 57 (3d ed. 1979).

Successor to an existing contract

This term is defined in § 2 of the NATURAL GAS POLICY ACT OF 1978 (*q.v.*) (Pub. L. No. 95-621) as any contract, other than a ROLLOVER CONTRACT (*q.v.*), entered into on or after the date of the enactment of this Act, for the first sale of natural gas which was previously subject to an EXISTING CONTRACT (*q.v.*), whether or not there is an identity of parties or terms with those of such existing contract.

In Superior Oil Co. v. Pioneer Corp., 532 F. Supp. 731, 73 *O.&G.R.* 412 (N.D. Tex. 1982), the court found that a purchaser's option to extend the term of a gas purchase contract was not an EVERGREEN CLAUSE (*q.v.*), and that the new contract arising from exercise of the option was, therefore, a ROLLOVER CONTRACT rather than a successor to an existing contract. This judgment was vacated and dismissed for want of jurisdiction. 706 F.2d 603 (5th Cir. 1983), *cert. denied,* 464 U.S. 1041, 104 S. Ct. 706 (1984).

Successor unit operator

The person, association, partnership, corporation, or other business entity selected to serve as UNIT OPERATOR (*q.v.*) when the original unit operator resigns or is removed.

Sucker rod

A rod or string of rods connecting a pump with a source of power.

Sulfinol solution

A chemical solution employed in a processing plant to absorb hydrogen sulphide and carbon dioxide from SOUR GAS (*q.v.*). See Piney Woods Country Life School v. Shell Oil Co., 539 F. Supp. 957, 74 *O.&G.R.* 485 (S.D. Miss. 1982), *aff'd in part, rev'd in part, and remanded,* 726 F.2d 225, 79 *O.&G.R.* 244 (5th Cir. 1984), *reh. denied,* 750 F.2d 69 (5th Cir. 1984), *cert. denied,* _____ U.S. ____, 105 S. Ct. 1868 (1985).

Sulfur differential

A DIFFERENTIAL (*q.v.*) in the price of oil from a given source from the MARKER PRICE (*q.v.*) of BENCHMARK CRUDE (*q.v.*) based upon the relative sulfur content of the crude in question and that of Benchmark crude. "The 'sulfur differential' amounts to about 4 cents per barrel per percentage point of sulfur content, and is seldom more than 10 cents per barrel." Danielsen, *The Evolution of OPEC* 65 (1982).

Sump hole or sump pit

A surface pit into which drilling MUD (*q.v.*) flows on reaching the surface of the well after being pumped through the drill pipe and bit, then up through the annular opening between the walls of the hole and the drill pipe, carrying with it cuttings from the well. Heavy cuttings settle out of the mud in the sump pits and the mud can be reused.

Syn.: MUD-PIT, SLUSH PIT.

Superior use

A relatively economic or beneficial use of gas. See END USE CONTROL; INFERIOR USE.

Superport

A loading and/or unloading facility capable of handling deep-draft supertankers.

Supertanker

A Very Large Cargo Carrier (VLCC) for sea transport, which can carry 1.5 million barrels or more of crude oil.

Supplementary depletion allowances

In Canada, additional depletion allowances are authorized to encourage investment in enhanced recovery systems and nonconventional oil and gas projects and are effective in respect of taxation years ending after April 10, 1978. See Katchen and Bowhay, *Federal Oil and Gas Taxation* 54 (3d ed. 1979).

See also DEPLETION.

Supplementary petroleum tax

A tax imposed in the United Kingdom for the eighteen-month period of January 1, 1981, to June 30, 1982. The tax, a levy of 20 percent on companies' gross revenues after an allowance of 7.3 million barrels of crude a year, is deductible from corporate tax and from the PETROLEUM REVENUE TAX (*q.v.*). *The Wall Street Journal,* March 20, 1981, p. 29.

See also ADVANCE PETROLEUM REVENUE TAX (APRT) SYSTEM.

Supplier/Purchaser Rule

A rule applied under the Mandatory Petroleum Allocation Regulations, 10 C.F.R. Parts 211 and 212, under which a supplier was obligated to supply a customer with product if that customer has "purchased or obtained" that product from the supplier during the base period. 10 C.F.R. § 211.9(a). See Hydrocarbon Trading & Transport Co. v. Exxon Corp., *CCH Energy Management* ¶ 9783 (S.D. N.Y. 1983).

Support agreement

The term applied by Lowe, *Oil and Gas Law in a Nutshell* (1983), for a variety of letter agreements such as DRY HOLE AGREEMENTS, BOTTOM HOLE AGREEMENTS, ACREAGE CONTRIBUTION AGREEMENTS (*q.v.*). See LETTER.

Surface and subsurface user provisions

Express lease clauses concerning the lessor's and the lessee's rights of surface and subsurface user, *viz.:* (1) reservations of surface and subsurface rights of the lessor subsequent to the execution of the lease; (2) express surface and subsurface easements of the lessee; (3) restrictions on the rights of user of the lessee; (4) fencing and buried pipe covenants; (5) obligation to restore condition of premises; and (6) obligation to compensate lessor or other person injured for surface damage. See TREATISE §§ 673–673.6.

Surface casing

See CASING.

Surface damage act

A statute providing for the payment to the surface owner of damages resulting from oil and gas operations. See *e.g.,* 52 Okla. Stat. §§ 318.2–318.9 (enacted in 1982); applied in Davis Oil Co. v. Cloud, ____ P.2d ____, ____ *O.&G.R.* ____ 57 *Okla. B.J.* 2885 (Okla, 1986). Anschutz Corp. v. Sanders, 734 P.2d 1290, ____ *O.&G.R.* ____ (1987), held that a mineral lessee was entitled to enter upon the premises for the purpose of seismic testing without complying with the Act. Somewhat similar acts in other states were said to be applicable to entry for seismic testing. Mont. Rev. Codes §§ 82–10–501 through 82-10-511; S.D. Codified Laws Ann. §§ 45-5A-1 through 45-5A-11; N.D. Cent. Code §§ 38-11.1-01 through 38-11.1-09.

For discussions of such statutes see the following:

Lowe, "Eastern Oil and Gas Operations," 4 *Eastern Min. L. Inst.* 20-1 at 20-18 (1983);

Pierson, "Oil and Gas: Legislative Damage to Surface Rights," 36 *Okla. L. Rev.* 386 (1983).

Surface damage clause

A provision, sometimes found in oil and gas leases, requiring the lessee to pay compensation for damages done to the leasehold in drilling and operating thereon. See Meyer v. Cox, 252 S.W.2d 207, 1 *O.&G.R.* 1810 (Tex. Civ. App. 1952 error ref'd). Such a provision is of particular importance to a lessor who joins in a community lease or whose lease contains authority for pooling or unitization, inasmuch as he may otherwise be unfairly dealt with if the well drilled under the community lease or pooling or unitization agreement is upon his land, in which event he will suffer all the surface damage and yet be entitled only to a proportionate share of the royalties. See TREATISE §§ 218.11, 673.5, 673.6.

Surface disturbance test

The name given a test, originated in the case of Acker v. Guinn, 464 S.W.2d 348, 38 *O.&G.R.* 273 (Tex. 1971), for determining what subsurface deposits are included in a grant or reservation of minerals. Norvell, "Developing Lands Characterized by Separate Ownership of Oil and Gas and Surface Coal and Uranium—The Other Side of *Acker v. Guinn* and Its Progeny," 33 *Sw. Legal Fdn. Oil & Gas Inst.* 183 at 196 (1982), describes the test as follows:

> "if the deposit is near the surface within the reasonably immediate vicinity of the tract in issue and any reasonable method of removal will consume, deplete or destroy the surface, the substance will not be included within a grant or reservation of minerals, absent explicit language to the contrary in the instrument of severance. The determination of whether surface mining constitutes a reasonable method of removal is to be made as of the date of trial as opposed to the date of the instrument of severance. Finally, if the substance is determined to be a part of the surface estate, the surface owner has title to the substance at whatever depth it may be encountered."

Surface easements

See EASEMENTS.

Surface estate

See SUBSURFACE ESTATE.

Surface lease

This term is defined in Ariz. Rev. Stat. § 27–551(9) (1976), as "a lease on the surface of any state land for grazing, agricultural, commercial, or homesite purposes."

When the fee is divided between the owner of a nonfreehold possessory interest (*e.g.,* estate for years) and the owner of a future interest, there has been some controversy over the right of the latter to develop mineral resources without the consent of the former. Clearly the owner of the possessory nonfreehold interest is not entitled to produce minerals or to share in any production from the premises, absent an express authorization, but it has been urged that the owner of the future interest might not interfere with the enjoyment of the land by the owner of the possessory interest by drilling operations. As a matter of practice, before operations are pursued, the owner of the future interest attempts to obtain the consent of the owner of the possessory interest to the operations. The consent of the tenant to the drilling operations is usually evidenced by a TENANT'S CONSENT AGREEMENT (*q.v.*).

Difficulty arose over surface leases and subsequent attempts to develop the minerals in Mississippi as a result of 99 year agricultural leases executed by the state. It was first held that the state could not give an oil and gas lessee a right to interfere with the exclusive right of possession that had previously been acquired by the agricultural lessee, but this case was later overruled. Pace v. State, 191 Miss. 780, 4 So.2d 270 (1941).

Surface management regulations

Regulations issued by the BUREAU OF LAND MANAGEMENT (*q.v.*) under the mining laws in an effort to strike a balance between mineral development activities under the mining laws and other competing surface resource uses of the public lands. See Kimball, "Impact of BLM Surface Management Regulations on Exploration and Mining Operations," 28 *Rocky Mt. Min. L. Inst.* 509 (1982).

Surface pit

A pit utilized for the disposal of oilfield brine by evaporation or seepage.

Surface right

The right of a mineral owner or an oil and gas lessee to use so much of the surface of land as may be reasonably necessary for the conduct of operations under the lease. See Ariz. Rev. Stat. § 27–560 (1976).

Applicable state or provincial laws or regulations sometimes require that compensation be paid by a mineral operator for damage to the surface resulting from mineral operations. See *e.g.*, the Saskatchewan Petroleum Regulations, 2 *O.&G.R.* 1194 at 1207 *et seq.* (1953).

See also EASEMENTS; RESIDUAL INTEREST.

Surface rights act

See ALBERTA SURFACE RIGHTS ACT; FOUR HEADS APPROACH; GLOBAL APPROACH; TREATISE § 218 at note 8.

Surface rights compensation

See FOUR HEADS APPROACH; GLOBAL APPROACH.

Surface string

See CASING.

Surface tension

The tendency of the surface of a liquid to behave as a thin elastic film. This is one property of oil that affects recovery. If specific gravity, viscosity and surface tension are low, the oil will flow more readily to the well bore. These properties can be kept low if gas in the reservoir is kept in solution.

Surface waste

"[T]he unnecessary or excessive surface loss or destruction without beneficial use, however caused, of casinghead gas, oil, or other product thereof, but including the loss or destruction, without beneficial use, resulting from evaporation, seepage, leakage or fire, especially such loss or destruction incident to or resulting from the manner of spacing, equipping, operating, or producing well or wells, or incident to or resulting from inefficient storage or handling of oil; the unnecessary damage to or destruction of the surface, soils, animal, fish or aquatic life or property from or by oil and gas operations; and the drilling of unnecessary wells." Comp. Laws Mich., § 319.2 (1)(2); Mich. Stat. Ann. § 13. 139(2)*(l)*(2) (1980 Supp.).

See also WASTE.

Surfactant flooding

WATER FLOODING (*q.v.*) in which surfactants (surface-active agents) are employed in the water, resulting in higher oil recoveries than can be obtained by flooding with water alone. See Morse, "Trends in Oil Recovery Methods," 1 *IOCC Committee Bull.* 1 (Dec. 1959).

For a discussion of surfactant-polymer flooding (also known as microemulsion or micellar flooding), see Lopez and Parsley, "Microbes, Simulators, and Satellites: The Prudent Operator Under the Implied Covenants," 58 *N.D. L. Rev.* 501 at 529 (1982).

Surplus gas clause

A provision common in gas purchase contracts in the 1950s and 1960s, and now condemned retroactively by the Federal Energy Regulatory Commission, which limited the amount of gas which the pipeline was required to take under the contract on a DAILY CONTRACT QUANTITY (DCQ) (*q.v.*) basis but then provided that if the pipeline was unwilling or unable to take gas in excess of such quantities, that the producer was free to sell the gas to third parties. See Johnson, "Natural Gas Sales Contracts," 34 *Sw. Legal Fdn. Oil & Gas Inst.* 83 at 116 (1983).

Surrender and refile procedure

A procedure formerly available in Arizona whereunder a lessee from the state could surrender a lease prior to the expiration of its term and simultaneously file application for a new lease on the same land. Since the lessee controlled the timing of the surrender, it could always be the first applicant for the available lease land. The procedure was held to be invalid in Sanchez-O'Brien Minerals Corp. v. State of Arizona, 149 Az. 258; 717 P.2d 937, 90 *O.&G.R.* 23 (Ariz. App. 1986).

Surrender clause

A lease clause authorizing the lessee to surrender all or part of the leased premises as follows:

> "Lessee shall have the right at any time without Lessor's consent to surrender all or any portion of the leased premises and be relieved of all obligations as to the acreage surrendered."

By virtue of this clause, a lessee may be able to retain that portion of leased acreage which appears most promising while relieving himself of obligations as concerns payment of rentals, protection, exploration or development of that portion of the leased premises which appears to him to be least promising. In earlier days it was strenuously argued that the inclusion of a surrender clause in a lease made it terminable at the will of the lessee, and that therefore the lease created an estate at will, terminable also at the will of the lessor, or that the inclusion of the surrender clause in the lease meant that the consideration moving from the lessee to the lessor for the lease was illusory. In states wherein these contentions created difficulty, the surrender clause was modified to provide that payment of a nominal sum, *e.g.*, $1, was required before the lessee might surrender the premises. See Cohn v. Clark, 48 Okla. 500, 150 Pac. 467 (1915). In an OR LEASE FORM (*q.v.*) giving the lessee the option to "drill or pay rentals or surrender," if the lessee fails to exercise his right to surrender the lease prior to the anniversary date for rental payments, the lessor has a cause of action to recover rentals. *Ibid.*

Occasionally community leases provide that the lessee may surrender part of the leased premises at his option. Such surrender of a portion of the leased premises does not alter the pre-existing rights of the community lessors under the original lease to an apportioned share of royalties from production anywhere on the communitized premises. It was held in Superior Oil Co. v. Dabney, 147 Tex. 51, 211 S.W.2d 563 (1948), that where a lessee surrendered all of the premises except that portion which was included in a unit area on which a well was drilled (but off the lessee's own lease), the lessee was excused from an express covenant to drill on the leased premises.

Surrender clauses are generally construed against the lessee, and the exact mode of surrender prescribed in the lease must be followed if the surrender is to be effective to relieve the lessee of his obligations under the lease. See TREATISE §§ 680–680.8.

Wiggins v. Warrior River Coal Co., 696 F.2d 1356, 77 *O.&G.R.* 8 (11th Cir. 1983), concluded that surrender of a coal lease under the provisions of its surrender clause did not extinguish the minimum royalty obligation of the lessee.

Surrendered part

See PRODUCTION LICENSE.

Survey

See ACID DIP SURVEY; BASE LINE; BASE SURVEY; CADASTRAL SURVEY; DEVIATIONAL SURVEY; DIRECTIONAL SURVEY; ELECTRICAL WELL LOG; GENERAL LAND OFFICE SURVEY; GEOLOGICAL SURVEY; GEOPHYSICAL AND GEOLOGICAL SURVEY; GEOPHYSICAL SURVEY; GRAVITY SURVEY; INCLINATION SURVEY; LEGAL SUBDIVISION; LOT; PLAT BOOK; PRINCIPAL MERIDIAN; RECTANGULAR SYSTEM OF PUBLIC LAND SURVEYS; REGULAR SUBDIVISION; SEISMOGRAPHICAL SURVEY; SMALLEST LEGAL SUBDIVISION.

Suspect price

A price eliminated in the determination of "in line price" by the Federal Power Commission because it was under litigation or Commission review or because similar to a price under a cloud. See Public Service Comm'n of State of N.Y. v. Federal Power Comm'n, 373 F. 2d 816 at 824, 26 *O.&G.R.* 523 at 531 (D.C. Cir. 1967), *rev'd,* Federal Power Comm'n v. Sunray DX Oil Co., 391 U.S. 9, 29 *O.&G.R.* 305 (1968); Morris, "Recent Independent Producer Certificate Cases: The 'Suspect Order' Rule," 32 *Geo. Wash. L. Rev.* 489 (1964).

See also IN LINE PRICE.

Suspended or no lease area

A category of federal lands where oil and gas leasing is suspended pending further planning or special studies. It includes areas that are too large in size to permit slant drilling or values that cannot be adequately protected by the other lease categories. Examples are some areas of potential wild and scenic river corridors, and larger unique primitive and natural areas where roads, pipelines, drilling activities, etc. are not compatible with management for these uses. As further information is obtained and public needs are better understood, these areas may continue to be closed to leasing or made available. Lundberg and Garver, "Federal Land Use Planning and Management—Its Effect on Oil and Gas Operations," Appendix III, in *Rocky Mt. Min. L. Fdn. Inst. on the Overthrust Belt—Oil and Gas Legal and Land Issues* (1980).

See also FEDERAL LEASE.

Suspended royalties

The term applied to that portion of the royalty withheld by a gas purchaser pending final determination by the Federal Power Commission of the lawfulness of a requested price. See Gray v. Amoco Prod. Co., 1 Kan. App. 2d 338, 564 P.2d 579, 59 *O.&G.R.* 14 (1977), *aff'd except as to computation of interest,* 223 Kan. 441, 573 P.2d 1080, 59 *O.&G.R.* 31 (1978).

See also SUSPENSE MONEY.

Suspense money

The term applied to money collected by a regulated NATURAL GAS COMPANY (*q.v.*) after filing a rate increase which is subject to a duty to refund to purchasers of the gas to the extent that the Federal Power Commission or its successor, the Federal Energy Regulatory Commission, ultimately fails to approve the increase. The company may collect the increased prices for years, using the funds collected as it pleases although it will ordinarily characterize the suspense money as a liability for accounting purposes. When the Commission ultimately passes on the rate increase the company must, in appropriate cases, recompute the price it must pay to its suppliers under percentage-of-proceeds purchase contracts or make refunds to those who purchased gas from it. See Phillips Petroleum Co. v. Adams, 513 F.2d 355, 51 *O.&G.R.* 370, *rehearing en banc denied,* 515 F.2d 1183 (5th Cir.), *cert. denied,* 423 U.S. 930 (1975).

That portion of suspense money required to be refunded after action by the Commission on the proposed rate increase has been termed "refundable money," and that portion which may be retained after the Commission action has been termed "sustainable money." Fuller v. Phillips Petroleum Co., 408 F.Supp. 643, 54 *O.&G.R.* 213 (N.D. Tex. 1976).

An assignment of an oil and gas lease was held not to pass any title to suspense money for production prior to the effective date of the assignment. Phillips Petroleum Co. v. Hazlewood, 490 F.Supp. 1193, 54 *O.&G.R.* 360 (N. D. Tex. 1975), *aff'd,* 534 F.2d 61 (5th Cir. 1976).

On the recovery by lessors in a class action of interest on suspense money, see Shutts v. Phillips Petroleum Co., 235 Kan. 195, 679 P.2d 1159, 81 *O.&G.R.* 46 (1984), *aff'd in part, rev'd in part and remanded sub nom.* Phillips Petroleum Co. v. Shutts, 472 U.S. 797, 105 S. Ct. 2965, 85 *O.&G.R.* 486 (1985), *on remand,*240 Kan. 764, 732 P.2d

1286, ____ O.&G.R. ____ (1987), and Sterling v. Marathon Oil Co., 223 Kan. 686, 576 P.2d 635, 62 *O.&G.R.* 21 (1978), and the cases cited therein.

For a detailed discussion of *Shutts* see Kennedy, "The Supreme Court Meets the Bride of Frankenstein: *Phillips Petroleum Co. v. Shutts* and the State Multistate Class Action," 34 *U. of Kansas L. Rev.* 255 (1985).

See also Wortman v. Sun Oil Co., 236 Kan. 266, 690 P.2d 385, 83 *O.&G.R.* 284 (1984), *cert. granted, judgment vacated, and case remanded for further consideration in the light of Phillips Petroleum Co. v. Shutts, sub nom.* Sun Oil Co. v. Wortman, ____ U.S. ____, 106 S.Ct. 40 (1985).

See also SUSPENDED ROYALTIES.

Suspension of operations and production

Relief from the producing requirements or from all operating and production requirements of oil and gas leases authorized by the Area Oil and Gas Supervisors of the Bureau of Land Management under the provisions of 43 C.F.R. § 3103.3–8 (1981). The term of any lease will be extended by adding thereto any period of suspension of all operations and production during such term pursuant to the direction or assent of the Area Oil and Gas Supervisor or the Director, Geological Survey. See Teton Energy Co., Inc., IBLA 81-528, GFS (O&G) 1982-38.

For a discussion of the authority of the Secretary of the Interior to suspend operations and production under federal lease see Peterson, "Extensions and Suspensions of Federal Oil and Gas Leases," *Rocky Mt. Min. L. Fdn. Inst. on the Overthrust Belt—Oil and Gas Legal and Land Issues* 12-1 at 12-19 (1980).

The provisions of the lease suspension provisions in sections 39 and 17(f) of the Mineral Leasing Act of 1920 are discussed in Oil & Gas Lease Suspension, 92 I.D. 293, GFS (O&G) 1985 SO-2 (Solicitor's Opinion, May 31, 1985). The opinion concludes that:

(1) A suspension of operations and production under section 39, which by law extends the term of the lease for the period of suspension, must be a suspension of both operations and production such that the lessee has been denied beneficial use of the lease by the Department in the interest of conservation. Lease activity (operations or production) is beneficial use and may not be allowed to commence or continue while the lease is suspended.

(2) Suspension of operations or of production under section 17(f) toll the running of the lease term but do not suspend the payment of rental or minimum royalty.

To avoid confusion and to clarify the differences in types of "extensions," the opinion refers to section 39 extensions as "tolling the running of the lease term."

See also Getty Oil Co. v. Clark, 614 F.Supp. 904; 88 *O.&G.R.* 174 (D. Wyo. 1985).

Suspension of prescription

Cessation of the running of prescription *liberandi causa* for some period of time.

The law concerning suspension of prescription in Louisiana is codified in Articles 58–61, 97–100 of the Louisiana Mineral Code [R.S. 31:58–61, 97–100 (1975)]. See TREATISE § 216.3(d).

See also PRESCRIPTION.

Suspensive condition

"Conditional obligations are such as are made to depend on an uncertain event. If the obligation is not to take effect until the event happen, it is a suspensive condition; if the obligation take effect immediately, but is liable to be defeated when the event happens, it is then a resolutory condition." La. Civ. Code Art. 2021 (1977).

Sustainable money

See SUSPENSE MONEY.

Swab

A device equipped with an upward-opening check valve that is designed to fit snugly within the well casing or tubing through which oil is produced. Lowered on a wire line to a point well below the surface of the fluid in the well, it is rapidly withdrawn to the surface, lifting above it the oil through which it has been lowered.

Swabbing

A trade term or colloquialism for the practice of securing information about oil and gas matters from someone without paying him for it or for his time. Consolidated Oil & Gas, Inc. v. Ryan, 250 F.Supp. 600 at 604, 24 *O.&G.R.* 237 at 242 (W.D. Ark. 1966), *aff'd,* 368 F.2d 177 (8th Cir. 1966).

Swabbing a well

Introduction of a swab into the tubing after casing is set, perforated and tubing run, in order to clean out drilling mud. This is a recognized method in the oil industry in producing the first oil. Swabbing may not be feasible if high pressures are encountered, in which event it may be necessary to conduct "periodic flowing." See Rogers v. Osborn, 152 Tex. 540, 261 S.W.2d 311, 2 *O.&G.R.* 304, 1439 (1953); Upshaw v. Norsworthy, 267 S.W.2d 566, 3 *O.&G.R.* 1558 (Tex. Civ. App. 1954).

See also CLEANING A WELL; REWORKING OPERATIONS; WORK OVERS.

Swabbing the hole

The suction pressure (pressure drop) created as the drill pipe is pulled from a well. The imposed pressure drop can create a negative pressure differential between the formation and the well bore with the well at a lower pressure, and thereby allow fluid to enter the well. Alberta Energy Resources Conservation Board, *Inquiry Report* 78–8, page 9 (June 9, 1978).

Swage

(1) A part of the CHRISTMAS TREE (*q.v.*). Continental Oil Co. v. Federal Power Comm'n, 266 F.2d 208, 10 *O.&G.R.* 601 (5th Cir. 1959), *cert. denied,* 361 U.S. 827, 11 *O.&G.R.* 305 (1959).

(2) A tool used to repair collapsed or damaged casing.

Sweep

A pattern for the location of input and producing wells in a fluid injection program, consisting of a line of input wells on the flank of the formation and the sweep carried forward by degrees, producing wells being converted into input wells as the flood reaches them and they cease to produce oil.

See also SECONDARY RECOVERY; WATER FLOODING.

Sweet gas

Natural gas not contaminated with impurities, such as sulphur compounds. Except for removal of any liquid constitutents that may be present, sweet gas is ready for commercial and domestic use.

See also SOUR GAS.

Sweetheart bill

A term applied to 52 Okla. Stat. §§ 541–547 (enacted in 1983) permitting all owners of interests in natural gas wells and wells producing casinghead gas to share ratably in revenues from the sale of the well's production, regardless of who may be producing it. Lowe and McKeown, "Mineral Law Section Annual Survey of Significant Developments," 57 *Okla. B.J.* 735 at 739 (1986). The avowed purpose of this bill was "to afford all such owners an equal opportunity to extract their fair share of gas and to sell and to be paid in proportion to their interest therein. It is further the intent of this act to protect such owners against discrimination in purchases in favor of one owner as against another." See TREATISE § 951.

Sweet oil

Crude oil containing only small quantities of hydrogen sulphide gas and carbon dioxide.

Swing

The amount, frequently stated as a percentage, above or below the average DAILY TAKE (*q.v.*), which may be taken by a purchaser under the provisions of a GAS PURCHASE CONTRACT (*q.v.*). See Matter of South Georgia Natural Gas Co., Docket No. G–9892, 22 F.P.C. 211 at 220 (Opinion No. 325, Aug. 7, 1959).

Switcher

An employee of a gas pipeline company whose job is to turn the valves at the well head, thus releasing the gas to the pipeline.

Syncline

A U or bowl-shaped geological structure, not favorable to the accumulation of oil and gas because of the tendency of the latter to rise in a structure until further escape is blocked. However, STRATIGRAPHIC TRAPS (*q.v.*) have been encountered in synclines.

See also GEOLOGICAL STRUCTURE.

Syncrude

Synthetic crude oil derived from coal or oil shale.

Synfuel

SYNTHETIC FUEL (*q.v.*).

Syngas

SYNTHETIC NATURAL GAS (SNG) (*q.v.*).

Synthesis gas

A mixture of approximately equal parts of hydrogen and carbon monoxide formed by reacting steam with hot coal or char. The mixture can be burned for fuel, and is thus similar to coal gas, but the primary use is in the production of methane or synthetic natural gas. Synthesis gas, also known as water gas, has an energy content of 980 to 1035 Btu per standard cubic foot, about the same as that of natural gas. See Hammond, Metz, and Maugh, *Energy and the Future* 165 (1973).

See also MANUFACTURED GAS.

Synthetic crude oil

In Alberta, a mixture, mainly of pentanes and heavier hydrocarbons, that may contain sulphur compounds, that is derived from crude bitumen and that is liquid at the conditions under which its volume is measured or estimated, and includes all other hydrocarbon mixtures so derived. Alberta Oil and Gas Conservation Act, R.S.A. 1970, c. 267, § 2(1)(41).

Synthetic fuel (Synfuel)

A catch-all term for a wide variety of non nuclear, non solar energy products which have the potential of serving as substitutes for petroleum or natural gas. See Office of Consumers' Counsel v. Federal Energy Regulatory Comm'n, 655 F.2d 1132, 21 FPS 6–197 (D.C. Cir. 1980) (holding that the Commission lacked jurisdiction to grant a certificate of public convenience and necessity pursuant to Section 7 of the Natural Gas Act for the construction and operation of a coal gasification plant. The court concluded that the Commission lacked authority over unmixed synthetic gas, Congress having given authority to a different governmental agency, the Synthetic Fuels Corporation, to provide governmental support for risky synfuel projects.).

See also Johnson, "Financing Synthetic Fuel Projects: An Overview," 43 *U. Pitt. L. Rev.* 103 (1981).

Synthetic fuels corporation

See UNITED STATES SYNTHETIC FUELS CORPORATION.

Synthetic natural gas (SNG)

Gas manufactured from coal or naphtha. Synthetic natural gas contains 95 to 98 percent methane and has an energy content of 980 to 1035 Btu per standard cubic feet, about the same as that of natural gas. Hammond, Metz, and Maugh, *Energy and the Future* 165 (1973).

Office of Consumers' Counsel v. Federal Energy Regulatory Comm'n, 655 F.2d 1132 (D.C. Cir. 1980), held that the Federal Energy Regulatory Commission lacked direct authority over the manufacture of unmixed synthetic gas under the Natural Gas Act. Although the Federal Power Commission and its successor, the Federal Energy Regulatory Commission, lacked jurisdiction over the sale of SNG unmixed with natural gas, it was held in Brooklyn Union Gas Co. v. Federal Energy Regulatory Comm'n, 627 F.2d 462 (D.C. Cir. 1980), that the Commission does have jurisdiction over sales in which SNG produced by one party was merely the consideration for the sale of natural gas in interstate commerce.

See American Petroleum Institute, *1972 Proceedings, Division of Refining* 283-333, (discussions of the qualities, utilization and manufacture of this product); Natural Gas Policy Issues, p. 9. Hearings before the Committee on Interior and Insular Affairs, United States Senate, Pursuant to S. Res. 45, 92nd Congress, 2d Sess., Feb. 25, 29, and March 2, 1972, Serial 92–22.

Syn.: SUBSTITUTE NATURAL GAS.

See also MANUFACTURED GAS.

Systems dispatching office

The office of a gas pipeline company which controls the flow of gas through the company's main lines. In this office, the demand for gas is estimated from a study of weather conditions, industrial fuel requirements and other factors, from which the volume of gas to be carried is determined.

..T..

Tail gas

The residue gas left after the completion of a treating process designed to remove certain liquid or liquefiable hydrocarbons. Clymore Production Co. v. Thompson, 11 F.Supp. 791 (W.D. Tex. 1935).

See also REFINERY TAIL GAS.

Tail gate

The delivery point for residue gas after processing and removal of liquid constituents in a processing plant.

Take

See GOVERNMENT TAKE.

Take-and-pay clause

A clause in a GAS PURCHASE CONTRACT (*q.v.*) requiring the purchaser to take a specified quantity of gas and to pay for the same. In the event the Buyer fails to take the quantity specified, the contract measure of damages is applicable, *viz.*, the difference between the contract price and the market price, and Seller is required to seek to mitigate damages.

In contrast is the TAKE-OR-PAY CLAUSE (*q.v.*) which requires the Buyer to pay the purchase price for the quantity specified, whether taken or not. See TREATISE § 724.5.

Amoco Production Co. v. Columbia Gas Transmission Corp., 455 So.2d 1260, 82 *O.&G.R.* 283 (La. App. 1984), *writs denied,* 459 So.2d 542, 543 (La. 1984), held that lessors, royalty owners and/or third party beneficiaries of gas purchase and sales contracts have sufficient justiciable interest to allow their intervention in an action seeking declaratory relief against a contracting purchaser of gas concerning performance of contracts and seeking specific performance of contractual obligations, including take-and-pay and take-or-pay provisions.

Take-aways

Clauses of gas purchase and sales contracts providing for reduction in prices under specified circumstances, *e.g.*, in the event the buyer exercises an option of compressing or processing the gas. See Watson, "The Natural Gas Policy Act of 1978 and Gas Purchase Contracts," 27 *Rocky Mt. Min. L. Inst.* 1407 at 1431 (1982).

Take imbalance

Failure of pipelines to take gas in the same ratio as their sellers' interest in production under normal property law concepts. See Mosburg, "Practical Effects of the 'Blanchard' Case," *35 Okla. B. A. J.* 2331 (1964).

See also BALANCING.

Take-or-lose provision

A provision of a BALANCING (*q.v.*) agreement to the effect that if a party fails to lift and dispose of its share of production (or sell it to another lifting party) the amount of the underlifted production "shall remain and accrue for and to the benefit of all the Parties according to their respective Percentage Interests." See UNDERLIFT/OVERLIFT PROVISION.

Take-or-pay clause

A clause in a GAS PURCHASE CONTRACT (*q.v.*) requiring the purchaser to take, or failing to take, to pay for the minimum annual contract volume of gas which the producer-seller has available for delivery. Under such clause the purchaser usually has the right to take the gas paid for (but undelivered) in succeeding years. Such gas is called MAKE-UP GAS (*q.v.*).

Take or Pay Provisions in Gas Purchase Contracts, 23 FPS 5–921 (Statement of Policy issued Dec. 16, 1982), 47 Fed. Reg. 57628, 57270 (1982) (to be codified at 18 C.F.R. § 2.103), announced the intent of the Commission concerning take or pay provisions in gas purchase contracts and amendments thereto between producers and interstate pipelines which become effective on or after the effective date of the statement of policy:

> "The Commission intends to apply a rebuttable presumption in general rate cases under sections 4 and 5 of the Natural Gas Act (NGA) that take or pay payments to producers which are made pursuant to requirements in such contracts in excess of 75 percent of annual deliverability are inappropriate and should not be given rate base treatment. In addition, the Commission will continue to review the extent of its other authority, if any, to deal with excessive take or pay payments under existing contracts."

A 1983 West Virginia public utilities reform bill declared "anticompetitive" take-or-pay, indefinite escalator, or most favored nation clauses in all natural gas purchase contracts to be against public policy and unenforceable to the extent "that such clause[s] require. . .[a] utility to buy more than a reasonable amount of gas at a greater than reasonable price." West Virginia Senate Bill No. 117 (1983).

For a discussion of the variety of efforts made by gas purchasers, legislatures and regulatory agencies to reduce the impact of take-or-pay clauses in gas purchase contracts, see Allison, "Natural Gas Pricing: The Eternal Debate," 37 *Baylor L. Rev.* 1 at 59 *et seq.* (1985).

Amoco Production Co. v. Columbia Gas Transmission Corp., 455 So.2d 1260, 82 *O.&G.R.* 283 (La. App. 1984), *writs denied,* 459 So.2d 542, 543 (La. 1984), held that lessors, royalty owners and/or third party beneficiaries of gas purchase and sale contract have sufficient justiciable interest to allow their intervention in an action seeking declaratory relief against a contracting purchaser of gas concerning performance of contracts and seeking specific performance of contractual obligations, including take-and-pay and take-or-pay provisions.

Markette, "Oil and Gas: 'Take or Pay' Gas Contracts: Are They Subject to Royalty?" 35 *Okla. L. Rev.* 150 (1982), argues that any income the producer receives from minimum payments under a take-or-pay clause should be subject to royalty.

For cases dealing with claims that performance by the buyer under a take-or-pay clause may be excused, see the following:

American Exploration Co. v. Columbia Gas Transmission Corp., 779 F.2d 310, 89 *O.&G.R.* 598 (6th Cir. 1985) (district court was not clearly erroneous in finding that buyer was authorized by language of contract to restrict its take on the basis of market demand);

International Minerals & Chemical Corp. v. Llano, Inc., 770 F.2d 879, 86 *O.&G.R.* 556 (10th Cir. 1985), *cert. denied,* ___ U.S. ___, 106 S.Ct. 1196 (1986) (holding that contract provision for adjustment of minimum bill under take-or-pay clause was triggered by Environmental Improvement Board regulation, compliance with which reduced buyer's natural gas consumption, and hence buyer should not be required to pay for any natural gas it did not take under the contract);

Sid Richardson Carbon & Gasoline Co. v. Internorth, Inc., 595 F.Supp. 497, 83 *O.&G.R.* 396 (N.D. Tex. 1984) (indicating court's view that take-or-pay provision does not violate the NGPA);

Stack v. Tenneco, Inc., 641 F.Supp. 199, ___ *O.&G.R.* ___ (S.D. Miss., E.D. 1986) (seller not entitled to preliminary injunction to enforce take-or-pay clause but seller is entitled to order that purchaser pay undisputed amount owed by purchaser);

Pogo Producing Co. v. Sea Robin Pipeline Co., 493 So.2d 909, ___ *O.&G.R.* ___ (La. App. 1986), *writs denied,* 497 So.2d 310 (La. 1986) (sustaining validity of preliminary injunction in favor of producer to enforce specific performance of take-or-pay covenant against pipeline).

For discussions of the take-or-pay clause see the following:

Roland, "Take-or-Pay Provisions: Major Problems for the Natural Gas Industry," 18 *St. Mary's L.J.* 251 (1986);

Medina, McKenzie and Daniel, "Take or Litigate: Enforcing the Plain Meaning of the Take-or-Pay Clause in Natural Gas Contracts," 40 *Ark. L. Rev.* 185 (1986);

Arbaugh, "Take or Pay Clauses: Pandora's Box Reopened?" 5 *Eastern Min. L. Inst.* 11-1 (1984);

Johnson, "Natural Gas Sales Contracts," 34 *Sw. Legal Fdn. Oil & Gas Inst.* 83 at 108 (1983);

Watson, "Take Or Pay Provisions in Producer Gas Sales Contracts," *Rocky Mt. Min. L. Inst. on Oil and Gas Agreements* Paper No. 11 (1983);

Tannenbaum, "Commercial Impracticability Under the Uniform Commercial Code: Natural Gas Distributors' Vehicle For Excusing Long-Term Requirements Contracts?" 20 *Houston L. Rev.* 771 (1983);

Turner, "Natural Gas—Impact of Deregulation or Reregulation on Sales Contracts," 29 *Rocky Mt. Min. L. Inst.* 501 (1983);

Howell, "Gas Purchase Contracts," 4 *Sw. Legal Fdn. Oil & Gas Inst.* 151 at 170 (1953);

TREATISE § 724.5.

The payment of royalty to the lessor on receipts by the lessee-seller under a take-or-pay clause in a gas sales contract is considered in Gulf Oil Corp., 21 IBLA 1, GFS (O&G) 1975–71.

In view of uncertainty in the right of a royalty owner to share in the proceeds realized under a take-or-pay clause of a gas sales contract, it is advisable for the lessor to consider inclusion of an express provision on the matter in the royalty clause of his lease. See Legg and Murrah, "Royalty Payments—Who Owes How Much to Whom and When?" 35 *Sw. Legal Fdn. Oil & Gas Inst.* 159 at 169, 181 (1984).

Mesa Petroleum Corp. v. U.S. Dept. of Interior, 647 F.Supp. 1350, ___ *O.&G.R.* ___ (W.D. La. 1986), held that the United

States as Lessor was not entitled to payment of royalties on proceeds realized by the lessee of offshore lands under a take-or-pay provision of a gas sales contract.

See also BUY-OUT; MARKET-OUT CLAUSE; MINIMUM COMMODITY BILL; MINIMUM TAKE PROVISION; SPECIAL MARKETING PROGRAM; TAKE-AND-PAY CLAUSE.

Take-or-pay contract

A contract whereby a purchaser agrees to take a minimum quantity of oil or gas over a specified term at a fixed price (or at a fluctuating price which cannot be reduced below a specified level) or to make minimum periodic payments to the producer even though oil or gas is not being delivered to the purchaser.

"[A] set of promises by the sponsor, nominally related to the production or use of the project facilities, which includes a promise to pay amounts specified or calculated to be at least equal to the amounts required to pay principal and interest on project borrowings." Hunt and Camp, "Project Financing—Oil and Gas Ventures," 27 *Sw. Legal Fdn. Oil & Gas Inst.* 215 at 228 (1976). The contract right of the project entity provides security for financing the project. "If the project in question is a pipeline or terminal, these contracts are called 'through put' or 'user' agreements, and if the project is a refinery or petrochemical plant, the contracts are called take-or-pay agreements (or, if the feedstock and output are owned other than by the project entity, they may be called 'refining' or 'tolling' agreements)." *Ibid.*

Freede v. Comm'r, 86 T.C. 340, 88 *O.&G.R.* 640 (1986), concluded that the purchaser of gas under a take-or-pay contract had an ECONOMIC INTEREST FOR TAX PURPOSES (*q.v.*) in the gas in place.

See also MAKE-UP GAS; MAXIMUM QUANTITY CLAUSE; PROJECT FINANCING.

Take-or-pay financing

A method of development financing involving the pledging of the benefits of a TAKE-OR-PAY CONTRACT (*q.v.*) to the lender as security for a development loan.

See also PROJECT FINANCING.

Take-out arrangement

Syn.: TAKE-OUT LETTER (*q.v.*).

Take-out letter

A letter agreement incident to an A-B-C Transaction (*q.v.*) in which the purchaser of the reserved production payment is guaranteed that if the payment is not satisfied within a specified period of time, a purchaser for the unpaid balance of such production payment will be secured or the obligor himself will buy such unpaid balance of the production payment. The obligor may be *B,* the purchaser of the operating interest [see Able Finance Co. v. Whitaker, 388 S.W.2d 437, 22 *O.&G.R.* 291 (Tex. Civ. App. 1965)] or *A,* the vendor of the developed property who reserved the production payment in the sale of the operating interest [see Burns v. United States, 22 *O.&G.R.* 841, 65–1 USTC ¶ 9835 (N.D. Tex. 1965).] See Treatise §§ 423.10, 423.11.

For other forms of letter agreements, see Letter.

Take-over clause

A clause found in an occasional oil and gas lease authorizing the lessor to "take over" a well on the leasehold upon lessee's abandonment. See D. Pierce, *Kansas Oil and Gas Handbook* § 12.08 (1986).

Take-over party

The party to a unit agreement who elects to take over the work of completing, reworking or operating a well at his sole cost, risk and expense after the unit operator has exercised an option to terminate such operations. See Upchurch, "Formation of the Exploration and Development Unit," *1959 Sw. Legal Fdn. Nat'l Inst. for Petroleum Landmen* 1 at 24 (1960).

Take-over periods

Periods of time during which the principal is in control of operations under the take-over provisions of a drilling contract. See Discussion Notes, 3 *O.&G.R.* 225 (1954).

Take-over provisions

Provisions in a Drilling contract (*q.v.*) giving the principal the right, or sometimes duty, to assume control as to defined operations. See Discussion Notes, 3 *O.&G.R.* 225 (1954).

Take-over well

A well which has been turned over to a Take-over party (*q.v.*).

Taker

"[A]ny person, who, acting alone, or jointly with any person or persons, is directly or indirectly purchasing or transporting by any means whatsoever or otherwise removing oil or gas from any common source of supply." Okla. Stat. Ann., § 52–86.1 (i) (1969).

Tank

A large, steel cylinder for the storage of oil.

Lease tanks (also called field tanks) store the oil from one or more wells on a single lease. Tank farms are a collection of a number of large storage tanks at the main pump station of the pipe line that carries the oil to the refinery. Tank farms may also be found at refineries and other places where oil storage is convenient.

See also STOCK TANK; TRIP TANK.

Tank battery

A group of tanks located at convenient points for storing oil prior to transportation by truck or pipeline to a refinery. See BATTERY SITE.

Syn.: TANK FARM.

Tank battery commingling agreement

An agreement used "when an operator of several producing properties wishes to consolidate the production facilities of various leases and store oil from all the leases in a single tank battery. This agreement allocates to each royalty and overriding royalty owner and each working interest owner a proportionate amount of the production from the common tank battery based on flow tests of all wells affected. The wells are usually retested once a year in order to readjust the allocation of production. The allocation formula is based on a direct ratio of each well's individual production test to the sum of all the wells' individual tests on a per lease basis." Himebaugh, "An Overview of Oil and Gas Contracts in the Williston Basin," 59 *No. Dak. L. Rev.* 7 (1983).

Tank battery consolidation agreement

Syn.: TANK BATTERY COMMINGLING AGREEMENT (*q.v.*).

Tank bottoms

Oil emulsified with water and other substances and concentrated at the bottom of stock tanks used for gathering and temporary storage of crude oil preparatory to its sale to pipe line companies. Usually the substance is removed from the stock tanks periodically to avoid contamination of crude oil sold. In Shoemake v. United States, 176 F. Supp. 746, 10 *O.&G.R.* 875 (D. Kan. 1959), *aff'd,* 280 F.2d 902, 12 *O.&G.R.* 624 (10th Cir. 1960), it was held that taxpayer who removed and processed such tank bottoms did not have a depletable interest therein.

Tank farm

A collection of large, steel cylinders for the storage of oil.
Syn.: TANK BATTERY.

Tank gas

See LIQUEFIED PETROLEUM GAS.

Tank settlings

Syn.: TANK BOTTOMS (*q.v.*).

Tank strappage deduction

See STRAPPAGE DEDUCTION.

Tank table

A table recording the capacity in barrels for each one-eighth or one-quarter inch of depth of a measuring tank.

Tapered royalty

A royalty which begins at a specified rate and declines each year by a specified amount or percentage, regardless of the rate of production. This type of royalty would tend to preclude early abandonment. McDonald, *The Leasing of Federal Lands for Fossil Fuels Production* 117 (1979).

Tapline

The Trans-Arabian Pipeline Co. organized in 1945. See Shwadran, *The Middle East, Oil and the Great Powers* 337 (3d ed. revised and enlarged, 1973).

TAPS agreement

The agreement entered into by several companies to design, construct, own, operate and maintain the pipeline system known as the Trans Alaska Pipeline System (TAPS).

For discussions of the construction of TAPS and of the ownership agreement, see the following:

Fox, *Federal Regulation of Energy* ch. 12 (1983);

Lenzner, *Management, Planning and Construction of the Trans-Alaska Pipeline System* (1977);

Hagle, "The Trans Alaska Pipeline System," in International Bar Ass'n, *Proceedings of the Energy Law Seminar* (organized by the Committee on Energy and Natural Resources, Section on Business Law) Topic L, Paper 1 (1979).

See also UNDIVIDED INTEREST PIPELINE.

Target area

A term employed in Section 9 (1) of the Canada Oil and Gas Land Regulations established by P.C. 1961–797, amended by P.C. 1963–408 as "an area of land six hundred feet square lying within a unit [*viz.*, 1/16 of a section] and oriented due north-south and east-west and situate symmetrically about the intersection of a line joining the midpoints of the east and west boundaries of the unit with a line joining the midpoints of the north and south boundaries of the unit."

In Alberta, the part of a DRILLING SPACING UNIT (*q.v.*) within which a well for the purpose of producing oil or gas may be completed without reduction of its ALLOWABLE (*q.v.*) because of its location. Oil and Gas Conservation Regulations (Alta. Reg. 151/71) § 1–020 (23). When a well is completed outside its primary and secondary target area, its base allowable, or, in the case of a gas well, its annual allowable, is reduced. See Province of Alberta Energy Resources Conservation Board Order No. SU 1088 (Aug. 10, 1981).

For a study of a proposal to change the target area requirements for future oil and gas wells in Alberta from the center to the northeast quadrant of the spacing units, see Board Staff Submission, Alberta's Oil and Gas Well Spacing and Target Area Regulations, Energy Resources Conservation Board Proceeding 9750 (19 April 1977).

See also CORNER TARGET AREA; DRILLING SPACING UNIT; DRILLING UNIT; OFF-TARGET PENALTY; SPACING UNIT; STANDUP DRILLING UNIT (STANDUP SPACING); WELL SPACING.

Target formation

"For the purposes of W. Va. Code ch. 22, arts. 4 and 4B, the phrase means the primary geological formation identified by the well operator in his application for a drilling permit filed under W. Va. Code § 22–4–1k." Snyder and Christian, "Oil and Gas Operations Through Coal Seams in West Virginia," 1 *Eastern Min. L. Inst.* 5–126 (1980).

Tariff (or FPC gas tariff)

A compilation, in book form, of all of the effective rate schedules of a particular natural gas company, and a copy of each form of service agreement. 18 C.F.R. § 154.14 (1980).

See also RATE SCHEDULE; VOLUME VARIATION ADJUSTMENT CLAUSE.

Tariff-and-service-agreement

An agreement between buyer and seller of gas which does not itself contain a price term but refers to rate schedules of general applicability on file with the Federal Power Commission or its successor, the Federal Energy Regulatory Commission. United Gas Pipe Line Co. v. Memphis Light, Gas & Water Division, 358 U.S. 103, 9 *O.&G.R.* 967 (1958), *rehearing denied,* 358 U.S. 942 (1958).

See also RATE SCHEDULE.

Tar sands

See PETROLEUM TAR SANDS.

Taxable income for depletion

See NET INCOME FOR THE DEPLETION ALLOWANCE.

Taxation of oil and gas

See ABANDONMENT LOSS; A-B-C TRANSACTION; ABERCROMBIE-TYPE CARRIED INTEREST; ACT; ADDITIONAL PROFITS TAX; ADDITIONAL ROYALTY; ADD-ONS; ADJUSTED BASE PRICE; ADJUSTMENT OF UNIT INTERESTS; AD VALOREM TAX; ADVANCE ROYALTY; AGGREGATION OF PROPERTIES; ANTICIPATION OF INCOME; ANTI-PASSTHROUGH PROVISION; AREA OF INTEREST; ASSOCIATION FOR TAX PURPOSES; "AT RISK" RULE; BONUS; BOOT; BOTTOM HOLE CONTRIBUTION; CAPITAL ASSETS; CAPITAL COST ALLOWANCE; CAPITAL EXPENDITURES; CAPITAL GAIN (OR LOSS); CARRIED INTEREST; CARVED OUT OIL PAYMENT; COMPLETE PAY-OUT PERIOD; CONNECTED PERSON; CONSORTIUM; CONVERTIBLE OVERRIDE

FARM OUT; COST COMPANY; CRUDE OIL EQUALIZATION TAX; CRUDE OIL WINDFALL PROFITS TAX OF 1980; DEFERRED BONUS; DEFERRED-PAYMENT OPEN-END SALE; DEFERRED PRODUCTION PAYMENT; DELAY RENTAL; DEPLETION; DEPLETION, COST; DEPLETION, PERCENTAGE; DEPLETION, RESTORATION OF; DEPRECIATION; DISQUALIFIED TRANSFEROR; DIVISIBLE SHARING ARRANGEMENT; DRILLING FUND; EARNED DEPLETION; ECONOMIC INTEREST FOR TAX PURPOSES; ENERGY TAX ACT of 1978; EQUIPMENT COSTS; EXCESS CASH; EXCLUDED OIL; EXEMPT ALASKAN OIL; EXEMPT FRONT-END OIL; EXEMPT INDIAN OIL; EXEMPT OIL; EXPENDABLE WELL; FARM-OUT AGREEMENT; FIRST MARKETABLE PRODUCT; FIRST USE TAX; FISKE FORMULA; FOREIGN TAX CREDIT; FRONT-END TERTIARY OIL; FRONT-END TERTIARY PROVISIONS; FRONTIER EXPLORATION ALLOWANCE; FUNCTIONAL ALLOCATION SHARING ARRANGEMENT; G AND G EXPENDITURES; GATHERING TAX; GEOPHYSICAL AND GEOLOGICAL COSTS; GOVERNMENT TAKE; HEAVY OIL; HERNDON-TYPE CARRIED INTEREST; HORIZONTAL CUT OIL PAYMENT; INCREMENTAL TERTIARY OIL; INDEPENDENT PRODUCER OIL; INJECTION WELL; INTANGIBLE DRILLING AND DEVELOPMENT COSTS; IPRO EXEMPTION; "IVY" OPTION; LEASE ACQUISITION COSTS; LIFTING COSTS; LIMITED CARRIED INTEREST; LIMITED WORKING INTEREST; MANAHAN-TYPE CARRIED INTEREST; MINERAL LAND TAX ACT; MINIMUM ROYALTY; NASSAU PLAN; NET INCOME FOR DEPLETION ALLOWANCE; NEWLY DISCOVERED CRUDE OIL; NON-EXCLUDED OIL; NON-OPERATING MINERAL INTEREST, FOR TAX PURPOSES; NORM PRICE; NORWEGIAN SPECIAL TAX; OBLIGATION WELL DOCTRINE; OIL PAYMENT; OPERATING EXPENSES; OPERATING MINERAL INTEREST, FOR TAX PURPOSES; OPERATING UNIT, FOR TAX PURPOSES; OWNER OF AN OPERATING MINERAL INTEREST; PERMANENT CARRIED INTEREST; PETROLEUM ADMINISTRATION ACT; PETROLEUM REVENUE TAX (PRT); PREPAID IDC; PRODUCTION FACILITIES; PRODUCTION TAX; PROPERTY UNIT, FOR TAX PURPOSES; PROPORTIONATE PROFITS METHOD; PROVEN OIL OR GAS PROPERTY TRANSFER; QUALIFIED CHARITABLE INTEREST; QUALIFIED GOVERNMENTAL INTEREST; QUALIFIED OVERRIDING ROYALTY INTEREST; QUALIFIED PRODUCTION; QUALIFIED TERTIARY INJECTANT EXPENSES; QUALIFIED TERTIARY RECOVERY PROJECT; REDRILLING; RELATED GROUP; REMOVAL PRICE; RESERVED OIL PAYMENT; RESOURCE ALLOWANCE; RESOURCE RENT TAX; RESPONSIBLE PERSON; RING FENCE; ROYALTY EXPENSING; ROYALTY SURCHARGE; ROYALTY TAX CREDIT; ROYALTY TAX REBATE; RRT; SADLEROCHIT OIL; SALE OF OIL AT ARMS' LENGTH; SEVERANCE BENEFICIARY; SEVERANCE PRODUCER; SEVERANCE TAX; SEVERANCE TAX CREDIT; SHARING ARRANGEMENT; SHOOTING OPTION; SHORT-LIVED IN-OIL PAYMENT; SLIDING SCALE ROYALTY; SUCCESSOR EARNED DEPLETION; SUPPLEMENTARY DEPLETION ALLOWANCES; SUPPLEMENTARY PETROLEUM TAX; TAX EXPORT VALUE;

TAX-PAID COST (TPC); TAX PARTNERSHIP AGREEMENT; TAX PREFERENCE ITEM; TAX REFERENCE PRICE; TAX REFERENCE VALUE AGREEMENT; TAX-REIMBURSEMENT CLAUSE; TAX SHIFTING CLAUSE; TIER 1 OIL; TIER 2 OIL; TIER 3 OIL; TOTAL OPERATING GROSS INCOME; TOTAL OPERATING NET INCOME; TRANSFER RULE; TURNKEY WELL DOCTRINE; WINDFALL PROFIT; WORTHLESSNESS, LOSS FROM; YIELD TAX.

For discussions of the taxation of oil and gas in various countries, see the following:

W. Hellerstein, *State and Local Taxation of Natural Resources in the Federal System* (1986);

van der Rest, "Oil and Gas Taxation in Denmark," [1982] 4 *OGLTR* 110;

Pombo, "Oil and Gas Taxation in Spain," [1983] 2 *OGLTR* 33;

Nee, "Taxation of the Offshore Oil and Gas Industry in China," [1983] 3 *OGLTR* 41;

Henderson and Martin, "Petroleum Taxation in Australia," [1983] 5 *OGLTR* 89;

Etikerentse, "Taxation under Nigerian Petroleum Law,‘ [1983] 6 *OGLTR* 121;

Bell, "Petroleum Taxation in Canada," [1982] 3 *OGLTR* 82;

Savelbergh, "Dutch Offshore Oil and Gas Taxation," [1983] 8 *OGLTR* 174.

Tax Equity and Fiscal Responsibility Act of 1982 (TEFRA)

Public Law 97-249. For discussions of the Act and its effects on the oil and gas industry, see the folowing:

Orbach, Curatola & Samson, "The Tax Equity and Fiscal Responsibility Act of 1982 and the Subchapter S Revision Act of 1982: Their Effect on the Oil and Gas Industry," 31 *O.&G. Tax Q. 503* (1983);

Stewart, Wilding, Hecht and Sommerfeldt, "Impact of TEFRA on Intangible Drilling Costs of Individuals," 31 *O.&G. Tax Q.* 733 (1983).

Tax export value

Prior to the negotiated TAX REFERENCE VALUE AGREEMENT (*q.v.*), the Venezuelan Income Tax Law authorized the administration to estimate the true value of goods exported from the country. This estimate, known as the tax export value, was the basis upon which taxes were assessed. See Imperial Oil Ltd. v. Nova Scotia Light &

Power Co., [1977] 2 S.C.R. 817, 77 D.L.R.3d 1 (Sup. Ct. of Canada 1977).

Tax-increase clause

See ESCALATOR CLAUSE.

Tax-paid cost (TPC)

A term used to indicate the price floor for oil from countries organized in OPEC, namely the cost of production plus the per-barrel tax. Note, "From Concession to Participation: Restructuring the Middle East Oil Industry," 48 *N.Y.U. L. Rev.* 776 at 779 (1973).

See also MID-WAY PRICE; OIL PURCHASE AND SALE CONTRACT; QUARTER-WAY PRICE.

Tax partnership agreement

A contract by which the parties attempt to accomplish a result which, except for tax consequences, is the same as that which could be obtained through a farm-out agreement. This form of agreement was a response to Rev. Rul. 77-176 which made possible adverse tax consequences for both parties to a farm-out agreement. See Arruebarrena, "Tax Partnership Agreements," 31 *L.S.U. Min. L. Inst.* 138 (1984).

Tax preference item

Under Internal Revenue Code § 56 a tax is imposed on the amount by which the sum of the items of "tax preference" exceeds the greater of $10,000 or the regular tax deduction for the taxable year (as determined under subsection (c)). Among the "items of tax preference" listed in § 57 are the excess of the deduction for depletion allowable under section 611 for the taxable year over the adjusted basis of the property at the end of the taxable year (item 7) and the excess of the intangible drilling and development costs paid or incurred in connection with oil and gas wells allowable for the taxable year over the amount which would have been allowable for the taxable year if such costs had been capitalized and straight-line recovery of intangibles had been used with respect to such costs (item 11).

Tax reference price

An arbitrary posted price for hydrocarbons utilized in a number of countries for the purpose of calculating taxes and other payments due the State from an operator. See OPEC Resolution XVI.90 of the Sixteenth Conference held in Vienna from 24th to 25th June 1968.

See also POSTED PRICE.

Tax reference value agreement

An agreement between the oil producers operating in Venezuela and the Government of that country fixing an amount the companies were deemed to receive, notwithstanding the market or sales prices which they declared, for purposes of Venezuelan taxes. See Imperial Oil Ltd., v. Nova Scotia Light & Power Co., [1977] 2 S.C.R. 817, 77 D.L.R.3d 1 (Sup. Ct. of Canada 1977).

Tax Reform Act of 1976

Public Law 94-455 (1976).

See also INTANGIBLE DRILLING AND DEVELOPMENT COSTS (IDC); RESERVED OIL PAYMENT.

Tax-reimbursement clause

A clause of a gas purchase and sale contract providing that the purchaser will pay any state severance tax imposed upon the producer-seller of the gas. Hoover & Bracken Energies, Inc. v. United States Department of the Interior, 723 F.2d 1488, 79 *O.&G.R.* 282 (10th Cir. 1983), *cert. denied,* ____ U.S. ____, 105 S. Ct. 93 (1984).

See also ESCALATOR CLAUSE; GAS PURCHASE CONTRACT.

Tax shifting clause

A provision of a lease or other agreement designed to shift the burden of a tax (*e.g.,* a severance tax) from one party to another. See Tenneco West, Inc. v. Marathon Oil Co., 756 F.2d 769, 84 *O.&G.R.* 609 (9th Cir. 1985), *cert. denied,* ____ U.S. ____, 106 S.Ct. 134 (1985) (holding that the tax-shifting clause there construed did not have the effect of shifting the burden of the Windfall Profits Tax from the royalty owner to the lessee).

Tcf

Trillion cubic feet.

TD

Abbreviation for total depth.

TECA

Temporary Emergency Court of Appeals.

Technical Corrections Act of 1982

Pub. L. No. 97-448, Jan. 12, 1983. Among other things, this Act added Internal Revenue Code Section 6430 under which each individual or estate income beneficiary of a trust is entitled to a credit or refund of windfall profit tax paid by the trust on his or her allocable share of the QUALIFIED ROYALTY PRODUCTION (*q.v.*) of the trust for taxable years beginning after December 31, 1981.

TEFRA

The TAX EQUITY AND FISCAL RESPONSIBILITY ACT OF 1982 (*q.v.*).

Teheran Agreement of 14 February 1971

An agreement entered into between the six Gulf States (Abu Dhabi, Iran, Iraq, Kuwait, Qatar and Saudia Arabia) and thirteen oil producing companies "to establish security of supply and stability in financial arrangements," for a period from 15 February 1971 through 31 December 1975. The agreement was designated to stabilize government take and financial obligations of the companies and increase the posted price of crude oil by regular escalations over the period of the agreement. The agreement was a casualty of the Arab-Israeli War of 1973.

See also ORGANIZATION OF PETROLEUM EXPORTING COUNTRIES (OPEC).

Temperature deduction

A conversion of the metered or otherwise measured volume of oil or gas produced on the basis of a standard or agreed temperature base. Crude oil in the reservoir at high temperature and pressure may contain considerable quantities of gas in solution which may materially increase the volume. As the oil is produced and temperature and pressure reduced, the dissolved gas will come out of solution. Hence crude oil may shrink in volume as it is brought to surface conditions of temperature and pressure. Similarly the volume of gas from a gas well changes as it is brought to surface conditions.

Templet-type platform

An offshore drilling and production platform with a large deck area on which are mounted derricks and other drilling paraphernalia, all supported above sea level by "templets," which are compound, trussed structures, analogous in function to table legs but composed of several large vertical steel beams and pipes (usually an even number) arranged in a rectangular fashion with bars running between the pipes for support and spacing. Several templets are ordinarily used to support one deck, the number depending on the size, weight, and other features of the deck and equipment to be installed thereon. Exxon Corp. v. United States, 547 F.2d 548 at n.4, 55 *O.&G.R.* 535 at n.4 (Ct. of Claims 1976).

Temporary abandonment

Cessation of work on a well pending determination of whether it should be completed as a producer or permanently abandoned. Some of the factors considered in determining whether an offshore well should be temporarily abandoned (and the methods employed in effecting a temporary abandonment) are discussed in Gates Rubber Co. & Subsidiaries v. Commissioner, 74 T.C. 1456, 67 *O.&G.R.* 647 (1980), *aff'd,* 694 F.2d 648 (10th Cir. 1982), and Sun Oil Co. v. Commissioner, 74 T.C. 1481, 68 *O.&G.R.* 353 (1980), *aff'd,* 677 F.2d 294, 76 *O.&G.R.* 619 (3d Cir. 1982), *acq.,* I.R.B. 1983-26 (1983).

See also ABANDONMENT.

Temporary allowable

An ALLOWABLE (*q.v.*) granted to wells in a newly discovered field prior to issuance of a final proration order for the field, which usually must be preceded by notice and hearing if such order is issued by a conservation commission.

Temporary cessation of production

A termination of production for a temporary period as a result of governmental action, sanding up or breakdown of the well, etc. A temporary, as opposed to a permanent cessation of production, does not cause the termination of the lessee's interest in the leasehold after the expiration of the primary term of a lease.

It is frequently a difficult question of fact whether a cessation of production is temporary or permanent in character. It is suggested in Garcia v. King, 139 Tex. 578, 164 S.W.2d 509 (1942), that in making the determination of whether the cessation is temporary or permanent in character the question is whether under "normal" conditions, the well or leasehold was producing enough oil or gas to pay a profit over and above the cost of operating the well. Some courts have been more than generous in finding that prolonged cessation of production was merely temporary in character. Stimson v. Tarrant, 132 F.2d 363 (9th Cir. 1942), *cert. denied,* 319 U.S. 751 (1943); Saulsberry v. Siegel, 221 Ark. 152, 252 S.W.2d 834, 2 *O.&G.R.* 1 (1952).

There is some indication that courts are more liberal in finding that a cessation of production is merely temporary when the matter in issue is the alleged termination of a TERM MINERAL OR ROYALTY INTEREST (*q.v.*) with a thereafter clause than they are when the matter in issue is the alleged termination of the interest of a lessee. This appears to be based on the theory that such a grantee does not have the duty to obtain production and, at least in the case of a royalty grantee, does not have the right to obtain production. Beatty v. Baxter, 208 Okla. 686, 258 P.2d 626, 2 *O.&G.R.* 1284 (1953); but *cf.* Owens v. Day, 207 Okla. 341, 249 P.2d 710, 1 *O.&G.R.* 1713 (1952). Certain of the policy considerations involved in a more liberal construction of the "thereafter" provisions in mineral and royalty deeds are discussed in Note, 32 *Tex. L. Rev.* 769 (1954); Cantwell, "Term Royalty," 7 *Sw. Legal Fdn. Oil & Gas Inst.* 339 (1956); TREATISE §§ 334.8, 604.4.

See also CESSATION OF PRODUCTION; PERMANENT CESSATION OF PRODUCTION.

Tenancy by the entirety

A form of CONCURRENT OWNERSHIP (*q.v.*) between husband and wife in which there is a right of survivorship.

Tenancy in common

A form of CONCURRENT OWNERSHIP (*q.v.*) not involving a right of survivorship.

Tenant's consent agreement

The consent of the owner of a possessory interest in land (*e.g.*, a surface lessee) to drilling operations by the lessee of the owner of the reversion. The agreement recites that for and in consideration of a stated sum, the tenant gives:

> "his consent and approval of all the rights, interests and privileges stipulated in the within and foregoing oil and gas mining lease and the full use and exercise thereof by the lessee, or lessee's successors

and assigns, subject to the conditions, however, that any and all damages or loss sustained by any of his crops and other property on said premises as a result of the exercise of said rights under said oil and gas mining lease, shall be paid him on the basis of the actual cash value thereof."

The surface tenant is not entitled to produce minerals or to share in any production from the premises, absent an express authorization, but in some instances there is doubt as to the right of a lessee of the reversioner to interfere with the possessory rights of the surface tenant by drilling operations. As a matter of practice, before operations are pursued, the owner of the reversion or his lessee attempts to obtain the consent of the owner of the possessory interest to the operations. The latter may have such a bargaining position that he will be able to exact a substantial consideration for his consent, which is usually evidenced by a Tenant's Consent Agreement. See TREATISE §§ 218.3, 515.

See also SURFACE LEASE.

Tender

A permit or certificate of clearance for the transportation of oil, gas, or products, approved and issued or registered under the authority of a regulatory board or commission.

In Texas the tender requirement was eliminated on January 1, 1963 on the ground that it had been rendered unnecessary by modern machine accounting methods. See Murray, "Recent Conservation Developments: Technical, Economic and Legal," 7 *Tulane Tidelands Institute* 3 at 7 (1963).

Tender allowance

An allowance made to a carrier for transportation losses arising from evaporation and other causes. The allowance is usually a small percentage, *e.g.*, one per cent. See Irving and Draper, *Accounting Practices in the Petroleum Industry* 100 (1958).

Tender, minimum

See MINIMUM TENDER

Ten per cent excessive acreage rule

When an offer to lease federal lands exceeds 2560 acres and the RULE OF APPROXIMATION (*q.v.*) was not directly applicable, regulations provided that as long as the offer contained no more than ten per cent in excess of the maximum allowable acreage of 2560 acres, a lease could issue under certain circumstances for 2560 acres or for the maximum acreage in excess of the 2560 acres allowed by the Rule of Approximation. See Vernon, "The Maximum Acreage Requirement of Noncompetitive Federal Oil and Gas Lease Offers on the Public Domain," 3 *Nat. Res. J.* 291 at 297 (1963); *Rocky Mt. Min. L. Fdn. Law of Federal Oil and Gas Leases* § 5.05 (1985).

Ten per cent (rental) rule

The rule applicable to federal noncompetitive leases that an offer deficient in the first year's rental by not more than ten per cent will be approved by the signing officer provided all other additional requirements are met. The additional rental must be paid within 30 days from notice, under penalty of cancellation of the lease. 43 C.F.R. §§ 3103.3–1 3111.1–1 (1978). See Edward Goodman, IBLA 80–409, 48 IBLA 152, GFS(O&G) 1980–119 (June 9, 1980); Earl F. Hartley, IBLA 80–322, 49 IBLA 140, GFS(O&G) 1980–148 (July 30, 1980).

See also NON-COMPETITIVE LEASE.

Tension leg platform

Floating platform for drilling or production which is restrained and located by tension cables or articulated supports from the ocean bottom. Kash, *et al., Energy Under the Oceans* 59, 368 (1973).

Term clause

The clause of a lease, mineral deed or royalty deed which fixes the duration of the interest granted or reserved.

Syn.: HABENDUM CLAUSE.

Term day-work contract

A DAY RATE CONTRACT (*q.v.*) providing for a specific amount of time during which the contractor receives payment for services. Wagner & Brown v. E. W. Moran Drilling Co., 702 S.W.2d 760, 90 *O.&G.R.* 571 (Tex. App., Fort Worth, 1986).

Terminable working interest

A WORKING INTEREST (*q.v.*) which is terminable upon the satisfaction of certain charges from the proceeds of production. See *Miller's Oil and Gas Federal Income Taxation* § 13–5 (1980 Edition).

See also NASSAU PLAN.

Terminal provision

A clause providing for the termination of an interest upon the happening of a stated event, either by limitation or by exercise of a power of termination. Typical terminal provisions are found in the DELAY RENTAL CLAUSE (*q.v.*) and the NOTICE AND DEMAND CLAUSE (*q.v.*).

Termination clause

A lease clause permitting termination of a lease by the lessor under specified circumstances. In State of Alaska v. Andrus, 580 F.2d 465, 61 *O.&G.R.* 1 (D.C. Cir. 1978), the court concluded, contrary to the position taken by the Secretary of the Interior, that the Secretary was authorized to include such a clause in OCS leases. Certiorari was granted in this case *sub nom.* Western Oil & Gas Assoc. v. Alaska, 439 U.S. 922 (1978), and in the memorandum decision the court said "Part II–C of the decision below [dealing with the conclusion of the Court of Appeals that the Secretary had authority to include a termination clause in the lease] vacated and case remanded to the United States District Court for the District of Columbia for dismissal of paragraph 37(j) of the complaint."

Termination of lease

Expiration, cancellation or forfeiture of a lessee's interest in leased premises.

A lease may be terminated by the lessee's exercise of a surrender clause in the lease, and under contemporary forms of leases, failure of production in paying quantities at or after the expiration of the primary term will cause the lease to be terminated unless it can be preserved by some savings clause in the lease such as a SHUT-IN GAS WELL CLAUSE (*q.v.*), DRILLING OPERATIONS CLAUSE (*q.v.*), or CONTINUOUS DRILLING OPERATIONS CLAUSE (*q.v.*). Under an UNLESS LEASE (*q.v.*) form, the leasehold interest will be terminated on an anniversary date during the primary term, if drilling operations are not then being prosecuted (or, under some lease forms, if there is not then production) unless timely payment of delay rentals is made. Under an OR LEASE (*q.v.*) form, failure of the lessee to perform one of the alternative acts required by the lease ("drill or pay"; "drill or pay or forfeit") may occasion termination of the lease during the primary term. Failure of the lessee to engage in drilling operations required by the express or implied covenants of the lease may result in a termination of the lease in whole or in part by judicial decree in the form of a CANCELLATION DECREE or CONDITIONAL DECREE OF CANCELLATION (*q.v.*).

See also ALTERNATIVE DECREE; AUTOMATIC TERMINATION OF LEASE; CANCELLATION DECREE; CONDITIONAL DECREE OF CANCELLATION; DEVOTIONAL LIMITATION DOCTRINE; 555 TERMINATION; FORFEITURE CLAUSE; FORFEITURE OF LEASE; JUDICIAL ASCERTAINMENT CLAUSE; LIMITATION CLAUSE; NOTICE AND DEMAND CLAUSE; PARTIAL CANCELLATION; PERMANENT CESSATION OF PRODUCTION; POSSIBILITY OF REVERTER; POWER OF TERMINATION.

Termination, power of

See POWER OF TERMINATION

Term mineral or royalty interest

A mineral or royalty interest of less than perpetual duration. Most such interests are created to endure for a fixed period and so long thereafter as oil, gas or other minerals are produced. But some endure for a fixed and definite period, such as twenty years, without the thereafter clause. It is suggested that clarity is promoted by calling the latter FIXED TERM INTERESTS and by calling those with a thereafter clause DEFEASIBLE TERM INTERESTS (*q.v.*).

In addition to these two types of term interests, there are also examples in the cases of royalty limited in duration to the life of an existing lease. Davis v. Collins, 219 Ark. 948, 245 S.W.2d 571 (1952); Bellport v. Harrison, 123 Kan. 310, 255 Pac. 52 (1927); Peacock v. Alexander, 253 S.W.2d 716, 2 *O.&G.R.* 298 (Tex. Civ. App. 1953). And there are rare examples of royalty or mineral interests to endure for the period of the life of some person. Howard v. Dillard, 198 Okla. 116, 176 P.2d 500 (1947); Bank v. Evans, 169 S.W.2d 754 (Tex. Civ. App. 1943).

A common problem regarding term interests with thereafter clauses is termination of the interest. It has been held that discovery of minerals during the term does not keep the interest in force if production comes after the term has expired. Holchak v. Clark, 284 S.W.2d 399, 5 *O.&G.R.* 595 (Tex. Civ. App. 1956, error ref'd). *Contra,* Panhandle Eastern Pipe Line Co. v. Isaacson, 255 F.2d 669, 9 *O.&G.R.* 363 (10th Cir. 1958). When production ceases permanently a term interest with thereafter clause also ceases. But where cessation of production is only temporary, it has been held that the interest does not terminate. Beatty v. Baxter, 208 Okla. 686, 258 P.2d 626, 2

O.&G.R. 1284 (Okla. 1953), 32 *Tex. L. Rev.* 769 (1954); Postier v. Postier, 296 P.2d 138, 5 *O.&G.R.* 1234 (Okla. 1956); but *cf.* Wilson v. Holm, 164 Kan. 229, 188 P.2d 899 (1948).

Another problem is the prompt exercise of the power to lease, since the term interest expires without production at the end of the primary term. If the term interest owner has the power to execute a lease, as in the case of a mineral interest, no controversy will arise. But in the case of term royalty, the owner has no power to lease. Speaking to a related situation, the court in Schlittler v. Smith, 128 Tex. 628, 101 S.W.2d 543 (1937), said that the EXECUTIVE (*q.v.*) had the duty of UTMOST FAIR DEALING (*q.v.*). See Jones, "Non-Participating Royalty," 26 *Tex. L. Rev.* 569 (1948); Cantwell, "Term Royalty," 7 *Sw. Legal Fdn. Oil & Gas Inst.* 339 (1956).

On term interests generally, see TREATISE §§ 331–337.

TERP

Tertiary enhanced recovery program. See TERTIARY RECOVERY.

Territorial sea

The sea immediately adjacent to a coastal nation within which it claims comprehensive jurisdiction.

Tertiary incentive program

A program set up by the Department of Energy "to provide front-end money to producers engaged in the initiation or expansion of tertiary enhanced crude oil projects." 10 C.F.R. § 212.78. See Union Oil Co. of Calif. v. Department of Energy, 688 F.2d 797 (Temp. Emer. Ct. App. 1982), *cert. denied,* 459 U.S. 1202, 103 S. Ct. 1186 (1983).

See also Exxon Corp. v. Department of Energy, 601 F.Supp. 1395 (D. Dela. 1985) (discussing the history of the ENTITLEMENT PROGRAM (*q.v.*) and the tertiary incentive program), *aff'd in part and rev'd in part,* 802 F.2d 1400 (Temp. Emer. Ct. of App. 1986).

Tertiary incentive revenue

In the case of first sales of crude oil subject to Department of Energy regulation 10 C.F.R. § 212.78 (1980), this term means the excess of the market clearing price over the otherwise applicable ceiling price less any ad valorem or severance taxes attributable to this excess.

Tertiary incremental crude oil

See TERTIARY INCREMENTAL PROGRAM.

Tertiary incremental program

A program set up by the Department of Energy providing that increased production of crude oil resulting from a qualified and certified enhanced recovery project would be exempt from price controls. 43 Fed. Reg. 33,678 (Aug. 1, 1978). This regulation created a new category of exempt crude oil known as "tertiary incremental crude oil." Subsequently, the Department concluded that further production incentives were needed, and it amended 10 C.F.R. § 212.78 to add the TERTIARY INCENTIVE PROGRAM (*q.v.*), designed "to provide front-end money to producers engaged in the initiation or expansion of tertiary enhanced crude oil projects." For discussions of these programs see Union Oil Co. of Calif. v. Department of Energy, 688 F.2d 797 (Temp. Emer. Ct. App. 1982), *cert. denied,* 459 U.S. 1202, 103 S. Ct. 1186 (1983).

See also QUALIFIED TERTIARY RECOVERY PROJECT.

Tertiary injectant expenses

See QUALIFIED TERTIARY INJECTANT EXPENSES.

Tertiary recovery

Enhanced recovery methods for the production of crude oil or natural gas.

Enhanced recovery of crude oil requires a means for displacing oil from the reservoir rock, modifying the properties of the fluids in the reservoir and/or the reservoir rock to cause movement of crude oil in an efficient manner, and providing the energy and drive mechanism to force its flow to a production well. Chemicals or energy are injected as required for displacement and for the control of flow rate and flow pattern in the reservoir, and a fluid drive is provided to force the oil toward a production well. Basic methods include (a) thermal methods wherein heat energy is added to the formation, (b) pseudo miscible methods wherein surface active agents are introduced into the reservoir rock, (c) carbon dioxide miscible methods wherein carbon dioxide is used as the agent to enhance oil/water miscibility, and (d) hydrocarbon miscible methods wherein a slug of hydrocarbon material with high oil miscibility is employed.

Enhanced recovery of natural gas requires (1) the creation of a production well with sufficiently large area penetration into the reservoir rock that flow rates result in economic production (*e.g.*, by nuclear stimulation or hydraulic fracturing), or (2) the solution of problems arising from the high temperatures and pressures associated with otherwise conventional recovery below 15,000 feet.

Rev. Rul. 85-141, 1985-36 I.R.B. 54, 85 *O.&G.R.* 439 (1985), held that the injection of a nonhydrocarbon gas into the gas cap of an oil reservoir is not an approved tertiary enhanced recovery method under Internal Revenue code section 4993(d)(1)(B), relating to the Windfall Profit Tax, because that method does not utilize a process that acts directly on the oil zone of the reservoir.

See the Draft Report on Planning Criteria Relative to a National Research, Development, Testing, and Evaluation Program Directed to the Enhanced Recovery of Crude Oil and Natural Gas, in "Fiscal Policy and the Energy Crisis." Hearings before the Subcommittee on Energy of the Committee on Finance, U.S. Senate, 93rd Cong., 1st Sess., Nov. 27–29, 1973, at 570 *et seq.*

On the question of the existence of a duty to engage in secondary or tertiary recovery operations, see Fant, "Legal Issues in Implementing Secondary and Tertiary Operations on Federal Oil and Gas Leases," 19 *Land & Water L. Rev.* 1 (1984); Armstrong and Peters, "Enhanced Recovery of Oil," 5 *Eastern Min. L. Inst.* 13-1 (1984).

See also PRODUCTION ENHANCEMENT PROCEDURES; QUALIFIED TERTIARY RECOVERY PROJECT; SECONDARY RECOVERY.

Test hole or well

An exploratory well drilled to determine whether a particular horizon will be productive of minerals.

Test well contribution agreement

An agreement to pay the owner of an adjacent tract a portion of the cost of drilling an exploratory well on his property. See CONTRIBUTION AGREEMENT.

Texas Railroad Commission

The administrative agency of the State of Texas charged with the duty of making and enforcing conservation rules in the state. The Commission is composed of three members elected by the state at large, and a small but efficient technical staff. In general, the Commission determines production allowables monthly, enforces spacing rules and grants exceptions, enters special field rules regarding waste (oil-gas ratios, etc.), adopts measures to prevent waste of natural and casinghead gas, and holds hearings on the approval of voluntary unitization agreements. The Commission occupies an exceedingly powerful position in the nation's industry; for many years it supervised nearly half of the total production of oil in the United States.

For an interesting and informative history of the Railroad Commission, see Prindle, *Petroleum Politics and the Texas Railroad Commission* (1981). See also Douglass & Whitworth, "Practice Before the Oil and Gas Division of the Railroad Commission of Texas," 13 *St. Mary's L.J.* 719 (1982).

Thereafter clause

The lease clause providing for continued validity of the lessee's interest [or a defeasible term mineral or royalty interest] subsequent to the expiration of the primary term "so long as" a specified state of affairs continues, *e.g.*, so long as there is production in paying quantities, or so long as drilling operations are prosecuted.

The habendum clause of a contemporary lease provides in general as follows:

> "It is agreed that this lease shall remain in force for a term of ten years from date [the primary term] and as long thereafter as oil, or gas, of whatsoever nature or kind, or either of them is produced from said land or drilling operations are continued as hereinafter provided."

See TREATISE §§ 603–604.12.

Earlier forms of lease were frequently for a long primary term without a thereafter clause. This form of lease was found to be unsatisfactory to both lessor and lessee. [See LONG TERM LEASE.] The result of the evolution of the lease was the relatively short primary term (*e.g.*, five or ten years) during which the lessee might keep the lease alive without drilling operations by the payment of rentals followed by the extension of the lessee's interest under the "thereafter" clause, during which extended period production (or, under some leases, drilling operations) was required for continued validity of the lessee's interest. The habendum clause in this form is generally construed to create a fee simple defeasible in the lessee, with the lessor retaining a possibility of reverter.

A "thereafter" clause may also be found in term mineral or royalty deeds or reservations, *e.g.*, a grant of minerals or royalties "for ten years and so long thereafter as oil and/or gas is produced from said land." See TREATISE §§ 333–334.10.

See also PRIMARY TERM; SECONDARY PRIMARY TERM; SECONDARY TERM.

Therm

A unit of heat. A small calorie is the amount of heat required to raise one gram of water one degree centigrade. A large or great calorie is the amount of heat required to raise a kilogram of water one degree centigrade, *viz.*, 1,000 small calories. A therm is equal to 1,000 great calories.

Thermal cracking

One type of CRACKING (*q.v.*) in the refining process. Gas oils obtained in the topping process are subjected to extreme temperatures under severe pressures. In the process, the gas-oil molecules are cracked and broken into new molecules. From the high boiling gas-oil fraction, a fraction is broken off consisting of light hydrocarbons having the low boiling range of gasoline, and is called cracked gasoline. A heavy, high-boiling residue of the cracking process finds its way into the market as heavy industrial fuel oils. Light cracked gases become essential components of aviation gasoline. Through the alkylation process they are liquefied into alkylate, which is a component of aviation gasoline. Hearings before the Special Committee Investigating Petroleum Resources, 79th Cong., 1st Sess., on War Emergency Pipe-Line Systems and Other Petroleum Facilities 133 (Nov. 1945).

Thermal method of oil recovery

A method of increasing recovery of low gravity crude oil by the application of heat. Methods include oil well heating, hot fluid injection, and in-situ combustion. See Nelson, "Oil Recovery by Thermal Methods," 17 *Interstate Oil Compact Bull.* 56 (Dec. 1958); Lopez and Parsley, "Microbes, Simulators, and Satellites: The Prudent Operator Pursues Enhanced Recovery Under the Implied Covenants," 58 *N.D. L. Rev.* 501 at 527 (1982).

See also DOWNHOLE STEAM GENERATION; SECONDARY RECOVERY; STEAM STIMULATION; TERTIARY RECOVERY.

Thick well

A well drilled into a portion of the producing horizon which is relatively wide or thick.

Thief

A container used to take samples of oil from stock tanks for a THIEF TEST (*q.v.*) to measure the quality of oil.

Thief formation

A FORMATION (*q.v.*) causing excessive fluid loss in drilling operations. Such a formation may sometimes be sealed by the addition of various fibrous or flaky materials in the drilling fluid.

Thief test

A test to determine the amount of BASIC SEDIMENT (*q.v.*) and water contained in petroleum as produced. A sample is taken of the fluid in stock tanks on the leased premises and is tested for the purpose of determining the proportion of these substances in the sample. A THIEF (a square can about one foot deep and about two inches across) is submerged into the fluid in the tank. The thief is open at the top and is also open at the bottom when being submerged but has a sliding bottom which is closed by a spring which can be released quickly when the thief is at the point at which it is desired to take the sample. Separate samples are taken by the thief at the top, in the middle, and at the bottom of the fluid in the tank. The samples are mixed and the proportion of basic sediment and water in the fluid determined by testing by a centrifugal process or a distillation process. See Hamilton v. Empire Gas & Fuel Co., 117 Kan. 25, 230 Pac. 91 (1924).

Thin well

A well drilled into a portion of the producing horizon which is relatively thin or narrow.

Third for a quarter deal

A drilling joint adventure described in Brountas v. Commissioner, 73 T.C. 491 at 496 (1979), 74 T.C. 1062, 67 *O.&G.R.* 477 (1980), *vacated and remanded,* 692 F.2d 152, 75 *O.&G.R.* 193 (1st Cir. 1982), *cert. denied,* 462 U.S. 1106, 103 S. Ct. 2453 (1983), as "a relatively 'standard' arrangement among partners within the [oil and gas] industry."

> "The operator transfers three-quarters of the leasehold interest in a prospect to another person (or persons) in return for payment of 100 percent of the cost of drilling and, if successful, completing

the test well on the prospect. For example, if the deal included three people plus the operator, each person (other than the operator) would put up one-third of the drilling cost and would receive a one-quarter interest in the well. The operator's quarter interest in the well is its reward for searching for, identifying, and leasing the prospect as well as the efforts it exerts in supervising the actual drilling and completion."

See also Pezold and Richey, "The 'Industry Deal' Among Oil and Gas Companies and the Federal Securities Acts," 16 *Texas Tech. L. Rev.* 827 (1985).

See also DRILLING FUND.

Third party beneficiary

One for whose benefit a promise is made in a contract but who is not a party to the contract. For cases dealing with the question whether a lease surface user clause may be enforced by the owner of an interest in the surface as a third party beneficiary see TREATISE § 673.6, note 29.

See also STIPULATION POUR AUTRI.

Third-party favored nation clause

See ESCALATOR CLAUSE; MOST FAVORED NATION CLAUSE.

Third-party top lease

See TOP LEASE.

Third term

See PRODUCTION LICENSE.

Thirty day-sixty day clause

A provision, common in the modern UNLESS LEASE (*q.v.*) form intended to keep the lease alive if a dry hole is drilled during the primary term, if production ceases during the primary term or thereafter, or if there is no production at the end of the primary term but drilling operations are then being pursued. The clause provides that under these (and certain other) circumstances the lease will remain in force if the lessee engages in drilling or reworking operations as specified.

While there are a number of variations in the wording and accordingly in the precise operation of the clause, the following is typical:

"If prior to discovery of oil or gas on said land Lessee should drill a dry hole or holes thereon, or if after discovery of oil or gas the production thereof should cease from any cause, this lease shall not terminate if Lessee commences additional drilling or re-working operations within sixty (60) days thereafter or (if it be within the primary term) commences or resumes the payment or tender of rentals on or before the rental paying date next ensuing after the expiration of three months from date of completion of dry hole, or cessation of production. If at the expiration of the primary term oil, gas or other mineral is not being produced on said land but Lessee is then engaged in drilling or reworking operations thereon, this lease shall remain in force so long as operations are prosecuted with no cessation of more than thirty (30) consecutive days, and if they result in the production of oil, gas or other mineral so long thereafter as oil, gas or other mineral is produced from said land."

A clause such as the above was in litigation in Stanolind Oil & Gas Co. v. Newman Bros. Drilling Co., 157 Tex. 489, 305 S.W.2d 169, 7 *O.&G.R.* 1496 (1957); Rogers v. Osborn, 152 Tex. 540, 261 S.W.2d 311, 2 *O.&G.R.* 304, 1439 (1953); St. Louis Royalty Co. v. Continental Oil Co., 193 F.2d 778, 1 *O.&G.R.* 538 (5th Cir. 1952); and Continental Oil Co. v. Boston-Texas Land Trust, 221 F.2d 124, 4 *O.&G.R.* 669 (5th Cir. 1955). See also Skelly Oil Co. v. Wickham, 202 F.2d 442, 2 *O.&G.R.* 559 (10th Cir. 1953). See TREATISE §§ 623–623.2.

See also CESSATION OF PRODUCTION CLAUSE; CONTINUOUS DRILLING OPERATIONS CLAUSE; DRILLING OPERATIONS CLAUSE; DRY HOLE CLAUSE.

Thousand cubic feet mile

For purposes of the Michigan Business Receipts Tax, this term was defined as the transportation of 1,000 cubic feet of gas, measured at 60 degrees Farenheit and a pressure of 30 inches of mercury, a distance of 1 mile for a consideration. Act No. 17 of the Public Acts of 1954, State of Michigan, Mich. Stat. Ann. § 7.557 (1)(d), 4 *O.&G.R.* 491 (1955) (subsequently repealed in 1967).

Threshold price

A standard for price fixing based upon prevailing prices. See Connole, "Threshold Prices: A Practical Proposal for Producer Pricing," 63 *Pub. Util. Fort.* 23 (Jan. 1, 1959).

Throughput and deficiency agreement

An agreement by producing oil companies with a company planning the construction of a new pipeline by which the producing companies commit themselves to ship quantities of petroleum products sufficient to enable the pipeline company to pay and discharge expenses and obligations which are or shall become due or payable in an accounting period and to make additional cash payments (as advance payment for transportation) required to meet deficiencies in the cash available to the pipeline company to pay and discharge such expenses and obligations. On the basis of this agreement the pipeline company is enabled to borrow money (frequently as much as 90 percent of the total cost) for the construction of the pipeline.

For discussions of the role of this kind of agreement in the financing of pipelines see the following:

Wolbert, U.S. Oil Pipe Lines 243 (1979);

American Petroleum Institute, *The Future of American Oil, the Experts Testify* chapters 8 and 9 (1976);

Shalley, "Legal Problems Encountered in Throughput Financing," in International Bar Ass'n, *Proceedings of the Energy Law Seminar* (organized by the Committee on Energy and Natural Resources, Section on Business Law) Topic L, Paper 6 (1979);

The Petroleum Industry, Hearings before the Subcommittee on Antitrust and Monopoly of the Committee on the Judiciary, U.S. Senate, 94th Cong., 1st Sess. on S. 2387 and Related Bills at pp. 264–266, 1110, 1116–1117, 1121–1123.

See also PIPELINE CONSENT DECREE OF 1941; PROJECT FINANCING; TAKE-OR-PAY CONTRACT.

Throughput financing

See THROUGHPUT AND DEFICIENCY AGREEMENT.

Throughput rental

A scheme for leasing land for pipeline purposes under which the rental is based on the volume of oil or gas passing through the pipeline. Western Oil & Gas Ass'n v. California State Lands Comm'n, 105 Cal.App.3d 468, 164 Cal.Rptr. 468 (1980).

The California throughput rental system was held to be unconstitutional under the Commerce Clause and the Import-Export Clause of the Constitution of the United States in Western Oil & Gas Ass'n v. Cory, 726 F.2d 1340 (9th Cir. 1984), *aff'd by an equally divided court*, ____ U.S. ____, 105 S.Ct. 1859, *reh. denied*, ____ U.S. ____, 105 S.Ct. 2349 (1985).

Ticket

See SCOUT TICKET.

Tidelands

Technically lands overflowed during floodtide, but the term, by reason of the so-called Tidelands cases, has been used to describe that portion of the continental shelf between the shore and the claimed boundaries of the states (3 or 9 miles at sea). The Tidelands cases held that the right to produce minerals from this portion of the continental shelf was in the Federal government; the question of title to or ownership of the land under the water was technically not decided. United States v. California, 332 U.S. 19 (1947); United States v. Louisiana, 339 U.S. 699 (1950); United States v. Texas, 339 U.S. 707 (1950). The so-called "Tidelands" within certain defined boundaries of the states have been released to the states by the SUBMERGED LANDS ACT OF 1953 (*q.v.*), 67 St. 29, P. L. 31, c. 65, May 22, 1953.

Tier

A term employed for purposes of price controls on oil and gas and for purpose of the CRUDE OIL WINDFALL PROFIT TAX ACT OF 1980 (*q.v.*).

See also FIRST TIER OIL; LOWER TIER OIL; SECOND TIER OIL; TIER 1 OIL; TIER 2 OIL; TIER 3 OIL; UPPER TIER CRUDE OIL.

Tier 1 oil

For purposes of the CRUDE OIL WINDFALL PROFIT TAX ACT of 1980 (*q.v.*), Tier 1 oil is defined as any taxable crude oil other than Tier 2 and Tier 3 oil. Internal Revenue Code Code § 4991.

Tier 2 oil

For purposes of the CRUDE OIL WINDFALL PROFIT TAX ACT OF 1980 (*q.v.*), Tier 2 oil is defined as any other oil other than Tier 3 oil (a) which is from a stripper well property within the meaning of the June 1979 energy regulations, and (b) any oil from an economic interest in the National Petroleum Reserve held by the United States. Internal Revenue Code § 4991.

Tier 3 oil

For purposes of the CRUDE OIL WINDFALL PROFIT TAX ACT OF 1980 (*q.v.*), Tier 3 oil is defined as (a) newly discovered oil, (b) heavy oil, and (c) incremental tertiary oil. Internal Revenue Code § 4991.

Tight formation

A sedimentary layer of rock cemented together in a manner that greatly hinders the flow of any gas through the rock. Because such a formation is characterized by low permeability, wells drilled into gas-bearing formations of this kind usually produce at very low rates, requiring producers to use enhanced recovery techniques, usually hydraulic fracturing. F.E.R.C. Order No. 99, 21 F.P.S. 5–289 (Aug. 15, 1980), established an incentive price ceiling for new and recompletion tight formation gas produced from designated tight formations. 18 C.F.R. §§ 271.701 *et seq.* (1980).

Tight formation gas

Gas produced from a TIGHT FORMATION (*q.v.*) entitled to an incentive price.

See also NEGOTIATED CONTRACT PRICE REQUIREMENT.

Tight gas well

A gas well with low permeability which is incapable of ever achieving production in paying quantities. Monsanto Oil Co., 95 IBLA 112 at 114, GFS(O&G) 1987-10 (Jan. 6, 1987).

Tight hole

(1) A well in which there are no caves or cavities in the earth at the bottom of the hole. Independent-Eastern Torpedo Co. v. Price, 208 Okla. 633, 258 P.2d 189, 2 *O.&G.R.* 1148 (1953).

(2) This term is also used colloquially in a situation in which the performance data of a well is closely guarded. Hardy, "Drainage of Oil and Gas From Adjoining Tracts—A Further Development," 6 *Nat. Res. J.* 45 at 55 (1966); Guyer Oil Co. Ltd. v. Fulton and Gladstone Petroleum Ltd., [1976] 5 W.W.R. 356 at 359 (Saskatchewan Ct. of Appeal 1976), *appeal dism'd,* [1977] 2 S.C.R. 791, [1977] 4 W.W.R. 112 (Sup. Ct. of Canada 1977).

Tight hole status

A procedure whereby an operator who has drilled a well upon and selected a lease from a permit area is enabled to restrict any information concerning the operations conducted by him on the wells dug to become public knowledge prior to the sale of CORRIDOR ACREAGE (*q.v.*). Pine Pass Oil & Gas Ltd. v. Pacific Petroleums Ltd., 70 D.L.R.2d 196 at 204 (British Columbia Supreme Court 1968).

Tight sands

"Gas-bearing geologic strata that holds gas too tightly for conventional extraction processes to bring it to the surface at economic rates without special stimulation." American Gas Ass'n, *Glossary for the Gas Industry* (3d ed. 1981). See TIGHT FORMATION.

Tight well

A well in the process of being drilled, or just completed, information about which the operator seeks to maintain secrecy, by denying outsiders access to the derrick floor and to drillers', electrical and other well logs, and by instructing employees not to reveal information about the well.

Tilting

See RATE TILTING.

Time of essence clause

A clause of a lease or other instrument providing that time is of the essence for performance of obligations of a party. In the absence of such a clause in an oilfield operating agreement, Argos Resources, Inc. v. May Petroleum Inc., 693 S.W.2d 663, 86 *O.&G.R.* 594 (Tex. App., Dallas, 1985, error ref'd n.r.e.), rejected the contention that time was of the essence of the agreement. Hence the court applied the substantial performance doctrine. The court indicated, however, that ordinarily time is of the essence of an oilwell drilling contract which is part of a lease arrangement even though the contract does not contain an express clause on the subject.

Time-trade exchange

A transaction in which a company needing oil to meet present customer demands receives oil from a second company, simultaneously promising that second company to repay it in the future by delivering oil of a similar quality and quantity. Standard Oil Co. v. Federal Energy Administration, 465 F. Supp. 274 at 276 (N.D. Ohio 1978), *aff'd,* 612 F.2d 1291 (Temp. Emer. Ct. App. 1979).

TIP

The TERTIARY INCENTIVE PROGRAM (*q.v.*).

TIPRO

The Texas Independent Producers and Royalty Owners Association.

Title committee

A committee set up by a pooling or unitization agreement charged with the examination of titles to interests included within the agreement. Rocky Mountain Unit Operating Agreement Form 2 (Divided Interest) January, 1955, Section 18.3, TREATISE § 920.4.

Title examination area

In one usage, an area covering lands outside any participating area under a unit operating agreement upon which a well is to be drilled. See Rocky Mountain Unit Operating Agreement Form 2 (Divided Interest) January, 1955, Section 18.2 (C), TREATISE § 920.4.

Title insurance

Insurance issued against hidden title defects and title defects of record which are missed by the abstractor or examiner. For a discussion of the use of such insurance in Oklahoma, see Epperson, "Lender's Mineral Title Insurance: A Mini-Primer," 53 *Okla. B.A.J.* 3089 (1982).

Title opinion

A statement of opinion by an attorney, often in the form of a letter, as to the state of the title to land, mineral, royalty or working interests. The opinion will often recommend that curative instruments be obtained before the property interest is purchased, drilled on, or otherwise dealt with. In the course of the leasing and development of a tract of land, there may be occasions for several title opinions. Before the payment of the bonus for the execution of a lease, a bonus title opinion may be rendered. Another title opinion, the DELAY RENTAL TITLE OPINION (*q.v.*), may be rendered before rentals are paid. A more complete and thorough title opinion, the DRILL SITE TITLE OPINION (*q.v.*), may be rendered before drilling operations are begun. Before payments are made by a purchaser under a division order, a division order title opinion may be prepared.

The title search made for the purpose of rendering a title opinion has been described by Kuntz, Lowe, Anderson and Smith, *Oil and Gas Law* 506 (1986), as follows:

> "Mineral title opinions are based on either 'stand-up' or 'sit-down' searches. In a stand-up search the examining attorney searches the official records of the county recorder's office and other offices for the county where the subject land is located. In a sit-down search, the attorney examines a verbatim abstract furnished by an abstract company."

See also the following:

Bate, "Federal Land Records and Title Examinations," *Rocky Mt. Min. L. Fdn. Law of Federal Oil and Gas Leases* ch. 20 (1984);

Morgan, "Oil and Gas—Understanding the Division Order Title Opinion in Oklahoma," 56 *Okla. B.J.* 735 (1985);

Cassidy, "Preparation and Use of Title Opinions," 6 *Eastern Min. L. Inst.* 21-1 (1985);

Harris, "Analyzing and Curing Title Requirements in Oil and Gas Title Opinions," 31 *Rocky Mt. Min. L. Inst.* 20-1 (1985);

Rocky Mt. Min. L. Fdn. Law of Federal Oil and Gas Leases ch. 20 (1985);

Herd, "Title Opinions for Oil and Gas Purposes—Structure and Information Needed by a Client," 33 *Sw. Legal Fdn. Oil & Gas Inst.* 285 (1982);

Rocky Mt. Min. L. Fdn. Mineral Title Examination Institute (1977).

See also DRILL SITE TITLE OPINION; RUN SHEET, SHUT-IN ROYALTY/ TITLE OPINION.

Token allowable

A very small ALLOWABLE (*q.v.*), sufficient only to continue "commercial production", designed to avoid placing a lease in jeopardy by a complete shut-in of the only producing well on a leasehold or to avoid damage to a well resulting from complete cessation of production. See IOCC, *General Rules and Regulations for the Conservation of Oil and Gas* 20 (1969).

Tolling agreement

See TAKE-OR-PAY CONTRACT.

Tolling of terms of a lease and rental payment

The term applied in Jicarilla Apache Tribe v. Andrus, 687 F.2d 1324 at 1340, 75 *O.&G.R.* 286 (10th Cir. 1982), to an order of the court that annual rentals need not be paid and the primary term of a lease is extended during the period when a lessor actively asserts to a lessee that his lease is terminated or subject to cancellation.

Tolling the running of the lease term

A SUSPENSION OF OPERATIONS AND PRODUCTION (*q.v.*) under section 39 of the Mineral Leasing Act of 1920 as distinguished from a section 17(f) suspension of operations and production.

Ton

A unit of weight equal to 2,000 pounds in the United States, Canada and the Union of South Africa, and to 2,240 pounds in Great Britain. The American ton is often called the short ton, while the British ton is called the long ton. The metric ton, or 1,000 kilograms, equals 2,204.62 pounds. Depending upon specific gravity, a long ton or metric ton will equal from 6.5 to 8.5 barrels of oil.

See also CONVERSION FACTORS; MEASUREMENT UNITS.

Tool pusher

The general supervisor of drilling operations in the field, who has subordinate to him the drilling crews of at least one well, and often of a number of wells. He is responsible for seeing that drilling is properly and diligently performed and that supplies and equipment are on hand when needed.

Top deed

A conveyance of a grantor's reversionary interest to become effective upon the termination of an outstanding term or defeasible term interest. Peveto v. Starkey, 645 S.W.2d 770, 75 *O.&G.R.* 166 (1982), discussed in TREATISE § 335 at note 6.7, invalidated under the Rule against Perpetuities a top deed to become effective on the expiration of a defeasible term interest. See Kemp and Newman, "Hidden Rule Against Perpetuities Problems in Oil and Gas Transactions," 32 *Rocky Mt. Min. L. Inst.* 16-1 at 16-19 (1986).

Top-filed application

An application for a federal lease that conflicts with an existing offer because a prior applicant has filed for the land. Top-filed cases must be suspended until the prior offer is resolved. Comptroller General's Report to the Congress, *Actions Needed to Increase Onshore Oil and Gas Exploration and Development* 91 (1981).

Topgas

(1) A term used to describe take-or-pay gas subject to a TAKE-OR-PAY CONTRACT (*q.v.*).

(2) A term sometimes applied to WORKING GAS (*q.v.*).

Topgas agreement

An agreement modifying the take-or-pay commitment of TransCanada PipeLines Limited. See Park, "Developments in Natural Gas Purchase Contracts," 22 *Alberta L. Rev.* 43 (1984).

Top lease

(1) A lease granted by a landowner during the existence of a recorded mineral lease which is to become effective if and when the existing lease expires or is terminated. See Nabors, "The Louisiana Mineral Servitude and Royalty Doctrines," 25 *Tulane L. Rev.* 485 at 493 (1951).

A top lease may include both a conveyance of a fractional interest in the lessor's interest arising under an existing lease and a lease or an option to make a lease on the reversionary interest of the lessor after the termination of the existing lease. A common Canadian form of top lease is contained in Prudential Trust Co., Ltd. v. Cugnet, 15 W.W.R. 385, [1955], 4 D.L.R. 18, 4 *O.&G.R.* 1267 (Saskatchewan Court of Appeal 1955), *appeal dism'd,* [1965], S.C.R. 914, 5 D.L.R. 2d 1 (Supreme Court of Canada 1956). Certain of the tax consequences of a top lease are discussed in Hughes, "Income Tax Consequences of a Lease and Sale of Mineral Interests," 5 *L.S.U. Min. L. Inst.* 24 at 27 (1957).

In Frankfort Oil Co. v. Snakard, 279 F.2d 436 at 445 n. 23, 12 *O.&G.R.* 901 at 911 n.23 (10th Cir. 1960), *cert. denied,* 364 U.S. 920, 13 *O.&G.R.* 623 (1960), the court observed:

> "In the oil and gas vernacular to toplease is to secure a lease on land covered by an existing lease to the end that the toplease will be effective after the expiration of the existing lease and the inter-

est of one or more lessees thereby eliminated. Topleasing has the same invidious characteristics as claim jumping."

Superior Oil Co. v. Devon Corp., 604 F.2d 1063, 65 *O.&G.R.* 368 (8th Cir. 1979), was concerned with a lease executed while a prior lease was held by production on other premises. Under the circumstances of the particular case, it was possible that the top lessees were entitled to protection as bona fide purchasers for value. If that were the case, the court indicated that the prior lessee was entitled to recourse against the lessor. 604 F.2d at 1072, 65 *O.&G.R.* at 382.

Envirogas Inc. v. Consolidated Gas Supply Corp., 98 App. Div. 3d 119, 469 N.Y.S.2d 499, 85 *O.&G.R.* 602 (4th Dept. 1983), sustained the standing of a top lessee to maintain an action to have the bottom leases declared expired.

When a leassee (or his successor in interest) secures a second lease from the original lessor (or his successor in interest) covering all or part of the same interest prior to the expiration of the first lease, the lease is sometimes described as a "two-party" or "same-party" top lease. When the original lessor (or his successor in interest) executes in favor of a title stranger to the first lessee a second lease covering all or part of the same interest prior to the expiration of the first lease, the new lease is sometimes described as a "third-party" top lease. Tracy, "The Effects of Top Leasing in the Louisiana Law of Oil and Gas," 43 *La. L. Rev.* 1189 (1983).

In Stoltz, Wagner & Brown v. Duncan, 417 F.Supp. 552, 55 *O.&G.R.* 315 (W.D. Okla. 1976), the court ordered reformation of a top lease to avoid invalidity of the lease under the Rule against Perpetuities. For a discussion of the perpetuities problem, see Roach, "The Rule Against Perpetuities: The Validity of Oil and Gas Top Leases and Top Deeds in Texas After Peveto v. Starkey," 35 *Baylor L. Rev.* 399 (1983).

See also the following:

Jackson and Weissbrod, "Top Leasing in the Appalachian Basin," 6 *Eastern Min. L. Inst.* 12-1 (1985);

Kemp, "Top Leasing for Oil and Gas: The Legal Perspective," 59 *Denver L.J.* 641 (1982);

Johnson, "The Top Lease—No Longer a Stranger in the Lease Block," 34 *Sw. Legal Fdn. Oil & Gas Inst.* 201 (1983);

Kemp, "Top Leasing for Oil and Gas: The Legal Perspective," 59 *Denver L.J.* 641 (1982);

Ernest, "Top Leasing—Legality v. Morality," 26 *Rocky Mt. Min. L. Inst.* 957 (1980);

Brown, "Effect of Top Leases: Obstruction of Title and Related Considerations," 30 *Baylor L. Rev.* 213 (1978).

The varieties of top leases and perpetuities problems created thereby are discussed in Curran, "Effect of Amendments to Petroleum and Natural Gas Leases," 4 *Alberta L. Rev.* 267 (1965). The writer groups top leases currently in use into the following four classes: (1) option to lease within a term certain, or on or before, but not after, a stated period from the date of receipt of notice by the optionee from the option or of the termination, cancellation or expiration of an existing petroleum and natural gas lease; (2) option to acquire a petroleum and natural gas lease without reference to an existing lease; (3) agreement for transfer of one half of mineral rights and option to lease all mineral rights; and (4) right of first refusal.

In Obelgoner v. Obelgoner, 526 S.W.2d 790 (Tex. Civ. App. 1975, error ref'd n.r.e.), the court concluded that the primary term of a top lease began on the date of its execution rather than upon the expiration of the prior oil and gas lease.

Mitchell v. Amerada Hess Corp., 638 P.2d 441, 72 *O.&G.R.* 104 (Okla. 1981), concluded that it was not champertous to obtain a contract for a top lease conditioned upon successful prosecution by the top lessee of a suit to be brought seeking cancellation of a bottom lease.

See also COVER LEASE; PROTECTION LEASE.

The definition in this MANUAL was quoted in Norman Jessen & Associates v. Amoco Production Co., 305 N.W.2d 648, 69 *O.&G.R.* 478 (N.D. 1981).

(2) The term top lease is also applied to a lease extension agreement entered into by the lessor and lessee prior to the expiration of the original lease. The tax consequences of such a lease are discussed in *Miller's Oil and Gas Federal Income Taxation* § 21–11 (1980 Edition).

Top of the pick

A term used to describe the top of the structure of a field as interpreted by a geologist; in other words, it is the high point of a pool. Murphy v. Amoco Production Co., 590 F.Supp. 455 at note 4, 83 *O.&G.R.* 108 (D. N.D. 1984).

Topped crude oil

Crude oil from which the "LIGHT END" PRODUCTS (*q.v.*) have been removed. Texas American Asphalt Corp. v. Walker, 177 F.Supp. 315 (S.D. Tex. 1959).

Topping process

This is the basic refining process and is simply a distillation process in which the crude petroleum is heated in a heater and then is run into a fractionating tower in which the different fractions are separated and drawn off at different levels at varying controlled temperatures. Raw gasoline, the lightest fraction remaining in a vapor state at the lowest temperature in the tower, is topped or drawn off the top of the tower; the heavy bottom fraction is drawn off from the bottom of the tower to become heavy fuel oils; the intermediate fractions of kerosene and gas oils are drawn off or stripped at in-between levels of the fractioning towers. Additional treating and purification of the raw products complete the simple refining process.

See also CRACKING; REFINER.

Top well allowable

The ALLOWABLE (*q.v.*) assigned a discovery well which has ceased to qualify for the DISCOVERY WELL ALLOWABLE (*q.v.*). See Blazier, "The Lease Allowable System: New Method of Regulating Oil Production in Texas," 47 *Tex. L. Rev.* 658 at 659 (1969).

Torsion balance

A device which measures the gravitational attraction of subsurface rock. From data recorded by these devices and from complex calculations, geophysicists can sometimes identify subsurface structures favorable to oil and gas production. In recent years, the gravity meter has been replacing the torsion balance. The primary utility of these devices is in locating a SALT DOME (*q.v.*)

See also GRAVITY METER.

TOSCO

The Oil Shale Corporation, founded in 1955 for the purpose of developing a commercially feasible, above-ground retorting system for the economic recovery of oil and other products from the oil shales in the western United States.

Total depth (T.D.)

The greatest depth reached by a well bore.

Total operating gross income

A term employed in the 1956 proposed Treasury regulations, § 1.612–4(a)(2), for the gross income from a well, excluding income attributable to royalty interests, production payments and net profits income; the term is usually synonymous with working interest income. See Stroud, "Major Points of Impact of New Natural Resources Regulations on Oil and Gas," 8 *Sw. Legal Fdn. Oil & Gas Inst.* 393 at 404 (1957).

Total operating net income

A term employed in 1956 proposed Treasury regulations, § 1.612–4(a)(2) for the TOTAL OPERATING GROSS INCOME (*q.v.*) from a well reduced by an amount equal to the costs of operating the well. These operating costs, however, do not include tangible or intangible development costs or deductions based thereon, such as depreciation and depletion. See Stroud, "Major Points of Impact of New Natural Resources Regulations on Oil and Gas," 8 *Sw. Legal Fdn. Oil & Gas Inst.* 393 at 405 (1957).

Totco test

A test to determine the DEVIATION (*q.v.*) of a well from the vertical, employing an instrument known as a Totco. See Justiss-Mears Oil Co. v. Pennington, 132 S.2d 700, 16 *O.&G.R.* 329 (La. App. 1961).

See also Prindle, *Petroleum Politics and the Texas Railroad Commission* 86 (1981).

Tour

(1) An eight-hour shift in drilling of a well. The word is frequently pronounced as if pronounced "tower." In offshore drilling, the length of a tour may be as much as twelve hours.

See also DRILLER; GRAVEYARD TOUR; TOWER REPORT.

(2) In the United Kingdom, a term of duty, usually overseas, lasting months or years.

TOVALOP

The Tanker Owners Voluntary Agreement Concerning Liability for Oil Pollution Damage, an agreement providing insurance for member owners to pay damages to governments for the costs of oil spill cleanup or, in case the owner cleans up the spill, to reimburse him. See Wurfel, *Emerging Ocean Oil and Mining Law* 18 (1974); Wood, "Requiring Polluters to Pay for Aquatic Natural Resources Destroyed by Oil Pollution," 8 *Nat. Res. Law.* 545 at 559 (1976).

See also CRISTAL; IMCO CONVENTIONS; PLATO.

Tower report

The term applied to daily drilling reports. "These reports are on forms labeled 'IADC-API Official Daily Drilling Report Form' and contain entries describing the daily operations, bit and drill records, footage and similar information." Matador Drilling Co., Inc. v. Post, 662 F.2d 1190 at 1198, 72 *O.&G.R.* 598 at 612 (5th Cir. 1981).

See also TOUR.

Town border station

See GATE STATION.

Town gas

Syn.: COAL GAS (*q.v.*)

TPAO

The TURKISH NATIONAL PETROLEUM COMPANY (*q.v.*).

TPC

TAX-PAID COST (*q.v.*).

Tracking rate change

An adjustment of rates to reflect certain cost increases without following the detailed requirements for a general rate change. See Tennessee Gas Pipeline Co. v. Federal Power Comm'n, 504 F.2d 199 (D.C. Cir. 1974).

Tract

See QUALIFIED TRACT.

Tract allocation method

A method of allocation of production volumetrically to each tract included in a pooled or unitized operation on an average basis whereunder production is treated for all purposes, including payment of royalty, as if it were actually produced from each separately owned tract or interest by a well drilled thereon. "Each lessee delivering gas to his purchaser would account to his lessor for royalty on the gas allocated to his particular tract, and each lessee not delivering gas to a purchaser would account, out of his own funds, to his lessor for royalty on the gas allocated to his lease. Any imbalance resulting from this method could be settled by the lessors through a balancing arrangement." Upchurch, "Split Stream Gas Sales and the Gas Storage and Balancing Agreement," 24 *Rocky Mt. Min. L. Inst.* 665 at 669 (1978). See TREATISE § 951.

See also ACCOUNTING METHODS.

Tract book

A book maintained in the District Land Offices of the Bureau of Land Management listing all entries affecting described lands. See *Rocky Mt. Min. L. Fdn. Landman's Legal Handbook* 116 (3d ed. 1977).

See also FEDERAL LEASE.

Tract value

A term used in some unitization agreements to describe that percentage which is the share of the unitized substances allocated under the agreement to each respective tract of land within the unitized area. Belridge Oil Co. v. Commissioner, 27 T.C. 1044, 7 *O.&G.R.* 673 at 676, (1957), *aff'd,* 267 F.2d 291, 10 *O.&G.R.* 662 (9th Cir. 1959).

Trans-Alaska Pipeline Authorization Act

Title II of Public Law 93–153, 93rd Congress, S. 1081, November 16, 1973.

See also TAPS AGREEMENT.

Transferee well

A well to which is allocated a TRANSFERRED ALLOWABLE (*q.v.*). Hunter v. Hussey, 90 So.2d 429, 6 *O.&G.R.* 1172 (La. App. 1956).

Transfer order

A direction to the purchaser under a DIVISION ORDER (*q.v.*) to pay another person a share in the oil or gas produced.

If, subsequent to the execution of a division order, a person entitled to a share of the proceeds of the sale disposes of some or all of his interest in the proceeds, the transfer order is the means by which notification is given to the purchaser of such disposition. Execution of a transfer order permits payment to be made by a purchaser in accordance with the terms thereof even though in conflict with the actual ownership of interests in production. Chicago Corp. v. Wall, 293 S.W. 2d 844, 6 *O.&G.R.* 703 (Tex. 1956). See TREATISE §§ 701–715.

Transferor well

A well the allowable of which is transferred to another well. Hunter v. Hussey, 90 So.2d 429, 6 *O.&G.R.* 1172 (La. App. 1956).

See also TRANSFERRED ALLOWABLE.

Transfer price

The price fixed by a vertically integrated enterprise for tax and internal accounting purposes on raw materials and intermediate products which various of its affiliates sell to each other.

"These transfer prices need not bear any relation to cost or to external market forces. In many multinational corporations, therefore, they are set at levels chosen chiefly to reduce overall tax liability." Krueger, *The United States and International Oil* 36 (1975).

For discussions of transfer prices, see the following:

Finn and Munter, "The Importance of Transfer Pricing to Oil and Gas Companies," 35 *O.&G. Tax Q.* 136 (1986);

Stecker and Winslow, "Federal Energy Administration," 8 *Law and Policy in International Business* 499 at 505 (1976);

"Multinational Oil Corporations and U.S. Foreign Policy," Report to the Committee on Foreign Relations, U.S. Senate, by the Subcommittee on Multinational Corporations, 93rd Cong., 2d Sess. (Jan. 2, 1975) at p. 170;

Statement by FEA Administrator Frank G. Zarb in "Oversight—Federal Energy Administration Programs," Hearings before the Senate Committee on Interior and Insular Affairs, 94th Cong., 1st Sess., Serial No. 94–16 (92–106) 471 at 496 (1975);

Id. at 607.

Transferred allowable

An ALLOWABLE (*q.v.*) for a well or a lease that is transferred by the operator to another well or lease, or that is sold by the operator to an owner of other leases in the field, who thereby is able to increase his production.

Transferred allowables seem to have grown up in Texas in connection with the East Texas Field. In order to encourage operators to shut down wells producing excessive amounts of salt water (which injured the field), the Railroad Commission permitted an operator to take the allowable of such a well and apply it to other wells he owned in the field. Thus the offending well was shut in without economical loss to the operator. Since some owners of offending wells did not hold other leases in the field, the commission permitted the sale of the transferred allowable to operators who did.

The transferred allowable referred to above is known as a SALT WATER SHUT-IN ALLOWABLE (*q.v.*). A transfer of allowable may be authorized in connection with unitized operations. See TREATISE § 937.4. Transferred allowables have also been granted for injecting salt water back into the reservoir, called a BONUS ALLOWABLE (*q.v.*), and for shutting in wells producing from a gas cap, called GAS CAP ALLOWABLE (*q.v.*).

It was held in Tidewater Oil Co. v. United States, 339 F.2d 633, 21 *O.&G.R.* 695 (Ct. Cl. 1964), that the transferor did not have an economic interest in the oil produced by the transferee of a salt-water shut-in allowable and hence the transferee and not the transferor was entitled to the depletion allowance on the oil produced. See "Depletion on Transferred Allowables," 14 *O.&G. Tax Q.* 133 (1965).

Marlin Oil Corp. v. Corporation Comm'n, 562 P.2d 851, 58 *O.&G.R.* 225 (Okla. 1977), sustained the power of the Commission to protect correlative rights by ordering the transfer to a new well drilled on a spacing unit the accumulated underages of a prior well on the unit which were due partly to the failure of the purchaser to take sufficient gas from the well but due largely to the inability of the prior well to produce its full allowable.

See "Transferred Allowables and Substitute Royalties," 5 *O.&G. Tax Q.* 59 (1956). For discussion of subject with reference to Louisiana law, see Hussey, "Conservation Developments of the Year," 4 *L.S.U. Min. L. Inst.* 148 at 161–165 (1956).

See also FLUID INJECTION WELL; OBSERVATION WELL; SUBSTITUTE ROYALTY; UNIT SURPLUS WELL.

Transfer rule

The rule designed to prevent proliferation of the so-called independent producers exemption in Section 613A of the Internal Revenue Code. Under this exemption, independent producers continued to be entitled to percentage depletion on a limited quantity of oil. The transfer rule provides that (with limited exceptions) when an interest in oil and gas in proved oil and gas property is transferred, the independent producers exemption will not apply to the transferee with respect to oil or gas produced from that property. See Linden, "An Analysis of the 'Transfer Rule' of the Proposed Regs. on Oil and Gas Depletion," 45 *J. Taxation* 112 (1976).

See also DEPLETION, PERCENTAGE.

Transition zone

An area where the wells produce both free oil and free gas. Union Texas Petroleum v. Corporation Comm'n, 651 P.2d 652 at 665 (Okla. 1981) (dissenting opinion).

Transit Pipeline Treaty

The Agreement Between the Government of the United States of America and the Government of Canada Concerning Transit Pipelines, 28 U.S.T. 7449, T.I.A.S. No. 8720.

See also AGREEMENT ON PRINCIPLES; PIPELINE.

Transmission line

A pipe line extending from a producing area to a refinery or terminal. *Syn.:* TRUNK LINE.

See also DISTRIBUTION LINE; GATHERING LINE; PIPELINE.

Transmission system

". . . the land, structures, mains, valves, meters, boosters, regulators, tanks, compressors, and their driving units and appurtenances, and other equipment used primarily for transmitting gas from a production plant, delivery point of purchased gas, gathering system, storage area, or other wholesale source of gas to one or more distribution areas. The transmission system begins at the outlet side of the valve at the connection to the last equipment in a manufactured gas plant, the connection to gathering lines or delivery point of purchased gas, and includes the equipment at such connection that is used to bring the gas to transmission pressure, and ends at the outlet side of the equipment which meters or regulates the entry of gas into the distribution system or into a storage area. It does not include storage land or structures." 18 C.F.R. Part 201, Definitions 26B (1980).

place the burden of transportation costs to market upon the operator.

Transportation gas

Gas which is purchased by a user directly from a producer and is carried by the pipeline company for a fee; to be distinguished from CONSUMER GAS (*q.v.*) which is gas purchased by an interstate pipeline company for resale to a utility for ultimate sale to the consumer.

See also DISPLACED GAS.

Transport cost differential

A DIFFERENTIAL (*q.v.*) in the price of oil from a given source from the MARKER PRICE (*q.v.*) of BENCHMARK CRUDE (*q.v.*) based upon the relative transport cost of the crude in question and that of benchmark crude. "The 'transport cost differential' is rarely more than $1.25 per barrel." Danielsen, *The Evolution of OPEC* 65 (1982).

Trap

That portion of any mass of porous, permeable rock which is sealed on top and down the sides by relatively nonporous and impermeable rock and which lies above the intersection of a horizontal plane passing through the lowest point of complete sealing.

See also ANTICLINE; COMBINATION TRAP; FAULT TRAP; REEF; RESERVOIR; SALT DOME; STRATIGRAPHIC TRAP; STRUCTURAL TRAP.

Trap test

A test employed to determine the gravity of crude oil for purposes of petroleum price regulations. See Atlantic Richfield Co. v. DOE, *CCH Energy Management* ¶ 81,053 (1982).

Traverse well

A well drilled through but not bottomed under the premises in question. See Sehle v. Producing Properties, Inc., 230 Cal.App.2d 430, 41 Cal.Rptr. 136, 21 *O.&G.R.* 529 (1964).

Treating plant

A plant for the removal of basic sediment and water from oil as produced.

Purchasing companies will not ordinarily accept oil having much more than 1% of water and other foreign matter, and therefore oil

Transportation by displacement

The "movement" of natural gas volumes from one point on a pipeline's transmission system to another, noncontiguous point on that pipeline's system. Displacement permits a lateral movement of gas through a transportation network. See Madigan, MacDonald, Dornan and Rosenthal, "Regulation and Deregulation of the Natural Gas Industry in the United States," 25 *Alta. L. Rev.* 2 at 9 (1986).

Transportation by exchange

"Transportation by exchange occurs when two companies each have gas supplies remote from their system but connected to the system of the other company. Each pipeline receives the gas belonging to the other, with imbalance volumes received being adjusted through deliveries at a third point. An exchange makes possible a 'movement' of gas between two points which do not have connecting pipeline facilities." Tennessee Gas Pipeline Co., 23 FERC.¶ 61,115 (1983) at 60,270. See Madigan, MacDonald, Dornan and Rosenthal, "Regulation and Deregulation of the Natural Gas Industry in the United States," 25 *Alta. L. Rev.* 2 at 9 (1986).

See also EXCHANGE AGREEMENT.

Transportation costs

The costs of transporting oil or gas to a market. The operator of a lease upon gaining production will seek to secure a pipe line connection at the well or lease and to make delivery of the oil or gas at such pipeline connection to the purchaser of the oil or gas. Prior to the extension of pipe lines to the lease by a purchaser, the operator of the well or lease may find it necessary to transport the product to a distant pipe line connection or to a railroad or refinery by truck or by his own pipe line.

The lessor is entitled to a royalty free and clear of costs at the wellhead; if the product cannot be disposed of at the wellhead to a purchaser, then the lessor must normally share in the expenses of transporting the product to market. Molter v. Lewis, 156 Kan. 544, 134 P.2d 404 (1943); TREATISE §§ 645–645.3. An occasional lease may provide, however, that the lessor shall receive his royalty free and clear of expenses at the well *or other delivery point.* In Robert v. Swanson, 222 S.W.2d 707 (Tex. Civ. App. 1949, error ref'd n.r.e.), which involved an oil payment, the italicized language was held to containing more than this proportion of such substances must be treated before it is delivered to the purchaser. The fluid taken from a well is run into tanks. Since water is heavier than oil, a considerable portion of it settles by gravity into the bottom of the tank and is drawn off without disturbing the oil. A large amount of water, however, remains mixed with the oil, and under ordinary temperature it will not separate. By heating the mixture, a still greater portion of the water, which has remained suspended in the oil, can be separated and precipitated to the bottom and again drawn off.

Even when the fluid is heated, the water descending carries with it considerable oil. This mixture, with such other impurities as are brought up by the pump, forms an emulsion at the bottom of the tank, which is called BASIC SEDIMENT (*q.v.*), or more generally "B.S." This B.S. gradually thickens in the bottom of the tank, and much of it has to be scraped out and thrown away. Many operators deposit it in large artificial ponds upon the lease, which occasionally is disposed of by burning.

The lessee may establish a steaming plant, and place steam pipes in the tanks to heat the fluid sufficiently to separate water from the oil to such an extent that the portion of the fluid above the pipe-line connection is of such purity that the purchaser will accept it. A more elaborate plant will save much of the volatile vapors which escape from a simple steaming plant and will also save the emulsion of B.S. See Hamilton v. Empire Gas & Fuel Co., 117 Kan. 25, 230 P. 91 (1924).

See also DEHYDRATION PLANT; GLYCOL DEHYDRATOR.

Treaty of Rome

The 1957 treaty establishing the European Economic Community.

Trem Carr case

The name commonly applied to Railroad Comm'n v. Shell Oil Co., 139 Tex. 66, 161 S.W.2d 1022 (1942), a Rule 37 case involving the "more wells, more oil" theory.

Trespass

See BAD FAITH TRESPASSER; GEOPHYSICAL TRESPASS; GOOD FAITH TRESPASSER; SUBSURFACE TRESPASS.

Tribal lands

See INDIAN LANDS.

Trip tank

A small calibrated tank used to measure the volume of drilling fluid required to fill the hole while pulling pipe from a well. Alberta Energy Resources Conservation Board, *Inquiry Report* 78–8, page 9 (June 9, 1978).

True casinghead gas

See CASINGHEAD GAS.

True roll-up

See EXCHANGE OFFER.

Truman proclamation

The Proclamation of September 1945 by President Truman claiming for the United States the natural resources of the subsoil and seabed of the continental shelf beneath the high seas but contiguous to the coasts of the United States as appertaining to the United States, subject to its jurisdiction and control. United States Department of State Bulletin, No. 327 (Sept. 30, 1945), p. 485.

See also OUTER CONTINENTAL SHELF.

Trunk line

A pipe line for the transportation of oil or gas from producing areas to refineries or terminals. *Syn.:* TRANSMISSION LINE.

Trust

See LANDOWNERS' ROYALTY POOL; ROYALTY TRUST.

Tubing

A string of pipe set into a well through which oil is produced. *Syn.:* OIL STRING.

Tubing a well

Setting and sealing into the well a string of pipe, called tubing, after perforations have been made in the casing or the well has been drilled to the desired total depth. The oil or gas is produced through the tubing which may have screens at the level of the producing stratum to strain out sand and other foreign matter.

Tubing pressure

See SHUT-IN PRESSURE.

Tubular goods

Well casing and tubing, drill pipe, standard pipe, line pipe, *etc.*

Turbodrilling

A method of drilling wells in which "the bit is turned not by rotation of the drill string, as in rotary drilling, but by a downhole turbine, driven by the fluid pumped down through the drill stem. The turbodrill can thus be thought of as using a hydraulic transmission system that gets power to the bottom of the hole in contrast to the rotary drilling system's dependence on mechanical transmission." Campbell, *The Economics of Soviet Oil and Gas* 108 (1968). For a discussion of the development and use of this method of drilling see *Id.* at 108–120.

See also CABLE TOOL DRILLING; ROTARY DRILLING.

Turkish National Petroleum Co. (TPAO)

For a discussion of this company see Shwadran, *The Middle East, Oil and the Great Powers* 491 (3d ed. revised and enlarged, 1973).

Turned into the line

A pipeline has begun to run oil from field tanks into which a well's production first goes, so that the well's production is being marketed. Ball, Ball, and Turner, *This Fascinating Oil Business* 109 (2d ed. 1965).

Turning to the right

A colloquialism for actual drilling of a well. Peterson, "Extensions and Suspensions of Federal Oil and Gas Leases," *Rocky Mt. Min. L. Fdn. Inst. on The Overthrust Belt—Oil and Gas Legal and Land Issues 12-1 at 12-7 (1980).*

Turnkey contract

A contract in which an independent drilling contractor undertakes to furnish all materials and labor and to do all the work required to complete a well in a workmanlike manner, place it on production and turn it over ready to "turn the key" and start the oil running into the tanks for an amount stipulated in the contract. See Continental Oil Co. v. Jones, 177 F.2d 508 (10th Cir. 1949); Murdock v. Reynolds, 180 Ark. 729, 22 S.W.2d 1007 (1929). See DRILLING CONTRACT.

"On a 'turnkey' basis, the parties agree on a fixed sum of money that will be paid to the drilling contractor in return for his furnishing a drilling crew, drilling equipment and certain specified materials and services, to be due and payable only after the hole is drilled to contract depth; all other services, materials and equipment are furnished at the cost of the well owner." Haas v. Gulf Coast Natural Gas Co., 484 S.W.2d 127 at 131, 43 *O.&G.R.* 381 at 389 (Tex. Civ. App. 1972).

Brountas v. Comm'r, 73 T.C. 491 at 497 (1979), 74 T.C. 1062, 67 *O.&G.R.* 477 (1980), *vacated and remanded,* 692 F.2d 152, 75 *O.&G.R.* 193 (1st Cir. 1982), *cert. denied,* 462 U.S. 1106, 103 S. Ct. 2453 (1983), made the following distinction between a "standard" turnkey contract and a "no-out" turnkey contract:

> "In a 'standard turnkey' the operator agrees to drill a well to a certain depth for a certain sum of money. However, in the standard turnkey, the operator is given what is commonly called a Gulf Coast Clause, which allows the operator 'outs' to cease drilling if certain specified unfavorable conditions are reached. Among the conditions usually specified in a Gulf Coast Clause are high or low pressure, impenetrable subsurface formations, loss of mud circulation, and salt." [This clause is not present in a "no-out" contract. Obviously the contract price is higher in a "no-out" contract than in a standard turnkey contract.]

For a discussion of a "no-out" turnkey contract, see Gibson Products Co. v. United States, 637 F.2d 1041 (5th Cir. 1981).

See also NO-LOG, NO-PAYMENT CONTRACT.

Turnkey job

The testing of the formation contemplated by the parties and completion of a producing well or abandonment as a dry hole, all done for a specific agreed-upon total consideration thereby putting the risk of rising costs, costs of well trouble, delays caused by the weather, *etc.,* upon the contracting driller. In the absence of a clear expression in the contract, the driller should not be held to guarantee a producing well. Totah Drilling Co. v. Abraham, 64 N.M. 380, 328 P.2d 1083, 9 *O.&G.R.* 682 (1958).

Turnkey well

A well drilled under a TURNKEY CONTRACT (*q.v.*).

Turnkey well doctrine

The rule in the Treasury Regulations that required, for tax years beginning before Jan. 1, 1943, a taxpayer to capitalize the cost of a well drilled under a TURNKEY CONTRACT (*q.v.*). Under the present regulations, the cost of such a well may be deducted as an expense. U. S. Treas. Reg. § 1.612–4(a)(3) (1980). See Burke and Bowhay, *Income Taxation of Natural Resources* § 14.03 (1981).

Turntable, rotary

A heavy, steel turntable, resting on bearings and mounted on a steel platform just above the derrick floor. The drill pipe is connected to the turntable, which is rotated to turn the bit in the hole and thus dig the well, in rotary-type drilling.

Syn.: Rotary.

Two-grant theory

The theory, founded on Hoffman v. Magnolia Petroleum Co., 273 S.W.828 (Tex. Com. App. 1925), that the SUBJECT-TO CLAUSE (*q.v.*) of a mineral or royalty deed referring to an existing lease may have the effect of a second grant so that the grantee will have one interest in production under the existing lease and a different interest in production under future leases. The theory is examined in detail in TREATISE §§ 340–340.4.

See also FUTURE LEASE CLAUSE.

Two-party favored-nation clause

See ESCALATOR CLAUSE; MOST FAVORED NATION CLAUSE.

Two-party top lease

See TOP LEASE.

Two-price system

A system for regulation of gas sales contracts by the Federal Power Commission involving separate prices for "old" gas and for "new" gas. See Permian Basin Area Rate Proceeding, 34 F.P.C. 159 at 185, 23 *O.&G.R.* 103 at 124 (Opinion No. 468, Aug. 5, 1965), *re-*

manded, Skelly Oil Co. v. Federal Power Comm'n, 375 F.2d 6, 26 *O.&G.R.* 237 (10th Cir. 1967), *aff'd in part and rev'd in part sub nom. In re* Permian Basin Area Rate Cases, 390 U.S. 747, 28 *O.&G.R.* 689 (1968).

See also Federal Power Commission; New gas; Old gas; One-price system; Replacement contract policy; Vintage.

Two-tier pricing system

A pricing system for oil established by the Cost of Living Council (*q.v.*) for New oil and Old Oil (*q.v.*). See Summers, "The Case for Decontrolling the Price and Allocation of Crude Oil," 53 *Texas L. Rev.* 1275 at 1281 (1975).

See also Produced and sold.

Two-to-one agreement

A term occasionally applied to an agreement whereby for a contribution to the financing of a well, the contributor is given an Oil payment (*q.v.*) in the amount of twice the contribution. See United States v. Adamant Co., 197 F.2d 1, 1 *O.&G.R.* 1072 (9th Cir. 1952), *cert. denied,* 344 U.S. 903 (1952).

See also Project financing.

. . U . .

UIC program

UNDERGROUND INJECTION CONTROL (UIC) PROGRAM (*q.v.*).

Ultimate recovery

The total expected recovery of oil and/or gas from a producing well, leasehold, pool or field.

"Ultimate recovery represents the estimated quantity of crude oil which has been produced from a reservoir and is expected to be produced in the future if there are no substantial changes in current economic and operating conditions. Ultimate recovery also may be expressed as the percentage of original oil-in-place which is expected to be eventually produced. This percentage will vary from one reservoir to another in accordance with the reservoir fluid, rock characteristics, and the producing mechanism or drive which is present." American Petroleum Institute Division of Statistics, *Organization and Definitions for the Estimation of Reserves and Productive Capacity of Crude Oil* 20 (Technical Report No. 2, June 1970).

See also RESERVES.

Ultradeep drilling

Drilling to depths greater than 15,000 feet below the surface. F.P.C. Opinion No. 699, 51 F.P.C. 2212 at 2296 (June 21, 1974).

Unaccrued royalty

The royalty which will become payable on future production of oil and/or gas, as opposed to ACCRUED ROYALTY (*q.v.*), which is royalty payable on oil and/or gas already produced. Accrued royalty is always treated as personalty but unaccrued royalty is frequently treated as realty. See United States v. Noble, 237 U.S. 74 at 80 (1915); TREATISE § 212.

UNCLOS

The acronym for the United Nations Conference on the Law of the Sea. UNCLOS I in 1958 produced, *inter alia,* the CONVENTION ON THE CONTINENTAL SHELF (1958) (*q.v.*).

Uncompensated drainage

Local migration of oil or gas which cannot be prevented by the landowner being drained because of the operation of proration and/or spacing rules.

A striking example is found in Railroad Comm'n v. Humble Oil & Ref. Co., 193 S.W.2d 824 (Tex. Civ. App. 1946, error ref'd n.r.e.). There the field was governed by a 20-acre spacing order. But on one side of the field, a much greater well density prevailed due to the granting of exceptions to the spacing rule. The proration order allocated the allowable 50% per well and 50% to acreage. Under this formula a well on a 20-acre unit was allowed to produce slightly over twice as much as a well on a one-acre unit. Drainage took place from that part of the field developed on a 20-acre spacing to that part more densely drilled. The operator of the land being drained could not drill offset wells to prevent the drainage, as this would violate the spacing rule. The operator brought suit to set aside the proration order, claiming that it operated to deprive him of an opportunity to capture the oil under his leases and being drained away. That is, the operator claimed that the conservation orders were invalid if they deprived a landowner of the opportunity to prevent uncompensated drainage from his land. The court found that uncompensated drainage was taking place but that the conservation orders were valid because they gave certain other advantages to the protesting operator.

In new fields, such orders resulting in uncompensated drainage are no longer valid. Halbouty v. Railroad Comm'n, 163 Tex. 417, 357 S.W.2d 364, 16 *O.&G.R.* 788 (1962), *cert. denied,* 371 U.S. 888 (1962).

See also DRAINAGE.

Unconformity

A layer of sedimentary rock deposited on an eroded and/or deformed rock surface so that the two strata are not parallel. Stratigraphic traps are often found in unconformities.

See also DISCONFORMITY.

Unconnected well

A well without a pipe line connection. Oil from such wells must be shipped by tank truck to a refinery.

In December 1956, 8,394 wells in Texas, about 5% of the total number of producing wells in that state, did not have a pipe line connection. The average daily production of each unconnected well in

Texas in that month was 12.69 barrels; the average daily production of each connected well in Texas that month was 18.46 barrels. Trucking charges for oil produced from unconnected wells range from 15 to 30 cents per barrel. 16 *Oil and Gas Compact Bulletin* 71 (Dec. 1957).

Underage

(1) The amount of allowable production from a well in excess of actual production therefrom. See Choctaw Gas Co. v. Corporation Comm'n, 295 P.2d 800, 5 *O.&G.R.* 1226 (Okla. 1956).

Syn.: UNDERPRODUCTION (*q.v.*).

(2) The amount of the UNDERLIFT (*q.v.*) by a party to a JOINT OPERATING AGREEMENT (*q.v.*), PRODUCTION SHARING CONTRACT (*q.v.*), SERVICE CONTRACT (*q.v.*) or other contract between two or more parties having an interest in production.

See also BALANCING; CANCELLED UNDERAGE; DEEMED PURCHASE FORMULA; DEFERRED PRODUCTION AGREEMENT; GAS BANK AGREEMENT; LIFTING; LIFTING TOLERANCE; "OUT OF BALANCE" PRODUCTION PLAN; OVERLIFT; SPLIT CONNECTION; UNDERLIFT; UNDERLIFT/OVERLIFT PROVISION.

Underground injection control (UIC) program

A program designed to protect surface and subsurface freshwater sources from possible pollution and contamination as a result of oil and gas operations. 41 *Oil & Gas Compact Bull.* 48 (June 1982).

A program of the ENVIRONMENTAL PROTECTION AGENCY (EPA) (*q.v.*) for dealing with fluid injection of salt water produced from oil fields and other hazardous fluid wastes produced as a consequence of either mining or other industry. See Baltay, "Current Status UIC Programs," 26 *IOCC Comm. Bull.* 6 (Dec. 1983); Minton, "Frankenstein UIC or the Great Salt Water Monster," *Id.* at 8.

Underground property

A term employed in certain insurance policies to cover and include "oil, gas, water or other mineral substance, including any title, interest or estate therein, which, at the time of the act or omission causing loss of, injury to or destruction of such substance, or loss, impairment or reduction of the value of such title, interest or estate, has not been reduced to physical possession above the earth's surface; such term also includes any well, bore, formation, strata or area beneath the surface of the earth in or through which exploration for or production of any such substance is carried on, or any casing, pipe, bit, tool, pump, or other drilling or well servicing machinery or equipment which is located in any such well or hole beneath the earth's surface at the time of the accident causing injury or destruction." See Burnett, "Underground Property Damage Liability," 7 *Tulane Tidelands Inst.* 133 at 136 (1963).

Underground reservoir

See RESERVOIR.

Underground storage

Storage of gas in a subsurface stratum or formation of the earth. Iowa Code Ann. § 479.2 (1980 Supp.). See GAS STORAGE, SUBSURFACE.

Underground waste

"[T]he inefficient, excessive, or improper use or dissipation of the reservoir energy, including gas energy and water drive, of any pool, and the locating, spacing, drilling, equipping, operating, or producing of any well or wells in a manner to reduce or tend to reduce the total quantity of oil or gas ultimately recoverable from any pool, and unreasonable damage to underground fresh or mineral waters, natural brines, or other mineral deposits from operations for the discovery, development, and production and handling of oil or gas." Comp. Laws Mich. § 319.2(l)(2), Mich. Stat. Ann. § 13.139(2)(1)(1) (1980 Supp.).

See also WASTE.

Underlift

The term utilized in a JOINT OPERATING AGREEMENT (*q.v.*), PRODUCTION SHARING CONTRACT (*q.v.*), SERVICE CONTRACT (*q.v.*), or other contract between or among two or more parties having an interest in production indicating that a party has failed during a given contract period to take and remove its obligated share of production for the period in question.

See also BALANCING; CANCELLED UNDERAGE; DEEMED PURCHASE FORMULA; DEFERRED PRODUCTION AGREEMENT; GAS BANK AGREEMENT; LIFTING; LIFTING TOLERANCE; "OUT OF BALANCE" PRODUCTION PLAN; OVERLIFT; SPLIT CONNECTION; UNDERAGE; UNDERLIFT/OVERLIFT PROVISION.

Underlift/overlift provision

(1) A provision of a JOINT OPERATING AGREEMENT (*q.v.*) designed to provide a mechanism whereby each party can take its share of the oil in the reservoir, independently of the other parties and, if any party or parties fail to take, or take less than its proportionate share, to allow the taking party to produce its respective share of the reservoir oil at a faster rate. A simple form of such a provision is as follows:

> "Any party not currently taking its share of the production in kind may notify the party or parties currently taking their shares of the production in kind that it desires to leave stored its share of the production in the reservoir for future taking. If any such notice is given, it shall be deemed that thereafter, and until such notice is given, it shall be deemed that thereafter, and until such time as the party electing to store its production again elects to commence to take its share of the production, the share in production of the party giving such notice remains in the reservoir. Thereafter by notice in writing to the other parties, the party once so electing to store its share of the production may elect again to take its normal share of the production, plus an excess not in excess of . . . percent of the normal share of any party then having a cumulative overproduction, until such time as all parties are in current balance. If, upon final abandonment of the last jointly-owned well, there is any net cumulative deficiency, it shall be deemed that the party with the net cumulative overproduction has purchased the net cumulative underproduction from the party having such net cumulative underproduction at the weighted average price upon which the party with the net cumulative overproduction has computed royalty, from the date of first production. Such party with the net cumulative overproduction shall settle in cash with the party having the net cumulative underproduction at that time." Stewart "Important Features of Joint Operating Agreements," 13 *Sw. Legal Fdn. Nat'l Inst. for Petroleum Landmen* 139 at 153–155 (1972).

A number of joint operating agreements impose upon each party the duty to lift and dispose of its share of production and then include a "take or lose" provision to the effect that in the event a party fails to lift its share of production (or sell it to another lifting party) the amount of the underlift "shall remain and accrue for and to the benefit of all Parties according to their respective Percentage Interests." United Kingdom Joint Operating Agreement Dated 20 December 1977 for Fifth Round Production License Number P264 Between the British National Oil Corporation (BNOC), Texaco North Sea U.K. Limited, & Texaco North Sea U.K. Company, Clause 16.

(2) A provision of a joint venture agreement relating to inability of one party to take some or all of his share of production (underlift) which authorizes another or other parties to take such share (overlift), subject to a later "makeup right" of the underlifter.

For discussion of the underlift/overlift provision of participation agreements in the Norwegian sector of the North Sea, see Swan, *Ocean Oil and Gas Drilling & The Law* 79 (1979):

> "If a party, for 'reasons beyond its control,' takes less oil than its proportional share, the amount not taken is referred to as 'underlift.' As soon as it becomes apparent that one or more parties will be in an underlift situation, the operator must notify all the parties so that any one or more of the others may dispose of the underlifted amount. When more than one party desires to dispose of the underlifted amount, it is shared in the same proportion as the interest of each party desiring to dispose of it bears to the total of all such parties' interests. Those who dispose of the amount not required by the underlifter, are referred to as 'overlifters.' The underlifter is presently entitled to exercise a 'makeup right.' This means that it can, to the extent of the overlift, claim 10 percent of each overlifter's share of the optimum production program each quarter until the cumulative volume reclaimed equals the overlift of each overlifter."

See also BALANCING; CANCELLED UNDERAGE; DEEMED PURCHASE FORMULA; DEFERRED PRODUCTION AGREEMENT; GAS BANK AGREEMENT; LIFTING; LIFTING TOLERANCE; "OUT OF BALANCE" PRODUCTION PLAN; OVERLIFT; SPLIT CONNECTION; UNDERAGE; UNDERLIFT.

Underproduction

The deficiency in production when the monthly production of a gas well is less than its monthly ALLOWABLE (*q.v.*). State proration orders frequently provide for the making up of the deficiency in a subsequent period. See, *e.g.*, State of Louisiana, Department of Conservation, Statewide Order No. 29–F, Nov. 8, 1955, 5 *O.&G.R.* 474, 476 (1956); Administrative Ruling, Railroad Commission of Texas, 5 *O.&G.R.* 1100 at 1104 (1956); Choctaw Gas Co. v. Corporation Comm'n, 295 P.2d 800, 5 *O.&G.R.* 1226 (Okla. 1956).

Syn.: UNDERAGE.

See also BALANCING PERIOD; OVERPRODUCTION.

Undeveloped acreage clause

A clause in a GAS LEASE-SALES AGREEMENT (GLA) (*q.v.*) providing that in the event development in the area of or adjacent to any drilling unit should evidence that such drilling unit would not be productive of gas in commercial quantities, the purchaser may promptly reassign any such drilling unit to the seller or the seller's designee and thereupon be relieved of its obligation to drill a test well thereon; but the purchaser could retain any commercial gas well completed thereon in a shallower or deeper formation, together with its rights in such drilling unit down through such shallower or deeper horizon. El Paso Natural Gas Co. v. American Petrofina Co. of Texas, 715 S.W.2d 177, ___ *O.&G.R.* ___ (Tex. App., Houston, 1986) (holding that for purposes of this clause the cost of the overriding royalties which the operator was required to pay was a cost necessarily to be considered in determining whether undeveloped acreage was capable of producing in commercial quantities).

Undiscovered resources

Unspecified bodies of mineral-bearing material surmised to exist on the basis of broad geologic knowledge and theory. 2 *OCS Oil and Gas—An Environmental Assessment,* A Report to the President by the Council on Environmental Quality (April 1974) at p. 10.

See also RESERVES.

Undivided interest clause

A lease clause negating any drilling or development obligation so long as some undivided interest in the premises remains unleased.

Undivided interest farm-out

A FARM-OUT AGREEMENT (*q.v.*) in which it is agreed to transfer a specified undivided interest in the farmed-out acreage if an obligation test well is drilled on said land to a specified depth or to the "casing point." See Bowden, "Federal Income Tax Consequences Under Typical Farm-Out Agreements," 3 *Nat. Res. J.* 470 at 475 (1964).

Undivided interest pipeline

A pipeline in which each owner has an undivided interest, as a tenant-in-common, in the pipeline properties. The system is generally operated by one of the participants as an agent. Each owner publishes its own tariffs, accepts shipments, and collects its own revenue.

The most noted example of this type of ownership is the Trans Alaska Pipeline System (TAPS). See TAPS AGREEMENT. Report to the Congress by the Comptroller General, *Petroleum Pipeline Rates and Competition* 2 (July 13, 1979). This form of pipeline can be conceived as a single line consisting of a bundle of different-sized lines, each with a different owner. Participants enjoy the economies of large-diameter pipe which they might not be justified in building just for themselves; each owner exercises full control over tenders, tariffs, and other requirements on his share of the line, and is entitled to throughput in proportion to his percentage of ownership. Allocation of costs, with the exception of those that vary directly with throughput, is based on this percentage of ownership. See Johnson, *Petroleum Pipelines and Public Policy, 1906–1959* 318, 406–407 (1967).

Undivided joint interest pipeline

See UNDIVIDED INTEREST PIPELINE.

Undivided type of unit operating agreement

See DIVIDED TYPE OF UNIT OPERATING AGREEMENT.

Unfinished gasoline

Gasoline of less than sixty-five octane, or gasoline that has been refined partially but not enough for use as an engine fuel. *N. Y. Times,* June 5, 1958, 45:1.

Uniform Limited Offering Exemption

An exemption under the BLUE SKY LAW (*q.v.*) of certain states drafted by a committee of The North American Securities Administrators Association, Inc. (NASAA) and approved at the 1981 annual meeting of the association. 1 *CCH Blue Sky L. Rept.* ¶ 5294. See TREATISE § 441.4.

Uniform system of accounts

A system adopted by the Federal Power Commission and required to be kept by natural gas companies. 18 C.F.R. Part 201 (1980).

Unit

(1) The total area incorporated in a unitization agreement.

This term is defined by Article 213 of the Louisiana Mineral Code [R.S. 31:213 (1975)] as "an area of land, deposit, or deposits of minerals, stratum or strata, or pool or pools, or a part or parts thereof, as to which parties with interests therein are bound to share minerals produced on a specified basis and as to which those having the right to conduct drilling or mining operations therein are bound to share investment and operating costs on a specified basis. A unit may be formed by convention or by order of an agency of the state or federal government empowered to do so. A unit formed by order of a governmental agency is termed a 'compulsory unit.' "

See also COMMISSIONER'S UNIT; COMPULSORY UNIT; CONTRACTUAL UNIT; CONVENTIONAL UNIT; DECLARED UNIT; DEVELOPMENTAL UNIT; EDGE UNIT SYSTEM; GEOGRAPHICAL UNIT; GEOLOGICAL UNIT; NON-STANDARD UNIT; OPERATIONAL UNIT; POOLED UNIT; SUBSIDENCE UNIT; VOLUNTARY UNIT.

(2) The acreage allocated to a particular well.

See also DRAINAGE UNIT, DRILLING SPACING UNIT; DRILLING UNIT; MARGINAL UNIT; PRORATION UNIT; SPACING UNIT; WELL SPACING.

Unit accounting agreement

The agreement providing for the apportionment of working interest and/or royalty interest benefits among the owners of unitized working and/or royalty interests.

Unit agreement

An agreement or plan of development and operation for the recovery of oil and gas made subject thereto as a single consolidated unit without regard to separate ownerships and for the allocation of costs and benefits on a basis as defined in the agreement or plan. See TREATISE §§ 920–921.19.

See also ABANDONING PARTY; ACREAGE BASIS; ACREAGE TOLERANCE; ACRE FOOT OF SAND; ADJUSTMENT OF UNIT INTERESTS; AFE; AFTER ACQUIRED RIGHTS CLAUSE; AUTOMATIC ELIMINATION CLAUSE; BALANCING; BENEFICIAL INTEREST; CARRYING PARTY; CASING POINT; COMMITTED WORKING INTEREST; CONTRIBUTION CLAUSE; DEEMED PURCHASE FORMULA; DIVIDED TYPE OF OPERATING AGREEMENT; DRILLING BLOCK; DRILLING PARTY; EDGE UNIT SYSTEM; EFFECTIVE PAY; EXCLUDED INTEREST; EXTRANEOUS GAS; GAS STORAGE AND BALANCING AGREEMENT; INDIVIDUAL LOSS PROVISION; JOINT ACCOUNT WELL; JOINT LOSS PROVISION; JOINT OPERATING AGREEMENT; LEASE BURDENS; LANDOWNERS' ROYALTY POOL; NON-ABANDONING PARTY; NON-CONSENT PENALTY; NON-CONSENT PRINCIPLE; NON-CONSENT WELL; NON-DRILLING PARTY; NON-JOINT DRILLING; NON-PARTICIPATING AREA; OPERATING AGREEMENT; OPERATING COMMITTEE; OPERATIONAL UNIT; OPERATOR;

OPERATORS AGREEMENT; OPERATORS COMMITTEE; PARTICIPANT; PARTICIPATING AREA; PARTICIPATING INTEREST; PARTICIPATION FORMULA; PENALTY CLAUSE; PLANT OPERATING AGREEMENT; POOLING AGREEMENT; PRODUCTION PAYMENT RESERVATION AGREEMENT; QUALIFIED SUBSCRIBER; QUALIFIED TRACT; REQUIRED WELL; RESULTING AREA; ROSS MARTIN FORM; ROYALTY OWNERS AGREEMENT; ROYALTY TRUST; ROYALTY UNITIZATION AGREEMENT; SEGREGATED LANDS; SOLE RISK CLAUSE; SUCCESSOR UNIT OPERATOR; TAKE-OVER PARTY; TITLE COMMITTEE; TITLE EXAMINATION AREA; TRACT VALUE; UNDERLIFT/OVERLIFT PROVISION; UNIT ACCOUNTING AGREEMENT; UNIT AREA; UNIT EXPENSE; UNITIZATION; UNITIZATION COMMITTEE; UNITIZED LAND; UNITIZED LEASE; UNITIZED SUBSTANCES; UNITIZED TITLE; UNIT MANAGER; UNIT OPERATOR; UNIT SURPLUS WELL; UNQUALIFIED SUBSCRIBER; UNSIGNED TRACTS; WEIGHTED AVERAGE METHOD; WINDOW.

Unit area

The area described in an agreement as constituting the land logically subject to development under such agreement.

United method

A method of classifying costs for purposes of cost allocation and rate design. The name comes from United Gas Pipeline Co., 50 F.P.C. 1348 (1973), *reh. denied,* 51 F.P.C. 1014 (1974), *aff'd sub nom.* Consolidated Gas Supply Corp. v. Federal Power Comm'n, 520 F.2d 1176 (D.C. Cir. 1975), wherein the Commission determined that 25 percent of a pipeline's fixed transmission costs were to be recovered through the demand component of the pipeline's two-part "demand-commodity" rate and the remaining 75% of fixed costs and all of the variable costs were to be recovered through the commodity charge. See Columbia Gas Transmission Corp. v. Federal Energy Regulatory Comm'n, 628 F.2d 578 (D.C. Cir. 1979), vacating a Commission order employing this method rather than the SEABOARD METHOD (*q.v.*) in allocating costs and designing pipeline rates. See Pierce, "An Overview of Regulation," in Pierce, *Natural Gas Regulation Handbook* 30 at 87 (1980).

See also COMMODITY CHARGE; DEMAND CHARGE.

United States Synthetic Fuels Corporation

A corporation established by the Energy Security Act, Pub. L. No. 96–294 (June 30, 1980) with power to: (1) make loans to any concern for development of synthetic fuel projects, (2) make loan guarantees on obligations to provide funds for synthetic fuel projects, (3) guarantee prices received by a concern for the production from a synthetic fuel project, (4) enter into purchase agreements for synthetic fuel production, (5) enter joint ventures for synthetic fuel project modules. The Corporation is authorized to construct and operate on its own no more than three synthetic fuel projects.

For discussions of the history of the corporation, see the following:

Humphrey, "Government Programs of Potential Assistance in Financing Mineral Projects," *Rocky Mt. Min. L. Inst. on Mineral Financing* 12-1 *et seq.* (1982);

Solomon and Mitchell, "The Development of Synthetic Fuels: A Legal and Policy Analysis," 17 *Tulsa L.J.* 375 (1982);

Young, "The New United States Synthetic Fuels Corporation and the Development of Synfuels in the 1980's," 2 *Eastern Min. L. Inst.* 4–1 (1981).

Unit expense

"[A]ny and all cost, expense, or indebtedness incurred by the unit in the establishment of its organization, or incurred in the conduct and management of its affairs or the operations carried on by it." Okla. Stat. Ann., § 52–287.13(e)(1969).

Unitization

A term frequently used interchangeably with POOLING (*q.v.*) but more properly used to denominate the joint operation of all or some portion of a producing reservoir as distinguished from pooling, which term is used to describe the bringing together of small tracts sufficient for the granting of a well permit under applicable spacing rules.

Pooling is important in the prevention of drilling of unnecessary and uneconomic wells, which will result in physical and economic waste. Unitization is important where there is separate ownership of portions of the rights in a common producing pool in order that it may be made economically feasible to engage in cycling, pressure maintenance or secondary recovery operations and to explore for minerals at considerable depth.

The best results in conservation can be attained only by unitization. Only in this way can appropriate use of reservoir pressures be made and secondary recovery operations utilized at the appropriate early stage in the exploration of the oil deposits. Moreover, only with unitization of fairly sizable tracts is it economically feasible to utilize advanced methods of cycling for maximum extraction of liquid constituents from gas. Cycling operations should be conducted under a program planned for a field as a whole in order to prevent wet gas from being segregated from producing wells by the dry gas fingering into the formation. Under a unitization program, input and production wells may be located in accordance with the best engineering practices and without regard to lease or property lines. See Hoffman, *Voluntary Pooling and Unitization* (1954); Hardwicke, *Antitrust Laws, et al. vs. Unit Operation of Oil or Gas Pools* (1948); TREATISE Vol. 6.

For a discussion of the arguments for compulsory unitization, see S. L. McDonald, *Petroleum Conservation in the United States: An Economic Analysis* (1971).

For an economic and political analysis of the difficulties encountered in obtaining joinder in a voluntary unit, see Libecap and Wiggins, "The Influence of Private Contractual Failure on Regulation: The Case of Oil Field Unitization," 93 *J. of Political Economy* 690 (1985).

For a detailed study of the extent Texas has achieved voluntary unitization without the impetus of a compulsory unitization statute, see Weaver, *Unitization of Oil and Gas Fields in Texas* (1986).

For discussions of unitization of international common petroleum products see the following:

Onorato, "Apportionment of an International Common Petroleum Deposit," 26 *Int. & Comp. L.Q.* 324 (1977):

Woodliffe, International Unitization of an Offshore Gas Field," *Id.* at 338 (1977).

See also COMPULSORY POOLING; COMPULSORY UNITIZATION; CONSENT PARTY; CROSS ASSIGNMENT; CROSS-TRANSFER OF ROYALTIES; OPERATING AGREEMENT; POOLING; UNITIZATION.

Unitization agreement

An agreement for the operation of separately owned interests as a unit. See UNIT AGREEMENT.

Unitization committee

A temporary committee of operators interested in reaching an agreement on unitization. See Myers, *The Law of Pooling and Unitization* § 4.01 (2d ed. 1967).

Unitization, compulsory

See COMPULSORY UNITIZATION.

Unitized land

The part of a unit area committed to an agreement.

Unitized lease

A term used to describe a lease subject to a unitization agreement; also, a community lease. See Southland Royalty Co. v. Humble Oil & Refining Co., 151 Tex. 324, 249 S.W.2d 914, 1 *O.&G.R.* 1431 (1952).

Unitized substances

Deposits of oil and gas recoverable by operation under and pursuant to an agreement.

The term is normally defined in a pooling or unitization agreement, *e.g.*, as "all oil, gas, gaseous substances, sulphur contained in gas, condensate, distillate and all associated and constituent liquid or liquefiable hydrocarbons within or produced from the Unit Area." See Myers, *The Law of Pooling and Unitization* § 5.02 (2d ed. 1967).

If fewer than all hydrocarbons are unitized, the definition must be more specific.

Unitized title

A term descriptive of the situation where parties other than the original well site owner share in production from the well site under an arrangement for reciprocal sharing, either actual or potential, from the production on their well sites. Masterson, "The Nature of Unitized Title," 10 *Sw. L.J.* 146 (1956).

Unit manager

The person charged with the management of a unit operation.

Unit of production method

A method employed for the calculation of depletion, depreciation or amortization based upon quantities produced in relation to reserves. For a discussion of the use of this method of depreciation see

Tennessee Gas Pipeline Co., 56 F.P.C. 120, 10 FPS 5–240.1 (Opinion No. 769, July 9, 1976).

Unit operating agreement

See UNIT AGREEMENT.

Unit operation

Exploration and development of an area included within a unitization agreement.

Unit operator

The person, association, partnership, corporation, or other business entity designated under a unit agreement to conduct operations on unitized land as specified in such agreement. See TREATISE § 921.18.

Unit surplus well

A producing well in a pool or portion of a pool operated as a unit which is not required for the efficient production of the unit MPR (*q.v.*) or MER (*q.v.*). In Alberta the Oil and Gas Conservation Board may authorize the temporary or permanent suspension of the well and the transfer of its economic allowance to another well or wells in the unit. Oil and Gas Conservation Board, Transfer of Oil Allowables (Sept. 30, 1957).

See also TRANSFERRED ALLOWABLE.

Unlawful oil or gas

See ILLEGAL OIL OR GAS.

Unless clause

The clause in an UNLESS LEASE (*q.v.*) providing for the termination of the lease interest unless the lessee commences drilling or pays rentals during the primary term. See TREATISE §§ 605–606.11.

See also DELAY RENTAL CLAUSE.

Unless lease

The type of lease most frequently employed in this country except on the west coast, where the OR LEASE (*q.v.*) is normally employed. There is no single form of the Unless lease in use, but generally leases are known as Unless leases because of the form of the delay rental clause, which in general is somewhat as follows:

> "If no well be commenced on said land on or before one year from the date hereof, this lease shall terminate as to both parties, *unless* the lessee on or before that date shall pay or tender to the lessor, or to the lessor's credit in the . . . . Bank at . . . ., or its successors, which shall continue as the depository for rental regardless of changes in the ownership of said land, the sum of . . . . Dollars, ($. . . . .) which shall operate as a rental and cover the privilege of deferring the commencement of a well for twelve months from said date. . . ." (Emphasis supplied.)

The "Producers 88" or "Form 88" lease, in common use in the mid-continent area, is an Unless type lease. The delay rental clause in the Unless lease is construed as a special limitation, and the leasehold interest of the lessee automatically terminates if neither of the events specified (commencement of a well or payment of rentals) occurs on or before the anniversary date or due date of the rentals. The clause is generally construed in favor of the lessor, and failure to make timely payment of the full amount of the rentals occasions termination of the leasehold interest, even though the failure is due to accident or mistake. The exceptions to this rule are few in number. See TREATISE §§ 601.5, 606–606.10.

See also "COMMENCE" LEASE; "COMPLETION" LEASE; 88 LEASE.

Unlimited carried interest

Syn.: PERMANENT CARRIED INTEREST (*q.v.*).

Unpooling

Termination of a pooling or unitization agreement.

Unprofitability clause

A clause in a GAS LEASE-SALES AGREEMENT (GLA) (*q.v.*) providing that in the event operation of any well should become unprofitable the purchaser could reassign the well and the unit on which it was situated to the seller and in such event the seller-assignee should have the option to sell gas produced therefrom to the purchaser-assignor at the highest price paid for gas of like kind and quality in the field and the purchaser-assignor agreed to purchase such gas at such price. El Paso Natural Gas Co. v. American Petrofina Co. of Texas, 715 S.W.2d 177, ____ *O.&G.R.* ____ (Tex. App., Houston, 1986), concluded that under this clause a lease could become unprofitable even though it was still producing in paying quantities because both the basic lease royalty and any overriding royalty burdening the property were to be considered in determining profitability whereas only the basic lease royalty was considered in determining whether the lease was producing in paying quantities.

Unproven area

An area in which it has not been established by drilling operations whether oil and/or gas may be found in commercial quantities.

Syn.: Wildcat territory.

Unqualified subscriber

A party to a unitization agreement who agrees to all the terms, provisions, and conditions of the agreement including the expenses attributable to the interest of a QUALIFIED SUBSCRIBER (*q.v.*).

Unsigned tracts

A phrase occasionally used to describe tracts located within the boundaries of a unit agreement in which there are interests not subject to the agreement (unsigned interests). See Myers, "Legal Problems Incident to Operation of a Unit," 8 *Sw. Legal Fdn. Oil & Gas Inst.* 255 at 306 (1957); TREATISE §§ 937–937.4.

Unstablized crude oil

Crude oil prior to treatment in a gas separation plant.

Up-dip lease

A lease on the higher part of a reservoir. Amoco Production Co. v. Alexander, 622 S.W.2d 563 at 566, 72 *O.&G.R.* 125 at 127, 18 A.L.R.4th 1 (Tex. 1981).

See also DOWN-DIP LEASE.

Up-dip well

A well located high on the structure where the oil is nearest the surface of the field. Hunter v. Hussey, 90 So.2d 429, 6 *O.&G.R.* 1172 (La. App. 1956).

Upper tier crude oil

This term is defined by Section 4988 of the National Energy Act (H.R. 8444), as passed by the House of Representatives on August 5, 1977, as controlled crude oil which is certified by the producer as having been sold pursuant to the upper tier ceiling price rule in effect (at the time of the purchase) under section 4(a) of the Emergency Petroleum Allocation Act of 1973.

Upper tier oil

Syn. for SECOND TIER OIL (*q.v.*).

Upstream

This term is used in describing operations performed before those at a point of reference. Production is an upstream operation and marketing is a downstream operation when the refinery is used as a point of reference. On a gas pipeline, gathering activities are considered to have ended when gas reaches a central point for delivery into a single line, and facilities used before this point of reference are upstream facilities used in gathering, whereas facilities employed after commingling at the central point and employed to make ultimate delivery of the gas are downstream facilities.

Up-structure

Toward the highest point on a STRUCTURE (*q.v.*). Because of the tendency of oil and gas to rise, the highest point on the structure is the most favorable for production, and accordingly wells located up-structure are more likely to produce than wells located down structure.

Syn.: Up-dip.

User agreement

See TAKE-OR-PAY CONTRACT.

USGS

United States Geological Survey.

Usufruct

(1) In Louisiana, "Usufruct is a real right of limited duration on the property of another. The features of the right vary with the na-

ture of the things subject to it as consumables or nonconsumables." La. Civ. Code Art. 535 (1980 Special Pamphlet). The Civil Code provisions dealing with the usufruct were extensively revised by the Louisiana legislatures in 1976, 1977, 1978 and 1979 on the recommendation of the Louisiana State Law Institute. Provisions relating to the Usufruct are found in Articles 535–629 (1980 Special Pamphlet). The rights of usufructuaries in minerals is dealt with in Chapter 11 of the Louisiana Mineral Code [R.S. 31:188 to 31:196 (1975) (1980 Supp.)]. See also TREATISE § 512.3.

Certain aspects of the usufruct were summarized by Oppenheim, "The Usufruct of the Surviving Spouse," 28 *Tulane L. Rev.* 181 at 182–183 (1943) as follows:

> "The person who holds the usufruct, the usufructuary, is entitled to all kinds of fruits, natural, cultivated, or civil, produced during the existence of the usufruct by the things subject to that usufruct. If the usufruct is a perfect usufruct, that is, one which consists of things which the usufructuary may use without changing their substance, the usufructuary must return the things subject to the usufruct as soon as that usufruct terminates. If the usufruct is imperfect, that is, one which consists of things which would be useless to the usufructuary unless he could consume or expend them, the usufructuary at the termination of the usufruct must return the same quantity, quality and value, or the estimated price, of the things subject to the usufruct which were consumed or expended. . . . The usufruct may terminate by the death of the usufructuary, by the happening of the condition stipulated in the title under which it was established, by the destruction of the thing subject to the usufruct, by prescription, by confusion, and finally the usufructuary may lose his rights through a violation of his duties. A usufruct may be established in three ways and is of three types: (1) the LEGAL USUFRUCT (*q.v.*); (2) the testamentary usufruct; and (3) the CONVENTIONAL USUFRUCT (*q.v.*). The usufruct of the surviving spouse is a legal usufruct, since it attaches by operation of law."

See also Yiannopoulos, "The Usufruct of Mineral Rights in Louisiana," 22 *L.S.U. Min. L. Inst.* 155 (1975).

(2) "The usufruct is well known to the civil law as a *ius in re aliena,* a right in the property of others, amounting to full possession." Henderson, "Canada's Indian Reserves: The Usufruct in Our Constitution," 12 *Ottawa L. Rev.* 167 (1980) (urging the abandonment of the usufruct concept in dealing with Indian proprietary interests).

Under the Hague Regulations [Hague Convention No. IV Respecting the Laws and Customs of War on Land and Annex thereto Embodying Regulations Respecting the Laws and Customs of War on Land, Oct. 18, 1907, 36 Stat. 2277, T.S. No. 539], an occupying force must administer immovables in accordance with the rules of usufruct. See Cummings, "Oil Resources in Occupied Arab Territories Under the Law of Belligerent Occupation," 9 *J. Int'l L. & Econ.* 533 at 559 (1974).

Utmost fair dealing, duty of

The obligation imposed on the EXECUTIVE (*q.v.*) with regard to the exercise of the power to lease, where the EXCLUSIVE LEASING POWER (*q.v.*) in land is separated from an interest in the oil and gas, as in the case of NONPARTICIPATING ROYALTY (*q.v.*) and NONEXECUTIVE MINERAL INTERESTS (*q.v.*). The precise term "utmost fair dealing" was used in the case of Schlittler v. Smith, 128 Tex. 628, 101 S.W.2d 534 (1937). See also McCall v. Nettles, 251 Ala. 349, 37 So.2d 635 (1948). However, the duty has also been characterized as one of ordinary care and diligence, Winterman v. McDonald, 129 Tex. 275, 102 S.W.2d 167 (1937).

There has been little judicial discussion of the duty, where it applies, or remedy for breach. The question arises with regard to (1) the terms of the lease negotiated by the executive (size of royalty, length of primary term, acceptance of drilling obligation in lieu of bonus, agreement to a pooling clause), (2) the time when the leasing power is exercised, and (3) enforcement of express and implied covenants.

See Jones, "Non-Participating Royalty," 26 *Texas L. Rev.* 569 (1948); Jones, "Exercise of Executive Rights in Connection with Non-Participating Royalty and Non-Executive Mineral Interests," 15 *Sw. Legal Fdn. Oil & Gas Inst.* 35 (1964); Williams, "The Fiduciary Principle in the Law of Oil and Gas," 13 *Sw. Legal Fdn. Oil & Gas Inst.* 201 (1962); TREATISE §§ 338–339.3.

..V..

Vacancy

For purposes of the sale or lease of a "vacancy," the term vacancy is defined by Tex. Nat. Res. Code § 51.172 (1978) as follows:

" 'Vacancy' means an area of unsurveyed public school land that:

(A) is not in conflict on the ground with land previously titled, awarded, or sold;

(B) has not been listed on the records of the land office as public school land; and

(C) was, on the date of filing, neither subject to an earlier subsisting application to purchase or lease by a discoverer or claimant nor involved in pending litigation brought by the state to recover the land."

See also APPLICANT; EXCESS LAND; GOOD FAITH CLAIMANT; QUALIFIED APPLICANT.

Vacant land

(1) Land which is unoccupied.

(2) Land which is included in a VACANCY (*q.v.*).

See also EXCESS LANDS.

Vacuum pump

A pump which by means of the creation of an artificial vacuum or partial vacuum in the well bore stimulates the flow of oil from the producing formation into the well bore.

For regulations governing the employment of a vacuum pump, see 16 Tex. Admin. Code § 3.24.

Validation well

A well the drilling of which is required to avoid loss of a lease or other interest in land. See Brown, "Independent Operations, Obligatory Operations and Challenge of Operator Provisions in Joint Venture Agreements," 8 *Alberta L. Rev.* 216 at 217 (1970).

Valuable mineral

In Gladys City Co. v. Amoco Production Co., 528 F. Supp. 624, 73 *O.&G.R.* 88 (E.D. Tex. 1981), the court rejected the contention that the term "valuable mineral" includes those minerals which later become valuable, concluding that the term is limited to substances which, at the time of the grant, reasonably prudent men would have been justified in an expenditure of time and resources to exploit.

Valuation methods

See NET-BACK PRICING; PROCEEDS-LESS EXPENSE METHOD; PROVEN OR SEMI-PROVEN ("DRAINAGE") METHOD OF EVALUATION; RANGE OF VALUES METHOD; RISK-FREE VALUE; WILDCAT ACREAGE METHOD OF EVALUATION; WORK-BACK EVALUATION METHOD.

Value in ground

The monetary value of proven reserves in the ground, that is, before removal.

After a well has been brought into production and an estimate made of the recoverable oil and gas under the property, it is possible to estimate the value of the oil or gas in the ground for the purpose of estimating the value of the property. In general, when the sale price of oil was approximately $3 per barrel, the value of royalty oil in the ground was approximately $1.25 per barrel and the value of working interest oil in the ground was approximately $1 per barrel. Fiske, "The Valuation of Oil and Gas Properties in Estates and Trusts," 2 *Rocky Mt. Min. L. Inst.* 371 (1956).

See also RISK-FREE VALVE.

Value-less-expenses method

Syn. for WORK-BACK VALUATION METHOD (*q.v.*).

Vapor

"The gaseous state of a substance, as distinguished from permanent gases. A gaseous fluid may be classified as either a vapor or a gas. If it is near the region of condensation it is called a vapor. If it is well above the region of condensation it is called a gas." American Gas Ass'n, *Glossary for the Gas Industry* (3d ed. 1981).

Variable dedication

In an A-B-C TRANSACTION (*q.v.*), a provision whereunder the production reserved by *A* to satisfy the production payment may be reduced as necessary to provide *B* with sufficient production to expense his operating costs. See Beatty, "Selected Problems in Oil and Gas Financing," 11 *Rocky Mt. Min. L. Inst.* 79 (1966).

Variable net profit share bidding system

A lease bidding system for Outer Continental Shelf lands proposed by the Department of Energy. 46 Fed. Reg. 15,484 (March 5, 1981), 46 Fed. Reg. 29,680 (June 2, 1981). Under this system, which provides for a fixed cash bonus and payment of a fixed annual rental, the bid variable is a percentage of net profits. See Proposed 10 C.F.R. § 376.110.

See also CAPITAL RECOVERY FACTOR; LEASE BIDDING SYSTEMS.

Variable royalty

(1) A SLIDING SCALE ROYALTY (*q.v.*).

(2) In Canada the term has been applied to the right reserved by the Crown in certain transfers to require the payment of royalty from time to time prescribed by regulations. Huggard Assets Ltd. v. Attorney-General for Alberta, [1949] 2 W.W.R. 370, [1949] 4 D.L.R. 211 (Supreme Court of Alberta, 1949), *appeal dismissed,* [1950] 1 W.W.R. 69, [1950] 1 D.L.R. 823 (Supreme Court of Alberta, App. Div. 1950), *appeal dismissed,* [1951] S.C.R. 427, [1951] 2 D.L.R. 305 (Supreme Court of Canada, 1951), *appeal allowed and action dismissed,* [1953] A.C. 420, 8 W.W.R. (N.S.) 561, [1953] 3 D.L.R. 225 (Privy Council, 1953).

See also REFERENTIAL INCORPORATION.

Variable work commitment bidding system

A lease bidding system for Outer Continental Shelf lands proposed by the Department of Energy. 46 F.R. 20522 (April 3, 1981). Under this system, which provides for a fixed cash bonus, a fixed royalty and a fixed annual rental, the bid variable is a dollar value exploration work commitment. See proposed 10 C.F.R. § 376.110.

The final rule, reported in 46 F.R. 35614 (July 9, 1981), summarizes the anticipated effect of various lease bidding systems.

See also LEASE BIDDING SYSTEMS.

Venting of gas

The release of gas into the atmosphere. See FLARING.

Verbatim abstract

A full ABSTRACT OF TITLE (*q.v.*) containing the exact language of conveyances in the chain of title.

Vertical cut oil payment

The assignment of part of an OIL PAYMENT (*q.v.*), whereby the part conveyed and the part retained pay out simultaneously. Thus, if *A* owns an oil payment of the first $50,000 out of 1/8 of 7/8, he may assign a vertical cut oil payment to *B* by transfering the first $20,000 out of 2/40 of 7/8, retaining the first $30,000 out of 3/40 of 7/8. See Burke and Bowhay, *Income Taxation of Natural Resources* ¶ 5.01 (1980).

See also HORIZONTAL CUT AND PAYMENT.

Vertical severance

A conveyance of all, or some portion, of the minerals in a portion of a tract subject to unified ownership or lease, *e.g.*, a conveyance of minerals or of the leasehold in the SE 1/4 of a section of land subject to unified ownership or lease.

See also HORIZONTAL SEVERANCE; PHASE SEVERANCE; SEVERANCE.

Vibroseis

A form of GEOPHYSICAL SURVEY (*q.v.*) carried out by seismic waves generated from vehicle-mounted vibrators. The waves are picked up by sensitive listening devices (geophones) and the waves so recorded are then subjected to computer analysis which produces a reasonable plan of the geological structures beneath the ground surface. J. Salter, *U.K. Onshore Oil and Gas Law* 1-202 (1986).

See also WAVE VIBRATOR.

Video barrel

Syn. for PAPER BARREL (*q.v.*).

Vintage

The term used in Area Rate Proceedings of the Federal Power Commission to indicate the period during which a gas sales contract was made. See Shell Oil Co. v. Federal Power Comm'n, 491 F.2d 82, 46 *O.&G.R.* 515 (5th Cir. 1974).

See also CONTRACT DATE VINTAGING; DEEPER DRILLING EXCEPTION; FEDERAL POWER COMMISSION; NEW GAS; OLD GAS; ONE PRICE SYSTEM;

PRICE CONTROL OF OIL, GAS AND PETROLEUM PRODUCTS; REPLACEMENT CONTRACT POLICY; TWO-PRICE SYSTEM; WELL COMPLETION DATE VINTAGING.

Viscosity

One of the physical properties of a liquid, *viz.*, its ability to flow. It is expressed inversely, *i.e.*, the less viscous the fluid the greater its mobility. The viscosity of oil in a reservoir affects the rate and amount of recovery. While viscosity is related to specific gravity, it is also affected by the amount of gas in solution in the oil. Thus greater recoveries can be obtained where the solution gas is not allowed to escape prior to the time the oil is removed from the reservoir.

VLCC

A Very Large Cargo Carrier (Supertanker) for sea transport which can carry 1.5 million barrels or more of crude oil.

Volumetric charge (or rate)

Syn.: THROUGHPUT RENTAL (*q.v.*).

Volumetric displacement rule for gas wells

A method of prorating production from a gas well producing from the same reservoir in which oil wells are completed. Statewide Rule 6B of the Texas Railroad Commission provides that:

> "Any gas well producing from the same reservoir in which oil wells are completed and producing shall be allowed to produce daily only that amount of gas which is the volumetric equivalent in reservoir displacement of the gas and oil produced from that oil well in the reservoir which withdraws the maximum amount of gas in the production of its daily oil allowable."

The validity of this rule was sustained in Murray v. R & M Well Servicing & Drilling Co., 297 S.W.2d 225, 7 *O.&G.R.* 357 (Tex. Civ. App. 1957), error ref'd n.r.e.).

See also ALLOWABLE.

Volumetric method of allocation

A method of allocation of costs of service between jurisdictional and non-jurisdictional sales on the basis of the volume of such jurisdictional and non-jurisdictional sales. In the Matter of Olin Gas

Transmission Corp., 17 F.P.C. 685 at 695, 7 *O.&G.R.* 936 at 941 (May 15, 1957).

See also ACCOUNTING METHODS; JURISDICTIONAL SALES.

Volumetric method of estimating reserves

The average net thickness of the producing sand under a property is multiplied by the acreage of the property to obtain the volume of producing sands (usually expressed in acre feet). If conditions are reasonably uniform an average value of recovery per acre-foot then is determined, considering such properties of the sand as porosity, permeability and connate water saturation, and such properties of the oil as viscosity, amount of dissolved gas and other appropriate factors.

A method of estimating gas reserves utilizing structural and isopachous maps based on data from electrical logs, cores, and drill-stem and production tests. The method is discussed in Leeston, Crichton and Jacobs, *The Dynamic Natural Gas Industry* 46, 50 (1963).

For a discussion of this and other methods of estimating reserves see Graham, "Fair Share or Fair Game?" 8 *Nat. Res. Law.* 61 at 70 (1975).

See also RESERVES.

Volume variation adjustment clause

A gas tariff provision designed to alleviate the erosion of revenues to cover fixed costs, due to the decreasing supply of natural gas to pipelines. Under this proposed method, the Volume Fixed Cost would be arrived at by deducting from the total cost of service all the variable costs plus the fixed costs recovered through the demand component of the pipeline company's jurisdictional rates. Volume Fixed Cost would be divided by the Standard Volume (the annual volume reflected in the total cost of service) to obtain the Base Unit Fixed Cost. Periodically the company would forecast the volume for a succeeding period. The difference between the Forecast Volume and the Standard Volume for the period would constitute the Volume Deficiency. The Volume Deficiency would be multiplied by the Base Unit Fixed Cost, and the product would be divided by the Forecast Volume to obtain the amount of the rate adjustment to be made to the commodity component of its two-part rates. United Gas Pipe Line Co., Docket No. RP74–21, 12 FPS 5–328 (Opinion No. 802, June 2, 1977).

See also ACCOUNTING METHODS; TARIFF (OR FPC GAS TARIFF).

Voluntary subdivision

Under Rule 37, the state-wide spacing rule in Texas, a tract of land created after Rule 37 became applicable to the area by discovery of oil therein or created with intent to evade the rule or with mineral development in mind.

Every tract of land in Texas, however small, is entitled to one well at least, as a matter of right, except those tracts which are "voluntary subdivisions." See RULE 37 for a citation of pertinent cases and articles.

The voluntary subdivision rule is also known as the "Rule of May 29th" for the day in 1934 on which it was adopted by the Railroad Commission. Douglass & Whitworth, "Practice Before the Oil and Gas Division of the Railroad Commission of Texas," 13 *St. Mary's L.J.* 719 at 728 (1982).

See also CENTURY CASE, RULE OF.

Voluntary unit

In Louisiana, a unit specifically created by joint agreement of the mineral lessee and the owners of all the other mineral or royalty interests affecting the land in question, as distinguished from a DECLARED UNIT (*q.v.*), *viz.,* one formed by the lessee acting under the provisions of a lease pooling clause. See Humble Oil & Refining Co. v. Jones, 157 So. 2d 110, 19 *O.&G.R.* 545 (La. App. 1963), *writ refused,* 245 La. 568, 159 So. 2d 284, 19 *O.&G.R.* 559 (1964).

VVAC

A VOLUME VARIATION ADJUSTMENT CLAUSE (*q.v.*).

..W..

WACOG

Weighted average cost of gas. See Johnson, "Gas Marketing—An Industry in Transition," 30 *Rocky Mt. Min. L. Inst.* 12-1 at 12-10 (1984).

Wagonwheel proposal

A proposed government-industry experiment for commercial gas stimulation by an underground nuclear explosion designed to create a chimney and a fracture system that surrounds and is connected to the chimney, thus stimulating the flow of gas through "tight" reservoirs characterized by low-permeability. See Rubin, Schwartz, and Montan, *An Analysis of Gas Stimulation Using Nuclear Explosives* (May 15, 1972).

Waiting on cement

See Woc time.

Walking beam

The beam, mounted on a fulcrum, and connected at one end to a source of power (*e.g.*, a steam engine) which in turn raises and drops the bit in the hole in cable tool drilling. *API Quarterly* 4 (Spring 1957). See Drilling rig.

Wall cake

A seal, formed by drilling Mud (*q.v.*), of the formations pierced by a well bore. Mud is introduced into the well bore during the drilling process, and a portion thereof plugs up the permeable face of the formation. As the wall cake builds up, it seals the bore hole, thereby reducing water flow into the formation, maintaining the desired pressure differential, and providing a smooth, slick conduit in which to operate. See J. C. Trahan Drilling Contractor, Inc. v. Cockrell, 225 So. 2d 599, 34 *O.&G.R.* 384 (La. App. 1969), *writ refused,* 254 La. 922, 228 So.2d 482.

Warranty

A covenant of title by a grantor, lessor, or assignor. The oil and gas lease typically includes a general warranty clause as follows:

> "Lessor hereby warrants and agrees to defend the title to the lands herein described."

The warranty, usually coupled with a SUBROGATION CLAUSE (*q.v.*), is the only covenant of title customarily included in oil and gas leases.

If a lessor has only an undivided concurrent interest in leased premises, care must be taken in the drafting of the warranty clause when the lessee seeks to have executed a lease purporting to convey the entire fee interest rather than the lessor's undivided interest in the premises. The lessee frequently seeks to have the lease drafted in this manner in order to be entitled to the entire interest of the lessor if he owns a greater interest than he is believed to own and in order to have the benefit of the doctrine of after-acquired title should the lessor later acquire an additional undivided interest in the land. When the lease of a concurrent owner is drafted in this manner, the warranty clause should purport to warrant only the lessor's title to the interest he is believed to own, since otherwise he may be subject to an action for damages on the warranty or he may not be able to recover all of the bargained-for consideration for the lease. See generally, TREATISE §§ 411–411.1(d), 505.3, 685–685.1.

See also GENERAL WARRANTY; SPECIAL WARRANTY.

Warranty contract

A contract for the sale of gas wherein the producer agrees to sell a specific amount of gas and the gas delivered in satisfaction of this obligation may come from fields or sources outside the designated fields. In a CONVENTIONAL SALES CONTRACT (*q.v.*), on the other hand, the producer promises to sell all the gas produced from either specific wells or specific fields. Shell Oil Co. v. Federal Power Comm'n, 531 F.2d 1324 at note 6, *petition for reh. denied,* 535 F.2d 957 (5th Cir. 1976).

Florida Power & Light Co. v. Federal Energy Regulatory Comm'n, 598 F.2d 370 (5th Cir. 1979), *cert. denied,* 444 U.S. 1013 (1980), held that prior issuance of certificates of public convenience and necessity approving warranty contracts did not preclude the Commission from conditioning new certificates to the seller to transport natural gas from new offshore wells so as to prohibit use of the gas for boiler fuel.

Louisiana Land & Exploration Co. v. Texaco, Inc., 478 So.2d 926, 89 *O.&G.R.* 472 (La. App. 1985), *rev'd and remanded on other grounds,* 491 So.2d 363, 89 *O.&G.R.* 479 (La. 1986), distinguished a warranty contract from a so-called DEDICATION CONTRACT (*q.v.*), whereunder the producer contracts to furnish all the gas produced from specified reserves, thus "dedicating" those reserves to the customer.

See also GAS PURCHASE CONTRACT.

War relief crude

The term applied to crude oil, believed to total about 550,000 barrels daily, supplied by Saudi Arabia to customers who had been purchasing crude oil from Iraq before the onset of its war with Iran. *The New York Times,* May 6, 1981, 31:3.

Wash oil

Oil injected into a well bore to remove various elements therefrom. See "'Wash' or 'Frac' Oil Not Subject to Windfall Profit Tax," 31 *O.&G. Tax Q.* 187 (1982); Rev. Rul. 82-41, 1982-11 I.R.B. 16, 72 *O.&G.R.* 196 (March 22, 1982).

Washout

(1) Elimination of an overriding royalty or other share of the working interest by the surrender of a lease by a sublessee or assignee and subsequent reacquisition of a lease on the same land free of such interest.

It is common to include in an instrument transferring a leasehold subject to a retained override or other interest an express provision [EXTENSION AND RENEWAL CLAUSE (*q.v.*)] to protect the assignor against a washout. See Berman v. Brown, 224 La. 619, 70 So. 2d 433, 3 *O.&G.R.* 608 (1954). See also TREATISE §§ 428.1, 442.3.

In Sunac Petroleum Corp. v. Parkes, 416 S.W.2d 798 at 804, 26 *O.&G.R.* 689 at 697 (Tex. 1967), the court discussed the "washout" transaction as follows:

> "Another situation in which some courts have protected the holder of the overriding royalty is called a 'washout' transaction, generally involving some bad faith on the part of the lessee. In this type of situation, the operator takes a new lease before the expiration of the old lease and then simply permits the old lease to expire. Oldland v. Gray, 179 F.2d 408 (10th Cir. 1950); 2 Williams and Meyers, Oil and Gas Law § 420.2 (1964)."

The court refused to protect the overriding royalty owner in the instant case where the lessee took a new lease after the expiration of the old lease.

(2) This term has also been used to refer to a hole in the drill pipe or a tool joint. ANR Production Co. v. Westburne Drilling, Inc., 581 F. Supp. 542 at n.1, 80 *O.&G.R.* 14 at n.1 (D. Colo. 1984).

See also ANTI-WASHOUT PROVISION.

Washover process

A process during which a larger wash pipe fitted with a rotary shoe at its base is lowered over stuck drill pipe. Mud is then pumped down the wash pipe under pressure which frees the pipe stuck in the hole, thus permitting removal of the drill pipe from the hole. Buster Gardner Drilling Co. v. Associated Oil & Gas Exploration, Inc., 214 So. 2d 267 at 273, 32 *O.&G.R.* 169 at 178 (La. App. 1968), *writ refused,* 253 La. 59, 216 So. 2d 306 (1968).

Waste

The term is too broad and has too many meanings for a one- or two-sentence definition. In the oil industry, it suggests the ultimate loss of oil or gas. The prevention of waste is conservation.

The term is best understood when broken down. There is PHYSICAL WASTE (*q.v.*) and ECONOMIC WASTE (*q.v.*). Physical waste is the loss of oil or gas that could have been recovered and put to use. Such waste can occur on the surface or underground. Examples of the former are flaring of gas and storage of oil in earthen pits. Examples of the latter are inefficient use of reservoir energy, excessive production rates resulting in CHANNELING (*q.v.*) and by-passing. An example of economic waste is the sale of natural gas at too low a price at the well-head. Some people also regard unrestricted production of oil in excess of market demand as economic waste.

While the above may give some indication of the scope of the term, the reader is directed to the specific statutes of the states for the precise meaning of the term in that state. Thus Colo. Rev. Stats. 1973 § 34–60–103 defines the term as follows:

> "(11) 'Waste,' as applied to gas, includes the escape, blowing, or releasing, directly or indirectly into the open air, of gas from wells productive of gas only, or gas in an excessive or unreasonable amount from wells producing oil, or both oil and gas; and the production of gas in quantities or in such manner as unreasonably reduces reservoir pressure or unreasonably diminishes the quantity of oil or gas that ultimately may be produced; excepting gas that

is reasonably necessary in the drilling, completing, testing, and in furnishing power for the production of wells.

"(12) 'Waste,' as applied to oil, includes underground waste; inefficient, excessive, or improper use or dissipation of reservoir energy, including gas energy and water drive; surface waste; open-pit storage; and waste incident to the production of oil in excess of the producer's aboveground storage facilities and lease and contractual requirements, but excluding storage, other than open-pit storage, reasonably necessary for building up or maintaining crude stocks and products thereof for consumption, use, and sale."

Tex. Nat. Res. Code § 85.046 (1978) (1980 Supp.) also gives a detailed definition of waste, setting forth the meaning in ten subdivisions. See also Model Conservation Act, § 18, published by the Interstate Oil Compact Commission.

The term "waste" is defined by McDonald, *Petroleum Conservation in the United States: An Economic Analysis* 235 (1971), as "a preventable loss the value of which exceeds the cost of avoidance." This book examines in detail the varieties of waste and offers a cost-benefit analysis of the problem.

Some of the leading cases on waste and prevention of waste are: Champlin Ref. Co. v. Comm'n, 286 U.S. 210 (1932); Cities Service Oil & Gas Co. v. Peerless Oil and Gas Co., 203 Okla. 35, 220 P.2d 279, *aff'd,* 340 U.S. 179 (1940); Phillips Petroleum Co. v. Oklahoma, 340 U.S. 190 (1950) (economic waste).

In Larsen v. Oil & Gas Conservation Comm'n, 569 P.2d 87, 61 *O.&G.R.* 246 (Wyo. 1977), the court concluded that the term waste as used in W.S. 1957 § 30–216(a) (Supp.) did not include so-called economic waste.

Kuykendall v. Corporation Comm'n, 634 P.2d 711 at 716, 71 *O.&G.R.* 364 at 373 (Okla. 1981), sustaining a Commission order establishing 1,440-acre drilling and spacing units, commented as follows:

"We are now called upon to consider whether general economic conditions such as an increase in the price of gas which effect financial inducements to drill and develop a common source are to be included within the kaleidoscope of 'waste.'

". . . That minerals are being found in increasingly deeper formations, that the cost of drilling and producing them is ever increasing, and that the market price being paid for the product will vary with time are economic realities which cannot be ignored. Yet they are shifting economic sands which change with the times, so that which is feasible from a monetary standpoint today, may not be tomorrow, not because the geological or scientific knowledge pertaining to the common source has changed, but because economic conditions have materially altered the feasibility of development of the field. We therefore hold, that if by increasing the size of a drilling or spacing unit, or if by decreasing it the practicable recoverability of minerals may be affected, the Corporation Commission may consider such factors as constituing 'waste.' "

Amoco Production Co. v. Alexander, 622 S.W.2d 563 at 572, 72 *O.&G.R.* 125 at 139 (Tex. 1981), concluded that an action for failure to protect against drainage is not a waste case:

"There has been no 'waste' as defined in section 85.046(a) of the Texas Natural Resource Code. There has been no negligent waste or destruction as occurred in *Elliff* [*v. Texon Drilling Co.,* 146 Tex. 575, 210 S.W.2d 558 (1948)], *supra.* Nor has there been an ultimate loss by a reversionary or remainder interest. The problem is the operation, by a common lessee, of some leases to the detriment of others."

Osborn v. Texas Oil & Gas Corp., 661 P.2d 71, 72 *O.&G.R.* 101 (Okla. App. 1982), held that "the corporation commission—once it found that a gas well offsetting a water driven secondary recovery unit maintained by gas pressure was 'causing waste and [would] continue to . . . so long as it is produced' had authority to either shut the well in or permanently limit its production to a nonwasteful level."

Big Piney Oil & Gas Co. v. Wyoming Oil and Gas Conservation Comm'n, 715 P.2d 557, ____ *O.&G.R.* ____ (Wyo. 1986), concluded that the power of the commission to prevent waste justified issuance of an order restricting gas cap production causing migration of oil from adjoining premises, which oil became nonrecoverable after migration, when the gas cap producer had produced more gas from the common pool than was estimated to have been under its lease originally.

See also CONSERVATION; MARKET WASTE; SURFACE WASTE; UNDERGROUND WASTE; WASTE OF RESERVOIR ENERGY.

Waste injection well

A well operated for the introduction of liquids for the disposal of sewage, industrial waste or other waste or the effluent therefrom. W. Va. Code § 22–4–2b.

Syn.: Waste disposal well.

See also INJECTION WELL.

Waste liquids

Oil field brine, cut oil, bottom sediments, concentrated sulphur water, and acid waters. Burns Ind. Stat. Ann., § 13–4–7–4 (K) (Code ed. 1973).

Waste of reservoir energy

"[T]he failure reasonably to maintain such energy by artificial means and also the dissipation of gas energy, hydrostatic energy, or other natural reservoir energy, at any time at a rate or in a manner which would constitute improvident use of the energy available or result in loss thereof without reasonably adequate recovery of oil." 30 C.F.R. § 221.2(n)(2) (1980).

See also RESERVOIR ENERGY.

Waste water lease

A lease for the drilling of a salt water disposal well and a plant to dispose of salt water produced in connection with the production of oil. Dunn v. Southwest Ardmore Tulip Creek Sand Unit, 548 P.2d 685, 54 *O.&G.R.* 515 (Okla. App. 1976).

Water

See AQUIFER; BOTTOM WATER; BRINE; BY PASSING; CHANNELING; CONNATE WATER; DROWNING; EDGE WATER; ENCROACHMENT; FINGERING; FORMATION WATER; GEOPRESSURED BRINE; HEATER-TREATER; INFILTRATING WATER; MAKE WATER, TO; MIST; SALT WATER DISPOSAL; UNDERGROUND INJECTION CONTROL (UIC) PROGRAM.

Water blocking

Injection of water into a structure in such a way as to prevent drainage to and from adjoining properties. See Walker, "Problems Incident to the Acquisition, Use and Disposal of Repressuring Substances Used in Secondary Recovery Operations," 6 *Rocky Mt. Min. L. Inst.* 273 at 277 (1961).

Water coning

See CHANNELING.

Water cut-percentage

The percentage of water produced per thousand barrels of oil. Pickens v. Railroad Comm'n, 387 S.W.2d 35 at 47, 21 *O.&G.R.* 644 at 658 (Tex. 1965).

Water drive

Energy for production of oil derived from compressed edge- or bottom-water in the reservoir.

See also RESERVOIR ENERGY.

Water-drive field

An oil field in which the primary natural energy for production is derived from edge- or bottom-water in the reservoir. While water is only slightly compressible, the expansion of great volumes of it in a reservoir will force the oil to the well bore. Recoveries are high in water drive fields, absent dissipation of the reservoir energy, because the water tends to push the oil ahead of it, washing out recalcitrant oil as the water table rises. The East Texas Oil Field is the largest water-drive field in the United States.

See also AQUIFER; HYDROSTATIC PRESSURE; RESERVOIR ENERGY; WATER.

Water encroachment

The movement of water into the oil or gas zone of a reservoir as that zone is depleted by production. The movement of the water may occur from expansion of water under compression or from hydrostatic pressure where a continuous reservoir horizon outcrops so that water flows through the reservoir like water through artesian basins.

Waterflood allowable

A special concession in the allowable of a well based upon the institution of waterflood operations. See 16 Tex. Admin. Code § 3.48.

Water flooding

One method of SECONDARY RECOVERY (*q.v.*) in which water is injected into an oil reservoir for the purpose of washing the oil out of the reservoir rock and into the bore of a producing well.

Depending on the reservoir, several methods of water flooding may be used. In one, the water is injected down structure and the oil floated up-structure to the producing wells. But when viscosities are high, or the reservoir rock relatively impermeable, spot flood patterns are used. For example, a FIVE-SPOT WATER FLOOD PROGRAM (*q.v.*) utilizes four input (or injection) wells which surround a producing well located in the center of the area covered by the input wells. Water moves from the input wells toward the producing well, creating an oil bank ahead of the advancing water front, as it moves through the oil zone. For brief discussions, see Buckley (ed.), *Petroleum Conservation* 187–190 (1951); Interstate Oil Compact Commission, *Oil and Gas Production* 50–54 (1951). For detailed technical discussions, see American Petroleum Institute, *Secondary Recovery in the United States* (2d ed. 1950).

In Sivert v. Continental Oil Co., 497 S.W.2d 482, 46 *O.&G.R.* 355 (Tex. Civ. App. 1973, error ref'd n.r.e.), the meaning of the phrase "conducting waterflood" operations as used in a unit agreement was in issue. The court concluded that there need not be continuous injection of water into the reservoir and continuous production of oil in order that the operations be described as waterflood operations. Expert testimony was admitted on the definition of the term and the court appears to have concluded that

> "waterflooding consists of an initial injection of the necessary amount of water to create sufficient energy or pressure to cause the oil to be produced; that the tremendous pressure and weight of the water is the force that pushes the oil to the recovery well bores; that there is no need of continuous injection of water; and that as long as the energy is present, waterflood operations are being conducted." 497 S.W.2d at 487, 46 *O.&G.R.* at 363.

For a report of the difficulties encountered in and the success of water flooding of the North Hobbs Unit in Lea County, N.M., see Lopez & Parsley, "Microbes, Simulators, and Satellites: The Prudent Operator Pursues Enhanced Recovery Under the Implied Covenants," 58 *N.D. L. Rev.* 501 at 521 (1982).

Briggs v. Gaddis, 133 Ill. App.3d 704, 88 Ill.D. 737, 479 N.E.2d 350, 87 *O.&G.R.* 10 (1985), concluded that use of an injection well to dispose of salt water was not, under the circumstances of this case, a water flooding secondary recovery program.

Oklahoma Water Resources Board v. Texas County Irrigation and Water Resources Ass'n, Inc., 711 P.2d 38, 88 *O.&G.R.* 331 (Okla. 1984), noted, 21 *Tulsa L.J.* 565 (1986), sustained the power of the Oklahoma Water Resources Board to determine that the use of fresh ground water in a tertiary recovery program may not constitute waste and to authorize use of fresh ground water off the lands from which it was produced. The case was remanded to the Board for the taking and consideration of further evidence and for further findings required by the applicable statute, in particular a finding on whether use of fresh water in tertiary oil recovery will cause waste by pollution.

For a discussion of the use of fresh water for waterflooding operations, see Dace, "Oil and Gas: Water and Watercourses: The Right to Use Fresh Groundwater in Waterflood Operations," 35 *Okla. L. Rev.* 159 (1982).

The definition in this MANUAL was cited in Day v. Commissioner, 54 T.C. 1417, 36 *O.&G.R.* 555 (1970), at note 2.

See also CIRCLE FLOOD; DUMP FLOOD; FLUID INJECTION; INJECTION WELL; LINE FLOOD; PRESSURE FLOODING; SEVEN-SPOT PATTERN; SURFACTANT FLOODING; SWEEP; WATER LOGGING.

Water gas

Syn.: SYNTHESIS GAS (*q.v.*).

Water gas generating equipment

Equipment used in the generation of water gas. 18 C.F.R. § 201.310 (1980).

Water imbition

The displacement of oil by water because of capillary forces. See Smith, "The Engineering Aspects of Pressure Maintenance and Secondary Recovery Operations," 6 *Rocky Mt. Min. L. Inst.* 211 at 236 (1961).

Water injection well

In WATER FLOODING (*q.v.*), the well used to inject water into the reservoir. Also called input well or water input well.

Water logging

A condition sometimes arising in a water flood project in which the water injected has failed to wash the oil out of the sands on account of insufficient movement of fluids. Brown and Myers, "Some Legal Aspects of Water Flooding," 24 *Tex. L. Rev.* 456 at 466 (1946).

Water-oil contact line

See OIL-WATER CONTACT LINE.

Water-oil ratio

See OIL-WATER RATIO.

Water-oil ratio penalty factor

"[A] variable penalty factor less than unity used to establish an Authorized MPR [MAXIMUM PERMISSIVE RATE] or Authorized EA [ECONOMIC ALLOWANCE] of a well, whichever is applicable, where the water-oil ratio for the well for the immediately preceding month is in excess of .0199." Provisions Governing the Limitation and Allocation of Production of Oil, Saskatchewan MRO 118/68 A 62, 5 Lewis and Thompson, *Canadian Oil and Gas* Division D, Part X [5] (1971).

See also ALLOWABLE.

Water shut-off

The sealing off of salt-water bearing formations from oil-bearing zones to prevent harmful underground water pollution. This is ordinarily done by cementing.

Water string

Casing used to shut off water bearing formations encountered in the drilling of a well.

Water-white oil

A clear petroleum liquid recovered by conventional surface separators from gas produced from a condensate gas reservoir. See CONDENSATE. Classification of this product as oil or as gas in many instances determined whether the well itself was an oil well or a gas well and a variety of consequences turned on that classification, *e.g.*, whether the gas was casinghead gas and could be flared. See Prindle, *Petroleum Politics and the Texas Railroad Commission* 59 (1981).

See also ALBINO OIL; GAS CONDENSATE; LOW TEMPERATURE EXTRACTION (LTX); NATURAL GASOLINE; WHITE OIL.

Water zone

That portion of an oil or gas reservoir occupied by water. The water zone is always the lowest in the reservoir.

See also OIL ZONE; GAS CAP.

Wave vibrator

An instrument employed in GEOPHYSICAL EXPLORATION (*q.v.*). "When placed on the ground, the instrument generates continuous low frequency sound waves which penetrate downward into the rock layers. Each formation reflects the sound waves back to the surface, where they are picked up and changed into electrical impulses by instruments called geophones." Rice, "Wrongful Geophysical Exploration," 44 *Mont. L. Rev.* 53 (1983).

See also VIBROSEIS.

WCTOGA

The West Central Texas Oil and Gas Association.

Weather window

The period of time when weather is expected to be good enough in the area in question to permit drilling or other operations to be conducted without interruption of danger to those participating. The weather window in Arctic operations may be as short as two months and in North Sea operations perhaps six months.

Weevil

An inexperienced rig or oil field worker. Also known as a BOLL WEEVIL.

Weighted average arm's length price

A field price for gas established by federally unregulated bargaining for gas in the fields. City of Detroit, Michigan v. Federal Power Comm'n, 230 F.2d 810, 5 *O.&G.R.* 279 (D.C. Cir. 1955), *cert. denied,* 352 U.S. 829, 6 *O.&G.R.* 897 (1956).

Weighted average method

A method of allocation of production from a pooled or unitized operation whereunder each royalty owner shares in the production in the proportion that his acreage bears to the entire acreage of the unit. The production so allocated is not characterized or considered as if produced on such lessor's acreage by a well drilled thereon; instead each operator taking production from a well accounts to each royalty owner in the unit on the basis of the price received by that operator for the sale of gas disposed of by it. See Upchurch, "Split Stream Gas Sales and the Gas Storage and Balancing Agreement,"

24 *Rocky Mt. Min. L. Inst.* 665 at 670 (1978). See also TREATISE § 951.

See also ACCOUNTING METHODS.

Well

An orifice in the ground made by drilling, boring or in any other manner, from which any petroleum or gas is obtained or obtainable or which is being so made for the purpose of obtaining any petroleum or gas.

Also an orifice in the ground for the introduction into an underground stratum of water or gas under pressure.

Well was defined in Gates Rubber Co. & Subsidiaries v. Commissioner, 74 T.C. 1456, 67 *O.&G.R.* 647 (1980), *aff'd,* 694 F.2d 648 (10th Cir. 1982), *acq.,* I.R.B. 1983-26 (1983), for purposes of the deduction for INTANGIBLE DRILLING AND DEVELOPMENT COSTS (*q.v.*) as:

> "a shaft drilled in search of hydrocarbons which shaft is designed and drilled in such a manner that it would be capable, upon encountering hydrocarbons and upon appropriate completion of the shaft by the operator, of conducting or aiding in the conduction of hydrocarbons to the surface. This definition of wells excludes shafts, such as core drillings, which, because of their design or the manner in which they are drilled, would not be capable of conducting or aiding in the conduction of hydrocarbons to the surface, but, rather, are capable of yielding G&G information. If an appropriately designed shaft is drilled in search of hydrocarbons, it is a 'well' regardless of the presence or absence of an intent to produce hydrocarbons from that particular shaft."

The term "well" is defined by the Alberta Oil and Gas Conservation Act, R.S.A. 1970, c. 267, § 2(1) (46), as "an orifice in the ground completed or being drilled

> (i) for the production of oil, gas or crude bitumen, or of water for injection to an underground formation, or
>
> (ii) for injection to an underground formation, or
>
> (iii) as an evaluation well or test hole, or
>
> (iv) to or at a depth of more than 500 feet, for any purpose, but does not include one to evaluate rock or solid inorganic mineral and that does not or will not penetrate a stratum capable of containing a pool or oil sands deposit."

In some contexts it is necessary to determine whether the term "well" includes operating rights. In an Illinois case the court rejected the view that the term meant only a hole in the ground;

"The word 'well', as used in the agreement between the parties here, meant not only the hole in the ground, but the casing and all the equipment that made it an oil well, above and below ground. By implication it included the right to operate the well." National Oil Co. v. R. C. Davoust Co., 51 Ill.App.2d 225 at 233, 201 N.E.2d 260 at 264, 21 *O.&G.R.* 6 at 9–10 (1964).

See also ABANDONED WELL; ACIDIZING OF WELL; AIR INJECTION WELL; ANNULUS OF WELL; APPRAISAL WELL; BLOWING OF WELL; BLOW OUT; BOTTLE WELL; BOTTOM HOLE WELL; BRADENHEAD GAS WELL; B RINE DISPOSAL WELL; CAPABLE WELL; CLEANING A WELL; COMBINATION WELL; COMMERCIAL WELL; COMMINGLED WELL; COMPLETED WELL; COMPLETION OF A WELL; CONDENSATE WELL; CONFIDENTIAL WELL; CONFIRMATION WELL; CONNECTED WELL; CONTROL WELL; COST; DEAD WELL; DEEP WELL; DEFICIENT WELL; DESERTION OF WELL; DEVELOPMENTAL PROGRAM WELL; DEVELOPMENT WELL; DIRECTIONAL WELL; DISCOVERY WELL; DISPOSAL WELL; DOWN-DIP WELL; DRY GAS WELL; DRY HOLE; DRY WELL; DUAL COMPLETION; EDGE WELL; ELECTRICAL WELL LOG; ESCROW WELL; EVALUATION WELL; EXCEPTION WELL; EXPENDABLE WELL; EXPERIMENTAL WELL; EXPLOITATION WELL; EXPLORATORY WELL; EXTENSION WELL; FIELD DEVELOPMENT WELL; FLOWING WELL; FLUID INJECTION WELL; FREEHOLD WELL; FREE WELL; FREE WELL FARM OUT; GAS INJECTION WELL; GAS WELL; GAUGING A WELL; GUSHER; HISTORY OF WELL; INCENTIVE EXPLORATORY WELL; INCENTIVE WILDCAT WELL; INFILL WELL; INJECTION WELL; JOINT ACCOUNT WELL; KILL A WELL; LIMITED CAPACITY WELL; LINE TEST WELL; MARGINAL WELL; MARKER WELL; MULTIPLE COMPLETION WELL; MULTI-ZONE WELL; NEW FIELD WILDCAT WELL; NEW GAS WELL; NEW, ONSHORE PRODUCTION WELL; NEW WELL; NON-COMMERCIAL WELL; NON-CONSENT WELL; OBLIGATION WELL; OBLIGATION WELL FARM OUT; OBSERVATION WELL; OFFSET WELL; OIL WELL; OLD WELL; OPEN HOLE; ORPHAN WELL; OUTPOST WELL; OUTSIDE WELL; PLUGGING OF WELL; PREPLATFORM WELL; PRODUCIBLE WELL; PRODUCING WELL; PUMPING WELL; RECOMPLETED WELL; RELIEF WELL; REQUIRED WELL; ROBBER WELL; SALT WATER DISPOSAL WELL; SEISMIC SHOT HOLE; SERVICE HOLE; SHALLOW WELL; SHOOTING A WELL; SHUT-IN WELL; SIDE-LINE WELL; SLIM HOLE; SPLIT STREAM GAS WELL; SQUEEZE A WELL; STEP-OUT WELL; STRAIGHT GAS WELL; STRATIGRAPHIC TEST HOLE; STRIPPER WELL; STRUCTURE TEST HOLE; TAKE-OVER WELL; TEST HOLE OR WELL; THICK WELL; THIN WELL; TIGHT GAS WELL; TIGHT HOLE; TIGHT WELL; TRANSFEREE WELL; TRANSFEROR WELL; TRAVERSE WELL; TUBING A WELL; TURNKEY WELL; UNCONNECTED WELL; UNIT SURPLUS WELL; UP-DIP WELL; VALIDATION WELL; WASTE INJECTION WELL; WATER INJECTION WELL; WELL HEAD; WET WELL; WILDCAT WELL; WILD WELL.

Well allowable

See ALLOWABLE; PRORATIONING.

Well bore

The hole made by a well.

Well commencement date vintaging

A system for determining the permissible price to be charged for natural gas subject to price control regulations under which price was based on VINTAGE (*q.v.*) of gas (*viz.*, as NEW GAS (*q.v.*) or OLD GAS (*q.v.*)) and the determination whether the gas was new or old was based on the date of commencement of the well producing the gas. City of Farmington v. Amoco Gas Co., 568 F. Supp. 1265, 78 *O.&G.R.* 504 (D. N.M. 1983), *aff'd,* 777 F.2d 554, ____ O.&G.R. ____ (10th Cir. 1985).

See also CONTRACT DATE VINTAGING.

Well completion clause

Syn.: DRILLING OPERATIONS CLAUSE (*q.v.*). See Freeland v. Edwards, 11 Ill.2d 395, 142 N.E.2d 701, 7 *O.&G.R.* 1382 (1957).

Well connection order

See CONNECTION ORDER.

Well cuttings

"[F]ragments of rock that are cut from subsurface formations by the chipping, cutting, and abrasive action of the drilling bit during drilling operations. The cuttings are collected at regular intervals, washed, dried, and placed in separate sample containers and labeled as to geographic location, well name and number, and sample depth. By examining well cutting samples, the character of the rock and depth of the formation penetrated in the course of drilling the well can be determined." Rev. Rul. 82-9.

Well density

The ratio between the number of wells drilled in a field and the acreage. Under a 20-acre spacing pattern, the well density is one well per 20 acres. See WELL SPACING.

Well determination

Under price control laws and regulations authorizing prices based on the classification of a well (*e.g.*, as a STRIPPER WELL (*q.v.*) or NEW WELL (*q.v.*), procedures are required to determine the classification of a particular well in order to determine the price to be paid for its product. Complex procedures adopted for this purpose by the Federal Energy Regulatory Commission were approved in Ecee, Inc. v. Federal Energy Regulatory Comm'n, 645 F.2d 339, 69 *O.&G.R.* 343 (5th Cir. 1981).

See also PRICE CONTROL OF OIL, GAS AND PETROLEUM PRODUCTS.

Well-head

A term usually defined as being at the CHRISTMAS TREE (*q.v.*) but which under exceptional circumstances may be defined as located at some other place. See Balfour v. Esso Exploration and Production Australia Inc., [1986] V.R. ____ (Supreme Court of Victoria, April 8, 1986) (holding that in the instant case the Designated Authority was authorized under Commonwealth and State of Victoria legislation to designate as the well-head certain valves located on a production platform situated some four kilometres from the Christmas tree), *appeal allowed sub nom.* BHP Petroleum Pty Ltd. v. Balfour, ____ A.L.J.R. ____ (High Court of Australia, 11 June 1987) (well-head is a valve in the Christmas tree located on the seabed immediately above the well and not a valve on a platform some four kilometres away which was connected to the Christmas tree by pipelines or flow lines).

Well-head pressure

See SHUT-IN PRESSURE.

Well-head price

The price paid at the well-head for gas produced. See MINIMUM WELL-HEAD PRICE.

For a discussion of the regulation of the well-head price of natural gas, see Gilliam, "Wellhead Regulation Under the Natural Gas Act and the Natural Gas Policy Act," American Gas Ass'n, *Regulation of the Gas Industry* ch. 20 (1981).

Well history

See HISTORY OF WELL.

Well log

A record of the formations penetrated by a well, their depth, thickness, and (if possible) contents. Cal. Pub. Res. Code § 3211 (1972) requires that a log

> "shall show the character and depth of the formation passed through or encountered in the drilling of the well, and particularly the location and depth of water-bearing strata, together with the character of water encountered from time to time, as far as ascertained, whether or not the water was shut off, and if so at what point. The log shall show completely the amounts, kinds, and size of casing used, the depth at which oil-bearing strata are encountered, the depth and character of such strata, and whether all water overlying and underlying such oil-bearing strata was successfully and permanently shut off so as to prevent the percolation or penetration of water into such oil-bearing strata; and whether strata bearing water that might be suitable for irrigation or domestic purposes are properly protected from the infiltration or addition of detrimental substances from the well."

See Hilchie, "Well Logging," *Rocky Mt. Min. L. Fdn. Basic Oil and Gas Technology for Lawyers and Landmen* (1979).

See also Acoustical well logging; Caliper log; Cemotron log; Electrical well log; Gamma ray—gamma ray logging; Natural gamma ray logging; Neutron logging; Radioactivity well logging; Schlumberger; Spectral logging; SPWLA.

Well name register

A record of official well names in which is entered: (a) the name and location of each well; (b) the name of the licensee and license number; (c) the name of the drilling contractor; and (d) any approved name or names subsequently assigned to the well. Saskatchewan Oil and Gas Conservation Regulations, 1969, O.C. 2272/68, § 200.

See also Oil and Gas Field Code Master List—1982.

Well permit

The authorization to drill a well.

In many states, the law requires an operator to obtain permission before drilling, so that Well spacing (*q.v.*) may be enforced. In some states the permit will not be issued unless the well site is the appropriate size. In this case the undersized tract may be united with other tracts by Compulsory pooling (*q.v.*). In other states, undersized tracts may be drilled on under certain circumstances, and the well permit is issued as an exception to the spacing rule. [See Rule 37.]

Generally, where well permits are required before drilling, the authority to issue them is in the administrative agency charged with enforcing conservation.

See also Drilling permit.

Well potential

The producing capacity of a well during a period of twenty-four hours.

Well potential is a somewhat artificial calculation in many cases as it refers to the producing capacity of one well while other wells in the area are shut down. Such a potential cannot be maintained when all wells drilled are operating simultaneously. Field potential, the producing capacity of a field during a period of twenty-four hours, is, therefore, considerably smaller than the sum of the potentials of the wells in the field. See Zimmermann, *Conservation in the Production of Petroleum* 151 (1957).

See also Potential.

Well servicing

A type of work done after the well is drilled and in operation. Peterson Truck Co. Ltd. v. Socony-Vacuum Exploration Co., 17 W.W.R. 257 (Alberta Supreme Court, App. Div. 1955).

Well site

That portion of the surface of land required for the conduct of drilling or completion operations of a well during the period next following the initial entry upon the land until the well is abandoned or completed; or that portion of the surface of land required for the conduct of producing operations of a well commencing from the completion date of the well. Saskatchewan Surface Right Acquisition and Compensation Act, 1968 (Stat. Sask. 1968, c.73) § 2(o).

Well spacing

The regulation of the number and location of wells over an oil or gas reservoir, as a conservation measure.

It is generally agreed today that increased recovery from a reservoir is not a function of the number of wells drilled. Thus to the extent that more wells are drilled than are necessary for maximum recovery, there is economic waste, since the cost of drilling the unnecessary wells need not have been incurred. It has been estimated by Mr. R.E. Hardwicke that over $100 million was spent annually in Texas in the period 1947–1952 for drilling, equipping and operating unecessary wells. See 31 *Texas L. Rev.* 99 at 111 (1952).

In addition to curbing such waste, well spacing also prevents injury to the reservoir. Excessive rates of withdrawal from a reservoir, particularly where the rate in one section of the field is disproportionate to that in another, can result in physical waste from irregular or premature water or gas encroachment. Well spacing, based on a uniform pattern (such as one well to 40 acres), will inhibit such physical waste by making unnecessary disproportionate withdrawals. See American Petroleum Institute, *Standards of Allocation of Oil Production* 27–30 (1942); Hardwicke, *supra,* 31 *Tex. L. Rev.* 99 (1952).

Well spacing is normally accomplished by order of the regulatory conservation commission. The order may be statewide in its application (subject to change for local conditions) or it may be entered for each field after its discovery. Some well spacing orders divide up the field into spacing units, using the grid system of the U.S. General Land Office Survey. Thus an order might prohibit the drilling of more than one well in each quarter, quarter section. Another system is to prohibit the drilling of a well closer than x feet from another well or closer than y feet to any surface boundary line. This is the method used in the Texas spacing rule, RULE 37 (*q.v.*).

The problem then arises of what to do with tracts of land smaller than those upon which drilling is permitted under the order. In general, two solutions have been adopted. The first is to permit drilling on such undersized tracts as an exception to the rule. This solution seriously impairs the value of well spacing, for it allows the evils to arise that uniform spacing would prevent. But it removes the spacing rule from the jeopardy of unconstitutionality, since with the granting of exceptions the rule does not deprive the land owner of the opportunity to produce the oil beneath his undersized tract. This is the well-spacing system in Texas [see RULE 37].

However, uniform spacing can be achieved without allowing exceptions and without depriving the landowner of a chance to recover his oil. This is accomplished by COMPULSORY POOLING (*q.v.*), whereby the regulatory agency combines small tracts into sufficient area to meet the standard of the well spacing order. To take a single example, if the spacing order calls for 40-acre drilling units, the owners of two twenty acre tracts would be required to combine their land to form one drilling unit. Usually, the landowners share production on the basis of surface acreage, but other formula may be used, such as acre feet of producing sand. The constitutionality of compulsory pooling statutes has been uniformly upheld. See TREATISE Ch. 9.

The development of well spacing and compulsory pooling in Oklahoma is discussed in Dancy and Dancy, "Regulation of the Oil and Gas Industry by the Oklahoma Corporation Commission," 21 *Tulsa L.J.* 613 (1986).

The development of well spacing legislation in the United States and Canada is traced in Harrison, "Regulation of Well Spacing in Oil and Gas Production," 8 *Alberta L. Rev.* 357 (1970).

Under appropriate circumstances, a regulatory commission may de-space existing drilling units and create new drilling units of a different size. See El Paso Natural Gas Co. v. Corporation Commission, 640 P.2d 1336, 72 *O.&G.R.* 93 (Okla. 1982)(finding that sufficient evidence was presented to the Commission to hold a substantial change of knowledge of conditions existed which authorized a change in spacing from 1,440 acres to 640 acres. One of the several factors considered by the Commission was the economic circumstances of a dramatic increase in gas prices in the period since the spacing was originally ordered.).

Kuykendall v. Corporation Comm'n, 634 P.2d 711, 71 *O.&G.R.* 364 (Okla. 1981), sustained a Commission order establishing 1,440-acre drilling and spacing units, concluding that it was permissible for the Commission to consider general economic conditions such as an increase in the price of gas which effect financial inducements to drill and develop a common source of supply as included within the kaleidoscope of "waste."

Anderson, "Compulsory Pooling in North Dakota: Should Production Income and Expenses Be Divided from Date of Pooling, Spacing, or 'First Run?' " 58 *No. Dak. L. Rev.* 537 at 573 (1982), argues that "a well spacing order should be retroactive to the date of first production and a compulsory pooling order should be retroactive to the effective date of spacing."

For a case giving retroactive operation to a compulsory pooling order, see Murphy v. Amoco Production Co., 590 F.Supp. 455, 83 *O.&G.R.* 108 (D. N.D. 1984), discussed in TREATISE § 953 note 1.

See also DOWN-SPACING; DRILLING SPACING UNIT; DRILLING UNIT; SPACING UNIT; STANDUP DRILLING UNIT (STANDUP SPACING); TARGET AREA.

Well stimulation

See STIMULATE.

Well symbol

A symbol used on a map or chart to indicate the nature of a well. The following standard symbols were adopted for use in American Petroleum Institute, *Secondary Recovery of Oil in the United States* 837 (2d ed. 1950):

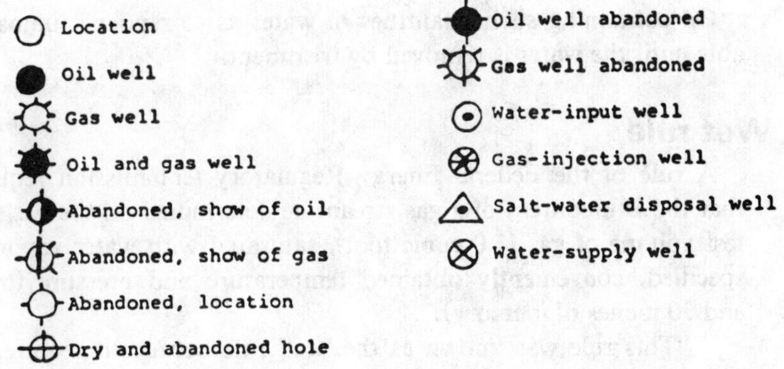

WEPCO

Western Desert Petroleum Co.

Western Accord

An agreement entered into on March 28, 1985, by the Governments of Canada, Alberta, Saskatchewan and British Columbia on Oil and Gas Pricing and Taxation. See Hollingsworth and Snider, "Some Aspects of 1985 Deregulation of Petroleum," 25 *Alta. L. Rev.* 36 (1986).

Western Governors' Regional Energy Policy Office, Inc.

An organization created by the governors of ten western states in 1975 to formulate a regional response to energy development. See White and Barry, "Energy Developments in the West: Conflict and Coordination of Governmental Decision-Making," 52 *N.D. L. Rev.* 451 at 508 (1976).

Wet gas

Natural gas containing liquid hydrocarbons in solution, which may be removed by a reduction of temperature and pressure or by a relatively simple extraction process.

See also Casinghead gas; Casinghead vapor; Dry gas.

Wet oil

Oil containing such quantities of water as to render it unmarketable until the water is removed by treatment.

Wet rule

A rule of the Federal Energy Regulatory Commission requiring that the Btu content of a gas stream be determined on the basis of a test volume of gas (1.0 cubic foot), saturated with water vapor at a specified, conveniently obtained temperature and pressure (60° F. and 30 inches of mercury).

> "This rule was known as the 'wet' rule because it required the gas sample to be saturated with water vapor at a temperature and pressure combination where the capacity of natural gas to absorb water vapor is markedly higher than that existing at the temperature and pressure conditions under which most natural gas is sold. In practical effect, therefore, the wet rule tended to overstate water vapor content for gas which, when actually delivered, was neither saturated with water vapor nor delivered at the 'standard' temperature or pressure. . . . This overstated water vapor, in turn, caused an understatement in the number of Btu's assumed to be in the test sample of natural gas." Interstate Natural Gas Ass'n of America v. Federal Energy Regulatory Comm'n, 716 F.2d 1 at 4, 81 *O.&G.R.* 631 at 634 (D.C. Cir. 1983), *cert. denied,* 465 U.S. 1108, 104 S. Ct. 1615, 1616 (1984) (overturning rule of the Commission adopting the dry rule in place of the wet rule for measuring the Btu content of natural gas for wellhead pricing purposes of the Natural Gas Policy Act (NGPA)).

Wetting

A natural phenomenon that affects the relative permeability of reservoir rock. Wetting of a solid by a liquid is commonly observed in the spreading of a liquid on a solid surface and the blotting of a liquid by a dry absorbent material. The effect on relative permeability occurs because wetting affects the curvature of the interface between reservoir fluids. This curvature causes the wetting fluid to occupy selectively the smaller interstices of the rock, the finer pores, and the corners adjacent to the grain contacts. The non-wetting fluid occupies the larger openings, thus decreasing the relative permeability of the rock. The phenomenon seems to occur when a small amount of gas is present with the oil in a reservoir. See Buckley (ed.), *Petroleum Conservation* 125 (1951).

See also PERMEABILITY OF ROCK.

Wetting the gas cap

A reservoir phenomenon that occurs when the pressure of the gas cap in a GAS CAP FIELD (*q.v.*) is depleted faster than that of the oil zone. The resulting pressure differential forces an upward movement of solution gas and oil into the gas cap. Capillary forces cause the pore spaces of the gas cap rock to retain the fluids moving into them. Consequently some of the oil from the oil zone that moved up to the gas cap becomes unrecoverable.

Wet tree

A CHRISTMAS TREE (*q.v.*) installed under water on the seabed in offshore drilling operations as distinguished from a DRY TREE which is one installed above water.

Wet well

A term used to describe a well drilled for oil or gas which produces only water. Levorsen, *Geology of Petroleum* 7 (1954).

WGREPO

The WESTERN GOVERNORS' REGIONAL ENERGY POLICY OFFICE, INC. (*q.v.*).

Whipsticking

Syn.: WHIPSTOCKING (*q.v.*). See Prindle, *Petroleum Politics and the Texas Railroad Commission* 81 (1981).

Whipstock

(1) A technique of drilling a well deviating from the vertical; a directional well; to drill a directional well.

(2) The drilling tool employed in drilling a directional well. It is a long, slender, tapered steel wedge with a concave groove on its inclined face, supported in the well in such a position that the drilling

tool is deflected from the previous course of the well toward the direction in which the inclined grooved surface faces.

Whipstocking

Use of a WHIPSTOCK (*q.v.*) to drill a directional well. For a discussion of some of the history and details of whipstocking, see Prindle, *Petroleum Politics and the Texas Railroad Commission* 81 (1981).

See DEVIATION; DIRECTIONAL DRILLING.

White oil

Colorado Interstate Gas Co. v. HUFO Oils, 626 F.Supp. 38, ____ *O.&G.R.* ____ (W.D. Tex. 1985), *aff'd,* 802 F.2d 133, ____ *O.&G.R.* ____ (5th Cir. 1986), *reh. en banc denied,* 806 F.2d 261 (5th Cir. 1986), and HUFO Oils v. Railroad Commission, 717 S.W.2d 405, ____ *O.&G.R.* ____ (Tex. App., Austin, 1986), held that white oil extracted from natural gas by LOW TEMPERATURE EXTRACTION (*q.v.*) could not be treated as "oil" for purposes of classification of a well as an oil well or gas well.

See also ALBINO OIL; GAS CONDENSATE; LOW TEMPERATURE EXTRACTION (LTX); NATURAL GASOLINE; WATER-WHITE OIL.

See ALBINO OIL.

Wholesale price escalation clause

See ESCALATOR CLAUSE.

Wide-open roll-up

See EXCHANGE OFFER.

Widowmaker

The term employed in Cormier v. Rowan Drilling Co., 549 F.2d 963 at 966–967 (5th Cir. 1977), to describe a smooth metal ramp with steps constructed on one side providing ingress and egress for material, equipment and personnel between a drilling tender and a fixed oil platform. The ramp is permanently affixed to the oil platform but because of the movement of the drilling tender in the water, it can not be affixed to the tender—the ramp extends from the platform out over the water and over the deck of the tender.

"One wishing to leave the oil platform and board the drilling tender had to walk down the steel ramp of the widowmaker until he reached its bottom step, which was no wider than any of the other steps. Then, waiting until the tender was either at the very top or very bottom of its movement up and down in the water, he would leap across the gap of two or three feet separating him from the drilling tender platform and ramp. The ramp presumably was labeled the widowmaker by the heirs, friends and co-workers of those who did not land safely or at all."

Wildcat acreage method of evaluation

A method of evaluation of bids received for leases on Outer Continental Shelf Lands, defined as follows:

"Unleased acreage is located on a structural feature which has not previously produced oil or gas, but which is in close proximity to other producing structures. Projection of these nearby reservoirs and sand conditions into the leasing area are possible through the use of geophysics, stratigraphy, and paleontology. It is also possible to obtain a reserve estimate based on reserve calculations performed in a nearby comparable producing structure. Values obtained are adjusted using the most appropriate risk factor." Exxon Company, U.S.A. 15 IBLA 345 at 355 note 6, GFS(OCS) 1974–55 (May 14, 1974).

See also PROVEN OR SEMI-PROVEN ("DRAINAGE") METHOD OF EVALUATION; RANGE OF VALUES METHOD; RISK-FREE VALUE.

Wildcatter

An operator who drills a WILDCAT WELL (*q.v.*).

Wildcat territory

Unproven territory; that is, an underground horizon from which there is no production in the general area.

Wildcat well

An exploratory well being drilled in unproven territory, that is, in a horizon from which there is no production in the general area. Since the meaning is vague, it should be observed that some wells are more wildcat than others.

See also NEW-FIELD WILDCAT WELL.

Wilderness Act of 1964

Pub. L. No. 88-577, 78 Stat. 890, 16 U.S.C.A. § 1131, establishing a system for the preservation of WILDERNESS AREAS (*q.v.*).

See also FEDERAL LAND POLICY AND MANAGEMENT ACT OF 1976 (FLPMA).

Wilderness areas

Federally owned areas designated by Congress and "administrated for the use and enjoyment of the American people in such manner as will leave them unimpaired for future use and enjoyment as wilderness, and so as to provide for the protection of these areas, the preservation of their wilderness character, and for the gathering and dissemination of information regarding their use and enjoyment as wilderness."

"A wilderness, in contrast with those areas where man and his own works dominate the landscape, is hereby recognized as an area where the earth and its community of life are untrammeled by man, where man himself is a visitor who does not remain. An area of wilderness is further defined to mean in this chapter an area of undeveloped Federal land retaining its primeval character and influence, without permanent improvements or human habitation, which is protected and managed so as to preserve its natural conditions and which (1) generally appears to have been affected primarily by the forces of nature, with the imprint of man's work substantially unnoticable; (2) has outstanding opportunities for solitude or a primitive and unconfined type of recreation; (3) has at least five thousand acres of land or is of sufficient size as to make practicable its preservation and use in an unimpaired condition; and (4) may also contain ecological, geological, or other features of scientific, educational, scenic, or historical value." The Wilderness Act of 1964, Pub. L. No. 88-577, 78 Stat. 890, 16 U.S.-C.A. § 1131.

See also Watson, "Mineral and Oil and Gas Development in Wilderness Areas and Other Specially Managed Federal Lands in the United States," 29 *Rocky Mt. Min. L. Inst.* 37 (1983).

See also CHERRYSTEMMING PRACTICE; OPEN LEASE AREA; OPEN LEASE AREA SUBJECT TO NO SURFACE OCCUPANCY; OPEN LEASE AREA SUBJECT TO SPECIAL STIPULATIONS.

Wilderness protection stipulation

A stipulation in leases issued after 1978 in areas under wilderness study informing the lessee that the area is a potential wilderness area, subject to the non-impairment standard. In Rocky Mountain Oil & Gas Ass'n v. Andrus, 500 F. Supp. 1338, 69 *O.&G.R.* 187 (D. Wyo. 1980), the court concluded that such stipulations in leases amounted to the issuance of "shell" leases with no developmental rights, and the practice was an unconstitutional taking, blatantly unfair to lessees and contrary to Congressional intent. The judgment was reversed and the case remanded in Rocky Mountain Oil and Gas Ass'n v. Watt, 696 F.2d 734, 78 *O.&G.R.* 152 (10th Cir. 1982).

Wilderness study area

An area of the public lands determined to have wilderness characteristics. See Rocky Mountain Oil & Gas Ass'n v. Andrus, 500 F. Supp. 1338, 69 *O.&G.R.* 187 (D. Wyo. 1980), *rev'd and remanded sub nom.* Rocky Mountain Oil & Gas Ass'n v. Watt, 696 F.2d 734, 78 *O.&G.R.* 152 (10th Cir. 1982).

Wild well

A well which has gone out of control and from which oil and/or gas is escaping into the air or onto the surface. *Syn.:* BLOW-OUT.

Windfall profit

For purposes of the CRUDE OIL WINDFALL PROFIT TAX ACT OF 1980 (*q.v.*), this term means the excess of the removal price of the barrel of crude oil over the sum of: (1) the adjusted price of such barrel, and (2) the amount of the severance tax adjustment provided by section 4996(c). Internal Revenue Code § 4988.

Window

A term used to describe an unsigned interest affecting a pooled or unitized area. See Myers, *The Law of Pooling and Unitization* § 14.03 (2d ed. 1967).

See also SINGLE WINDOW APPROACH; WEATHER WINDOW.

Winner's curse

The term applied to the phenomenon that given the uncertainty of offshore oil and gas leases, the winners at the auctions may be the firms which most overvalue the leases, and thus the winning bidders will ultimately earn a relatively low rate of return on their leases. Mead, Moseidjord, Muraoka and Sorensen, *Offshore Lands: Oil and Gas Leasing and Conservation on the Outer Continental Shelf* 75 (1985).

Withdrawal

(1) The designation by the executive branch of the federal government of lands not available for settlement, location, sale or entry. Major withdrawls have been made for reclamation projects, power sites, stock driveways, grazing districts and leases, national forests, wildlife refuges, military and naval purposes. See *Rocky Mt. Min. L. Fdn. Law of Federal Oil and Gas Leases* Ch. 3 (1985); Peck, "'And Then There Were None'—Evolving Federal Restraints on the Availability of Public Lands for Mineral Development," 25 *Rocky Mt. Min. L. Inst.* 3–1 (1979).

In Mountain States Legal Foundation v. Andrus, 499 F.Supp. 383, 69 *O.&G.R.* 160 (D. Wyo. 1980), the court held that inaction by the Secretary of the Interior, in concert with the Secretary of Agriculture, to act on outstanding lease applications in non-wilderness portions of United States forests in Wyoming, Idaho and Montana fell within the statutory definition of withdrawal. An order issued that the Secretary report the withdrawal to Congress, as required by statute, or cease withholding said lands from oil and gas leasing, exploration and development.

Pacific Legal Foundation v. Watt, 529 F. Supp. 982 (D. Mont. 1981), 539 F.Supp. 1194 (D. Mont. 1982), held that the term "withdrawal," as used in the FEDERAL LAND POLICY AND MANAGEMENT ACT OF 1976 (FLPMA) (*q.v.*), includes withdrawal of public lands from mineral exploration and leasing. The scope and duration of a withdrawal order under Section 204(e) of the Act are within the sound discretion of the Secretary of the Interior, to be exercised in accordance with the goals and procedural requirements of the Act, subject to judicial review.

(2) The designation by the appropriate executive officer of Crown mineral lands not open for prospecting and staking out and for disposition. See The Mineral Resources Act, Rev. Stat. Saskatchewan 1965, c. 50, as amended, R.S.S. 1966, c.69, § 16.

Withering clause

A clause found in numerous joint venture operating agreements providing that in the event of default in the development stage the interest of the defaulting member could (after the applicable grace period) be forfeited, and the defaulting member released from the obligation to contribute anything further to the development, but with a right to re-acquire a reduced interest at the production stage, representing a predetermined proportion of the defaulting member's share based on the actual contributions made prior to the default.

See Willoughby, "Forfeiture of Interests in Joint Operating Agreements," 3 *J. of Energy & Nat. Res. L.* 256 at 258 (1985); Doeh, "Default Clauses: No Relief in Sight," [1985/86] 7 *O.&G.R.* 187 at 188.

Woc time

Waiting-on-cement time. That period between the end of actual cementing operations and drilling out the cement plug or perforating the casing to permit fluid entry to the well bore. See Curtis, " 'Woc' or 'Cow' Time," 16 *Oil and Gas Compact Bull.* 39 (June 1957).

WOGA

The Western Oil & Gas Association.

Won and saved

A term employed in United Kingdom Petroleum (Production) Regulations 1976, clause 10, but left undefined. Daintith and Willoughby, *A Manual of United Kingdom Oil and Gas Law* 441 (1977), suggest that "won" refers to the winning of access to minerals prior to the start of extraction processes and that "saved" means "brought into possession and under control and that, as regards the extraction of petroleum, this stage is reached either when the petroleum has passed the well head or when it is passed through the initial separation and stabilization processes on the production platform."

WOR

Water-oil ratio.

See OIL-WATER RATIO.

Work-back valuation method

A method for calculating market value of oil or gas at the wellhead when value cannot be calculated on the basis of comparable sales. Under this method costs of transportation, processing and treatment are deducted from the ultimate proceeds of sale of the oil or gas and any extracted or processed products to ascertain wellhead value. See Rev. Rul. 83-161, 1983-44 I.R.B. 8, 77 *O.&G.R.* 605 (Oct. 31, 1983) (removal price of Alaska North Slope oil for purpose of Windfall Profit Tax);Scott Paper Co. v. Taslog, Inc., 638 F.2d 790, 69 *O.&G.R.* 1 (5th Cir., Unit B, 1981); Ashland Oil, Inc. v. Phillips Petroleum Co., 554 F.2d 381 at 387, 57 *O.&G.R.* 390 at 300 (10th Cir. 1977), *cert. denied,* 434 U.S. 921, *reh. denied,* 434 U.S. 977

(1977), *on remand,* 463 F.Supp. 619, 62 *O.&G.R.* 483 (N.D. Okla. 1978), *aff'd in part and rev'd in part,* 607 F.2d 335, 64 *O.&G.R.* 332 (10th Cir. 1979), *cert. denied,* 445 U.S. 936 (1980), *on subsequent appeal,* Northern Natural Gas Co. v. Grounds, 666 F.2d 1279, 72 *O.&G.R.* 531 (10th Cir. 1981), *cert. denied,* 457 U.S. 1126 (1982).

After several trips back and forth from the district court to the Supreme Court via the Court of Appeals for the Tenth Circuit, appeals from the Northern District of Oklahoma in Ashland Oil, Inc. v. Phillips Petroleum Co., and from the District of Kansas in Northern Natural Gas Co. v. Grounds, were consolidated, and the Court of Appeals held that the district court had erred in failing to employ the work-back method for computing the value of the helium content of processed natural gas. Northern Natural Gas Co. v. Grounds, 666 F.2d 1279 (10th Cir. 1981).

See Leftwich, "The Workback Method of Valuing Raw Materials: The Helium Cases," 35 *O.&G. Tax Q.* 292 (1986); Yu and Leftwich, "Court Errors in the Use of Internal Rates of Return in the Valuation of Helium," 35 *O.&G. Tax Q.* 7 (1987).

See also Marathon Oil Co. v. United States, 604 F.Supp. 1375, 87 *O.&G.R.* 455 (D. Alaska 1985), *aff'd,* 807 F.2d 759, 90 *O.&G.R.* 6 (9th Cir. 1986) (sustaining the use of a net-back method for computing gas royalties).

See also NET-BACK PRICING; PROCEEDS-LESS-EXPENSE METHOD; RECONSTRUCTION APPROACH.

Work commitment bidding

A system of bidding for leases designed to encourage rapid exploration in which the variable is the work commitment made by the bidder.

> "When compared with cash bonus bidding, though, there seems little economic justification for it. An operator who obtains oil and gas rights by payment of a cash bonus has taken into account in submitting his bid the cost of exploring the area in the most efficient way possible. If a government believes that this exploration will be slower than the socially-desired rate, it may specify operations to be conducted within time limits as a condition of bidding and still use the cash bonus system. Work commitment bidding is likely to result in government loss of a portion of the economic rents either by promoting inefficiency in exploration or by allowing excess private profits." Crommelin, "Offshore Oil and Gas Rights: A Comparative Study," 14 *Nat. Res. J.* 457 at 494 (1974).

See also LEASE BIDDING SYSTEMS.

Work contract

A term employed to describe a type of government-company relationship in which the company, instead of being a property owner as under the concession concept, is simply a service contractor to the government, receiving the right to purchase a certain percentage of the oil produced in exchange for providing the capital and expertise necessary for exploration, development and production of the host country's oil reserves. Ely, "Changing Concepts of the World's Mineral Development Laws," in International Bar Ass'n, *World Energy Laws* (Proceedings of the IBA Seminar on World Energy Laws held in Stavanger, Norway) 4 at 34 (1975).

See also CONCESSION.

Working agreement

An agreement between or among concurrent owners of a leasehold concerning the method of operating the premises, the division of responsibility and allocation of costs. See Discussion Notes, 3 *O.&G.R.* 1479 (1954).

Working date

A term used in certain lease forms with reference to the last day of the period during which the lessee must commence drilling operations, pay rentals, or quit-claim and surrender the lease.

Working gas

The term applied to gas stored for varying periods of time in an underground gas storage reservoir pending its further transportation and delivery to customers. Mississippi River Transmission Corp. v. Simonton, 442 So. 2d 764 (La. App. 1983), *writ denied,* 444 So.2d 1240 (La. 1984), *cert. denied,* ____ U.S. ____, 105 S. Ct. 58 (1984); United Gas Pipe Line Co. v. Whiteman, 390 So. 2d 913 (La. App. 1980).

Working gas is sometimes referred to as Topgas. Arkla, Inc. v. United States, 592 F.Supp. 502, 83 *O.&G.R.* 209 (W.D. La. 1984), *rev'd and remanded,* 765 F.2d 487, 85 *O.&G.R.* 431 (5th Cir. 1985), *reh. denied,* 772 F.2d 904 (5th Cir. 1985), *cert. denied,* 106 S.Ct. 1374 (1986).

See also CUSHION GAS; GAS STORAGE, SUBSURFACE; NATIVE GAS; NATIVE GAS ENTITLEMENT.

Working interest

The operating interest under an oil and gas lease. The owner of the working interest has the exclusive right to exploit the minerals on the land.

In the simple situation of a lessor who executes a lease, reserving 1/8th royalty, to a lessee who creates no burdens on his estate, the working interest consists of 7/8ths of production subject to all costs of exploration and development; the lessor receives his 1/8th of production free of such costs. However, a lessee may transfer out of his working interest an OVERRIDING ROYALTY (*q.v.*), OIL PAYMENT (*q.v.*), NET PROFIT INTEREST (*q.v.*), or CARRIED INTEREST (*q.v.*), leaving himself still as owner of the working interest (and therefore exclusively entitled to operate on the premises) but as the owner of very little production and the recipient of a small fraction of the income from the property.

Although the term working interest ordinarily refers to an interest acquired by a lease, special context may indicate that it is used to describe a mineral interest. See Schnitt v. McKellar, 244 Ark. 377, 427 S.W.2d 202, 30 *O.&G.R.* 1 (1968).

This term is defined by Federal Power Commission Order No. 411, 46 F.P.C. 1178 at 1180 (Nov. 10, 1971), as an interest "embodying operating rights and/or the right to share in production or revenues from the producing venture, so that its receipt of production or revenues will increase as the production or revenues from the producing venture increase, without any termination of such right to receive production or revenues after the return of the amount of any related advance payment."

For some purposes (*e.g.*, indicating who bears what proportion of expenses in a situation where the working interest is divided) the working interest is stated as a unity and the share of expenses borne by each party is stated in decimal or percentage (usually decimal) terms. To be distinguished from working interest is NET REVENUE INTEREST (*q.v.*), also stated in decimal or percentage terms. Thus where a lease reserving a one-eighth royalty is executed to *A*, who thereafter assigns one-fourth of his interest to *B*, the lessor owns none of the working interest but has a O.125 net revenue interest, *A* owns O.75 of the working interest and has a net revenue interest of O.65625, and *B* owns O.25 of the working interest and has a O.21875 net revenue interest.

See also Miller v. Schwartz, 354 N.W.2d 685, 84 *O.&G.R.* 143 (N.D. 1984), quoting a portion of this MANUAL'S definition and concluding that "it appears that the term 'working interest,' as commonly used in the oil industry, is generally synonymous with the term 'leasehold interest.' "

See also COMMITTED WORKING INTEREST; EXCLUDED INTEREST; FULL TERM WORKING INTEREST; LIMITED WORKING INTEREST; OPERATING INTEREST; NET LEASEHOLD; NON-OPERATING WORKING INTEREST; TERMINABLE WORKING INTEREST.

Working interest bidding

A proposed bidding system for leases on federal lands in which bids are made for undifferentiated interests in a large area overlying a geological structure:

> "Each bidder would offer a bonus per acre on a specified amount of acreage (for example, 640 acres). Bids would be opened and arrayed in the order of the bonus offered per acre. The winners would be those, selected in order of bonus bid per acre, whose total acreage bid summed to the total acreage in the structure. . . . Since the bidders receive undifferentiated acreage in the total area, it is necessary for them to commit themselves in advance to participation in a cooperative plan of exploration and, in the event of a discovery, to development and production, sharing in costs and revenues on the basis of acreage shares." McDonald, *The Leasing of Federal Lands for Fossil Fuels Production,* 113–114 (1979).

See also LEASE BIDDING SYSTEMS.

Work overs

Operations on a producing well to restore or increase production. A typical workover is cleaning out a well that has sanded up. Tubing is pulled, the casing and bottom of the hole washed out with mud, and (in some cases) explosives set off in the hole to dislodge the silt and sand.

See also CLEANING A WELL; PRODUCTION ENHANCEMENT PROCEDURES; REWORKING OPERATIONS.

Work programme

The scheme of prospecting and test drilling required under the provisions of a PRODUCTION LICENSE (*q.v.*).

Worldscale

The Worldwide Tanker Nominal Freight Scale, issued jointly by the Association of Ship Brokers and Agents, Inc., and the International Tanker Nominal Freight Scale Association Limited.

See also AFRA.

Worst case analysis

An analysis by a regulatory agency of the worst case that might happen if the agency permits a proposed action. See Hill, "The Requirement of Worst Case Analysis When Approving Oil Leasing Under the Outer Continental Shelf Lands Act: Village of False Pass v. Clark," [1985] *Brigham Young U. L. Rev.* 347.

Worthlessness, loss from

In federal income tax law, a deduction for ordinary losses (not compensated by insurance) incurred in a trade or business or resulting from a transaction entered into for profit though not connected with a trade or business, exclusive of losses from a sale or exchange of capital assets. Internal Revenue Code (1954) § 165 (a) and (c).

Establishment of loss is governed by Treas. Reg. § 1.165–1(b) (1980), which requires for the deduction "closed and completed transactions, fixed by identifiable events" bona fide and actually sustained in the tax year.

The deduction of a loss from worthlessness, in the case of completion of dry holes on a property, is considered in Louisiana Land & Exploration Co. v. Commissioner, 161 F.2d 842 (5th Cir. 1947); Pool v. U.S., 119 F. Supp. 202, 3 *O.&G.R.* 518 (Ct. Claims 1954); Harmon v. Commissioner, 1 T.C. 40 (1942); L. M. Fischer, 14 T.C. 792 (1950). See Burke and Bowhay, *Income Taxation of Natural Resources* ¶ 15.11 (1980).

WOW

Waiting on weather, *viz.*, an operation is being held up by bad weather.

See also WEATHER WINDOW.

WPS

WILDERNESS PROTECTION STIPULATION (*q.v.*).

WPT

The CRUDE OIL WINDFALL PROFIT TAX ACT OF 1980 (*q.v.*).

Wrap-around carved-out production payment

Conceived as part of a mine financing package, this form of production payment consists of one development carved-out production payment for each of several fields to finance intangible drilling costs or equipment costs, and one conventional carved-out production payment wrapped around the entire package to finance operating and overhead expenses. Stockmar, "Money Magic: Pulling the Golden Rabbit From the Hat," *Rocky Mt. Min. L. Inst. on Mineral Financing* 13-32, note 39 (1982).

WSA

WILDERNESS STUDY AREA (*q.v.*).

WWR

Abbreviation of *Western Weekly Reports,* a set of reports containing decisions of various Canadian courts.

. . XYZ . .

X-Y-Z transaction

Syn.: A-B-C TRANSACTION (*q.v.*).

Yacimentos Petroliferos Fiscales (YPF)

The national oil company of Argentina. For discussions of this company and the Argentine situation, see the following:

Dabinovic, "The New Argentine Legal Regime for the Petroleum Industry: Decree 1443 of 6 August 1985," [1985/86] 3 *OGLTR* 75 (1985);

Chester, *United States Oil Policy and Diplomacy* 185 (1983);

Bosch, "Present, Past and Future of Oil and Gas Legislation in Argentina," International Bar Ass'n Section on Energy and Natural Resources, *International Energy Law* (1984) (Topic 2);

Cardenas, "Argentina. Oil Policies. A Glance Over the Next Future," *ibid.;*

Dabinovic, "The Argentine National Oil Company," International Bar Ass'n, *Energy Law 1981* at p. 57;

Amadeo, "Legal and Contract Provisions to Implement the Present Argentine Hydrocarbon Policy," *id.* at 285.

Yacimentos Petroliferos Fiscales Bolivianos (YPFB)

The national oil company of Bolivia. See Chester, *United States Oil Policy and Diplomacy* 166 (1983).

Yamburg-Urengoi pipeline

A pipeline designed to provide western Europe with gas from the USSR. The building of this pipeline was the occasion for substantial political controversy in the early 1980s. See Russell, *Geopolitics of Natural Gas* 138 (1983).

Yardstick allowable

A uniform formula worked out in 1947 by the Texas Railroad Commission for the determination of daily per well allowables. The yardstick employed two factors: depth of the well and spacing pattern. Under this yardstick, reservoir characteristics were ignored, and the individual well, not the reservoir, was viewed as the unit of production in the proration formula. See McKie and McDonald, "Petroleum Conservation in Theory and Practice," 64 *Q.J. Econ.* 98 at 112 (1964).

Several states (Kansas, Louisiana, New Mexico, North Dakota, Oklahoma and Texas) have adopted so-called yardstick allowables, *viz.*, formulae based on depth of well and acreage assigned to the particular well. See Governors' Special Study Committee of Interstate Oil Compact Commission, *A Study of Conservation of Oil and Gas in the United States* 92, 96–105 (1964); Lovejoy and Homan, *Economic Aspects of Oil Conservation Regulation* (1967).

A revised oil allowable yardstick became effective in Texas on January 1, 1965. The details of this yardstick are reported in 24 *Oil and Gas Compact Bull.* 66 (June, 1965). See 16 Tex. Admin. Code § 3.45.

For an analysis indicating that the yardstick allowable system benefits low-production fields at the expense of flush fields, and that thereby independent producers were the primary beneficiaries, see Prindle, *Petroleum Policies and the Texas Railroad Commission* 42 (1981).

See also ALLOWABLE; DEPTH-BRACKET METHOD OF PRORATION.

Yield tax

A SEVERANCE TAX (*q.v.*). See, *e.g.*, the California Timber Yield Tax, Cal. Rev. & Tax. Code § 38101 *et seq.* (1979), which has been proposed as a model for a tax on oil and gas properties. Cal. Assembly Revenue and Taxation Committee, *Taxation of Oil and Gas Properties* (Dec. 1980).

YPF

YACIMENTOS PETROLIFEROS FISCALES (*q.v.*), the national oil company of Argentina.

YPFB

YACIMENTOS PETROLIFEROS FISCALES BOLIVIANOS (*q.v.*), the national oil company of Bolivia.

Zone

This term was defined by the Seeligson Field Unit Agreement as "a stratigraphic interval containing one or more reservoirs." See Myers, *The Law of Pooling and Unitization* 104 (1957).

30 La. R.S. 1950 § 9(E) (as amended in 1980) provides:

"Each zone of a general structure which is completely separated from any other zone in the structure is covered by the term 'pool', to promote the development and production of marginally commercial sands, a zone may contain one or more common accumulations and the overall stratigraphic intervals of the zone may be considered and treated as a pool.

Hystad v. Industrial Comm'n, 389 N.W.2d 590, 90 *O.&G.R.* 260 (N.D. 1986), concluded that under a North Dakota statute dealing with the creation of spacing units the term "zone" referred to a geographic area rather than a stratigraphic interval.